dental plaque revisited
oral biofilms in health and disease

proceedings of a conference held at
the Royal College of Physicians, London,
3-5 November, 1999

edited by
Hubert N Newman and Michael Wilson

Eastman Dental Institute
University College London

ISBN 0-9520432-7-0

BioLine

Cardiff School of Biosciences, Cardiff University
PO Box 915, Cardiff CF10 3TL, UK

© BioLine 1999

Printed and bound in the UK by Antony Rowe Ltd,
Bumper's Farm, Chippenham, Wiltshire

Preface

It is now thirty years since our colleague Bill McHugh held his benchmark symposium on Dental Plaque in Dundee, Scotland. In many ways this set the pace for much of what followed in plaque research over the following thirty years. At the close of this millennium of the Common Era, we felt it opportune to review plaque knowledge with a view to doing our bit to set the pace for future plaque research. We are delighted and honoured that our distinguished colleagues agreed with alacrity to join in our venture, and it is an especial pleasure that Bill McHugh himself is to start the proceedings. We welcome all our colleagues to the Royal College of Physicians, and are particularly appreciative, given their other commitments, that their efforts have enabled us to provide the full publication at the time of the Symposium.

We owe thanks to several other colleagues who have been so supportive in all the complex organisation associated with such a meeting, not least Ramya Senaratna, Michael's secretary. We are grateful indeed to our publishers, particularly Barbara Evans, for their co-operation, patience and speed, and trust that readers will concentrate on the vast body of knowledge in these pages, and excuse any minor errors in the text. We also wish to thank Clive Ostler, Angela Bachtler, Arpita Bhose and their team at the College, whose infrastructure support in their superb surroundings has been invaluable.

A very special expression of gratitude is extended to our sponsors. We deeply appreciate their generous support of this basic science meeting, and we have acknowledged them individually on another page. Without their support it would be very difficult indeed to effect the research we do that is aimed at treating and preventing the most widespread of human diseases, the aetiological agent of which is the focus of this Symposium.

Hubert N. Newman   **Michael Wilson**

Conference Sponsors

This conference would not have been possible without the generous financial support of our sponsors to whom we would like to express our deep appreciation:

Braun Oral-B
GABA International Ltd
Optiva Corporation
Procter & Gamble
Unilever Research

We are also most grateful to the following for their support of this conference:

Atrix Laboratories Inc
Block Drug/Stafford Miller
Coca Cola Company
Colgate-Palmolive Limited
CollaGenex Pharmaceuticals Inc
Don Whitley Scientific Ltd
Dumex Alpharma Limited
Mars UK Ltd
Pharma Nord
SmithKline Beecham
Teledyne Water Pik
3M Dental Products Division
Warner-Lambert
Wellcome Trust

We would also like to thank the *Society for Applied Microbiology* and the *Federation of European Microbiological Societies* for generously providing travel awards for many of the student delegates.

Contents

BioLine © 1999

Medical Implications of Oral Biofilms

Treatment of Plaque-related Diseases

Authors

David G. Allison *School of Pharmacy and Pharmaceutical Sciences, University of Manchester, Manchester, M13 9PL, UK*

Roxanna N. Andersen *Oral Infection and Immunity Branch, National Institute of Dental and Craniofacial Research, National Institutes of Health, Bethesda, Maryland 20892, USA*

Catherine Bass *School of Biological Sciences, Exeter University, Exeter, EX4 4PS, UK*

Roger Bayston *Biomaterials - Related Infection Group, Division of Microbiology & Infectious Diseases, Faculty of Medicine & Health Sciences, University of Nottingham, UK*

J.D. Beck *Center for Oral and Systemic Diseases, University of North Carolina at Chapel Hill, School of Dentistry, CB # 7455, Chapel Hill, NC 27599-7455, USA*

David Beighton *Department of Oral Microbiology, Guy's, King's and St Thomas' Dental Institute, Caldecot Road, Denmark Hill, London, SE5 9RW, UK*

George H.W. Bowden *Departments of Oral Biology and Medical Microbiology, Faculties of Dentistry and Medicine,, University of Manitoba, 780 Bannatyne Avenue, Winnipeg, Manitoba R3E 0W2, CANADA*

John D. Boyle *School of Engineering and Computer Science, North Park Road, Exeter University, Exeter, EX4 4QF, UK*

Melanie Brading *Unilever Research, Port Sunlight Laboratories, Wirral, L63 3JW, UK*

David J. Bradshaw *Research Division, CAMR, Salisbury, SP4 0JG, UK*

Susan R. Brailsford *Department of Oral Microbiology, Guy's, King's and St Thomas' Dental Institute, Caldecot Road, Denmark Hill, London, SE5 9RW, UK*

C.M.E. Champagne *Center for Oral and Systemic Diseases, University of North Carolina at Chapel Hill, School of Dentistry, CB # 7455, Chapel Hill, NC 27599-7455, USA*

H.J. Chung *Center for Oral and Systemic Diseases, University of North Carolina at Chapel Hill, School of Dentistry, CB # 7455, Chapel Hill, NC 27599-7455, USA*

Daniel L. Clemans *Oral Infection and Immunity Branch, National Institute of Dental and Craniofacial Research, National Institutes of Health, Bethesda, Maryland 20892, USA*

Charles M. Cobb *Department of Periodontics, School of Dentistry, University of Missouri-Kansas City, 650 East 25th Street, Kansas City, Missouri 64108, USA*

Guy Cook *Bacterin, P.O. Box 6743, Bozeman, MT 59715, USA*

J.W. Costerton *Center for Biofilm Engineering, Montana State University – Bozeman, 366 EPS Building, P.O. Box 173980, Bozeman, MT 59717-3980, USA*

Michael A. Curtis *MRC Molecular Pathogenesis Group, Dept of Oral Microbiology, St Bart's and the Royal London School of Medicine & Dentistry, 32 Newark Street, London E1 2AA, UK*

Connie Hastings Drisko *School of Dentistry, University of Louisville, Kentucky 40202, USA*

Jeremy M. Hardie *Department of Oral Microbiology, St. Bartholomew's and the Royal London, School of Medicine and Dentistry, Queen Mary and Westfield College, Turner Street, London E1 2AD, UK*

M. Feres *The Forsyth Institute, 140 The Fenway, Boston MA 02114, USA*

S Geva *Center for Oral and Systemic Diseases, University of North Carolina at Chapel Hill, School of Dentistry, CB # 7455, Chapel Hill, NC 27599-7455, USA*

Peter Gilbert *School of Pharmacy and Pharmaceutical Sciences, University of Manchester, Manchester, M13 9PL, UK*

James R. Giordano *University of Detroit School of Dentistry, Detroit MI, USA*

J.Max Goodson *The Forsyth Institute, 140 The Fenway, Boston MA 02114, USA*

John Greenman *Department of Biological and Biomedical Sciences, University of the West of England, Bristol, BS16 1QY, UK*

Ian C. Hancock *School of Microbiological, Immunological, and Virological Sciences, The Medical School, Newcastle University, Framlington Place, Newcastle upon Tyne, NE2 4HH, UK*

Pauline S. Handley *Department of Biological Sciences, 1.800 Stopford Building, Oxford Road, Manchester University, Manchester M13 9PT, UK*

Brian Henderson *Cellular Microbiology Research Group, Division of Surgical Sciences, Eastman Dental Institute, University College London, 256 Gray's Inn Road, London WC1X 8LD, UK*

Jeffrey D. Hillman *University of Florida College of Dentistry, Box 100424, 1600 SW Archer Road, Gainesville, FL 32610, USA*

Laura S. Houston *Department of Periodontics and the Regional Clinical Dental Research Center, School of Dentistry, and the Department of Pathology, School of Medicine, University of Washington, Seattle, WA 98195, USA*

Howard F. Jenkinson *Department of Oral and Dental Science, Bristol University, Lower Maudlin Street Bristol BS1 2LY, UK*

Paul E. Kolenbrander *Oral Infection and Immunity Branch, National Institute of Dental and Craniofacial Research, National Institutes of Health, Bethesda, Maryland 20892, USA*

Christiane M. Klier *Oral Infection and Immunity Branch, National Institute of Dental and Craniofacial Research, National Institutes of Health, Bethesda, Maryland 20892, USA*

Richard Lamont *University of Washington, School of Dentristry, Dept. of Oral Biology, Box 3 57132, Seattle, WA 98195-7132, USA*

Hilary Lappin-Scott *School of Biological Sciences, Exeter University, Exeter, EX4 4PS, UK*

Y. Liu *Center for Oral and Systemic Diseases, University of North Carolina at Chapel Hill, School of Dentistry, CB # 7455, Chapel Hill, NC 27599-7455, USA*

Max A. Listgarten *Microbiological Testing Laboratory, University of Pennsylvania, School of Dental Medicine, 4001 Spruce Street, Philadelphia, PA 19104-6003, USA*

Walter J. Loesche *University of Michigan School of Dentistry, Ann Arbor MI.48109, USA*

P.N. Madianos *Center for Oral and Systemic Diseases, University of North Carolina at Chapel Hill, School of Dentistry, CB # 7455, Chapel Hill, NC 27599-7455, USA*

Philip D. Marsh *Research Division, CAMR, Salisbury, SP4 0JG, UK* and *Leeds Dental Institute, University of Leeds, LS2 9LU, UK*

T. Wallace MacFarlane *Infection Research Group, Glasgow Dental School, 378 Sauchiehall Street, Glasgow, UK*

William D. McHugh *303 Sandringham Road, Rochester, NY, 14610, USA*

Roderick McNab *Department of Microbiology, Eastman Dental Institute, University of London, Gray's Inn Road, London WC1X 8LD, UK*

Søren Molin *Department of Microbiology, Technical University of Denmark, Building 301, DK-2800 Lyngby, Denmark*

Nicola J. Mordan *Eastman Dental Institute for Oral Healthcare Sciences, 256, Gray's Inn Road, London, WC1X 8L, UK*

Hubert N. Newman *Eastman Dental Institute for Oral Healthcare Sciences, 123, Gray's Inn Road, London, WC1X 8TZ, UK*

Steven Offenbacher *Center for Oral and Systemic Diseases, University of North Carolina at Chapel Hill, School of Dentistry, CB # 7455, Chapel Hill, NC 27599-7455, USA*

Roy C. Page *University of Washington, Research Center in Oral Biology, 1959 NE Pacific, HSB B530, Box 357480, Seattle, WA 98195, USA*

Jonathan Pratten *Department of Microbiology, Eastman Dental Institute for Oral Health Care Sciences, University College London, 256 Gray's Inn Road, London WC1X 8LD, UK*

James I Prosser_*Department of Molecular and Cell Biology, University of Aberdeen, Institute of Medical Sciences, Foresterhill, Aberdeen AB25 2ZD, Scotland, UK*

Sara K. Roberts *School of Biological Sciences, Exeter University, Exeter, EX4 4PS, UK*

Jennifer M. Slaney *MRC Molecular Pathogenesis Group, Dept of Oral Microbiology, St Bart's and the Royal London School of Medicine & Dentistry, 32 Newark Street, London E1 2AA, UK*

Andrew Smith *Infection Research Group, Glasgow Dental School, 378 Sauchiehall street, Glasgow, UK*

S.Sigmund Socransky *The Forsyth Institute, 140 The Fenway, Boston MA 02114, USA*

S. Som *The Forsyth Institute, 140 The Fenway, Boston MA 02114, USA*

Janice K. Stoll *University of Michigan School of Dentistry, Ann Arbor MI.48109, USA*

Paul Stoodley *School of Biological Sciences, Exeter University, Exeter, EX4 4PS, UK*

Ian W. Sutherland *Institute of Cell and Molecular Biology, Edinburgh University, Mayfield Road, Edinburgh EH9 3JH, Scotland< UK*

William Wade *Department of Oral Microbiology, Guy's, King's and St Thomas' Dental Institute, Floor 28, Guy's Tower, Guy's Hospital, London, SE1 9RT, UK*

Catherine J. Whittaker *Oral Infection and Immunity Branch, National Institute of Dental and Craniofacial Research, National Institutes of Health, Bethesda, Maryland 20892, USA*

Ray C. Williams *Center for Oral and Systemic Diseases, University of North Carolina at Chapel Hill, School of Dentistry, CB # 7455, Chapel Hill, NC 27599-7455, USA*

Robert A. Whiley *Department of Oral Microbiology, St. Bartholomew's and the Royal London, School of Medicine and Dentistry, Queen Mary and Westfield College, Turner Street, London E1 2AD, UK*

Michael Wilson *Department of Microbiology, Eastman Dental Institute for Oral Health Care Sciences, University College London, 256 Gray's Inn Road, London WC1X 8LD, UK*

Opening Address

DENTAL PLAQUE: THIRTY YEARS ON

William D. McHugh

Soft microbe-containing deposits on the teeth were probably first described by Antony van Leeuwenhoek in 1683, using his "new" microscope. These soft deposits were subsequently referred to by many terms, and it was generally believed the they consisted mostly of food debris. Black (1898) described "gelatinous microbial plaques" on teeth and this term was variously used to include all soft material developing on or adhering to tooth surfaces, including food debris, leukocytes, and epithelial cells (Stephan, 1953; Winkler and Backer-Dirks, 1958.) or gelatinous polysaccharide microbial products (Schroeder, 1969a), or a structureless bacteria-free cuticle (Millin and Smith, 1961).

Even when the predecessor of this symposium was held thirty years ago, the term dental plaque did not have a clear and widely-accepted definition. One outcome of that symposium was general agreement among the participants that dental plaque consists predominantly of micro-organisms plus extra-cellular polysaccharides, and usually an underlying pellicle of salivary origin (McHugh, 1970). It was also recognized that the oral and gingival surfaces of dental plaque are often covered with leukocytes and desquamated epithelial cells and, at times, food debris.

Probably the biggest breakthrough in our understanding of plaque was the demonstration by Socransky, Gibbons and their co-workers that the number of microorganisms in plaque is of the same order of magnitude as an equal weight of a centrifuged culture of streptococci (Socransky *et al.*, 1963; Gibbons *et al.*, 1964). The predominantly microbial composition of plaque was confirmed by ultrastructural studies (Schroeder and deBoever, 1970; Frank and Houver, 1970).

In a series of conceptually simple but elegant studies, Egelberg and his colleagues followed the development of plaque on cleaned tooth surfaces (Bjorn and Carlsson, 1964; Carlsson and Egelberg, 1965; Egelberg, 1965a, 1965b, 1970). A structureless pellicle, presumably of salivary origin, formed within a day and, in from 1-4 days, small discrete colonies of microorganisms formed on the surface of this pellicle, especially near the gingival margin. These colonies gradually grew until they became confluent and covered large parts of the tooth surface. These workers also showed that plaque formation is greatly influenced by both the consistency and composition of the diet. More plaque forms when the diet is soft (Egelberg, 1965a) although, as later tube-feeding experiments have shown, food is not necessary for abundant plaque formation. Dietary sucrose leads to the formation of distinctive large confluent colonies of strepto-coccal plaque in contrast to the thin structureless plaque with small scattered colonies which forms when the diet contains protein and fat, with or without supplemental glucose or fructose (Carlsson and Egelberg, 1965). Plaque formed on a cleaned tooth surface in 2 days consists of approximately 90% of gram-positive cocci and rods, with the remaining organisms being gram-negative cocci and rods. Thereafter, the proportions of gram-negative cocci and rods increases, and filamentous organisms and fusobacteria appear in the deeper layers of the plaque (Theilade *et al.*, 1966). Depending on its site, plaque reaches maturity in 20 - 40 days when the type and proportions of different organisms reaches relative stability.

Subgingival plaque forms in a different environment with little influence from saliva (Baumhammers and Stallard, 1966) but direct effects from the gingival fluid and the migrating leukocytes and desquamating epithelial cells it contains. A complex flora seems to develop much more rapidly in subgingival plaque (Oshrain *et al.*, 1969), probably because of its more anaerobic environment.

The microbial composition of plaque can be substantially influenced by diet and by the selective effect of antibiotics and anti-microbials, Plaque formation can be largely inhibited by topical application of penicillin or tetracycline (Larson *et al.*, 1963; Keyes, 1966) while topical application of vancomycin, which suppresses gram-positive organisms, changes the plaque flora but does not alter plaque thickness at the gingival margin or affect the development of gingivitis (Jensen *et al.*, 1968), the antibacterial, chlorhexidine gluconate, has been shown to totally inhibit plaque formation and the development of gingivitis (Löe and Schiött, 1969).

Plague and disease

Much of our interest in plaque is due to its potential to cause disease. Dental caries will not develop in the absence of plaque (Löe, 1970). Plaque formed when monkeys were tube-fed had no capacity to form acid (Bowen, 1970) and plaque formed in the presence of dietary sucrose had much greater acid-producing potential than that formed in the presence of monosaccharides (Bowen, 1970). However, in the absence of plaque, frequent rinsing with sucrose does not cause caries (Löe, von der Fehr and Schiött, 1970). Caries can be prevented by inhibiting plaque formation with chlorhexidine rinses (Löe, von der Fehr and Schiött, 1970). However, removal of plaque by oral hygiene has little effect on caries (Horowitz, 1998), probably because of the overriding effects of fluoride in dentifrice and diet.

The relationship between plaque and gingivitis is clear-cut. When plaque is allowed to form on cleaned tooth surfaces associated with healthy gingivae, sub-clinical gingivitis develops within 3 days and clinical gingivitis in from 10 - 21 days (Löe *et al.*, 1965; Theilade *et al.*, 1966; Löe *et al.*, 1967; Jensen *et al.*, 1968). This gingivitis was reversible and resolved completely when plaque was eliminated by toothbrushing or rinsing with chlorhexidine (Löe, 1970). Clinical attachment loss (a measure of periodontitis) in susceptible adults can be halted almost completely by self-performed plaque control combined with professional

2

prophylaxis, 3 - 6 times a year (Axelsson, Lindhe and Nystrom, 1991). In epidemiological studies, there is a high positive correlation between plaque and gingivitis (Pattanaporn and Navia, 1998).

However, plaque and subgingival calculus, accumulations correlate poorly with severe periodontitis (Löe, Anerud, Boysen and Morrison, 1986). It is clear, therefore, that plaque plays a critical and essential role in the initiation and early development of caries, gingivitis and periodontitis. Its role in their subsequent progression is less clear because of the confounding effects of other factors.

It has been known for many years that plaque can lead to severe destruction of the periodontal and other tissues when the body's immune systems are compromised by diseases such as leukemia, agranulocytosis and AIDS. It has recently been shown, however, that maternal periodontal disease is a statistically significant risk factor for low birth-weight as a consequence of pre-term labor or premature rupture of membranes (Offenbacher *et al.,* 1996). Dental plaque and periodontitis are also strongly correlated with subacute bacterial endocarditis, and are risk factors for cardiovascular disease (AmericanAcademy of Periodontology, 1998).

A new era dawned in the last decade when it was found that dental plaque is not unique, as had been assumed, but is a specialized example of the microbial biofilms that form on many surfaces in the human body as well as in many environmental aquatic systems. These studies combined with newer more sophisticated methods of investigation are yielding new insights which form the substance of this very timely symposium.

References

American Academy of Periodontology. 1998. Periodontal disease as a potential risk factor, for systemic disease. *J. Periodontol.* **69**: 841-850.

Axelsson, P., Lindhe, J. and Nystrom, B. 1991. On the prevention of caries and periodontal disease: results of a 15-year longitudinal study in adults. *J. Clin.Periodontol.* **18**: 182-189.

Baumhammers, A. and Stallard, R.E. 1966. Salivary mucoprotein contribution to dental plaque and calculus. *Periodontics* **4**: 229.

Bjorn, H. and Carlsson, J. 1964. Observations on a dental plaque morphogenesis. *Odont. Revy* **15**: 23.

BIack, G.V. 1898. Dr. Black's conclusions reviewed again. *Dent. Cosmos* **40**: 440.

Carlsson, J. and Egelberg, J. 1965. Effect of diet on early plaque formation in man, *Odont. Revy* **16**: 112.

Egelberg. J. 1965a. Local effect of diet on plaque formation and development of gingivitis in dogs. I. Effect of hard and soft diets. *Odont. Revy* **16**: 31.

Egelberg, J. 1965b. Local effect of diet on plaque formation and development of gingivitis in dogs. II. Effect of frequency of meals and tube feeding. *Odont.Revy* **16**: 50.

Egelberg, J. 1970. A review of the development of dental plaque. In: McHugh, W.D. (Ed.) *Dental Plaque.* pp 9-16. E. S. Livingstone, Edinburgh.

Frank, R.M. and Houver, G. 1970. An ultrastructural study of human supragingival dental plaque formation. In: McHugh, W.D. (Ed.) *Dental Plaque*, pp 85-108. E.S. Livingstone, Edinburgh.

Horowitz, H.S. 1998. The halcyon days of clinical field studies of dental caries prevention. *J. Dent. Res.* **77**: 1380-1383.

Gibbons, R.J., Socransky, S. S., Araujo, W. C. de, and van Houte, J. 1964. Studies of the predominant cultivable microbiota of dental plaque. *Arch. Oral Biol.* **9**: 365-370.

Jensen, S.B., Löe, H., Schiött, C.R. and Theilade, E. 1968. Experimental gingivitis in man. IV. Vancomycin-induced changes in bacterial plaque composition as related to development of gingival inflammation *J. Periodont. Res.* **3**: 284-293.

Larson, R.H., Zipkin, I. and Fitzgerald, R.J. 1963. Effect of dehydroacetic acid and tetracycline on caries activity and its transmission in the rat. *J. Dent. Res.* 42-95.

Löe, H. 1970. A review of the prevention and control of plaque. In: McHugh, W.D. (Ed). *Dental Plaque* pp. 259-270. E. S. Livingstone, Edinburgh.

Löe, H. and Schiött, C.R. 1970. The effect of suppression of the oral microflora upon The formation of dental plaque. In: McHugh, W.D. (Ed) *Dental Plaque*, pp-247-255. E.S. Livingstone, Edinburgh.

Löe, H., Theilade, E. and Jensen, S.B. 1965. Experimental gingivitis in man. *J. Periodontol.* **36**: 177-187.

Löe, H., Theilade, E., Jensen, S.B. and Schiött, C.R. 1967. Experimental gingivitis in man. III. The influence of antibiotics on gingival plaque development. *J. Periodontal Res.* **2**: 282.

Löe, H. Anerud, A., Boysen, H. and Morrison, E. 1986. Natural history of periodontal disease in man. Rapid, moderate and no loss of attachment in Sri Lankan laborers, 14-46 years of age. *J. Clin. Periodontol.* **13**: 431-445.

McHugh, W.D. (Ed.) 1970. *Dental Plaque.* E. S. Livingstone, Edinburgh.

Millin, D.J. and Smith, M.H. 1961. Nature and composition of dental plaque. *Nature* **189**: 664.

Oshrain, H.I. and Salkind, A. 1969. Studies of the histology and bacteriology of subgingival plaque and calculus. *J. Periodont. Res.* **4**: suppl. 4.

Offenbacher, S., Katz, V. Fertig, G., Collins, J. Boyd, D., Maynor, G. McKaig, R. and Beck, J. 1996. Periodontal infection as a possible risk factor for pre-term low birth weight. *J. Periodontol.* **67**: 1103-1112.

Schroeder, H.E. 1969. *Formation and Inhibition of Dental Calculus.* H. Huber, Berne.

Schroeder, H.R. and de Boever, J. 1970. The structure of microbial dental plaque. In: McHugh, W.D. (Ed.) *Dental Plaque*, pp. 49-74. E. S. Livingstone, Edinburgh.

Socransky, S.S., Gibbons, R.J., Dale, A.C., Bortnick, L., Rosethal, E. and Macdonald, J.B. 1963. The microbiota of the gingival crevice area in man. I Total microscopic and viable counts of specific organisms. *Arch. Oral Biol.* **8**: 275-280.

Stephan, R.M. 195 3. The dental plaque in relation to the etiology of caries. *Int. Dent. J.* **4**:180.

Theilade, E., Wright, W.H., Jensen, S.B. and Löe, H. 1966. Experimental gingivitis in man. II A longitudinal, clinical and bacteriological investigation. *J. Periodont. Res.* **1**: 1-13.

Van Leeuwenhoek, A. 1683. Quoted from Dobell, C. (1932). *Antony van Leeuwenhoek and His "Little Animals".* Harcourt Brace and Co., New York.

4

Bacterial Biofilms

THE COMMUNITY ARCHITECTURE OF BIOFILMS: DYNAMIC STRUCTURES AND MECHANISMS

J.W. Costerton, Guy Cook and Richard Lamont

Introduction

People who deal with bacteria, for fun and profit, divide their somewhat arcane field along antrocentric lines, and we speak of Dental Microbiology and Industrial Microbiology amongst many artificial prdgeonholes. Bacteria however, being simple but honest creatures, do not recognize these antrocentric divisions, and they go about their business using effective strategies that were successful millions of years before man evolved. Microbiology is one of the sciences in which the structure and function of the subjects must largely be deduced, because their size usually precludes direct observation. Since the time of Pasteur we have, therefore, recovered bacteria from nature, and we have grown those few whose requirements we can anticipate *in vitro* in monospecies cultures of floating (planktonic) cells. As we gather to think about the complex community of bacteria that actually populate the human oral environment, in the penultimate year of this century, it will be useful to abandon these traditional microbiological approaches and to "catch the wave" of the new century.

Because we now know that bacteria are very sensitive and reactive to their environments, we must resolve to study them *in situ*, using modern direct observation techniques. Some previous deductions, and some conclusions from pure culture studies will be correct, but biofilms predominate in the oral environment and it is troubling that the biofilm phenotype of some species has been shown to differ radically from the planktonic phenotype of the same organism. One of the facets in which biofilm bacteria differ the most profoundly from their planktonic counterparts, is in the critical matter of resistance to antibacterial agents (Nickel *et al.*, 1985). Direct observation are also very important in the definition of community structure, where they can usefully replace our tentative efforts to reconstruct complex communities by mixing cells from highly adapted pure cultures in simulated oral environments. Perhaps the most useful strategy that we can adopt is to anticipate that the strategic basis of biofilm formation and community development is approximately similar in all ecosystems. We can now begin to use new methods of direct observation to study the structure and function of biofilms, independent of whether they impact man in the dental or the environmental sphere, and we can begin to use methods of direct observation in all areas of Biofilm Microbiology if they have produced useful data in any examination of one of these sessile communities. If all of the anthrocentric microbiology communities continue in isolation, modern biofilm concepts and methods will penetrate their structure at different rates, and some will lag far behind. If the new methods are adopted more universally, and are used to examine each system for common features, a great surge of understanding may occur, but we must be forewarned that this choice will threaten the "great guru" status of all of us who enjoy pre-eminence in a field built on authrocentric lines.

It is almost prophetic that these universal perceptions concerning sessile bacterial communities had their origins in interdisciplinary research. Microbiologists were at a loss when it came to making direct observations of bacterial cells in biofilms, and no one in this community had reliable methods for the simple determination of the physical and chemical parameters that obtain in a particular location in a complex biofilm community. This work required a laser confocal microscope that could resolve bacterial cells deep in biofilms on opaque surfaces (Lawrence *et al.*, 1991), miniature microelectrodes that could measure local parameters with a resolution of <50 microns (Lewandowski *et al.*, 1989), and a programmed microscope stage that could correlate these data and produce an accurate image in three dimensions (Lewandowski *et al.*, 1993). Engineers were able to provide all of these new techniques, which have produced revelations when they have been applied to industrial and environmental biofilms, and they are now available to biofilm boffins in all antrocentric divisions of Microbiology. The combination of the "mapping" capability of the biofilm methods developed by engineers, with the equally direct observations made possible by new molecular probes, offers biofilm proponents in all fields the unique opportunity to redefine their research areas and to make very useful contacts in traditionally separated areas. For all of these reasons, we will now offer a compendium of new biofilm concepts and methods that may be useful if applied to long-standing questions and problems in the ecosystem in which biofilms were first discovered and described – the human oral environment.

Biofilm characteristics
The Architecture of Discrete Microcolonies

The blurred images of non-confocal light microscopes, and the dehydration-wracked wreckage seen by electron microscopy of specimens dehydrated for Scanning (SEM) or Transmission (TEM) modes, both contributed to an incorrect image of these slime-enclosed communities. The sessile cells were opaque and solid, and the exopolysaccharide slime was ephemeral, and we concluded that biofilms consist of bacterial cells randomly distributed in a slab-like matrix. When the confocal scanning laser (CSLM) microscope was used to image living biofilms, without dehydration, even the most obtuse operators could see that these sessile communities are actually composed of discrete matrix enclosed microcolonies. These microcolonies, many of which are shaped like mushrooms (Figure 1), were composed of cells (15-20% of volume) non-randomly distributed in a shaped matrix (75-80% of volume) and their shape was responsive to shear forces (Stoodley *et al.*, 1998). At low shear the matrix of the microcolony was shaped like a tower (Figure 1), or a mushroom but, at high shear the matrix was radically elongated and capable of rapid oscillation (Stoodley *et al.*, 1999)

6

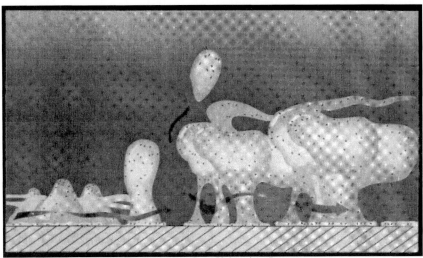

© Center for Biofilm Engineering - Montana State University - Bozeman

Figure 1 Diagramatic representation of the structure of dozens of single species *in vitro* biofilms, and mixed species natural biofilms, in which the sessile bacteria form matrix-enclosed microcolonies. These microcolonies assume various shapes, from "stacks" to mushrooms, and they are interspersed between water channels in which convective flow occurs.

before it broke and detached at the limit of its tensile strength. Individual microcolonies within mixed species biofilms sometimes contain cells of a single morphotype but, more frequently, they contain cells of several different shapes, and molecular techniques often reveal several different species in a single microcolony.

As the microcolonies that make up a young biofilm were seen essentially to comprise a "field of (discrete) mushrooms" (Figure 1), we speculated on the degree of actual separation of these discrete elements when they are packed tightly together in a thick mature biofilm. Studies of the very thick (>5mm) biofilms that develop on surfaces in sewage treatment plants have shown that the water channels that separate discrete microcolonies in the biofilm are maintained, and the exposure of these sessile communities to high shear produces images that resemble the independent movement of kelp fronds in a mature kelp bed in which each plant is anchored and moves independently. If the microcolonies that make up the biofilm are structurally independent, and functionally coherent, it follows that the open spaces between these subunits of the sessile community must contain water and function as channels. Early in his examination of biofilms, Zbigniew Lewandowski had used nuclear magnetic resonance (NMR) to detect the physical state of the water within these accreted communities, and the signals that he obtained indicated connective flow in defined channels (Lewandowski *et al.*, 1992). Later he used confocal microscopy to study the behavior of latex beads that had become entrained in water channels, and he showed that convective flow does indeed occur, in the same direction as the flow in adjoining bulk fluid, but at a reduced rate. This discovery of the discrete microcolony architecture of environmental and industrial biofilms has changed the biofilm concept. Any nutrient or antagonist must enter this anastomosing network of passages, and make contact with each sessile cells by diffusion from the channel into the microcolony, and not from the bulk fluid interface as previously assumed. Very few direct confocal examinations of dental biofilms have been made (Assmus *et al.*, 1997), and none has been made at high shear, so we simply do not know whether some or all dental biofilms lack the water channels that are an integral part of all other biofilms examined to date.

Physiological Heterogeneity

Most of our knowledge of bacterial physiology concerns metabolic processes in cells that are floating in water, in which the interface of greatest importance is with the bulk fluid, in which they move or float. Sessile cells in biofilms are inherently stationary within a hydrated anionic matrix (Sutherland, 1977), that limits diffusion (Stewart, 1996) and then from the bulk fluid by hundreds of microns. Even the simple matter of energy generation by proton extrusion may therefore be profoundly different in biofilms, where protons extruded from the cell displace mobile cations associated with the matrix polymer to produce an acidic "halo" that has been detected by high resolution chemical probes (Korber *et al.*, 1995). Organic acids produced by individual sessile cells may intensify the local acidity in specific locations within biofilms and direct measurements, using pH microelectrodes, have shown that proton concentrations may vary sharply over remarkably short distances within a biofilm. Because the chemical composition of the matrices produced by different species of bacteria may differ, the number of metal ions associated with different microcolonies may vary over a wide range and these differences in local ion concentrations are sufficient to produce measurable potential differences between locations only hundreds of microns apart in a biofilm. Corrosion Microbiologists measure these gradients, which they call "corrosion potentials," because they are sufficiently steep to drive corrosion that may consume a full cm of steel pipe in a few months, if the biofilm is on a conductive surface. If a biofilm has equally steep ion and proton gradients, and it has formed on a nonconductive surface, the physico-chemical gradients within the community may affect the movement of charged molecules (e.g. antibiotics) in ways that we have only began to think about.

Cells that live in a matrix can produce enzymes that associate with the negatively charged matrix polymer, or that diffuse readily through its hydrated interstices. Some biofilm cells produce defensive enzymes that protect them from antibiotics (Beta lactamases), or from oxidizing ions released by phagocytes (catalase, superoxide dismutase), and these enzymes can be arrayed in the proximal matrix to provide a line of defense that is almost impregnable. Similarly, sessile cells can produce aggressive enzymes (e.g. elastase, cellulases) that remain in the proximal matrix and can therefore reach very high local

8

concentrations, and effect a focused attack (Costerton *et al.*, 1995) upon some structural element of plant or animal tissues.

Direct measurements of oxygen, and of other respiratory gases in biofilms, have produced surprising data in that the centers of 50 micron think microcolonies are seen to be completely anaerobic, even when a biofilm composed of a single facultative species is growing in ambient air (deBeer *et al.*, 1994). CO_2 and methane have been shown to reach very high concentrations within specific microcolonies in environmental biofilms, and these very local concentrations of metabolites indicate that individual sessile cells growing in mixed species biofilms actually exist in an almost infinite range of chemical and physical microniches (Costerton *et al.*, 1994) within these microbial communities.

The practical consequences of this remarkable physiological heterogeneity of sessile cells growing in biofilms may be of paramount importance to dental practitioners. Antibacterial agents that kill planktonic cells of periodontal pathogens *in vitro*, may encounter chemical and physical conditions within the biofilm that are inimical with their modes of action. More importantly, sessile cells within biofilms may respond to the conditions in their particular microniche by adopting a whole series of different phenotypes (e.g. aerobic vs. anaerobic) that vary in their susceptibility to a given agent. Regrowth studies in Biofilm Engineering routinely show that biofilms can recover, in a matter of hours, from the bactericidal activities of agents that kill as much as 99% of their component cells. The sessile cells that survive these challenges are located in discrete microcolonies (Figure 2), and they inherit an ideal nutrient microniche when their competitors/compatriots are dead and freshly lysed within the biofilm matrix. We suggest that the direct assessment of bacterial killing, using a modern viability probe and a confocal microscope, is the most logical way to evaluate the efficacy of any agent or procedure designed to kill or remove the sessile bacteria in the biofilms that mediate virtually all dental problems of bacterial origin.

The Biofilm Phenotype

Biofilm Engineers (Stewart, 1996) have used mass transfer calculations, and penetration measurements made by Attenuated total Reflectance Fourrier Transform Infrared Spectroscopy (ATR-FTIR), to study the inherent resistance of biofilms to antibacterial agents (Suci *et al.*, 1994). Analysis of these conceptual and mathematical models has led these engineers to conclude that this resistance does not devolve completely from a penetration limitation (mass transfer resistance), but that there is an important component of resistance at the cellular level, that appears to involve an altered phenotype in the sessile cell. Most of the studies of the biofilm phenotype have concentrated on *Pseudomonas aeruginosa*, and the use of reporter constructs (Davies and Geesey, 1995; Yu and Costerton, unpublished data) has shown that two alginate synthesis genes (*alg C* and *alg D*) are up regulated within 15 minutes of the irreversible adsorbtion of planktonic cells to a surface. Parallel studies suggest (Deretic

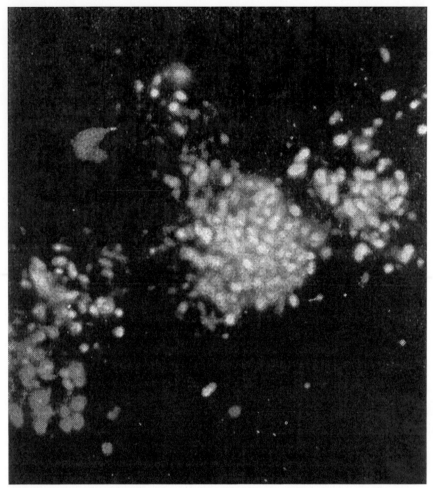

Figure 2 Cells within a *Pseudomonas aeruginosa* biofilm stained with a tetrazolium dye (CTC) to detect respiratory activity. The surviving cells (orange) in this biofilm, which had been treated with chloramine, are clustered in discrete microcolonies amongst the wreckage of dead cells and matrix material that stain weakly green.

et al., 1994) that all of the alginate synthesis genes are turned on, as a "cassette," by the *alg U* gene which produces a sigma factor (epsilon 32) that controls this process of adhesion and matrix production. More detailed examinations of the phenotypic changes that occur when a planktonic cell adheres to a surface, and initiates biofilm formation, show even more profound changes in the Outer Membrane Protein (OMP) fraction of cells of *Pseudomonas aeruginosa* (Figure 3). The dozens of genes that appear to be up regulated to initiate biofilm formation are presently being identified, by two dimensional electrophoresis and by

10

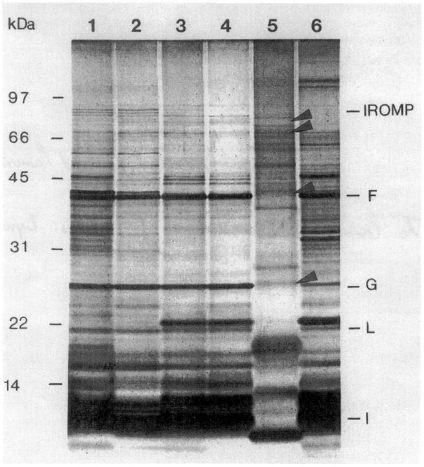

Figure 3 PAGE gel preparation of the Outer Membrane Protein (OMP) fraction of cells of *Pseudomonas aeruginosa* grown as planktonic cells (lanes 1-4 and 6), or as a biofilm (lane 5), showing profound differences in OMP of cells growing in the biofilm phenotype.

proteomics, but there is now unequivocal evidence that the planktonic and biofilm phenotypes of *P. aeruginosa* differ by a number of genes easily sufficient to explain the much increased antibiotic resistance of those sessile organisms (Nickel *et al.*, 1985). A very small number of other environmental species have been examined, vis-à-vis phenotypic difference between planktonic and biofilm cells, and profound differences have been found in each case.

It is much too early to make sweeping assumptions but, if even a few pivotal species of dental bacteria show similar differences between planktonic and biofilm phenotypes, this will mandate that the biofilm phenotype must be used in all definitive examinations of pathogenic processes in dental systems. Many strategies, from the selection of antibiotics to the design of vaccines, depend on the gene products that comprise that bacterial cell envelope. If these gene products are distinctive in the cell envelope of cells growing in biofilms, virtually all of the studies of the etiology of dental disease should be redone using cells of the same species growing in the biofilm phenotype. The somewhat muted success of dental vaccines, and the strategies based on interference with adhesion strategies, may be sharply improved when we realize that tactics directed against targets in planktonic cells may be effective against planktonic invaders but ineffective against cells of the same organism growing in nascent or established biofilm.

Biofilm Signaling

The direct demonstration (Davies *et al.*, 1998) that acyl homoserine lactone (AHL) signal molecules are instrumental in the formation of biofilms, by cells of *P. aeruginosa,* is less important than the deduction that some type of signal must be involved in the sequential development of any structural community as complex as a microbial biofilm. Certainly, mushroom-shaped towers in which bacterial cells grow in defined spatial patterns, which are separated by intervening open water channels from other similar towers, clearly implies the existence of a signaling system that resembles the hormones that control embryogenesis in multicellular organisms. Our knowledge of bacterial signaling (Fuqua *et al.*, 1994) and dozens of different classes of compounds from AHLs, to polyphosphate kinase to cydic peptides (Dunny and Leonard, 1997) have been implicated in the control of the development of structural microbial communities, of which dental biofilms are paramount examples. Again, the biofilm field is just getting its collective mind around the concept of signal-directed community development. For this reason the pivotal question is, are oral biofilms sufficiently similar to other types of biofilms, that we should begin to look for the presence of known or unknown classes of signal molecules in these communities. While this is generally true, the complex structure of these communities strongly suggests some form of organizational control, and the response of gingival tissues to subgingival plaque strongly suggests some form of signaling between biofilm bacteria and host tissues. The good news that follows from this preliminary deduction is that any chemical signaling system lends itself to manipulation by signal analogues that either block or promote the bacterial cell activity controlled by the signal. Signal analogues that prevented *Fusobacterium nucleatum* from joining a biofilm, or that promoted the detachment of *Porphyromonas gingivalis* from subgingival plaque, might be of some interest to clinicians who treat this notably recalcitrant biofilm disease (Costerton *et al.*, 1999).

Valete

The anthrocentric divisions of microbiology will always serve their practical clients well. Dental Microbiology will serve dental practitioners, just as

Agricultural Microbiology will serve agricultural scientists and practitioners. However, it is important that microbiologists within the anthrocentric disciplines who are interested in specific and universal bacterial "behaviors," like the formation and development of biofilms, join the mainstream of the science to develop these common themes. Because biofilms constitute a microbial community that is protected from a wide variety of antibacterial factors, from simple drying to antibiotic challenge, it is likely that they will predominate in any nutrient-sufficient ecosystem. Because all biofilms are structurally and physiologically complex, and because most described to date create and maintain a system of open water channels, we deduce the activity of some form of cell-cell signaling that controls both structure and function. Simple *sine qua non* experiments can be designed to determine whether open water channels exist in dental biofilms. Somewhat more complex analyses can be used to determine whether known signal molecules are produced in dental biofilms, and whether gingival tissues respond to chemical signals from subgingival plaque. If dental biofilms are similar to the sessile communities that predominate in most other ecosystems, there is a vast wealth of new direct methods and fresh biofilm concepts that can accelerate progress in Dental Microbiology, just as they have accelerated progress in Environmental and Industrial Microbiology. I am sure that the organizers of this exciting meeting intended that such a synthesis should take place, and I salute their wonderful perceptions and their open-mindedness.

References

Assmus, B., M. Hausner, D. Genier, M. Schloter, A. Hartman and M. Goldmen. 1997. Direct examination of subgingival plaque from a diseased periodontal site using confocal laser scanning microscopy (CLSM). *New Microbiol.* **20**: 155-159.

Costerton, J.W., Z. Lewandowski, D. DeBeer, D. Caldwell, D. Korber and G. James. 1994. Minireview: Biofilms, the customized micronich. *J. Bact.* **176**(8): 2137-2142.

Costerton, J. W., Z. Lewandowski, D.E. Caldwell, D.R. Korber and H.M. Lappin-Scott. 1995. Microbial biofilms. *Ann. Rev. Micro.* **49**: 711-745.

Costerton, J.W., P.S. Stewart and E.P. Greenberg. 1999. Bacterial Biofilms: A Common Cause of Persistent Infections. *Science* **284**: 1318-1322.

Davies, D.G. and G.G. Geesey. 1995. Regulation of the alginate biosynthesis gene *alg*C in *Pseudomonas aeruginosa* during biofilm development in continuous culture. *Appl. Environ. Microbiol.* **61**(3): 860-867.

Davies, D.G., M.R. Parsek, J.P. Pearson, B.H. Iglewski, J.W. Costerton and E.P. Greenberg. 1998. The involvement of cell-to-cell signals in the development of a bacterial biofilm. *Science* **280**: 295-298.

deBeer D., P. Stoodley, F. Roe and Z. Lewandowski. 1994. Effects of biofilm structures on oxygen distribution and mass transport. *Biotechnol. Bioeng.* **43**: 1131-1138.

Deretic, V., M.J. Schurr, J.C. Boucher,and D.W. Martin. 1994. Conversion of *Pseudomonas aeruginosa* to mucoidy in cystic fibrosis: Environmental stress and regulation of bacterial virulence by alternative sigma factors. *J. Bact.* **176**: 2773-2780.

Dunny, G.M. and B.A. Leonard. 1997. Cell-cell communication in Gram-positive bacteria. *Ann. Rev. Microbiol.* **51**: 527-564.

Fuqua,W.C., E.P. Winans and E.P. Greenberg. 1994. Quorum sensing in bacteria: The Lux R - Lux I family of cell density-responsive transcriptional regulators. *J. Bacteriol.* 176: 269-275.

Korber, D.R., J.R. Lawrence, H.M. Lappin-Scott and J.W. Costerton. 1995. Growth of microorganisms on surfaces. In: *Microbial Biofilms*, H.M. Lappin-Scott and J.W. Costerton (Eds.), Cambridge University Press, Cambridge.

13

Lawrence J.R., D.R. Korber, B.D. Hoyle, J.W. Costerton, and D.E. Caldwell. 1991. Optical sectioning of microbial biofilms. *J. Bacteriol.* **173**: 6558-6567.

Lewandowski Z., W. Lee, W.G. Characklis and B. Little. 1989. Dissolved oxygen and pH microelectrode measurements at water immersed metal surfaces. *Corrosion,* **45**: 92-98.

Lewandowski, Z., S.A. Altobelli, P.D. Majors and E. Fukushima. 1992. NMR imaging of hydrodynamics near microbially colonized surfaces. *Wat. Sci. Tech.* **26**: 577-584.

Lewandowski, Z., S.A. Altobelli and E. Fukushima. 1993. NMR and microelectrode studies of hydrodynamics and kinetics in biofilms. *Biotechnol. Prog.* **9**: 40-45.

Nickel, J.C., I. Ruseska, J.B. Wright and J.W. Costerton. 1985. Tobramycin resistance of *Pseudomonas aeruginosa* cells growing as a biofilm on urinary catheter material. *Antimicrob. Agents Chemother.* **27**(4): 619-624.

Stewart, P.S. 1996. Theoretical aspects of antibiotic diffusion into microbial biofilms. *Antimicrob. Agents & Chemother.* **40** (11): 2517-2522.

Stoodley, P., Z. Lewandowski, J.D. Boyle and H.M. Lappin-Scott. 1998. Oscillation characteristics of biofilm streamers in turbulent flowing water as related to drag and pressure drop. *Biotechnol. Bioeng.* **57**: 536-544.

Stoodley, P., I. Dodds, Z. Lewandowski, A.B. Cunningham, J.D. Boyle and H.M. Lappin-Scott. 1999. Influence of hydrodynamics and nutrients on biofilm structure. *J. Appl. Microbiol.* **85**: 19S-28S.

Suci, P.A., M.W. Mittelman, F.P. Yu and G.G. Geesey. 1994. Investigation of ciprofloxacin penetration into *Pseudomonas aeruginosa* biofilms. *Antimicrob. Agents Chemotherapy* **38**(9): 2125-2133.

Sutherland, I.W. 1977. *Surface Carbohydrates of the Prokaryotic Cell.* Academic Press, London.

BIOFILM FORMATION AND STRUCTURE: WHAT'S NEW?

Sara K. Roberts, Catherine Bass, Melanie Brading, Hilary Lappin-Scott and Paul Stoodley

Biofilms form under a variety of different physical , chemical and biological conditions. After the initial attraction to surfaces the bacteria grow, the biofilm increases in thickness and detachment events occur. We have developed microscopy flow cells which can be used to monitor, in real time, all of these processes. The image analysis microscopy system captures data and supports interpretation of these important biofilm processes.

The incorporation of different surfaces into flow cells and Robbins devices has allowed the investigation of different surfaces on biofilm formation. For example, clear differences were observed in bacterial attachment on a range of surface materials. An appreciation of the surface roughness characteristics of the surfaces showed that this was an important consideration for initial colonisation by Pseudomonads.

Scanning electron microscopy has shown that bacteria (but not filamentous fungi) 'nesting' within crevices in different materials and this has been supported by atomic force microscopy data. Specifically, higher populations of bacteria were recorded on surfaces with higher surface roughness. These data will be discussed in the context of the mouth environment where different hydrodynamics (caused by different salivary flow rates) and different surface roughnesses (from dental acrylic, cements and catheter material) may contribute to differing susceptibilities of bacterial colonisation and biofilm structure.

Thus far our research has concentrated on aerobic bacteria. However, we have also developed a system to study in situ biofilm formation by communities of anaerobes using flow cell technology and image analysis. To date these have focused on the sulphate-reducing bacteria but the model is useful to study growth rates, biofilm thickness and detachment of mixtures of aerobes and anaerobes as pertinent to dental plaque.

Introduction

Since the mid 1940's the existence of biofilms has been recognised and it is now widely accepted that biofilm environments are the preferred mode of growth for bacteria. There still remain many aspects of biofilm development and control that require investigation. Work reported in the literature has shown biofilms may be considered to be stable microenvironments in which the microbial community is protected from environmental and antimicrobial challenges (Stewart *et al.*, 1998; Allison and Gilbert, 1995; Brown and Gilbert, 1993).

The aim of this review is to discuss current research and recent findings on the initial attachment of cells to surfaces and to assess how far our understanding of the complex nature of biofilms has progressed. Some recently developed methodology is also described.

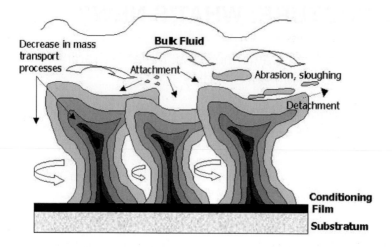

Figure 1 Conceptual model for the chemical and physical factors that affect a maturing biofilm. White arrows indicate flow over the biofilm and through the interstitial channels. The number of interstitial channels decrease over time resulting in changes in flow and decreases in mass transport processes. Shading indicates the development of chemical and physical gradients that develop as a result of reduced mass transport (darker areas represent areas of lowest availability). The overall structure of the biofilm will ultimately depend on the flow velocity of the system. It has been reported (unpublished data) that instead of existing as collection of individual microcolonies in close proximity (as above) the upper sections of the biofilm are connected forming bridge like structures.

Factors that affect attachment

The factors that affect attachment of organisms to a surface have been broadly categorised into chemical, physical and biological. Although much research has been carried out in these areas they will not all be discussed; the reader is directed instead to a recent review of this topic (Brading *et al.*, 1995). Those topics that are covered in this review include the physical and chemical properties of the surface. A conceptual model summarising physical and chemical factors that affect a maturing biofilm and how they influence biofilm structure is illustrated in Figure 1. Costerton *et al.*, (1985) proposed that initial rate of biofilm formation by bacterial adhesion is to a degree dependent on the chemical nature of the surface. Recent research has also shown that the physical nature of the surface is important (Hissett *et al.*, 1995). In many instances, contaminated surfaces require cleaning/disinfecting to reduce microbial fouling. It has been shown that not only is the type of surface important in attachment but that the type of surface often dictates how easily the surface may be cleaned or disinfected.

Physical Characteristics Affecting Biofilm Development

Dagnall (1986) described surface texture as being comprised of three parameters: form, waviness and roughness. Form describes the general shape of the surface, whereas roughness and waviness are considered to be primary and

16

secondary textures respectively. Waviness describes the component of texture upon which roughness is superimposed. Roughness is caused by irregularities inherent in the production process and dictates the number of peaks and valleys. A rough surface has been defined from a mechanistic point of view as a folded, flat surface with an extended surface area from which similar interaction forces arise as from a smooth surface (Bos *et al.*, 1999). Another factor to consider when examining surface structure is the lay of the surface. There are some machining processes that cause patternation on the surface resulting in distinct directional characteristics. For example, a ground surface exhibits a distinct lay when compared to a sandblasted surface which has a random topography and no lay direction.

Surface roughness may affect attachment for a number of reasons. On a rough surface there is more area available for bacterial attachment and growth. A rougher surface also provides more protection for colonising bacteria. Mueller *et al.* (1992) found a positive correlation between surface roughness and bacterial attachment. In plaque formation, bacterial colonisation of tooth enamel has been shown to start in the surface irregularities, cracks and grooves, suggesting that these areas provide protection (Quriyynen, 1994). Quriyynen (1994) also found that following initial colonisation, growth rate and maturation of the supragingival plaque increased when the intra-oral surfaces were roughened. A number of authors have reported that microscopic surface irregularities associated with fine roughening of the surface provide entrapment areas for microbial cells, including yeast (Verran *et al.*, 1991), and promote adhesion. Increased adhesion associated with these surfaces has been attributed to the protection of cells from shear forces and to the increase in surface area available for adhesion (Quirynen and Bollen, 1995). Although other reports suggest that gross surface defects found in rougher surfaces do not protect bacteria from shear forces great enough to displace microbial cells (Taylor *et al.*, 1995; Verran and Taylor, 1995).

Work conducted by Brading (PhD Thesis, 1996) at Exeter University confirmed that not only is the protection afforded to the bacteria on rougher surfaces important but that the increase in surface area associated with rougher surfaces is also significant. In her study the influence of the physical nature of the surfaces on biofilm formation by a binary culture of *Pseudomonas fluorescens* EX101 and *Pseudomonas putida* EX102 was examined on a range of different surfaces (stainless steel, PVC, brass and glass). These surfaces are all of environmental and industrial importance, being used commonly in water distribution pipelines, plumbing and food processing systems. The surfaces were examined by atomic force microscopy (AFM). The arithmetic roughness average (R_a) values obtained from AFM analysis provide quantitative measurements of surface roughness. The R_a values obtained ranked the degree of roughness of each surface as follows: stainless steel > PVC > brass > glass. The numbers of *Ps. fluorescens* and *Ps. putida* attached to the surfaces were plotted against the R_a values. The results showed that there was a corresponding increase in viable cell numbers with the type and roughness of the surface.

A

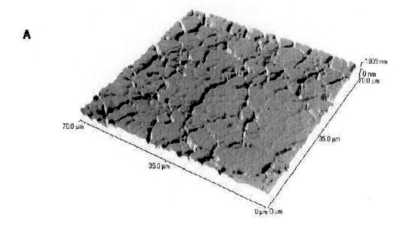

B

Figure 2 3-D images of the surface treatments of stainless steel AISI 316. **A** Untreated surface; **B** polished surface; **C** ground surface; **D** sandblasted surface.

To study the effect of surface roughness on biofilm formation, stainless steel AISI 316 was roughened by three different methods (polishing, grinding and sandblasting). AFM was used to obtain 3-D images of the surfaces (Figure 2). The R_a values obtained ranked the degree of roughness as follows: sandblasted > ground > polished. The three treatments provided very different environments for biofilm formation. Initially the results showed that there was no significant difference in biofilm accumulation observed for the three roughened stainless

18

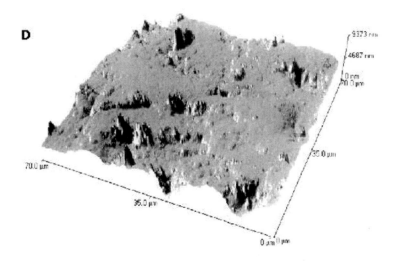

Figure 2 continued Diagrammatic representation of an MRD showing direction of flow and position of studs. Block arrows indicate direction of flow.

steel samples. However statistical analysis revealed that after 24h growth there was significantly greater biofilm accumulation on the sandblasted steel than on the polished steel. Thus any effect seen was attributed to increased surface roughness and surface area for bacterial colonisation as well as the added protection from the effects of bulk fluid flow. This is a particularly important factor when considering flow conditions where shear forces are operating. The results from these data indicate that roughness of the surface was not affecting initial attachment of the bacteria, rather the subsequent persistence and growth of these bacteria on that surface (see also, Bos *et al.*, 1999).

Quantifying the effects of surface roughness as a means of providing protection is difficult. It can be considered that a polished surface is more exposed, with fewer sites for initial attachment. Preferential colonisation within surface irregularities on rougher surfaces, for example ground and sandblasted stainless steel (AISI 316), was not observed (Bos *et al.*, 1999; Brading, PhD Thesis, 1996). However it is possible that initial attachment occurred preferentially in these areas (only qualitative visual assessments were conducted). Quantification of preferred colonisation sites has been achieved by Geesey *et al.*, (1996), however the attachment in many instances is believed to be random (Hamilton *et al.*, 1995, Camper *et al.*, 1994).

In summary the data obtained from the investigation (Brading, PhD Thesis, 1996) indicated that the surface roughness is most important for bacterial accumulation and persistence on the surface. The influence of surface roughness is then more likely to influence surface cleanability (Bos *et al.*, 1999). According to published research, stainless steel is comparable in its biological cleanability to glass and significantly better than polymers, aluminium or copper. A biofilm developing on a stainless steel surface can be treated with lower concentrations of disinfectant than those on polymer surfaces (Boulangé-Petermann, 1996; Dhaliwal *et al.*, 1992; Krysinski, *et al.*, 1992). As surface roughness is increased biofilm accumulation would also be expected to be greater due to the additional surface area available and the protection provided by the surface irregularities. It should also be taken into account that the exposed surface area is dependent on roughness rather than the overall dimension of the sample. However, this is scale dependent, and the roughness itself must be measured on a similar or larger scale than the overall dimensions of the bacterial cells.

Chemical Characteristics Affecting Biofilm Development

The chemical composition of the surface is important for bacterial colonisation particularly if the surface possesses components which are either beneficial or detrimental to the adhering/adherent population. For instance with brass, an alloy of copper and zinc, dezincification may occur and copper has antimicrobial properties. In spite of this biofilm formation on copper has been reported. It is believed that the production of exopolymeric substances (EPS) immobilise copper ions (Mueller *et al.*, 1992) or that the some cells behave altruistically by taking up toxic heavy metals from the surroundings to allow the continued activity of the remaining bacterial population (Southam *et al.*, 1995). In contrast surfaces such as PVC may well possess components that bacteria could utilise. PVC is largely composed of carbon, hydrogen and chlorine although these are unlikely to be available to the bacteria. Added UV stabilisers and colourant may well influence attachment (Rogers *et al.*, 1994). Other components may also be associated with the surface including calcium stearate, which is used as a lubricant in manufacturing process, and glycol. Both of these compounds would have a beneficial effect on biofilm formation; for example calcium acts as a cross-linking agent in EPS production. In the case of glass, a supercooled mixture of sodium and calcium silicates (Sharp, 1985), it is unlikely that any component would be available to the bacteria to influence the colonisation process. Consequently, any effect of the surface on biofilm formation is most likely attributed to the physicochemical properties of the glass surface and also cannot be ruled out in the case of other surfaces.

The physicochemical properties of a surface are related to the chemical nature of the surface. These properties, including surface charge, hydrophobicity, surface free energy and surface bonding, rather than influencing the entire colonisation process, have an important role on the actual attachment process from the moment a bacterium comes into contact with the surface. The immersion of a surface into an aquatic environment results in the formation of a layer of organic deposits of biological origin, for example, proteins and humic acids. This is termed the conditioning film. Molecules and small particles (<0.01-0.1 µm) rapidly adhere to the surface and can induce change in the surface properties which include: acquisition of a net negative charge; decrease in hydrophobicity; variations in zeta potentials, surface contact angles, critical surface tension and free energy as a function of their original surface energy. The composition of the conditioning film will vary with the type of surface. It is generally assumed, though with no conclusive evidence, that the conditioning film across the surface is uniform in both composition and coverage. The manner in which conditioning films influence microbial attachment remains unclear. Korber *et al.* (1995) suggested the occurrence of interactions between the chemical groups of the organic molecules and bacterial appendages, such as pili, flagella or bacterial EPS. It has also been proposed more recently that the strength of biofilm formation becomes dependent upon the cohesiveness of the conditioning film rather than upon the direct bacterial contact with the bare substratum surface (Bos *et al.*, 1999).

The liquid medium surrounding the substratum also plays a role in bacterial attachment. The availability of metabolites has been shown by a number of authors not only to play a role in bacterial attachment but has an overall effect on biofilm morphology (Stoodley *et al.*, 1999; Mohamed *et al.*, 1997). Although a physical factor the flow rate of the medium is also crucial in determining the rate of bacterial attachment (Camper *et al.*, 1998) and biofilm morphology (Stoodley *et al.*, 1999), as this directly relates to mass transport processes (Figure 1). Stoodley *et al.* (1999) reported that biofilms grown under laminar flow conditions developed as patchy microcolonies and consisted of roughly circular cell clusters separated by interstitial voids. Biofilms grown under turbulent flow conditions on the other hand were also patchy but these biofilms consisted of patches of ripples and elongated "streamers" which oscillated in the flow. It has been demonstrated that these interstitial voids act as transport channels (Lewandoski *et al.*, 1995; De Beer *et al.*, 1994; Stoodley *et al.*, 1994; Drury *et al*, 1993). As the biofilm develops the interstitial void fractions

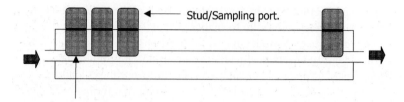

Experimental surface attached.The surfaces are 1cm in diameter and are

fixed to black rubber backing discs which fit directly into the stud. The

surfaces are easily removed from the stud for analysis.

Figure 3 Scanning electron micrograph illustrating mixed biofilm formation after 24 h growth on stainless steel AISI 321. The biofilm was established under laminar flow conditions, *Re* = 2.72. The model organisms were all environmental isolates and consisted of four Gram negative rod shaped bacteria *Stenotrophomonas maltophilia*, *Pseudomonas alcaligenes*, *Alcaligenes denitrificans* and *Flavobacterium indologenes*. Also the inoculum included one non-fermentative yeast *Rhodotorula glutinis* and two filamentous fungi *Fusarium solani* and *Fusarium oxysporum* which were not captured in this frame. Scale bar = 5μm.

decrease. Reductions in these voids would decrease the mass transport characteristics within the bulk liquid phase and therefore ultimately control growth rate of the biofilm by a reduction in nutrient and possibly oxygen availability (Characklis, Turakhia and Zelver, 1990).

Experimental systems to study biofilms
Biofilms represent a complex community. The parameters that can be evaluated when studying biofilms are restricted by the nature of the experimental model. As such experimental biofilms generally only represent certain aspects of the system under investigation. There are several models currently in use to study biofilms, however, only two will be discussed at length providing a comparison between destructive and non-destructive techniques.

Modified Robbin's Device (MRD)
The MRD (Figure 3) was initially developed to study biofouling in industrial pipelines (Bale *et al.*, 1988). Since then it has been modified and used to study biofilms from a number of different systems. The MRD consists of an enclosed lumen with twenty five replaceable sampling studs. Different surfaces can be attached to the studs and removed for analysis by a number of different techniques. Some of the parameters evaluated by researchers at these laboratories include viable and total cell counts, scanning electron microscopy (SEM) and AFM. The MRD can be incorporated into a variety of experimental models such as a batch recirculating and flow through culture systems (Roberts *et al.*, 1999 in press; Elvers *et al.*, 1997; Elvers *et al.*, 1998; Brading *et al.*, 1995) or it can be

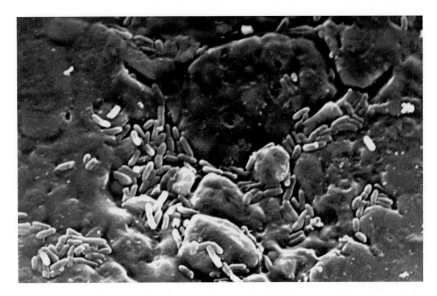

Figure 4 Scanning electron micrograph illustrating mixed biofilm formation after 24 h growth on stainless steel AISI 321. The biofilm was established under the same conditions described in the previous figure and shows *Rhodotorula glutinis* (**Y**) nesting in the surface irregularities. Scale bar = 5μm.

connected to a chemostat as a recirculating or flow through culture system (Linton *et al.*, 1999; Jass *et al.*, 1995).

In work reported by Roberts *et al.*, (in press, 1999) the stainless steel used in MRD experiments was analysed by AFM for assessment of the surface topography. The cross-sectional view of the surface illustrated numerous surface irregularities. SEM analysis of mixed biofilm formation on stainless steel, taken from the MRD after 24 h growth, revealed that bacteria and yeast were 'nesting' within the surface irregularities. Examples of this nesting phenomenon are illustrated in Figures 4 and 5. As discussed previously the protection offered to micro-organisms in grain boundaries has serious implications concerning the cleanability of this particular surface which is commonly used in industry and may harbour and retain pathogens.

The main drawback with the MRD system is that it is a destructive technique and involves scraping of the biofilm for analysis of biofilm accumulation and metabolic counts. Other drawbacks with the MRD system include: the biofilm can not be visualised *in situ*; possible nutrient gradients along the length of the lumen from the inlet to the outlet. Hydrodynamics around the sampling stud may also be compromised (Hall-Stoodley *et al.*, 1999a). Nevertheless the information obtained from the MRD model is valuable and allows comparisons to be drawn with other techniques.

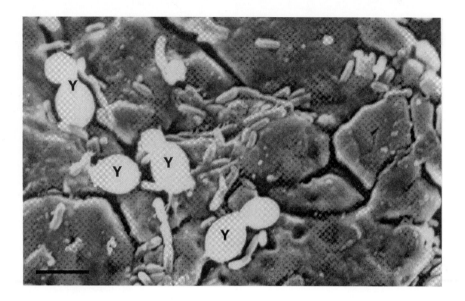

Figure 5 Scanning electron micrograph illustrating mixed biofilm formation after 24 h growth on stainless steel AISI 321. The biofilm was established under the same conditions described in the previous figure and shows *Rhodotorula glutinis* (**Y**) nesting in the surface irregularities. Scale bar = 5 μm.

Image Analysis and Flow Cells

Although valuable information can be obtained from models that involve the disruption of the biofilm, the continuous and non-destructive analysis of biofilms is essential in understanding biofilm processes (McCoy *et al.*, 1981). *In situ* monitoring techniques have advanced with recent developments in image analysis technology. The advantages of this technique include the monitoring of the biofilm in a hydrated state and real time analysis. Using digital image capture, accumulation rates can be calculated by comparing captured images with those at the outset of the experiment, allowing quantification of the growth kinetics of the biofilm; qualitative information regarding surface colonisation is also possible (Hall-Stoodley *et al.*, 1999b).

At Exeter University, two types of flow cells are currently used the flat plate reactor (Figure 6) and the square glass tube reactor (Figure 7). The flat plate reactor was developed at the Centre of Biofilm Engineering, Bozeman Montana. In this apparatus different surfaces can be examined and compared (Hall-Stoodley *et al.*, 1999a). The surface can also be removed for other types of analyses. The disadvantage of the flat plate reactor is that it is constrained by the channel thickness. This model of flow cell is limited by the nature of the working distances of the microscope objectives, resulting in a compromise between magnification and hydrodynamics (Characklis, 1990). Use of the square glass tube reactor can overcome this problem which facilitates higher

24

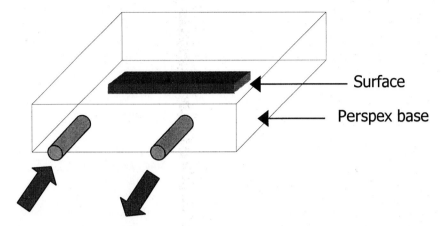

Figure 6 Diagrammatic representation of a flat plate reactor. Block arrows indicate direction of flow.

magnification of the biofilm allowing the flow cell to be viewed from above (Hall-Stoodley *et al.*, 1999b). The square glass tube reactor flow cell was initially designed to replicate biofilm fouling in industrial pipelines. Biofilm formation can be monitored under both laminar and turbulent flow conditions comparable to industrial flow rates. Stoodley *et al.*, (1998) have characterised the flow hydrodynamics of this system using the relationship between the friction factor and the Reynolds number and found that they fit established equations describing laminar and turbulent flow through a smooth pipe. This system also permits visualisation of biofilm formation under both laminar and turbulent flow concurrently (Stoodley *et al.*, 1999).

Assessing biofilm growth by image analysis can be monitored by measuring the surface area covered and biofilm thickness. Biofilm thickness is defined, in this instance, to be the distance between the substratum and the peaks of the highest cell clusters. By using this definition, the channels (void fraction) and the cell clusters (biomass fraction) are considered integral components of the biofilm (Stoodley *et al.*, 1998). The height of the biofilm may be measured microscopically by focusing on the substratum and moving the stage through a pre-calibrated distance until the upper biofilm cells are in focus. Calibration of the stage stepper is achieved by measuring a known vertical distance to determine the correction factor. The distance travelled by the stage, as measured on the integral Vernier scale, is multiplied by the correction factor to give the biofilm height. The images are processed with a Macintosh G3 computer and captured using the public domain NIH-Image 1.59 program (developed at the National Institute of Health). In order to obtain surface coverage measurements a binary threshold (black:white) was applied to captured images. The relative surface coverage of the biofilm is the proportion of black to white within the field of view.

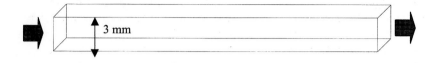

Figure 7 Diagrammatic representation of a glass tube reactor. Block arrows indicate direction of flow.

Summary of Experimental Systems to Study Biofilms

The models described above are very versatile, pure and mixed cultures can be examined under a variety of different conditions depending on the type of system under investigation. Information obtained from these systems could be extrapolated with relevance to dental biofilms. For instance the nesting of bacteria and yeast within surface irregularities will have direct implications for the cleanability of tooth surfaces. Removal of bacteria from gingival pockets, interproximal spaces and other retention sites is difficult (Bos *et al.*, 1999) and some cleaning agents and disinfectants have been shown to strengthen bacterial attachment (Eginton *et al.*, 1997). This is especially important where dental hygiene is concerned as yeasts are emerging more as life threatening pathogens in hospitalised and immunodeficient patients (Millsap *et al.*, 1998). Monitoring biofilms under different dynamic conditions is particularly relevant in studying dental biofilms as there are a number of different flow velocities and shear forces operating within the oral cavity.

Dental biofilms – an introduction

Dental plaque has been defined as the microbial community found on tooth surfaces embedded in a matrix of polymer of bacterial and host origin (Landa, *et al.*, 1996; Douglas, 1994; Scheie, 1994). It is found in the mouth both in healthy and diseased individuals and is the aetiological agent of the two most prevalent diseases affecting industrialised societies, dental caries and periodontal disease.

Colonisation of the oral cavity is a continuous process. The relatively smooth surfaces of the teeth are exposed to frequent mechanical cleaning by the tongue, cheek, saliva or toothbrush, however these actions have proved ineffective at preventing tooth decay/biofilm removal alone. The very structure of teeth, a non-shedding surface, favours the retention of food and thus provides numerous sites for harbouring dental biofilms and it has been reported that there are between 200-500 resident bacterial species in the mouth. Between 10 and 30 species of subgingival plaque bacteria have been implicated in the aetiology of periodontitis in humans (Page, 1995) and the adherent population may stimulate the adhesion of planktonic micro-organisms present in saliva in vast amounts, up to 10^8 CFU ml^{-1} (Bos, *et al.*, 1999). The diversity of the plaque microflora is believed to be due primarily to the endogenous nutrients supplied by the host, rather than by the exogenous factors in the diet.

Initially an organic film is formed by the presence of foods, namely acidic glycoproteins from the saliva, gingival crevicular fluid and bacteria (Bradshaw *et al.*, 1997). This film provides attachment sites for the colonisation and growth of bacterial microcolonies and may also dictate the adhesive strength of the biofilm (Bos *et al.*, 1999; Busscher *et al.*, 1995). It has been found that the initial attachment of bacteria to this film is relatively species specific and involves the co-operation and co-aggregation of only a few Gram positive streptococci including *S. sanguis*, *S. sobrinus*, *S. mutans* and *S. mitis* are involved (Pratten *et al.*, 1998; Bradshaw *et al.*, 1997). The growth of this microbial film encourages the proliferation of other organisms including filamentous Gram negative *Fusobacterium* species (*F. nucleatum*) and spirochetes such as *Borrelia* species. In thick plaque anaerobic organisms including *Actinomyces* species may predominate. It is likely that anoxia develops through the action of facultative bacteria growing aerobically on organic materials on the tooth because the dense matrix of the plaque decreases oxygen diffusion onto the tooth surface. It is therefore relevant to discuss here methods for studying anaerobic biofilms which have recently been developed at Exeter University.

Anaerobic Biofilms

The development of an anaerobic system to study biofilms in flow cells and micromodels has extended the range of characteristics which may be investigated in the laboratory. These techniques have been used primarily to study consortia of organisms derived from oil-field reservoirs (Bass *et al.*, 1993, Bass *et al.*, 1996, Bass *et al.,* 1998a, 1998b) and allow direct visualisation of attachment and biofilm development in different conditions of flow, nutrient status and temperature, simulating deep terrestrial subsurface habitats.

At first glance such relentlessly anaerobic and extreme environments might be considered to bear little relation to the oral cavity. Closer investigation reveals more similarities however. One feature of fluid-filled rock matrices away from the immediate vicinity of injection and production wells is slow flow rates, which are not necessarily constant. Variability in nutrient status, water availability and temperature are determined either by changes influenced by groundwater flow dynamics, or influxes of fluids resulting from surface injected secondary recovery waters and these are controlled by remote operational decisions. Abstraction of hydrocarbons also has an effect on subsurface flow characteristics and pressure variation may occur. Physically, growth of biofilm can cause pore blocking and subsequent flow diversion, leaving stagnant rock pores where no flow occurs. Sudden changes of flow direction or pressure may also cause movement of rock particles, clay fines and other abrasive agents which affect attached bacteria and biofilm on exposed surfaces.

On a smaller scale, many analagous effects can be considered to occur in the mouth. Fluid flow rate is variable and contains a wide range of nutrient; water availability and temperature are also variable. Fluid influences range from the constant presence of saliva, to intermittent flooding with a variety of fluids according to the whim of the oral cavity's owner! The highly abrasive action of chewing and swallowing different foodstuffs will affect bacteria attached to exposed tooth surfaces, whereas those bacteria in biofilms deeply embedded in dental crevices can be likened to those in a blocked rock pore. Shear forces will also act on exposed dental surfaces during chewing , drinking and swallowing processes.

Gaseous Environment

Flow cells for image analysis of anaerobic biofilms are centred around an Olympus BH2 microscope fitted with a customised acrylic and aluminium support to accommodate a flow cell. The adaptor fits directly to the microscope objective plane to allow observation via the objectives by a Cohu CCTV camera interfaced with a Macintosh Power PC. Images are transferred to disk using computer software (Scion Image, NIH software) and stored as digitised images for printing and analysis as described for the flat bed reactor. Oxygen is excluded from developing anaerobic biofilms by preparing media in de-oxygenated water, using redox poising agents where appropriate. Vessel contents are overlaid with a blanket of oxygen-free-nitrogen (OFN) at all times to restrict access of oxygen to the experimental media and biofilm. Gas impermeable tubing is employed wherever feasible. This is essential for the culture of biofilms of organisms from deep subsurface environments; for modelling dental biofilms the opportunity exists for supplying a range of micro-aerobic conditions by sparging fluids with suitable gases prior to passage through the flow cell, enabling the development of anaerobic plaque models.

Flow Rates

Fluid movement in deep subsurface oil-bearing rock matrices is often slow, particularly in consolidated chalk and sandstone formations where rock is highly porous and fluid permeates from its source over a three dimensional flood front. Unconsolidated sandstone and fractured chalk offer different conditions, where fluids take the path of least resistance through fissures and faults, occasionally bypassing large reservoir zones. Analagous conditions may be considered to co-exist in the mouth, in which the entire surface is constantly bathed in saliva, yet localised areas are likely to be subjected to intermittent shear forces. To model slow water movement on a laboratory scale using flow cells, it is necessary to operate a system which can control flow rates at 3–5 mL h^{-1} (Reynolds number 3 in flow cell). Standard peristaltic pumps are unable to provide a suitable flow regime at this rate as the slow rotation of the pump head imposes a visible pulse which influences attachment and growth. A system has been devised which allows fluid passage under a constant hydraulic head. Flow rates are adjusted by altering the relative height of supply and effluent reservoirs thus generating differential pressure between the inlet and outlet of the cell (Figure 8).

The influent constant volume reservoir is supplied with fresh medium pumped from a further reservoir and the volume maintained by means of a weir overflow inserted in the vessel to allow excess fresh medium to return to the supply vessel for recirculation. Fluid moves to the flow cell on the microscope stage via a submerged port in the constant volume reservoir. All vessels in the

28

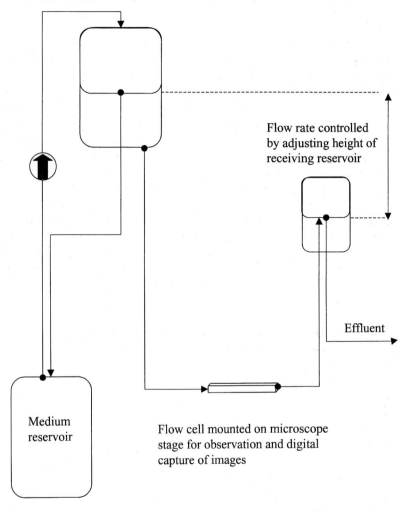

Constant hydraulic head maintained through circulation of sterile medium to constant volume reservoir

Flow rate controlled by adjusting height of receiving reservoir

Effluent

Medium reservoir

Flow cell mounted on microscope stage for observation and digital capture of images

Figure 8 Schematic showing use of hydraulic pressure to control low flow rates to flow cell or micromodel.

system are open to the atmosphere by means of sterile filter attachments to ensure free flow of fluid through the model; anaerobiosis is maintained by continuous sparging of the constant volume reservoir with sterile filtered oxygen free nitrogen (OFN).

Biofilm developed under these very low flow conditions does not exhibit the

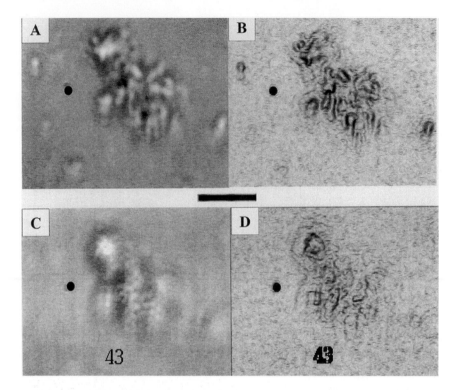

Figure 9 Microcolony development on lower surface of square section glass flow cell. Anaerobic biofilm development of sulphate-reducing consortium EX258, grown at 65∞C.
A : coverage at substratum, no image enhancement, B: image enhancement to locate edges of focussed cells in A, C: objective raised to focus on upper cells of biofilm margin, D: image enhancement to locate edges of upper focussed cells in C .
• Reference mark to locate images correctly.
'43' refers to number of Vernier scale divisions separating substratum from upper focussed cells. Conversion factor 1.45, therefore microcolony height is 62µm.   Bar = 20µm

directional influence which is evident at much higher rates in pipe flow experiments where, for example, R=3600 (Stoodley *et al.*, 1999). Points of attachment become the centre of microcolony development and growth often extends away from the surface into the lumen of the flow cell (Figure 9). Figure 9A shows an anaerobic microcolony developed from a consortium of thermophilic oil field reservoir bacteria, growing at 65°C in low nutrient medium based on a seawater formulation. The microcolony was approximately 30µm in diameter and extended unevenly into the lumen of the flow cell to the same extent. The outermost layer of cells is visible after focussing up from the substratum (Figure 9B). Laminar flow (0.1cm sec[-1], R=3) was from right to left and did not influence the form of the microcolony. Similar microcolonies were visible all over the substratum, interspersed with single attached cells which were not apparently dividing and growing under the same imposed conditions.

30

Temperature

The temperature of the experiment may be raised by clamping the flow cell to an aluminium plate attached to the microscope stage, heated by brass resistors wired back to a microprocessor. A thermocouple, applied to the flow cell, controls the heat input to the system. The temperature of the constant volume medium reservoir may also be regulated, to preheat the medium before passage through the flow cell. Experiments were conducted on mesophilic and thermophilic consortia between ambient and 65°C. Figure 10A-C shows members of the mesophilic subsurface consortium EX246 grown at 30, 37 and 45°C respectively, demonstrating the dominance of morphologically different consortium members at the two lower temperatures and the relatively low incidence of microcolony formation at the upper temperature. Members of thermophilic consortia are able to grow at temperatures as low as 45°C, indicating a very broad range of bacterial activity in many environments.

While the range of temperatures encountered in the oral cavity may not be as wide, nor will any extremes be experienced for sustained periods of time, nevertheless there is value in understanding the altered dynamics within bacterial plaque and dental biofilms resulting from temperature variation. The apparatus described here is able to model such changes, while allowing direct observation of biofilms.

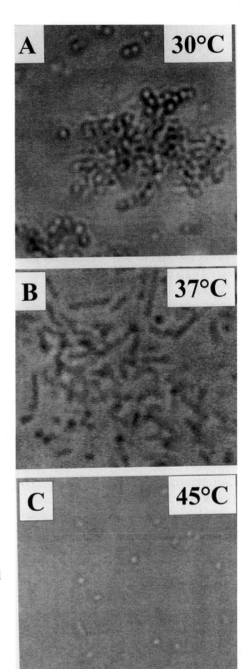

Figure 10 Growth of consortium EX246 at 30 (**A**), 37 (**B**) and 45°C (**C**) in a glass flow cell. Note the difference in morphology between bacteria in all three frames, and low adhesion and growth in **C**. Bar = 20μm

Nutrients and Treatment Evaluation

Preliminary work on determining the effect of varying available nutrients or reservoir chemicals on developed biofilms also has an application in the field of dental microbiology, since again, the direct effect of applying specific treatments to attachment and growth may be observed in real time. Further details of the work on subsurface consortia are in preparation for publication, in which methodology for setting up slow flow rate, controlled atmosphere flow cells will be described in full.

Glass Micromodels

A recent addition to the range of observation chambers used for image analysis is the glass micromodel. These are prepared by photographically transferring a specific pattern to a glass surface, acid-etching the pattern and annealing a second piece of glass over the first to enclose etched area. Inlet and outlet grooves are ground prior to annealing the second layer, and the micromodel is ready to use in the same way as a square section glass flow cell. Pore throats of as little as 30μm are attainable in micromodels, with similar distances between the upper and lower layers of glass. The pore volume of the micromodel can be less than 1mL. The cross sectional area and pore size of the model under observation contribute to the range of achievable experimental flow rates depending on the constriction factor through the model. On passage through the micromodel, inoculated bacteria encounter obstacles within the flow path. Following adhesion and growth, the flow through the micromodel is diverted due to biomass blocking the pore throats, altering shear forces in other zones of the micromodel. Patterns mimicking gingival pockets and dental crevices may be reproduced in a similar way to observe growth and blocking of areas by representative organisms.

Concluding remarks

In summary, McEldowney and Fletcher (1986) believed that adhesion can not be attributed to any one type of adhesive interaction and Marshall (1992) agreed, concluding that the same bacterial strain may attach to a greater or lesser extent to substrata with different surface properties. We now have an increased knowledge and understanding of the complex nature of biofilm dynamics and anticipate continued improvement of experimental regimes. These should incorporate relevant variables that need to be accounted for to ensure that information obtained from laboratory models can be extrapolated with confidence to *in vivo* circumstances.

Acknowledgements

We would like to thank Luanne Hall-Stoodley, Peter Sanders, Braden Dunsmore and Gillian Moore for their help, advice and discussions. We would also like to thank Tony Davey and Gavin Wakely for their technical assistance.

References

Alison, D.G. and Gilbert, P. 1995. Modification by surface association of antimicrobial susceptibility of bacterial populations. *J. Indust. Microbiol.* **15**, 311-317.

Bale, M. J., Fry, J. C. and Day, M. J. 1988. Transfer and occurrence of large mercury resistance plasmids in river epilithon. *Appl. Environ. Microbiol.*,**54**, 972-978.

Bass, C.J., Davey, RA. and Lappin-Scott, H.M. 1998. Long term starvation survival of a thermophilic sulfidogen consortium. *Geomicrobiol.J.* **15**, 29-36.

Bass, C.J., Lappin-Scott, H.M. and Sanders, P.F. 1993. Bacteria that sour reservoirs. *J. Off. Technol.* **1**, 31-36.

Bass, C.J., Sanders, P.F. and Lappin-Scott, H.M. 1998. Study of biofilms of sulfidogens from North sea oil production facilities using continuous-flow apparatus. *Geomicrobiol.J.* **15**, 101-120

Bass, C.J., Webb, J.S., Sanders, P.F. and Lappin-Scott, H.M. 1996. Influence of surfaces on sulphidogenic bacteria. *Biofouling* **10**, 95-109.

Bos, R., van der Mei, H. C. and Busscher, H. J. 1999. Physico-chemistry of initial microbial adhesive interaction – its mechanisms and methods for study. *FEMS Microbiol. Rev.* **23**, 179-230.

Boulangé-Petermann, L. 1996. Process of bioadhesion on stainless steel surfaces and cleanability: a review with special reference to the food industry. *Biofoul.* **10**, 275-300.

Brading, M. G. 1996. The influence of fluid dynamics and surface material on pure and binary culture biofilms. PhD thesis, University of Exeter.

Brading, M. G., Boyle, J. and Lappin-Scott, H. M. 1995. Biofilm formation in laminar-flow using *Pseudomonas fluorescens* EX101. *J. Indust. Microbiol.* **15**, 297-304.

Brading, M. G., Jass, J. and Lappin-Scott, H. M. 1995. Dynamics of bacterial biofilm formation. In: Lappin-Scott, H. M. and Costerton, J. W. (ed.), *Microbial biofilms*, pp. 46-63, Cambridge University Press, Cambridge, UK.

Bradshaw, D. J., Marsh, P. D., Watson, G. K. and Allison, C. 1997. Effect of conditioning films on oral microbial biofilm development. *Biofoul.* **11**, 217-226.

Brown, M. R. W. and Gilbert, P. 1993. Sensitivity of biofilms to antimicrobial agents. *J. Appl. Bacteriol.* S. S. **74**, 87S-97S.

Busscher, H. J., Bos, R., and van der Mei, H. C. 1995. Initial microbial adhesion is a determinant for the strength of biofilm adhesion. *FEMS Microbiol. Lett.* **128**, 229-234.

Characklis, W. G. 1990. Laboratory biofilm reactors. In: Characklis, W. G. and Marshall, K. C. (ed.), *Biofilms*, pp. 55-92, John Wiley and Sons, New York.

Characklis, W. G., Turakhia, M. H. & Zelver, N. 1990. Transport and interfacial transport phenomena. In: Characklis, W. G. and Marshall, K. C. (ed.), *Biofilms*, pp. 265-340, John Wiley and Sons, New York.

Costerton, J. W., Marrie, T. J. and Cheng, K. J. 1985. Phenomena of bacterial adhesion. In Savage, D. C. and Fletcher, M. (ed.) *Bacterial Adhesion*, pp 3-43, Plenum Press, New York.

Dagnall, H. 1986. *Exploring surface texture.* Rank Taylor Hobson Ltd., Leicester, England.

De Beer, D., Stoodley, P. and Lewandoski, Z. 1994. Liquid flow in heterogeneous biofilms. *Biotechnol. Bioengin.* **44**, 636-641.

Dhaliwal, D. S., Cordier, J. L. and Cox, L. J. 1992. Impedimetric evaluation of the efficiency of disinfectants against biofilms. *Lett. Appl. Microbiol.*, **15**, 217-221.

Douglas, C. W. I. 1994. Bacterial-protein interactions in the oral cavity. *Adv. Dent. Res.* **8**, 254-262.

Drury, W. J., Stewart, P. S. and Characklis, W. G. 1993. Transport of 1-mm particles in *Pseudomonas aeruginosa. Biotechnol. Bioeng.* **42**, 111-117.

Eginton, P. J., Holah, J., Allison, P. S., Handley, P. and Gilbert, P. 1997. Changes in the strength of attachment of micro-organisms to surfaces following treatment with disinfectants and cleansing agents. *Lett. Appl. Microbiol.* **27**, 101-105.

Elvers, K. T., Leeming, K., Moore, C. P. and Lappin-Scott, H. M. 1998. Bacterial-fungal biofilms in flowing water photo-processing tanks. *J. Appl. Microbiol.* **84**, 607-618.

Elvers, K. T., Leeming, K., Moore, C. P. and Lappin-Scott, H. M. 1997. Control of bacterial fungal biofilms using Kathon‰. In: Wimpenny, J., Handley, P., Gilbert, P., Lappin-Scott, H. M. and Jones, M. (ed.), *Biofilms Community interactions and control*, pp. 251-257, Bioline, Cardiff.

Geesey, G. G., Gillis, R. J., Avci, R., Daly, D., Hamilton, M., Shope, P. and Harkin, G. 1996. The influence of surface features on bacterial colonization and subsequent substratum chemical changes of 316L stainless steel. *Corr. Sci.* **1**, 73-95.

Hall-Stoodley, L., Rayner, J. C., Stoodley, P. and Lappin-Scott, H. M. 1999a. Establishment of experimental biofilms using the Modified Robbins Device. In: Edwards, C. (ed.), *Environmental monitoring of bacteria*, pp. 307-319, Humana Press, Totowa, New Jersey.

Hall-Stoodley, L., Keevil, C. W. and Lappin-Scott, H. M. 1999b. *Mycobacterium fortuitum* and *Mycobacterium chelonae* biofilm formation under high and low nutrient conditions. *J. Appl. Microbiol.* SS **85**, 60S-69S.

Hissett, T., Verran, J. and Marshall, G. P. 1995. Abstract submitted to the 132nd Ordinary Meeting of the Society of General Microbiology, University of Aberdeen, 10-13th September.

Jass, J., Costerton, J. W. and Lappin-Scott, H. M. 1995. Assessment of a chemostat-coupled Modified Robbins Device to study biofilms. *J. Indust. Microbiol.* **15**, 283-289.

Korber, D. R., Lawrence, J. R., Lappin-Scott, H. M. and Costerton, J. W. 1995 Growth of micro-organisms on surfaces. In: Lappin-Scott, H. M. and Costerton, J. W. (ed.), *Microbial Biofilms*, pp. 15-45Cambridge University Press, Cambridge, U.K.

Krysinski, E. P., Brown, L. J. and Marchisello, T. J. 1992. Effect of cleaners and sanitizers on *Listeria monocytogenes* attached to product contact surfaces. *J. Food Prot.* **55**, 246-251.

Landa, A. S., van der Mei, H. C. and Busscher, H. J. 1996. A comparison of the detachment of adhering oral Streptococcal strain stimulated by mouthrinses and pre-brushing rinse. *Biofoul.* **4**, 327-339.

Lewandowski, Z., Stoodley, P. and Altobelli, S. 1995 Experimental and conceptual studies on mass transport in biofilms. *Wat. Sci. Tech.* **31**, 153-162.

Linton C. J., Sherriff A. and Millar M. R. 1999. Use of a modified Robbins device to directly compare the adhesion of *Staphylococcus epidermidis* RP62A to surfaces. *J. Appl. Microbiol.* **2**, 194-202.

Marshall, K. C. 1992. Biofilms: an overview of bacterial adhesion, activity and control at surfaces. *Am. Soc. Microbiol. News*, **58**, 202-207.

McCoy, J. C., Bryers, J. D., Robbins, J. and Costerton, J. W. 1981. Observations in fouling biofilm formation. *Can. J. Microbiol.* **15**, 263-276.

McEldowney, S. and Fletcher, M. 1986. Variability of the influence of physicochemical factors affecting bacterial adhesion to polystyrene substrata. *Appl. Env. Microbiol.* **52**, 460-465.

Millsap, K. W., van der Mei, H. C., Bos, R. and Busscher, H. J. 1998. Adhesive interactions between medically important yeasts and bacteria. *FEMS Microbiol. Rev.* **21**, 321-336.

Mohamed, M. N., Lawrence, J. R. and Robarts, R. D. 1998. Phosphorus limitation of heterotrpohic biofilms from the Fraser river, British Columbia, and the effect of pulp. *Mic. Ecol.* **36**, 121-130.

Mueller, R. F., Characklis, W. G., Jones, W. L. and Sears, J. T. 1992. Characterisation of initial events in bacterial surface colonisation by two *Pseudomonas* species using image analysis. *Biotech. Bioengin.* **39**, 1161-1170.

Page, R. C. 1995. Critical issues in periodontal research. *J. Dent. Res.* **74**, 1118-1128.

Pratten, J., Barnett, P. and Wilson, M. 1998. Composition and susceptibility to chlorhexidine of multispecies biofilms of oral bacteria. *Appl. Env. Microbiol.* **64**, 3515-3519.

Quirynen, M. 1994. The clinical meaning of the surface roughness and the surface free energy of intra-oral hard substrata on the microbiology of the supra- and subgingival plaque: results of *in vitro* and *in vivo* experiments. *J. Dent.* **22**, SS1 S13-S16.

Quirynen, M. and Bollen, C. M. L. 1995. The influence of surface roughness and surface-free energy on supra- and subgingival plaque formation in man. *J. Clin. Periodont.* **22**, 1-14.

Roberts, S. K., Lappin-Scott, H. M. and Leeming, K. 1999. The control of bacterial-fungal biofilms. *In press.*

Rogers, J., Dowsett, A. B., Dennis, P. J., Lee, J. V. and Keevil, C. W. 1994. Influence of plumbing material on biofilm formation and growth of *Legionella pneumophila* in potable water systems. *Appl. Env. Microbiol.* **60**, 1842-1851.

Scheie, A. A. 1994. Mechanisms of dental plaque formation. *Adv. Dent. Res.* **8**, 246-253.

Scheuerman T. R., Camper A. K. and Hamilton M. A. 1998. Effects of substratum topography on bacterial adhesion. *J. Colloid Interface Sci.* **208**, 23-33.

Sharp, D. W. A. 1985. *The Penguin Dictionary of Chemistry*. Penguin Books Ltd, Middlesex, England.

Southam, G., Ferris, F. G. and Beveridge, T. J. 1995. Mineralised bacterial biofilms in sulphide

34

tailings and in acid mine drainage systems. In: Lappin-Scott, H. M. and Costerton, J. W. (ed.), *Microbial biofilms*, pp. 148-170, Cambridge University Press, Cambridge, U.K.

Stewart, P. S., Grab, L. and Diemer, J. A. 1998. Analysis of biocide transport limitation in a n artificial biofilm system. *J. Appl. Microbiol.* **85**, 495-500.

Stoodley, P., Dodds, I., Boyle, J. D. and Lappin-Scott, H. M. 1999 Influence of hydrodynamics and nutrients on biofilm formation. *J. Appl. Microbiol.* SS **85**, 19S-28S.

Stoodley, P., Lewandowski, Z., Boyles, J. D. and Lappin-Scott, H. M. 1998 Oscillation characteristics of biofilm streamers in turbulent flowing water as related to drag and pressure drop. *Biotechnol. Bioeng.* **57**, 536-544.

Stoodley, P., DeBeer, D. and Lewandowski, Z. 1994. Liquid flow in biofilm systems. *Appl. Env. Microbiol.* **60**, 2711-2716.

Taylor, R. L., Verran, J. and Lees, C. G. 1995. Abstract submitted to the 132nd Ordinary Meeting of the Society of General Microbiology, University of Aberdeen, 10-13th September.

Verran, J. and Taylor, R. L. 1995. The effect of surface roughness and conditioning on adhesion. In: Wimpenny, J., Handley, P., Gilbert, P. and Lappin-Scott, H. M. (ed.), *The life and death of Biofilm*, pp. 53-59, Bioline, Cardiff, UK.

Verran, J., Lees, G. and Shakespeare, A. P. 1991. The effect of surface roughness on the adhesion of *Candida albicans* to acrylic. *Biofoul.* **3**, 183-192.

BACTERIAL SURFACE COMPOSITION AND PROPERTIES

Ian C. Hancock

*The surfaces bacteria present to their environment vary not only between strains and species, but also phenotypically within a single strain. Their physico-chemical properties of the bacterial cell surface, and the ways in which these might contribute to interactions with other biological and non-biological surfaces and with the extracellular matrix of biofilms. The physicochemical interactions of bacterial ce present to their environment vary not only between strains and species, but also phenotypically within a single strain. Their physicochemical interactions depend on a mosaic of ionic, polar and apolar domains contributed by cell wall components and a variety of non-covalently linked ions and macromolecules that associate with the cell envelope. Wall components may give rise to diffuse surface properties such as anionic surfaces of Gram-positive bacteria or the hydrophobic surfaces of mycobacteria. On the other hand, they may be responsible for very specific interactions with receptors on other cells or non-biological surfaces. There are many examples of these in the oral environment, such as the interactions between oral streptococci, human epithelial cells and **Actinomyces**. Increasingly glycoproteins, such as those in **Mycobacterium** are being recognised as bacterial cell surface components, offering the possibility of highly specific mutual lectin-binding interactions. The dynamic nature of cell wall structure, due to autolysin-catalysed turnover of peptidoglycan and the activities of wall-bound proteases, polysaccharases and lipases, ensures the fluidity of surface interactions, and contributes wall macromolecules to the extracellular matrix. These may be capable of competing with bacterial surface-bound receptors for binding sites. The "spheres of influence" of these different components will be discussed in the context of the porous cell wall itself, the bacteria's interactions with their environment and with other cells in that environment.*

Introduction
Composition of walls and their physico-chemical properties

The aim of this review is to consider the varied compositions of bacterial cell walls, the effects of chemical composition on the physicochemical properties of the bacterial cell surface, and the ways in which these might contribute to interactions with other biological and non-biological surfaces and with the extracellular matrix of biofilms. The physicochemical interactions of bacterial cell surfaces depend on a mosaic of ionic, polar and apolar domains contributed by cell wall components and a variety of non-covalently linked ions and macromolecules that associate with the cell envelope. The "spheres of influence" of these different components will be discussed in the context of the porous cell wall itself, the bacteria's interactions with their environment and with other cells in that environment. The wall of a growing bacterial cell is a dynamic structure whose continuous growth and turnover may allow high rates of phenotypic change and correspondingly rapid changes in its contribution to the surrounding environment. The implications of this for bacterial interactions *in vivo* will be discussed.

Bacterial cell wall structure

With the exception of the group known as mollicutes (mycoplasmas), all bacteria have an external cell wall whose structural "scaffolding" consists of peptidoglycan, a macro-polymer of polysaccharide chains, cross-linked by short oligopeptides that have the potential to interlink three polysaccharide chains in three dimensions. This cross-linking creates a single porous, macromolecular net of peptidoglycan around the whole cell. Due to improved techniques of enzymic and chemical analysis, our knowledge of the structural architecture of this material has escalated in the last few years. Although the main constructional principles are the same in peptidoglycan from all species of bacteria, the design of the polymer allows a substantial degree of variation in architecture. These variations result from differences in polysaccharide chain length, differences in the degree of cross-linking of polysaccharides through their peptide side chains and, most significantly, differences in the relative extent to which crosslinked peptide side chains are attached to one or two further peptide side chains on other polysaccharide strands. These variations can result in "single sheet" and "multilayered" architectures, with variations in the mesh size of the net. In general, Gram-negative bacteria are characterised by the single sheet form, while Gram-positive bacteria, mycobacteria and actinomycetes possess multilayered peptidoglycan.

Although cell wall shape and integrity depend on the peptidoglycan, quantitatively it is frequently not the predominant component of the wall. In all bacteria other macromolecules, "accessory polymers", occur covalently linked to the peptidoglycan matrix or interact strongly and specifically with it, and these in turn support a variety of other more or less strongly absorbed molecules, from small ions to large proteins, polysaccharides and lipids. All these contribute to the properties and functionality of the intact cell wall. In most Gram-positive bacteria and actinomycete bacteria the principal accessory polymer is a polyanionic polysaccharide, frequently termed a teichuronic acid, or an equally polyanionic teichoic acid in which phosphate groups contribute the negative charges. These in turn support intercalated proteins, polysaccharides and small cations. Mycobacteria and their *Rhodococcus*, *Corynebacterium* and *Nocardia* relatives possess an uncharged accessory polysaccharide, arabinogalactan, which is esterified with long chain acyl groups, mycolic acids, at its distal end, providing sites in turn for adsorption of free lipids. In Gram-negative bacteria a specific lipoprotein, linked by its hydrophilic end to peptidoglycan, provides distal hydrophobic acyl groups that attach the lipid bilayer outer membrane to the peptidoglycan layer. The outer membrane in turn may support a capsule consisting of polysaccharide chains with reducing-terminal lipid groups that interact with the lipid bilayer of the outer membrane.

38

The Surface Negative Charge of Bacteria

Zeta potential measurements for bacteria reveal that, irrespective of their hydrophobicity, the cells bear a net negative surface charge. In Gram-positive bacteria this charge is provided mainly by wall teichoic acids and anionic polysaccharides. Lipoteichoic acids (LTA), though they possess terminal membrane anchor groups, also penetrate the network of the cell wall and contribute to the net surface charge. While all these polymers occur together in the cell walls of a few bacteria, such as *Bacillus licheniformis*, the predominant anionic wall polymers in aerobic and microaerophilic species are teichoic acids, in which the negative charges are provided by a phosphodiester group in the regular repeating units of the polymer chain. This group is strongly acidic, with a pK_a of about 1.5, and therefore contributes a full negative charge at all physiological pH values. There is growing evidence that a wall-bound anionic polymer and LTA are both essential for viability. In the few Gram-positive genera not known to contain teichoic acids, teichuronic acids (TU), which contribute negative charge by virtue of carboxylate groups in their repeating structure, are present instead (Archibald *et al.*, 1993).

Gram-negative bacteria also exhibit a substantial negative surface charge, in this case contributed by phosphate groups and the carboxylate groups of KDO residues in the lipid A and core regions of lipopolysaccharide in the outer leaflet of the outer membrane, in the polar headgroups of the phospholipids in the inner leaflet, and in encapsulated bacteria by the polyanionic capsular polysaccharides (K antigens), where again the negative charges may be provided by phosphates or the carboxylate groups of uronic acids.

The teichoic acids are a family of macromolecules in which alditols (glycerol, ribitol or mannitol), sugars (most commonly N-acetylhexosamines) or glycosylalditols are linked in a linear chain by phosphodiesters. Glycosylation of the alditol residues is common. The viridans group of streptococci contain an interesting variant of this type of polymer, in which hexa-or hepta-saccharide repeating units are linked by phosphodiesters. In contrast to this diversity of polymer chain structure, the mode of covalent attachment of the teichoic acids to the peptidoglycan of the cell wall is highly conserved. A small oligomeric "linkage unit" intervenes between the phosphate terminus of the polymer chain and the primary hydroxyl at C-6 of an N-acetylmuramic acid residue in peptidoglycan. This unit consists of between one and three glycerol phosphate residues linked in turn to the N-acetylmannosamine residue of the disaccharide N-acetylmannosamine-β1->4 N-acetylglucosamine-1-phosphate. The 1-phosphate group on the N-acetylglucosamine forms a phosphoester linkage to the primary hydroxyl at C6 of the muramic acid. The reason for evolutionary conservation of this structure is unknown, but its similarity to the mode of attachment of cell wall arabinogalactan in *Mycobacterium* (Mikusova, K. *et al.*, 1996) and of some teichuronic acids, which also involve N-acetylglucosamine-1-phosphate, is intriguing. The possibility that it could act as a hinge region allowing less restricted orientation of the rather rigid polyanions is borne out by molecular modelling studies.

Until recently, specific interactions involving anionic cell wall polymers have received relatively little attention, in comparison to their capsular and extracellular relatives. However, the increasing recognition of the roles of such polysaccharides in cell-cell interactions, such as those of the viridans group of streptococci with oral *Actinomyces* strains (Cisar *et al.*, 1997a) is causing renewed interest. The extensive knowledge of the conformational and physico-chemical properties of anionic polysaccharides generated from studies of extracellular polysaccharides and animal proteoglycans should lead to a rapid expansion in our understanding of the behaviour of these cell wall components in cell surface interactions (Xu *et al.*,1996; see I.W. Sutherland, this volume).

Covalently linked cell wall teichoic acids and teichuronic acids are absent from Gram-negative bacteria. However, there are many examples of teichoic acid-like and teichuronic acid-like capsular polymers. In these cases the polymer chains are much longer than the Gram-positive cell wall analogues (typically 100-150 repeating units) and are synthesised with a terminal phospholipid group that probably serves to anchor them to the outer surface of the outer membrane during assembly of the capsule. Several examples of immunological cross-reaction between these capsular "polysaccharides" and cell wall teichoic acids from Gram-positive bacteria have been reported (Jann & Jann, 1990; Myerowitz *et al.*, 1973).

An interesting modification of the structure and net charge of some anionic wall polymers results from attachment of small cationic substituents. In teichoic acids this is usually D-alanine, esterified to the secondary hydroxyls of some of the alditol repeating units of the polymer. The positively charged amino group of the alanine is within electrovalent interaction distance of a neighbouring phosphodiester negative charge , and this charge neutralisation dramatically reduces the like-charge repulsion that is a dominant determinant of the confor-mation of the un-alanylated polymer. In the lipopolysaccharide of Gram-negative bacteria, ethanolamine and aminoarabinose substituents contribute positive charges to the lipid A and core regions (Rietschel *et al.*, 1994).

The impact of such modifications can be profound. Mutation of the *dlt* operon responsible for teichoic acid alanylation greatly enhances the interaction of the cell wall of staphylococci with membrane-damaging cationic peptides, resulting in increased sensitivity (Peschel *et al.*,1999). Similarly, *E.coli* can acquire greater resistance to the cationic antibacterial agents polymyxin and protamine by increased substitution of phosphate groups in the lipid A and core regions of its LPS with ethanolamine and aminoarabinose (Nummila *et al.*, 1995).

Charge neutralisation within the wall by mobile cations can also have gross effects on bulk wall properties, reducing like-charge repulsion leading in Gram-positive bacteria to contraction of the elastic peptidoglycan network and reduc-tion in porosity (ref). On an even larger scale, reversible biofilm compaction can occur due to electrical charge neutralisation or protonation of acidic groups in the biofilm matrix and bacterial walls (Stoodley *et al.*,1997). Such effects are likely to be relevant to the effects of cationic antimicrobials that are active against oral biofilms (Helmerhorst *et al.*,1999).

Bacterial Surface Proteins

Most bacteria display some proteins on their surface. These range from extra-cellular proteins that are in transit through the cell wall, outer membrane structural proteins in Gram-negative bacteria, fimbrial and fibrilar proteins which frequently have specific receptor functions (see below) and others. S-layer proteins that form semi-crystalline arrays of globular polypeptide units over the whole surface of some Gram-positive and Gram-negative strains are a very distinctive group (Beveridge *et al.*, 1997). They self-aggregate into sheet-like structures from aqueous solution, but it has been demonstrated in some Gram-positive bacteria such as *Lactobacillus* and *Bacillus* that their association with the cell wall is mediated in addition by specific domains interacting with structural wall polymers such as peptidoglycan and teichoic acid (Sara *et al.*, 1998). The distribution of S-layer proteins amongst bacterial species is still incompletely investigated and their roles *in vivo* are poorly understood, but it has been demonstrated that they form effective permeability barriers to large molecules. The extent to which they mask other surface molecules and functions is not known in any detail.

The molecular biology of specific targeting of receptor proteins to the cell wall in some streptococci and staphylococci has recently been elucidated (Navarre & Schneewind, 1999) and involves specific C–terminal sequences in the newly translated pro-proteins. Strains that lack a functional targeting system, and hence secrete the protein, are selected for in populations under some environmental conditions, with potential consequences for their interactions in biofilms. Moreover, surface proteins are prime candidates for regulation by global quorum-sensing systems (see J. Prosser, this volume) as exemplified by the *agr* system of staphylococci, and are released from their wall-bound state into the environment by cell wall turnover. All these factors contribute to the roles played by these proteins in the dynamics of biofilms.

Bacterial Surface Hydrophobicity

Some bacterial strains exhibit considerable hydrophobicity, as observed by an ability to stick to hydrophobic surfaces or to collect at a hydrocarbon-water interface. In many cases this property is due to the presence of species-specific or even strain-specific surface proteins which in some cases may have evolved as adhesins but in other cases have other receptor functions and only "acciden-tally" stabilise adhesion. The increasing recognition of proteins at the surface of Gram-positive bacteria that are specifically targeted to the cell wall, and in some cases covalently attached to the wall peptidoglycan makes the exploration of this phenomenon in relation to protein "hydrophobins" important as it imposes particular constraints on the dynamics of the proteins in growing and non-growing bacteria (Navarre & Schneewind, 1999; see below). The ability of some of these hydrophobic proteins, such as the CshA protein of *Streptococcus gordonii* to form cell-surface fibrils extends their sphere of influence around the cell, and may thus increase the chance of hydrophobic interactions with other cells and surfaces by allowing these to occur at a greater distance from the negatively charged surface of the cell wall (McNab *et al.*, 1999; see Handley, this volume).

The interactions of attractive and repulsive electrostatic and hydrophobic forces, and the opposite effects of ionic strength on the two processes, lead to very complex effects that are only poorly understood (Bos *et al.*, 1996; Ellen *et al.*, 1994)

In rare cases the hydrophobicity of wall proteins entirely dominates the surface properties of the bacteria. This is exemplified by the coat proteins of bacterial spores (Setlow, 1993; Guijarro *et al.*, 1988). The only bacteria that exhibit similar hydrophobicity in the vegetative state are mycobacteria and some strains of *Rhodococcus*, *Corynebacterium* and *Nocardia* . In these bacteria, however, hydrophobicity is due to acylation with long chain fatty acids (mycolic acids) of the accessory wall polysaccharide, rather than to protein. These bacteria have a very much higher concentration of hydrophobic domains, each with a much higher degree of hydrophobicity, than those whose hydrophobicity is due to protein. For example, mycobacteria up to half their weight of the surfactant oleyl polyethylene glycol (Noda & Kanemasa, 1986). However, the exposure of the extremely hydrophobic alkyl chains at the outermost surface of the mycobacterial cell is limited by strong adsorption of other non-covalently linked mycobacterial glycolipids oriented so that their polar head-groups form the outer surface (Minnikin, 1991). The exposure of the sugar residues of these glycolipids on the wall surface may explain how some of these bacteria can retain very hydrophilic, loosely attached polysaccharide layers on their surface (Ortalo-Magné *et al.*, 1995; Sutcliffe, 1998).

Mobile Molecular Species in the Cell Wall

As well as the more or less organised components of the cell wall described above, more mobile molecular species may be present. Lipoteichoic acid (LTA), is associated with the outer face of the cytoplasmic membranes of many Gram-positive bacteria (Aasjord &Grov, 1980; Fischer, 1988) and also, often in a partly deacylated form (Kessler *et al.*,1979), in loose association with the cell wall. Although this macromolecule bears a superficial resemblance to a wall teichoic acid, the two differ in their biosynthetic origins, their stereochemistry and their chain termination - attachment to peptidoglycan in WTA and attach-ment to a glycolipid in LTA. LTA makes up between 1 and 2% of the cell dry weight and with only a very few exceptions, such as the LTA-like Forsman antigen of *Streptococcus pneumoniae* LTA is based on a poly(glycerol-phos-phate) backbone. The repeating units have the opposite stereochemistry to those in WTA, due to differences in biosynthesis. Like WTAs, however, these glycerol phosphate polymers can be glycosylated with a variety of monosaccharides or oligosaccharides and also almost invariably exhibit some degree of D-alanylation.

Little is known about the physicochemical properties of the membrane and wall-bound forms of LTA. Immunochemical labelling indicates exposure of the poly(glycerol-phosphate) domain of LTA on the outer surface of *Lactobacillus*

(Wicken & Knox, 1980). However, the conclusion that the anionic chains must therefore adopt an extended conformation, perpendicular to the membrane surface, allowing them to penetrate the cell wall while the terminal lipid is intercalated with the outer leaflet of the cytoplasmic membrane bilayer, is now recognised to be an oversimplification. LTA has been shown to make a major contribution to the hydrophobicity of the bacterial surface (Miörner *et al.*, 1983; Op den Camp *et al.*, 1985), implying exposure of the lipid domains of some of the LTA molecules.

In aqueous solution LTAs form micelles with critical micellar concentrations in the range 0.28 to 5µM (Wicken *et al.*, 1986). The solution properties of LTA from *Staphylococcus aureus* and from *Streptococcus pneumoniae* have been studied by X-ray scattering analysis (Labischinski *et al.*, 1991) which reveal that LTAs form micelles of about 150 molecules, arranged spherically with the polyanionic chains extending outwards from a lipid interior. Some biological activities of LTA demonstrated *in vitro* are dependent on the formation of micelles in solution (Courtney *et al.*, 1986). However, the extent to which their solution properties reflect their behaviour *in vivo* in membrane-attached, non-micellar form, and in the poorly understood wall-associated form, remains to be determined. How such highly polyanionic macromolecules can enter and apparently transit the equally anionic matrix of the cell wall is an important but unanswered question.

Several species of Gram-positive bacteria appear not to contain a lipoteichoic acid, but instead possess lipid-substituted polysaccharides for which the name macroamphiphile has been coined (Sutcliffe & Shaw, 1991). Though they do not contain phosphate these polymers may be anionic by virtue of acidic substituents such as ester-linked succinate or acetal-linked pyruvate, which provide negatively charged carboxylate groups. Analogous lipo-oligosaccharide polymers such as lipoarabinomannan (LAM) occur in mycolate actinomycetes (Hunter *et al.*, 1986) but these are uncharged except for a single phosphate in the region of attachment to the lipid terminus.

As well as proteins specifically targeted to the cell wall (see above) walls contain exoproteins in transit to the external environment. In the thick peptidog-lycan-accessory polyanion wall of a Gram-positive bacterium this may be a slow process and there is evidence that it requires specific protein properties, though these are poorly understood (Müller & Harwood, 1998; Stephenson *et al.*, 1998). Not surprisingly, positively charged proteins (those with a high pI) are more likely to remain associated with the wall than those with a low pI.

The mobile molecular species present in the largest numbers in cell walls are metal cations, held within the matrix of the wall and in the electrical double layer at the surface by electrostatic interactions with fixed anions and, in Gram-positive bacteria, also with LTA. At high ionic strengths up to 20% of the weight of the cell walls of many bacteria may consist of electrostatically bound mono-valent and, predominantly, bivalent metal cations. Subject to differences in association constants due to differences in ionic radius, and to the Debye-Huckel principle, the wall-bound population of metal ions reflects the composition of the surrounding aqueous environment, but at much higher concentrations. This also applies to anionic capsular polysaccharide layers and to anionic exopolysaccharides (see I.W. Sutherland, this volume). The roles of the Group II metal cations such as Mg2+ and Ca2+ are particularly significant in this context since they have relatively low affinities for the wall anionic sites (though much higher than monovalent Na+ and K+) and therefore exchange relatively freely with cations in the external environment. The release of calcium in soluble form in dental caries, for example, has been shown to depend on, among other things , the concentration of anionic binding sites in the dental plaque. These have been identified in *S. oralis* as predominantly the phosphodiester groups of teichoic acids, whereas carboxylate anionic groups are more significant in other oral species (Rose *et al.*, 1997a,b).

Specific interactions of cell surface components

As already discussed, cell surface components may give rise to diffuse surface properties such as negative charge and hydrophobicity. On the other hand, they may be responsible for very specific interactions, sometimes localised at particular sites on the cell surface, with receptors on other cells or non-biological surfaces. A central theme of this meeting is the role of microbial co-aggregation in oral biofilms (see P. Handley, S.S. Socransky, Kolenbrander, this volume), the best understood of which are the interactions of oral streptococci with each other and with *Actinomyces naeslundii* cells (Kolenbrander *et al.*, 1993). The oligosaccharide units of the phosphodiester-containing wall polysaccharides of the viridans group streptococci are involved in specific lactose-sensitive interactions with fimbrial surface lectins of *A. naeslundii* involving, depending on the polysaccharide, a β-N-acetylgalactosaminyl-galactose or a ß-galactosyl-N-acetylgalactosamine motif. The streptococci themselves also possess surface lectins, since lectin-mediated, N-acetylgalactosamine-sensitive and lactose-sensitive, co-aggregation of some of these strains with *S.sanguis and S.gordonii* also occurs, dependent on the CshA fibrilar surface protein that also has fibronectin-binding properties (McNab *et al.*, 1999; Cisar *et al.*,1997a; McNab *et al.*, 1996; see Handley, this volume) and other surface proteins, such as SspA and B, which are also involved in co-aggregation with *A.naeslundii* (Holmes *et al.*, 1998). Additional *Streptococcus gordonii* and *A.naeslundii* lectins specific for sialic acid residues have also been identified as important factors in interactions of the bacteria with salivary and human cell glycoproteins (Takahashi *et al.*, 1997; Sandberg *et al.*, 1995; Vernier *et al.*, 1996).

Increasingly glycoproteins are being recognised as bacterial cell surface components, offering the possibility of further highly specific mutual lectin-binding interactions between bacteria and other cells, and the possibility of mimicking of host glycoproteins (Messner, 1997). The best studied of these are the glycoprotein S-layer proteins and the cell wall glycoproteins of the mycobacteria (Herrman *et al.*, 1996; Khoo *et al.*, 1999; Sara *et al.*, 1998).

The cell wall is a dynamic structure

The dynamic nature of cell wall structure, due to autolysin-catalysed turnover of peptidoglycan and the activities of wall-bound proteases, polysaccharases and lipases, ensures the fluidity of surface interactions, and contributes wall macro-molecules to the extracellular matrix. In fast-growing populations, as much as 50% of the cell wall can turn over into the surrounding medium within one cell generation, though the trunover rate is in general proportional to the growth rate (Archibald *et al.*, 1993). One implication of this is that specific wall components may be eliminated from the cell surface, in response to changing environmental factors, in less than one cell generation. Another is that wall components can also be present in the extracellular matrix at very high concentrations, where they may compete with bacterial surface-bound receptors for binding sites. In this solubilised form they may also reach sites in an infected host not accessible to the intact bacteria. Such effects have been noted for a variety of periodontopathic bacteria, for example (Hancock, 1989; Hancock & Cox, 1991; Reddi *et al.*, 1996).

The release of separate polar and hydrophobic components into the extracel-lular environment could have important implications for the segregation of macromolecules in biofilm, and hence the structural organisation of the biofilm matrix. The lipooligosaccharides of some Gram-negative bacterial outer mem-branes (Bacteroides and Prevotella, for example), the mycolate actinomycetes (Kawabata *et al.*, 1998) (products such as lipoarabinomannan and the mycolylarabinogalactan-peptidoglycan complex) and of Gram-positive bacteria (lipoteichoic acid) will all be important in this respect. The apparently pro-grammed death of some bacteria in populations during colony development, well established for the soil myxobacteria (Kim *et al.*, 1992.), has recently also been demonstrated to occur in *Streptomyces* (Miguelez *et al.*, 1999) and may prove to be much nore widely distributed, contributing to biofilm development and flux.

These processes become even more significant when the bacteria are exposed to antibiotics and other antimicrobial agents. ß-lactam antibiotics in particular, by virtue of the fact that they inhibit attachment of newly synthesised peptidoglycan to the cell wall, can cause and stimulate the release of cell wall components, even at sub-lethal concentrations (van Langevelde *et al.*, 1998; Periti & Mazzei, 1998).

References

Aasjord, P. and Grov, A. (1980) Immunoperoxidase and electron microscopy studies of staphylococcal lipoteichoic acid. *Acta Path. Mic. Scand.* B. **88**, 47-52.

Archibald A.R., Hancock I.C. & Harwood C.R. (1993) Cell wall structure, synthesis and turnover. In: Sonenshein A.L., Hoch J.A. & Losick R. (Eds) *Bacillus subtilis and other Gram-positive Bacteria.* American Society for Microbiology, Washington. pp. 381-410.

Beveridge T.J., Pouwels P.H., Sara M., Kotiranta A., Lounatmaa K., Kari K., Kerosuo E., Haapasalo M., Egelseer E.M., Schocher I., Sleytr U.B., Morelli L., Callegari M.L., Nomellini J.F., Bingle W H , Smit J., Leibovitz E., Lemaire M., Miras I., Salamitou S., Beguin P., Ohayon H., Gounon P., Matuschek M., Sahm K., Bahl H., GrogonoThomas R., Dworkin J., Blaser M.J. , Woodland R.M., Newell D.G., Kessel M., Koval S.F. (1997) Functions of S-layers. *FEMS Microbiol. Rev.*

20, 99-149.

Bos R., vanderMei H.C. & Busscher H.J. (1996) Influence of ionic strength and substratum hydrophobicity on the co-adhesion of oral microbial pairs. *Microbiol.* **142**, 2355-2361.

Cisar, J.O., Sandberg A.L., Reddy G.P., Abeygunawardana C. & Bush C.A. (1997) Structural and antigenic types of cell wall polysaccharides from viridans group streptococci with receptors for oral actinomyces and streptococcal lectins. *Infect. Immun.* **65**, 5035-5041.

Courtney, H.S., Simpson, W.A. and Beachey, E.H. (1986) Relationship of critical micellar concentration of bacterial lipoteichoic acids to biological activities. *Infect. Immun.* **51**, 414-418.

Ellen R.P., Veisman H., Buivids I.A. & Rosenberg M. (1993) Kinetics of lactose-reversible coadhesion of *Actinomyces naeslundii* WVU 398a and *Streptococcus oralis* 34 on the surface of hexadecane droplets. *Oral Microbiol. Immunol.* **9**, 364-371.

Fischer W. (1988) Physiology of lipoteichoic acids in bacteria. *Adv. Microbial Physiol.* **29**, 233-303.

Guijarro J.A., Santamaria R., Schauer A. &Setlow P. (1988) Promoter determining the timing and spatial localisation of transcription of a cloned *Streptomyces coelicolor* gene encoding a spore-associated polypeptide. *J. Bacteriol.* **170**, 1895-1901.

Hancock I.C. (1989) Encapsulation of coagulase-negative staphylococci. *Z. Bakt.* **272**: 11-18.

Hancock I.C. and Cox C.M. (1991) Turnover of cell surface-bound capsular polysaccharide in *Staphylococcus aureus. FEMS Microbiol. Lett.* **77**: 25-30.

Helmerhorst E.J., Hodgson R., vantHof W., Veerman E.C.I., Allison C.& Amerongen A.V.N. (1999)The effects of histatin-derived basic antimicrobial peptides on oral biofilms. *J. Dental Res.* **78**, 1245-1250.

Herrmann J.L., O'Gaora P., Gallagher A., Thole J.E.R. & Young D.B. (1996) Bacterial glycoproteins: A link between glycosylation and proteolytic cleavage of a 19 kDa antigen from *Mycobacterium tuberculosis. EMBO J.* **15**, 3547-3554.

Holmes A.R., Gilbert C., Wells J.M. & Jenkinson H.F. (1998) Binding properties of *Streptococcus gordonii* SspA and SspB (antigen I/II family) polypeptides expressed on the cell surface of *Lactococcus lactis* MG1363. *Infect. Immun.* **66**, 4633-4639.

Jann K. & Jann B. (1990) Structure and biosynthesis of the capsular antigens of *Escherichia coli.* Curr. *Topics in Microbiol. Immunol.* **150**, 623-628.

Kawabata Y., Semba I., Hirayama Y., Koga T., Nagao S., Takada H. (1998) Wax D of *Mycobacterium tuberculosis* induced osteomyelitis accompanied by reactive bone formation in Buffalo rats. *FEMS Immunol. Med. Microbiol.* **22**, 293-302.

Kessler, R.E., Van de Rijn, I. and McCarty, M. (1979) Characterisation and localisation of the enzymatic deacylation of lipoteichoic acid in group A streptococci. *J. Exp. Med.* **150**, 1498-1509.

Khoo K.H., Jarboe E., Barker A., Torrelles J., Kuo C.W. & Chatterjee_D (1999) Altered expression profile of the surface glycopeptidolipids in drug-resistant clinical isolates of *Mycobacterium avium* complex. *J. Biol. Chem.* **274**, 9778-9785.

Kim S.K., Kaiser D. & Kuspa A. (1992) Control of cell density and pattern by intercellular signaling in *Myxococcus* development. *Ann. Rev. Microbiol.* 46, 117-139.

Kolenbrander P.E. & Ganeshkumar N. (1993) Coaggregation - specific adherence among human oral plaque bacteria. *FASEB J.* **7**, 406-413.

Labischinski, H., Naumann, D. and Fischer, W. (1991) Small and medium-angle x-ray analysis of bacterial lipoteichoic acid phase structure. *Eur. J. Biochem.* **202**, 1269-1274.

McNab R., Holmes A.R., Clarke J.M., Tannock G.W. & Jenkinson H.F. (1996) Cell surface polypeptide CshA mediates binding of *Streptococcus gordonii* to other oral bacteria and to immobilized fibronectin. *Infect. Immun.* **64**, 4204-4210.

McNab R., Forbes H., Handley P.S., Loach D.M., Tannock G.W. & Jenkinson H.F. (1999) Cell wall-anchored CshA polypeptide (259 kilodaltons) in *Streptococcus gordonii* forms surface fibrils that confer hydrophobic and adhesive properties. *J. Bacteriol.* **181**, 3087-3095.

Messner, P. (1997) Bacterial glycoproteins. *Glycoconjugate J.* **14**, 3-11.

Mikusova K., Mikus M., Besra G.S., Hancock I.C. & Brennan P.J. (1996) Biosynthesis of the linkage region of the mycobacterial cell wall. *J. Biol. Chem.* **271**: 7820-7828.

Miguelez E.M., Hardisson C.& Manzanal M.B. (1999) Hyphal death during colony development in *Streptomyces antibioticus*: Morphological evidence for the existence of a process of cell deletion in a multicellular prokaryote. *J. Cell Biol.* **145**, 515-525.

Minnikin D.E (1991) Chemical principles in the organisation of lipid components in the mycobacterial cell envelope. *Res. Microbiol.* **142**, 423-427.

Miörner, H., Johansson, G. and Fronvall, G. (1983) Lipoteichoic acid is the major cell wall component responsible for surface hydrophobicity in group A streptococci. *Infect. Immun.* **39**, 336-343.

Muller J.P. & Harwood C.R. (1998) Protein secretion in phosphate-limited cultures of *Bacillus subtilis* 168. *Appl. Microbiol. Biotechnol.* **49**, 321-327.

Myerowitz R.L., Gordon R.E. & Robbins J.B. (1973) Polysaccharides of the genus *Bacillus* cross-reactive with the capsular polysaccharides of *Diplococcus pneumoniae* type III, *Haemophilus influenzae* type b and *Neisseria meningitidis* Group A. *Infect. Immun.* **8**, 896-900.

Navarre W.W. & Schneewind O. (1999) Surface proteins of Gram-positive bacteria and mechanisms of their targeting to the cell wall envelope. *Microbiol. Mol. Biol. Rev.* **63**, 174-232.

Noda Y. & Kanemasa Y. (1986) Determination of the hydrophobicity on bacterial surfaces by nonionic surfactants. *J. Bacteriol.* **167**, 1016 - 1019.

Nummila K., Kilpeläinen I., Zahringer U., Vaara M. & Helander I.M. (1995) Lipopolysaccharides of polymyxin B-resistant mutants of *Escherichia coli* are extensively substituted by 2-aminoethylpyrophosphate and contain aminoarabinose in lipid A. *Mol. Microbiol.* **16**, 271-278.

Op den Camp, H.J.M., Oosterhof, A. and Veerkamp, J.H. (1985) Cell surface hydrophobicity of *Bifidobacterium bifidum* subsp. *pennsylvanicum* . Antonie van Leeuwenhoek *J. Microbiol.* **51**, 303-312.

Ortalo-Magné A., Dupont M.-A., Lemassu A., Andersen A.B., Gounon P. & Daffé M. (1995) Molecular composition of the outermost capsular material of the tubercle bacillus. *Microbiol.* **141**, 1609-1620.

Periti P. & Mazzei T. (1998) Antibiotic-induced release of bacterial cell wall components in the pathogenesis of sepsis and septic shock: a review. *J. Chemother.* **10**, 427-448.

Peschel A., Otto M., Jack R.W., Kalbacher H., Jung G. & Gotz F. (1999) Inactivation of the *dlt* operon in *Staphylococcus aureus* confers sensitivity to defensins, protegrins, and other antimicrobial peptides. *J. Biol. Chem.* **274**, 8405-8410.

Reddi K., Wilson M., Nair S., Poole S. & Henderson B. (1996) Comparison of the pro-inflammatory cytokine stimulating activity of the surface associated proteins of periodontopathic bacteria. *J. Periodont. Res.* **31**, 120-130.

Rietschel E.T., Kirikae T., Schade U., Mamat U., Schmidt G., Loppnow H., Ulmer A.J., Zähringer U., Seydel U. Padova F., Schreier M. & Brade H. (1994) Bacterial endotoxins: molecular relationships of structure to activitiy and function. *FASEB J.* **8**, 217-225.

Rose R.K., Matthews S.P. & Hall R.C. (1997a) Investigation of calcium-binding sites on the surfaces of selected gram-positive oral organisms. *Arch. Oral Biol.* **42**, 595-599.

Rose R.K., Turner S.J. & Dibdin G.H. (1997b) Effect of pH and calcium concentration on calcium diffusion in streptococcal model-plaque biofilms. *Arch. Oral Biol.* **42**, 795-800.

Sandberg A.L., Ruhl S., Joralmon R.A., Brennan M.J., Sutphin M.J., Cisar J.O. (1995) Putative glycoprotein and glycolipid polymorphonuclear leukocyte receptors for the *Actinomyces naeslundii* WVU45 fimbrial lectin. *Infect. Immun.* **63**, 2625-2631.

Sara,M., Egelseer, E.M., Dekitsch, C. and Sleytr, U.B. (1998) Identification of two binding domains, one for peptidoglycan and another for a secondary cell wall polymer, on the N-terminal part of the S-layer protein SbsB from *Bacillus stearothermophilus* PV72/p2. *J. Bacteriol.* **180**: 6780-6783.

Sandberg A.L., Ruhl S., Joralmon R.A., Brennan M.J., Sutphin M.J. & Cisar J.O. (1995) Putative glycoprotein and glycolipid polymorphonuclear leukocyte receptors for the *Actinomyces naeslundii* WVU45 fimbrial lectin. *Infect. Immun.* **63**, 2625-2631.

Setlow, P. (1993) Spore structural proteins. In: Sonenshein A.L., Hoch J.A. & Losick R. (Eds) ***Bacillus subtilis** and other Gram-positive Bacteria.* American Society for Microbiology, Washington. pp. 801-809.

Stephenson K., Carter N.M., Harwood C.R., Petit-Glatron M.F. & Chambert R.G. (1998) The influence of protein folding on late stages of the secretion of alpha-amylases from *Bacillus subtilis. FEBS Lett.* **430**, 385-389.

Stoodley P., de Beer D. & Lappin-Scott H.M. (1997) Influence of electric fields and pH on biofilm structure as related to the bioelectric effect. *Antimic. Ag. Chemother.* **41**, 1876-1879.

Sutcliffe I.C. (1998) Cell envelope composition and organisation in the genus *Rhodococcus*. Antonie Van Leeuwenhoek Int. *J. Gen.Mol. Microbiol.* **74**, 49-58.

Sutcliffe, I.C. and Shaw, N. (1991) Atypical lipoteichoic acids of Gram-positive bacteria. *J. Bacteriol.* **173**, 7065-7069.

Takahashi Y., Sandberg A.L., Ruhl S., Muller J. & Cisar J.O. (1997) A specific cell surface antigen of *Streptococcus gordonii* is associated with bacterial hemagglutination and adhesion to alpha 2-3-linked sialic acid-containing receptors. *Infect. Immun.* **65**, 5042-5051.

van Langevelde P., vanDissel J.T., Ravensbergen E., Appelmelk B.J., Schrijver I.A. & Groeneveld P.H.P. (1998) Antibiotic-induced release of lipoteichoic acid and peptidoglycan from *Staphylococcus aureus*: Quantitative measurements and biological reactivities. *Antimic. Ag. Chemother.* **42**, 3073-3078.

Vernier A., Diab M., Soell M., Haan Archipoff G., Beretz A., Wachsmann D.& Klein J.P. (1996) Cytokine production by human epithelial and endothelial cells following exposure to oral viridans streptococci involves lectin interactions between bacteria and cell surface receptors. *Infect. Immun.* **64**, 3016-3022.

Wicken, A.J. and Knox, K.W. (1980) Bacterial cell surface amphiphiles. *Biochim. Biophys. Acta* **604**, 1-26.

Wicken,A.J., Evans, J.D. and Knox, K.W. (1986) Critical micellar concentrations of lipoteichoic acids. *J. Bacteriol.* **166**, 72-77.

Xu Q.W., Mohan S. & Bush C.A. (1996) A flexible model for the cell wall polysaccharide of *Streptococcus mitis* J22 determined by three-dimensional C-13 edited nuclear overhauser effect spectroscopy and C-13-H-1 long-range coupling constants combined with molecular modeling. *Biopolymers* **38**, 339-353.

BIOFILM MATRIX POLYMERS – ROLE IN ADHESION

Ian W. Sutherland

The composition, primary, secondary and tertiary structures of the exopolysaccharide (EPS) components of all biofilms differ widely yet play an extremely important role in determining the properties of any type of biofilm. Their role in determining biofilm structure is widely recognised. They may also play either a positive (promotional) or negative (inhibitory) role in adhesion of microbial cells. While relatively little is yet known about the secondary or tertiary structures of most of the EPS found in oral biofilms, our increasing knowledge of structure function/relationships in microbial polysaccharides in general, now enables us to predict some of the attributes of these complexes.

Introduction

In any type of biofilm, whether in oral, natural or industrial environments, water and aqueous solutes represent most of the volume of the matrix. The dry material present is composed of a mixture of exopolysaccharides, proteins, salts and cell material. The development of the biofilm is dependent on the physico-chemical nature of the surface to which it is attached; the microbial species present; the surface macromolecules secreted by these species and the sequence in which they attach. Exopolysaccharides (EPS) are major components of the biofilm; they may comprise from 50-95% of the dry weight and play a major role in maintaining the integrity of the biofilm. Depending on the chemical structures of the EPS and their physicochemical properties, these polymers also confer many other properties on biofilms. They may act as receptors to cell-induced adhesins through coating of the cells which synthesise them as well as adjacent microbial cells and inert surfaces. The entire biofilm matrix can be regarded as an ever-changing layer of immobilised water and solutes attached to either an inert surface or to epithelial cells. A further complication is seen in the ability of some bacterial species to synthesise several polysaccharides. The actual polymer produced may depend on the physiological state of the bacteria, but it may also depend on the presence of a specific substrate.

Clearly, biofilms are not all alike and it is probably not valid to extrapolate some of the findings from one system to another, dissimilar environment. However, all biofilms do contain EPS and the general properties of these polymers may significantly affect each of the biofilms in which they are found. Wimpenny and Colosanti (1997) suggested that, of the three models in current vogue for biofilm composition and structure – namely, water-channel model, heterogeneous mosaic model and dense biofilm model – oral biofilms con-formed most closely to the last of these, the dense biofilm model. Oral biofilms also differ from some of the other systems studied in that they are formed in the presence of high concentrations of available nutrients for microbial growth. They share this property with biofilms formed in food processing plants and similar environments, and with some of those studied in the laboratory where again, relatively high concentrations of specific substrates are commonly available.

The composition and the physicochemical nature of different EPS from a wide range of microbial species vary greatly. Some EPS are neutral as in the case of mutan from *Streptococcus mutans* or curdlan from *Agrobacterium* spp., while many others are highly charged polyanionic macromolecules. The charge may be conferred by the presence of uronic acids in the polysaccharide structure or by organic or inorganic substituents. These may include pyruvate ketals, succinyl half-esters, phosphate groups or (in a very few polymers) sulphate groups. The presence or absence of cations or the nature of other molecules present can thus greatly affect the overall interactions. It is also probable that the ionic strength will vary within different sectors of any biofilm, with resultant localised effects. Different ions and concentrations will alter the conformation and may cause rapid changes in the three-dimensional gel network of polysaccharides. Similar effects may be found with sucrose or other sugars. There may consequently be localised alterations in the strength of the biofilm. Neu and Marshall (1990) suggested that ions might also affect the orientation of molecules in the initial conditioning film. Although it is very unusual to find that the EPS provide an extracellular carbon and energy reserve for the bacteria which synthesise them, they can undoubtedly be degraded to utilisable fragments by heterologous micro-organisms present in a biofilm. Extrapolation of our knowledge of the properties of bacterial EPS and of their roles in other biofilm systems may contribute to the understanding of their multifaceted roles in oral biofilms but should also be viewed with caution. The micro-organisms associated with any biofilm also comprise representatives from many different species and genera ranging from aerobes to strict anaerobes. Some but not all of these cell types are capable of synthesising EPS. In contrast to this property, probably only a relatively small number of species or strains are capable of degrading complex heteropolysaccharides, although many bacteria are now known to possess genes for EPS-degrading enzymes associated with those for biosynthesis. In general homopolysaccharides including dextrans of the mutan type are more readily degraded. It may also be a distinguishing feature of oral biofilms that many of the component micro-organisms can both synthesise and degrade EPS.

Physicochemical aspects of bacterial EPS structure
Physical studies on exopolysaccharides have indicated that many of these macromolecules can exist either in ordered or disordered forms. At elevated temperatures and (frequently) at extremely low ionic concentrations, the disordered form is generally favoured. In only a few examples among the polysaccharide systems which have so far been examined, has the total absence of an ordered structure been demonstrated. Thus, in the natural environment, most of these polymers will frequently be found in some sort of ordered configuration (Sutherland, 1990). It is possible that some microbial exopolysaccharides even

50

resemble crystalline cellulose in their behaviour. Each crystal of cellulose contains numerous glycan chains in parallel orientation (Teeri, 1997). The reducing ends are at one terminus while the non-reducing ends are at the other. Despite the high degree of crystallinity, the structure is non-uniform and amorphous regions may be present in addition to highly crystalline regions. A number of bacterial exopolysaccharides including the commercial product xanthan from *Xanthomonas campestris* adopt a helical configuration in the ordered form. There is still some discussion as to whether polymers like xanthan exist as single helices or whether association of two individual chains yields double helices. In this, the association between double helices is facilitated by ions and by water molecules. They can thus almost be regarded as resembling the double helix of DNA. Confirmation of these structural features has recently been obtained for several bacterial EPS by Kirby *et al.* (1996) using atomic force microscopy, a technique which shows considerable promise for the direct examination of biofilm polymers. A structure of this type may also result in a series of exposed carboxylate residues each capable of binding a cation. This was confirmed for the binding of potassium ions to gellan molecules by Chandrasekaran *et al.* (1992). In this polymer produced by strains of *Sphingomonas paucimobilis* (Kang *et al.*, 1982) most of the potential ion-binding sites are exposed on the 'outer' portions of the macromolecule and can thus interact with other components of the biofilm. In other polysaccharide structures, the exposed carboxylic acid groups may be 'internal' leading to enhanced interaction between the polymer strands through divalent cations such as Ca^{2+}. Even in gellan, sufficient carboxylate residues are available to allow cation-mediated aggregation of double helices with subsequent formation of the ordered microcrystalline regions required for the formation of rigid gels (Larwood *et al.*, 1996). Some structuring of the water surrounding these binding sites was also reported.

Although they are essentially linear macromolecules (with short side-chains in some cases), many water-soluble EPS exhibit gelation. As in the case of gellan when in association with cations, this may yield stable polysaccharide gels. An interaction of this type would thus enhance the rigidity of the biofilm structure. The specificity of binding of different cations is dependent on the polysaccharide structure. This has long been recognised for algal alginates which readily form gels with Ca^{2+} or Sr^{2+} due to the 'fit' of these ions into the 'egg-box' structure provided by sequences of L-guluronosyl residues (Grant *et al.*, 1973). Some polysaccharides such as the Enterobacterial polymer XM6 show preference for ions with a distinct cationic radius - in this case 1.0, others appear to be less restrictive (Nisbet *et al.*, 1984). The binding of ions by polyanionic bacterial polysaccharides is also greatly affected by the presence of acyl groups as was demonstrated for bacterial alginates (Geddie and Sutherland, 1994). This may also be true of other properties such as polysaccharide crystallinity. Acetyl groups also greatly affect the interactions between different polysaccharides as was demonstrated for mixtures of xanthans and plant polysaccharides (Ross-Murphy *et al.*, 1996). Acetyl groups in several of these systems weakened the gel network while their removal reversed the effect.

Some neutral β-D-glucans, including curdlan from *Agrobacterium* and other spp. form a triple helix. This tight structure effectively excludes water molecules and renders the polysaccharide insoluble (Kanzawa *et al.*, 1989). It is possible that the corresponding a-D-glucan mutan may behave similarly. It certainly exhibits a highly crystalline structure (Ogawa *et al.*, 1981). The conformation was stabilised by intramolecular hydrogen bonding and packing was stabilised by intermolecular hydrogen bonding. The resultant sheet-like structure with its extensive hydrogen bonding and its insolubility in water was thought to resemble regenerated cellulose. Within the sheet, there was alternating polarity of the chain directions. At the molecular level, the physical properties of the polysaccharides and hence of the biofilms, are dependent on inter- and intramolecular interactions and may be very greatly influenced by the presence or absence of free anionic groups derived from uronic acids, phosphate groups, pyruvate ketals or succinyl half-esters. Exposed hydroxyl groups can also cause significant hydrogen bonding. Localised hydrophobic regions may also exert considerable influence; these may be derived from either *O*-acetyl groups, methyl groups or 6-deoxyhexoses such as L-rhamnose or L-fucose. One atypical polymer is the linear glucosaminoglycan from biofilm-forming *Staphylococcus epidermidis*. Its structure contains 80-85% N-acetylated residues, while the remainder are non-acetylated and hence provide one of the very few examples of basic biofilm exopolysaccharides so far reported (Mack *et al.*, 1996). An associated and structurally related polymer showed greater acetylation and was anionic due to the presence of ester-linked succinyl residues and also phosphate groups.

As larger numbers of microbial polysaccharides have been analysed and more structures have been determined, an increased number of these polymers have also been subjected to studies on their physical properties. A consequence of this, is a better knowledge of structure-function relationships for bacterial EPS (Sutherland, 1995). Picullel (1998) pointed out that a common type of EPS gelation involved a coil-to-helix transition which could yield various types of gel. The exact type depended on the nature of the polysaccharide and on the solvent present. Xanthan from *Xanthomonas campestris* formed very weak gels which dissolved in excess solvent, whereas other EPS formed brittle gels unaffected in shape by the presence of excess solvent. In the case of gellan, the nature of the gel has been shown to be highly dependent on the extent of acylation present on the EPS. Alterations in acylation produced a range of weak or strong gels, the latter favoured by removal of acyl groups.

The availability of improved imaging techniques has shown that a number of EPS, again including gellan, can form a dense network of thin fibres (Gunning *et al.*, 1996; Kirby *et al.*, 1996). This has sometimes been observed also in electron micrographs of individual, capsulated bacterial cells (e.g. Moorhouse *et al.*, 1977; Koval and Bayer, 1977). Thus, the various proposed models of biofilms can only be regarded as simplifications of the actual structures in which it seems probable that masses of fibres of varying size, structure, composition and rigidity interact with each other, with cells and with surface matrices. As demonstrated by Burton and Brant (1983), a wide range of possible conformations, flexibility and configurations can be expected among the different classes of polysaccharides. The density of these fibrillar masses will clearly affect the accessibility of both cells and surfaces to nutrients and to other solutes.

Role of EPS in biofilms

The chemical composition and the tertiary structure of the EPS will determine whether it forms an effective adhesive. It will also affect the hydrophilic or hydrophobic nature of the surface. The EPS assist in the protection of microbial cells within the biofilm from desiccation and from injurious agents. They may also bind essential nutrients including cations and create a local, nutritionally rich environment in which growth of specific types of micro-organism is favoured. Indeed, Freeman and Lock (1995) have suggested that the EPS matrix of the biofilm could act as a buffer against changes in the available organic substrates. The EPS may assist in retention of extracellular enzymes (and their substrates) in the biofilm complex and thus enhance substrate utilisation by the bacterial cells within it. The result of enzyme action depends very much on the extent of polysaccharide degradation and on the nature of the polysaccharide matrix. There may be very localised degradation of the polysaccharide matrix without release of cells and other polymers. Indeed, in polymers such as xanthan, complete removal of the terminal monosaccharide residues on the side-chains, and even partial removal of complete side-chain trisaccharides, had relatively minor effects on the polysaccharide conformation (Christensen *et al.*, 1995). On the other hand, Hughes *et al.* (1998a,b) demonstrated that highly specific phage-induced endopolysaccharases could effectively remove single species or dual species biofilms.

Exopolysaccharides are effective in maintaining the biofilm structure through the formation of a network of cross-linked linear macromolecules. Binary networks may be independent of each other but may either be interpenetrating or phase separated. One possibility is that one polysaccharide forms the polymer network within which a second soluble component exits. Alternatively two independent but inter-penetrating networks could exist and these might even show distinct regions of phase separation. Finally, intermolecular binding could yield a new coupled type of network. Ross-Murphy and Shatwell (1993) have distinguished three categories of networks: i) those in which covalent cross-linking leads to the formation of junctions; ii) physical junctions which can be readily disrupted through alteration of temperature; and iii) entanglement networks which result from local chain entanglements. A further possibility can be envisaged in which in a single polymer network, a second component is soluble and diffuses through the polysaccharide mesh without resulting in any direct interaction. In most mixed biofilms in which there are numerous types of polysaccharide present, the network structure will inevitably become even more complicated. A consequence of the polysaccharide interactions is the variability in the extent of hydration within the biofilm. Studies on hyaluronic acid from

53

Streptococcus zooepidemicus indicated that for this particular polymer, which was capable of bonding 9-15 moles of water/ disaccharide repeat unit, different states of water could be recognised – non-freezable bound water, freezable bound water and free water (Jouon *et al.*, 1995). Although the ionic form of the polymer had relatively little effect on the water binding, this represents a further factor in the inhomogeneity of biofilms relating directly to their component polysaccharides and their three dimensional structures. It will also greatly affect the accessibility or otherwise of solutes into the interior of biofilms.

One possibility, which has not yet been addressed, is that of cellulosome-like complexes (Beguin and Aubert, 1994). Given that in the oral microflora, there are many polysaccharides and glycoproteins as well as micro-organisms with polysaccharase activity, might there be complexes analogous to cellulosomes in which the microbial cell surface, hydrolytic enzymes and polymers form closely linked structures? A further consequence of such interactions could be the release of monosaccharides or oligosaccharides yielding localised, relatively high concentrations. In solutions of some EPS in the presence of high sugar concentrations, formation of junction zones is promoted (Miyoshi *et al.*, 1998). The fructans synthesised by a range of bacterial species including *Streptococcus mutans*, *Streptococcus salivarius*, *Streptococcus sanguis* and *Actinomyces viscosus* (Birkhed *et al.*, 1979) although found associated with oral biofilms, probably function as carbon and energy reserves rather than having any struc-tural role. Their degradation by *exo*-fructanases including that from *S. mutans*, releases single fructose residues (Burne *et al.*, 1987; 1999) so has a less drastic effect on solution viscosity and polysaccharide tertiary structure than do the more common endopolysaccharases.

It is clear that the amount of a specific EPS in a biofilm does not necessarily reflect the proportion of cells of the bacteria which produce it. If two bacterial species are present in roughly equal numbers, the amount of EPS derived from one type may greatly exceed that from the other (Skillman, 1998). Similarly, loss or removal of one of the EPS may have a much more drastic effect on the biofilm matrix than removal of the other even if the polymer which is removed is not the dominant component of the biofilm (Skillman *et al.*, 1999). This merely reflects the role that one particular polymer plays in the biofilm struc-ture. It appears to be particularly true of a polysaccharide which is poorly soluble, and might thus be applicable to mutan in oral biofilms. The ability of streptococcal cells to bind to such a polymer through glucose-binding proteins (Banas *et al.*, 1990), then enhances accretion of the biofilm. In oral biofilms, the situation is complicated by the availability or otherwise of a carbohydrate substrate from which EPS can be synthesised. *S. mutans* requires sucrose for mutan synthesis whereas under laboratory conditions, *Actinomyces viscosus* can produce a viscous EPS from glucose. The composition of the EPS from strain T14Av contained galactose, *N*-acetyl-D-glucosamine and glucose in the molar ratio 2:2:1 with small amounts of mannose also present (Imae and Kuramitsu, 1983). In a comparative study of these two bacterial species Beckers and van der Hoeven (1984) observed that on a glucose diet, *S. mutans* exceeded Actinomyces cells by a factor of 4, whereas on sucrose twice as many Actinomyces cells were present. This was attributed to the synthesis of EPS from glucose by *A. viscosus* providing a biofilm matrix in which the *S. mutans* were retained. Bowden and Lee (1998) concluded that in the biofilm, production of EPS enabled both the bacteria which synthesised it and other bacteria to persist in plaque.

It is also possible that the mixture of two (or more) EPS may possess physical properties, conferred through synergistic interactions, which differ from or are markedly enhanced relative to those of the individual polymers. While this is seen in the interactions observed between the bacterial polysaccharide xanthan and plant gluco- and galacto-mannans, it might also occur between two microbial polysaccharides synthesised in the close proximity of a biofilm. Skillman (1998) suggested that this might explain the additive effects found when two EPS-producing enterobacterial species formed a mixed biofilm.

The oral biofilm

As well as work on oral biofilms in healthy and diseased individuals, studies on oral biofilms have provided one of the first good examples of an experimental system in which there are artificial biofilms composed of complex mixtures of microbial species. The mouth has various features which provide a useful model and permit discovery of some of the basic principles which apply to all types of biofilm. There is a wide variety of surfaces including those of buccal epithelial cells, tooth surfaces and in some patients – implanted materials of differing composition. As pointed out by Gibbons (1989) the location is readily accessible, the surfaces are continuously bathed by secreted fluids and the oral bacterial flora are varied and basically benign. However, the nature of the surfaces is constantly changing due to loss of epithelial and microbial cells, microbial interactions and accumulation of products. Further alterations leading to loss of some receptors and formation of others results from modification through the action of enzymes of human and microbial origin.

Nyvad and Fejerskov (1989) noted that some microbial deposits in their experimental study were 'dominated by large mucoid colonies'. Associated with this type of material were randomly distributed cells. This was in contrast to material from other individuals in which the micro-organisms formed a layered pattern parallel to the surface of the tooth. Thus the presence of large amounts of EPS may significantly influence the nature of the oral biofilm and the distribution and arrangement of microbial cells within it. However, only one person in their study exhibited this type of material, possibly due to a unique microflora. It was considered similar to the large sucrose-induced colonies observed earlier by Carlsson and Engelberg (1965). EPS may play several roles in the oral biofilm. EPS in the oral biofilm may act directly, as adhesins to exposed surfaces within the oral cavity, on epithelial cells, on dental materials and on other bacteria although this function of EPS is probably less significant in oral biofilms than in other environments in which biofilms are present. Although they may be adhesins, Kolenbrander and London (1993) have indicated that probably their most significant function is that of forming the major 'building bricks' in the architecture of the oral biofilm. Undoubtedly they will trap and retain some of the proteins and glycoproteins with lectin-like specificity which are thought to be the major 'players' in terms of interactions at the molecular level. Again, this is probably more noticeable for the poorly soluble EPS of the mutan type than for the highly charged and soluble EPS of other microbial species.

The properties and interactions of the EPS types found in the oral cavity and associated surfaces

As shown by Busscher *et al.* (1995) considerable differences may be observed between oral streptococci adhering directly to a surface and those adhering via a conditioning film. Detachment through application of shear forces was not significant when the adhesion was directly onto a glass surface but was very marked when it was through the intermediary salivary conditioning film. A major feature of oral biofilms is that within them, the bacterial EPS serve not only as adhesins binding the cells to each other and to surfaces, but in the case of glucans, also as receptors for the many glucose-binding proteins of heterologous species which play such an important role (Jenkinson and Lamont, 1997). As these authors indicated, the glucans thus function as bridging molecules. They also differentiated between the function in adhesion and microbial cell accumulation, and the role of soluble EPS as a potential nutrient source in nutrient-limited environments.

The ability of oral bacteria to synthesise glucans similar to mutan when exposed to high concentrations of sucrose appears to be fairly widespread in *Streptococcus* spp. (Jenkinson and Lamont, 1997). Molecular studies have revealed glucosyltransferases in *S. gordonii* as well as *S. mutans* (e.g. Sulavik and Clewell, 1996; Monchois *et al.*, 1999). In one major respect the synthesis of α-D-glucans in the presence of sucrose by *S. mutans* and related species differs from other types of biofilm. Each of these oral bacteria may possess several glucosyl transferases, and they are capable of synthesising both water-soluble and water-insoluble glucans in which the dominant linkage types are α-1,6 and α-1,3 respectively. Typically, the product from *S. mutans* contains 85-87% α-1,3 linkages, the remainder being α-1,6. The main characteristics of the glucansucrases from several of these

Table 1 Synthesis of glucans and levans by oral bacteria

Species	Glucan synthesis	Levan synthesis
Streptococcus sanguis	+	+
S. oralis	+	+
S. gordonii	+	+
S. mitis	+	+
S. mutans	+	+
S. sobrinus	+	+
S. salivarius	+	+
Actinomyces israelii	-	+
A. naeslundii	-	+
A. viscosus	-	+

Additionally, several of these bacteria may produce heteropolysaccharides in the absence of sucrose
From Ofek and Doyle (1994)

→-[3-α-D-Gl*cp*-(1→3)-α-D-Gl*cp*-(1→3)-α-D-Gl*cp*-(1→3)-α-D-Gl*cp*-(1→3)-α-D-Gl*cp*-]→
Mutan from *Streptococcus mutans*

→-[3-β-D-Gl*cp*-(1→3)-β-D-Gl*cp*-(1→3)-β-D-Gl*cp*-(1→3)-β-D-Gl*cp*-(1→3)-β-D-Gl*cp*-]→
Curdlan from *Agrobacterium* spp.

Figure 1 The structure of glucan homopolysaccharides mutan and curdlan.

Streptococcus spp. have been summarised by Monchois *et al.* (1999). Additionally the cells possess several distinct glucan-binding proteins (e.g. Kuramitsu, 1993; Smith *et al.*, 1994). In other biofilm systems these activities are more commonly found as individual attributes of strains rather than as common features. In addition to synthesis of mutan and soluble dextrans, the presence of sucrose may permit levan synthesis. This is a feature of oral isolates of both *Streptococcus* and *Actinomyces* spp. although the latter fail to form mutan or dextrans (Table 1). In oral biofilms there are therefore a number of different types of neutral EPS synthesised, the exact range depending on the strains present within the oral microflora and on the diet of the individual.

The EPS of *Streptococcus mutans*

The polysaccharide mutan from *S. mutans*, is a poorly soluble 1,3-linked-α-D-glucan (Figure1) in which a small proportion of α-1,6-linkages are normally also present. Change to its physical structure can be effected through the action of depolymerase enzymes from heterologous oral bacteria such as *Actinomyces viscosus*. This will alter the binding of not only cells of *S. mutans* but also of other microbial cells, together with proteins and glycoproteins which have receptors for the glucan. Similar effects may be found following degradation of fructans by Streptococci located in the oral cavity although fructans differ considerably in their properties from mutan. The net effect may either be to loosen the whole biofilm or to cause localised 'pores' from which the EPS has been removed and from which other macromolecules may then escape. Removal of some of the EPS matrix may also lead to increased sensitivity to antimicrobial agents or antagonists. *S. mutans* is one of a number of oral bacteria which can synthesise fructans in the presence of sucrose as carbon substrate. The *S. mutans* products are predominantly β2,1-linked (Birkhed *et al.*, 1979). The role of the fructans is probably as a carbon and energy reserve rather than forming part of the biofilm structure, as *S. mutans* also secretes a fructanase which permits catabolism of the polymer (Burne *et al.*, 1999).

Loss of polysaccharide from the biofilm may also occur due to the action of other enzymes than glycanases. Thus, Lee *et al.* (1996) demonstrated that an endogenous enzyme activity which they termed 'surface-protein releasing enzyme' (SPRE) caused the release of cells of *S. mutans* from a monolayer biofilm in a chemostat. The removal of cells could be associated with accompanying release of any polysaccharide which was firmly attached to them rather than to the oral surfaces. The observation also reflects the earlier report by

Mukasa and Slade (1973) that binding of either viable or heat-killed cells of *S. mutans* required synthesis of water-insoluble polymer and the involvement of a binding site on the cell-surface. Does this represent a further analogy to cellulosomes?

EPS from other oral *Streptococcus* spp.

In the presence of sucrose many oral bacterial species can synthesise homopolysaccharides which are either levans or dextrans. These may however vary in structure. Thus the fructans from *Streptococcus salivarius*, *Streptococcus sanguis* and *Actinomyces viscosus* are mainly β2,6-linked as opposed to the β2,1-linked product from *Streptococcus mutans* (Birked *et al.*, 1979). The dextrans from strains such as *S. gordonii* contain fewer α-1,3-linkages (40%) than do some of those from *S. salivarius* (90%) (Table 2). Whereas mutan, dextrans and levans are neutral homopolymers, most other Streptococcal EPS which have been studied, are heteropolysaccharides. Very marked differences in interaction behaviour can be expected from the EPS of *Streptococcus oralis* strains. These are polyanionic heteropolymers which are charged due to the presence of phosphate groups on each repeat unit of the structure (Figure 2) (Kolenbrander, 1991). They thus have the capacity to involve both specific (lectin-type) adhesion to the various carbohydrate residues present and bridging with other polyanionic materials through the mediation of multivalent cations. This may account for some of the types of co-aggregation noted by Kolenbrander (1997) in which one cell type carried a thermolabile (or protease degradable) surface molecule while the other possessed a thermostable macromolecule. Clearly EPS, including the phosphorylated heteroglycans of *S. oralis*, are excellent candidates

-[α-L-Rhap-(1→2)-α-L-Rhap-(1→3)-α-D-Galp-(1→3)-β-D-Galp(1→4)-β-D-Glcp-(1→3)-α/β-D-Galp -]-
Streptococcus oralis H1
Each hexasaccharide repeat unit carries a phosphate substituent

-[α-D-GalpNAc-(1→3)-β-L-Rhap (1→4)-β-D-Glcp-(1→6)-b-D-Galf(1→6)-β-D-GalpNAc-(1→3)-α-D-Galp -]$_n$-

→PO$_4$'
Streptococcus oralis 34

-[→6)-α-D-GalpNAc-(1→3)-β-L-Rhap (1→4)-β-D-Glcp-(1→6)-β- D-Gal(1→6)-β-D-Galp-(1→3)-α-D-GalpNAc-]$_n$-
↑2
1
α-L-Rhap

→PO$_4$'
Streptococcus oralis (*mitis*) J22

Results of Kolenbrander (1991)

Figure 2 The structure of *Streptococcus oralis* exopolysaccharides.

for the latter role. As many examples of coaggregation were inhibited by lactose, exposed epitopes containing β-D-galactosyl-$(1{\rightarrow}4)$-... linkages are likely to be involved. This was confirmed in various studies which were reviewed by Whittaker *et al.* (1996). Kolenbrander (1997) has suggested that as cells of *Fusobacterium* spp. coaggregate with so many other species, they could form the focus for the attach-

Table 2 The composition of the glucans from oral strains of Streptococcus .

Strain	gene product	α-1,3	α-1,6
S. downei	*gtfI*	88%	12%
	gtfS	10%	90%
S. mutans (Strain GS5)	*gtfB*	87%	13%
	gtfC	85%	15%
	gtfD	30%	70%
S. gordonii	*gtfG*	40%	60%
S. sobrinus (Strain OMZ176)	*gtfT*	27%	73%
S. salivarius	*gtfJ*	90%	10%
	gtfK	0%	100%
	gtfL	50%	50%
	gtfM	5%	95%

Adapted from Monchois *et al.* (1999)

ment of other bacteria, effectively bridging the many types present. Cationic bridges involving calcium are inhibited by fluoride (Rose and Turner, 1998a,b). The fluoride decreases the calcium-binding affinity of *S. mutans* and enhances diffusion of the cation. This probably also decreases the stability of the plaque and its associated polymeric material and enables improved penetration of other solutes into the biofilm.

Other EPS from oral micro-organisms

An important member of the oral bacterial flora is *Actinomyces viscosus*. Although some strains produce relatively large amounts of EPS, such isolates may not colonise oral surfaces as readily as do other isolates of this species. This may result from occlusion of sialic acid-containing polymers on the surface of these bacteria (Jones *et al.*, 1986). The sialic-acid residues appeared to play a significant role in adhesion but could be released through the action of either the cell-bound or extracellular forms of the neuraminidase from the bacteria. Similarly, although *Streptococcus salivarius* is a major component of the salivary microbial flora, it displays both biosynthetic and degradative capacities in respect of EPS. It coaggregates with *Veillonella parvula* due to material that appears to be a fibrillar polyanionic polysaccharide and also appears capable of synthesising another electron-dense polysaccharide detectable by the ruthenium red staining procedure, under various growth conditions (Handley *et al.*, 1988; Harty and Handley, 1989). The chemical nature of the stainable material was not investigated. The *S. salivarius* was capable of dextran synthesis when exposed to sucrose as carbon substrate, but also secreted extracellular endodextranases (Lawman and Bleiweis (1991). One endodextranase which has been isolated yields isomaltose from dextran, but the bacteria were unable to utilise this as a growth substrate, indicating other possible roles for the polysaccharase. The function of the enzyme may therefore be concerned with bacterial cell detachment from a dextran-containing biofilm or with the alteration of the physical properties of that polysaccharide. This bacterium appears to belong to the group of strains which can synthesise several apparently different polysaccharides, some of which (the dextrans) are substrate dependent. Probably in oral biofilms even more than in other environments, the presence or absence of a specific substrate (sucrose) greatly influences biofilm composition, structure and properties. Many of the interactions in oral biofilms are therefore dextran-mediated <u>and</u> sucrose dependent! Similar biosynthetic and degradative activities have been observed in other oral Streptococcal species (Ellis and Miller, 1977).

As yet, relatively few EPS from microbial plaque or oral biofilm isolates have been thoroughly investigated. Among those which have been studied are those microbial cultures which have yielded relatively large amounts of polysaccharides. Other types which may only synthesise a small amount of EPS, or a thin layer surrounding the cell, could also play a very significant role in oral biofilms. A study of these might well elucidate some of the many complex interactions which occur in the biofilms associated with the oral environment. Improved and more sensitive assay and investigative procedures such as atomic force microscopy, may well cast light on these.

References

Banas,J.A., Russell,R.R.B. and Ferreti,J.J. 1990. Sequence analysis of the gene for the glucan-binding protein of *Streptococcus mutans* Ingbritt. *Infect. Immun.* **58**, 667-673.

Beckers,H.J.A. and van der Hoeven,J.S. 1982. Effect of microbial interaction on the colonization rate of *Actinomyces viscosus* or *Streptococcus mutans* in the dental plaque of rats. *Infect. Immun.* 38, 8-13.

Beguin,P. and Aubert,J.-P. 1994. The biological degradation of cellulose. *FEMS Microbiol. Rev.* **13**, 25-58.

Birkhed,D., Rosell,K.-G. and Granath,K. 1979. Structure of extracellular water-soluble polysaccharides sunthesised from sucrose by oral strains of *Streptococcus mutans, Streptococcus salivarius, Streptococcus sanguis* and *Actinomyces viscosus. Arch. Oral Biol.* **24**, 53-61.

Bowden, G.H. and Li, Y.H. 1998. Nutritional influences on biofilm development. *Adv. Dental Res.* **11**, 81-99.

Burne, R.A., Schilling, K.M., Bowen, W.H. and Yasbin, R.E. 1987. Expression, purification and chatacterization of an exo-b-D-fructosidase of *Streptococcus mutans* . *J. Bacteriol.* **169**, 4507-4517.

Burne, R.A., Wen, Z.T., Chen, Y.-W.M. and Penders, J.A.E.C. 1999. Regulation of expression of the fructan hydrolase gene of *Streptococcus mutans* GS-5 by induction and carbon catabolite repression. *J. Bacteriol.* **181**, 2863-2871.

Burton, B.A.. and Brant, D.A. 1983. Comparative flexibility, extension and conformation of some simple polysaccharide chains. *Biopolym.* **22**, 1769-1792.

Busscher, H.J., Bos, R. and Vandermei, H.C. 1995. Initial microbial adhesion is a determinant for the strength of biofilm adhesion. *FEMS Microbiol. Lett.* **128**, 229-234.

Carlsson,J. and Engelberg,J. 1965. Effect of diet on early plaque formation in man. *Odontol. Rev.* **16**, 112-125.

Chandrasekaran, R., Radha, A. and Thailambal, V.G. 1992. Roles of potassium ions, acetyl and L-glyceryl groups in the native gellan double helix. *Carbohydr. Res.* **224**, 1-17.

Christensen, B.J., Stokke, B.T. and Smidsrød, O. 1995. Xanthan - the natural water soluble cellulose derivative. In Kennedy, J.F., Phillips, G.O. and Williams, P.A.(eds.): *Cellulose and cellulose derivatives: physico-chemical aspects and industrial applications*, pp. 265-278, Woodhead Publishing.

Ellis,W. and Miller,C. (1977. Extracellular dextran hydrolase from *Streptococcus mutans* strain 6715. *J. Dent. Res.* **56**, 57-69.

Freeman,C. and Lock,M.A. 1995. The biofilm polysaccharide matrix: A buffer against changing organic substrate supply? *Limnol. Oceanograph.* **40**, 273-278.

Geddie, J.L. and Sutherland, I.W. 1994. The effect of acetylation on cation binding by algal and bacterial alginates. *Biotech. Appl. Biochem.* **20**, 117-129.

Gibbons,R.J. 1989. Bacterial adhesion to oral tissues: A model for infectious disease. *J. Dent. Res.* **68**, 750-760.

Grant, G.T., Morris, E.R., Rees, D.A., Smith, P.J.C. and Thom, D. 1973. Biological interactions between polysaccharides and divalent cations: the egg-box model. *FEBS Lett.* **32**, 195-198.

Gunning, A.P., Kirby, A.R., Ridout, M.J., Brownsey, G.J. and Morris, V.J. 1996. Investigation of gellan networks and gels by atomic force microscopy. *Macromol.* **29**, 6791-6796.

Handley, P.S., Hargreaves, J. and Harty, D.W.S. (1988. Ruthenium red staining reveals surface fibrils and a layer external to the cell wall in Streptococcus. *J. gen. Microbiol.* **134**, 3165-3173.

Harty, D.W.S. and Handley, P.S. 1989. Expression of the surface properties of the fibrillar *Streptococcus salivarius* HB and its adhesion deficient mutants grown in continuous culture under glucose limitation. *J. gen. Microbiol.* **135**, 2611-2621.

Hughes,K.A., Sutherland,I.W., Clark,J. and Jones,M.V. 1998. Bacteriophage and associated polysaccharide depolymerases – novel tools for study of bacterial biofilms. *J. appl. Microbiol.* **85**, 583-590.

Hughes,K.A., Sutherland,I.W. and Jones,M.V. 1998. Biofilm susceptibility to bacteriophage attack: the role of phage-borne polysaccharide depolymerases. *Microbiol.* **144**, 3039-3047.

Imai, S. and Kuramitsu, H. 1983. Chemical characterization of extracellular polysaccharides produced by *Actinomyces viscosus* T14V and T14Av. *Infect. Immun.* **39**, 1059-1066.

Jenkinson, H.F. and Lamont, R.J. 1997. Streptococcal adhesion and colonization. *Crit. Rev. Oral. Biol. Med.* **8**, 175-200.

Jones, A.H., Lee, C.-C., Moncla, B.J., Robinovitch, M.R. and Birdsell, D.C. 1986. Surface localization of sialic acid on *Actinomyces viscosus. J. gen. Microbiol.* **132**, 3381-3391.

Jouon, N., Rinaudo, M., Milas, M. and Desbrieres, J. 1995. Hydration of hyaluronic acid as a function of the counterion type and relative humidity. *Carbohydr. Polymers* **26**, 69-73.

Kang, K.S., Veeder, G.T., Mirrasoul, P.J., Kaneko, T. and Cottrell, I.W. 1982. Agar-like polysaccharide produced by a Pseudomonas species: production and basic properties. *Appl. Env. Microbiol.* **43**, 1086-1091.

Kanzawa, Y., Harada, A., Koreeda, A., Harada, T. and Okuyama, K. 1989. Difference of molecular association in two types of curdlan gel. *Carbohydr. Polymers* **10**, 299-313.

Kirby, A.R., Gunning, A.P. and Morris, V.J. 1996. Imaging polysaccharides by atomic-force microscopy. *Biopolymers* **38**, 355-366.

Kolenbrander,P.E. 1991. Coaggregation: Adherance in the human oral microbial system. In Dworkin, M.(ed.) : *Microbial Cell-Cell interactions*, Chapt. 10, pp. 303-329, ASM, Washington.

Kolenbrander,P.E. 1997. Biofilm developmental biology. *Trends in Microbiol.* **5**, 475.

Kolenbrander,P.E. and London, J. 1993. Adhere today, here tomorrow: Oral bacterial adherance. *J. Bacteriol.* **175**, 3247-3252.

Koval, S.F. and Bayer, M.E. 1997. Bacterial Capsules - no barrier against *Bdellovibrio. Microbiol.* **143**, 749-753.

Kuramitsu, H.K. 1993. Virulence factors of mutans streptococci: role of molecular genetics. *Crit. Rev. Oral. Biol. Med.* **4**,159-176.

Larwood, V.L., Howlin, B.J. and Webb, G.A. 1996. Solvation effects on the conformational behaviour of gellan and calcium ion binding to gellan double helices. *J. Mol. Modeling* **2**, 175-182.

Lawman, P. and Bleiweis, A.S. 1991. Molecular cloning of the extracellular endodextranase of Streptococcus salivarius. *J.Bacteriol.* **173**, 7423-7428.

Lee, S.F., Li, Y.H. and Bowden, G.H. 1996. Detachment of *Streptococcus mutans* biofilm cells by an endogenous enzymatic activity. *Infect. Immun.* **64**, 1035-1038.

Mack, D., Fischer, W., Krokotsch, A., Leopold, K., Hartmann, R., Egge, H. and Laufs, R. 1996. The intercellular adhesin involved in biofilm accumulation of *Staphylococcus epidermidis* is a linear b-1,6-linked glucosaminoglycan: purification and structural analysis. *J. Bacteriol.* **178**, 175-183.

Miyoshi, E., Takaya, T. and Nishinari, K. 1998. Effects of glucose, mannose and konjac glucomannan on the gel-sol transition in gellan gum aqueous solutions by rheology and dsc. *Polymer Gels And Networks* **6**, 273-290.

Monchois,V., Willemot, R.M., and Monsan, P.F. 1999. Glucansucrases: mechanism of action and structure-function relationships. *FEMS Microbiol. Rev.* **23**, 131-151.

Moorhouse, R., Winter, W.T., Arnott, S. and Bayer, M.E. 1977. Conformation and molecular organization in fibers of the capsular polysaccharide from *Escherichia coli* M41 mutant. *J. Mol. Biol.* **109**, 373-391.

Mukasa,H. and Slade,H.D. 1973. Mechanism of adherence of *Streptococcus mutans* to smooth surfaces. *Infect. Immun.* **8**, 555-562.

Neu,T.R. and Marshall,K.C. 1990. Bacterial polymers: Physicochemical aspects of their interactions at interfaces. *J. Biomaterials Applic.* **5**, 107-133.

Nisbet, B.A., Sutherland, I.W., Bradshaw, I.J., Kerr, M., Morris, E.R. and Shepperson, W.A. 1984. XM6 a new gel-forming bacterial polysaccharide. *Carbohydr. Polymers* **4**, 377-394.

Nyvad,B. and Fejerskov,O. 1989. Structure of dental plaque and the plaque-enamel interface in human experimental caries. *Caries Res.* **23**, 151-158.

Ofek,I. and Doyle,R.J. 1994. *Bacterial adhesion to cells and tissues*. Chapman and Hall:New York and London.

Ogawa, K., Okamura, K. and Sarko, A. 1981. Molecular and crystal structure of the regenerated form of (1Æ3)-a-D-glucan. *Intern. J. Biol. Macromol.* **3**, 31-36.

Piculell, L. 1998. Gelling polysaccharides. *Current Opinion in Colloid and Interface Science* **3**, 643-650.

Rose, R.K. and Turner, S.J. 1998a. Extracellular volume in streptococcal model biofilms - effects of pH, calcium and fluoride. *Biochim. Biophys. Acta - General Subjects* **1379**, 185-190.

Rose, R.K. and Turner, S.J. 1998b. Fluoride-induced enhancement of diffusion in streptococcal model plaque biofilms. *Caries Res.* **32**, 227-232.

Ross-Murphy, S.B. and Shatwell, K.P. 1993. Polysaccharide strong and weak gels. *Biorheol.* **30**, 217-227.

Ross-Murphy, S.B., Shatwell, K.P., Sutherland, I.W. and Dea, I.C.M. 1996. Influence of acyl substituents on the interaction of xanthans with plant polysaccharides. *Food Hydrocolloids* **10**, 117-122.

Skillman,L.C. 1998. Enterobacterial mixed species biofilms. Ph.D. Thesis, Edinburgh University.

Skillman,L.C., Sutherland,I.W. and Jones,M.V. 1999. The role of exopolysaccharides in dual species biofilm development. *J. Appl. Microbiol.* **85**, (In press).

Smith, D.J., Akita, H., King, W.F. and Taubman, M.A. 1994. Purification and antigenicity of a novel glucan-binding protein of *Streptococcus mutans*. *Infect. Immun.* **62**, 2545-2552.

Sulavik, M.C. and Clewell, D.B. 1996. *Rgg* is a positive transcriptional regulator of the *Streptococcus gordonii* gtfG gene. *J. Bacteriol.* **178**, 5826-5830.

Sutherland, I.W. 1990. *Biotechnology of Exopolysaccharides*, C.U.P., Cambridge.

Sutherland, I.W. 1995. Structure function relationships in microbial exopolysaccharides. *Biotech. Adv.* **12**, 393-448.

Teeri, T.T. 1997. Crystalline cellulose degradation: new insight into the function of cellobiohydrolases. *Trends in Biotech.* **15**, 60-167.

Whittaker,C.J., Klier,C.M. and Kolenbrander,P.E. 1996. Mechanisms of adhesion by oral bacteria. *Ann. Rev. Microbiol.* **50**, 513-552.

Wimpenny, J.W.T. and Colasanti, R. 1997. A unifying hypothesis for the structure of microbial biofilms based on cellular automaton models. *FEMS Microbiol. Ecology* **22**, 1-16.

BIOFILM STRUCTURE AND BEHAVIOUR: INFLUENCE OF HYDRODYNAMICS AND NUTRIENTS

Paul Stoodley, John D. Boyle and Hilary M. Lappin-Scott

Micro-organisms attached to surfaces in biofilms contaminate industrial processes and are responsible for many types of microbial infections and disease. Of more specific relevance to the dental profession, biofilms are directly associated with both caries and periodontal diseases. Biofilms have also been recently linked with dental associated infective endocarditis. Once established, biofilms are difficult to eradicate. A more complete understanding of how biofilms form and behave is crucial if we are to predict, and ultimately control, biofilm processes. A breakthrough in biofilm research came in the early 1990's when confocal scanning laser microscopy showed that biofilms formed complex structures that could facilitate nutrient exchange. It has been documented that surfaces, nutrients, and hydrodynamics may all influence biofilm structure but it remains unclear whether the biofilm structure is merely a consequence of the environmental conditions and forces acting upon it, or whether the biofilm can organise its structure to optimise growth conditions in a certain environment.

Using microscopic time lapse imaging techniques, we have discovered that, as well as being spatially complex, biofilms can exhibit a high degree of temporal complexity. We have found that biofilm structures can be transported along a surface and can form micro-scale migratory ripples. Further, we have observed biofilm ripples and cell clusters detaching at regular intervals. The shedding of biofilm micro-colonies has serious implications for the spread of plaque to other areas of the mouth as well as disseminating infective endocarditis during dental procedures. These discoveries give new insights into biofilm behaviour and add to our understanding of how surfaces are colonised by bacteria.

Introduction

In the field of biofilm research it is the prevention of biofilm formation that is arguably of the greatest concern to the dental and medical professions and their associated support industries. However, the accumulation of bacteria on wetted surfaces has proven to be extremely difficult, if not impossible, to prevent. At best biofilm prevention strategies tend to be exercises in damage limitation. Biofilms persist in environments as diverse as the mouth and industrial heat exchangers, despite continued attempts at dispersal using a multitude of mechanical and chemical treatments. Because of the chronic nature of a biofilm colonisation, treatment is usually a long term proposition.

In the last five years combined developments in confocal scanning laser microscopy (CSLM), fluorescent *in situ* hybridisation (FISH), microelectrodes and flow cell design, have allowed the ecology, activity, mechanical properties and structure of fully hydrated, living biofilms to be studied *in situ* with minimal

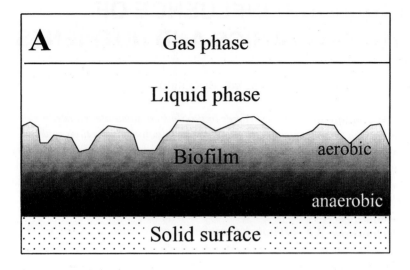

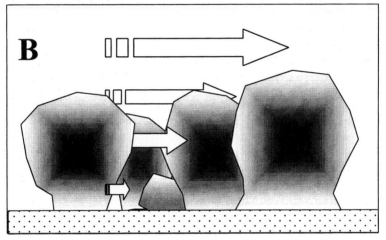

Figure 1 Changes in the conceptual view of biofilm structure which have occurred over the last decade. A) A planar layered biofilm was depicted at the 1988 Dahlem conference on microbial biofilms (Wilderer, P.A. and Characklis, W.G. 1989). Although simplified the model was useful for identifying the main components of a biofilm system. It was assumed that there was only diffusional mass transfer within the biofilm and that concentration gradients were perpendicular to the solid surface. These assumptions allowed mass transfer – reaction process within the biofilm system to be modelled in 1 dimension. B) Biofilms are now thought of as a complex 3D arrangement of cell clusters separated by water channels. Such a system greatly increases the surface area available for nutrient and waste product exchange with the bulk liquid. The formation of "mushroom" like structures and clusters attached to the surface on "legs" (see ASM Biofilms Collection available online at www.asmusa.org/edusrc/biofilms/infopage/011i.html) resulted in oxygen depleted regions in the centre of the cell clusters away from the substratum (deBeer *et al.*, 1994a), not in an anaerobic layer parallel to the solid surface as predicted by the old model.

intrusion. Hopefully, as we better understand biofilm processes at the microscale, we will be able to design more sophisticated and effective methods of biofilm control. In this paper we will concentrate on some of our recent findings concerning the influences of hydrodynamics and nutrients on structure, mechanical properties, and behaviour of bacterial biofilms.

Biofilm structure

With the application of confocal microscopy to observe fully hydrated biofilms at high resolution, it has become apparent that biofilms can have very complex structures. Detailed observations of biofilms grown in a laminar or low shear environment show that bacterial cells in biofilms tend to be concentrated into discrete aggregates or cell clusters and are held together by a highly hydrated extra-cellular polysaccharide (EPS) matrix (Caldwell *et al.*, 1993; Costerton *et al.*, 1994; deBeer *et al.* 1994a; Lawrence *et al.*1991; Møller *et al.*, 1996). The bacterial cell clusters are surrounded by a network of voids or water channels. It was directly demonstrated that water could flow through the channels (deBeer *et al.* 1994b; Stoodley *et al.* 1994) and facilitate the mass transfer of nutrients to biofilm bacteria (deBeer and Stoodley, 1995; deBeer *et al.*, 1996). Okabe *et al.* (1998) have shown that water channels can facilitate convective flow throughout wastewater biofilms with thickness of 640 µm. After 2 months the water channels had remained open, suggesting that such a network was in some way beneficial to the biofilm and supporting an earlier hypothesis made by Costerton *et al.* (1995) that the water channels may serve as a rudimentary circulatory system by which to supply nutrients to biofilm cells.

Over the last decade the examination of biofilms with CSLM has resulted in a fundamental change in the way we conceptualise biofilm structure: from that of a simplified planar layered arrangement (Wilderer and Characklis, 1989) to that of a spatially complex heterogeneous system (Figure 1). This shift now allows us to consider the possibility of different functional morphotypes within diverse biofilm systems.

Hydrodynamics

Hydrodynamics affects both the physical shear stress at a wetted surface as well as the rate at which nutrients are transported to the surface and both shear and mass transfer can influence biofilm development. It has been shown that biofilms grown under high shear are generally thinner and denser than those grown under lower shear (Vieria and Melo 1999). We have also demonstrated that hydrodynamics can profoundly influence on biofilm structure. We have grown non-defined tap water, defined mixed species, and pure culture *Pseudomonas. aeruginosa* biofilms in parallel glass flow cells under laminar (low shear, poorly mixed) and turbulent (high shear, well mixed) flows Stoodley *et al.*, (1999a,b,c). In all of these experiments the biofilms grown in laminar flow consisted of cell clusters, which were roughly circular in shape, separated by surrounding voids (Figure 2). However, the biofilm clusters grown in turbulent flow became elongated in the downstream direction to form filamentous streamers

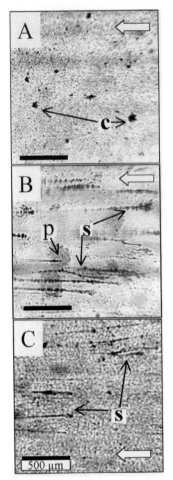

Figure 2 Influence of hydrodynamics on the structure of an undefined mixed population biofilm. A) 17 d biofilm grown in laminar flow consisted of cell clusters "c" surrounded by voids. Flow direction is indicated by the open arrow. Approximately 50% of the void areas were covered by a layer of single cells. B) 17 d biofilm grown in turbulent flow consisted of filamentous streamers "s" and patches "p" of cells of 1 to 2 cells thick. The streamers oscillated rapidly in the flow and consequently appear blurred in the image. C) After 3 d of increasing from laminar to turbulent flow the biofilm clusters had elongated to form streamers "s" (same biofilm as shown in panel "A"). Scale bars = 500 µm.

(Stoodley *et al.*, 1998) (Figure 2). Some of the streamers oscillated rapidly in the flow and were anchored to the solid surface by an upstream cluster "head". Other streamers appeared to be more firmly attached to the surface and only oscillated at the tip. When a 17 d undefined culture biofilm was switched from laminar to turbulent flow some of the clusters began to elongate noticeably within 24 h (Figure 2). It is likely that the elongated forms were caused by the constant unidirectional shear to which they were subjected. As cells divide, daughter cells would be more likely to assume a downstream location as they are "pushed" by the fluid shear.

An elongated structure may have certain advantages for the biofilm organisms. In addition to streamlining, which may help reduce drag and allow the streamers to remain attached, the oscillation of the streamers close to the wall may contribute to mixing in the boundary layer and increase the transport of solutes through the biofilm as found by Siegrist and Gujer (1985). Another potential advantage of a filamentous structure is that there is a large surface area to volume ratio which will tend to minimise mass transfer limitations. Although it appears that some minimum shear is required for the formation of streamers, at high shear streamer length is inversely related to shear (Bryers and Characklis, 1981) as predicted by Boyle *et al.* (1997) for conical shaped structures. It may be expected that, in the widely fluctuating multidirectional stress environment of the mouth, the shape of biofilm structures will differ regionally and elongation may occur if there is a prevailing shear direction.

In addition to streamers, ripple-like structures also developed in some biofilms grown under turbulent flow, these will be discussed in following sections.

Nutrients

Nutrient concentration can influence both the amount of biomass and the structure of biofilms. Generally, there is a greater accumulation of biofilm biomass in copiotrophic environments than in oligotrophic environments as demonstrated by the influence of carbon loading rate on biofilm thickness (Characklis, 1990). The nutrient composition can also influence biofilm structure (Møller *et al.* 1997). In recent work we have demonstrated that an increase in nutrients resulted not only in an increase in biomass (measured as biovolume) of an established biofilm, but also a change in structure (Stoodley *et al.*, 1999b). The structure of a 21 d mixed species biofilm grown under turbulent flow changed from an arrangement of ripples and streamers to large cell clusters (up to 500 μm in length) when the carbon and nitrogen concentration was increased by a factor of 10 (Stoodley *et al.*, 1999b). The thickness of the biofilm increased from 26 ± 2.6μm (n=5 measurements from one flow cell) to 129 ± 6.9μm (n=5) within 24 h. The ripples had completely disappeared after 9 h. When the nutrients were reduced back to their original level (on day 26) there was an immediate loss of biomass, through detachment of the clusters and, after a further 3 d, the ripples and streamers had begun to reappear. It was thought that the structural changes may have been drag related and caused by variations in fluid shear within the biofilm as a result of changes in thickness and surface coverage. The time scale of the observed structural response to nutritional changes suggest that the structure of oral biofilms may also vary as a result of nutrient fluctuations caused by eating patterns.

Material properties of biofilms

The material properties of intact biofilms have received very little attention but will determine the strength, flexibility, and viscosity of a biofilm and consequently influence the detachment and behaviour of a biofilm which is subjected to physical forces. In previous sections we have discussed the impact of hydrodynamics over long term (days to weeks) biofilm development, now we will discuss the influence of short term (seconds to minutes) variations in hydrodynamic shear and how consequent changes in biofilm shape were used to investigate material properties. Pure culture *Ps. aeruginosa* and mixed culture biofilm streamers grown in turbulent flow were subjected to cycles of increasing and decreasing shear stress (by changing flow velocity) and the displacement of fiducial points on the biofilm were monitored over time (Stoodley *et al.*, 1999d). Repeated extension and contraction of streamers below the shear at which the biofilm was grown demonstrated that the biofilm was elastic and suggested a very low elastic modulus (≈ 60 Pa), i.e. the biofilms were highly compliant. However, when the shear stress was increased to between 120 to 200 % of the shear at which the biofilm was grown, the biofilm behaved like a liquid and began to flow. These characteristics are similar to those of the non-Newtonian class of Bingham fluids which behave as elastic solids below a critical yield point but as viscous liquids when the yield point is exceeded. Creep curves demonstrated that the biofilm was behaving as predicted for a non-cross linked

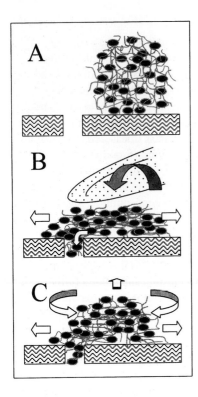

Figure 3 Hypothetical schematic showing how mechanical forces may cause structural changes to a dental plaque. A) Biofilm cell cluster showing cells and strands of EPS. B) Pressure from the tongue may squeeze the biofilm flat and squeeze fluid out of the EPS matrix, temporarily increasing the cell density. The biofilm may also be squeezed into crevices in the teeth and gums. C) When the pressure is released the biofilm may spring back, drawing in fresh nutrients.

polymer gel, which suggests that the material properties were largely determined by the EPS. Since biofilms can have a complex rheology, their response to an applied force will not only be dependant on the magnitude and direction of shear but also on the rate of change of shear . Rapid shape changes by the biofilm in response to shear may influence both mass transfer (surface area dependant)   and the drag acting on individual biofilm structures (shape dependant) which may consequently affect both the growth and detachment processes.

It was also found that the biofilm could be repeatedly flattened. The thickness of mixed culture and pure culture *Ps. aeruginosa* biofilms was reduced by approximately 30% when the bulk liquid flow velocity was increased from 0 to 1.5 m s^{-1}. Similar thickness changes have been induced electrochemically by applying a voltage with an oscillating polarity to a platinum wire colonised with biofilm (Stoodley *et al.* 1997). It may be expected that when a biofilm is flattened water in the matrix would be "squeezed" out like a sponge. Then when the biofilm re-expands, surrounding water would be drawn back into the matrix, thereby increasing the nutrient flux. In the mouth such mechanical squeezing could come from the motion of the tongue, jaw, and teeth (Figure 3). In dental plaque the co-aggregation of different species, a high protein content and the presence of cross linking divalent cations will all influence the material properties and might be expected to increase biofilm strength and rigidity. Further hardening will occur if plaque, not removed by brushing, becomes calcified to form calculus.

Biofilm behaviour - surface migration and detachment

In addition to collecting structural information, an advantage of observing biofilms non invasively *in vivo* is that digital time lapse microscopy (DTLM) can also reveal aspects of biofilm behaviour. For example, it has been shown

Figure 4 Downstream migration of a mixed species biofilm cell cluster (Stoodley *et al.*, 1999e). A) Cell cluster is outlined for clarity. The surrounding surface was covered by single cells. B) After 35 minutes the cell cluster had moved downstream approximately 30 μm, at a velocity of ≈ 20 μm h⁻¹. The average velocity of the bulk liquid was 1 m s⁻¹, in the direction indicated by the arrow.

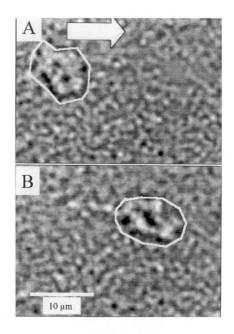

that in some marine species cell clusters can repeatedly form and disperse from the motion of single cells across the substratum (Dalton *et al.*, 1996).

Biofilm Ripples

We have found that complete biofilm structures can migrate steadily downstream in high shear unidirectional flows (Stoodley *et al.*, 1999e). In a mixed species biofilm growing in turbulent pipe flow, both ripple-like structures and cell clusters moved steadily downstream over time (Figure 4). The ripple morphology and migration velocity were a function of the bulk liquid flow rate. The maximum migration velocity of the ripples was approximately 1 mm h⁻¹. These data demonstrate that biofilm structures can move across solid surfaces while remaining attached. This has some important implications for the colonisation of surfaces by biofilms. It is generally assumed that biofilm colonisation of a surface follows two stages, 1) single planktonic cells are transported to a solid surface and 2) these cells attach and grow. Our data suggests that surfaces can also be colonised by "pre-formed" biofilm structures that have moved into a new area from an adjacent area. This mode of colonisation may be advantageous in some circumstances because it does not rely on a planktonic phase of single cells, which are known to be more susceptible to antimicrobial agents (Gilbert and Brown, 1995).

Biofilm Detachment

The detachment of biofilm is of concern in a dental context because it may contribute to the spread of biofilm within the mouth. Also, periodontal disease has been linked with systemic diseases ["More reasons to look after your teeth", Lancet (1998) **352,**121]. In one study group of patients suffering from infective endocarditis 33% of the cases were associated with a dental procedure as a predisposing event (Somerville, 1998).

Bryers (1988) proposed five types of biofilm detachment processes, of these erosion (the continual shedding of individual cells from a biofilm, sloughing (the sporadic detachment of large pieces or entire biofilms), and human intervention

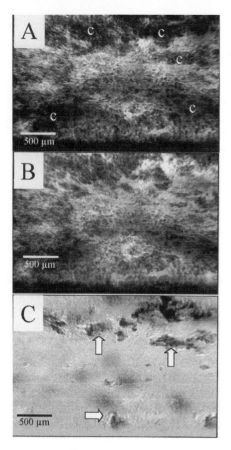

Figure 5 Detachment of cell clusters from a mixed species biofilm consisting of *Ps. aeruginosa*, *Ps. fluorescens*, *Klebsiella. pneumoniae*, and *Xanthamonas. maltophilia* growing on a minimal salts medium with glucose (400 mg l⁻¹) as the carbon source (Stoodley *et al.*, 1999b). The biofilm was grown in a glass flow cell with an average bulk liquid flow velocity 1 m s⁻¹. A) The biofilm consisted of cell clusters "c" separated by water channels. B) Same area as shown in panel "A" 30 minutes later. C) Image "B" was digitally subtracted from image "A" to show the differences over the 30 min. time period. Clusters which had detached during this time appear as dark patches (three representative clusters are indicated by the open arrows).

(including chemical treatment and mechanical removal) are of most relevance to dental biofilms. Detachment is arguably the least understood biofilm process and to date much of the available information remains anecdotal. By using time lapse microscopy we have observed the continual growth and subsequent detachment of cell clusters from a mixed culture biofilm (Figure 5). The continual detachment of large pieces of biofilm in a predictable manner represents an intermediate process (both in terms of spatial and temporal scales) between erosion (single cells - continuous) and sloughing (large groups of cells - sporadic and unpredictable) as they are currently understood. The larger clusters had length and width dimensions on the order of several hundred microns and the thickness was approximately 60μm. By selectively removing cell clusters from the biofilm with a micropipette, then dispersing and plating, we estimated that there were ≈ 10¹⁰ CFU (colony forming units) cm⁻³ of cell cluster material. This gives an estimate ≈ of 10⁴ CFU per detached cluster. Clusters in this size category detached at a rate of approximately 6 clusters cm⁻² of surface h⁻¹ over a 19 h period. The detached cell clusters may retain the protective properties against the host's defence systems that are attributed to attached biofilms (Hoiby *et al.*, 1995).

Concluding remarks

In recent years the use of flow cells and improved microscopy techniques have allowed living biofilms to be observed non intrusively *in vivo*. These techniques have made it clear that biofilm structure can quickly adapt to changing nutrient and hydrodynamic conditions. The complex structures which allow fluid to flow through the biofilm have opened up a new way of thinking about biofilms and the role of biofilm structure in terms of functional morphology. It is likely that biofilm structures are not incidental, but rather represent an adaptive arrangement which balances the need to maximise the available surface area for nutrient exchange, while maintaining the form and strength required to hold the biofilm together at a solid surface, according to a given set of environmental conditions. Time lapse imaging is also revealing different biofilm behaviours such as the migration of single cells and larger structures across surfaces and the growth and detachment of cell clusters from surfaces. In this paper we have drawn together observations and data primarily from flow cell systems and attempted to extrapolate the significance of these results in a dental context. However, the variations in nutrients and forces exerted on biofilms in the mouth are much more complex than in our laboratory flow cells. Complex dental biofilm communities have been cultured in the laboratory (Bradshaw *et al.*, 1997, Pratten *et al.*, 1998) but are usually grown under steady flow and nutrient conditions. Further work is required to characterise the nutrient fluctuations and physical forces to which biofilms may be subjected in the mouth and to observe how biofilms behave under similar conditions in the laboratory.

Acknowledgements

Original research by the authors reported in this paper was supported by the University of Exeter and in part by the co-operative agreement EEC-8907039 between the National Science Foundation and Montana State University - Bozeman. Thanks to Luanne Hall-Stoodley for careful review of this manuscript.

References

Boyle, J.D., Dodds, I., Stoodley, P., and Lappin-Scott, H.M. 1997. Stress management in biofilms. In: Wimpenny, J.W.T., Handley, P.S., Gilbert, P., Lappin-Scott, H.M. and Jones, M. (eds.), *Biofilms: community interactions and control,* pp. 15-22, BioLine, Cardiff, UK.

Bradshaw, D.J., Marsh, P.D., Watson, G.K., and Allison, C. 1997. Effect of conditioning films on oral microbial biofilm development. *Biofouling.* **11,**217-226.

Bryers, J.D. and Characklis, W.G. 1981. Early fouling biofilm formation in a turbulent flow system: overall kinetics. *Water Res.* **15,**483-491.

Bryers, J.D. 1988. Modeling biofilm accumulation. In: Bazin, M.J., and Prosser, J.I. (eds.) *Physiological models in microbiology vol. 2.,* pp. 109-144, CRC, Boca Raton.

Caldwell, D.E., Korber, J.R. and Lawrence, D.R. 1993. Analysis of biofilm formation using 2D vs 3D digital imaging. *J. Appl. Bacteriol.* **74,**S52-S66.

Characklis, W.G. 1990. Microbial fouling. In: Characklis, W.G. and Marshall, K.C. (eds.), *Biofilms,* pp.523-584. Wiley, New York.

Costerton, J.W., Lewandowski, Z., deBeer, D., Caldwell, D., Korber, D., James, G. 1994. Biofilms, the customized microniche. *J. Bacteriol.* **176,**2137-2142.

Costerton, J.W., Lewandowski, Z., Caldwell, D.E., Korber, D.R., and Lappin-Scott, H.M. 1995. Microbial Biofilms. *Annu. Rev. Microbiol.* **49,**711-745.

Dalton, H.M., Goodman, A.E., and Marshall, K.C. 1996. Diversity in surface colonization behavior in marine bacteria. *J. Ind. Microbiol.* **17,**228-234.

deBeer, D., Stoodley, P., Roe, F., and Lewandowski, Z. 1994a. Effects of biofilm structures on oxygen distribution and mass transfer *Biotechnol. Bioeng.* **43,**1131-1138.

deBeer, D., Stoodley, P., and Lewandowski, Z. 1994b. Liquid flow in heterogenous biofilms.

Biotechnol. Bioeng. **44,**636-641.

deBeer, D. and Stoodley, P. 1995. Relation between the structure of an aerobic biofilm and mass transport phenomena. *Water Sci. Tech.* **32,**11-18.

deBeer, D., Stoodley, P., and Lewandowski, Z. 1996. Liquid flow and mass transfer in heterogeneous biofilms. *Water Res.* **30,**2761-2765.

Gilbert, P. and Brown, M.R.W. 1995. Mechanisms of the protection of bacterial biofilms from antimicrobial agents. In: Lappin-Scott, H.M. and Costerton, J.W. (eds.), *Microbial Biofilms, Plant and microbial biotechnology research series; 5*, pp. 118-130.Cambridge University Press, Cambridge.

Hoiby, N., Fomsgaard, A., Jensen, E.T., Johansen, H.K., Kronborg, G., Pedersen, S.S., Pressler, T., and Kharazmi, A. 1995. The immune response to bacterial biofilms.. In: Lappin-Scott, H.M. and Costerton, J.W. (eds.), *Microbial Biofilms, Plant and microbial biotechnology research series; 5*, pp. 233-250, Cambridge University Press, Cambridge.

Lawrence, J.R., Korber, D.R., Hoyle, B.D., Costerton, J.W., and Caldwell, D.E. 1991. Optical sectioning of microbial biofilms. *J. Bacteriol.* **173,**6558-6567.

Møller, S., Pedersen, A.R., Poulsen, L.K., Arvin, E., and Molin, S. 1996. Activity and three-dimensional distribution of toluene-degrading *Pseudomonas putida* in a multispecies biofilm assessed by quantitative in situ hybridization and scanning confocal laser microscopy. *Appl. Environ. Microbiol.* **62,**4632- 4640.

Møller, S., Korber, D.R., Wolfaardt, G.M., Molin, S., and Caldwell, D.E. 1997. Impact of nutrient composition on a degradative biofilm community. *Appl. Environ. Microbiol.* **63,**2432-2438.

Okabe, S., Kuroda, H., and Watanabe, Y. 1998. Significance of biofilm structure on transport of inert particulates into biofilms. *Water Sci. Technol.* **38,**163-170.

Pratten, J., Barnett, P., and Wilson, M. 1998. Composition and susceptibility to chlorhexidine of multispecies biofilms of oral bacteria. *Appl. Environ. Microbiol.* **64,** 3515-3519.

Siegrist, H. and Gujer, W. 1985. Mass transfer mechanisms in a heterotrophic biofilm. *Water Res.* **19,**1369-1378.

Somerville, L.W. 1998. Infective endocarditis in the grown-up congenital heart (GUCH) population. *European Heart Journal.* **19,**166-173

Stoodley, P., deBeer, D., and Lewandowski, Z. 1994. Liquid flow in biofilm systems. *Appl. Environ. Microbiol.* **60,**2711-2716.

Stoodley, P., deBeer, D., and Lappin-Scott, H.M. 1997. The influence of electrical fields and pH on biofilm structure as related to the bioelectric effect. *Antimicrob. Agents. Chemother.* **41,**1876-1879.

Stoodley, P., Lewandowski, L., Boyle, J.D., and Lappin-Scott, H.M. 1998. Oscillation characteristics of biofilm streamers in turbulent flowing water as related to drag and pressure drop. *Biotechnol. Bioeng.* **57,**536-544.

Stoodley, P., Boyle, J.D., Cunningham, A.B., Dodds, I., Lappin-Scott, H.M. and Lewandowski, Z. 1999a. Biofilm structure and influence on biofouling under laminar and turbulent flows. In: Keevil C.W., Dow C.S., Godfree A.F., Holt D. (eds), *Biofilms in Aquatic Systems.* Cambridge: Royal Society of Chemistry. In press.

Stoodley, P., Dodds, I., Boyle, J.D., Lappin-Scott, H.M. 1999b. Influence of hydrodynamics and nutrients on biofilm structure. *J. App. Microbiol.* **85,**S19-S28.

Stoodley, P., deBeer, D., Boyle, J.D., and Lappin-Scott, H.M. 1999c. Evolving perspectives of biofilm structure. *Biofouling* **14,**1-16. In press.

Stoodley, P., Lewandowski, Z., Boyle, J.D., and Lappin-Scott, H.M. 1999d. Structural deformation of bacterial biofilms caused by short term fluctuations in flow velocity: an in-situ demonstration of biofilm viscoelasticity. *Biotechnol. Bioeng.* In press.

Stoodley, P., Lewandowski, Z., Boyle, J.D. and Lappin-Scott, H.M. 1999e. The formation of migratory ripples in a mixed species bacterial biofilm growing in turbulent flow. *Environ. Microbiol.* In the press.

Vieira, M.J. and Melo, L.F. 1999. Intrinsic kinetics of biofilms formed under turbulent flow and low substrate concentrations. *Bioprocess Engineering* **20,**369-375.

Wilderer, P.A. and Characklis, W.G. 1989. Structure and function of biofilms. In: Characklis, W.G. and Wilderer P.A. (eds.), *Structure and function of biofilms*, pp 5-17, John Wiley and Sons Ltd., New York.

MICROBIAL ACTIVITY IN BIOFILM COMMUNITIES

Søren Molin

*Reporter genes have been used extensively in molecular microbiology for studies of specific gene expression in cases where direct monitoring of gene activity is very complicated or impossible. The **lac** operon has been very popular in this respect because of the existence of useful indicator substrates and an easy quantitative enzyme assay. The green fluorescent protein and its variant molecules are well suited as reporters for **in situ** single-cell gene expression studies due to the lack of substrate requirement and the compatibility between the fluorescence signal and the fluorescence microscope (incl. the scanning confocal microscope). The construction of fusions between a promoter of interest and the **gfp** gene allow on-line non-destructive monitoring of gene expression in almost any type of microbial community. Moreover, this reporter may also be used in combination with other types of fluorescent indicators such as those used in **in situ** hybridization of rRNA molecules for identification of specific organisms. We have recently designed a series of variant Gfp reporters with reduced stability. These proteins are very useful as gene expression reporters in populations where the conditions change over time, because they allow monitoring of both turn-on and turn-off of gene expression. We have investigated biofilm communities in flow chambers, and through the use of Gfp reporters it has been possible to monitor a number of important microbial activities in relation to the specific organisms and their location in the community. In particular, expression from an rRNA promoter was used as an indicator of growth. The fluorescent proteins are also useful as tagging markers in situations where different strains of the same organism need to be specifically identified. The recent construction of Gfp tagged streptococci has opened up possibilities of investigating other types of ecological niches such as dental plaques.*

Complex microbial communities

Life of bacteria in their natural settings is most often associated with colonization of surfaces, and if the conditions allow it, mixed populations will proliferate and spread in the formation of bacterial biofilms. Microbial biofilm communities can be viewed as random aggregates of a number of different organisms, which happen to be together in a specific place at a specific time. Alternatively, they may be seen as multi-cellular 'organisms' with developed internal interdependencies and coordinated activities. The perspective favored here is that it is not a question of either one or the other, but instead a matter of choice of the observer. Experience from the laboratory shows that many different species of bacteria may be brought together in stable biofilm communities, even though the organisms most likely never meet under natural conditions; at the same time, such random consortia may display activities and form structures which are indicative of coordinated performance. Therefore, in the description of biofilm communities it is useful to define a set of parameters which on one hand lead to an overall phenotypic description of the system independent of its composition or location, and on the other hand may be used to define both views of microbial communities (random aggregates/multicellular organisms).

The four principal parameters forming the basis for experimental descriptions of multi-species biofilm communities are: Organisms (who is there?), Structure (where are they?), Interactions (what are they doing?), and Coordination (how and why?). In the present context, the major focus is on bacterial activity as it unfolds in microbial surface communities, and it is consequently the organism/interaction platform that is dealt with.

Organism Identification

Natural microbial communities most often consist of complex mixtures of microbial species whose relative frequency may vary significantly. The classical approach towards an analysis of such populations is to cultivate bacteria on laboratory substrates as pure cell lines, followed by identification of the individuals. This is often an impossible task due to the complexity of the community, and also because the majority of the bacteria are not culturable. The most powerful technique at present for organism identification in environmental samples is that of rRNA identification (Pace *et al.*, 1986). Bacterial taxonomy is changing rapidly these years due to the systematic analysis of rRNA sequences, which are almost ideal indicators of evolutionary relationships (Woese, 1987). Direct analysis of rRNA sequences present in complex samples is possible without any step of cultivation using the PCR method to create libraries of probes (Giovannoni *et al.*, 1988; Ward *et al.*, 1992). The simplicity and speed of the PCR based methods make detailed analyses of microbial communities possible. The obtained information relates to the complexity of the community, but also provides specific data on identification at a number of different taxonomic levels (Amann *et al.*, 1995).

The method of rRNA hybridization is furthermore useful in the context of *in situ* identification of single cells (Amann *et al.*, 1995). Specific rRNA probes labeled with fluorochromes are precise and highly sensitive tools for single-cell identification in the fluorescence microscope, and when used in combination with the flow-cytometer they may also provide quantitative information such as the relative proportion of a certain organism (Amann *et al.*, 1990; Møller *et al.*, 1995). To some extent similar quantitative information can be obtained by fluorescence microscopy. The limitation of the method is that only a few species can be investigated at the time.

Molecular tagging of a distinct organism is an interesting possibility in cases where the purpose is to follow specifically one particular strain in a complex community (Chalfie *et al.*, 1994; Jansson, 1995; Prosser, 1994). Introduction of such tags requires growth and manipulation of the organism followed by introduction of the tagged cells to the community. This scenario is often not possible in natural ecosystems, but in laboratory model systems it represents an excellent choice of specific organism analysis.

74

Monitoring Bacterial Growth

In situ rRNA hybridization provides information, not only about organism identity, but also in some cases about organism activity (DeLong *et al.*, 1989; Poulsen *et al.*, 1993). This possibility is a direct consequence of the careful steady-state measurements of RNA contents in exponentially growing bacteria performed 40 years ago (Maaløe and Kjeldgaard, 1966). Several ways of quantifying the hybridization of fluorescent probes to the rRNA molecules have been presented, and controls have been described showing that potential changes in probe permeability or variations in probe accessibility to its target sequence did not seem to interfere significantly with the growth rate correlation experiments (Poulsen *et al.*, 1993). Care was taken to compare quantification of fluorescence intensities as measures of hybridization efficiencies with other methods of rRNA determinations without coming across serious problems (Møller *et al.*, 1995). However, although the well-known correlation between growth rate and ribosome concentration in the cell has been found in a number of different organisms, there may be several problems in uncritical extrapolations from the data obtained in balanced cultures of *E. coli* and *S. typhimurium* (Amann *et al.*, 1995).

The inherent problem in the ribosome counting approach is that the quantification defines the accumulated level of rRNA without providing any information about the changing rates of synthesis, let alone the actual on-line state of growth activity. Control of macromolecular synthesis in bacteria is primarily exerted at the level of intitiation of synthesis, be it DNA replication, transcription or translation. Thus, for rRNA the rate of transcription is an important target for the growth rate associated control system, and in *E. coli* genetic and physiological evidence has shown that only one of the two *rrn* promoters located upstream of the rRNA operons, the P1 promoter, is subject to growth rate directed control (Gourse *et al.*, 1986). Monitoring the *rrn* promoter activity in single cells should therefore yield on-line information about the growth physiological status of the cells.

In molecular microbiology there is a fairly long and successful tradition for employing reporter genes for determinations of promoter activities. The *lac* genes of *E. coli* constituted the first useful reporter system, and later the *lux/luc* bioluminescence genes have been added to the list. The gene expression reporter, Gfp (green fluorescent protein), is the latest example of highly useful gene expression reporters. It harbors several interesting and relevant characteristics that make it an excellent tool in molecular ecology. Most importantly, the protein carries in the polypeptide chain a fluorophore, which is excitable with blue light; thus, there is no requirement for any externally added substrate. Second, the green fluorescence emitted from the expressed protein upon excitation with light of the right wave length is compatible with fluorescence microscopy, including scanning confocal microscopy, which makes it a relevant marker for biofilm cells. Finally, a number of variant *gfp* genes have been constructed with the following properties: better intensities (Cormack *et al.*, 1996), changed excitation and emission wave lengths (Heim *et al.*, 1994), reporters for both transcriptional and translational gene fusions (Ludin *et al.*, 1996), and lately also genes expressing Gfp molecules with much reduced stability in bacteria (Andersen *et al.*, 1998). The latter is relevant for design of reporter systems, in which it is important to monitor changing gene expression activities in complex environments.

In a particular application of the unstable Gfp reporter proteins, fusions have been made between the rRNA P1 promoter from *E. coli* and the relevant mutated *gfp* genes (Molin *et al.*, 1998; Sternberg *et al.*, 1998). The activity of this promoter reflects directly the growth activity of the cells, since its rate of transcription is proportional to the cellular growth rate. If growth is reduced or totally blocked the stringent response controlling the rRNA promoter immediately shuts down the promoter, and due to the instability of the Gfp protein the cellular fluorescence fades out under such conditions. If growth is increased or resumed the promoter is induced and fluorescence reappears. The introduction of this kind of growth reporter system in a community of bacteria thus monitors the rate of rRNA transcription in individual cells, which in general may be an indicator of growth rate (although caution in interpreting such signals is important). The finding that the *E. coli* rRNA promoter seems to be regulated in an identical fashion in *P. putida* provides hope that at least in the proteobacteria it may be a useful common growth reporter. It should be emphasized that if the cells are growing very slowly – as they most often are in natural environments – this reporter system will not distinguish between non-growth and poor growth. This means that the major value of it is in connection with localization of growth activity hot-spots.

Obviously, the various *gfp* reporters may be fused to a large number of promoters which in one way or another will be useful for monitoring microbial activity. Among such alternative promoters are starvation induced, stress induced (various types of stress), stationary phase induced, density induced (quorum sensing) and other growth physiology related promoters. In all cases, similar approaches as described above for the rRNA promoter may be applied. This use of genetic modification in the design of specific growth physiology reporter systems opens up for a range of very detailed studies of bacterial life in complex adaptive communities, and in connection with future applications of genetically engineered microorganisms in agriculture and for environmental purposes such strains will become highly useful as 'informers' of microbial life in natural environments. In the meantime, we will see a rapid increase of their use in model communities, from which we can formulate new questions to the field of microbial ecology.

Thus, if genetic manipulation of the strain of interest is at all possible, clones comprising chromosomal insertions of rRNA promoter fusions to the gene for unstable Gfp may be obtained and used to monitor growth activity in the biofilm communities. Preliminary applications of such strains in biofilms have provided the first insights in the distribution of actively growing bacteria in simple biofilm communities, and a considerable heterogeneity has been observed, even in micro-niches of such communities, which would never have been detected with any of the other monitoring methods described previously. Through this - and similar - approaches it will be possible to reach a deeper understanding of the creation of micro-environments in microbial surface communities, and due to the non-destructive characteristic of analytical like this one, dynamic developments in the community can be recorded.

Molecular Tools for Oral Gram-positive Bacteria

Although there has been a rapid development of a range of molecular methods and tools for investigations of complex bacterial community features, most of these have so far mainly been applied to Gram-negative bacteria. The major reason for that is the broad knowledge about organisms like *E. coli* and various Pseudomonads, and the large collections of genetic tools for these organisms that have been designed in many places. In several interesting fields within microbiology the Gram-positive bacteria are in focus, and molecular genetics has also contributed to the understanding of these in recent years. We have initiated an attempt to transfer several of our molecular methods described above to a number of Gram-positive bacteria, among which is the dental plaque related species *Streptococcus gordonii*. In particular, a strain of this organism has now been tagged with a fusion between a synthetic, strong and constitutive promoter and the *gfp* gene in order to monitor its presence in mixed species communities. In a further series of constructions we have transferred similar fusions with *gfp* genes expressing unstable fluorescent proteins, and shown that also in Gram-positive lactococci the variant proteins are degraded. Since these bacteria preferentially grow anaerobically it was important to determine the lower level of oxygen concentrations allowing the Gfp fluorophore to be formed, since it is known that molecular oxygen is required for this conformational change of the protein. The finding that extremely low levels of oxygen are needed for Gfp fluorescence to establish was very promising for future applications of this reporter gene in studies of a very broad range of bacteria. These results open up for detailed investigations of gene expression and other bacterial activities concerning organisms living in the oral ecological niche.

Concluding remarks

Combining the fluorescence microscope, and in particular the scanning confocal laser microscope, with the application of molecular techniques and tools has introduced new and very promising approaches to studies of bacterial performance and organization in heterogeneous environments and complex populations. The most important conclusion from the last years' developments is that these approaches are apparently equally useful and informative in very diverse ecological contexts. What has proven already to result in significant new information about enterics or pseudomonads in water, soil, laboratory based reactors and waste water treatment plants, seems to be relevant also for investigations of anaerobic bacteria living in oral microniches, such as streptococci and other Gram-positive bacteria.

References

Amann, R. I., Binder, B. J., Olson, R. J., Chrisholm, S. W., Devereux, R. and Stahl, D. A. 1990. Combination of 16S rRNA-Targeted Oligonucleotide Probes whith Flow Cytometry for analyzing Mixed Microbial Populations. *Appl.Environ.Microbiol.* **56,** 1919-1925.

Amann, R. I., Ludwig, W. and Schleifer, K. H. 1995. Phylogenetic identification and in situ detection of individual microbial cells without cultivation. *Microbiol.Rev.* **59,** 143-169.

Andersen, J. B., Sternberg, C., Poulsen, L. K., Bjorn, S. P., Givskov, M. and Molin, S. 1998. New unstable variants of green fluorescent protein for studies of transient gene expression in bacteria. *Appl. Environ. Microbiol.* **64,** 2240-2246.

Chalfie, M., Tu, Y., Euskirchen, G., Ward, W. W. and Prasher, D. C. 1994. Green fluorescent protein as a marker for gene expression. *Science* **263,** 802-805.

Cormack, B. P., Valdivia, R. H. and Falkow, S. 1996. FACS-optimized mutants of the green fluorescent (GFP). *Gene* **173,** 33-38.

DeLong, E. F., Wickham, G. S. and Pace, N. R. 1989. Phylogenetic stains: ribosomal RNA-based probes for identification of single cells. *Science* **243,** 1360-1362.

Giovannoni, S. J, DeLong, E. F., Olsen, G. J. and Pace, N. R. 1988. Phylogenetic group-specific oligodeoxynucleotide probes for identification of single microbial cells. *J.Bacteriol.* **170,** 720-726.

Gourse, R. L., de Boer, H. A. and Nomura, M. 1986. DNA determinants of rRNA synthesis in E. coli: Growth rate dependent regulation, feedback inhibition, upstream activation, antitermination. *Cell* **44,** 197-205.

Heim, R., Prasher, D. C. and Tsien, R. Y. 1994. Walelength mutations and posttranslational autoxidation of green fluorescent protein. *Proc.Natl.Acad.Sci.USA.* **91,** 12501-12504.

Jansson, J. K. 1995. Tracking genetically engineered microorganisms in nature. *Curr.Opinion. Biotechnol.* **6,** 275-283.

Ludin, B., Doll, R., Meili, S., Kaech, S. and Matus, A. 1996. Application of novel vectors for GFP-tagging of proteins to study microtubule-associated proteins. *Gene* **173,** 107-111.

Maaløe, O. and Kjeldgaard, N. O. 1966. Control af macromolecular synthesis. New York, W.A. Benjamin.

Molin, S., Nielsen, A. T., Christensen, B. B., Andersen, J. B., Licht, T. R., Tolker-Nielsen, T., Sternberg, C., Hansen, M. C., Ramos, C. and Givskov, M. 1998. Molecular ecology of biofilms. In James Bryers (ed.), *Biofilms.* **2nd.** J. Wiley & Sons, Inc., in press.

Møller, S., Kristensen, C. S., Poulsen, L. K., Carstensen, J. M. and Molin, S. 1995. Bacterial Growth on Surfaces: Automated Image Analysis for Quantification of Growth Rate-Related Parameters. *Appl.Environ.Microbiol.* **61,** 741-748.

Pace, N. R., Stahl, D. A., Lane, D. L. and Olsen, G. J. 1986. The analysis of natural microbial populations by rRNA sequences. *Adv. Microb. Ecol.* **9,** 1-55.

Poulsen, L. K., Ballard, G. and Stahl, D. A. 1993. Use of rRNA fluorescence *in situ* hybridization for measuring the activity of single cells in young and established biofilms. *Appl.Environ.Microbiol.* **59,** 1354-1360.

Prosser, J. I. 1994. Molecular marker systems for the detection of genetically modified microorganisms in the environment. *Microbiology* **140,** 5-17.

Sternberg, C., Christensen, B. B., Johansen, T., Nielsen, A. T., Andersen, J. B., Givskov, M. and Molin, S. 1999. Bacterial activity in microbial communities analyzed in situ by unstable variants of Green Fluorescent Protein fused to ribosomal promoters. *Appl. Environ.Microbiol.,* in press.

Ward, D. M., Bateson, M. M., Weller, R. and Ruff-Roberts, A. L. 1992. Ribosomal RNA analysis of microorganisms as they occur in nature. In Marshall, K. C. (ed.), *Advances in microbial ecology* pp. 219-228, New York, Plenum Press.

Woese, C. R. 1987. Bacterial evolution. *Microbiol.Rev.* **51,** 221-271.

QUORUM SENSING IN BIOFILMS

James I. Prosser

*The control of a wide range of density-dependent phenomena has been shown to depend on bacterial communication via intercellular signalling mechanisms. Such quorum sensing phenomena include plasmid transfer and the production of antibiotics, exoenzymes and surfactants and are dependent on the accumulation of signal molecules, notably N-acyl homoserine lactones (AHLs). These molecules, which are often produced constitutively by cells at low concentrations, accumulate at high cell densities through autoinduction mechanisms and activate expression of specific genes. In biofilm populations, accumulation will also be affected by the diffusion of signalling molecules through the biofilm and the establishment of concentration gradients. One important ecological property of biofilm populations is their ability to recover rapidly following prolonged periods of starvation, one example being biofilm populations of ammonia oxidising bacteria. Rapid recovery of one ammonia oxidiser, **Nitrosomonas europaea**, can be achieved at low cell concentrations following simultaneous addition of substrate and the AHL N-(3-oxo-hexanoyl) homoserine lactone (OHHL), suggesting a similar function for this signalling molecule in biofilms. Quorum sensing is also involved in the differentiation and resistance of complex biofilms of **Pseudomonas aeruginosa** on glass surfaces. Quorum sensing phenomena in natural multispecies biofilms will be determined by the specificity of signalling molecules, in addition to their rates of diffusion and degradation, and are likely to contribute community structure and to the properties of biofilms which distinguish them from planktonic cells.*

Quorum sensing

Quorum sensing in bacteria involves the regulation of expression of specific genes through the accumulation of signalling compounds that mediate intercellular communication. At low cell densities, these compounds may be produced constitutively at low levels but autoinduction leads to dramatic increases in concentration as cell density increases. Gene expression is activated through accumulation of the signalling compound to a threshold level, equivalent to a quorum cell density, and subsequent interaction of the signalling compound with transcriptional activators (Salmond *et al.*, 1995; Fuqua *et al.*, 1996). The phenomenon is best characterised in the luminescent bacterium *Photobacterium fischeri*, where cell signalling is mediated by a *N*-acyl homoserine lactone (AHL) which is encoded by a *lux*I gene. The AHL interacts with a transcriptional activator, *lux*R, activating expression of genes encoding luciferase and leading, through autoinduction, to increased expression of *lux*I.

In Gram-negative bacteria, quorum sensing systems homologous to *lux*I/*lux*R control in luminescent bacteria encompass a variety of processes, including conjugation in *Agrobacterium tumefaciens*, carbapenem production and virulence determinants in *Erwinia carotovora* and virulence factors in *Pseudomonas aeruginosa* (see Fuqua *et al.*, 1996; Salmond *et al.*, 1995; Swift *et al.*, 1996). In each case, the signalling compound is an AHL with specificity for different processes provided by differences in the length and/or degree of substitution of the *N*-acyl side chain.

Differences between attached and planktonic populations

Bacteria in natural environments are most commonly found attached to particulate material. Surface colonisation typically begins with attachment of single cells, which develop into microcolonies and, if conditions are favourable for extensive growth, into complex, three-dimensional biofilms with apparent differentiation and structural organisation. The widespread occurrence of surface-associated populations in itself demands study of the mechanisms controlling attachment and colonisation. A major additional feature of such populations, of equal significance, is the existence of major differences between their properties and those of much more intensively studied cell suspensions or planktonic populations. Some of these differences arise directly from the physico-chemical properties of biofilms. For example, restrictions to diffusion of oxygen through monoculture biofilms of facultative anaerobes will lead to close proximity of cells metabolising aerobically and anaerobically. The subsequent diffusion of products of their respective metabolic processes will enable the establishment of interactions between physiologically different cells over short distances which would not be possible in well-dispersed, homogeneous cell suspensions. In mixed communities, the scope for such interactions is increased considerably and in heterogeneous environments such as dental plaque and marine or soil aggregates, aerobic and anaerobic mixed populations can interact and coexist in close proximity.

Other differences between biofilm and planktonic cells indicate differences in the physiological characteristics of the populations. There is evidence, for example, that the metabolic activities of biofilms cells may differ from those of planktonic cells under equivalent environmental conditions (Turley *et al.*, 1995). Biofilm populations are also believed to be more resistant to environmental stress and perturbation than equivalent populations of suspended cells, with significant consequences for biofilms of clinical importance. Biofilms have been shown to have increased resistance to antibacterial agents (Costerton *et al.*, 1981) and to protect cells from desiccation and phagocytosis by amoebae (Atkins *et al.*, 1979). These properties are of considerable medical significance in increasing resistance to antibiotics of populations colonising surfaces such as heart valves, bronchial tissue, catheters and prosthetic joints (Nichols, 1993; Gilbert *et al.*, 1997).

In the majority of cases, the mechanistic basis for differences in the properties of cells in biofilms and the same cells freely suspended in homogeneous liquid systems is, at best, poorly understood. Biofilm cells commonly produce extracellular polymeric material (Allison & Matthews, 1992), which may function to increase adhesion of cells to surfaces (Marshall *et al.*, 1971). This has been proposed as an explanation for antibiotic resistance (Allison & Matthews, 1992) and provides a feasible explanation for desiccation resistance.

The nature and properties of such extracellular material are, however, generally poorly characterised and specific mechanisms for protection are difficult to propose and test. Alternative explanations have been proposed for protection from antibiotic activity, for example differences in specific growth rate of organisms within biofilms (Gilbert *et al.*, 1990).

Quorum sensing and biofilms

The high cell concentrations found in biofilms present an ideal situation for the operation of quorum sensing mechanisms. Indeed, microcolonies containing less than ten cells may provide the opportunity for cell-density based induction of gene expression if the signalling compounds do not diffuse from the microcolony and are not degraded. Quorum sensing may therefore provide a mechanism for cell communication and expression of genes that give biofilm populations their distinctive properties, such as those described above. For example, expression of genes for antibiotic resistance at high cell densities may provide protection from competitors or invaders while expression of gene encoding virulence determinants may explain the phenomenon of 'inoculum potential' in both plant and animal bacterial infections. Co-ordinated induction of genes encoding degradation and antibiotic resistance could accelerate decomposition of particulate substrates while simultaneously reducing the exploitation of degradation products by competing organisms. Quorum sensing also has the potential for influencing the community structure of complex biofilms and biological interactions. In natural biofilms, consisting of mixed microbial communities, signalling compounds may encourage growth of beneficial organisms and discourage that of competitors and may influence the physiological properties of other organisms within the community, through cross-talk. The traditional view of temporal and spatial heterogeneity influenced by the production, utilisation and diffusion of nutrients and by-products and end products of metabolism should therefore be modified by to include a role for signalling compounds, with more specific effects on gene expression, cell physiology and community structure.

The possible role of quorum sensing mechanisms in controlling the properties of biofilms was first suggested in 1995 (Cooper *et al.*, 1995) but there are currently few published reports of experimental evidence supporting an effect of AHLs on biofilm characteristics. These will be discussed along with evidence for production of AHLs in natural biofilms and the issues surrounding quorum sensing which must be addressed for a full understanding of its potential influence on biofilms.

Biofilms of nitrifying bacteria

Biofilm populations of autotrophic nitrifying bacteria exhibit many of the properties of heterotrophic bacteria and have been studied in experimental laboratory systems that provide controlled conditions, enabling direct comparison of attached and planktonic cells. Attached cells of ammonia and nitrite oxidising bacteria are more active when attached to charged surfaces that adsorb their respective substrates (Underhill & Prosser, 1987). In addition, both groups of organisms can grow and maintain activity in biofilms at pH values significantly lower than minimum pH values supporting growth of planktonic cells (Keen & Prosser, 1987; Allison and Prosser, 1993). Surface growth increases survival of these organisms (Allison & Prosser, 1991) and protects them from the effects of specific inhibitors of nitrification, including nitrapyrin (Powell & Prosser, 1991) and potassium ethyl xanthate (Underhill & Prosser, 1985). Consequently, greater concentrations of these compounds are required for inhibition of nitrifying bacteria in soil than for the same organisms in liquid culture. Growth of nitrifying bacteria on surfaces is frequently associated with production of extracellular polymeric substances (Cox & Bazin, 1980; Keen & Prosser, 1987). This material does not appear to be involved in initial attachment but forms a 'blanket' over cells in mature biofilms. This may provide protection from the effects of low pH and inhibition but, as discussed above, the nature and properties of the extracellular material are not characterised and its effects on physiology are difficult to predict.

An additional characteristic of biofilm formation by nitrifying bacteria, which is of enormous significance in natural environments, is a reduction in the lag phase following resupply of nutrients to starved cells. For example, the lag period for starved suspended cells of the ammonia oxidising bacterium *Nitrosomonas europaea* may extend for several days but are reduced or eliminated when this strain is grown on clay minerals (Armstrong & Prosser, 1988; Prosser & Powell, 1991). The mechanisms controlling the length of lag phases prior to growth and of recovery from starvation are poorly understood but there is evidence that recovery may be faster at high cell densities. For example, lag phases during resuscitation of *Micrococcus luteus* are significantly reduced at high cell concentrations (Votyakova *et al.*, 1994). The 'biofilm' effect on the lag phase of starved nitrifying bacteria may therefore be due to the close proximity and high concentrations of cells and may provide a significant advantage for natural populations, which are usually associated with particulate material and which are subjected to intermittent substrate supply leading to a fast:famine existence.

Batchelor *et al.* (1997) determined the effect of starvation on lag periods of *N. europaea* in liquid medium and in mature biofilms. For the former, cells at a concentration of 10^7 ml^{-1} were starved in inorganic medium lacking ammonium for periods of up to 42 days before addition of ammonium. Growth during subsequent incubation was then followed by measuring changes in product (nitrite) concentration. The results confirmed previous work with these and other organisms that the length of the lag period prior to growth increased with the length of the preceding starvation period (Figure 1). Cells starved for 42 days had a lag phase of 150 h, which would represent a significant disadvantage for organisms in the natural environments, where competition for ammonium would be strong.

Starvation in biofilms was studied in columns packed with sand, or a mixture of sand and soil, inoculated with the same strain of *N. europaea* and

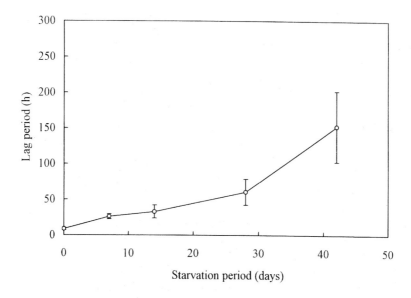

Figure 1 Changes in the length of the lag period prior to exponential nitrite production following starvation of *Nitrosomonas europaea* in ammonium-free mineral salts medium. Error bars represent standard errors. (From Batchelor *et al.*, 1997, with permission.)

supplied continuously with the same inorganic medium with ammonium. Following establishment of a biofilm population, indicated by high, steady state nitrite concentrations in effluent from the columns, biofilms were starved by removal of ammonium from the inorganic medium supplied to the column. This resulted in rapid decreases in ammonium and nitrite concentrations (Figure 2). After starvation periods of up to 43 days, biofilms were resuscitated by supply of medium containing ammonium. In all cases, this resulted in rapid, exponential increases in nitrite in the column effluent. The exponential nature of these increases indicated some cell death during starvation, resulting in growth to the previous steady state biomass level. Kinetic analysis of these data showed that lag phases in both growth and activity were not detectable for these biofilm communities.

To determine whether the reduction in lag phase resulted from an AHL-mediated, density dependent phenomena, suspensions of starved cells in liquid inorganic medium were supplemented with both ammonia and *N*-(3-oxo-hexanoyl homoserine lactone (OHHL). The presence of OHHL significantly decreased the length of the lag phase (Figure 3) with effects at concentrations of OHHL similar to those affecting other cell density dependent secondary metabolic processes. Further analysis of culture supernatants from high cell density (10^{10} cells ml^{-1}) cultures of *N. europaea*, using a *lux E. coli* AHL reporter, demonstrated the presence of high levels of AHL, although its chemical composition was not determined. Cell densities in biofilms will be greater than 10^{10} ml^{-1}

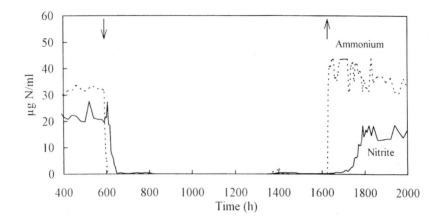

Figure 2 Recovery of a *Nitrosomonas europaea* biofilm starved for 42 days. Changes in ammonium (- - - -) and nitrite concentrations (——) in effluent from continuous flow sand columns supplied with mineral salts medium containing ammonium or ammonium-free medium. Arrows indicate times at which ammonium was supplied (upward arrows) or removed (downward arrows). Samples were taken at intervals of 5 h. (From Batchelor *et al.*, 1997, with permission.)

and AHL production is likely to have taken place in biofilm cultures, providing evidence that cell density signalling has a direct role in activating cell growth in biofilms and may be responsible for other distinctive properties of biofilms. This activation will enable cells to respond immediately to increased concentrations of nutrients, providing significant benefits in the face of competition for ammonium.

Pseudomonad biofilms

The molecular basis for quorum sensing in *P. aeruginosa* has been studied intensively, due to the importance of this organism in chronic infections in cystic fibrosis patients and infection of catheters. At least two quorum-sensing systems exist in this organism, with roles in determination of virulence. The *las*I-*las*R system involves *N*-(3-oxododecanoyl) homoserine lactone and regulates synthesis of elastase and a protease. The *rhi*I-*rhi*R system is mediated by *N*-butyryl homoserine lactone and activates genes involved in rhamnolipid synthesis and the stationary-phase sigma factor, rpoS.

To determine the role of these AHLs in biofilm formation, Davies *et al.* (1998) created *P. aeruginosa* mutants in *las*I, *rhi*I and a double mutant. The wild type *P. aeruginosa* strain forms differentiated biofilms on glass surfaces, with groups of cells separated by water channels, associated with extracellular polysaccharide matrix or glycocalyx. In addition, wild type biofilms are not affected by 0.2% sodium dodecyl sulphate (SDS). The double mutant and the *las*I mutant formed biofilms which were thinner, lacked apparent differentiation and were sensitive to SDS, which led to detachment. Cells were more densely

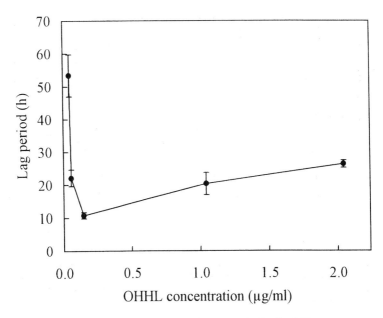

Figure 3 The effect of OHHL on the lag phase prior to growth of cells of *Nitrosomonas europaea* starved in inorganic, ammonium-free medium for 28 d. Error bars indicate standard errors for triplicate flasks. (From Batchelor *et al.*, 1997, with permission.)

packed and were distributed evenly over the glass surface. A glycocalyx was produced, with no evident difference from the wild type. There is, however, evidence that production of extracellular polysaccharide material by planktonic cells differs from that of biofilm cells. The authors therefore suggested that wild type planktonic cells differentiated following attachment, possibly through changes in the glycocalyx, and that these changes were activated through a quorum sensing mechanism activated by *las*I and mediated by the AHL, *N*-(3-oxododecanoyl) homoserine lactone. The absence of the *las*I gene product prevented activation and led to undifferentiated biofilm. To test this hypothesis, biofilms of the *las*I mutant were developed in the presence of the AHL. These biofilms possessed a differentiated structure, typical of the wild type strain, and were also resistant to the effects of 0.2% SDS.

Further evidence for AHL involvement in pseudomonad biofilms comes from growth of *Pseudomonas fluorescens* on glass coverslips (Allison *et al.*, 1998), where biofilm formation is followed by a period of detachment. In the presence of spent growth medium, initial biofilm growth was increased and detachment of cell occurred sooner, i.e. the whole process of biofilm formation and detachment occurred faster and to a greater extent. AHL production was not detected using an *A. tumefaciens* indicator strain, but it was assumed that this strain, like other pseudomonads, produces AHLs but that they were not detectable by the indicator strain. In the presence of *N*-hexanoyl-L-homoserine lactone biofilm accumulation was greater and more rapid than by the wild type strain, but not as great as in the presence of culture supernatant, and detachment was unaffected. This may be due to the absence of polysaccharide lyase activity, which was detected in cell supernatants, particularly from older cultures. The authors therefore proposed that quorum sensing was involved in attachment and biofilm formation, but not with short chain AHLs detectable by their indicator system, and that detachment through degradation of the extracellular polysaccharide matrix was not density-dependent.

AHL production in natural biofilms

AHL production by biofilms was not assessed in the above studies, but has been demonstrated by others in naturally occurring biofilms. McLean *et al.* (1997) used an *A. tumefaciens* indicator strain to investigate AHL production by biofilms colonising limestone rocks collected from a river bed. Activity was detected during incubation of biofilm covered rocks with the indicator strain and during incubation with biofilm supernatant. Activation did not occur during incubation with autoclaved rocks but this was not due to inactivation of the AHL. AHL activity therefore arose from growth-associated production during incubation. Stickler *et al.* (1998) used the same indicator to demonstrate AHL production by infected catheters taken from patients and by 14 *P. aeruginosa* strains isolated from these catheters. Other Gram negative isolates did not activate the indicator strain but may produce AHLs to which it is not responsive. They also demonstrated AHL production by *P. aeruginosa* biofilms produced on silicone catheters in a model system.

Factors influencing quorum sensing in biofilms

There is now strong evidence, in a limited number of situations, for the role of density dependent control of gene expression through AHL signalling compounds in biofilms of Gram negative bacteria and the production of AHLs has been demonstrated in naturally occurring biofilms of environmental and clinical importance. It is not yet possible, however, to predict the importance of quorum sensing in biofilms. For single species biofilms a number of factors, on which we currently have little information, will determine the ability of signalling compounds to have an effect.

Accumulation of AHLs to the 'threshold' level required for activation of gene expression will depend on AHL uptake systems and efflux systems, which will differ for different AHLs. Free diffusion has been demonstrated for two short chain AHLs, OHHL, produced by *P. fischeri* (Kaplan & Greenberg, 1985), and *N*-butyryl homoserine lactone, produced by *P. aeruginosa*, with six- and four-carbon side chains respectively. In contrast, transport of *N*-(3-oxododecanoyl) homoserine lactone, with a twelve-carbon side chain, was recently shown to be more complex (Pearson *et al.*, 1999). Although some free diffusion occurred, there was also evidence for active efflux and for partitioning of this AHL into cell membranes. These differences in transport are believed to be due to a combination of side chain length and hydrophobicity and will affect

86

accumulation within cells and in the immediate extracellular medium. Accumulation of an AHL within biofilms will depend on its rate of degradation and removal, both of which are required in the long term to prevent continuous activation, and the rate of production. Diffusion through the liquid phase of biofilms will depend on the hydrophobicity and molecular weight of signalling compounds and on the density of cell packing. Diffusion may also be affected by production of extracellular polymeric material. Little quantitative information is available on these factors, or on the rates of production and degradation.

For multispecies biofilms, the potential for quorum sensing to activate genes controlling processes which may benefit or inhibit other species provides limitless permutations for the regulated establishment of mixed communities. The specificity provided by variation in AHL chemical structure provides a mechanism for establishment of complex metabolic interactions within a community; activation of specific AHL degradation pathways may provide a new mechanism for competition and induction of detachment processes may reduce biofilm stability. It must be remembered, however, that quorum sensing will not be the sole mechanism controlling biofilm characteristics that distinguish them from planktonic populations. Factors leading to spatial heterogeneity in substrate and product concentrations, oxygen gradients, etc., will remain of significance and should not be ignored. Nevertheless, the characterisation of specific processes under density dependent control does suggest a role for quorum sensing and indicates the need for further studies in this area.

References

Allison, D.G. and Matthews, M.J. 1992. Effect of polysaccharide interactions on antibiotic susceptibility of *Pseudomonas aeruginosa*. *Biofouling* **4**, 243.

Allison, S.M. and Prosser, J.I. 1991. Survival of ammonia oxidising bacteria in air-dried soil. *FEMS Microbiol. Lett.*, **79**, 65-68.

Allison, S.M. and Prosser, J.I. 1993. Ammonia oxidation at low pH by attached populations of nitrifying bacteria. *Soil Biol. Biochem.*, **25**, 935-941.

Allison, D.G., Ruiz, B., San Jose, C., Jaspe, A. and Gilbert, P. 1998. Extracellular products as mediators of the formation and detachment of *Pseudomonas fluorescens* biofilms. *FEMS Microbiol. Lett.*, **167**, 179-184.

Armstrong, E.F. and J.I. Prosser. 1988. Growth of *Nitrosomonas europaea* on ammonia-treated vermiculite. *Soil Biol. Biochem.*, **20**, 409-411.

Atkins, E.D.T., Isaac, D.H. and Elloway, H.F. 1979. Conformations of microbial extracellular polysaccharides by X-ray diffraction: progress on the *Klebsiella* serotypes. In: Berkeley, R.C.W., Gooday, G.W. and Ellwood, D.C. (ed.), *Polysaccharides and Polysaccharases*, pp. 161-189, Academic Press, London.

Batchelor, S.E., Cooper, M., Chhabra, S.R., Glover, L.A., Stewart, G.S.A.B., Williams, P. and Prosser, J.I. 1997. Cell-density regulated recovery of starved biofilm populations of ammonia oxidising bacteria. *Appl. Environ. Microbiol.*, **63**, 2281-2286.

Cooper, M., Batchelor, S.M. and Prosser, J.I. 1995. Is cell density-signalling applicable to biofilms? In: Wimpenny, J., Nichols, W., Stickler D. and Lappin-Scott, H. (ed.), *The Life and Death of a Biofilm*, pp. 93-96, BioLine, Cardiff.

Costerton, J.W., Irvin, R.T. and Cheng, K.J. 1981. The bacterial glycocalyx in nature and disease. *Ann. Rev. Microbiol.*, **35**, 299-324.

Cox, D.J., Bazin, M.J. and Gull, K. 1980. Distribution of bacteria in a continuous-flow nitrification column. *Soil Biol. Biochem.*, **12**, 241-246.

Davies, D.G., Parsek, M.R., Pearson, J.P., Iglewski, B.H., Costerton, J.W. and Greenberg, E.P. 1988.

The involvement of cell-to-cell signals in the development of a bacterial biofilm. *Science*, **280**, 295-298.

Fuqua, C., Winans, S.C. and Greenberg, E.P. 1996. Census and consensus in bacterial ecosystems: the LuxR-LuxI family of quorum-sensing transcriptional regulators. *Ann. Rev. Microbiol.*, **50**, 727-751.

Gilbert, P., Collier, P.J. and Brown, M.R.W. 1990. Influence of growth rate on susceptibility to antimicrobial agents: biofilms, cell cycle, dormancy, and stringent response. *Antimicrobial Agents and Chemotherapy*, **34,** 1865-1868.

Gilbert, P., Das, J. and Foley, I. 1997. Biofilm susceptibility to antimicrobials. *Adv. Dent. Res.,* **11**, 160-167.

Kaplan, H.B. and Greenberg, E.P. 1985. Diffusion of autoinducer is involved in regulation of the *Vibrio fischeri* luminescence system. *J. Bacteriol.,* **163**, 1210-1214.

Keen, G.A. and Prosser, J.I. 1987. Interrelationship between pH and surface growth of *Nitrobacter*. *Soil Biol. Biochem.*, **19**, 665-672.

Marshall, K.C., Stout, R. and Mitchell, R. 1971. Mechanism of the initial events in the sorption of marine bacteria to surfaces. *J. Gen. Microbiol.*, **68**, 337-348.

McLean, R.J.C., Whiteley, M., Stickler, D.J. and Fuqua, W.C. 1997. Evidence of autoinducer activity in naturally occurring biofilms. *FEMS Microbiol. Lett.*, **154**, 259-263.

Nichols, W.W. 1993. Sensitivity of bacteria in biofilms to antibacterial agents. In: Denyer, S.P. and Gorman S.P. (ed.), *Microbial Biofilms: Formation and Control*, Society for Applied Bacteriology Technical Series No. 30.

Pearson, J.P., van Delden, C. and Iglewski, B.H. 1999. Active efflux and diffusion are involved in transport of *Pseudomonas aeruginosa* cell-to-cell signals. *J. Bacteriol.*, **181**, 1203-1210.

Powell, S.J., and J.I. Prosser. 1991. Protection of *Nitrosomonas europaea* colonising clay minerals from inhibition by nitrapyrin. *J. Gen. Microbiol.*, 137, 1923-1929.

Salmond, G.P.C., Bycroft, B.W., Stewart, G.S.A.B. and Williams, P. 1995. The bacterial 'enigma': cracking the code of cell-cell communication. *Mol. Microbiol.*, **16,** 615-624.

Stickler, D.J., Morris, N.S., McLean, R.J.C. and Fuqua, W.C. 1998. Biofilms on indwelling urethral catheters produce quorum-sensing signal molecules *in situ* and *in vitro*. *Appl. Environ. Microbiol.*, **64**, 3486-3490.

Swift, S., Throup, J.P., Salmond, G.P.C. and Stewart, G.S.A.B. 1996. Quorum sensing: a population density component in the determination of bacterial phenotype. *Trends Biochem. Sci.*, **21**, 214-219.

Turley, C.M., Lochte, K. and Lampitt, R.S. 1995. Transformations of biogenic particles during sedimentation in the northeastern Atlantic. *Phil. Trans. Roy. Soc. Lond.*, Ser. B, **348**, 179-189.

Underhill, S.E. and Prosser, J.I. 1985. Inhibition of nitrification by potassium ethyl xanthate in soil and in liquid culture. *Soil Biol. Biochem.*, **17**, 229-233.

Underhill, S.E. and Prosser, J.I. 1987. Surface attachment of nitrifying bacteria and their inhibition by potassium ethyl xanthate. *Microbial Ecol.*, **14**, 129-139.

Votyakova, T,V, Kaprelyants, A.S. and Kell, D.B. 1994. Influence of viable cells on the resuscitation of dormant cells in *Micrococcus luteus* cultures held in an extended stationary phase: The population effect. *Appl. Environ. Microbiol.*, **60**, 3284-3291.

LABORATORY MODELS OF BIOFILM

Julian Wimpenny

There are four different approaches to investiging microbial communities. These are (1) in situ studies of communites growing in their natural habitat; (2) the use of microcosms which are parts of natural communities brought into the laboratory. The latter are homologues of in situ samples retaining all of their complexity; (3) using experimental model systems which are analogues of natural communities constructed from well understood components and (4) mathematical models of community interactions. Each approach has its advantages and disadvantages, its proponents and its opponents. The difference between laboratory models and microcosms is sometimes small but theoretically significant and equipment devised to investigate one can often be applied to the other. For instance growth of natural dental plaque grown in a film fermenter is a microcosm experiment whilst investigating a biofilm of seven different oral bacteria using the same equipment is considered to be a model. Laboratory models can be divided into numerous categories with emphasis on different processes. Some examples to be discussed include (i) adhesion and early colonisation models including glass plate flow cells; (ii) flow systems with removable studs on which biofilm grows such as the Robbins device, (iii) constant shear devices of which the Rototorque is one example; (iv) steady state systems like the constant depth film fermenter and fluidised bed reactors; (v) immersed surface systems linked to chemostats and (vi) constant growth rate reactors such as percolating filter systems or 'baby factories'

Introduction

Paul Feyeraband was famous as a scientific philosopher for 'epistemological anarchy' or in crude terms 'anything goes' as far as methods of scientific research is concerned. This approach really means that almost any activity can help to create the body of information (hard facts, speculation, theories, discussions, interactions between scientists, imagination, debate etc.) which generates the received wisdom or current paradigm about a scientific topic. This is undoubtedly true in biofilm research as it is in any other investigative sphere. It can be clearly seen in methodology and outlook. Many biofilm scientists believe in the somewhat holistic view that biofilm should be studied where it occurs naturally, even though natural biofilm can often be both complex and irreproducible.

The alternative is to generate biofilm in the laboratory. Here two approaches are possible though sometimes the difference between these can be small. Microcosms consist of samples of natural material brought into the laboratory and cultivated under controlled conditions. They always retain the same complexity as the system from which they derived. Of course in the laboratory their composition can alter since the environmental conditions here will almost certainly be different from that in the natural habitat.

The second main class are laboratory model systems. The model as I have defined it several times before (Wimpenny, 1981; 1988; 1996) is a system whose constituent elements are completely defined. For example we used a model community consisting of nine different species grow in the constant depth film fermenter, (CDFF) (Kinniment *et al.*, 1996). It is important to stress that the *same* equipment can be used for either model experiments or for microcosm experiments. Addition of a natural dental plaque sample into the CDFF makes the experiment a microcosm. The main reason for saying this is that we can never, however carefully we analyse a community cultivated in the laboratory be absolutely sure that it does not contain components which we have not identified.

Laboratory models have been reviewed by the author (Wimpenny, 1988; 1996). Earlier oral growth systems were exhaustively discussed by Tatevossian (1988).

In this chapter we will discuss laboratory systems for investigating biofilm with the clear assumption that such equipment can be used to do model *or* microcosm experiments.

Surface adhesion and early biofilm formation
Flow Cells

It has been know for many years before biofilm was really recognised as a particular type of microbial ecosystem, that microbes can concentrate on surfaces especially glass (Zobell, 1943, 1946; Wood, 1950; Larsen and Dimmick, 1964). If a glass plate is used as the basis for a flow cell and if the latter is examined by visible or by confocal laser scanning microscopy associated with image analysis we have a powerful tool for examining the early stages in biofilm formation (Figure 1). Such a system was developed by Caldwell and his colleagues (Caldwell and Lawrence, 1988). Wolfaardt *et al.* (1994) used Plexiglas chambers having of up to ten flow channels each 1 mm deep by 3 mm wide by 42 mm long. The whole array was then covered by a glass coverslip held in place by silicone adhesive. Another type of flow cell was the parallel plate flow cell (Van Kooten *et al.*, 1992; Sjollema *et al.*, 1989; Bos *et al.*, 1994). Bos (1996) gives a useful and complete description of a flow system in his Doctoral thesis. The flow cell consisted of two parallel plates separated by Teflon spacers, held in a nickel plated chamber whose temperature was controlled via power resistors and thermocouples. The dimensions of the flow channel were 76 x 38 x 0.6 mm. The depth of the chamber could be regulated by altering the size of the Teflon spacers. Flow in the chamber was laminar: this was enhanced by the tapering design of the inlet and outlet ports. The chamber was placed beneath an ultra long working distance x40 objective using an Olympus microscope. The latter was fitted with a CCD camera for image processing purposes. The dynamics of attachment and growth in the flow chamber were carefully analysed by Bos (1996). The system was used to investigate adhesion of pairs of microbial species.

A related model was a flat plate reactor used by Mirpuri *et al.* (1997). This was used to examine toluene supplied as humidified vapour diffusing into a

90

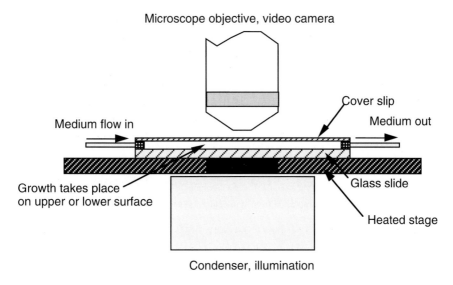

Figure 1 Slide culture apparatus in diagrammatic form.

basic mineral salts medium which flowed across the plate. The model was established in this way since all the relevant parameters could be controlled accurately. It also allowed the deployment of oxygen microelectrodes directly into the biofilm.

Channel Reactor
A channel reactor related to the above, was constructed by de Beer and Stoodley (1995) and de Beer, *et al* (1997) to measure diffusion in and around biofilm by the micro-injection of fluorescein dye. The channel was made of polycarbonate and was 10 mm deep X 5 mm wide. It was connected in a recycle loop with an aeration mixing chamber. The inlet port was tapered to minimize entrance effects. Biofilm grew on the underside of a coverslip fitted to the top of the channel. A 'J' shaped micropipette was located so that the tip was just below the biofilm. The film was observed using laser confocal microscopy. Diffusion rates were calculated from the spread of the fluorescent image.

Flow systems
The Robbins Device
The original Robbins device was described by McCoy *et al.* (1981) and by Ruseska *et al.* (1982). The Robbins device was quite simple conceptually and consisted of a tubular flow system in whose walls were located removable studs (Figure 2). These were usually held in place with 'O' rings. Test pieces of substratum material were fixed to the end of the stud so that, when fitted, these were flush with the lumen of the tube. Most of the specific design features were

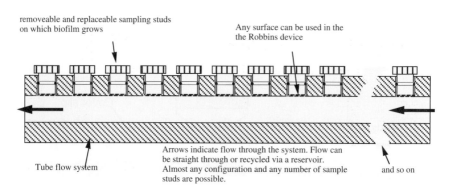

removeable and replaceable sampling studs
on which biofilm grows

Any surface can be used in the
the Robbins device

Tube flow system

Arrows indicate flow through the system. Flow can
be straight through or recycled via a reservoir.
Almost any configuration and any number of sample
studs are possible.

and so on

Figure 2 The Robbins device (modified from Wimpenny, 1996).

associated with medium feed. This could be straight through or more commonly recirculating. Whilst the earlier Robbins device was large and made of materials which included admiralty brass, newer smaller machines are commonly called 'modified Robbins devices' (MRD). MRD have become standard equipment for many biofilm laboratories. A few of the more recent applications are listed below.

Hall-Stoodley and Lappin Scott (1998) used the Robbins device to grow biofilms of Mycobacteria. Hughes *et al.* (1998) also used the Robbins device. They demonstrated that certain bacteriophage produced lytic enzymes that removed EPS from their host bacteria. Linton *et al.* (1999) investigated bacterial adhesion to different surfaces (siliconized glass, plasma-treated glass, titanium, stainless steel and teflon) in a modified Robbins device. An MRD was used to investigate the effects of marine paints on biofilm development using *Pseudomonas* PAO-1 as a test organism. The main conclusion was that though toxic additives in the coatings could delay growth of the biofilm for from 72 – 96 hours the total amount of growth after this time was much the same. An MRD was used to explore the effects of argon plasma treated silicone voice prostheses on biofilm colonisation. The increasing hydrophilicity of plasma treatment led to a reduction in biofilm formation in vitro but not in vivo. It was concluded that hydrophobicity influenced biofilm formation (Everaerts *et al.*, 1998). An MRD was evaluated as a test system for encrustation of urinary catheters. Silicone and polyurethane were both used with the former less prone to encrustation (Tunney *et al.*, 1997)

Staphylococcus epidermidis was grown in a Robbins device on PVC discs (Sanford *et al.*, 1996) Cell growth was monitored by green autofluorescence excited at 488 nm whilst polysaccharide was detected after staining with Texas red labelled wheat germ agglutinin which binds to slime lectin specifically. The red fluorescence was excited at 568 nm with a krypton laser. Cells showed up as cell clusters embedded in EPS interspersed with porous water channels.

Leung *et al.* (1998) used chemostats as source of inoculum for a Robbins

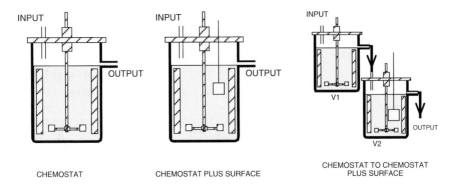

Figure 3 Chemostat based biofilm systems (modified from Wimpenny, 1996).

device. The latter was used to model biofilm formation on biliary stents. A Gram negative organism (*Escherichia coli*) were grown together with a Gram positive bacterium (*Enterococcus* spp.) to investigate their adhesion patterns. The surfaces used in the Robbins device were 5 mm segments of polyethylene stent pieces. For use each species was grown in a chemostat and mixed as it was fed into the Robbins device.

Systems based on the chemostat

The chemostat is an ideal device for generating steady state homogeneous cultures. Immersion of surfaces into such a culture leads to attachment, growth and biofilm formation (Figure 3). Unfortunately the biofilm is not itself in a steady state, since biomass may increase or decrease over the life cycle of the biofilm. It can only become steady state at some imprecise moment when or if biofilm removal (by sloughing or attrition due to shear forces applied by the stirrer system) exactly equals growth.

Chemostat Fed Systems

Another approach favoured by some workers is to use a two stage culture system. Here the first stage is a conventional chemostat where an inoculum of cells grows to a steady state. The feed from this first vessel provides cells which can then attach to surfaces immersed in the second stage (Rogers and Keevil, 1992). These surfaces can therefore be exposed to non-growing cells. This techniques has been applied by a number of workers (Keevil *et al.*, 1987; Keevil, 1989; Marsh, 1995) to the formation of oral biofilm communities.

Such systems allow one to investigate the importance of different surfaces. Keevil *et al*, (1993) investigated surfaces from copper, glass and several different plastics to a latex elastomer to examine colonisation by a natural flora and by *Legionella pneumophila*. Thames river water was used as the basic growth medium. Chemostat systems were used to investigate colonisation of plumbing materials by *L. pneumophila* (Rogers *et al.*, 1994). Episcopic differential

Insoluble particulate supports

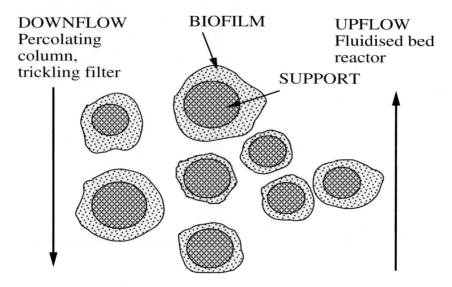

DOWNFLOW
Percolating
column,
trickling filter

BIOFILM

UPFLOW
Fluidised bed
reactor

SUPPORT

Figure 4 Insoluble supports. Used in trickling filters but also in airlift and fluidised bed fermenter systems (modified from Wimpenny, 1996).

interference microscopy (Nomarski optics) was used to visualise the biofilm which formed since this system can give greater depth of focus than conventional microscopy (Rogers and Keevil, 1992). Results of this work led to formulation of a heterogeneous mosaic model for biofilm structure (Walker *et al.*, 1995).

A chemostat was used by Herles *et al.* (1994) to feed a number of flow cells each containing hydroxyapatite and germanium surfaces. Germanium was used to allow the measurement of growth by attenuated total reflectance fourier transform infra red (ATR/FT-IR) spectroscopy. Glass surfaces pre-conditioned with mucin were used by Li and Bowden (1994) to follow the adhesion of gram positive oral bacteria. Four development phases were noted from attachment without growth through to the formation of a mature biofilm.

Irrigated Surfaces

Instead of immersing surfaces in a chemostat it is of course possible to irrigate different surfaces by dropping medium or culture on them. Sutton *et al.* (1994) used such a system to investigated the structure of *Streptococcus crista* biofilms using different electron microscopic techniques. Watson *et al.* (1995) described a more complex device where the discs were held in a chamber which could be irrigated either with a chemostat culture, with fresh medium or by recycling the output from the growth chamber.

Packed bed reactors

There are many examples of the use of packed bed reactors (Figure 4), generally in the form of trickling filters used in the waste water industry. These will not be discussed in this chapter. Diz & Novak (1999) and Novak (1999) have used a column packed with polystyrene beads to generate a chemolithotrophic community to catalyse ferrous iron oxidation simulating acid mine drainage conditions.

A variant of the filter is the upflow anaerobic sludge bed (UASB) reactor. Here the organisms themselves produce particulate 'granules' which can be regarded as quasi-spherical biofilm! These are often very highly organised sometimes distinctly layered communities capable of generating methane from fermentable substrates (MacLeod *et al.*, 1990; Tartakovsky & Guiot, 1997)

Airlift reactors

Another model biofilm system that has had an important part to play in biofilm research is the Biofilm Airlift Suspension (BAS) system, described first by Gjaltema *et al.* (1994). Here a solid particle (sometimes basalt granules) is placed in the central column of a tubular reactor. This is aerated to fluidise the particles. Entrained liquid and particles pass down around the outside of the inner tube and up again through the latter. Biofilm forms on the surface of the solid substratum (Figure 4). The biofilm system is subject to shear stresses which removes biomass and in the end the system approximates to steady state. Shear control in the BAS is good. Van Loosdrecht *et al.* (1995) employed this system to compare the effects of shear and nutrient concentration on biofilm structure. When shear forces are high any protuberances on the biofilm surface will be removed leading to a smooth structure. Low shear combined with high substrate loading should generate very heterogeneous biofilm with many extensions and outgrowths. The authors equated low shear with high loading rates and vice versa, however it might have been better to regard these as independent variables.

A related suspended-carrier biofilm reactor was described in 1994 by Lee & Welander (1994) to investigate the effects of predation on natural mixed culture nitrifying biofilms. Use of inhibitors nystatin and cycloheximide which both target eukaryotic microbes, led to elimination of predators and hence stimulated nitrification twofold.

vanBenthum *et al.* (1999) describe a biofilm airlift suspension extension reactor used to investigate the nitrification and denitrification of waste water. The internal airlift part consists of an ideally mixed pool of liquid air bubbles and solid particles on which the biofilm develops. The additional down comer is free of air bubbles and allows plug flow of liquid plus solid particles to move to the base of the reactor.

Constant shear devices

The Rototorque

If a knowledge of shear stress is important to biofilm researchers the Rototorque

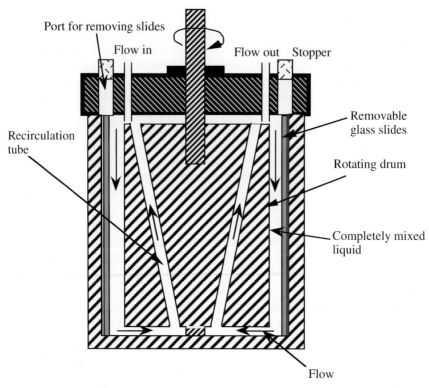

Figure 5 The Rototorque. Redrawn from Gjaltema *et al.* (1994).

(Trulear & Characklis, 1982; Bakke *et al.,* 1984) is an approriate model to use (Figure 5). It is an elaboration of the Couette viscometer consisting as it does of of two concentric cylinders the outer of which is stationary whilst the inner rotates. The system incorporates a torque converter to monitor drag forces which, with a knowledge of rotational speed, allows fluid frictional forces to be determined. The walls of the outer cylinder are fitted with removable slides on which biofilm grows. The device is equipped with draft tubes that help to mix the nutrient feed. In this system liquid residence time is independent of shear stress.

The Rototorque was used by Gjaltema *et al*, (1994) to characterise biofilms of pure and mixed cultures. Careful examination revealed that the structure was always very heterogeneous. They concluded that small imperfections and changes in the flow pattern rather than cell motility were the most important causes of the observed heterogeneity.

Arcangeli and Arvin (1995) have used a similar device, the Biodrum. This consists of Plexiglas cylinders one rotating at 200 rpm within the other. Biofilm grows on both rotor and stator surfaces. The Biodrum was used to compare aerobic and anaerobic (nitrate reducing) growth on a toluene degrading natural microbial community. Biofilm grew under either condition: it was smooth and continuous anoxically but irregular and rough in the presence of oxygen.

Other rotating drum bioreactors have been used where biofilm forms on the outer walls of the rotating drum as well as on the inner walls of the outer stationary cylinder (Figure 6). Such a system was used on a laboratory scale by Zhang & Bishop (1995) to investigate the degradation of azo dyes. In a typical reactor the liquid volume was 954 ml, the total surface area for growth was 1590 cm^2. The mean hydraulic retention time of this system was 2 hours. The RDBR was operated in a recycling mode with a recycle rate of 500 l min^{-1}. The system generated biofilm which could be investigated using microelectrodes and by micro-slicing and was also used to monitor competition in biofilms as a function of oxygen gradients and of cell density across the biofilm.

A radial reactor for developing biofilm was described by Allison *et al.* (1999) to generate a range of four different shear rates (Figure 7). This consisted of a stationary vessel containing four concentric steel cylinders and a rotor with complementary cylinders designed to fit within the former. Provision was made to add nutrient to each of the separate chambers as well as a weir system to take the overflow. The system was tested in an investigation into the role of signal molecules on adhesion.

Fowler Cell Adhesion Measurement Module (CAMM)
Fowler and Mackay (1980) described a simple device to measure the strength of attachment of biofilm to solid surfaces. This consisted of two precisely parallel discs, one rotating against a second stationary one. Nutrient solution was fed into the centre of the system: as the latter flowed outward its velocity slowed as the surface area increased so that shear gradient was formed. The system was inoculated and incubated in zero shear to allow attachment and growth before the rotor was switched on. By examining growth after further incubation, a cut off point could be determined at the precise position where shear forces exceeded the attachment strength of the organisms (Fowler, 1988).

Steady state systems
The concept of a steady state system really originates with continuous culture systems including the chemostat. A steady state is most useful from an experimental point of view because it allows the experimenter to alter parameters and interpret any resulting changes unequivocally. It is easy to see that this might work well in a well mixed, homogeneous reactor with inputs and outputs of nutrient, less so in a spatially heterogeneous system like a biofilm. Many biofilm systems can operate in a quasi-steady state. For example under high shear conditions growth can approximately equal removal by shear and the resultant attrition of biomass. Air lift systems in which biomass accumulates on a solid carrier can approximate steady state conditions as contact between the moving particles removes some of biofilm.

A more reliable method of generating steady state biofilm first recognised by Atkinson and colleagues (Atkinson & Fowler, 1974) was to grow the film in

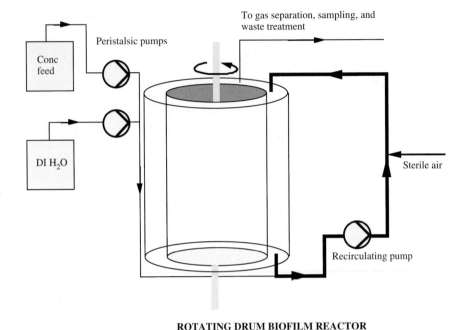

Peristalsic pumps

Conc feed

DI H$_2$O

To gas separation, sampling, and waste treatment

Sterile air

Recirculating pump

ROTATING DRUM BIOFILM REACTOR

Figure 6 A rotating drum biofilm fermenter (redrawn from Zhang and Bishop, 1995).

recesses which are swept in some way by a blade which removes any material above the level of the recess. Atkinson developed two systems. In the first a roughened glass surface was used as a substratum, in the second a metal plate with a series of cut-outs was placed over the substratum. Both systems were swept regularly to remove excess growth. The same principle was used by us (Coombe *et al.*, 1981, 1982, 1984; Peters and Wimpenny, 1988a,b) in the Constant Depth Film Fermenter (CDFF) (Figure 8). The CDFF was designed to fulfil a number of criteria. It was necessary to operate in an aseptic environment which would allow any combination of medium flow and gas composition. Temperature should be controllable. To allow reproducibility to be assessed a sufficient number of substratum samples of any kind should be included in the design. The latter should be removable and replaceable during operation of the fermenter.

The system is built around a QVF tubing section which is fitted with a stainless steel top and bottom plate secured via sterilisable Teflon gaskets with retaining bolts. The bottom plate is equipped with bearings and a bearing housing through which is a shaft connected at its upper end to a rotating stainless steel ring and its bottom end to a gear box and small 12 volt DC motor. The ring is drilled with 15 holes each fitted with a single recessed 'O' ring. Each hole receives a film pan made of Teflon drilled to receive five or six film plugs on which the biofilm grows. The plugs (which can be made of any material) are

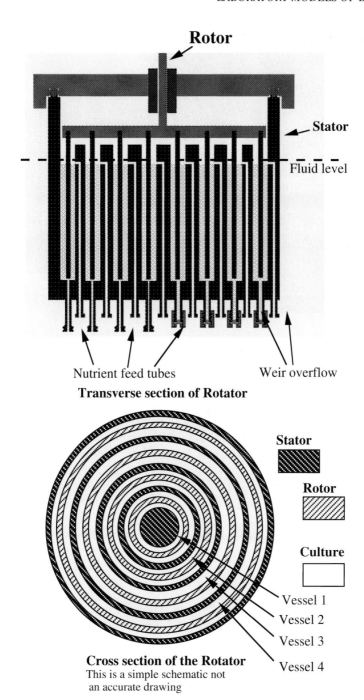

Figure 7 The Rotator shear generating system. (courtesy of Peter Gilbert, modified by the author).

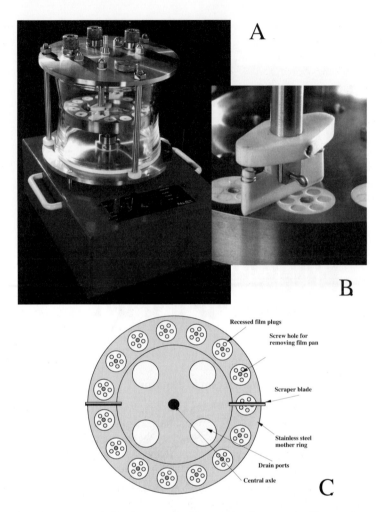

Figure 8 The Constant Depth Film Fermenter. A. The complete fermenter; B. Close up of scraper assembly; C. Diagram of turntable, film pans and film plugs.

recessed a measured amount, normally from 100 to 500 µm, with stainless steel templates. The 'mother' ring rotates at from 1-3 rpm beneath a pair of spring loaded Teflon or most recently, nylon, scraper blades attached to the top plate. These remove any material which appears above the film pan recesses. Nutrient feed enters the system via a tubing pump, grow back traps and a stainless steel tube which allows medium to drop directly onto the top of the mother ring. Also in the top plate is a large port through which sample pans can be removed and replaced using an extractor tool and a tamping tool to push the new pan down so that it is exactly flush with the mother ring surface.

In use the sterile fermenter is inoculated from a small batch culture and this is recycled via a tubing pump for 24 h to allow cell attachment before switching to straight through operation from a large medium reservoir.

The CDFF has been used in a variety of applications. These include

(i) Development of a fresh water biofilm (Peters and Wimpenny, 1988)

(ii) development of oral biofilms from natural plaque or from consortia of specific oral bacteria (Kinniment *et al.*, 1996a,b);

(iii) development of biofilms from indwelling catheter-related combinations of species (Ganderton, 1994).

(iv) investigations into biofilms derived from contaminated metal working fluids (Kinniment and Wimpenny, 1992; Wimpenny *et al.*, 1993). Some of these are described in more detail below:

Kinnniment and Wimpenny (1992) isolated a pseudomonad from contaminated metal working fluids. This was grown in a CDFF using a mixture of carboxylic acids and triethanolamine (normal constituents of cutting fluids) as the basis for a nutrient solution. Full depth biofilm was generated and a number of characteristics of the structure determined, for example oxygen penetration, the distribution of adenylates and the distribution of viable counts. In addition the effects of a range of antimicrobials was tested. It was shown in common with many other workers, that cells established in a biofilm were much more resistant to biocides than were planktonic organisms (Wimpenny *et al.*, 1993). The CDFF has been used quite extensively by us and by Professor M. Wilson of The Eastman Dental Hospital to investigate oral microbial system. Kinniment *et al.* (1996a) used a nine membered collection of oral bacteria, to develop a steady state community in the CDFF. The system was maintained in a stable state for 8 weeks. In separate experiments this community was challenged with chlorhexidine at timed intervals and the dynamics of inhibition measured (Kinniment *et al.*, 1996b).

Wilson *et al.* (1997) employed the same system to investigate the corrosion of intra-oral magnets by microbial communities in growth media with and without a fermentable substrate. Loss of magnet weight was 28 times greater in the presence compared to the absence of sucrose. Pratten *et al.* (1998) used three surfaces in the CDFF to monitor the effect of three antimicrobial agents on *Streptococcus sanguis* biofilms. They showed that the substratum could influence the effectiveness of the antimicrobial treatment. Wood *et al.* (1998) used the CDFF to investigate the possibility that binding a catalytic molecule to the substratum would kill bacteria in biofilms *from below* if a substrate which reacted with the catalyst, (in this case persulphate which liberated toxic free radicals), was allowed to diffuse through the biofilm.

Membrane systems

Membrane bioreactors rely on the diffusion of nutrients, often gases such as oxygen, across a permeable membrane. In one common configuration, one side of the membrane is in contact with nutrient solution containing an organic substrate, the biofilm forms on this side: oxidant as oxygen, generally supplied

Table 1

Membrane material	Permeability g mm m^{-2} h^{-1} bar^{-1}
Teflon (PTFE)	0.016
Natural rubber	0.092
PVC	O.093
Demethyl silicone (silicone rubber, General Electric)	1.929
Silastic 500-1 (Dow Corning)	2.226

as air, diffuses from the other. The Membrane Biofilm Reactor (MBR) was used to treat waste water using this principle (Rothemunde *et al.*, 1994). A biofilm membrane reactor was used to grow white rot fungi *Phanerochaete chrysosporium*, which degrades lignin using the extracellular enzyme lignin peroxidase (Venkatadri *et al.*, 1992). Watanabe *et al.* (1997) described a novel membrane bioreactor. Here the membrane was part of a rotating disc system. Waste water was in contact with the outer parts of the rotating disc and a biofilm formed here. Suction applied to the space between the membranes and also to the hollow shaft of the disc allowed purified water to flow through. Here a combination of filtration and BOD removal led to clean water.

The properties of membranes used for this purpose are important specifically the permeability of the membrane to gases. Table 1 (from Wilderer, 1995) shows how valuable silicone plastics are in this respect.

Materials other than plastic membranes can be used in particular materials with different sized pores or even particular fabrics. Various alternatives are reviewed by Wilderer.

Wilderer developed a sequencing batch membrane biofilm reactor (SBMBR). This consisted of plates of porous plastic. These were arranged to form liquid and gaseous compartments alternately. All the liquid compartments were connected together as were the gas compartments. Waste water to be treated passed into the liquid compartments and air was passed through the gas compartments. The former compartments were filled with water to be treated leading to biofilm formation: the liquid phase was circulated around via a holding tank for a predetermined period. The tanks were then part drained and the effluent passed through an activated carbon column for final polishing. The sequence continued by the addition of more waste water. Nitrification-denitrification cycling membrane bioreactor behaviour has been modelled by de Silva *et al.* (1998). Model generation was based on results from a pilot scale membrane bioreactor.

Hollow fibre reactors

Hollow fibre systems are really another form of membrane reactor (Figure 9). These are made of materials which are permeable to liquid or gas phase solutes. Generally the material to be treated is passed down the hollow lumen and diffuses across the fibre wall to a biofilm which form using the outer side of the

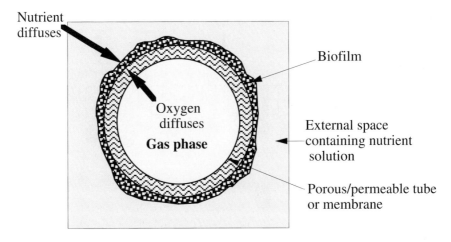

Nutrient diffuses

Biofilm

Oxygen diffuses

Gas phase

External space containing nutrient solution

Porous/permeable tube or membrane

Permeable membrane reactor

Figure 9 A hollow fibre system.

fibre as support. These systems use numerous fibres in parallel to provide a large surface area. They can make efficient treatment systems. For example Ergas *et al.*(1999) used such a fermenter to control air emissions of biodegradable volatile organic compounds (VOC's). Here the gas stream was passed through the lumen of the reactor and compounds were degraded as they diffused into the biofilm outside the fibre. In another application Pressman *et al.* (1999) grew a *Methylosinus trichosporium* in a chemostat which fed the space outside hollow fibres allowing a biofilm to form. A waste stream carried trichloroethylene (TCE) (160 to 1450 µg /l) through the lumen of the fibres. Between 80 to 90% of the TCE was removed from the water stream.

Filter based biofilm systems
The Perfused Biofilm Fermenter was developed by Gilbert *et al.* (1989). Its principle of operation is based on the Cooper:Helmstetter method for cell synchronisation which was sometimes referred to as 'the baby factory'. The principle on which it operates is very simple (Figure 10). Bacteria are forced onto one side of a bacterium-proof filter membrane. The membrane is then reversed into a filter holder and irrigated from the sterile side with fresh medium. Microbial growth takes place on the lower surface at a rate which is governed by the concentration of nutrients in the growth medium. As cells grow the attached mother cells remain associated with the membrane whilst the offspring that are formed drop of into the permeate. The biofilm is generally very thin (roughly 10-20 µm thick) so the sort of gradients seen in thicker film systems is not present here. In addition much of the film biomass is EPS so the actual cell density is low (ca 6 X 10^6/cm^2). Biofilm can be removed from the

MEDIUM FLOW

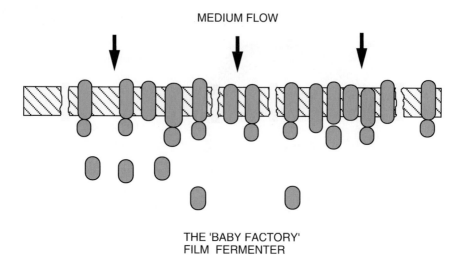

THE 'BABY FACTORY'
FILM FERMENTER

Figure 10 The perfused membrane system.

filter and cells in it compared with the recently shed 'young' organisms or with steady state cultures grown in a chemostat. After a period during which the system equilibrates pseudo-steady state conditions prevail. The doubling time is given by the total membrane population divided by the rate of elution of cells and the specific growth rate, as usual, is merely the natural log of 2 divided by the doubling time. Because the cells shed in the PBF are initially synchronous this reactor allows investigation of biofilm-related properties at different times in the cell cycle.

As stressed above growth rate can also be controlled as in a chemostat, so that the PBF is a versatile piece of equipment. Comparisons between position in cell cycle, growth rate, and attachment or not have been monitored and big changes in surface characteristics of cells, resistance to antibiotics ability to colonise surfaces etc. have been observed (Gilbert and Brown, 1995; Allison *et al,* 1999 in press).

A modified version of the PBF was developed by these workers using commercially available Swinnex filters produced by Millipore Corporation. The filters were 22 mm in diameter with 0.22 μm pore size. Whilst these units seem to achieve steady state conditions quicker than the PBF, they can, depending on the cultures used, block relatively easily.

Yet another version is based on Sorbarod filters, initially developed for plant cell culture (Figure 11). Sorbarods resemble cigarette filters. They are 10 mm in diameter by 20 mm long and contain folded filter elements. They provide a much larger surface area for biofilm attachment and a single Sorbarod can yield 10^{10} to 10^{11} cells, allowing biochemical assays to be performed. Allison *et al,* in press)

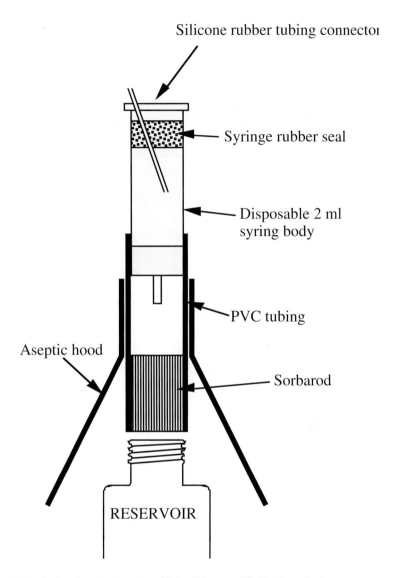

Silicone rubber tubing connector

Syringe rubber seal

Disposable 2 ml syring body

PVC tubing

Aseptic hood

Sorbarod

RESERVOIR

Figure 11 The Sorbarod system (courtesy of Peter Gilbert, modified by the author).

Gel trapped models

Jouenne *et al.* (1994) A culture of *Escherichia coli* was trapped within an agar layer and incubated for 2 days in the presence of a glucose mineral salts medium. This was then incubated for three weeks under metal ion depletion. The cell distribution in this artificial biofilm became very heterogeneous. Immobilised cells survived a range of environmental extremes far better than did sessile or free living bacteria (Perrot *et al.*, 1998).

Cunningham *et al.* (1995) made an artificial biofilm by resuspending a known number of *Pseudomonas aeruginosa* 8830 evenly within an alginate preparation which originated from the same organism. The experimental model was used to validate a theoretical model of mass transport in biofilms.

It is possible to immobilise bacterial cells in thick gels. These stretched gel models do not behave exactly like biofilms however they can give useful information on the effects of environment on the distribution of cells. Such a system has been used by Jonathan Baker (personal communication) to examine the effects of oxygen tension and antimicrobials on a six membered community of oral microorganisms.

Conclusions

On reading this chapter, I am only too aware of the vast range of different experimental systems with which to cultivate biofilm. Choice very much depends on the nature of the problem. Investigations of attachment and early colonisation processes are best examined on transparent surfaces such as glass slides. This is essential if light microscopy is planned as an investigative tool. If biofilm formation in a flow regime is envisaged then the Robbins device has a great deal of potential value as it is a flexible and versatile system allowing a choice of substratum surfaces which can be removed and replaced during operation as well as the ability to operate over a wide range of flow rates in recycling or straight through modes. If shear rate needs to be determined the rototorque has many advantages though interestingly the biofilm that forms is often quite irregular. Biofilm airlift systems using solid substrata can achieve reasonably reproducible steady state conditions although the mode of operation may not be appropriate for some biofilm investigations. Better steady states are possible using the constant depth film fermenter given that the biofilm under investigation is sufficiently cohesive that it is capable of filling the film pan and not being detached due to the rather slight shear forces generated by the scraper bar.

No single system is ideal and the researcher needs to examine a range of techniques to see which is most suitable for the problems under investigation.

Bibliography

Allison, D., Maitra-Litran, T., and Gilbert, P. in press. Perfused biofilm fermenters. *Methods in Enzymology* **310**.

Allison, D.G., Heys, S.J.D., Willcock, L., Holah, J. and Gilbert, P. (1999) Cellular detachment and dispersal from bacterial biofilms: a role for quorum sensing. In *Biofilms: the Good the Bad and the Ugly*. J. Wimpenny, P. Gilbert, J. Walker, M. Brading and R. Bayston eds. Bioline, Cardiff, pp279-286

Arcangeli, J. P. and Arvin E. (1995). Growth of an aerobic and an anoxic toluene degrading biofilm - a comparative study. *Water Science and Technology* **32**:125-132.

Atkinson, B. and Fowler, H.W. (1974). The significance of microbial film in fermenters. *Advances in Biochemical Engineering* **3**, 224-277.

Bakke, R., Trulear, M.G., Robinson, J.A. and Characklis, W.G. (1984). Activity of *Pseudomonas aeruginosa* in biofilms: steady state. *Biotechnology and Bioengineering* **26**, 1418-1424.

Bos, R., van der Mei, H.C., Meinders, J.M. and Busscher, H.J. (1994) Quantitative method to study co-adhesion of microorganisms in a parallel plate-flow chamber - basic principles of the analysis. *Journal of Microbiological Methods*, **20**, 289-305

Bos, R. (1996) Coadhesion of oral microbial pairs a physico-chemical approach. PhD Thesis, University of Groningen, Nederlands

Caldwell, D.E. and Lawrence, J.R. (1988) Study of attached cells in continuous flow slide culture. In: *CRC Handbook of Laboratory Model Systems for Microbial Ecosystems*. Wimpenny JWT, (ed.). CRC Press, Boca Raton, USA. pp 117 - 138.

Coombe R.A., Tatevossian, A. and Wimpenny, J.W.T. (1982) An *in vitro* model for dental plaque. Paper given at the 30th Meeting of the *International Association for Dental research*, British Division, University of Edinburgh, Scotland.

Coombe, R. A., Tatevossian, A. and Wimpenny, J. W. T. (1981) Bacterial thin films as *in vitro* models for dental plaque. In: Frank, R. M., Leach, S. A. (eds) *Surface and Colloid Phenomena in the Oral Cavity: Methodological Aspects*. Information Retrieval, London, pp. 239-249

Coombe, R. A., Tatevossian, A. and Wimpenny, J. W. T. (1984) Factors affecting the growth of thin bacterial films *in vitro*. In: ten Cate, J. M., Leach, S. A., Arends, J. (eds) *Bacterial Adhesion and Preventative Dentistry*. IRL Press, Oxford, page 193

Cunningham, A. B., Visser, E., Lewandowski, Z. and Abrahammson M. (1995). Evaluation of a coupled mass transport biofilm process model. *Water Science and Technology* **32**:107-144.

de Beer, D. and Stoodley, P. 1995. Relation between the structure of an aerobic biofilm and transport phenomena. *Water Science and Technology* **32**:11-18.

de Beer, D., Stoodley, P. and Lewandowski, Z. (1997). Measurement of local diffusion coefficients in biofilms by microinjection and confocal microscopy. *Biotechnology and Bioengineering* **53**:151-158.

de Silva, D. G. V., Urbain, V.,. Abeysinghe, D. H. and Rittmann, B. E. (1998). Advanced analysis of membrane-bioreactor performance with aerobic-anoxic cycling. *Water Science and Technology* **38**:505-512.

Diz, H. R. and Novak, J. T. (1999). Modelling bio-oxidation of iron in a packed-bed reactor. *Journal of Environmental Engineering-ASCE* **125**:109-116.

Ergas, S. J., Shumway, L., Fitch, M. W. and. Neeman, J. A. (1999). Membrane processes for biological treatment of contaminated gas streams. *Biotechnology and Bioengineering* **63**:431-441.

Everaert, E. P. J M., Van de BeltGritter, B., Van der Mei, H. C., Busscher, H. J., Verkerke, G. J., Dijk, F., Mahieu, H. F. and Reitsma, A. (1998). *In vitro* and *invivo* microbial adhesion and growth on argon plasma-treated silicone rubber voice prosthesis. *Journal of Materials Science - Materials in Medicine* **9**:147-157.

Fowler, H.W. (1988) Microbial adhesion to surfaces. *in Handbook of Laboratory Model Systems for Microbial Ecosystems*. Wimpenny JWT (ed.). CRC Press. Boca Raton, Fla. pp 139-153.

Fowler, H.W. and Mackay A.J. (1980) The measurement of microbial adhesion. In *Microbial Adhesion to Surfaces,* Berkeley, R.C.W., Lynch, J.M., Melling, J., Rutter, P.R. and Vincent, B. (eds.) Ellis Horwood, Chichester, UK. pp 143-161.

Ganderton, L. (1994) PhD Thesis. *A Study of Bacterial Biofilms Found on Indwelling Urethral Catheters*. University of Wales College of Cardiff.

Gilbert, P., Allison, D.G., Evans, D.J., Handley, P.S. and Brown, M.R.W. (1989) Growth rate control of adherent bacterial populations. *Applied and Environmental Microbiology*. **55**: 1308-1311.

Gilbert P. and Brown, M.R.W. (1995) Mechanisms of the protection of bacterial films from antimicrobial agents. In: *Microbial Biofilms*. Lappin-Scott HM, Costerton JW (eds.). Cambridge University Press. Cambridge, UK pp 118-130.

Gjaltema, A., Arts, P.A.M., van Loosdrecht, M.C.M., Kuenen, J.G. and Heijnen , J.J. (1994) Heterogeneity of biofilms in rotating annular reactors. *Biotechnology and Bioengineering*, **44**:194-204

Hall-Stoodley, L. and H. Lappin-Scott. (1998). Biofilm formation by the rapidly growing *Mycobacterium fortuitum* *FEMS Microbiological Letters* **168**:77-84.

Herles, S., Olsen, S., Afflito, C., and Gaffar, A. (1994) Chemostat flow system - an *in-vitro* model for the evaluation of antiplaque agents. *Journal of Dental Research*, **73**, 1748-1755

Hughs, K. A., Sutherland, I. W. and Jones, M. V. (1998) Biofilm susceptibility to bacteriophage attack: the role of phage borne polysaccharide depolymerase. *Microbiology UK* **144**:3039-3047.

Jouenne, T., Tresse, O. and Junter, G.A. (1994) Agar entrapped bacteria as an in vitro model of biofilms and their susceptibility to antibiotics. *FEMS Microbiology Letters*. **119**: 237-242.

Keevil, C.W., (1989) Chemostat models of human and aquatic corrosive biofilms. In *Recent Advances in Microbial Ecology* Hattori T, (ed.). Japan Scientific Society Press, Tokyo pp 151-156.

Keevil, C.W., Bradshaw D.J., Dowsett, A.B. and Feary, T.W. (1987) Microbial film formation: dental plaque deposition on acrylic tiles using continuous culture techniques. *Journal of Applied Bacteriology* **62**, 129-138

Keevil, C.W., Dowsett, A.B. and Rogers, J. (1993) *Legionella* biofilms and their control. In *Microbial Biofilms and their Control* Denyer SP, Gorman SP, Sussman M Academic Press pp 200-215.

Kinniment, S.L., Wimpenny, J.W.T., Adams, D. and Marsh, P.D. (1996) Development of a steady state oral microbial film community using the constant depth film fermenter *Microbiology* **142**: 631-638

Kinniment, S.L., Wimpenny, J.W.T., Adams, D., and Marsh, P.D. (1996)The effect of chlorhexidine on defined, mixed culture oral biofilms grown in a novel model system. *Journal of Applied Bacteriology*, **81**:120-125

Kinniment, S. L. and Wimpenny, J. W. T. (1992). Measurements of the distribution of adenylate concentrations and adenylate energy charge across *Pseudomonas aeruginosa* biofilms. *Applied and Environmental Microbiology* **58**, 1629-1635.

Larsen, D.H. and Dimmick, R.L. (1964) Attachment and growth of bacteria on surfaces of continuous culture vessels. *Journal of Bacteriology*, **88**: 1380-1387

Lee, N. M. and Welander, T. (1994). Influence of predators on nitrification in aerobic biofilm processes. *Water Science and Technology* **29**:355-363.

Leung, J. W., Liu, Y. L., Desta, T., Inciardi, J. F. and Lam, K. (1988). Is there a synergistic effect between mixed bacterial infection in biofilm formation on biliary stents? *Gastrointestinal Endoscopy* **48**:250-257.

Li, Y.H. and Bowden, G.H. (1994) Characteristics of accumulation of oral gram positive bacteria on mucin-conditioned glass surfaces in a model system. *Oral Microbiology and Immunology*, **9**, 1-11

Linton, C. J., Sherriff A., and M. Millar. (1999). Use of a modified Robbins device to directly compare the adhesion of *Staphylococcus epidermidis* RP62a to surfaces. *Journal of Applied Microbiology* **86**:194-202.

MacLeod, F. A., Guiot, S. R. and Costerton, J. W. (1990). Layered structure of bacterial aggregates produced in an upflow anaerobic sludge bed and filter reactor. *Applied and Environmental Microbiology* **56**:1598-1607.

Marsh, P. D. (1995) Dental plaque. In: *Microbial Biofilms*, Lappin-Scott, H. M., Costerton, J. W. (eds). Cambridge University press, Cambridge, pp. 282-300

McCoy, W.F., Bryers, J.D., Robbins, J. and Costerton, J.W. (1981) Observations of fouling biofilm formation. *Canadian Journal of Microbiology*. **29**: 910-917.

Mirpuri, R., Sharp, W., Villaverde, S., Jones, W., Lewandowski, Z. and Cunningham A. (1997). Predictive model for toluene degradation and microbial phenotypic profile in flat plate vapour phase bioreactor. *Journal of Environmental Engineering* **June, 1997**:586-592.

Peters, A.C. and Wimpenny, J.W.T. (1988a). A constant depth laboratory film fermenter. In *Handbook of Laboratory Model Systems for Microbial Ecosystems*, Vol 1, Edited by J. W. T. Wimpenny. Boca Raton, Florida: CRC Press, pp. 175-195.

Peters, A.C. and Wimpenny, J.W.T. (1988b). A constant depth laboratory model film fermentor. *Biotechnology and Bioengineering* **32**: 263-270.

Pratten, J., Wills, K., Barnett, P., and M. Wilson. 1998. In vitro studies of the effect of antiseptic-containing mouthwashes on the formation and viability of *Streptococcus sanguis* biofilms. *Journal of Applied Microbiology* **84**:1149-1155.

Pressman, J. G., Georgiou, G. and Speitel, G. E. (1999). Demonstration of efficient trichloroethylene biodegradation in a hollow-fibre membrane bioreactor. *Biotechnology and Bioengineering* **62**:681-692.

Rogers, J. and Keevil, C. W. (1992). Immunogold and fluorescein immunolabelling of *Legionella pneumophila* within an aquatic biofilm visualised by using episcopic differential interference contrast microscopy. *Applied and Environmental Microbiology* **58**.

Rogers, J., Dowsettt, A. B., Dennis, P. J., Lee, P. J. and Keevil, C. W. (1994). Influence of plumbing materials on biofilm formation and growth of *Legionella pneumophila* in potable water systems. *Applied and Environmental Microbiology* **60**:1842-1851.

Rothemund, C., Camper, A. and Wilderer, P.A. (1994) Biofilms growing on gas permeable membranes. *Water Science and Technology*. **29**: 447-454.

Ruseska, L., Robbins, J., Costerton, J.W. and Lashen, E. (1982) Biocide testing against corrosion causing oil-field bacteria helps control plugging. *Oil and Gas Journal*, **March 1982**, 153-164

Sanford, B. A., de Feijter, A. W., Wade, M. H. and Thomas V. L. (1996). A dual fluorescence technique for visualisation of *Staphylococcus epidermidis* biofilm using scanning confocal microscopy. *Journal of Industrial Microbiology* **16**:48-56.

Sjollema, J., Busscher, H. J. and Weerkamp, A. H. (1989). Real time enumeration of adhering microorganisms in a parallel plate flow cell using automated image analysis. *Journal of Microbiological Methods* **9**:73-78.

Sutton, N.A., Hughes, N. and Handley, P.S. (1994) A comparison of conventional SEM techniques, low temperature SEM and the electroscan electron microscope to study the structure of a biofilm of *Streptococcus crista* CR3. *Journal of Applied Bacteriology* **76**: 448-454

Tartakovsky, B. and Guiot, S. R. (1997). Modeling and analysis of layered stationary anaerobic granular biofilms. *Biotechnology and Bioengineering* **54**:122-130.

Tatevossian, A. (1988) Film fermenters in dental research. In: *Handbook of Laboratory Model Systems for Microbial Ecosystems*. Wimpenny JWTW) (ed.). CRC Press, Boca Raton, pp I197-227.

Trulear, M.G. and Characklis, W.G. (1982) Dynamics of biofilm formation. *Journal of Water Pollution Control Federation*, **54**: 1288-1301

van Kooten, T. G., Schakenraad, J. M., Van der Mei, H. C. and Busscher, H. J. (1992). Development and use of a parallel plate flow chamber for studying cellular adhesion to solid surfaces. *Journal of Biomedical Materials Research* **26**:725-738.

van Loosdrecht, M. C. M., Eikelboom, D., Gjaltema, A., Mulder, A., Tijhuis, L., and Heijnen, J. J. (1995). Biofilm structures. *Water Science and Technology* **32**:235-243.

van Benthum, W. A. J., van den Hoogen, J. H. A., van der Lans, R. G. J. M., van Loosdrecht, M. C. M. and Heijnen J. J. (1999). The biofilm airlift suspension reactor. Part 1: Design and two phase hydrodynamics. *Chemical Engineering Science* **54**:1909-1924.

Venkatadri, R., Tsai, S.P., Vukanic, N., Hein, L.B. (1992) Use of a biofilm membrane reactor for the production of lignin peroxidase and treatment of pentachlorophenol by *Phanerochaete chrysosporium*. *Hazardous Waste and Hazardous Materials* **9**: 231-243

Walker, J.T., Mackerness, C.W., Rogers, J. and Keevil, C.W. (1995) Heterogeneous mosaic biofilm - a haven for water borne pathogens. In *Microbial Biofilms* Edited by Lappin-Scott, H.M. and Costerton, J.W. Cambridge University Press, Cambridge, pp 196-204

Watanabe, Y., Kimura, K., Okabe, S., Ozawa, G. and N. Ohkuma . (1997). A novel biofilm-membrane reactor for ammonia oxidation at low concentrations. *Water Science and Technology* **36**:51-60.

Watson, G.K., Halliday, D., Albiston, I., Singleton, S. and Allison, C. (1995) An *in vitro* biofilm system for the study of plaque ecology and physiology. *Journal of Dental Research*. **74**: 853

Wilderer, P. A. (1995). Technology of membrane biofilm reactors operated under periodically changing process conditions. *Water Science and Technology* **31**:173-183.

Wilson, M., Patel, H., Kpendama, H., Noar, J. H., Hunt, N. P. and Mordan, N. J. (1997). Corrosion of intra-oral magnets by multi-species biofilms in the presence and absence of sucrose. *Biomaterials* **18**:53-57.

Wimpenny, J.W.T. (1988) Introduction. In: *Handbook of Laboratory Model Systems for Microbial Ecosystems*, Wimpenny, J.W.T. (ed.). CRC Press, Boca Raton, Fla. pp 1-17

Wimpenny, J.W.T., Kinniment, S.L. and Scourfield, M.A. (1993) The physiology and biochemistry of biofilm. *Society for Applied Bacteriology Technical Series* **30**: 51-94

Wimpenny, J. W. T. (1981). Spatial order in microbial ecosystems. *Biological Reviews* **56**:295-342.

Wimpenny, J.W.T. (1996) Laboratory growth systems in biofilm research. *Scanning Microscopy International* **6**:221-232

Wood, P., Caldwell, D. E., Evans, E., Jones, M., Korber, D. R.,. Wolfaardt G. M, Wilson M. and

Gilbert P. (1998). Surface catalysed disinfection of thick *Pseudomonas aeruginosa* biofilms. *Journal of Applied Microbiology* **84**:1092-1908.

Wolfaardt, G.M., Lawrence, J.R., Robarts, R.D., Caldwell, S.J., Caldwell, D.E. (1994) Multicellular organization in a degradative biofilm community. *Applied and Environmental Microbiology*, **60:** 434-446

Wood, E.J.F. (1950) Investigation on underwater fouling. I. The role of bacteria in the early stages of fouling. *Australian Journal of Marine and Freshwater Research* **1**: 85-91 .

ZoBell CE (1943) The effect of solid surfaces on bacterial activity. *Journal of Bacteriology*, **46**: 39-56

ZoBell, C.E. (1946) *Marine Microbiology*, Chronicia Botanica, Waltham, Mass. USA 240 pp

MEDICAL PROBLEMS DUE TO BIOFILMS: CLINICAL IMPACT, AETIOLOGY, MOLECULAR PATHOGENESIS, TREATMENT AND PREVENTION

Roger Bayston

As populations age, and those with former life - threatening conditions survive for longer periods, the number of implantable devices of all kinds will continue to increase. While infection rates vary considerably, the impact on the individual can range from the trivial nuisance to the devastating or even fatal. The cost in terms of resources is enormous and yet is ipoorly assessed. It is vital that we understand the periods of risk of infection, sources of organisms and the gross and molecular pathogenesis of biomaterials-related infection in order to develop sound strategies for treatment and prevention. Currently, treatment consists of device removal in most cases. Though prevention rests on good surgical and aseptic technique in certain categories of device, in others infection arises later during use of the device. The use of prophylactic antibiotics may in some device categories be helpful, but in others is irrelevant or even hazardous. Antimicrobial polymers are often disappointing in practice, though some promise to reduce infection in certain devices. The use of "new" principles such as surfactants from lactobacilli will hopefully also contribute to this reduction.

Introduction

Implantable medical devices made from biomaterials are used to repair or replace a structure or function which has been lost or become defective through congenital imperfection, trauma, surgery or disease. A further application is for local drug delivery. The use of tissues or organs from human or animal sources involves the major problem of immune rejection which can be overcome only to a relatively limited extent. Another concern is transmission of known or unknown infective agents to the recipient. Biomaterials, which by definition are biocompatible with host tissues (though this might not be absolute), do not involve these risks, but they do carry others. One of these is biodegradation or mechanical malfunction, and another is infection; the two may also be causally linked. Many of the infections in implants are caused by organisms which otherwise would not be considered pathogenic for the human or animal host, and and for many years biomaterials - related infection (BRI) remained an enigma. In more recent years, considerable progress has been made in the understanding of its aetiology and pathogenicity, and this has led to advances in prevention and treatment, though the problem still constitutes one of the largest, in terms of resource consumption, facing the changing health care system in the next millenium.

Table 1 Incidence of infection in implantable devices.

Implant	Site	Infection rate
Prosthetic hip / knee joint	Hip or knee	1-3%
Vascular grafts	Thoracic aorta	1%
	Abdominal aorta / groin	3-6%
Hydrocephalus shunts	Brain to abdomen	3-20%
Prosthetic heart valves	Heart	1.5%
Central venous catheters (Cuffed)	Central venous system (Cuffed)	3-10% (0.5%)
CAPD catheters	Abdominal wall /peritoneum	1.3 per patient / year
Voice prostheses	Trachea / oesophagus	100%

Types of Implantable Devices in Use

The devices now in common use were developed in the last three or four decades, though prototypes were used sporadically long before that. "Implantable" devices can be divided into three categories: totally implanted, partially implanted, and non - implanted. In the first category are hip, knee and other joint prostheses, hydrocephalus shunts, prosthetic heart valves, pacemakers, vascular grafts, artificial urinary sphincters, ascites shunts, intraocular lenses and certain types of vascular access devices (e.g. Portacath) and intraspinal drug delivery devices. In the second category are central venous catheters (eg Hickman, Boviac), external ventricular drains, and Tenckhoff catheters for continuous ambulatory peritoneal dialysis (CAPD), while the third category includes urinary catheters and voice prostheses, which do not require an invasive surgical procedure to remove or replace them.

Aetiology, rates and risks of infection

Main Sources of Infection

The general principle applies that for the totally implanted devices in the first category, the main period of risk of infection is during surgical insertion, though in some cases there is a well - defined but small group of late haematogenous infections; while in the other two categories the period of risk equates to the duration of use of the device. This principle has obvious implications for prevention.

Before surgical implantation of a Category 1 device, the patient's skin in the area of the incision is rigorously cleaned using antiseptics in alcohol, and this reduces the number of commensals on the skin surface to almost zero. However, the deeper layers of the skin, including hair follicles and glands, are heavily colonised with a resident flora which recolonises the skin surface within about 15 minutes. These organisms then gain access to the incision and from there to the biomaterial being implanted.

In the case of a central venous catheter, a Category 2 device, the risk of infection at insertion is not known but this is not the main source. Skin microorganisms at the site of entry of the catheter can track down the outside of the catheter and may reach the bloodstream, or microorganisms from the intravenous fluids or introduced when the administration bags are changed can colonise the inner surfaces of the catheter and reach the bloodstream by this route. A very similar situation exists with CAPD catheters. In both cases the implant is intended to be in place for weeks or months, being used at least once daily.

Voice prostheses, Category 3 devices used to restore vocalisation after laryngectomy, are situated in an aperture, created surgically, between trachea and oesophagus. However, they are not surgically implanted and can be removed and replaced without a further operation. They are continuously exposed to saliva and food, and rapidly become colonised from these sources.

Rates of Infection

Table 1 shows the reported rates of infection in some implanted devices. Such figures are of limited usefulness as they obscure important subgroups, and this can be illustrated by the case of hydrocephalus shunts. Here the rate is 3 - 20%, and is often cited as an average of 10%. However, the lower figure of 3% relates to shunts inserted in older children and adults, and a rate of 15% or more is applicable to infants less than 6 months of age. Stratifications can also be made in hip or knee replacements, where patients with rheumatoid arthritis have a three-fold higher rate. In Category 3 devices the manner in which rates are reported often does not allow differentiation between infection, ie inflammation, tissue damage etc, and colonisation without these features, and their sites of use make the presence of microorganisms inevitable. However in the case of the voice prosthesis, which is virtually always colonised eventually, the main reason for removal is interference with its function by fungal growth (Mahieu *et al.*, 1986).

Periods of Risk of Infection

It follows from the above that the periods of risk of infection for various categories of device, as shown in Table 2, are different. However, there are also important differences within categories, and late infections of proven non - surgical origin have not been reported in hydrocephalus shunts, despite prolonged monitoring of patients (Bayston, 1989). In other devices in this category, late haematogenous infections do occur, due to microorganisms seeded from the large intestine, mouth, respiratory or urinary tracts and elsewhere (Atkins and Bowler, 1998). However, in all devices in Category 1, most infections are associated with initial surgery.

Table 2 Periods of risk of infection in implantable devices.

Implant	Source	Period of Risk
Category 1		
Prosthetic hip / knee joint	Skin flora	At surgery
Late infections	Gut, respiratory tract etc	Constant
Vascular grafts	Skin flora	At surgery
Late infections	Gut, respiratory tract etc	Constant
Hydrocephalus shunts	Skin flora	At surgery
Prosthetic heart valves	Skin flora	At surgery
Late infections	Mouth, respiratory tract	Constant
Category 2		
Central venous catheters	Skin flora, iv fluids, contamination of system	Constant
CAPD catheters	Skin flora, dialysis fluids, contamination of system	Constant
Category 3		
Voice prostheses	Saliva, food, drink	Constant
Urinary catheters	Skin / gut / genital flora, environmental organisms	Constant

Causative Organisms

Staphylococci, and particularly *S. epidermidis*, are the commonest causative organisms of infection in most devices (Table 3). In many, they cause a late - presenting infection (not to be confused with a late, haematogenous infection) due to their "low - grade" pathogenicity, while *S. aureus, Pseudomonas aeruginosa* and other aerobic gram negative bacilli (AGNB) when surgically acquired tend to be associated with more serious illness and an earlier acute presentation. Prosthetic heart valves, while prone to infection with surgically acquired *S. epidermidis* and other coagulase - negative staphylococci (CoNS), may also be infected late by oral streptococci (Horstkotte *et al.,* 1995). Recently, *Propionibacterium acnes* was isolated from over half of removed hip prostheses (Tunney *et al.,* 1997) calling into question the belief that CoNS are the common- est cause of these infections. *Candida* spp, while they are found sporadically in all BRI, account for the majority of infective agents in voice prostheses (Neu *et al.,* 1994).

A fundamental difference between biofilm infections of medical devices, at least in Category 1, and oral or environmetal biofilms is that the medical ones almost always consist of a single species, though there is considerable phenotypic variation within them. Those found on Category 3 devices may closely resemble the multispecies biofilms found in the oral cavity or the gut.

Table 3 Causative microorganisms of biofilm infections in implants.

Implant	Causative micro–organisms
Category 1	
Prosthetic hip / knee joint	*S. epidermidis, S. aureus*; Peptococci, Streptococci, AGNB, *P. acnes*
Vascular grafts	*S. epidermidis, S. aureus*, AGNB
Hydrocephalus shunts	*S. epidermidis, S. aureus*, coryneform,s AGNB
Prosthetic heart valves	*S. epidermidis, S. aureus*, oral streptococci enterococci
Category 2	
Central venous catheters	*S. epidermidis, S. aureus*, AGNB, *Candida* spp
CAPD catheters	*S. epidermidis, S. aureus*, AGNB, *Candida* spp
Category 3	
Voice prostheses	*Candida* spp, *S. aureus*
Urinary Catheters	AGNB, enterococci, *S. epidermidis, Candida* spp

AGNB = aerobic gram negative bacilli, such as *Escherichia coli* or *Pseudomonas aeruginosa*.

Clinical impact

Resource Consequences of Infection

One of the major impacts of BRI is on health resource consumption. An example is the prosthetic hip, in which the surgical insertion and related hospital costs are approximately £4.5k. Treatment of an infected hip prosthesis costs approximately £18k, assuming treatment is effective at the first attempt. This is because the prosthesis has to be removed in order to eradicate the infection. With an infection rate of 2%, and with approximately 70,000 operations annually in UK, this presents a total cost to the health service of approximately £25M. While the infected patient is undergoing treatment, a hospital bed is being used which could have been used for the next hip replacement patient, so waiting lists increase. Also, the costs do not include travel for family, loss of earnings (or even employment), followup visits, physiotherapy and increased dependence on social services.

Morbidity and Effect on Quality of Life

The symptomatology and consequences of infection to the patient vary considerably. In the patient with a *S. epidermidis* infection in a hip replacement, the suddenly enhanced, painfree quality of life is slowly lost again as pain and poor mobility increase over several months. Due to absence of specific features of infection and similarity to those of non - infective conditions, diagnosis might be delayed for a year or more. In the case of a child with a hydrocephalus shunt infection, again the features are generally non-specific but the diagnosis is precipitated within about six months by obstruction of the shunt and return of the hydrocephalus. This requires removal of the device for a time, during which the patient is at risk of further brain damage due to poor control of the hydro-cephalus as well as secondary infection including meningitis (Bayston *et al.,* 1995). If a patient with an aortic vascular graft has in infection with *S. aureus,* the graft material can separate from the aorta due to bacterial protease produc-tion, causing sudden fatal exsanguination before treatment of the infection itself can be instituted. This happens in approximately 40-50% of those with such infections; the survivors will lose one or both lower limbs due to thrombosis and interruption of blood supply (Bunt, 1994). CoNS cause a serious but much more chronic infection in these patients, with much less risk of death or amputation.

Similarly, the majority of infections associated with CAPD are peritonitis caused by CoNS, but morbidity due to this is low and the cause of the worst clinical outcome in CAPD is removal of the tenckhoff catheter and reversion to haemodialysis. This is associated with relapsing infections due to *S. aureus* or *P aeruginosa* (Bayston *et al.,* 1999).

Infection of central venous catheters often requires catheter removal though some success can be achieved by filling the infected catheter with a concen-trated solution of antibiotic and clamping it for a few hours (Krzywda *et al.,* 1995). If the catheter must be removed, this can interrupt a vital course of anticancer therapy or lead to serious nutritional problems, depending on the use for which the catheter was inserted.

When Category 3 devices become infected, they can usually be removed and replaced easily, though this may not be without distress to the patient.

The two key characteristics of BRI are chronicity or persistence, and insus-ceptibility to antimicrobials.

Molecular pathogenesis

The relationships between microorganisms and biomaterials have been studied mainly in the context of staphylococcal infections, and as these are the common-est causative agents of BRI in most devices, they will be the focus of the following discussion, though much of what is known regarding staphylococci will relate in some degree to other organisms.

The sequence of events in establishment of BRI consist of access of microor-ganisms to the implant, adherence to either biomaterial or, more commonly, to the conditioning film, microbial proliferation, and development of biofilm.

Microbial Access to the Device

Most microorganisms causing BRI are not capable of invasion of the host and reach the device after gaining access to the host during surgery, or in the case of Category 2 and 3 devices, from contamination of the device during use. Late infections of hip or knee replacements can arise from bacteraemia from a distant site such as the large intestine, especially after colonoscopy or as a result of malignancy. However, *S. aureus,* which in terms of pathogenicity is a very versatile organism, is capable of invasion of the host from a trivial injury, and may give rise to prosthetic valve endocarditis or infection of virtually any other implanted device. Oral streptococci can infect prosthetic heart valves following bacteraemia (Horstkotte *et al.*, 1995). The oral cavity is also a neglected source of staphylococci in prosthetic valve endocarditis (Rams *et al.*, 1990).

Adherence

The adherence of the microorganism is a prerequisite for BRI, as without it there is no chance of progression to biofilm formation. In a few cases, bacteria may adhere to the naked biomaterial, and this is true of the inner surfaces of hydrocephalus shunts and central venous catheters. A 220kDa peptide adhesin has been identified in *S. epidermidis* which mediates adherence to polystyrene and other biomaterials (Timmerman *et al.*, 1991) though it is clear that other adhesins are also involved in adherence to hydrophilic materials (Heilman *et al.*, 1996b) and other biomaterials (Tojo *et al.*, 1988). However, in most other cases adherence takes place to a host – derived conditioning film. In the oral cavity, dental implants are coated in salivary glycoproteins and other components, while in tissues or the vascular system, fibronectin, fibrinogen, collagen, laminin, albumen, platelets and other factors are involved. Staphylococci, and particularly *S. aureus*, express surface binding proteins for conditioning film components (Hogt *et al.*, 1986, Herrmann *et al.*, 1988, Brokke *et al.*, 1991). Staphylococci also possess adhesins specific for platelets (Scheld *et al.*, 1978), an important factor in pathogenesis of endocarditis, though this adherence can be considerably offset by the expression of thrombin - induced platelet microbicidal proteins (Yeaman *et al.*, 1994). *S. epidermidis Tn917* mutants lacking four surface – associated proteins have been found to lack adherence to polystyrene, and to show decreased surface hydrophobicity. A 60kDa protein was shown to be able to reverse the effects of the mutagenesis by complementation (Heilmann *et al.*, 1996b).

Biofilm Formation

After adherence has been established and microbial proliferation has begun, some strains of some microorganisms begin to produce exopolymers which act as cell - to cell adhesins allowing a much more extensive biofilm to be produced. The exoploymers are polysaccharide - based, often containing uronic acids and glucosamines, and may be acetylated or phosphorylated. The exopolymer of *Pseudomonas aeruginosa* is polymannuronic acid. While it has been the subject of considerable investigation, that of *S. epidermidis* has until recently remained unidentified, but it is now known to be a glucosaminoglycan (Bayston *et al.*, 1990, Mack *et al.*, 1996) with β-1,6 linkages, and has been named polysaccharide intercellular adhesin (PIA) (Mack *et al.*, 1996). The genetics of PIA production in *S. epidermidis* have been elucidated by Heilmann *et al.*, (1996a). PIA is coded for by the *icaABC* operon. Of the gene products, icaA is a *N* – acetylglucosaminyltransferase (Gerke *et al.*, 1998), and icaC is probably a transmembrane helical peptide functioning as a porin.

The Biofilm Phenotype and Small Colony Variants

As the biofilm develops, cells in the deeper layers are subjected to low oxygen concentrations and nutrient limitation. This results in decreased electron transport and reduced ATP production. In staphylococci the reduction in microbial ATP levels causes increase in sigma factor B (by unbinding of Rsb-W, an anti-sigma factor) and this in turn activates the promoter (particularly P3) for the staphylococcal accessory regulator, *sar*. The upregulation of *sar* activates the promoter for the accessory global regulator, *agr* which leads to transcription of RNAIII and upregulation of toxin production. In *S. aureus* this results in production of α – toxin (coded for by *hla*) and toxic shock syndrome toxin (coded for by *tst*) among others (Chan and Foster, 1998). In *S. epidermidis*, production of fatty acid modifying enzyme (FAME), which esterifies potentially antibacterial host fatty acids to cholesterol, is also regulated in this way (Novick *et al.,* 1993).

However, another result of reduced oxygen tension and nutrient limitation in biofilms is selection of small colony variants (SCV). These subpopulations of staphylococci have defects in electron transport (Proctor *et al.,* 1994), and the result is a drastic decrease, rather than an increase, in toxin production (Proctor 1996). The lesions in the electron transport system amount to auxotrophy for haemin, menadione, menaquinone and thiamine, though a spectrum of auxotrophs is usually found having auxotrophy for one or more of these. The net results are very slow growth, with much decreased synthesis of proteins, including toxins, very little cell wall synthesis, and very low membrane potential. This is expressed phenotypically in *S. aureus* SCV as colonies which show such pleomorphology that they are often mistaken for mixed cultures, and which are non - pigmented, non - haemolytic, α - toxin - negative, coagulase - negative, and may be DNAse - negative and catalase - negative (Bayston and Wood, 1997). The low membrane potential leads to insusceptibility to aminoglycosides as well as to platelet microbicidal proteins and other antibacterial substances which rely on microbial energy to reach their intracellular target (Proctor and von Humboldt, 1998). These negative factors explain why SCV are able to evade the inflammatory response and the immune system (by not producing α - toxin, peptidoglycan etc which activate cytokine release), and are insusceptible to therapeutic concentrations of antimicrobials (as either target sites are inactive or membrane potential is insufficient). The two key features of BRI, chhronicity with persistence of infection and treatment failure or relapse, are thus accounted for by SCV status. It has been suggested that SCV represent the true biofilm mode phenotype (Bayston and Wood 1997).

Selection of staphylococcal SCV *in vitro* can be achieved by progressive nutrient limitation, antibiotic pressure, prolonged growth as a biofilm (Bayston and Wood 1997), or intracellular growth in endothelial cell lines (Vesga *et al.,* 1996).

Selection of SCV can occur *in vivo*. SCV are frequently seen on primary cultures from prosthetic devices removed because of longstanding infection, and though they are often ignored, or the culture discarded as mixed, they should probably be selected as the most deserving population for antimicrobial susceptibility testing, though using current methods this is technically demanding. They can occur spontaneously without antibiotic pressure (Spagna *et al.,* 1978) though they have most often been reported following longterm antibiotic use. A recent example of this is their isolation from persistent infections after treatment with gentamicin - polymethylmethacrylate beads (von Eiff *et al.,* 1998).

Treatment of biomaterials-related infection
Principles of Treatment
In view of the general insusceptibility of biofilm cells to antimicrobials (Foley and Gilbert 1996), the basis of which has been discussed above, conventional antimicrobial sensitivity tests are not clinically predictive, and treatment failure and relapse are common. The minimum inhibitory concentration of an antimicrobial such as vancomycin for an organism in planktonic mode might be 1mg/L, whereas in the biofilm mode it will be >1000mg/L. As the plasma concentration after normal dosage might reach 50mg/L (but decline rapidly soon afterwards), there is no hope of eradicating BRI in such circumstances. Treatment often brings about symptomatic improvement, but relapse occurs soon after "successful" treatment is stopped. This is why most regimens for treatment of BRI include early device removal, followed by long courses of antimicrobials in conventional doses, usually in combination. The need for removal and, if possible, eventual replacement of the device, and long hospital stay during treatment, accounts for the high resource costs outlined earlier. However, attempts are being made to improve this situation. In the case of hip replacements treatment with a combination of rifampicin and ciprofloxacin, originally cautioned against on spurious theoretical grounds, has proved effective without device removal (Zimmerli *et al.,* 1998). However, all the cases reported were diagnosed within a few weeks of surgery, and this is not always possible. In addition, antibiotics had to be administered for between three and six months. The reason for this success is probably related to the ready penetration of phagocytes by these two drugs, and their ability to act on SCV inside the cells. Another avenue of research has involved enhancement of antimicrobial action on biofilms using microcurrents - the "bioelectric effect" (Costerton *et al.,* 1994) and this interesting concept continues to be investigated.

Prevention of biomaterials-related infection
Antimicrobial Prophylaxis
Despite considerable advances in understanding of the aetiology and pathogenesis of BRI, there have been few effective improvements in their prevention. In Category 2 devices, where the period of risk is constant during the use of the implant, improvements in their management can play an important role in prevention of infection. The use of longterm prophylactic antibiotics is not indicated as they are associated with development or selection of resistant organisms. The same principle applies to Category 3 devices, though Candida infection in voice prostheses has been reduced by daily oral application of an

anticandida drug (Leder *et al.,* 1997). Another advance has been the use of buccal bioadhesive slow - release lozenges containing miconazole (van Weissenbruch *et al.,* 1997). A promising approach which does not use antibiotics but which exploits the surfactants produced by dietary lactobacilli and *Strepto-coccus thermophilus* has been shown *in vitro* to reduce significantly candida biofilm on voice prostheses (van der Mei and Busscher 1999), and there is also evidence *that live yoghurt can significantly delay candida colonisation.*

In Category 1 devices where the period of risk is confined mainly to the surgical implantation procedure, the administration of a broad spectrum antibi-otic immediately preoperatively often reduces the incidence of infection, with or without the use of special theatre conditions, and the risk of selection or genera-tion of resistance is very low. However, in some Category 1 devices this ap-proach has not been found useful (Brown *et al.,* 1994).

Antimicrobial Polymers

Antibiotic powder mixed into the uncrosslinked polymethylmethacrylate bone cement in theatre immediately before use is released from the cement after crosslinking (Bayston and Milner 1982), and has been associated with consider-able reduction of relapse rate when used in cases of already - infected hip prostheses (Bucholz and Gartmann 1972, Strachan 1995). A variety of processes for coating the surfaces of intravenous catheters with antimicrobials such as minocycline and rifampicin (Raad *et al.,* 1996), antiseptics such as chlorhexidine (Sherertz *et al.,* 1996, Maki *et al.,* 1997) or silver (Heard *et al.,* 1998, Kampf *et al.,* 1998) have been described, with mixed results. Coatings are rapidly eluted from the surface by blood or infusate, and they are easily obliter-ated by conditioning film. They are also sometimes applied on only one surface of the catheter (Wilcox *et al.,* 1999). The best protection has been obtained with minocycline – rifampicin impregnated catheters, which prevented infection for approximately eight days (Darouiche *et al.,* 1999). The approach taken in the case of CSF shunts, where prophylactic antibiotics are not helpful and the infection rate, especially in young children, is high, is to use an impregnation process rather than a coating. This results in the whole silicone material from which the shunt is made becoming impregnated with antimicrobials, protecting both inner and outer surfaces for periods of up to 2 months (Bayston and Lambert 1997), and the shunts are now available commercially. The advantage of impregnation is that the conditioning film does not reduce the activity of the antimicrobials. In addition, a very low concentration of antimicrobials, 0.05 - 0.1% by weight, is capable of exerting the desired protective effect. This is because, for an enduring effect, it is necessary only to maintain saturation of the Nernst layer, an affinity layer a few molecules thick at the interface of biomate-rial and host tissue (Nernst 1904). The layer is emptied continuously by diffu-sion into the surrounding tissue fluids, and coatings are very soon depleted, failing to maintain the antimicrobial concentration for longer than a few hours or days. Impregnation, assuming that the release kinetics of the polymer / drug matrix are optimal, is capable of maintaining a replete Nernst layer for periods of several weeks (Bayston and Lambert, 1997) with undetectable tissue or plasma concentrations of drug. This principle is now being applied to other devices.

Conclusion

As many implantable devices are used in the very young, the elderly or the disabled, all social groups which are increasing in size world – wide, it is almost certain that their use will become more wide – spread. Though considerable advances in knowledge of BRI have taken place in the last two decades, the major growing points in medical science, such as vaccine development, gene therapy and new drug development, are unlikely to solve the problems of infection in implantable devices. Some, but not many, devices will perhaps be dispensed with as biological approaches become more successful, but for the foreseeable future we can expect to face increasing numbers of cases of BRI.

References

Atkins, B.L. and Bowler, I.C.J.W. 1998. The diagnosis of large joint sepsis. *J. Hosp. Infect* .**40**, 2263-2274

Bayston, R. 1989. *Hydrocephalus Shunt Infections.* Chapman & Hall Medical, London.

Bayston, R., Andrews, M., Rigg, K. and Shelton, A. 1999. Recurrent infection and catheter loss in patients on continuous ambulatory peritoneal dialysis. *Perit. .Dial. Int* . (in press)

Bayston, R., de Louvois, J., Brown, E.M., Hegdes, A.J., Johnston, R.A. and Lees, P. 1995. Treatment of infections associated with shunting for hydrocephalus. *Brit. J. Hosp. Med.* **53**, 368-373.

Bayston R., Lambert E. (1997). Duration of activity of cerebrospinal fluid shunt catheters impregnated with antimicrobials to prevent bacterial catheter - related infection. *J Neurosurg* **87**: 247-251

Bayston R., Milner R.D.G. (1982). The sustained release of antimicrobial drugs from bone cement . *J Bone Joint Surg* **64B**: 460-464

Bayston, R. and Wood, H. 1997. Small colony variants: are they anything to do with biofilms? In: Wimpenny, J., Handley, P., Gilbert, P., Lappin - Scott, H. and Jones, M. (eds.), *Biofilms: Community Interactions and Control,* pp 161-165, BioLine, Cardiff.

Brokke, P., Dankert, J., Carballo, J. and Feijen, J. 1991. Adherence of coagulase - negative staphylococci onto polyethylene catheters *in vitro* and *in vivo*: A study on the influence of various plasma proteins. *J. Biomater. Appl.* **5**, 204-226.

Brown, E.M., de Louvois, J., Bayston, R., Hedges, A.J., Johnston, R.A. and Lees, P. 1994. Antimicrobial prophylaxis in neurosurgery and after head injury. *Lancet* **344**, 1547-1551.

Bucholz, H.W. and Gartmann, H.D. 1972. Infektionsprophylaxe und operative behandlung der Schleichenden teifen Infektion bei der totalen Endoprosthese. *Chirurg.* **43**, 446-453.

Bunt, T.J. 1994. Treatment options for graft infections. In: Bunt, T.J. (ed.) *Vascular Graft Infections.* Pp 175-210, Futura Pubs, New York.

Chan, P.F. and Foster, S.J. 1998. Role of *SarA* in virulence determinant production and environmental signal transduction in *Staphylococcus aureus. J. Bacteriol.* **180,** 6232-6241.

Costerton, J.W., Ellis, B., Lam, K., Johnson, F. and Khoury, A.E. 1994. Mechanisms of electrical enhancement of efficacy of anitbiotics in killing biofilm bacteria. *Antimicrob. Ag. Chemother.* **38**, 2803-2809.

Darouiche, R.O., Raad, I.I., Heard, S.O., Thornby, J.I., Wenker, O.C., Gabrielli, A., Berg, J., Khardori, N., Hanna, H., Hachem, R., Harris, R.L., Mayhall, G. 1999. A comparison of two antimicrobial – impregnated central venous catheters. *N. Eng. J. Me.d* **340**, 1-8

Foley, I. and Gilbert, P. 1996. Antibiotic resistance of biofilms. *Biofouling.* **10**, 331-346.

Gerke, C., Kraft, A., Süßmuth, R., Schweitzer, O. and Götz, F. 1998. Characterisation of the *N*-acetylglucosaminyltransferase activity involved in the biosynthesis of the *Staphylococcus epidermidis* polysaccharide intercellular adhesin. *J. Biol. Chem.* **273**, 18586-18593.

Heard, S.O., Wagle, M., Vijayakumar, E., McClean, S., Brueggemann, A., Napolitano, L.M., Edwards, P., O'Connell, F., Puyuna, J.C. and Doern, G.V. 1998. Influence of triple lumen central venous catheters coated with chlorhexidine and silver sulfadiazine on the incidence of catheter – related bacteraemia. *Arch. Int. Med.* **158,** 81-87

Heilmann, C., Schweitzer, O., Gerke, C., Vanittanakom, N., Mack, D. and Götz, F. 1996. Molecular basis of intercellular adhesion in the biofilm – forming Staphylococcus epidermidis. *Mol. Microbiol.* **20,** 1083-1091.

Heilmann, C., Gerke, C., Perdreau – Remington, F. and Götz, F. 1996b. Characterisation of *Tn917* insertion mutants of *Staphylococcus epidermidis* affected in biofilm formation. *Infect. Immun.* **64,** 277-282.

Herrmann, M., Vaudaux, P.E., Pittet, D., Auckenthaler, P.D., Leew, F., Schumaker - Perdreau, F., Peters, G. and Waldvogel, F.A. 1988. Fibronectin, fibrinogen and laminin act as mediators for adherence of clinical staphylococcal isolates to foreign material. *J.Infect.Dis.* **158,** 693-701.

Hogt, A.H., Dankert, J., de Vries, J.A. and Feijen, J. 1983. Adhesion of coagulase - negative staphylococci to biomaterials. *J.Gen.Microbiol.* **129,** 2959-2968.

Horstkotte, D., Piper, C., Niehues, M., *et al.,*. 1995.. Late prosthetic valve endocarditis. *Europ. Heart J.* **16(SB),** 39-47.

Kampf, G., Dietze, B., Große - Seistrup, C., Wendt, C. and Martiny, H. 1998. Microbicidal activity of a new silver - containing polymer, SPI-ARGENT II. *Antimicrob. Ag. Chemother.* **42,** 2440-2442.

Krzywda, E.A., Andris, D.A., Edmiston, C.E. and Quebbeman, E.J. 1995. Treatment of Hickman catheter sepsis using antibiotic lock technique. *Infect. Control Hosp. Epidemiol* .**16**, 596-598

Leder, S.B. and Erskine, M.C. 1997. Voice restoration after laryngectomy: experience with the Blom - Singer extended – wear indwelling tracheoesophageal voice prosthesis. *Head and Neck* **19,** 92-97

Mack, D., Fischer, W., Krokotsk, A., Leopold, K., Hartmann, R., Egge, H. and Laufs, R. 1996. The intercellular adhesin involved in biofilm accumulation of *Staphylococcus epidermidis* is a linear β–1,6-linked glucosaminoglycan: purification and structural analysis. *J. Bact.* **178,** 175-183.

Mahieu, H.F., van Saene, H.K.F., Rosingh, H.J. and Schutte, H.K. 1986. Candida vegetations on silicone voice prostheses. *Arch. Otolaryngol. Head Neck Surg* .**112,** 321-325.

Maki, D.G., Wheeler, S.J. and Stolz, S.M. 1991. Study of a novel anti - septic coated central venous catheter. *Crit. Care Med.* **19,** 599.

Nernst, W. Z. 1904. Theorie der Reaktionsgeschwindigkeit in heterogenen Systemen. *Z. Phys. Chem.* **47,** 52-55.

Neu, T.R., Verkerke, G.J., Herrmann, I.F., Schutte, H.K., van der Mei, H.C. and Busscher, H.J. 1994. Microflora on explanted silicone rubber voice prostheses: taxonomy, hydrophobicity and electrophoretic mobility. *J. Appl. Bact.* **76,** 521-523.

Novick, R.P., Ross, H.F., Projan, S.J., Kornblum, J., Kreiswirth, B. and Moghazeh, S. 1993. Synthesis of staphylococcal virulence factors is controlled by a regulatory RNA molecule. *E.M.B.O.J.* **12,** 3967-3975.

Proctor, R.A., Balwit, J.M. and Vesga, O. 1994. Variant subpopulations of *Staphylococcus aureus* as a cause of persistent and recurrent infections. *Infect. Ag. Dis.* **3,** 302-312.

Proctor, R.A., and von Humboldt, A. 1998. Bacterial energetics and antimicrobial resistance. *Drug Res. Updates* **1,** 227-235.

Proctor, R.A., Vesga, O., Otten, M.F., Koo, S.-P., Yeaman, M.R., Sahl, H.-G. and Bayer, A.S. 1996. *Staphylococcus aureus* small colony variants cause persistent and resistant infections. *Chemother.* **42** (Suppl 2), 47-52.

Raad, I., Darouiche, R., Hachem, R., Mansouri, M. and Bodey, G.P. 1996. The broad - spectrum activity and efficacy of catheters coated with minocycline and rifampin. *J. Infect. Dis.* **173,** 418-424.

Rams,T.E., Feik, D. and Slots, J. 1990. Staphylococci in human periodontal diseases. *Oral Microbiol. Immunol.* **51,** 29-32.

Scheld W.M., Valone, J.A. and Sande, M.A. 1978. Bacterial adherence in the pathogenesis of endocarditis: interaction of bacterial dextran, platelets and fibrin. *J. Clin. Invest.* **61,** 1394-1404.

Sherertz, R.J., Heard, S.O., Raad. I.I., Gentry, L., Bowton, D., Scuderi, P., Hu, J., Carruth, W., Satishchandra, B., Pepe, J., Mosenthal, A., Burke, T. and Dupuis, J. 1996. Gamma radiation –

sterilised, triple lumen catheters coated with a low concentration of chlorhexidine were not efficacious at preventing catheter infections in intensive care unit patients. *Antimicrob. Ag. Chemother.* **40**, 1995-1997.

Spagna, V.A., Fass, R.J., Prior, R.B. and Slama, T.G. 1978. Report of a case of bacterial sepsis caused by a naturally - occurring variant form of *Staphylococcus aureus. J. Infect. Dis.* **138**, 277-278.

Strachan, C.J.L. 1995. The prevention of orthopaedic implant and vascular graft infections. *J. Hosp. Infect.* **30**: 54-63.

Timmerman, C.P., Fleer, A., Besnier, J.M., de Graaf, L., Cremers, F. and Verhoef, J. 1991. Characterisation of a proteinaceous adhesin *of Staphylococcus epidermidis* which mediates attachment to polystyrene. *Infect. Immun* .**59**, 4187-4192.

Tojo, M., Yamashita, N., Goldman, D.A. and Pier, G.B. 1988. Isolation and characterisation of a capsular polysaccharide adhesin from *Staphylococcus epidermidis. J.Infect.Dis.***157**, 713-722.

Tunney, M.M., Patrick, S., Gorman, S.P., Nixon, J.R., Anderson, N., Hanna, D., Rammage, G. and McKenne, J.P. 1997. Isolation of anaerobes from orthopaedic implants. *Rev Med Microbiol* **8 (S1)**, S92-S93.

van der Mei, H.C. and Busscher, H.J. 1999. Microbial and host factors influencing adhesion to prosthetic devices. Abstract In:21st International Congress of Chemotherapy, Birmingham.

van Weissenbruch, R., Bouckaert, S., Remon, J-P., Nelis, H.J., Aerts, R., and Albers, F.W.J. 1997. Chemoprophylaxis of fungal deterioration of the Provox silicone tracheoesophageal prosthesis in postlaryngectomy patients. *Ann. Otol. Rhinol. Laryngol.* **106**, 329-337.

Vesga, O., Groeschel, M.C., Otten, M.F., Brar, D.W., Vann, J.M. and Proctor, R.A. 1996. Staphylococcus aureus small colony variants are induced by the endothelial cell intracellular milieu. *J. Infect. Dis.* **173**, 739-742.

von Eiff, C., Lindner, N., Proctor, R.A., Winkelmann, W. and Peters, G. 1998). Auftreten von Gentamicin - resistenten Small Colony Variants von *S. aureus* nach Einsetzen von Gentamicin - Ketten bei Osteomyelitis als Mögliche Ursache für Rezidive. *Z. Orthop.* **136**, 268-271.

Wilcox, M., Kite, P. and Dobbins, B. 1999. Antimicrobial intravascular catheters- which surface to coat? *J. Hosp. Infect.* **40**, 322-323.

Yeaman, M.R., Sullam, P.M., Dazin, P.F. and Bayer, A.S. 1994. Platelet microbicidal protein alone and in combination with antibiotics reduces *Staphylococcus aureus* adherence to platelets in vitro. *Infect.Immun.* **62**, 3416-3425.

Zimmerli, W., Widmer, A.F., Blatter, M., Frei, R. and Ochsner, P.E. 1998. Role of rifampin for treatment of orthopedic implant - related staphylococcal infections - a randomised controlled trial. *J. Amer. Med. Assoc.* **279**, 1537-1541.

BIOFILMS AND THEIR RESISTANCE TOWARDS ANTIMICROBIAL AGENTS

Peter Gilbert and David G. Allison

*Exopolymers not only immobilise biofilm-bacteria at colonised surfaces but also provide for interactions between the component species. Such interactions give the community both metabolic and physiological capabilities which are present for individual, unattached cells. A notable property of biofilms is their high level resistance towards antibiotics, biocides and disinfectants. Attributions of resistance most frequently relate to the properties of the exopolymer matrix. Whilst the matrix is not a significant barrier to the diffusion of antimicrobial molecules it can restrict access to the depths of the biofilm by quenching chemically-reactive agents or through binding highly charged agents. Additionally, extra-cellular enzymes, bound within the matrix, are sometimes able to augment the restriction of access through the enzymic destruction of the agent. A close proximity of cells within the biofilm causes the acquisition of nutrients and oxygen to be problematic for the deeper lying cells. During exposure to antimicrobials these slower-growing cells, at the core of the biofilm, will generally out-survive the faster metabolising ones found at the periphery. Slow growing cells will, in addition, express dormant, starvation-phenotypes which often over-express non-specific defences such as shock proteins, multi-drug efflux pumps (**acrAB**) and also further exopolymer synthesis. Finally, attachment causes the expression, possibly regulated through quorum sensing mechanisms, of biofilm-specific phenotypes which might contribute to resistance. None of these processes can alone provide an explanation for **in situ** resistance, more likely they collectively delay eradication of the treated population and provide opportunities for other selection events to occur.*

Introduction

There is now widespread concern that the indiscriminate use of antibiotics, and possibly biocides, has led to the development and emergence of resistant bacteria (Dixon, 1998; Levy, 1998). Moreover, the prospect of resistance to one type of antimicrobial agent, such as a biocide, leading to cross-resistance to a separate, unrelated agent such as an antibiotic, has serious potential (Levy, 1998). This, coupled to increasing demands by society on the control of bacteria in an ever-widening sphere of applications, has heightened the need to understand those mechanisms associated with antimicrobial tolerance development and resistance.

Microbial biofilms are well known for their ability to resist the actions of antibiotic, biocide and/or disinfectant treatment that would adequately contend with the same organisms growing in suspension culture (Allison and Gilbert, 1995). Indeed, given the close proximity of cells within the biofilm matrix, then if such resistance were genotypic and if the genotype were transferable, then biofilms would be a nidus of both the genesis and propagation of resistance phenotypes. In medicine, biofilm-related problems are associated not only with the surfaces of implanted medical devices such as prostheses, endocardial pacemakers and catheters, but also with soft-tissues of the nasopharynx, mouth and gut, and hard surfaces such as tooth and bone (Costerton *et al.,* 1987). Serious infections may also arise from a failure to disinfect adequately the organisms attached to medical equipment such as fibre-optic endoscopes and washers (Spach *et al.,* 1993; Griffiths *et al.,* 1997). Biofilm infections, associ- ated with indwelling medical devices are often chronic and, act as the reservoir of bacteraemia. Bacteraemia respond readily to antibiotic treatments that are dictated by the results of conventional sensitivity testing (Thomson *et al.,* 1995). The biofilms from which they are derived display greatly enhanced resistance and often fail to respond to even the most aggressive antibiotic prescribing (Costerton *et al.,* 1993; Gristina *et al.,* 1987; Kunin and Steel, 1985; Nickel *et al.,* 1985).

Whilst in medicine biofilms are now firmly associated with a majority of chronic infection scenarios (Costerton *et al.,* 1987), such problems related to microbial biofilm are not unique to this field. Indeed in many industrial settings, fouling and corrosion of plant and pipe-work have been related to the presence of biofilms (Characklis, 1990; Little *et al.,* 1990). In food-processing biofilms, formed on food contact surfaces, contribute substantially both to the contamina- tion and spoilage of product (Holah *et al.,* 1994; Eginton *et al.,* 1998). In all of these aspects resistance is demonstrated by the developed biofilms, not only towards antibiotics and antiseptics, but also towards highly reactive chemical biocides. The latter include isothiazolones (Costerton and Lashen, 1984), halogens and halogen-release agents (Favero *et al.,* 1983), and quaternary ammonium compounds (Costerton and Lashen, 1984; Evans *et al.,* 1990b). Failure of most available antimicrobials to contend adequately with microbial biofilms, together with an increasing dependence of modern medicine upon the implantation of devices, has stimulated the search for antimicrobials which have activity directed primarily towards the biofilm phenotype (Gilbert and Brown, 1995). Current strategies for the control of microbial biofilms involve the design of antimicrobial agents that are specifically targeted at cells growing within the biofilm. Such approaches have, to date, only met with limited success and the need to develop efficient, low cost hygienic cleansing systems remains as urgent as ever. To aid the search for novel antimicrobial targets there is a need not only to develop our knowledge of biofilm physiology, but also to examine the various mechanisms associated with resistance development within biofilm communi- ties. The failure of antimicrobial treatments may be related to:

    (i)   Inherent insusceptibility of the target cells to the agents employed,

    (ii) The acquisition of resistance, by previously susceptible strains, either by genetic mutation or by transfer of genetic material from another species or genus, or,

    (iii) An emergence of pre-existing but unexpressed resistance phenotypes.

The extent to which such adaptation towards less susceptible phenotypes is influenced through growth as a biofilm is still a matter for debate. This contribution considers our current understanding of resistance mechanisms associated with microbial biofilms and gained as a result of attachment to surfaces and growth as polymer-entrapped micro-colonies. Such understanding reflects diffusional resistance of the extracellular matrix, augmented by chemical / enzymic modification of the agent (reaction-diffusion limitation), physiological changes due to slow growth rate and starvation responses, and the induction of attachment-specific, drug-resistant physiologies. It is unlikely that any single mechanism will account for the general observation of resistance. Rather, all such mechanisms are compounded to render the biofilms recalcitrant and to create an environment which is ideally suited for the selection and emergence of tolerant genotypes.

Biofilm physiology

Biofilms are functional consortia of microbial cells enveloped within matrices of extracellular polymers (glycocalyx) and the concentrated products of their own metabolism. The latter include ions and nutrients sequestered from the general environment and extra-cellular enzymes such as lyases, proteases, ß-lactamases *etc*. In the majority of natural habitats, the consortia comprise of a variety of species and genera. In biomedical situations, particularly those associated with soft tissue infection or infections of indwelling devices, mono-cultures are more commonly isolated.

The structural organisation of the inter-cellular matrix (glycocalyx) varies according to the prevailing physico-chemical environment, such that under high shear (*ie* tooth surface during mastication, gastro-intestinal tract *etc*.), the biofilm population is organised within stratified compacts of exopolymeric material that define boundaries between different component organisms (Marsh, 1995; Newman and Barber, 1995). Under moderate to low shear, with few nutrients being derived from the substratum, biofilms appear as floccules, anchored to the substratum yet maximising the surface interaction with the nutrient-bearing liquid phase (Costerton *et al.,* 1994). If the growth rate limiting nutrient is derived directly from the substratum, rather than the bathing fluids, then the biofilm cells completely coat the available surface, and gradients of growth rate relative to the bathing fluid are reversed. Such conditions would prevail in the biodeterioration of materials and in microbial colonisation of the respiratory tract, skin and nasopharynx. With the exception of those cells that are located at the boundary to the biofilm community, access to nutrients, and the ease with which metabolic by-products may be eliminated is less easy than for single cells growing in liquid culture. In this fashion, organisation as a dense community causes cells deep within the biofilm matrix to have available to them only those materials that have not been sequestered by the more out-lying cells. Conversely, microorganisms within the core of the community will have a more ready access to the secreted metabolic products of their neighbours. Such cross-feeding, and the development of functional inter-species dependence, leads to spatial organisation of sub-communities within the biofilm community. In all biofilm communities, nutrient and gaseous gradients, generated by metabolism, will cause nutrient availability, growth rate, and the nature of metabolism (aerobic, microaerobic, anaerobic, fermentative etc.) to vary according to the location of cells relative to each other, the substratum and biofilm/liquid phase interface. In well-mixed, suspension cultures, at any given time each member of the community will experience a common environment. Single phenotypes will therefore dominate such the cultures, as a consequence, demonstrate a singular response towards antimicrobial treatment. At any given time within biofilm communities, however, a plethora of phenotypes is represented for each component species, the breadth of which reflects the extent of chemical and structural heterogeneity within the film (Gilbert *et al.*, 1990). The outcome of any antimicrobial treatment of the biofilm community will, therefore, reflect the susceptibility of the most resistant phenotype represented within it. As biofilms mature, and exopolymer deposition increases, the magnitude of the nutrient and gaseous gradients will become increased and the net growth rate of the community will become further reduced, possibly with an onset of dormancy and the triggering of stringent response genes (Zambrano and Kolter, 1995). The latter might in turn initiate escape mechanisms whereby the production of polymer-lyase enzymes is increased and the biofilm community is dispersed (Willcock *et al.*, 1997).

Resistance mechanisms
Since the presence and nature of the exopolymeric biofilm matrix is thought to confer much of the resistance property towards antimicrobial agents, it is imperative to consider its physical property, biosynthesis and regulation before an examination of its possible roles in limiting the access of antimicrobial chemicals.

The Extracellular Polymeric Matrix
Light and electron microscopy show that the extracellular polymers (EPS) form a matrix in biofilms that is comprised of an ordered array of fine fibres. These arrays provide a relatively thick, hydrated coating to the cells. Up-regulation of extracellular polymer synthesis occurs within several minutes of the irreversible attachment of cells to a surface (Allison and Sutherland, 1987), whilst its deposition within the microcolony proceeds over a period of hours. Whilst the matrices are often given the generic term of 'glycocalyx' there is no common definition of its structure. The predominant components of the EPS matrix are gelled, highly hydrated, extracellular polysaccharides, held in an ordered configuration (Sutherland, 1997) with other macromolecules, such as nucleic acids, proteins, globular glycoproteins and lipids and ions, bound loosely within (Sutherland, 1995). It is unknown whether or not the chemical nature, and physico-chemical properties, of the matrix polymers differs from that either of the EPS produced by planktonic cells, or the 'foot-print polymers' which cement the primary colonisers to the substratum (Allison, 1998; Sutherland, 1997). Bacterial polysaccharides are heterogeneous chemically and contain some non-carbohydrate moeties. The latter are usually negatively charged and may be species specific (Sutherland, 1985). Neutrally-charged, or more rarely

128

positively-charged, polymers may be represented according to the nature of the repeat components. Furthermore, whilst polysaccharides are generally regarded as being hydrophilic in nature, they may sometimes possess a degree of hydrophobic property (Neu and Marshall, 1990; Sutherland, 1997). In such respects we must therefore regard the matrix polymers associated with individual species and particularly when organsised within a multi-species community as being highly heterogeneous (Sutherland, 1997; Cooksey, 1992). The physicochemical properties of blended exopolymers, as might be found at the mosaic-boundary between community members, differs significantly from that of the purified components. The properties of such blends will also be substantially affected by the nature of any adsorbed cations and by the ionic-strength of the surrounding medium (Allison and Matthews, 1992).

Regulation of Exopolymer Synthesis

The synthesis of matrix polymers appears to be regulated by a variety of factors, of which attachment to a surface appears to be paramount. In this respect, Davies *et al.* (1993) showed that exopolysaccharide (alginate) production by *Pseudomonas aeruginosa* forming a biofilm was de-repressed relative to planktonic cells, and Evans *et al.* (1994), working with *Staphylococcus epidermidis,* showed that exopolysaccharide production was not only substantially higher for biofilm than planktonic cells but was also much increased at low growth rates. The latter effect would cause increased deposition of exopolymers within the slow-growing heart of a thick micro-colony/ biofilm. Thus, the distribution and density of cells would be affected throughout the matrix and, once again, some degree of structural organisation would be conferred upon the community (Costerton *et al.,* 1994). In such respects it is notable that with the exception of the alginates the majority of the extracellular polysaccharides are soluble, to a reasonable degree in water. Biofilm communities should therefore be regarded as being dynamic structures with solubilisation of matrix-polymers at the periphery being balanced by an increased production within the depths. Recent work (Davies *et al.,* 1998), with *P. aeruginosa,* suggests that the regulation of exopolysaccharides, such as alginate, is under the control of global regulatory systems responding to *N*-acyl homoserine lactone (HSL) accumulation. Such signalling systems, and their equivalent in Gram-positive cells (Kleerebezem *et al.,* 1997) may also act as regulators of biofilm specific physiology (Cooper *et al.,* 1995; Gambello *et al.,* 1993; Williams *et al.,* 1992; Heys *et al.,* 1997). In order for cell-cell signalling to play a role in biofilm regulation then the signal molecules must become concentrated either within the geometric centre of the micro-colony/biofilm or at the interface between individual cells and the sub-stratum. Such accumulation of signal, were it to upregulate polymer biosynthesis, would alter the relative distribution and density of cells throughout the community (Costerton *et al.,* 1994). The extent and nature of exopolymer production is also dependent upon physiological factors such as the relative availability of carbon- and nitrogen-containing nutrients (Sutherland, 1985).

Diffusion-limitation and the Glycocalyx

Deposition within a charged, hydrated extra-cellular polymer matrix will have a profound influence upon cells ability to access of molecules and ions, including protons, from the surrounding liquid environment. Such effects on the diffusion of agents from the surrounding medium occur through a combination of ionic-interaction and molecular-sieving events. In such respects, the extra-cellular polymer matrix acts as an ion-exchange resin, actively removing strongly charged molecules from solution. In order to access deeply embedded cells then either all of the binding sites within the matrix must be saturated or the affinity of cells for that substrate must exceed the binding affinity to the matrix. It is not surprising therefore that the intuitive explanation of biofilm resistance towards antimicrobials has been one of the physical exclusion of antimicrobials (Costerton *et al.,* 1987; Slack and Nichols, 1981; 1982; Suci *et al.,* 1994). This is most probably a major contributor to recalcitrance when the antimicrobial agents are strongly charged (*ie* tobramycin) or chemically highly reactive (*ie* halogens/peroxygens). For antibiotics such as tobramycin and cefsulodin (Gordon *et al.,* 1988; Nichols *et al.,* 1988; 1989), however, the reductions in the diffusion coefficient within the polymer matrix are insufficient to account for the observed change in susceptibility. In this context Gristina *et al.* (1987) failed to find any difference in the antibiotic susceptibility of slime-producer and non-slime producer strains of *Staphylococcus epidermidis.* When however, Evans *et al.* (1991) assessed the susceptibility biofilms of mucoid and non-mucoid strains of *P. aeruginosa* to the quinolone ciprofloxacin differences were noted between intact and resuspended biofilms. Resuspension in this instance would remove the majority of the glycocalyx from the community. The concensus of opinion, from the various studies of this nature, is that whilst a mucoid phenotype is often associated with a general decrease in susceptibility, this is unlikely to be as a direct result of changes in the diffusion coefficient. Similar conclusions were reached by Stewart (1996) who used a theoretical model to investigate the extent of antibiotic penetration into microbial biofilms. The situation may be regarded as somewhat different in biofouling than in the biomedical sphere. The dimen-sions of biofilms *in vivo* are in the order of tens of micrometres thick, whereas in some industrial situations thickness may be several orders of magnitude greater (Nichols *et al.,* 1989). Whilst the thickness of a matrix will have no influence on its diffusion property *per se,* it will affect the net-flux of charged antimicrobials across it (Nichols, 1993).

Reaction-diffusion-limitation and the Glycocalyx

Any interaction between the glycocalyx and solute resulting in adsorption, covalent binding or chemical modification of the solute will significantly reduce the net-flux of solute across the matrix. In this respect exopolymers and cellular materials derived from dead cells in the peripheral regions of a treated biofilm may react chemically with, and neutralise, the treatment agent. Such effects will be most pronounced for chemically, highly-reactive biocides that are capable of oxidising extracellular matrix rather than the target cells. Such biocides would include iodine and iodine-polyvinylpyrollidone complexes (Favero *et al.*, 1983), chlorine and peroxygens (Huang *et al.*, 1995) which are notable for their lack of effect against extant biofilm. Similar situations may be 'engineered' by the enveloped cells however by the deposition of drug-inactivating enzymes, such as ß-lactamases (Giwercman *et al.*, 1991), formaldehyde lyase and formaldehyde dehydrogenase (Sondossi *et al.*, 1985) within the glycocalyx. In such instances, catalytic (e.g. enzymic) reactions can lead to severe antibiotic penetration failure, provided that turn-over is sufficiently rapid, (Stewart, 1996). It is particularly interesting in this respect that hydrolytic enzymes such as ß-lactamases are induced/de-repressed in adherent populations, and in populations exposed to sub-lethal concentrations of imipenem and/or piperacillin (Lambert *et al.*, 1993; Giwercman *et al.*, 1991). These enzymes become trapped and concentrated within the biofilm matrix and further impede the action of susceptible antibiotics. Similarly, inactivation of formaldeyde by the enzymes formaldeyde lyase and formaldehyde dehydrogenase (Sondossi *et al.*, 1985) has also been observed within biofilms of *P. aeruginosa* . Such effects would be in addition to the loss, through irreversible binding to the matrix, of highly charged drug molecules, such as the glycopeptides (Hoyle *et al.*, 1992). Curiously, macrolide antibiotics, which are also positively charged, but which are also very hydrophobic, are relatively unaffected by the presence of the exopolymers (Ichimiya *et al.*, 1994). Poor penetration through anionic matrices might, therefore, be a phenomenon restricted to the more hydrophilic, positively charged agents. It is apparent that the function of the exopolymeric matrix as a physical barrier to antimicrobial penetration depends not only upon the nature of the agent and the binding capacity of the polymeric matrix towards it but also upon the levels of agent used therapeutically (Nichols, 1993). In this latter respect reaction of treatment agent with the glycocalyx must deplete the bulk phase available agent. This will depend in turn upon the volume of the bulk phase relative to the biomass of the biofilm, and local hydrodynamics (DeBeer *et al.*, 1994) together with the rate of turnover of the microcolony relative to antibiotic diffusion rate (Kumon *et al.*, 1994). For antibiotics such as tobramycin and cefsoludin such effects are therefore likely to be minimal (Nichols *et al.*, 1988; 1989), but are high for positively charged antibiotics such as the aminoglycosides, which will bind strongly to polyanionic matrix polymers (Nichols *et al.*, 1988).

Reaction-diffusion limitation resistance of microbial biofilms is typified by their recalcitance towarfds oxidising biocides. In an elegant study Huang *et al.* (1995) grew biofilms of *Klebsiella pneumoniae* and *P. aeruginosa* on stainless steel surfaces using a continuous-flow annular reactor. These were treated with 2mgL^{-1} of monochloramine for 2h and stained using a fluorogenic redox indicator that could differentiate respiring from non-respiring cells. Epifluorescent micrographs of frozen, cross-sections revealed gradients of respiratory activity within the biofilms in response to the monochloramine treatment. Cells near the biofilm-bulk fluid interface lost respiratory activity early in the treatment whereas residual respiratory activity persisted near the substratum or in the centre of small, viable cell-clusters, even after 2h treatment. This clearly indicated not only a progressive killing of the biofilm which progressed from the exposed face, but also distinct heterogeneity within the biofilm with small clusters of cells (possibly clones) with greater tolerance towards the agent than the majority of cells. A further study, using both oxidising and non-oxidising biocides (Stewart *et al.*, 1998), used alginate-entrapped biofilm constructs of *Enterococcus faecalis* to demonstrate a similar lack of penetration and action against the entrapped cells by chlorine, gluteraldehyde, isothiazolone and quaternary ammonium biocides. In the real world, the volume and overall reactive-capacity of a biofilm would, however, be insufficient to deplete the applied phase of available biocide. The net effect would therefore be to delay, rather than prevent, the inhibitory process (Huang *et al.*, 1995). Provided that the exposure to biocide were brief or that the biocide was not in a vast excess of requirements then reaction diffusion limitation could allow the survival of cells at the base of the biofilm which would flourish once the biocide were removed.

Modification of Exopolymer and Altered Susceptibility to Anti-microbial Drugs
The adsorption of ionic materials within the biofilm matrix will have profound effects upon its net charge and antibiotic-exclusion properties. Thus, Hoyle *et al.* (1992) showed that the binding capacity of exopolysaccharides towards tobramycin was less important than the diffusivity of the matrix. Diffusivity may in turn be changed by the adsorption of Ca^{2+} which causes the polymer-matrix to become much condensed. Similar effects have long been associated with the binding of ions and the molecular size exclusion properties of peptidoglycan (Marquis, 1968). The extent of the condensation can be highly dependent upon the nature of the adsorbed cation and is not seen, for example, with Mg^{2+}. Such disparities find explanation in the fact that within a mixture of polysaccharides a three-dimensional 'weak-gel' network, cross-linked by calcium ions can be formed by non-covalent interaction (Allison and Matthews, 1992). These observations become important since body fluids at the site of an infection normally show relatively high concentrations of soluble salts. Once again, however, modification of the physico-chemical properties of the glycocalyx through ion-adsorption is insufficient to account totally for biofilm resistance, since biofilm bacteria are found to be resistant to biocides even when found growing and treated in purified, de-ionised water.

Modulation of the growth environment

It is well established that the susceptibility of bacterial cells not only towards antibiotics, but also towards biocides and preservatives, is significantly affected by their nutrient status and growth rate, as well as by their temperature and pH, and prior exposure to sub-effective concentrations of antimicrobial (Brown and Williams, 1985; Brown *et al.*, 1990; Williams, 1988). This reflects adaptive changes in a variety of cellular components including membrane fatty-acids, phospholipids and envelope proteins, and the production of extracellular enzymes and polysaccharides. Adherent microcolonies form functional consortia and influence their micro-environment through the localised concentration of enzymes and metabolic products, and the relative exclusion of gases such as oxygen (Costerton *et al.,* 1987). Variations in nutrient status and growth rate within a biofilm will therefore cause it to possess an equally varied response to antimicrobial treatments. In this fashion, the exopolymeric matrix performs a homeostatic function, minimising the consequences of fluctuations in the surrounding macro-environment. A major consequence of such homeostasis is that cells deep within the biofilm are exposed to concentrations of substrates, hydrogen ions and also oxidation-potentials that are substantially altered from those experienced by cells on the periphery and by cells growing planktonically in the same medium. Growth rates will therefore be reduced within biofilms through the imposition of nutrient deficiences, which may or may not reflect the composition of the bulk aqueous phase.

Since mature biofilms are composed of dense communities of bacteria embedded within an exopolysaccharide matrix, then diffusion and transport of nutrients through the biofilm becomes an important consideration. In nutrient-rich environments, oxygen and nutrients are rapidly utilised by aerobic bacteria at the biofilm:liquid interface, thereby diminishing the availability of such nutrients in the depths of the biofilm. This leads to the formation of anaerobic and anoxic zones (Marshall, 1992). In this manner, nutrient gradients will be established within thick biofilms and will generate cell-populations which are very heterogeneous with respect to growth rate. As a consequence, growth rates are likely to decrease with depth of location of the cells within the biofilm. At any particular time a plethora of phenotypes is represented within the commu-nity which reflects the chemical heterogeneity of the biofilm. This has long been considered to be the case for biofilm communities (Brown *et al.,* 1990; Gilbert *et al.,* 1990). Such a notion has recently been visualised (Wentland *et al.,* 1996; Xu *et al.,* 1998) using epifluorescence microscopy and confocal microscopy to show that the regions of fastest growth occurred in the outer 30 microns of the biofilm, closest to the bulk liquid. Dispersed regions of slow growth, tending towards the substratum have also been observed. A major contributor towards the observed resistance of biofilms is therefore associated with physiological gradients of growth rate and nutritional status.

A distinction can be made between those effects related to the nature of the least available nutrient (nutrient limitation/depletion) at various points within a biofilm and the cellular growth rate imposed by that limitation. Within the depths of a biofilm growth rates will generally be suppressed relative to cells growing planktonically in the same medium. In this respect Ashby *et al.* (1994) used biofilm:planktonic ratios of isoeffective concentration (growth inhibition and bactericidal activity), determined for a wide range of antibiotics against cells grown either in broth or on urinary catheter discs, to indicate the extent of biofilm resistance. They noted that such ratios followed closely those generated between non-growing and actively growing cultures. With the exception of ciprofloxacin, antibiotic agents that were most effective against non-growing cultures (i.e. imipenem, meropenem) were also the most active against these biofilms. Other workers have used perfused biofilm fermenters (Gilbert *et al.,* 1989) to directly control and study the effects of growth rate within biofilms. Using control populations of planktonic cells grown in a chemostat, the separate contributions of growth rate, and association within a biofilm, can be evaluated. Decreased susceptibility of *S. epidermidis* to tobramycin (Duguid *et al.,* 1992) and of *Escherichia coli* to tobramycin (Evans *et al.,* 1990a) and cetrimide (Evans *et al.,* 1990b) could be explained largely in terms of growth rate. Cells resuspended from growth rate controlled biofilms and planktonic cells of the same growth rate possessed virtually identical susceptibilities to these agents. When intact biofilms were treated, however, susceptibility was decreased somewhat from that of planktonic and resuspended biofilm cells. This indicated some benefit to the cells of organisation within an exopolymeric matrix.

Stewart (1994) developed a mathematical model, which incorporated the concepts of metabolism-driven oxygen-gradients and growth-rate dependent killing, to examine the susceptibility of *S. epidermidis* biofilms to various antibiotics. The model accurately predicted that susceptibility would be reduced in thicker biofilms due to oxygen limitation. Oxygen gradients within the biofilm may also directly influence the activity of some antibacterials (Shepherd *et al.,* 1988; Zabinski *et al.,* 1995). Since nutrient and gaseous gradients will increase in extent as biofilms thicken and mature, then growth-rate effects on susceptibility, such as these, will become particularly marked in aged biofilms (Anwar *et al.,* 1989; Anwar and Costerton, 1990). Such changes probably contribute to reports that aged biofilms are more recalcitrant to antibiotic and biocide treatment than are younger ones (Anwar *et al.,* 1989).

Unfortunately, as for the other proposed mechanisms of biofilm resistance, the physiological heterogeneity of biofilms cannot be the sole explanation of their recalcitrance. Gradients of growth rate are established because the metabolism of the peripheral cells consumes nutrient before it can be utilised by the more deeply placed cells. Such peripheral cells will have a growth rate and nutrient status that is not very dissimilar from that of the sensitive planktonic cells. They will therefore be relatively sensitive to the treatments imposed and will quickly succumb. This will immediately increase the availability of nutrients to the underlying survivors that having been growth-rate limited in their physiology will increase both metabolism and growth rate. As a consequence they too will adopt a more susceptible phenotype and die. Indeed the growth rate of cells within this layer might even exceed that of untreated peripheral cells through the mobilisation of nutrients from the dead-biomass. This process would be continuous and lead eventually to the complete eradication of the biofilm proceeding, as visualised for monochloramine (Huang *et al.,* 1995), from the outside, inwards. Should the supply of antimicrobial agent cease then the biofilm could re-establish almost as fast as it was destroyed because of the relative abundance of nutrients. Growth-rate cannot therefore account solely for the observed levels of resistance in biofilm communities. Rather, once again, the effect will be to delay the lethal effects of treatment with respect to the underlying cells. No explanation of the long-term tolerance of biofilms towards antimicrobial agents is provided. For this to occur, the biofilm population must adapt to a resistant phenotype during the 'time-window' of opportunity provided by this buffering effect.

Antibiotic resistance phenotypes

Of the potential mechanisms of resistance described above none, alone or in combination, can account for the extreme tolerance towards antibiotics and biocides observed both in the field and in medicine. Each can provide a mechanisms by which the action of antimicrobial substances is delayed for a proportion of the community but cannot, unless turnover of the matrix polymers and cells is very rapid, account for long term recalcitrance. This must relate to the adoption of more resistant phenotypes during the delayed action of the treatment agent or to a shift in the balance of phenotypes represented. One obvious consequence of delayed action, with respect to the least susceptible phenotypes within a biofilm, is that these will be exposed, for an extended period, to sub-inhibitory levels of treatment agent that will gradually escalate. Such exposure might in itself cause the induction of a more tolerant phenotype. It is interesting to note, in this light, that the expression of multi-drug resistance operons, such as *mar,* and efflux pumps (i.e. *acrAB*) are upregulated during exposure to sub-effective concentrations of antibiotics such as tetracycline and chloramphenicol, and xenobiotics such as salicylate (George and Levy, 1983; Levy, 1992; Ma *et al.,* 1993). Under such circumstances it is possible to select, with a relative high frequency of recovery, for cells constitutive for the expression of such genes. *mar* is chromosomal, variously induced and represented within a wide range of Gram-negative bacteria. Induction of operons such as *mar*, during the delayed onset of the action of inducer-antibiotics directed at biofilms, is a tempting explanation of the biofilms long-term resistance. The importance of *mar* would be far greater, however, if it were induced by growth as a biofilm *per se*. Ciprofloxacin exposure will not induce the expression of *mar* or *acrAB* in *E. coli* but such expression will confer limited protection against this agent. *E. coli* biofilms, in which expression of the *mar* locus was either constitutive or absent, were perfused for 48h with various concentrations of ciprofloxacin. These experiments, demonstrated reduced susceptibility in the *mar* constitutive strain but showed little or no difference between wild-type and *mar*-deleted strains (Maira *et al.,* 1998). Similar experiments using biofilms constructed from strains in which the efflux pump *acrAB* was either deleted or constitutively expressed (Maira-Litran, 1998) showed the *acrAB* deletion to not significantly affect susceptibility over that of the wild-type strain. Clearly neither *mar* nor *acrAB* is induced by sub-lethal treatment of biofilms with anything other than inducer substances. On the other hand, constitutive expression of *acrAB* protected the biofilm against low concentrations of ciprofloxacin, and studies conducted in continuous culture with a *lacZ* reporter gene fused to *marO* showed *mar* expression to be inversely related to specific growth rate (Maira *et al.,* 1998). Hence, following exposure of biofilms to sub-lethal levels of ß-lactams, tetracyclines and salicylates *mar* expression will be greatest within the depths of the biofilm, where growth rates are suppressed, and might account of the long-term survival of the community. Other multidrug efflux pumps, under the regulation of different inducer agents might extend this explanation of biofilm tolerance to include other treatment agents.

Attachment specific phenotypes

A final explanation of biofilm resistance is that all of the organisms within a biofilm possess a biofilm-specific phenotype towards which the majority of marketed-antimicrobial substances are ineffective. Such an explanation requires that as a consequence of attachment to a surface the organisms are able to activate genes/operons that confer an attachment-specific phenotype. Variations of the 'bottle-effect', whereby the metabolic activity of microorganisms is stimulated by their attachment to surfaces, have been reported in the literature since the early 1940's (Fletcher, 1984; 1986; Zobell, 1943). Only recently, however, have attempts been made to define the genetic and physiological bases of such phenomena. Dagostino *et al.* (1991) utilised transposon mutagenesis to insert, randomly, into the chromosome of *E. coli* a marker gene that lacked its own promoter element. They then went on to isolate mutant cell lines which expressed the gene when attached to a polystyrene surface but not when grown on agar or in liquid media. The isolation of genes that respond to attachment onto a surface, has not diminished the level of debate as to the cause of surface-induced metabolic stimulation. The actions of such genes may reflect derepression or induction of specific operons/genes following contact, or they may simply reflect the physical (*ie* localised concentration of nutrients, viscosity changes, pH effects *etc.*) proximity of a surface (van Loosdrecht *et al.*, 1990).

Evidence in favour of proximity sensing includes work on the regulation of lateral flagella gene transcription in *Vibrio parahaemolyticus*. This organism produces a single polar flagellum in liquid media, and numerous lateral, un-sheathed flagella on solid culture media (Belas *et al.*, 1984; 1986; McCarter *et al.*, 1988). Changes in flagellation, in this instance, have been shown to reflect an increased viscosity at the surface which restricts the movement of the polar flagellum and regulates the *laf* genes. Similarly, Lee and Falkow (1990) recognised that reduced oxygen tension, as experienced by cells enveloped within a biofilm or in association with a surface, triggers the expression of invasins in *Salmonella* spp. Other examples of surface-induced behaviour, such as an enhanced degradation of nitrilotriacetate by attached organisms in the absence of substrate adsorption to the surface (McFeters *et al.*, 1990), and the synthesis of extracellular polymers by gliding bacteria being dependent upon the cells becoming irreversible bound to a surface (Abbanat *et al.*, 1988; Humphrey *et al.*, 1979), might equally well reflect the physical chemical characteristics of an interface.

It now seems probable that bacteria can sense the close proximity of surfaces, and, through cell density transcriptional activation (Cooper *et al.*, 1995) the close proximity of other cells. Thus, Davies and Geesey (1995) used a *lacZ*

136

reporter gene fused to *algC* of *P. aeruginosa* to demonstrate that alginate production was upregulated within minutes of the organisms attachment to a surface. The expression of *algC* generally ceases when large amounts of alginate are accumulated (Davies *et al.*, 1993); accumulation at an interface contravenes such positive feedback. The ability of biofilm bacteria to modulate exopolymer production as a consequence of changes in population density, through HSL mediated quorum sensing, is a phenomenon that is only just beginning to be understood (Davies *et al.*, 1998; Allison *et al.*, 1998). Since such density sensing systems are global regulators of physiology, then not only might polymer synthesis be affected, but also numerous (according to some estimates > 60) separate gene products may be differentially affected (Costerton, this volume), leading to a biofilm specific phenotype.

Das *et al.* (1998) used a novel spectrophotometric method to monitor simultaneously the growth rate of planktonic and biofilm bacteria. Susceptibility towards a wide range of different biocides changed rapidly after attachment and biofilm formation was initiated. In some instances 3 to 5 -fold decreases in susceptibility occurred within minutes and even occurred in the presence of biocide concentrations that exceeded the minimum inhibitory concentration for planktonic populations. Such changes occurred before there had been any significant growth of the microorganisms on the surface and before any extra-cellular polymers had accumulated, pointing to a rapid switch towards a less susceptible phenotype. Such results were largely confirmed in a similar study involving *P. aeruginosa*, *Serratia marcescens* and *Proteus mirablis* (Fujiwara *et al.*, 1998). The decrease in susceptibility that was observed after bacterial attachment, but before biofilm formation, were generally far less marked than those observed in mature biofilms. This indicates that adoption of attachment-specific phenotypes is unlikely to explain the high levels of resistance seen in biofilms.

Conclusions

Whilst the unique physiological properties of microbial biofilms are now becoming recognised as essential to many aspects of life and commerce, there is inevitably a down-side. This relates not only to oral disease and dental caries, but also to infection, public health and industry i.e. infections associated with indwelling medical devices, cross-contamination in food manufacturing, domestic and domiciliary hygiene, biofouling of pipes, biodeterioration of materials etc. In this respect a major aspect of biofilm research has centred upon their prevention and control in a wide variety of situations. Central to the theme of biofilm control has been the use of antimicrobial agents, preservatives and antibiotics. Inimical agents such as these have often been developed and optimised for their activity against fast growing, dispersed, planktonic-populations of individual species of the problematic organisms. When deployed against microbial communities growing as biofilms then their failure to eradi-cate has been spectacular. To date there have been only a few developments that look to remedy the situation. Recalcitrance of biofilm communities to antimicrobials has been attributed to a variety of mechanisms. Firstly the dense organisation of the biofilm population within an exopolymeric matrix, the glycocalyx, sets up a reaction diffusion limitation of the access of agent from its point of application to the deeper lying cells i.e. on substratum or at the core of a floccule. These deeper lying cells will out survive those on the surface and, if the bulk of the treatment agent is depleted or the exposure transient, will multiply and divide. Nutrients, as well as biocides and antibiotics, will suffer from reaction diffusion limitation of their availability to individual cells within biofilms. This will lead to the establishment of spatial gradients of growth-rate and redox-potential within the community structure. Different growth-limiting nutrients will also prevail at different points in the biofilm. This will provide for a plethora of phenotypes within the biofilm, each reflecting the physico-chemical micro-environment of individual cells and their proximity to neighbours. Faster-growing, more susceptible cells will generally lie on the periphery of the biofilm with slow growing recalcitrant ones being more deeply placed. As for reaction-diffusion limitation, these slow growing cells will out survive those on the surface and, if the bulk of the treatment agent is depleted or the exposure transient, will multiply and divide. In both instances, at the fringes of action, selection pressures will enrich the populations with the least susceptible genotype. This is strictly analogous to 'resistance training' experiments where bacterial cells are passaged up a series of plates each containing antibiotic at sub-effective levels (Brown *et al.*, 1969; Gilleland *et al.*, 1989). It is possible under such circumstances for repeated chronic exposure to sub-lethal treatments to select for a resistant population that shows cross-resistance to other forms of antimicrobial. Whilst neither of these mechanisms can provide a complete explanation of recalcitrance, together they will delay eradication of the treated population and allow other selection, regulation events to occur. A third explanation of the resistance of biofilm communities lies with their expression of a biofilm-specific phenotype that is so different to that of planktonic cells that agents developed against the latter fail to operate. Whilst such phenotypes are known to be expressed and might be regulated through quorum sensing mechanisms associated with homoserinelactone and cyclic peptides they do not appear to contribute greatly to the susceptibility pattern of individual biofilm-cells. Similarly multi-drug export pumps such as *acrAB* and *Mar* do not appear to be directly implicated in biofilm resistance. Such processes do however offer the possibility of novel agents that might prevent the formation of dense, polymer enclosed communities and thereby circumvent the problem of killing intact, mature biofilms.

References

Abbanat D.R., Godchaux, W. and Leadbetter, E.R. 1988. Surface-induced synthesis of new sulphonolipids in the gliding bacterium *Cytophaga johnsonae. Arch. Microbiol.,* **149**, 358-364.

Allison, D.G. 1998. Exopolysaccharide production in bacterial biofilms. *Biofilm,* **3**, BF98002.

Allison, D.G. and Gilbert, P. 1995. Modification by surface association of antimicrobial susceptibility of bacterial populations. *J. Ind. Microbiol.,* **15**, 311-317.

Allison, D.G. and Matthews, M.J. 1992. Effect of polysaccharide interactions on antibiotic susceptibility of *Pseudomonas aeruginosa. J. Appl. Bacteriol.*, **73**, 484-488.

Allison, D.G. and Sutherland, I.W. 1987. The role of exopolysaccharides in adhesion of freshwater bacteria. *J. Gen. Microbiol.*, **133**, 1319-1327.

Allison, D.G., Ruiz, B., SanJose, C., Jaspe, A. and Gilbert, P. 1998. Extracellular products as mediators of the formation and detachment of *Pseudomonas fluorescens* biofilms. *FEMS Microbiol. Lett.*, **167**, 179-184.

Anwar, H., and Costerton, J.W. 1990. Enhanced activity of combination of tobramycin and piperacillin for eradication of sessile biofilm cells of *Pseudomonas aeruginosa. Antimicrob. Ag. Chemother.*, **34**,1666-7161.

Anwar, H., Dasgupta, M., Lam, K. and Costerton, J.W. 1989. Tobramycin resistance of mucoid *Pseudomonas aeruginosa* biofilm, grown under iron-limitation. *J. Antimicrob. Chemother.*, **24**, 647-565.

Ashby, M.J., Neale, J.E., Knott, S.J. and Critchley, I.A. 1994. Effect of antibiotics on non-growing cells and biofilms of *Escherichia coli, J. Antimicrob. Chemother.*, **33**, 443-452.

Belas, R., Mileham, A., Simon, M. and Silverman, M. 1984. Transponson mutagenesis of marine *vibrio* spp. *J. Bacteriol.*, **158**, 890-896.

Belas, R., Simon, M. and Silverman, M. 1986. Regulation of lateral flagellar gene transcription in *Vibrio parahaemolyticus. J. Bacteriol.* **167**, 210-218.

Brown, M.R.W. and Williams, P. 1985. The influence of environment on envelope properties affecting survival of bacteria in infections. *Ann. Rev. Microbiol.* **39**, 527-556.

Brown, M.R.W., Watkins, W.M. and Foster, J.H. 1969. Step-wise resistance to polymyxin and other agents by *Pseudomonas aeruginsa. J. Gen. Microbiol.* **55**, 17-18.

Brown, M.R.W., Collier, P.J. and Gilbert, P. 1990. Influence of growth rate on the susceptibility to antimicrobial agents: Modification of the cell envelope and batch and continuous culture. *Antimicrob. Ag. Chemother.*, **34**, 1623-1628.

Characklis, W.G. 1990. Microbial fouling. In *Biofilms*, edited by W.G. Characklis, and K.C. Marshall, pp. 523-584. New York: Wiley.

Cooksey, K.E. 1992. Extracellular polymers in biofilms. In *Biofilms:Science and Technology*, edited by L. F. Melo, T. R. Bott, M. Fletcher and B. Capdeville, pp. 137-47. Dordrecht: Kuluwer Academic Press.

Cooper, M., Batchelor, S.M.and Prosser, J.I. 1995. Is cell density signalling applicable to biofilms? In *The Life and Death of Biofilm*, edited by J. Wimpenny, P. Handley, P. Gilbert and H. Lappin-Scott, pp.93-97.Cardiff: Bioline Press.

Costerton, J.W. and Lashen, E.S. 1984. Influence of biofilm on the efficacy of biocides on corrosion-causing bacteria. *Mat. Perform.*, **23**, 34-37.

Costerton, J.W., Cheng, K.J., Geesey, G.G., Ladd, T.I., Nickel, J.C., Dasgupta, M. 1987. Bacterial biofilms in nature and disease. *Ann. Rev. Microbiol.* **41**, 435-464.

Costerton, J.W., Khoury, A.E., Ward, K.H. and Anwar, H. 1993. Practical measures to control device-related bacterial infections. *Int. J. Artific. Org.*, **16**, 765-770.

Costerton, J.W., Lewandowski, Z., DeBeer, D., Caldwell, D., Kober, D. and James, G. 1994. Biofilms, the customised microniche . *J. Bacteriol.* **176**, 2137-2142 .

Dagostino, L., Googman, A.E. and Marshall, K.C. 1991. Physiological responses induced in bacteria adhering to surfaces. *Biofouling* **4**, 113-119.

Das, J.R., Bhakoo, M., Jones, M.V. and Gilbert, P. 1998. Changes in the the biocide susceptibility of *Staphylococcus epidermidis* and *Escherichia coli* cells associated with rapid attachment to plastic surfaces. *J. Appl. Microbiol.* **84**, 852-858.

Davies, D.G. and Geesey, G.G. (1995) Regulation of the alginate biosynthesis gene algC in *Pseudomonas aeruginosa* during biofilm development in continuous culture. *Applied and Environmental Microbiology*, **61**, 860-867.

Davies, D.G., Chakrabarty, A.M. and Geesey, G.G. 1993. Exopolysaccharide production in biofilms: Substratum activation of alginate gene expression by *Pseudomonas aeruginosa. Appl. Environ. Microbiol.*, **59**, 1181-1186.

Davies, D.G. Parsek, M.R., Pearson, J.P., Iglewski, B.H., Costerton, J.W. and Greenberg, E.P. 1998. The involvement of cell-to-cell signals in the development of a bacterial biofilm. *Science*, **280**, 295-298.

DeBeer, D., Srinivasan, R. and Stewart, P.S. 1994. Direct measurement of chlorine penetration into biofilms during disinfection. *Appl. Environ. Microbiol.*, **60**, 4339-4344.

Dixon, B. 1998. New and resurgent infections - new and future prospects. *Sci. Prog.*, **81**, 273-285.

Duguid, I.G., Evans, E., Brown, M.R.W. and Gilbert, P. 1992. Growth-rate-independent killing by ciprofloxacin of biofilm-derived *Staphylococcus epidermidis*: evidence for cell-cycle dependency. *J. Antimicrob. Chemother.*, **30**, 791-802.

Eginton, P.J., Holah, J,. Allison, D.G., Handley, P.S. and Gilbert, P. 1998. Changes in the strength of attachment of microorganisms to surfaces following treatment with disinfectants and cleansing agents. *Lett. Appl. Microbiol.*, **27**, 101-106.

Evans, D.J., Brown, M.R.W., Allison, D.G. and Gilbert, P. 1990a. Susceptibility of bacterial biofilms to tobramycin: role of specific growth rate and phase in the division cycle. *J. Antimicrob. Chemother.*, **25**, 585-591.

Evans, D.J., Brown, M.R.W., Allison, D.G., Gilbert, P. 1990b. Growth rate and resistance of Gram-negative biofilms towards Cetrimide USP. *J. Antimicrob. Chemother.*, **26**, 473-478.

Evans, D.J., Brown, M.R.W., Allison, D.G. and Gilbert, P. 1991. Susceptibility of *Escherichia coli* and *Pseudomonas aeruginosa* biofilms to ciprofloxacin: effect of specific growth rate. *J. Antimicrob. Chemother.*, **27**, 177-184.

Evans, E., Brown, M.R.W. and Gilbert, P. 1994. Iron cheletor, exopolysaccharide and protease production of *Staphylococcus epidermidis*: a comparative study of the effects of specific growth rate in biofilm and planktonic culture. *Microbiol.*, **140**, 153-157.

Favero, M.S., Bond, W.W., Peterson, N.J. and Cook, E.H. 1983. Scanning electron microscopic observations of bacteria resistant to iodophor solutions. In *Proc. Intern. Symp. Povidone*, pp158-166. University of Kentucky, Lexington, USA

Fletcher, M. 1984. Comparative physiology of attached and free-living bacteria.In *Microbial Adhesion and Aggregation*, edited by K.C. Marshall, pp 223-232, Berlin:Springer Verlag.

Fletcher, M. 1986. Measurement of glucose utilisation by *Pseudomonas fluorescens* that are free living and that are attached to surfaces. *Appl. Environ. Microbiol.*, **52**, 672-676.

Fujiwara, S., Miyake, Y., Usui, T. and Suginaka, H. 1998. Effect of adherence on antimicrobial susceptibility of *Pseudomonas aeruginosa*, *Serratia marcescens* and *Proteus mirablis*. *Hiroshima J. Med.*, **47**, 1-5.

Gambello, M.J., Kaye, S. and Inglewski, B.H. 1993. *LasR* of *Pseudomonas aeruginosa* is a transcriptional activator of the line protease gene (*apr*) and an enhancer of exotoxin A expression. *Infect. Immun.*, **61**, 1180-1184.

George, A.M. and Levy, S.B. 1983. Amplifiable resistance to tetracycline, chloramphenicol, and other antibiotics in *Escherichia coli*: involvement of a non-plasmid-determined efflux of tetracycline. *J. Bacteriol.*, **155**, 531-540.

Gilbert, P. and Brown, M.R.W. 1995. Screening for novel antimicrobial activity/compounds in the pharmaceutical industry. In *Microbial Quality Assurance: A Guide Towards Relevance and Reproducibility of Inocula,* edited by M.R.W. Brown and P. Gilbert, pp247-260. Boca Raton, USA: CRC Press.

Gilbert, P., Allison, D.G., Evans, D.J., Handley, P.S. & Brown, M.R.W. 1989. Growth rate control of adherent bacterial populations. *Appl. Environ. Microbiol.*, **55**, 1308-1311.

Gilbert, P., Collier, P.J. & Brown, M.R.W. 1990. Influence of growth rate on susceptibility to antimicrobial agents: biofilms, cell cycle and dormancy. *Antimicrob. Ag. Chemother.* **34**, 1865-1868.

Gilleland, L.B., Gilleland, H.E., Gibson, J.A. and Champlin, F.R. 1989. Adaptive resistance to aminoglycoside antibiotics in *Pseudomonas aeruginosa*. *J. Med. Microbiol.*, **29**, 41-50.

Giwercman, B., Jensen, E.T., Hoiby, N., Kharazmi, A. and Costerton, J.W. 1991. Induction of ß-lactamase production in *Pseudomonas aeruginosa* biofilms. *Antimicrob. Ag. Chemother.*, **35**, 1008-1010.

Gordon, C.A., Hodges, N.A., Marriot, C. 1988.. Antibiotic interaction and diffusion through alginate and exopolysaccharide of cystic fibrosis derived *Pseudomonas aeruginosa. J. Antimicrob. Chemother.*, **22**, 667-674.

Griffiths, P.A., Babb, J.R., Bradley, C.R. and Fraise, A.P. 1997. Glutaraldehyde-resistant *Mycobacterium chelonae* from endoscope washer disinfectors. *J. Appl. Microbiol.*, **82**, 519-526.

Gristina, A.G., Hobgood, C.D., Webb, L.X. and Myrvik, Q.N. 1987. Adhesive colonisation of biomaterials and antibiotic resistance. *Biomat.*, **8**, 423-426.

Heys, S.J.D., Gilbert, P. and Allison, D.G. 1997. Homoserine lactones and bacterial biofilms. In: *Biofilms:Community Interactions and Control*, edited by J. Wimpenny, P. Handley, P. Gilbert, H. Lappin-Scott and M. Jones, pp. 103-112. Cardiff: Bioline Press.

Holah, J.T., Bloomfield, S.F., Walker, A.J. and Spenceley, H. 1994. Control of biofilms in the food industry. In *Bacterial Biofilms and their Control in Medicine and Industry*, edited by J.T. Wimpenny, W.W. Nichols, D. Stickler and H. Lappin Scott, pp163-168. Cardiff: Bioline Press..

Hoyle, B.D., Wong, C.K. and Costerton, J.W. 1992. Disparate efficacy of tobramycin on Ca(2+)-, Mg(2+)-, and HEPES-treated *Pseudomonas aeruginosa* biofilms. *Can. J. Microbiol.*, **38**, 1214-1218.

Huang, C.T., Yu, F.P., McFeters, G.A. and Stewart, P.S. 1995. Non-uniform spatial patterns of respiratory activity within biofilms during disinfection. *Appl. Environ. Microbiol.*, **61**, 2252-2256.

Humphrey, B.A., Dixon, M.R. and Marshall, K.C. 1979. Physiological and in-situ observations on the adhesion of gliding bacteria to surfaces. *Arch. Microbiol.*, **120**, 231-238.

Ichimiya, T., Yamaski, T. and Nasu, M. 1994. *In-vitro* effects of antimicrobial agents on *Pseudomonas aeruginosa* biofilm formation. *J. Antimicrob. Chemother.*, **34**, 331-341.

Kleerebezem, M., Quadri, L.E.N., Kuipers, O.P. and deVos W.M. 1997. Quorum sensing by peptide pheramones and two component signal transduction in Gram-positive bacteria. *Med. Microbiol.*, **24**: 895-904.

Kumon, H., Tomochika, K-I., Matunaga, T., Ogawa, M. and Ohmori, H. 1994. A sandwich cup method for the penetration assay of antimicrobial agents through *Pseudomonas* exopolysaccharides. *Microbiol. Immun.*, **38**, 615-619.

Kunim, C.M. and Steel, C. 1985. Culture of the surfaces of urinary catheters to sample urethral flora and study the effect of antimicrobial therapy. *J. Clin. Microbiol.*, **21**, 902-908.

Lambert, P.A., Giwercman, B. and Hoiby, N. 1993. Chemotherapy of *Pseudomonas aeruginosa* in cystic fibrosis. In *Bacterial Biofilms and their Contriol in Medicine and Industry*, edited by J. Wimpenny., W. Nichols, D. Stickler, and H. Lappin-Scott, pp151-153. Cardiff: Biolone Press.

Lee, C.A. and Falkow, S. 1990. The ability of *Salmonella* to enter mammalian cells is affected by bacterial growth state. *Proc. Nat. Acad. Sci., USA*, **87**, 4304-4308.

Levy, S.B. 1992. Active efflux mechanisms for antimicrobial resisitance. *Antimicrob. Ag. Chemother.*, **36**, 695-703.

Levy, S.B. 1998. The challenge of antibiotic resistance. *Sci. Amer.*, **278**, 46-53.

Little, B.J., Wagner, P.A., Characklis, W.G. and Lee, W. 1990. Microbial corrosion. In *Biofilms*, edited by W.G. Characklis and K.C. Marshall, pp635-670. New York: Wiley.

Ma, D., Cook, D.N., Alberti, M., Pong, N.G., Nikaido, H. and Hearst, J.E. 1993. Molecular cloning and characterization of *acrAB* and *acrE* genes of *Escherichia coli*. *J. Bacteriol.*, **175**, 6299-6313.

Maira-Litran, T. 1998. An investigation into the potential of the *mar* operon to moderate the antibiotic resistance of biofilms. *PhD Thesis*, School of Pharmacy and Pharmaceutical Sciences, University of Manchester, Manchester, England.

Maira, T., Levy, S.B., Allison, D.G. and Gilbert, P. 1998. Influence of growth environment and biofilm formation on the expression of *mar* in *Escherichia coli* (abstract). 98th General Meeting of the American Society for Microbiology, May 17-21, 1998. Washington DC: ASM Press.

Marsh, P. 1995. Dental plaque. In *Microbial Biofilms*, edited by H.M. Lappin-Scott HM and J.W. Costerton, pp 282-300. Cambridge: Cambridge University Press.

Marshall, K.C. 1992. Biofilms: an overview of bacterial adhesion, activity and control at surfaces. *ASM News*, **58**, 202-207.

Marquis, R.E. 1968. Salt induced contraction of bacterial cell walls. *J. Bacteriol.*, **95,** 775-781.

McCarter. L., Hilmen, M. and Silverman, M. 1988. Flagellar dynamometer controls swarmer cell differentiation of *Vibrio parahaemolyticus*. *Cell*, **54**, 345-351.

McFeters, G.A., Egil, T., Wilberg, E., Adler, A., Schneider, R., Snozzy, M. 1990. Activity and adaptation of nitrilo(NTA)-degrading bacteria: Field and laboratory studies. *Water Res.*, **24**, 875-881.

Neu, T.R. and Marshall, K.C. 1990. Bacterial polymers: physicochemical aspects of their interactions at surfaces. *J. Biomat. Appl.*, **5**, 107-133.

Newman, H.N. and Barber, P.M. 1995. Dental plaque structure in-vivo. In *The Life and Death of*

141

Biofilm, edited by J. Wimpenny, P. Handley, P. Gilbert and H. Lappin-Scott, pp. 27-32. Cardiff: Bioline Press.

Nichols. W.W., Dorrington, S.M., Slack, M.P.E. and Walmsley, H.L. 1988. Inhibition of tobramycin diffusion by binding to alginate. *Antimicrob. Ag. Chemother.*, **32**, 518-523.

Nichols, W.W., Evans, M.J., Slack, M.P.E. and Walmsley, H.L. 1989. The penetration of antibiotics into aggregates of mucoid and non-mucoid *Pseudomonas aeruginosa*. *J. Gen. Microbiol.*, **135**, 1291-1303.

Nichols, W.W. 1993. Biofilm permeability to antibacterial agents. In *Bacterial Biofilms and their Control in Medicine and Industry*, edited by J. Wimpenny, W.W. Nichols, D. Stickler, H. Lappin-Scott, pp.141-149. Cardiff: Bioline Press.

Nickel, J.C., Ruseska, I., Wright, J.B. and Costerton, J.W. 1985. Tobramycin resistance of Pseudomonas aeruginosa cells growing as a biofilm on urinary catheter materials. *Antimicrob. Ag. Chemother.*, **27**, 619-624.

Shepherd, J.E., Waigh, R.D. and Gilbert, P. 1988. Antimicrobial action of 2-bromo-2-nitropropan-1,3-diol (Bronopol) against *Escherichia coli. Antimicrob. Ag. Chemother.*, **32**, 1693-1698.

Slack, M.P.E. and Nichols, W.W. 1981. The penetration of antibiotics through sodium alginate and through the exopolysaccharide of a mucoid strain of *Pseudomonas aeruginosa. Lancet*, **11**, 502-503.

Slack, M.P.E. and Nichols, W.W. 1982. Antibiotic penetration through bacterial capsules and exopolysaccharides. *J. Antimicrob. Chemother.*, **10**, 368-372.

Sondossi, M., Rossmore, H.W. and Wireman, J.W. 1985. Observation of resistance and cross-resistance to formaldehyde and a formaldeyde condensate biocide in *Pseudomonas aeruginosa. Intern. Biodeter.*, **21**, 105-106.

Spach, D.H., Siverstein, F.E. and Stamm, W.E. 1993. Transmission of infection by gastrointestinal endoscopy and bronchoscopy. *Annal Intern. Med.*, **118**, 117-128.

Stewart, P.S. 1994. Biofilm accumulation model that predicts antibiotic resistance of *Pseudomonas aeruginosa* biofilms. *Antimicrob. Ag. Chemother.*, **38**, 1052-1058.

Stewart, P.S. 1996. Theoretical Aspects of antibiotic diffusion into microbial biofilms. *Antimicrob. Ag. Chemother.*, **40**, 2517-2522.

Stewart, P.S., Grab, L. and Diemer, J.A. 1998. Analysis of biocide transport limitation in an artificial biofilm system. *J. Appl. Microbiol.*, **85**, 495-500.

Suci, P.A., Mittelman, M.W., Yu, F.U. and Geesey, G.G. 1994. Investigation of ciprofloxacin penetration into *Pseudomonas aeruginosa* biofilms. *Antimicrob. Ag. Chemother.*, **38**, 2125-2133.

Sutherland, I.W. 1985. Biosynthesis and composition of Gram-negative bacterial extracellular and wall polysaccharides. *Ann. Rev. Microbiol.*, **39**, 243-270.

Sutherland, I.W. 1995. Biofilm specific polysaccharides: do they exist? In *Life and Death of Biofilm*, edited by J. Wimpenny, P. Handley, P. Gilbert and H. Lappin-Scott, pp103-7. Cardiff: Bioline Press.

Sutherland, I.W. 1997. Microbial biofilm exopolysaccharides - superglues or velcro? In *Biofilms: Community Interactions and Control*, edited by J. Wimpenny, P. Handley, P. Gilbert, H. Lappin-Scott and M. Jones, pp 33-39, Cardiff: Bioline Press.

Thomson, K.S., Bakken, J.S. and Sanders, C.C. 1995. Antimicrobial Susceptibility Testing in the Clinic. In *Microbial Quality Assurance: A Guide Towards Relevance and Reproducibility*, edited by M.R.W. Brown and P. Gilbert, pp275-89. Boca Raton, USA: CRC Press.

van Loosdrecht, M.C.M., Lyklema, J., Norde, W. and Zehnder, A.J.B. 1990. Influence of interfaces on microbial activity. *Microbiol. Rev.*, **54**, 75-87.

Wentland, E.J., Stewart, P.S., Huang, C.T. and McFeters, G.A. 1996. Spatial variations in growth rate within *Klebsiella pneumoniae* colonies and biofilm. *Biotech. Prog.*, **12**, 316-321.

Willcock, L., Allison, D.G., Holah, J. and Gilbert, P. 1997. Population dynamics in steady-state biofilms: effects of growth environment upon dispersal. pp23-32, In, *'Biofilms: community interactions and control'* (Wimpenny, J., Handley, P.S., Gilbert, P., Lappin-Scott, H. and Jones, M., Editors), Bioline Press, Cardiff.

Williams, P. 1988. Role of the cell envelope in bacterial adaption to growth *in vivo* in infections. *Biochimie*, **70**, 987-1011.

Williams, P., Bainton, N.J., Swift, S., Chhabra, S.R., Winson, M.K., Stewart, G.S.A.B. *et al.* 1992.

Small molecule-mediated density dependent control of gene expression in prokaryotes: bioluminescence and the biosynthesis of carbapenem antibiotics. *FEMS Microbiol. Lett.*, **100**, 161-168.

Xu, K.D., Stewart, P., Xia, F., Huang, C.-T and McFeters, G.A. 1998. Spatial physiological heterogeneity in Pseudomonas aeruginosa biofilm is determined by oxygen availability. *Appl Environ. Microbiol.*, **64,** 4035-4039.

Zabinski, R.A., Walker, K.J., Larsson, A.J., Moody, J.A., Kaatz, G.W. and Rotschafer, J.C. 1995. Effect of aerobic and anaerobic environments on antistaphylococcal activities of five fluoroquinolones. *Antimicrob. Ag. Chemother.*, **39**, 507-512 .

Zambrano, M.M. and Kolter, R. 1995. Changes in bacterial cell properties on going from exponential growth to stationary phase. In *Microbial Quality Assurance: A Guide Towards Relevance and Reproducibility*, edited by M.R.W. Brown and P. Gilbert, pp21-30. Boca Raton, USA: CRC Press.

Zobell, C.E. 1943. The effect of solid surfaces upon bacterial activity. *J. Bacteriol.*, **46**, 39-56.

ADHESIVE SURFACE STRUCTURES ON ORAL BACTERIA

Pauline S. Handley, Roderick McNab and
Howard F. Jenkinson

*Oral bacteria usually carry one of two types of surface structure, either fibrils or fimbriae. These structures are implicated in adhesion of bacteria to host oral surfaces including the buccal mucosa and the glycoprotein pellicle of teeth, and to other bacteria. Fimbriae on oral bacteria are comprised of protein sub-units assembled into thin (3-5 nm wide), flexible, peritrichous structures ranging from 0.2 to <3.0μm long. The structure, functions and composition of the fimbriae on **Actinomyces naeslundii** and **Porphyromonas gingivalis** are distinct and will be reviewed. In contrast, less is known about the composition and function of surface structures that are found on the majority of oral streptococci. Fibrils on streptococci are comprised of either protein or glycoprotein and are relatively short structures (50-400 nm) that are present with a dense or sparse distribution on the cell surface. Fibrils are predominantly peritrichous but they can be organised into lateral or polar tufts on **Streptococcus crista** and **S. oralis**. For most oral streptococci it has proved difficult to demonstrate an unequivocal link between surface structures and adhesion and difficult to define their composition. However, recent data indicate that the sparse 60 nm fibrils expressed by **S. gordonii** DL1(Challis) are probably composed of individual molecules of the large (259kDa), cell wall-anchored, multifunctional protein adhesin CshA. The review will also assess the evidence linking fibrils on **Streptococcus salivarius** and fimbriae on **Streptococcus parasanguis**, with a functional role in adhesion.*

Introduction

Adhesion is essential for growth and survival of bacteria in the mouth and organisms can adhere to a wide range of surfaces such as the oral epithelia, the glycoprotein pellicle of teeth and to other bacteria. A great deal of information has accumulated detailing the nature of the adhesins and receptors involved in the highly specific protein (lectin)-carbohydrate and protein-protein interactions occurring between the bacteria and the surfaces to which they adhere. The mouth contains as many as thirty seven genera (Moore *et al.,* 1985), however specific adhesion mechanisms have been studied in a relatively small number of these organisms. Most emphasis has been put on understanding attachment mechanisms of the oral streptococci (Jenkinson & Lamont 1997), *Actinomyces naeslundii* (to include the former *Actinomyces viscosus*) (Li *et al.,* 1999) and periodontal pathogens such as *Porphyromonas gingivalis* (Lamont & Jenkinson, 1998). All of these organisms carry multiple adhesins and many of the adhesins have multiple binding functions. Molecular and genetic techniques have enabled enormous advances to be made in the understanding of the composition, structure and function of cell surface located adhesins on these organisms.

There are very clear correlations between adhesive abilities and fimbriae for *A.naeslundii* and *P. gingivalis,* however the association between surface structures and adhesive properties for the many different species of streptococci is more equivocal. Thus, while most oral streptococci carry fibrils, structures that are morphologically distinct from fimbriae (Handley, 1990) the involvement of fibrils in adhesion has so far only been made for *Streptococcus salivarius* (Weerkamp *et al.,* 1986a) and *Streptococcus gordonii* (McNab *et al.,* 1999). This chapter will review the structure and functions of fimbriae and fibrils on oral bacteria, using the examples of the surface structures on *A. naeslundii, P. gingivalis* and the oral streptococci to illustrate the properties of these adhesive appendages.

Terminology for surface structures on non-oral and oral bacteria
Fimbriae On Non-oral Bacteria
Fimbriae (sometimes known as pili) on non-oral Gram-negative bacteria, particularly on *Escherichia coli* and *Salmonella typhimurium* have been studied extensively (Low *et al.,* 1996). Fimbriae are proteinaceous, hairlike appendages from 2 to 8 nm in diameter (Duguid *et al.,* 1955), and are composed primarily of helically arranged, identical, protein subunits called fimbrillins (fimbrins) or pilins that range in mass from 14 to 30 kDa. Some fimbriae are known to carry adhesins as minor protein components either along their sides or at their tips. At least thirty four different types of fimbriae have been identified on different strains of *E. coli.* Classification of these fimbriae has been attempted using phenotypic traits, adhesive properties and on the basis of primary amino acid sequence data for the major fimbrial subunit proteins (Low *et al.,* 1996). Fimbriae on Gram-negative bacteria have also been grouped according to the type of molecular mechanism used for their assembly. On this basis, four major fimbrial assembly mechanisms have been described: (i) the chaperone usher pathway, (ii) the general secretion pathway, (iii) the extracellular nucleation/ precipitation pathway, (iv) the alternate chaperone pathway (Soto & Hultgren, 1999).

The majority of fimbriae so far described utilise chaperones and outer membrane usher proteins for subunit assembly. A number of morphologically distinct *E. coli* fimbriae are assembled by this mechanism, including the thicker, rigid, type 1 fimbriae, the thin, flexible K99 'fibrillae' and some non-fimbrial adhesins. The type 4 fimbriae found in polar tufts on enterotoxigenic *E. coli* (ETEC), enteropathogenic *E. coli* (EPEC), *Pseudomonas aeruginosa, Vibrio cholerae* and other Gram-negatives that cause twitching motility utilise a general protein secretion pathway for fimbrial assembly (Pugsley, 1993; Tennent & Mattick, 1994). The curli structures on *E. coli* and *Salmonella enteritidis* that bind fibronectin use a third, completely different fimbrial assembly process termed the extracellular nucleation/precipitation pathway (Hammar *et al.,* 1996).

146

Finally the CS1 fimbriae and related structures on *E. coli* are assembled via an alternate chaperone pathway (Soto & Hultgren, 1999)

Fimbrial genes are organised into operons with genes encoding either major or minor fimbrial subunit proteins. The fimbrial gene clusters also include genes for chaperone and assembly proteins and for regulation of fimbrial gene expression. Understanding of fimbrial biogenesis and structure in *E. coli* is now extremely detailed (for reviews see Paranchych & Frost, 1988; de Graff & Mooi, 1986; Low *et al.,* 1996; Hultgren *et al.,* 1996).

Fimbriae on Oral Bacteria

Structures fitting the morphological description of fimbriae have been detected on *A. naeslundii, P. gingivalis* and some species of oral streptococci. All the fimbriae so far detected on oral bacteria are very thin, flexible structures, 3 to 5 nm wide and between 0.2 and 3 μm long. They are peritrichously arranged on the cell surface and have a measurable diameter all along their length. The fimbriae on oral bacteria are similar to the very thin, flexible 2 to 3 nm diameter K88, K99, F41 and CS3 fimbriae found on some strains of *E. coli* (Paranchych & Frost 1988). Oral bacterial fimbriae are different from the thicker, rigid 7.0 nm diameter structures, with a central axial hole, typified by the type 1 fimbriae of *E. coli*. Fimbriae are found on *A. naeslundii* (including *Actinomyces viscosus)* (Handley *et al.,* 1985), *P. gingivalis* (formerly *Bacteroides gingivalis*), (Yoshimura *et al.,* 1984), *Streptococcus salivarius* (Handley *et al.,* 1984), *Streptococcus parasanguis* (formerly *Streptococcus sanguis*) (Elder *et al.,* 1982) and rarely on other strains in the mitis group streptococci (including former *S. sanguis* biotype I & II strains) (Handley *et al.,* 1985). Studies of fimbriae on oral bacteria are less well advanced than for fimbriae on enteric bacteria. However information on the structure, function, and genes involved in biogenesis of *P. gingivalis,* and *A. naeslundii* fimbriae in particular is accumulating, and is summarised in this review.

Fibrils on Oral Bacteria

The term fibril has been used to describe a second type of surface structure that is morphologically distinct from fimbriae and that has been detected on a wide range of oral bacteria (Handley, 1990). Some strains of *S. salivarius* (Handley *et al.,* 1984) and of various species in the mitis group streptococci (Handley *et al.,* 1985) were found to express surface structures that did not fit the description of fimbriae previously described on Gram-negative organisms. Fibrils are shorter than fimbriae and extend only 50 to 200nm from the cell wall, although they may be up to 400nm long on some strains. Fibrils are often peritrichously distributed over the cell surface and it is difficult to reliably measure their width as on the cell surface they can be densely packed or clumped together, appearing as tapered, thicker structures. Sometimes what appear to be individual fibrils are found on the cell surface but width measurements of these have not been made. Fibrils may be densely or sparsely distributed on cells in a strain, or species, dependent manner or alternatively they may be localised in lateral or polar tufts,

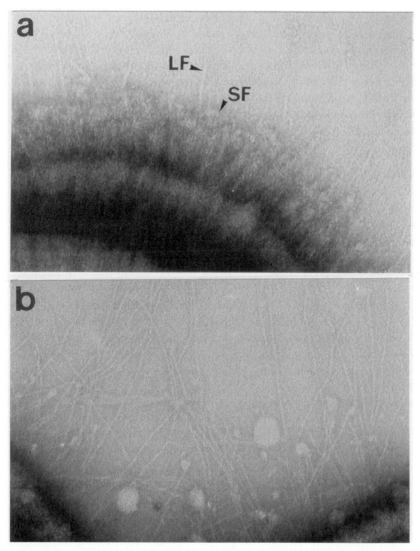

Figure 1 Cells were stained with 1% methylamine tungstate
Figure 1a. *S. salivarius* HB (Lancefield K⁺ strain) carries a dense fringe of peritrichous fibrils. Sparse long fibrils (LF) (168+/-5.0nm) project through a dense mass of shorter fibrils (SF) (90 +/-4.0nm) x129,000.
Figure 1b. *S. salivarius* CHR (Lancefield K⁻ strain) carries peritrichous fimbriae, 3-4.0nm wide and 0.5 –1.0 μm long. x294,000. Reproduced with permission from Handley *et al.* (1984).

that are comprised of fibrils of one or two lengths. In particular *Streptococcus crista* (Handley *et al.*, 1991), and a *Streptococcus oralis* strain in the mitis group (Jameson *et al.*, 1995) have a prominent crest, or tuft of fibrils located on one side of the cell only. Surface structures fitting the morphological description of fibrils have also been detected on *Prevotella intermedia* and *Prevotella nigrescens* (formerly *Bacteroides intermedia* and *Bacteroides nigrescens*) (Devine *et al.,*1989) and *Streptococcus mutans* (Hogg *et al.,* 1981).

The evidence for distinguishing between fibrils and fimbriae as two distinct adhesive structures will be assessed in light of the recent molecular approaches that have been used to understand the composition and functions of adhesins on oral bacteria. The purpose of this chapter is therefore to present our current understanding of surface structures on oral bacteria. This will be achieved by reviewing the structure and functions of fibrils on *S. salivarius,* and the mitis group streptococci, and of fimbriae on *A. viscosus, P. gingivalis and S. parasanguis.*

Streptococcus salivarius fibrils
Correlation Between Surface Structure Type and Adhesion
A very clear morphological distinction between fibrils and fimbriae has been made on *S. salivarius* strains isolated from the tongue dorsum. Two structural subgroups of strains have been described that carry either fibrils or fimbriae (Handley *et al.,* 1984). Dense, short, peritrichous fibrils (Figure 1a) have been described on 50% of strains (Lancefield K$^+$ strains) while the other 50% of strains (Lancefield K$^-$ strains) carry longer, flexible, peritrichous fimbriae (Figure 1b), that are morphologically similar to the fimbriae found on *Enterococcus faecalis* (Handley & Jacob 1981). Fibrillar K$^+$ strains generally exhibit a wider range of adhesion properties than the K$^-$ fimbriate strains (Weerkamp & McBride, 1980; Handley *et al.,* 1987). The K$^+$ fibrillar *S. salivarius* strains carry three categories of adhesins. The first category mediates host related adhesion and aggregation reactions, including saliva-induced aggregation, haemagglutination, and adherence to buccal epithelial cells (BEC). The second category mediates coaggregation with *Veillonella parvula* V1, and the third mediates coaggregation with *Fusobacterium nucleatum* LF. In contrast the K$^-$ fimbriate *S. salivarius* strains have a reduced affinity for red blood cells and do not cause haemagglutination, and are not aggregated by saliva, although they do coaggregate with *V. parvula* V1 and *F. nucleatum* LF (Weerkamp & McBride, 1980; Handley *et al.,* 1987). Fibrils from the surface of *S. salivarius* have been purified, and shown to possess the adhesive functions to host surfaces and other bacteria.

Morphology, Composition and Functions of **S. salivarius** *Fibrils*
Electron microscopy has shown that the surfaces of the fibrillar strains are morphologically complex. Strains generally express two lengths of fibrils; short, very densely packed fibrils ranging in from 76 to 111nm long, and longer, more sparsely distributed fibrils, 159 to 209nm long, projecting out through the shorter structures (Figure 1a). Fibril length for each strain is highly reproducible. The lengths of fibrils on different batches of the same strain show only small variations indicating that these structures have a finite length. The shorter fibrils have been shown to be comprised of a number of functionally distinct

149

fibril sub-classes (Weerkamp *et al.,* 1986a,b). Two cell surface protein antigens exhibiting adhesive functions were purified and characterised from *S. salivarius* HB, a typical Lancefield K$^+$ fibrillar strain (Weerkamp & Jacobs 1982). Antigen B (AgB) is the *Veillonella* binding protein (VBP), while Antigen C (AgC) is responsible for adhesion to buccal epithelial cells (BEC), haemagglutination and salivary agglutination and is called the host associated adhesion factor (HAF).

The purified antigens are both glycoproteins and have fibrillar morphologies. Low angle rotary shadowing of both AgB and AgC shows that they form rod-like structures, approximately 2 nm wide with swollen globular portions at both ends (Weerkamp *et al.,* 1986b). The fibrillar central portions are protease sensitive indicating a difference in composition along the length of the fibrils. Ag B (320 kDa) is 184 nm long and AgC (220-280 kDa) is 87 nm long. (Weerkamp & Jacobs 1982) and while both molecules consist of protein and carbohydrate AgC is only 57% protein by weight compared with AgB (80% protein). Weerkamp *et al.,* (1986a) proposed a model in which AgB is repre-sented by a 91 nm long fibril sub-class and AgC is represented by a 72 nm fibril sub-class, both being expressed simultaneously on the cell surface. The 72 nm fibrils on the cell surface could sometimes be seen with globular ends, similar to those on the ends of the purified fibrils.

While purified fibrillar AgC glycoprotein molecules are only slightly longer (87.0+/-3.5 nm) than the corresponding surface fibrils (72.0+/-3.0 nm), purified AgB is twice as long (184.0+/-9.0 nm) as surface bound AgB (91+/-5 nm). Possibly AgB forms dimers *in vitro,* or alternatively may adopt a hairpin like conformation *in situ.* The location of adhesin activity on the fibrils is not known. It seems most likely that the globular ends of the fibrils carry the adhesins because the fibrils are tightly packed and only the ends of the fibrils are exposed on the cell surface (Weerkamp *et al.,* 1986a). Also, it is not known how the shorter AgC (72 nm) functions in the presence of the longer AgB fibrils (91 nm) since they are proposed to be co-expressed on the same cells. The *S. salivarius* cell surface therefore carries multiple classes of fibril, each of a specific length, and at least one of which carries multiple adhesins.

Although *S. salivarius* represents an excellent model for studying the co-expression of multiple classes of adhesins there is an almost complete lack of information on the biogenesis of *S. salivarius* fibrils and no molecular genetic studies have been done to investigate the genes involved in biosynthesis and assembly. However, it is known that intact AgC fibrils can be accumulated in the cytoplasm as they have been purified from the cytoplasm of mutants lacking the cell wall associated form of AgC. The two forms have different lengths and different molecular weights although no explanation for this discrepancy has been proposed.

No information is available concerning the biochemical composition of the *S. salivarius* fimbriae and no adhesive function has yet been assigned to them. Fimbriate strains (K$^-$) are consistently less adhesive than the fibrillar strains in host associated adhesion assays, although they are able to coaggregate with *V. parvula* V1 (Weerkamp & McBride 1980; Handley *et al.,* 1987). The location

Table 1 Surface structures on strains of *S. sanguis*, *S. gordonii* and *S. crista* previously designated as *S. sanguis* biotype II strains.

Current species designation	Strain number and characteristics of surface structures		Length of fibrils[a] (nm +/-SEM)	
	Strain	**Fibril density[b]**	**Long**	**Short**
S. sanguis	GW2	6+	150±39.8	75.3±22.3
S gordonii	PAR	3+	179±59.4	86.7±9.8
S. gordonii	JF2	3+	190±6.5	78.8±10.9
S. gordonii	GEO2	2+	Absent	78.3±20.7
S. gordonii	LMH	2+	Absent	71.0±11.5
S. gordonii	MJ2	1+	Absent	66.0±8.4
S. gordonii	CH2	1+	Absent	66.0±8.4
S. gordonii	DL1	1+	Absent	60.7+/-14.5
S.. gordonii	CR2b	1+	Absent	57.8±7.2
S. crista	311	Asymmetrical	420+39.3	242±13.9
S. crista	AK1	lateral tufts	318±24.1	227±19.8
S. crista	CR3	of fibrils	386±40.1	Absent

Data modified from Handley *et al.* (1985)
a - fibril length +/- standard error of the mean length of fibrils
b - score of fibril density as assessed by negative staining

and composition of the *Veillonella*-binding adhesins in these fimbriate strains of *S. salivarius* is not known and there is no evidence to suggest that they carry the AgB (VBP) antigen.

Fibrils On The **Mitis** Group Streptococci

Fibrils are a common feature on the cell surfaces of the mitis group streptococci. In the current classification of the oral streptococci this group includes *S. mitis*, *S. oralis*, *S. sanguis*, *S. gordonii*, *S. parasanguis*, *S. crista* and *S. pneumoniae* (see Whiley & Beighton, 1998). These authors point out that according to the International Code of Nomenclature of Bacteria the specific epithets *sanguis, parasanguis and crista* are grammatically inaccurate and have to be changed to *sanguinis, parasanguinis* and *cristatus* respectively. However, the epithets in long term usage have been retained for this article. The species currently recognised in this group have a confused taxonomic history and since fibrils were first described on oral streptococci in the mid 1980s, species definitions have changed and new species have been described. Handley *et al.* (1985) described surface structures on strains from dental plaque, identified as *S. sanguis* biotype I and *S. sanguis* biotype II using the biochemical classification scheme proposed by Facklam (1977). The electron microscope survey found surface structures on all strains, but the morphology and cell surface distribution of the structures varied depending on the strain. The majority of the strains (38 out of 44) carried peritrichous fibrils. Fibril density was characteristic for each strain and ranged from very sparse (Figure 2a) to very dense and sometimes globular ends on the fibrils were detected. Many strains carried fibrils of one length only (Tables 1 & 2) whereas some strains expressed both

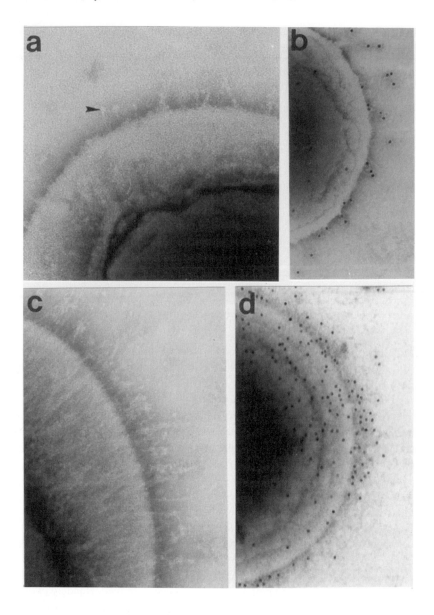

Figure 2 Cells were stained with 1% methylamine tungstate only (a & c) or with 1% methylamine tungstate together with CshA specific antibodies and 10 nm gold conjugated secondary antibody (b & d).
Figure 2a. *S. gordonii* DL1 Challis with sparse, 60.7+/-14.5 nm long, peritrichous fibrils projecting away from the cell surface. Fibrils may have globular ends (see arrow) x45,000.
Figure 2b. *S.gordonii* DL1 Challis showing the gold particles and antiserum labelling the CshA molecules. Gold particles extended 61.0+/-19.2nm away from the cell surface, some unlabelled fibrils are visible x147,000. Figure 2c. *E. faecalis* OB516 cell with dense, peritrichous fibrils 70.3+/-9.1 nm long. Figure 2d. *E. faecalis* OB516 (pAMCshA) cell showing gold particles extending 61.7+/-12.2 nm from the cell surface. Fibrils are masked by the gold and antiserum x121,500. Reproduced with permission from McNab *et al.* (1999)

Table 2 Surface structures on strains of *S. oralis and S. mitis,* previously designated as *S. sanguis* biotype I strains

Current species designation	Strain number and characteristics of surface structures		Length of fibrils[a] (nm +/-SEM)	
	Strain	**Fibril density[b]**	**Long**	**Short**
S. oralis	KN	1+	Absent	53.2±7.7
S. oralis	EY3	1+	Absent	47.8±4.4
S. oralis [e]	CN3410	Asymmetrical	289+/-15	159+/-5
S. mitis	PSH1a	lateral tufts	156.6±71.6	Absent
S. mitis	PSH1b	of fibrils	461±42.2	111.2±14.1
S. mitis	PSH2	Polar tufts of fibrils	374±65.5	Absent
S. oralis	834	Peritrichous fibrils & fimbriae	4.7±0.3wide ≤0.7 μm long[c]	76.5±11.9[d]

Data modified from Handley *et al.* (1985);
a - length ± standard error of the mean length of fibrils
b - score of fibril density as assessed by negative staining
c - dimensions of fimbriae
d - fibril length
e – data from Jameson *et al.* (1995)

long and short fibrils (Table 1) and fibril length was always characteristic for every strain examined. Another group of six strains carried instead of peritrichous fibrils, lateral tufts of very densely packed fibrils on the side of the cells (Figure 3)

In order to better understand the ecological significance of the presence of fibrils on strains from dental plaque it is necessary to reallocate these strains to their correct species using the current classification system (Whiley & Beighton 1998). Thus according to the identification scheme of Beighton *et al.,* (1991) the biotype I strains are now re-classified as *S. sanguis, S. gordonii* or *S. crista* (Table 1) and the biotype II strains are now *S. mitis* or *S. oralis* (Table 2), on the basis of salivary amylase binding ability and chromogenic substrate utilisation (P.S.Handley & J. Rose. Unpublished observations). Reclassification has shown that most of the strains isolated from smooth surface plaque and originally screened for surface structures were *S. gordonii* with only one *S. sanguis* strain (GW2).The fibrils elaborated by *S. gordonii* were relatively sparse and mostly consisted of one apparent length of fibril, ranging from approximately 58 to 87 nm in length depending on the strain. Fibrils of 60.7 +/- 14.5 nm on the surface of *S. gordonii* DL1 (Table 1) have now been shown by molecular means, to consist of cell wall-anchored CshA polypeptide of high molecular mass (259 kDa) (McNab *et al.,* 1999) and which will be described in detail later in this chapter. It can be speculated that the short structures expressed by the *S. gordonii* strains listed in Table 2 represent CshA fibrils. Expression of fibrils on all the *S. gordonii* strains was variable and many cells in a population were smooth walled, an observation consistent with the expression pattern of CshA fibrils on *S. gordonii* DL1 (McNab *et al.,* 1999). Two strains of *S. gordonii,* PAR and JF2, also express a second class of long fibril, approximately 180 nm in length (Table 1).

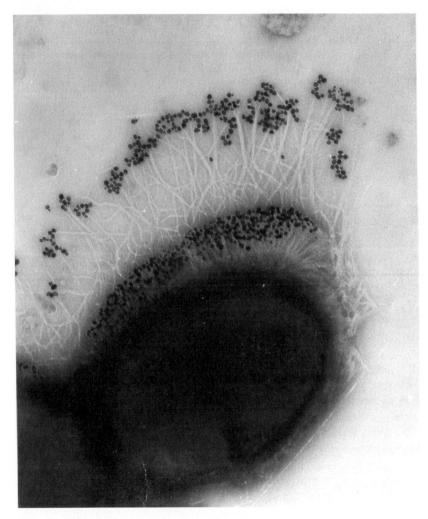

Figure 3 *S. mitis* PSH1b stained with 1% methylamine tungstate and labeled with colloidal gold at pH 3.7. Gold particles are attached to the ends of the short and long tuft fibrils and no gold is attached to any other part of the cell x 92,000. Reproduced with permission from Handley *et al.,* (1991).

In contrast to *S. gordonii,* the *S. sanguis* GW2 cell surface demonstrated a density and distribution of fibrils, very similar to those exhibited by fibrillar *S. salivarius* strains (see above). Very little is known about the structure and functions of *S. sanguis* adhesins although a fibrillar glycoprotein has been isolated and purified from *S. sanguis* 12 (Morris *et al.,* 1987), a strain yet to be reclassifed. This strain carries short (~70nm) and long (~200nm) fibrils and rare fimbriae (Willcox *et al.,* 1989), and a large glycoprotein, termed the long fibril protein (LFP) (300 kDa) was predicted to be involved in adhesion to saliva

154

coated hydroxyapatite (SHA). Antibodies raised to a purified preparation of long fibrils reduced by 85% the attachment of *S. sanguis* 12 to SHA. In addition a naturally occurring mutant strain, 12na, lacked both long and short fibrils (Willcox *et al.,* 1989), lacked LFP (Morris *et al.,* 1987) and showed a 50% reduction in adhesion to BEC (Willcox *et al.,* 1989). The suggested link between fibrils and adhesion for *S. sanguis* 12 has not been confirmed by molecular methods and the existence of three different types of surface structure on this strain illustrates well the complexity of the cell surface structures on oral streptococci and the continued challenge of identifying their functions and composition.

The *S. crista* strains represent a structurally specialised group of organisms that carry a characteristic tuft of very densely packed fibrils, containing one or more types of different length of fibrils on the side of the cells (Table1). *S. crista* 311, the type strain for the species (NCTC 12479), has long (420±39.3 nm) fibrils that project outwards through an extremely dense shorter crest of fibrils (242±13.9 nm) on the side of the cell (Handley *et al.,* 1991). *S. crista* is a secondary coloniser of the tooth surface and coaggregates with both *Corynebacterium matruchotii* and *Fusobacterium nucleatum* (Lancy *et al.,* 1983) to form 'corn-cobs' that are prevalent in mature plaque.

After reclassification, the biotype II strains (Handley *et al.*, 1985) are now strains of *S. oralis* and *S. mitis* (Table 2). Two *S. oralis* strains (KN & EY3), isolated from coronal smooth surface plaque, carry sparse, short, peritrichous fibrils. In contrast, the strains redesignated *S. mitis* comprise a second group elaborating lateral or polar tufts of fibrils. These tufted strains of *S. mitis* (PSH 1a, PSH 1b & PSH 2) have no known coaggregation partners and were originally found in the gingival crevice. Subsequently a strain of *S. oralis*, CN3410, has also been shown to carry lateral tufts of fibrils. Sparse longer 289±15.0 nm fibrils project through the shorter, dense 159±5.0 nm fibrils, with the longer fibrils possibly carrying adhesins (Jameson *et al.*, 1995) and which will be described in more detail in the next section. The tufted morphotype is therefore not restricted to *S. crista* strains, but is relatively widespread amongst species of the mitis group of streptococci. Fibrils have been found together with fimbriae on the cell surface of one *S. oralis* strain (834) (Table 2), although this is an unusual occurrence.

All strains isolated from dental plaque had surface structures, indicating the importance of fibrils to the survival of streptococci in the oral cavity (Handley *et al.,* 1985). One of the predominant tooth colonisers in plaque development is *S. gordonii* and all strains of this species carry peritrichous fibrils. All strains of the secondary plaque coloniser *S. crista* carry tufts (crests) of fibrils. It is less clear however what the predominant surface structure morphotype is on *S. oralis* and *S. mitis,* as these strains demonstrate a range of surface structure types (fibrils and fimbriae) and different distribution patterns on the cell surface (peritrichous, polar or lateral). A survey of a larger number of *S. oralis* and *S. mitis* strains is necessary as only a relatively small number of strains have so far been screened for surface structures.

Streptococcus gordonii *Dl1(challis) Fibrils*

The biochemical and electron microscopy studies of Weerkamp and co-workers successfully identified the fibrils of *S. salivarius* to be large glycoproteins involved in adhesion of streptococcal cells to human and bacterial receptors, as has been described. A molecular approach to understanding the adhesion mechanisms of *S. gordonii* DL1(Challis) has now taken the inferred link between large wall-anchored surface proteins, surface structures and adhesion a step further by demonstrating that the adhesive fibrils of this organism are encoded by a single gene product. Thus, the *S. gordonii* cell wall-anchored protein CshA (259kDa) appears to be the structural and functional component of fibrils on the surface of *S. gordonii* (McNab *et al.*, 1999). CshA is one of a large number of wall anchored proteins expressed by oral streptococci (Jenkinson and Lamont, 1997). The polypeptide has multiple binding functions and is essential for oral colonization by *S. gordonii* (McNab *et al.*, 1994).

The structural component of **S. gordonii** *DL1 fibrils*

Cells of *S. gordonii* DL1 carry thin fibrils that project 60.7 +/-14.5 nm away from the cell surface (Figure 2a). These fibrils are sparsely distributed, and vary in surface density from cell to cell. The fibrils bind CshA specific antibodies (Figure 2b) and are absent from isogenic mutants of *S. gordonii* DL1 in which the *cshA* gene is inactivated (McNab *et al.*, 1999). When the *cshA* gene was cloned and expressed in *Enterococcus faecalis* JH2-2 which does not normally carry surface fibrils, fibrils of 70.3 +/- 9.1 nm (Figure 2c) were produced that were not significantly different in length from those on *S. gordonii* (McNab *et al.*, 1999). These fibrils bind CshA specific antibodies as detected by immunoelectron microscopy (Figure 2d). These results provide evidence that the product of the *CshA* gene contains all the necessary structural information for the synthesis and assembly of fibril structures in an appropriate host. It is not possible to discern simply by electron microscopy whether the *S. gordonii* fibrils consist of single CshA molecules or of dimers or multimers of CshA . The correlation between CshA expression and the occurrence of surface fibrils may extend also to *S. sanguis* and *S. oralis* strains. These bacteria often carry short (48 – 75 nm), sparse fibrils (Tables 1 & 2) and also express high molecular mass proteins that are antigenically related to CshA from *S. gordonii* DL1 (McNab *et al.*, 1995).

CshA polypeptide structure and function

The primary sequence of CshA can be delineated into 4 distinct regions: (i) a 41-amino acid residue leader peptide directing export, (ii) a non-repetitive region (residues 42 to 878), (iii) an extensive amino acid repeat block region (residues 879 to 2417) comprising 13 repeat blocks of 101 residues and 3 shorter blocks, and (iv) a carboxy-terminal cell wall anchor domain (Figure 4). The wall anchor domain is common to a super-family of surface proteins from Gram positive bacteria and comprises a conserved Leu-Pro-Xaa-Thr-Gly motif (where Xaa is any amino acid) followed by a hydrophobic sequence and a short,

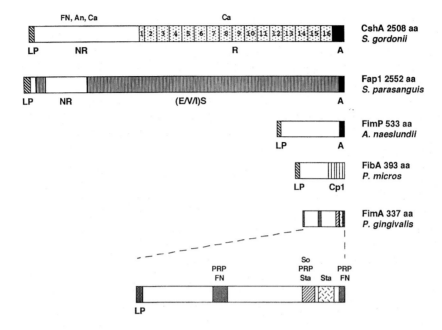

Figure 4 Schematic diagram of the features of fibril- or fimbriae- associated proteins of oral bacteria. Protein sequence features discussed in the text have been labeled below each protein (LP, leader peptide; NR, non-repetitive region; A, wall anchor domain; (E/V/I)S, dipeptide repeat region; Cp1, repeats with homology to Cp1 family of carbohydrate binding repeats (see text). Binding functions are annotated above the relevant region of each protein (FN, fibronectin; An, *A. naeslundii*; Ca, *C. albicans*; PRP, proline rich proteins; So, *S. oralis*; Sta, Statherin). *P. gingivalis* Fim A protein (337 amino acid residues) has been magnified to show the multiple binding regions.

charged cytoplasmic tail (Navarre and Schneewind, 1999). These C-terminal sequences assist retention of the secreted polypeptide at the cell surface while proteolytic cleavage of the protein occurs between the Thr and Gly residues of the LPxTG motif . The carboxyl group of the threonine is subsequently amide-linked to a free amino group present within the peptidoglycan cross-bridge and the polypeptide becomes wall anchored.

Mature CshA protein contains, at 25 sites, the motif AsnXaa[Ser/Thr] which is a potential signal for *N*-linked glycosylation. However, in contrast to the fibrillar antigens of *S. salivarius* (Weerkamp and Jacobs, 1982), there is currently no evidence to suggest that CshA is extensively glycosylated.

Adhesive functions of CshA have been defined by using a combination of genetic techniques and by antibody inhibition experiments. Mutants of *S. gordonii* deficient in CshA were up to 50% impaired in adhesion to other oral microorganisms (*A. naeslundii*, *S. oralis*, and *Candida albicans*) and to immobilized human fibronectin (McNab *et al*., 1996) and are markedly reduced in surface hydrophobicity (McNab *et al*., 1994). The CshA fibrils produced by heterologous *E. faecalis* impart hydrophobicity on the enterococci, promote attachment of cells to human fibronectin and the ability to coaggregate with *A. naeslundii* T14V (McNab *et al.*, 1999). Thus CshA polypeptide appears to contain the information necessary for the functional properties of adhesion as well as for fibril formation.

The adhesion-mediating sequences within CshA are localized to the N-terminal 93-kDa segment of mature CshA polypeptide on the basis of antibody blocking experiments (McNab *et al.*, 1996). Further, it appears from immunogold electron microscopy using antiserum to the 93-kDa region of CshA that these adhesive domains are present at the ends or tips of fibrils with gold particles located at a distance of approximately 60-70 nm from the surface of cells (Figure 2b & 2d). Some of the CshA fibrils expressed on the surface of *E. faecalis* have globular regions at their tips (Figure 2c), reminiscent of the 72nm fibrils of *S. salivarius.*

These observations have led to the hypothesis that the repeat block region of CshA may act as a scaffold to present the adhesive domain(s) distal from the cell surface (McNab *et al.*, 1999). However, CshA is not predicted to adopt either of the two well-known structural conformations of fibrous proteins. For example tropomyosin demonstrates a periodic distribution of apolar residues within an extensive heptad repeat block region that allows the protein to adopt an alpha-helical coiled-coil structure (Beck and Brodsky, 1998). This structural motif is present also in the fibrillar M-like proteins of group A streptococci that bind human serum components (Navarre and Schneewind, 1999). The heptad repeats are present throughout almost the entire M protein sequence that is proposed to form an alpha-helical coiled-coil dimer extension 50-60 nm from the cell surface (Fischetti, 1989). Although the N-terminal region of CshA is predicted to be predominantly alpha helical, neither this nor other regions of the polypeptide contain heptad repeats. Moreover, although the repeat block region of CshA is rich in Pro, Gly and Thr, the absence of any contiguous GxP sequence suggests it is unlikely that CshA adopts a collagen-like structure. It is speculated that owing to the repeat structure, CshA adopts an open conformation with elastic properties, with folding of the predominantly α-helical N-terminal region providing an adhesive tip (or globular end).

Tufts of Fibrils on **S. mitis** *Group Streptococci*

As previously outlined, strains with tufts of fibrils either in a polar or lateral position on the cell surface represent a structurally specialised group of oral streptococci. *S. crista* strains adhere specifically to *C. matruchotii* and *F. nucleatum* (Lancy *et al.*, 1983) via their tuft of fibrils and the specific attachment can be seen in thin sections of the 'corncobs' that form between the cocci and the central rod (Listgarten *et al.*, 1973). Most *S. crista* strains carry two lengths of fibril in the tuft (Table 1) (Handley *et al.*, 1985). The fibrils probably contain protein components as heat and trypsin treatment reduce corncob formation (Lancy *et al.*, 1983) and protease completely removes tuft fibrils (Hesketh *et al.*, 1987). The tuft fibrils react with antiserum specific for the

158

backbone of lipoteichoic acid (LTA) (Mouton *et al.,* 1980), although it is not clear if LTA acts as an adhesin. Attempts to identify adhesins on *S. crista* strains have been largely unsuccessful. Interestingly, *S. crista* CC5A carries a homologue (*scbA*) of the *fim*A gene (Correia *et al.,* 1996), the product of which has been associated with the adhesion of *S. parasanguis* FW213 to saliva coated hydroxyapatite (S-SHA) (see below). However *S. crista* CC5A itself adheres only poorly to S-SHA and a *scbA* mutant could still successfully form 'corn-cobs'. A mutant strain of *S. crista* CC5A from a transposon mutagenesis library, had a reduced binding capacity in the corn-cob assay, and the transposon insertion locus was sequenced and had the characteristics of an ATP-binding cassette (ABC) transport operon (Correia *et al.,* 1995). While the associations of adhesion with ABC transporters is not yet understood, it has been proposed that the lipoprotein component of an ABC transport system could recognise a receptor ligand on receiving surfaces and thus act as an adhesin (Whittaker *et al.,* 1996). The *S. crista* CC5A mutant was also reported to have 'disorganised' fibrils (described as fimbriae in the paper) but it was not clear whether the short or long fibrils were affected (Rosan *et al.,* 1998).

Tufts of fibrils are also found on *S.oralis* and *S. mitis* strains (Table 2) although detailed biochemical tests are needed on these strains to confirm their identity. *S. oralis* CN3410 carries a lateral, prominent crest of two lengths of fibrils and an indistinct 'fuzzy' surface component covering the rest of the cell surface, which may also consist of fibrils (Jameson *et al.,* 1995). The longer fibrils were purified from strain CN3410 by release from the cell surface with trypsin and the trypsin extracted polypeptides (TEPs) contained two groups of high molecular weight polypeptides. It was suggested that while the TEPs were components of the long fibrils, they were not determinants of adhesion to salivary pellicle or to epithelial cells. No coaggregation partner has yet been identified for *S. oralis* CN3410. Unfortunately no further molecular or genetic information is available at this time on the structure and function of some of the largest extracellular structures produced by streptococci.

Evidence exists to suggest that the ends of the short and long fibrils in the tuft have unique physico-chemical properties in comparison to the sides of the fibrils and this may in turn indicate that the ends of the fibrils are important in adhesion. (Handley *et al.,* 1991). The ends of the short fibrils on two tufted strains (*S. crista* CR311 and *S. mitis* PSH1b) could be specifically labelled with colloidal gold (Figure 3) in a pH dependent manner so these short fibrils may be charged depending on the extracellular pH. Also the short fibrils are protease sensitive (Hesketh *et al.,* 1987), therefore the short fibrils consist of proteins that in some way confer electrostatic properties to the ends of the short tuft fibrils. The long fibrils bound colloidal gold at their tips in a pH independent manner (Figure 3), indicative of hydrophobic interactions with the gold particles. The ends of the long fibrils are proposed to be hydrophobic based on this and other physico-chemical information (Busscher *et al.,* 1991) and the fibril tips may therefore be involved with the adhesion process (Handley *et al.,* 1991). The electrostatic and hydrophobic properties were exhibited only by the ends of the fibrils and not by any other part of the cell surface, indicating the unique adhesive potential of the ends of the tuft fibrils.

Fimbriae on oral bacteria

As discussed above, it is convenient to distinguish between fibrils and fimbriae present on streptococci on the basis of their morphological structure on the cell surface. However, there is no firm evidence for biochemical distinction either with respect to the nature of their protein components, or to the extent to which the structures may be glycosylated. Short fibrils on *S. gordonii* DL1 (Challis) that have been characterized at the molecular level appear to be comprised of CshA, a typical cell-wall-linked protein (see above). Other examples of wall-linked proteins forming fibrillar surface structures are the anti-phagocytic M proteins present on pathogenic Group A streptococci (Fischetti, 1989) and P1 (SpaP) protein that is present on the surface of *Streptococcus mutans* (Lee *et al.*, 1989), and that functions as a major adhesin (Jenkinson & Demuth, 1997). Because each of these proteins carries the C-terminal wall-anchorage sequence, including the LPxTG cleavage recognition site, it is presumed that the protein molecules are held at the cell surface by becoming covalently bound to cell wall peptidoglycan through the C-terminal Thr residue, as discussed above. However, recent findings that proteins with wall-anchorage sequences are also associated with production of longer fimbrial structures in gram-positive oral bacteria (see below), suggests that cell-wall linkage might not be the only consequence of C-terminal LPxTG recognition cleavage. This finding also raises the possibility that fibrillar structures, such as those formed by CshA, could themselves be polymeric consisting of more than one CshA molecule, and perhaps also having other minor associated protein components.

Streptococcus parasanguis

Amongst the oral streptococci, *S. parasanguis* FW213 is somewhat unusual in producing a dense surface array of peritrichous fimbriae (Figure 5a). Chemically-induced mutants lacking fimbriae are deficient in adhesion to saliva-coated hydroxylapatite beads (Fives-Taylor and Thompson, 1985) implicating a role for these structures in colonization. Some of these afimbrial mutants carry peritrichous fibrils, that may also be present on the wild-type cells but are masked by the fimbrial structures (Harty *et al.*, 1990) (Figure 5b). Early attempts to purify the fimbrial components resulted in the identification of a 35-kDa protein, designated FimA (Fenno *et al.*, 1989). This protein is probably not the structural sub-unit of fimbriae (Fenno *et al.*, 1995) and it has subsequently been recognised as a member of the LraI family of streptococcal lipoproteins (Jenkinson, 1994) found in all species of *Streptococcus* and *Enterococcus* tested. In *S. gordonii* and *S. pneumoniae* the FimA homologues, designated ScaA and PsaA respectively, are thought to be binding-protein components of ATP-binding cassette type transport systems associated with manganese uptake (Dinthilac *et al.*, 1997; Kolenbrander *et al.*, 1998). Nevertheless, *fimA* mutants of *S. parasanguis* are deficient in binding to fibrin (Burnette-Curley *et al.*, 1995) and

160

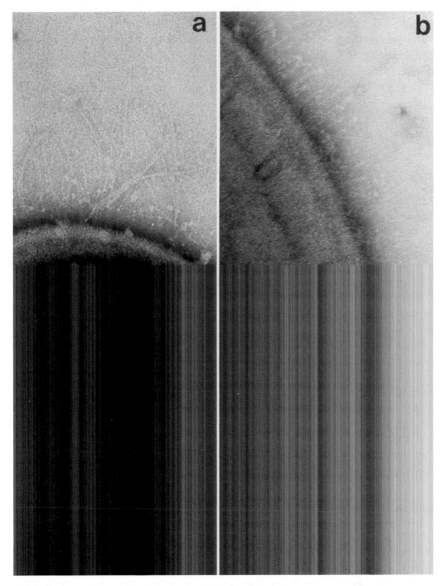

Figure 5 All cells were negatively stained with 1% methylamine tungstate.
Figure 5a. *S. parasanguis* FW213 with peritrichous, flexible fimbriae, 3-4nm wide and 216+/-28nm long x264,000.
Figure 5b *S. parasanguis* VT 324, a mutant of *S. parasanguis* FW213, carries dense, short fibrils that are 78.4+/-12.2 nm long. Some fibrils have globular ends x248,000. Reproduced with permission from Harty *et al.,* (1990). Figure 5c. *Actinomyces* serovar WVA963 mutant strain PK407 which is unable to coaggregate with streptococcal coaggregation partners (for details of the strain see Klier *et al.,* (1997)) carries flexible, peritrichous (3.30+/-0.05nm wide) type I fimbriae only x204,000. Figure 5d. *P. gingivalis* WPH 35 carries peritrichous, 'curly' fimbriae, 4-5nm wide x175,000.

purified FimA blocks adhesion of *S. parasanguis* cells to saliva-coated hydroxylapatite (Oligino and Fives-Taylor, 1993), implicating a role for this protein in adhesion. It is not altogether clear at this time how the adhesive and transport functions of the LraI proteins are related. Moreover, FimA has been shown to be located at the tips of *S. parasanguis* fimbriae (Fenno *et al.*, 1995). This is a potentially unusual location for a lipoprotein serving a membrane transport system, but is nevertheless consistent with observations that gram-positive bacterial lipoproteins, which demonstrate high-affinity substrate-binding activities, are released from the confines of the cell envelope (see Sutcliffe and Russell, 1995).

Recent evidence suggests that *S. parasanguis* fimbriae are comprised of a novel protein, designated Fap1, with a highly repetitive amino acid residue structure (Wu and Fives-Taylor, 1999). This polypeptide is a typical gram-positive wall-associated protein comprising a precursor of 2,552 aa residues with a 50 aa residue leader peptide and a cell wall-anchorage sequence at the C-terminus (Figure 4). It is an unusually acidic protein containing 1,000 repeats of the dipeptide (E/V/I)S. Similar extensive dipeptide repeats XS occur also in the fibrinogen-binding clumping factors A and B of *Staphylococcus aureus* (Ni Eidin *et al.*,1998). The functional significance of this dipeptide repeat is not understood at present. Although it is also not clear how Fap1 might be associated with fimbrial formation, it is speculated that Fap1 might become assembled into fimbriae in a process analogous to curli formation (Hammar *et al.*, 1996) whereby sub-units nucleate upon a surface-anchored polypeptide. This model has to take into account that each Fap1 molecule has a putative cell-wall-anchorage region. Thus, a mechanism must be invoked whereby the C-terminally cleaved Fap1 molecule may be protected from cell-wall-anchorage and instead polymerized into fimbriae. An alternative explanation for how this might occur has been proposed by Yeung *et al.* (1998) for the assembly of *A. naeslundii* fimbrial structures that also appear to be comprised of a polypeptide carrying a putative cell-wall-anchorage sequence at the C-terminus.

Actinomyces naeslundii

A. naeslundii fimbriae are perhaps the best characterized of the gram-positive oral bacterial structures and are ca. 3-4 nm wide and <1.5µ long. Two major fimbrial types have been identified; some strains bear both types of fimbriae while others carry only type 2 fimbriae (Yeung and Cisar, 1990). The two fimbrial types cannot be distinguished from each other ultrastructurally (Klier *et al.,* 1997). Type 1 fimbriae (Figure 5c) are associated with adhesion of *A. naeslundii* to salivary acidic proline rich proteins and to statherin deposited within salivary pellicles on oral surfaces (Clark *et al.*, 1989). However, antibodies raised to the type 1 fimbrial subunit protein FimP do not block adhesion of *A. naeslundii* cells to salivary pellicle (Cisar et al., 1991). Therefore, it is currently thought that the acidic proline rich protein adhesin, while being intimately associated with the production of type 1 fimbriae, is not the fimbrial subunit. Type 2 fimbriae are, on the other hand, implicated in the adhesion of *A.*

162

naeslundii to glycosidic receptors on epithelial cells, polymorphonuclear leukocytes, and oral streptococal cells. The lectin-like adhesion of *A. naeslundii* to these substrates is inhibited by galactose and N-acetylgalactosamine (see Whittaker *et al.*, 1996). More recent evidence suggests that the type 2 fimbrial lectin adhesin is a 95 kDa polypeptide that, like the type 1 fimbrial adhesin, is distinct from the structural FimA subunit (Klier *et al.*, 1997).

The genes encoding the structural subunits of type 1 and type 2 fimbriae encode proteins of molecular masses 54 kDa to 59 kDa . The structural sub-unit protein FimP of type 1 fimbriae is 34% identical in amino acid sequence to the sub-unit protein FimA of type 2 fimbriae (Yeung and Cisar, 1990). Each subunit protein precursor contains an N-terminal leader peptide and a C-terminal wall-anchorage region containing the LPxTG cleavage recognition sequence, al-though the proteins themselves do not contain internal amino acid repeat blocks (Figure 4). The detection of the cell wall-anchorage region within the fimbrial subunit proteins, as was shown for *S. parasanguis* Fap1 protein, again raises the issue that to form fimbriae the individual sub-units would need to become linked or assembled to one another and not individually bound to cell wall peptidoglycan. A possible component gene in the assembly of these type 1 or type 2 sub-units has been identified. Downstream of the *fimA* gene in *A. naeslundii* T14V is a gene designated *orf365* that encodes a polypeptide of 365 amino acid residues. Mutants in which the *fimA* or *orf365* genes were inacti-vated do not participate in coaggregation with *Streptococcus oralis* 34 (Yeung *et al.*, 1998). Although mutations in *orf365* resulted in cells deficient in cell surface fimbriae, production of the type 2 fimbrial subunit protein was still detected in cell lysates. Moreover, antibodies to a sequence C-terminal to the LPxTG motif of the FimA precursor reacted with the polypeptide produced by *orf365* mutants, but not with FimA protein isolated from mature fimbriae produced by wild-type *A. naeslundii* T14V. These results imply that type 2 fimbrial assembly requires expression of *orf365* as well as C-terminal process-ing of the FimA polypeptide. How this assembly process occurs is open to conjecture, but two possibilities have been proposed. One hypothesis suggests that FimA is processed by the general gram-positive wall-protein cleavage (sortase) machinery, linked to a peptidoglycan precursor and then, instead of being incorporated into cell wall, becomes linked to another fimbrial subunit. An alternative hypothesis, also proposed for the assembly of Fap1 protein (Wu and Fives-Taylor, 1999), is that the processed subunit becomes associated with a cell-wall-linked subunit. This then acts as a nucleator upon which C-terminally processed polypeptides become polymerized, analogous to the assembly of curlin during the formation of *E. coli* curli (pili) (Hultgren *et al.*, 1996). Each of these hypotheses requires that the cell-wall-anchorage machinery distinguish between C-terminally-cleaved protein destined for cell-wall-linkage and protein destined for polymerization into fimbriae. On the other hand, it is also possible that C-terminal peptide cleavage and assembly of fimbrial subunits are com-pletely independent events. In this regard it is of note that the type 1 fimbrial gene cluster *in A. naeslundii* T14V contains seven genes, amongst which are *fimP* and a downstream gene *orf4* the product of which shows 40% amino acid identity to the *orf365* peptide (Yeung and Ragsdale 1997). Thus it may turn out that *A. naeslundii* fimbrial production involves a genetic complexity approaching or paralleling that associated with *E. coli* pili production (Hultgren *et al.*, 1996).

Porphyromonas gingivalis

The best-characterized fimbriae of the oral gram-negative bacteria are those produced by *P. gingivalis*. At least three different types have been identified, but all are peritrichous, up to 3 µm long and 5 nm in width. The major class of fimbriae is composed of a protein subunit designated fimbrillin, that varies in molecular mass between 41 kDa and 49 kDa depending upon the strain (Lee *et al.*, 1991). Purified fimbriae are curly filaments composed of a single strand, 4-5nm wide with a pitch of about 34nm (Yoshimura *et al.,* 1984) (Figure 5d). The region downstream of the *fimA* gene contains four open reading frames. Two of these encode 50-kDa and 80-kDa polypeptides that appear to be minor structural components of fimbriae (Yoshimura *et al.*, 1993). Expression of the cloned *fimA* gene in *E. coli* does not result in fimbriae formation (Dickinson *et al.*, 1988), indicating that accessory genes from *P. gingivalis* are necessary for this process to occur. Indeed, it is known that precursor (pre)fimbrillin is cleaved by the arginine-specific proteinase RgpA or RgpB produced by *P. gingivalis* (reviewed by Lamont and Jenkinson, 1998). This proteolytic activity is essential for fimbrial formation since mutants in which the *rgpA* and *rgpB* genes are inactivated possess very few fimbriae on their surfaces (Nakayama *et al.*, 1996). In addition, *rgp-1* mutants show reduced transcription of *fimA* (Tokuda *et al.*, 1996). Thus it is likely that fimbrial assembly in *P. gingivalis* is under complex genetic control and involves at least several *P. gingivalis*-specific gene products that do not have functional homologues in *E. coli*.

Fimbriae appear to be the major adhesion-mediating determinants in *P. gingivalis*. The fimbrillin (FimA) polypeptide binds proline rich proteins, statherin, lactoferrin, oral epithelial cells, oral streptococci and *A. naeslundii*, fibrinogen and fibronectin (see Lamont and Jenkinson, 1998). Binding of fimbrillin to salivary proteins involves several separate regions on the molecule, deduced from antibody-blocking experiments and studies with synthetic peptides or recombinant truncated FimA polypeptides. The most adhesion active regions are located within the C-terminal half of the protein and especially between residues 266 and 337 (see Figure 4) (Amano *et al.*, 1996; 1997). The combined activities of multiple binding sites are probably important in enhancing interaction of fimbrillin with salivary receptors, thus establishing adhesion of cells to saliva-coated surfaces. Statherin is bound by fimbrillin only when the former is deposited upon a surface such as hydroxylapatite (Amano *et al.*, 1996). It is believed that upon binding to a surface, conformational changes occur within the C-terminal regions of statherin molecules, thus exposing hidden residues to which fimbrillin binds. Salivary acidic proline rich proteins are also believed to change conformation upon adsorption to a surface, and the

164

sequence PQGPPQ, which occurs four times within proline rich protein 1 is recognized by fimbrillin (Kataoka *et al.*, 1997). The fimbriae are therefore highly significant in *P. gingivalis* adhesion. They also demonstrate chemotactic properties and cytokine induction, and are necessary for *P. gingivalis* invasion of epithelial cells (Weinberg *et al.*, 1997) and endothelial cells (Deshpande *et al.*, 1998).

Electron-microscopy of strains in which the *fimA* gene has been inactivated reveals the presence of shorter fimbriae, composed of a protein subunit of molecular mass 67 kDa that is antigenically distinct from fimbrillin (Hamada *et al.*, 1996). A third fimbrial structure has also been identified comprising of a 72-kDa protein subunit (Ogawa *et al.*, 1995). The relationship between these fimbriae and their corresponding adhesive functions and roles in colonization and pathogenesis have not yet been determined.

Peptostreptococcus micros

It has recently been proposed that some isolates of the periodontal pathogen, *Peptostreptococcus micros*, carry fimbrial-like structures which can exceed 4 mm in length (Kremer *et al.*, 1999a). Smooth colony variants of *P. micros* arise readily during broth culture and lack fimbrial structures though they appear to release structures from the cell surface (Kremer *et al.*, 1999a). It is thought that the fimbriae may not be directly involved in adhesion of *P. micros* to human epithelial cells since smooth colony variant cells show no loss of adhesive properties (Kremer *et al.*, 1999b). The structural component of fimbriae is a protein (FibA) of 393 amino acid residues that possesses an N-terminal signal peptide and a C-terminal repeat region, but no cell-wall anchorage motif (Figure 4). The repeat region demonstrates similarity to sequences present in other surface and secreted proteins of Gram positive bacteria that bind carbohydrate residues associated with glucans, LTA, and peptidoglycan (Wren, 1991). How these fimbrial-like structures are assembled is open to conjecture, but the mechanism must be different from that occurring in the assembly of *S. parasanguis* and *A. naeslundii* fimbriae. At least two further genes (ORF2 and ORF3 flanking *fibA*) demonstrate significant homology to *fibA* and may be involved in fimbrial structure or assembly (Kremer *et al.*, 1999a). The molecular studies indicate that the fimbrial structures of *P. micros* consist of subunits and are therefore more similar to the fimbriae of *A. naeslundii* and *B. gingivalis,* rather than the non-subunit fibrils found on *S. gordonii*. So far, detailed studies on the incidence and ultrastructure of the fimbrial-like structures on different strains of *P. micros* are lacking

Summary

The oral environment contains at least 300 species of oral bacteria and these express the widest range of surface structures so far described in any ecosystem. Although some fibrils and fimbriae have a proven role in adhesion, a considerable number of structures detected by electron microscopy still have no known function. It is possible that they may have as yet unidentified functions, other than adhesion, which could be important in colonisation and survival. Oral bacteria have evolved different ways of supporting their adhesins and extending them away from the cell wall, either on longer fimbriae or shorter fibrils. Molecular biology techniques have resolved some questions regarding the structural location of the adhesins on fibrils and fimbriae. For example, the adhesion mediating sequences can be incorporated into the structural sub-units of both fibrils (*S. gordonii* DL1 CshA fibrillar protein) and fimbriae (*P. gingivalis* fimbrillin subunits). The adhesins of the CshA fibrillar protein are probably located at the distal end of the fibril whereas the *P. gingivalis* adhesin sequences are located all along the length of the fimbriae. Alternatively, some fimbrial subunits have only a structural role and not an adhesive role (FimP protein subunits of *A. naeslundii*) and the adhesins are likely to be separate, as yet unidentified proteins.

Current data indicate that fimbriae are protein subunit structures while fibrils may be single protein structures. However, although fibrils cannot be dissociated into smaller subunits (*S. salivarius* HB, *S. gordonii* DL1 and *S. oralis* CN3410), neither can the fimbriae of *A. naeslundii*. The fibril protein CshA (259 kDa) of *S. gordonii* DL1 forms surface fibrils of 60-70 nm. However the composition of the longer 100-400nm streptococcal fibrils has not yet been elucidated. It could be speculated that the longer fibrils or fimbriae are polymerised fibrillar proteins consisting of several copies of the same molecule. The mechanisms of export and assembly for fibrils and fimbriae on oral bacteria are not known in any detail. It will not be possible to understand better the similarities and differences between fibrils and fimbriae until further molecular and genetic studies, backed up by ultrastructural studies, are available to define the structural properties of adhesive surface appendages.

References

Amano, A., Fujiwara, T., Nagata, H., Kuboniwa, M., Sharma, A., Sojar, H.T., Genco, R.J., Hamada, S. and Shizukuishi. 1997. *Porphyromonas gingivalis* fimbriae mediate coaggregation with *Streptococcus oralis* through specific domains. *J. Dent. Res.*, **76**, 852-857.

Amano, A., Sharma, A., Sojar, H.T., Kuramitsu, H.K. and Genco, R.J. 1996. Structural domains of *Porphyromonas gingivalis* recombinant fimbrillin that mediate binding to salivary proline-rich proteins and statherin. *Infect. Immun.*, **64**, 1631-1637.

Beck, K., and Brodsky, B. 1998. Supercoiled protein motifs: the collagen triple-helix and the a-helical coiled coil. *J. Struct. Biol.*, **122**, 17-29.

Beighton, D., Hardie, J.M. and Whiley, R.A. 1991. A scheme for the identification of viridans streptococci. *J. Med. Microbiol.*, **35**, 367-372.

Burnette-Curley, D., Wells, V., Viscount, H., Munro, C.L., Fenno, J.C., Fives-Taylor, P. and Macrina, F.L. 1995. FimA, a major virulence factor associated with *Streptococcus parasanguis* endocarditis. *Infect. Immun.*, **63**, 4669-4674.

Busscher, H.J., Handley, P.S., Rouxhet, P.S., Hesketh, L.M. and Van der Mei, H.C. 1991. The relationship between structural and physico-chemical surface properties of tufted *Streptococcus sanguis* strains. In: Mozes, N., Handley, P.S., Busscher, H.J. and P.G. Rouxhet (eds), *Microbial cell surface analysis: Structural and physico-chemical methods,* pp. 317-338. New York, VCH Publishers.

Cisar, J.O., Barsumian, E.L., Siraganian, R.P., Clark, W.B., Yeung, M.K., Hsu, S.D., Curl, S.H., Vatter, A.E. and Sandberg, A.L. 1991. Immunochemical and functional studies of *Actinomyces viscosus* T14V type 1 fimbriae with monoclonal and polyclonal antibodies directed against the fimbrial subunit. *J. Gen. Microbiol.*, **137**, 1971-1979.

Clark, W.B., Beem, J.E., Nesbitt, W.E., Cisar, J.O., Tseng, C.C. and Levine, M.J. 1989. Pellicle receptors for *Actinomyces viscosus* type 1 fimbriae in vitro. *Infect. Immun.*, **57**, 3003-3008.

Correia, F.F., Di Rienzo, J.M., McKay, T.L. and Rosan, B. 1996. *ScbA* from *Streptococcus crista* CC5A: an atypical member of the *lra*1 gene family. *Infect. Immun.*, **64**, 2114-2121.

Correia, F.F., Di Rienzo, J.M., Lamont, R.J., Anderman, C., McKay, T.L. and Rosan, B. 1995. Insertional inactivation of binding determinants of *Streptococcus crista* CC5A using TN916. *Oral Microbiol. Immunol.*, **10**, 220-226.

de Graff, F.K. and Mooi, F.R. 1986. The fimbrial adhesins of *Escherichia coli*. In: Rose, A.H. and Tempest, D.W. (eds) *Advances in Microbial Physiology*, vol 28, Academic Press, pp 65-143.

Deshpande, R.G., Khan, M.B. and Genco, C.T. 1998. Invasion of aortic and heart endothelial cells by *Porphyromonas gingivalis*. *Infect. Immun.*, **66**, 5337-5343.

Devine, D.A. Gmür, R., Handley, P.S. 1989. Ultrastructure, serogrouping and localisation of surface antigens of *Bacteroides intermedius*. *J. Gen. Microbiol.*, **135**, 967-979.

Dickinson, D.P., Kubiniec, M.A., Yoshimura, F. and Genco, R.J. 1988. Molecular cloning and sequencing of the gene encoding the fimbrial subunit protein of *Bacteroides gingivalis*. *J. Bacteriol.*, **170**, 1658-1665.

Dintilhac, A., Alloing, G., Granadel, C. and Claverys, J.P. 1997. Competence and virulence of *Streptococcus pneumoniae*: Adc and PsaA mutants exhibit a requirement for Zn and Mn resulting from inactivation of putative AMB metal permeases. *Mol. Microbiol.*, **25**, 727-739.

Duguid, J.P., Smith, I.W., Dempster, G. and Edmunds, P.N. 1955. Non-flagella filamentous appendages ("fimbriae") and haemagglutinating activity in *Bacterium coli*. *J. Pathol. Bacteriol.*, **70**, 335-348

Elder.B.L., Boraker, D., Fives-Taylor, P. 1982. Whole bacterial cell enzyme linked immunosorbent assay for *Streptococcus sanguis* fimbrial antigens. J. Clin. Microbiol. **16**, 141-144.

Facklam,R.R. 1977 Physiological differentiation of viridans streptococci. J. Clin. Microbiol. **5**, 184-201.

Fenno, J.C., LeBlanc, D.J. and Fives-Taylor, P.M. 1989. Nucleotide sequence analysis of a type 1 fimbrial gene of *Streptococcus sanguis* FW213. *Infect. Immun.*, **57**, 3527-3533.

Fenno, J.C., Shaikh, A., Spatafora, G. and Fives-Taylor, P. 1995. The *fimA* locus of *Streptococcus parasanguis* encodes an ATP-binding membrane transport system. *Mol. Microbiol.*, **15**, 849-863.

Fischetti, V.A. 1989. Streptococcal M protein: molecular design and biological bevavior. *Clin. Microbiol. Rev.*, **2**, 285-314.

Fives-Taylor, P.M. and Thompson, D.W. 1985. Surface properties *of Streptococcus sanguis* FW213 mutants nonadherent to saliva-coated hydroxyapatite. *Infect. Immun.*, **47**, 752-759.

Hamada, N., Sojar, H.T., Cho, M-L. and Genco, R.J. 1996. Isolation and characterization of a minor fimbria from *Porphyromonas gingivalis*. *Infect. Immun.*, **64**, 4788-4794.

Hammar, M., Bian, Z. and Normark, S. 1996. Nucleatur-dependent intercellular assembly of adhesive curli organelles in *Escherichia coli*. *Proc. Natl. Acad. Sci. USA*, **93**, 6562-6566.

Handley, P.S. 1990. Structure, composition and functions of surface structures on oral bacteria. *Biofouling*, **2**, 239-264.

Handley, P.S., Carter, P. and Fielding, J. 1984. *Streptococcus salivarius* strains carry either fibrils or fimbriae on the cell surface. *Infect. Immun.*, **157**, 64-72.

Handley, P.S., Carter, P., Wyatt, J.E. and Hesketh, L. 1985. Surface structures (peritrichous fibrils and tufts of fibrils) found on S*treptococcus sanguis* strains may be related to their ability to coaggregate with other oral genera. *Infect. Immun.*, **47**, 217-227.

Handley, P.S., Coykendale, A., Beighton, D., Hardie, J.M. and Whiley, R.A. 1991. *Streptococcus crista* sp. nov., a viridans streptococcus with tufted fibrils, isolated from the human oral cavity and throat. *Int. J. Syst. Bacteriol.*, **41**, 543-547.

Handley, P.S., Hargreaves, J. and Harty, D.W.S. 1988. Ruthenium red staining reveals surface fibrils and a layer external to the cell wall in *Streptococcus salivarius* HB and adhesion deficient mutants. *J. Gen. Microbiol.*, **134**, 3165-3172.

Handley, P.S., Harty, D.W.S., Wyatt, J.E., Brown, C.R., Doran, J.P. and Gibbs, A.C.C. 1987. A comparison of the adhesion, coaggregation and cell surface hydrophobicity properties of fibrillar and fimbriate strains of *Streptococcus salivarius*. *J. Gen. Microbiol.*, **133**, 3207-3217.

Handley, P.S., Hesketh, L.M. and Moumena, R.A. 1991. Charged and hydrophobic groups are localised in the short and long tuft fibrils on *Streptococcus sanguis* strains. *Biofouling*, **4**, 105-111.

Handley, P.S. and Jacob, A.E. 1981. Some structural and physiological properties of fimbriae of *Streptococcus faecalis*. *J. Gen. Microbiol.*, **127**, 289-293.

Harty, D.W.S., Willcox, M.D.P., Wyatt, J.E., Oyston, P.C.F. and Handley, P.S. 1990. The surface ultrastructure and adhesive properties of a fimbriate *Streptococcus sanguis* strain and six non-fimbriate mutants. *Biofouling*, **2**, 75-86.

Hesketh, L.M., Wyatt, J.E. and Handley, P.S. 1987. Effect of protease on cell surface structure, hydrophobicity and adhesion of tufted strains of *Streptococcus sanguis* biotypes I and II. *Microbiol.*, **50**, 131-145.

Hogg, S.D., Handley, P.S., Embery, G. 1981. Surface fibrils.may be responsible for the salivary glycoprotein-mediated aggregation of the oral bacterium *Streptococcus sanguis*. Arch. Oral Biol., **26**, 945-949.

Hultgren, S.J., Jones, C.H. and Normark, S. 1996. Bacterial adhesins and their assembly. In: Neidhardt, F.C. (ed.), In: *Escherichia coli and Salmonella*, 2nd Edition, pp. 2730-2756, ASM Press, Washington, D.C.

Jameson, M.W., Jenkinson, H.F., Parnell, K. and Handley, P.S. 1995. Polypeptides associated with tufts of cell-surface fibrils in an oral *Streptococcus*. *Microbiology*, **141**, 2729-2738.

Jenkinson, H.F. 1994. Cell surface protein receptors in oral streptococci. *FEMS Microbiol. Lett.*, **121**, 133-140.

Jenkinson, H.F. and Demuth, D.R. 1997. Structure, function and immunogenicity of streptococcal antigen I/II polypeptides. *Mol. Microbiol.*, **23**, 183-190.

Jenkinson, H.F. and Lamont, R.J. 1997. Streptococcal adhesion and colonisation. *Crit. Rev. Oral Biol. Med.*, **8**, 175-200.

Kataoka, K., Amano, A., Kuboniwa, M., Horie, H., Nagata, H. and Shizukuishi, S. 1997. Active sites of salivary proline-rich protein for binding to *Porphyromonas gingivalis* fimbriae. *Infect. Immun.*, **65**, 3159-3164.

Klier, C.M., Kolenbrander, P.E., Roble, A.G., Marco, M.L., Cross. S. and Handley, P.S. 1997. Identification of a 95-kDa putative adhesin from *Actinomyces* serovar WVA963 strain PK1259 that is distinct from type 2 fimbrial subunits. *Microbiology*, **143**, 835-846.

Kolenbrander, P.E., Andersen, R.N., Baker, R.A. and Jenkinson, H.F. 1998. The adhesion-associated *sca* operon in *Streptococcus gordonii* encodes an inducible high-affinity ABC transporter for Mn^{2+} uptake. *J. Bacteriol.*, **180**, 290-295.

Kremer, B.H.A., Bijlsma, J.J.E., Kusters, J.G., De Graaff, J. and van Steenbergen, T.J.M. 1999a Cloning of *fibA*, encoding an immunogenic subunit of the fibril-like surface structure of *Peptostreptococcus micros*. *J. Bacteriol.*, **181**, 2485-2491.

Kremer, B.H.A., Herscheid A.J., Papaioannou, W., Quirynen M. and van Steenbergen, T.J.M. 1999b Adherence of *Peptostreptococcus micros* morphotypes to epithelial cells *in vitro*. *Oral. Microbiol. Immunol.*, **14**, 49-55.

Lamont, R.J. and Jenkinson, H.F. 1998. Life below the gum line: pathogenic mechanisms of *Porphyromonas gingivalis*. *Microbiol. Mol. Biol. Rev.*, **62**, 1244-1263.

Lancy, P., DiRienzo, J.M., Apelbaum, B., Rosan, B. and Holt, S.C. 1983. Corn-cob formation between *Fusobacterium nucleatum* and *Streptococcus sanguis*. *Infect. Immun.*, **40**, 303-309.

Lee, J.Y., Sojar, H.T., Bedi, G.S. and Genco, R.J. 1991. *Porphyromonas* (*Bacteroides*) *gingivalis* fimbrillin: size, aminoterminal sequence, and antigenic heterogeneity. *Infect. Immun.*, **59**, 383-389.

Lee, S.F., Progulske-Fox, A., Erdos, G.W., Piacentini, D.A., Ayakawa, G.Y., Crowley, P.J. and Bleiweis, A.S. 1989. Construction and characterization of isogenic mutants of *Streptococcus mutans* deficient in major surface protein antigen P1 (I/II). *Infect. Immun.*, **57**, 3306-3313.

Li, T., Johansson, I., Hay, D.I. and Stromberg, N. 1999. Strains of *Actinomyces naeslundii* and *Actinomyces viscosus* exhibit structurally variant fimbrial protein subunit proteins and bind to different peptide motifs in salivary proteins. *Infect. Immun.*, **67**, 2053-2059.

Listgarten, M., Mayo, H. and Amsterdam, M. 1973. Ultrastructure of the attachment device between coccal and filamentous microorganisms in "corn-cob" formations of dental plaque. *Arch. Oral Biol.*, **18**, 651-656.

Low, D., Braaten, B. and van der Woude 1996. 'Fimbriae' In Escherichia coli and Salmonella; cellular and molecular biology. ed in chief F. C. Neidhardt. Chapter 11 pp 146-157. ASM press, Washington.

McNab, R., Forbes, H., Handley, P.S., Loach, D.M., Tannock, G.W. and Jenkinson H.F. 1999. Cell wall-anchored CshA polypeptide (259 kilodaltons) in *Streptococcus gordonii* forms surface fibrils that confer hydrophobic and adhesive properties. *J. Bacteriol.*, **181**, 3087-3095.

McNab, R., Holmes, A.R., Clarke, J.C., Tannock, G.W. and Jenkinson, H.F. 1996. Cell-surface polypeptide CshA mediates binding of *Streptococcus gordonii* to other oral bacteria and to immobilized fibronectin. *Infect. Immun.*, **64**, 4204-4210.

McNab, R., Jenkinson, H.F., Loach, D.M. and Tannock, G.W. 1994. Cell-surface-associated polypeptides CshA and CshB of high molecular mass are colonization determinants in the oral bacterium *Streptococcus gordonii*. *Mol. Microbiol.*, **14**, 743-754.

McNab, R., Tannock, G.W. and Jenkinson, H.F. 1995. Characterization of CshA, a high molecular mass adhesin of *Streptococcus gordonii*. *Dev. Biol. Stand.*, **85**, 371-375.

Moore, W.E.C., Holdman, L.V., Cato, E.P., Smibert, E.M., Burmeister, J.A., Paleanis, K.G., Ranney, R.R. 1985. Comparative bacteriology of juvenile periodontitis. *Infect. Immun.*, **48**, 507-519.

Morris, E.J., Ganeshkumar, N., Song, M. and McBride, B.C. 1987. Identification and preliminary characterisation of a *Streptococcus sanguis* fibrillar glycoprotein. *J. Bacteriol*, **169**, 164-171.

Mouton, C., Reynolds, H.S. and Genco, R.J. 1980. Characterisation of tufted streptococci isolated from the "corn-cob" configuration of human dental plaque. *Infect. Immun.* **27**, 235-245.

Nakayama, K., Yoshimura, F., Kadowaki, T. and Yamamoto, K. 1996. Involvement of arginine-specific cysteine proteinase (Arg-gingipain) in fimbriation of *Porphyromonas gingivalis*. *J. Bacteriol.*, **178**, 2818-2824.

Navarre, W.W. and Schneewind, O. 1999. Surface proteins of gram-positive bacteria and mechanisms of their targeting to the cell wall envelope. *Microbiol. Mol. Biol. Rev.*, **63**, 174-229.

Ni Eidhin, D., Perkins, S., Francois, P., Vaudaux, P., Hook, M. and Foster, T.J. 1998. Clumping factor B (ClfB), a new surface-located fibrinogen-binding adhesin of *Staphylococcus aureus*. *Mol. Microbiol.*, **30**, 245-257.

Ogawa, T., Yasuda, K, Yamada, K., Mori, H, Ochiai, K. and Hasegawa, M. 1995. Immunological characterization and epitope mapping of a novel fimbrial protein (Pg-II fimbria) of *Porphyromonas gingivalis*. *FEMS Immunol. Med. Microbiol.*, **11**, 247-256.

Oligino, L. and Fives-Taylor, P. 1993. Over expression and purification of a fimbria-associated adhesin of *Streptococcus parasanguis*. *Infect. Immun.*, **61**, 1016-1022.

Parancnych W. and Frost, L.S. 1988. The physiology and biochemistry of pili. In: Rose, A.H. and Tempest, D.W. (eds) In *Advances in microbial physiology*, vol 29, pp 53-114. Academia Press.

Pugsley, A. 1993. The complete general secretory pathway in Gram negative bacteria. *Microbiol. Rev.*, **57**, 50-108.

Rosan, B., Correia, F.F. and Di Rienzo, J.M. 1998. Corn-cobs: a model for oral microbial biofilms. In: Busscher, H.J. and Evans, L.V. (eds), *Oral Biofilms and Plaque Control,* Harwood Academic Pub., pp. 145-162.

Soto, G.E. and Hultgren, S.J. 1999. Bacterial adhesins: Common themes and variations in architecture and assembly. *J. Bacteriol.*, **181**, 1059-1071.

Sutcliffe, I.C. and Russell, R.R.B. 1995. Lipoproteins of gram-positive bacteria. *J. Bacteriol.*, **177**, 1123-1128.

Tennent, J.M. and Mattick, J.S. 1994. Type 4 pili. In P. Klemm (ed.), *Fimbriae, Adhesion, Genetics, Biogenesis and Vaccines*, pp 127-147. CRC Press, Ann. Arbor, Mich.

Tokuda, M., Duncan, M., Cho, M.I. and Kuramitsu, H.K. 1996. Role of *Porphyromonas gingivalis* protease activity in colonization of oral surfaces. *Infect. Immun.*, **64**, 4067-4073.

Weerkamp, A.H. and Jacobs, T. 1982. Cell wall associated protein antigens of *Streptococcus salivaruis*: purification, properties and function in adherence. *Infect. Immun.*, **38**, 233-242.

Weerkamp, A.H., Handley, P.S., Baars, A. and Slot, J.W. 1986. Negative staining and immunoelectron microscopy of adhesion deficient mutants of *Streptococcus salivarius*, reveal that the adhesive protein antigens are separate classes of cell surface fibril. *J. Bacteriol.*, **165**, 746-755.

Weerkamp, A.H., van der Mei, H.C., Liem, R.S. 1986b. Structural properties of fibrillar proteins isolated from the cell surface and cytoplasm of *Streptococcus salivarius* K+ cells and non-adhesive mutants. *J. Bacteriol.* **165**, 756-762.

Weerkamp, A.H. and McBride, B.C. 1980. Characterisation of the adherence properties of *Strepfococcus salivarius. Infect. Immun.*, **29**, 459-468.

Weinberg, A., Belton, C.M., Park, Y. and Lamont, R.J. 1997. Role of fimbriae in *Porphyromonas gingivalis* invasion of gingival epithelial cells. *Infect. Immun.*, **65**, 313-316.

Whiley, R.A. and Beighton, D. 1998. Current classification of the oral streptococci. *Oral. Microbiol. Immunol.*, **13**, 195-216.

Whittaker, C.J., Klier, C.M. and Kolenbrander, P.E. 1996. Mechanisms of adhesion by oral bacteria. *Ann. Rev. Microbiol.* **50**, 513-552.

Willcox, M.D.P., Wyatt, J.E., and Handley,P.S. 1989. A comparison of the adhesive properties and surface ultrastructure of the fibrillar *Streptococcus sanguis* 12 and an adhesion deficient non-fibrillar mutant 12na. J.Appl.Bact. **66**, 291-299.

Wren, B.W. 1991. A family of clostridial and streptococcal ligand-binding proteins with conserved C-terminal repeat sequences. *Mol. Microbiol.* **5,** 797-803.

Wu, H. and Fives-Taylor, P. 1999. Characterization of dipeptide repeats and a cell wall sorting signal in the fimbriae-associated adhesin, Fap1 of *Streptococcus parasanguis. Mol. Microbiol.*, submitted.

Yeung, M.K. and Cisar, J.O. 1990. Sequence homology between the subunits of two immunologically and functionally distinct types of fimbriae of *Actinomyces* spp. *J. Bacteriol.*, **172**, 2462-2468.

Yeung, M.K. and Ragsdale, P.A. 1997. Synthesis and function of *Actinomyces naeslundii* T14V type 1 fimbriae require the expression of additional fimbria-associated genes. *Infect. Immun.*, **65**, 2629-2639.

Yeung, M.K., Donkersloot, J.A., Cisar, J.O. and Ragsdale, P.A. 1998. Identification of a gene involved in assembly of *Actinomyces naeslundii* T14V type 2 fimbriae. *Infect. Immun.*, **66**, 1482-1491.

Yoshimura, F., Takahashi, Y., Hibi, E., Takasawa, T., Kato, H. and Dickinson, D.P. 1993. Proteins with molecular masses of 50 and 80 kilodaltons encoded by genes downstream from the fimbrillin gene (*fimA*) are components associated with fimbriae in the oral anaerobe *Porphyromonas gingivalis. Infect. Immun.*, **61**, 5181-5189.

Yoshimura, F., Takahashi, K., Nodaska, Y., Susuki,T. 1984. Purification and characterisation of a novel type of fimbriae from the oral anaerobe *Bacteroides gingivalis*. J. Bacteriol., **160**, 949-957.

POTENTIAL ROLE OF FUNCTIONALLY SIMILAR COAGGREGATION MEDIATORS IN BACTERIAL SUCCESSION

Paul E. Kolenbrander, Roxanna N. Andersen, Daniel L. Clemans, Catherine J. Whittaker and Christiane M. Klier

Examination of the coaggregation patterns among more than 1000 oral bacterial strains indicates that cell-to-cell recognition of these oral bacteria is not random. Rather, each strain has a defined set of coaggregation partners. Further examination of these coaggregation patterns has led to the idea of functional similarity of adhesion-relevant surface molecules among members of phylo-genetically distinct genera. For example, functionally similar adhesins on cells from distinct genera may recognize the same complementary receptors on a co-aggregation partner cell. The significance of functionally similar molecules in cell-to-cell recognition and their contributions to the changeable nature of bacterial successions in dental plaque are discussed as three stages of plaque development.

Introduction

Most if not all human oral bacteria adhere to certain other oral bacteria. Cell-to-cell adherence among partner cells in suspension is called coaggregation. A network of both cell types settles from suspension as a coaggregate when a homogeneous, dense suspension of each cell type is mixed. The potential in vivo relevance of such in vitro interactions has been tested by using a variety of substrata to hold one of the cell types and measure the binding of the partner to the bacteria-coated surface: this process is termed coadhesion. Substrata employed include saliva-coated hydroxyapatite (Ciardi *et al.*, 1987), a nitrocellulose membrane filter (Lamont *et al.*, 1991), a hexadecane droplet (Ellen *et al.*, 1994), a glass surface in a parallel plate flow chamber (Bos *et al.*, 1995; Palmer & Caldwell, 1995), plastic discs (Skopek & Liljemark, 1994), or the plastic surface of a microtiter plate (Jenkinson *et al.*, 1993). Coaggregation and coadhesion may be important in development of dental plaque. Also, understanding the mechanisms of coaggregation and coadhesion may be of significance in designing compounds that prevent progression of oral diseases by altering oral bacterial community structure on the tooth surface.

Bacterial succession

All the bacteria examined in our laboratory for their ability to coaggregate have also been the subject of two extensive ecological population studies of the kinds of bacteria found in periodontally healthy and diseased sites (Moore & Moore, 1994; Socransky *et al.*, 1998). In this paper we integrate the results of those studies to describe the succession of bacteria observed in samples taken from healthy sites compared to diseased sites (Table 1). The study of Socransky *et al.* (1998) was an important advance in understanding communities of subgingival plaque bacteria on the tooth surface. They identified bacteria by DNA-probe analyses, and found that certain species of bacteria were found together or clustered. If one of the members of a particular cluster was present in the sample, then it was likely that other members were also there. Five clusters were reported and were designated by color. Besides species within clusters being tightly grouped, specific associations between some of the clusters were also reported. *Actinomyces naeslundii*, the most frequently found gram-positive organism found by Moore and Moore (Moore and Moore, 1994) in all periodontal health conditions, was an outlier to the clusters; however, occasionally it did join the purple cluster consisting of *Actinomyces odontolyticus* and *Veillonella atypica* (Socransky *et al.,* 1998). Interestingly, *A. naeslundii* and the yellow and green clusters were more commonly associated together than with members of the red or orange clusters. The red cluster was closely associated with the orange cluster but not with the other clusters. These data suggest that although the species within clusters were closely associated, the clusters themselves associate non-randomly with other clusters.

One or more representatives of the five clusters described by Socransky *et al.* (Socransky *et al.,* 1998) were also reported by Moore and Moore (1994) in their study of the most numerous species from subgingival crevices of subjects with different periodontal health conditions. Those species that are the same as the ones clustered in the study by Socransky *et al.* (Socransky *et al.* , 1998) are identified by listing the color (as described by Socransky *et al.*) of their respective cluster in Table 1. Table 1 is separated into two panels. In the top panel the species are arranged according to their prevalence in healthy sites. The numerical rank of each species in healthy sites is noted under the column labeled "Health", and their rank in each of three other clinical conditions, gingivitis, moderate periodontitis and adult periodontitis, is given, respectively, in each of the three adjacent columns labeled "Gingivitis", "Moderate", and "Adult". The bottom panel of Table 1 lists the eleven most numerous species found in gingivitis sites and gives their ranking in the other three clinical conditions. It is clear from the results of both studies that the most numerous bacteria found in gingivitis sites are in large part distinct from those found in healthy sites, since 5 of the top 11 species in gingivitis sites are ranked number 30 or below in health. Actinomyces and streptococci dominate the healthy site constituting 22 and 23 %, respectively, of the bacteria isolated. Six streptococci constitute the yellow cluster (Socransky *et al.* , 1998), and four of them are listed among the most numerous species found in healthy sites (Table 1). Both members of the purple cluster and *Capnocytophaga gingivalis* of the green cluster are common in healthy sites, but they are generally less frequently found in diseased sites. The same is observed for two other species, *Actinomyces meyeri* and *Gemella morbillorum*, not reported by Socransky *et al.* (1998). Two species of the orange cluster, *Fusobacterium nucleatum* and *Peptostreptococcus micros*, are

172

Table 1 Oral bacterial species in health and disease. Most numerous species, listed in order of percentage of isolates taken at random, from subgingival crevices of subjects with different periodontal health conditions.[a]

A. Arranged in order of rank in health

Species	Cluster[b]	Rank in different periodontal health conditions			
		Health	Gingivitis	Moderate	Adult
A. naeslundii[c]		1 (18)[d]	2	1	1
F. nucleatum	orange	2 (11)	1	2	2
S. sanguis	yellow	3 (9)	14	32	3
S. oralis	yellow	4 (7)	24	17	8
S. intermedius	yellow	5 (5)	19	14	11
P. micros	orange	6 (2)	7	3	4
A. meyeri		7 (2)	43+	30	31
S. gordonii	yellow	8 (2)	40	35	47+
G. morbillorum		9 (2)	31	44+	27
A. odontolyticus	purple	10 (2)	18	22	12
C. gingivalis	green	12 (2)	43+	44+	36
V. atypica	purple	14 (1)	37	44+	21

B. Arranged in order of rank in gingivitis

Species	Cluster[b]	Rank in different periodontal health conditions			
		Health	Gingivitis	Moderate	Adult
F. nucleatum[c]	orange	2	1 (12)[d]	2	2
A. naeslundii		1	2 (9)	1	1
L. uli		38+	3 (4)	9	9
C. concisus	green	30	4 (3)	44+	6
S. sputigena		36	5 (3)	15	10
B. gracilis		17	6 (3)	21	5
P. micros	orange	6	7 (3)	3	4
P. anaerobius ID		38+	8 (2)	20	23
A. israelii		21	9 (2)	38	22
L. rimae		11	10 (2)	29	13
P. gingivalis	red	38+	11 (2)	6	20

[a] Species rank based on data obtained from W. E. C. Moore and L. V. H. Moore. 1994. The bacteria of periodontal diseases. *Periodontology 2000* **5**:66-77.

[b] Cluster designations based on data obtained from S.S. Socransky, et al. 1998. Microbial complexes in subgingival plaque. *J. Clin. Periodontol.* **25**:134-144.

[c] *Actinomyces israelii, Actinomyces meyeri, Actinomyces naeslundii, Actinomyces odontolyticus, Bacteroides gracilis, Campylobacter concisus, Capnocytophaga gingivalis, Fusobacterium nucleatum, Gemella morbillorum, Lactobacillus rimae, Lactobacillus uli, Peptostreptococcus anaerobius, Peptostreptococcus micros, Porphyromonas gingivalis, Streptococcus gordonii, Streptococcus intermedius, Streptococcus oralis, Streptococcus sanguis,* and *Veillonella atypica.*

[d] Number in parentheses is the percentage of isolates taken at random from subgingival samples.

found in high numbers both in healthy sites and diseased sites. These data indicate that the most numerous species found in healthy sites include all or nearly all of the members of two clusters, purple and yellow, respectively, that are found in lower abundance in diseased sites. Further, these data suggest that these clusters represent early colonizers of the tooth surface that precede the colonization of additional genera that comprise other clusters.

One of the interesting events that occur in the transition from health to gingivitis is the reduction in numbers of the bacteria from the yellow and purple clusters. The two members of the orange cluster dominate and comprise 15 % of the bacteria isolated. In contrast to the decrease in yellow and purple clusters, a representative, *Porphyromonas gingivalis*, of the red cluster appears and is found consistently in the other two periodontal conditions. This event is clearly delineated by Socransky *et al.* (1998) in their study, where they found that members of the red cluster are rarely found without members of the orange cluster. Their data suggest that members of the orange cluster precede colonization by the red cluster members, i.e. succession of genera occurs on oral surfaces. Furthermore, the major changes in the species from healthy sites compared to gingivitis sites also suggests that the yellow and purple cluster members are more related to health than to gingivitis.

Our laboratory has surveyed these bacteria for their ability to coaggregate with a variety of potential partners spanning more than 16 genera; we found that they have a defined set of coaggregaton partners (Whittaker *et al.*, 1996). We (Cisar *et al.*, 1979; Kolenbrander, 1988) and others (Gibbons & Nygaard, 1970; McIntire *et al.*, 1978) have proposed that partnerships are often a result of surface molecules on one cell type that recognize their cognates on another genetically distinct cell type. The remainder of this chapter is a discussion of merging the two ideas of cell-to-cell recognition of partners and of succession of genera relevant to colonization of tooth surfaces and to progression of oral diseases. It is important to recognize that this discussion is limited to the contribution of adherence to colonization and does not address an equally important function of growth of bacteria in biofilms. Growth of bacteria in mixed-species microbial communities is an active area of research, and its role in colonization and biofilm community structure is being investigated.

Acquired pellicle

Within the first few hours after professional cleaning, the tooth surface is coated by a 200 to 1000 nm thick layer called the acquired pellicle (Hannig, 1997). This layer is predominantly derived from host secretions including saliva and crevicular fluid, a serous secretion. Several molecules within the acquired pellicle have been identified as receptors for binding oral bacteria. Acidic proline-rich proteins bind *Streptococcus gordonii* (Gibbons *et al.*, 1991; Hsu *et al.*, 1994) and *Actinomyces naeslundii* (Gibbons & Hay, 1988) that bear type 1 fimbriae on their surface (Cisar *et al.*, 1991; Nesbitt *et al.*, 1992). While the streptococci bind to the Pro-Gln dipeptide at the carboxy terminus of the proline-rich proteins (Gibbons *et al.*, 1991), the actinomyces appear to bind to a

174

different site within the molecule (Gibbons *et al.,* 1988). Strains of *S. gordonii* also bind to salivary a-amylase (Scannapieco *et al.,* 1995). Both fusobacteria and actinomyces bind to the phosphoprotein statherin (Gibbons*et al.,* 1988), and fusobacteria and streptococci bind to salivary proline-rich glycoproteins (Gillece-Castro *et al.,* 1991; Murray *et al.,* 1992). Other receptors include mucins and secretory immunoglobulin A molecules (Kilian & Nyvad, 1990).

The acquired pellicle also contains bacterial products like glucosyltransferases, which in the presence of sucrose catalyze the synthesis of glucans that, in turn, can mediate the binding of *Veillonella* species (McCabe & Donkersloot, 1977) and *Streptococcus mutans* (Schilling & Bowen, 1992). In addition, bacterial cell wall fragments and appendages are likely constituents of the acquired pellicle and may serve as receptors for binding oral bacteria. For example, lipoteichoic acid has been shown to inhibit adherence of *S. gordonii* to an insoluble bacterial glucan-polymer mass (Vickerman & Jones, 1992). It is well known that binding to receptors in the acquired pellicle and coaggregations between oral bacteria do not require living cells (Kolenbrander, 1988), suggesting that the molecules necessary for the interactions are constitutively expressed and, therefore, important to the oral biofilm.

The formation of the acquired pellicle precedes adherence of the initial colonizing bacteria. The focus of this chapter is on the events subsequent to adherence to receptors of the acquired pellicle. A description of the potential role of coaggregation in the development of dental plaque is presented diagrammatically in the set of three figures that follow. For illustrative purposes, specific strains are shown in these figures so that specific kinds of interactions can be discussed. For example, *Fusobacterium nucleatum* PK1594 coaggregates with numerous strains by lactose-inhibitable interactions (Figure 3), whereas other strains of fusobacteria (not shown in Figure 3) may also exhibit coaggregations with numerous strains. These interactions of other fusobacteria and their respective partners exhibit their own characteristic properties of inhibition by lactose or other sugars (Andersen *et al.,* 1998; Kolenbrander *et al.,* 1989). The selection of specific strains for this discussion permits our focus on a recurrent theme in our studies of coaggregations: different genera exhibit a functional similarity of their respective surface molecules that mediate coaggregations with common partners. Several examples of functional similarity will be discussed in the three hypothetical stages (Figures 1, 2, and 3) of formation of oral microbial communities (dental plaque) on the tooth surface. Other critical aspects of biofilm formation such as cell growth and nutritional communication are part of other presentations at this conference.

Stage 1

Streptococci constitute the majority of bacteria (47-82%) (Nyvad & Kilian, 1987) that attach to receptors of the acquired pellicle immediately following professional tooth cleaning. In consideration of this dominance, we have chosen to emphasize the presence of streptococci (Figure 1), although they are not the only initial colonizers. Other members of the early-colonizing microbial

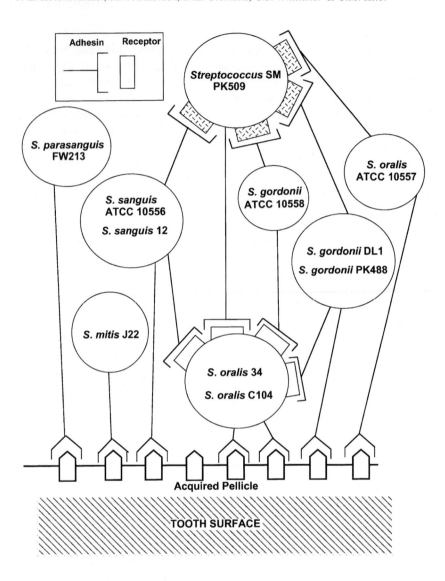

Figure 1 Depiction of intrageneric coaggregation among streptococci and their binding to the acquired pellicle. In all three figures the cell-to-cell interactions are depicted by a complementary set of symbols. An example is shown in the upper left. Adhesins are depicted as symbols with stems, and the receptor is depicted as its complementary-shaped cognate. The linking of the complementary symbols represents a coaggregation partnership. A cell that bears the adhesin (protein) is inactivated by heating or protease treatment. The cell bearing the complementary symbol without a stem (usually a polysaccharide receptor) is not affected by either treatment. Although identically shaped and shaded symbols may or may not be chemically identical, they are functionally similar. The different shading within the receptor rectangles indicates different specificity of the carbohydrate receptors (Cisar *et al.*, 1995). The interactions depicted here are the simplest representations. Binding to receptors in the acquired pellicle is shown as a juxtapositioning of a complementary set of obelisk-shaped symbols that are located near the bottom of the figure.

community are discussed below in Stage 2.

Most viridans streptococci adhere to saliva-coated hydroxyapatite (SHA), but a few like *S. gordonii* ATCC 10558 do not bind (Gibbons *et al.,* 1991; Hsu *et al.,* 1994). An unusual feature of viridans streptococci compared to other oral bacteria is the prevalence of coaggregations among strains within the genus (Kolenbrander *et al.,* 1990; Kolenbrander *et al.,* 1995). Most of these intrageneric coaggregations are inhibited by N-acetylgalactosamine and/or lactose (Figure 1, rectangle-shaped symbols) (Hsu *et al.,* 1994; Kolenbrander *et al.,* 1990). However, some viridans streptococci like *Streptococcus parasanguis* FW213 and *Streptococcus mitis* J22 do not coaggregate with any of the other streptococci. Others like *Streptococcus oralis* ATCC 10557, coaggregate with *Streptococcus* SM PK509, but not with other strains. Considering that more than 80% of the bacteria on an enamel surface initially are streptococci, the ability to participate in intrageneric coaggregation may be a significant advantage and may contribute to the dominance of streptococci as early colonizers.

Receptors on the surface of *S. oralis* 34/*S. oralis* C104 are recognized by adhesins on five streptococci (*S. gordonii* strains DL1, PK488, and ATCC 10558 and *S. sanguis* strains ATCC 10556 and 12). These receptors are cell wall polysaccharides composed of linear phosphodiester-linked hexasaccharide repeating units (Cisar *et al.,* 1995). While the receptors on *S. oralis* 34 and *S. oralis* C104 are not chemically identical, they do contain an identical disaccharide, GalNAcβ1—>3Gal, at the reducing end of the hexasaccharide repeating unit, which is recognized by the adhesins on the partner streptococci (Cisar *et al.,* 1995). Coaggregation-defective mutants of both *S. oralis* 34 and *S. oralis* C104 have been isolated. They lost the ability to coaggregate with all five streptococcal partners simultaneously, but both mutants retained their coaggregation with *Streptococcus* SM PK509 (Figure 1, open rectangle). The chemical structure of the receptor mediating this latter coaggregation is unknown.

The adhesins recognizing the shaded rectangle-shaped symbols on *S. oralis* 34/*S. oralis* C104 are functionally similar but not identical (Clemans & Kolenbrander, 1995). Antiserum raised against *S. gordonii* DL1 and absorbed with cells of a coaggregation-defective mutant PK1897, which fails to coaggregate with *S. oralis* 34/*S. oralis* C104 (Clemans and Kolenbrander, 1995), blocks coaggregation between *S. gordonii* DL1 and *S. oralis* 34/*S. oralis* C104 (Clemans and Kolenbrander, 1995). This absorbed antiserum (A-1897) also blocks coaggregation between *S. gordonii* PK488 and *S. oralis* 34/*S. oralis* C104, but it does not block coaggregations between *S. oralis* 34/*S. oralis* C104 and the other three streptococcal partners (*S. gordonii* ATCC 10558 and *S. sanguis* strains ATCC 10556 and 12). Besides blocking coaggregation, the absorbed antiserum also identified a 100-kDa protein on the surface of both *S. gordonii* DL1 and PK488 (Clemans and Kolenbrander, 1995). A cross-reacting protein of slightly larger molecular size was observed in surface extracts of the other partners of *S. oralis* 34/*S. oralis* C104 including *Streptococcus* SM PK509 and the non-partner *S. oralis* ATCC 10557 (Clemans and Kolenbrander, 1995).

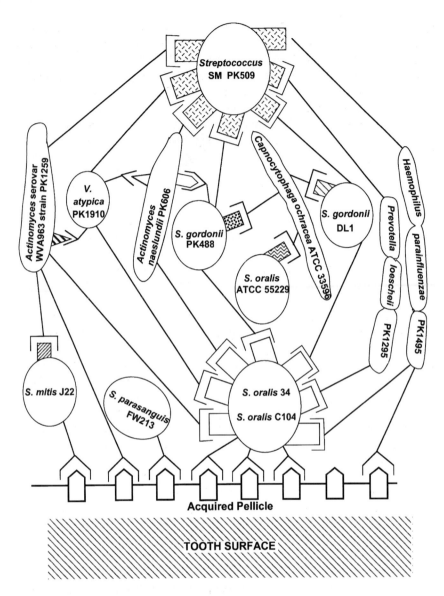

Figure 2 Depiction of intergeneric coaggregation among early colonizers of oral biofilms on the tooth surface. Species abbreviations: *Veillonella atypica* PK1910.

The putative GalNAc-sensitive 100-kDa adhesin on *S. gordonii* DL1 is associated with surface-located glycerol lipoteichoic acid (LTA) (Clemans *et al.*, 1999). Mutants in the *dlt* operon encoding genes for D-alanylation of LTA fail to express the 100-kDa protein suggesting that D-alanylated LTA forms a scaffold for presenting the 100-kDa adhesin on the streptococcal surface (Clemans *et al.*,

1999). Immunoreactive proteins of 100-kDa were notably absent in extracts of *S. parasanguis* FW213, *S. mitis* J22, *S. oralis* 34 or *S. oralis* C104 (Clemans and Kolenbrander, 1995). The association of the 100-kDa adhesin with LTA and the absence of both in *S. mitis* J22 and *S. oralis* strains 34 and C104 are supported by the reports that neither of these species possess detectable amounts of glycerol LTA (Hogg *et al.*, 1997; Kilian *et al.*, 1989). Since all of the streptococcal strains bearing GalNAc-reactive adhesins exhibit a surface protein of about 100 kDa, it is proposed that these functionally similar proteins mediate intrageneric coaggregations.

The absorbed antiserum A-1897 also blocks coaggregation between *S. gordonii* DL1 and *Streptococcus* SM PK509, suggesting that the same adhesin that mediates coaggregation with *S. oralis* 34/*S. oralis* C104 also mediates coaggregation with *Streptococcus* SM PK509 (Clemans and Kolenbrander, 1995). Support for this idea comes from two additional observations. Coaggregation-defective mutants of *S. gordonii* DL1 simultaneously lose the ability to coaggregate with *S. oralis* 34/*S. oralis* C104 and *Streptococcus* SM PK509 (Clemans & Kolenbrander, 1995; Whittaker *et al.*, 1996), and they do not exhibit the 100-kDa surface protein in immunoblots (Clemans and Kolenbrander, 1995; Whittaker *et al.*, 1996). The receptor on *Streptococcus* SM PK509 is distinct (Figure 1, stippled rectangle) from those on *S. oralis* 34/*S. oralis* C104, because it is recognized by *S. oralis* ATCC 10557, whereas ATCC 10557 does not coaggregate with *S. oralis* 34/*S. oralis* C104 or any of the other streptococci shown (Kolenbrander *et al.*, 1990). Furthermore, the strain PK509 receptor is known to be chemically distinct from the receptor on *S. oralis* 34/*S. oralis* C104 (Mary Ritchie, MS thesis, University of Maryland Baltimore County, 1996). Thus, functional similarity of adhesins and receptors provides specificity to intrageneric coaggregations among the initial colonizers of the human tooth.

Stage 2

As has been noted for other ecosystems, oral biofilms also become more complex after initial colonization of the site. The initial colonizers are joined by other species and in some cases are replaced by the secondary colonizers. Six additional species are shown in Figure 2 to illustrate further the idea of functional similarity of adherence among early colonizers. A total of five genera recognize *S. oralis* 34/*S. oralis* C104 by GalNAc-inhibitable coaggregations. It is proposed that the adhesins on *Haemophilus parainfluenzae* PK1495 (*H. parainfluenzae* HP28 (Liljemark *et al.*, 1985)), *Prevotella loescheii* PK1295 (Weiss *et al.*, 1987), *S. gordonii* DL1 (Clemans and Kolenbrander, 1995; Whittaker *et al.*, 1996), *S. gordonii* PK488 (Kolenbrander *et al.*, 1990), *A. naeslundii* PK606 (Kolenbrander & Andersen, 1990), *Veillonella atypica* PK1910 (Hughes *et al.*, 1988), and *Actinomyces* serovar WVA963 PK1259 (Klier *et al.*, 1997), are functionally similar and recognize the same carbohydrate receptor on *S. oralis* 34/*S. oralis* C104. Coaggregation-defective mutants of *S. oralis* 34/*S. oralis* C104 that were selected on the basis of their inability to

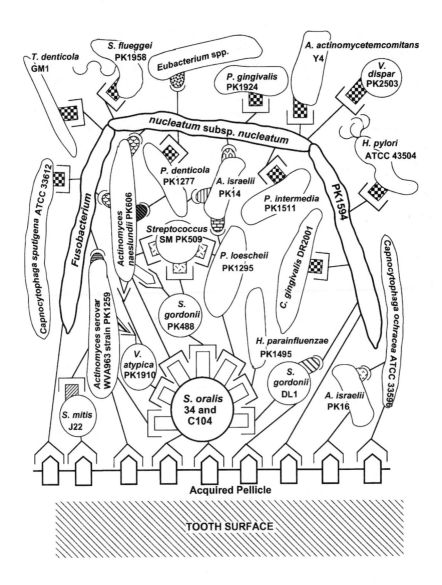

Figure 3 Depiction of multigeneric coaggregation among bacteria found in mature dental plaque. Species abbreviations: *Actinobacillus actinomycetemcomitans, Actinomyces israelii, Capnocytophaga gingivalis, Haemophilus parainfluenzae, Helicobacter pylori, Porphyromonas gingivalis, Prevotella denticola, Prevotella intermedia, Prevotella loescheii, Selenomonas flueggei, Streptococcus gordonii, Streptococcus mitis, Streptococcus oralis, Treponema denticola, Veillonella atypica,* and *Veillonella dispar.*

coaggregate with one of the seven partners, fail to coaggregate with all seven. A *S. oralis* 34 mutant, isolated by its failure to bind to a plant GalNAc-reactive lectin, does not have the surface polysaccharide receptor (Cisar, 1986), and it does not coaggregate with these partners. While the adhesins may be function-ally similar, they appear to be different structurally. Adhesins on *H. parainfluenzae* of 35 kDa (Lai *et al.*, 1990), on *P. loescheii* of 75 kDa (Weiss *et al.*, 1988), on *S. gordonii* DL1 and PK488 of 100 kDa (Clemans and Kolenbrander, 1995; Whittaker *et al.*, 1996), on *A. naeslundii* PK606 of un-known size, on *V. atypica* PK1910 of 45 kDa (Hughes *et al.*, 1992), and on *Actinomyces* serovar WVA963 strain PK1259 of 95 kDa (Klier *et al.*, 1997; Klier *et al.*, 1998) have been reported. Thus, functional similarity among the adhesins may contribute directly to the increased complexity of the ecosystem.

Antiserum raised against strain PK1259 and absorbed with a mutant that cannot coaggregate with *S. oralis* 34/*S. oralis* C104 blocks coaggregation between PK1259 and *S. oralis* 34/*S. oralis* C104 or *Streptococcus* SM PK509 (Klier *et al.*, 1997). Two classes of mutants of PK1259 defective in coaggregation with *S. oralis* 34/*S. oralis* C104 were isolated; one possesses type 2 fimbriae and no 95-kDa putative adhesin, and the other has no type 2 fimbriae and excretes the 95-kDa protein (Klier *et al.*, 1998). This is the first evidence that the type 2 fimbrial subunits and the lactose-reactive adhesin are distinct actinomyces proteins; only the lactose-reactive adhesin is involved in coaggregation. The 95-kDa putative adhesin also mediates coaggregation with *S. mitis* J22 and *Streptococcus* SM PK509, since both classes of coaggregation-defective mutants of PK1259 also fail to coaggregate with these streptococci (Klier *et al.*, 1997). Mutant-absorbed antiserum blocks coaggregation between PK1259 and all four of the streptococcal partners (Klier *et al.*, 1997). It is known that the surface polysaccharide-receptors on strains J22, PK509, 34 and C104 are chemically different (Mary Ritchie, MS thesis, University of Maryland Baltimore County, 1996) (Cisar *et al.*, 1995), however, the evidence indicates that they are functionally similar in coaggregation reactions.

The same pattern of simultaneous loss of coaggregation with multiple partners by coaggregation-defective mutants and blocking of coaggregation by mutant-absorbed antiserum was observed with *V. atypica* PK1910 (Hughes *et al.*, 1992; Hughes *et al.*, 1990). The two remaining interactions (Figure 2, triangle-shaped symbols), between the veillonella and two actinomyces is mediated by a different mechanism and illustrates the independent nature of different kinds of coaggregations possible by an oral bacterial cell. The respec-tive complementary molecules (Figure 2, triangle-shaped symbols) on the veillonella and the actinomyces are unknown.

The interactions between *Capnocytophaga ochracea* ATCC 33596 and three streptococci are unusual in that they are inhibited by lactose but are inhibited 16-fold more strongly by L-rhamnose (Weiss *et al.*, 1987). Indeed, the polysac-charide receptor on *S. oralis* ATCC 55229 contains two residues of L-rhamnose in the repeating hexasaccharide (Cassels *et al.*, 1990). The polysaccharide receptors on the other two streptococcal partners DL1 and PK488 have not been studied. Coaggregation-defective mutants of *C. ochracea* ATCC 33596 have simultaneously lost the ability to coaggregate with all three streptococcal partners (Weiss *et al.,* 1987), and the structure that appears to mediate these coaggregations is about 155 kDa (Weiss *et al.,* 1990). While *S. oralis* ATCC 55229 bears the polysaccharide receptor for coaggregation with the capnocytophaga, it does not bear the GalNAc-reactive adhesins (rectangle-shaped symbols with stems) seen on *S. gordonii* strains PK488 and DL1 that react with polysaccharide receptors on *Streptococcus* SM PK509 and the *S. oralis* strains 34 and C104. Thus, coaggregation between *C. ochracea* ATCC33596 and the three streptococcal partners revealed functionally similar streptococcal receptors that were undetected by coaggregations among strepto-cocci discussed in Figure 1.

Stage 3

The gram-negative organism that numerically dominates in dental plaque is *Fusobacterium nucleatum* (Moore and Moore, 1994). Interestingly, members of this species coaggregate with all other oral bacteria so far tested (Andersen *et al.,* 1998; Kolenbrander *et al.,* 1989; Kolenbrander *et al.,* 1995). *F. nucleatum* also binds to statherin, a phosphoprotein in the acquired pellicle (Gibbons *et al.,* 1988). For these reasons *F. nucleatum* is proposed to play a major role in the development of a more complex biofilm on the tooth surface. Our laboratory has studied *F. nucleatum* subsp. *nucleatum* PK1594, and interactions with some of its partners are shown in Figure 3. It exhibits two basic types of coaggregations: lactose-inhibitable (Figure 3, rectangle-shaped symbol) and lactose non-inhibitable (Figure 3, semi-circle shaped symbol). All lactose-inhibitable interactions appear to be mediated by the same surface structure, since a mutant unable to coaggregate with *P. gingivalis* PK1924 is unable to coaggregate with all the other partners that bear functionally similar receptors (Figure 3, checkered rectangle-shaped symbols) (Andersen *et al.,* 1998). Ten species are shown to participate in lactose-inhibitable interactions with strain PK1594 indicating the wide range of partnerships of this one strain of fusobacteria. In sharp contrast is the inability of some of its partners to coaggregate with bacteria other than fusobacteria (Andersen *et al.,* 1998; George & Falkler, 1992; Kolenbrander *et al.,* 1989; Kolenbrander *et al.,* 1995).

Two central foci are highlighted in Figure 3 by heavy outlines around the cell shapes of *F. nucleatum* subsp. *nucleatum* PK1594 and *S. oralis* strains 34 and C104. Important contributions by streptococci and fusobacteria to the development of a biofilm on human teeth seem certain, because they are present in high numbers in the oral bacterial communities. The *S. oralis* 34 and C104 cell (Figure 3, bottom center) illustrates the functional similarity of adhesins from seven species that recognize a surface polysaccharide on the streptococci. Conversely, the fusobacterium cell illustrates the functional similarity of receptors on ten species that are recognized by the same putative adhesin on the fusobacterium. It is unlikely that these two examples of functional similarity are the only ones occurring in oral biofilm formations. Thus, the observation that

182

coaggregations are not random among oral bacteria could be explained, in part, by functional similarity of coaggregation-relevant molecules on the surfaces of a wide range of genetically distant oral bacteria.

Shown in Figures 1, 2, and 3 are several examples of functional similarity among coaggregation-relevant surface molecules. As we learn more about each molecule it becomes evident that many of them are structurally closely related (Cisar *et al.*, 1995). Such evidence suggests that the genes that encode these molecules may have been transmitted horizontally within the oral bacterial community.

The ecological pressure to possess such functionally similar surface components could have arisen within the oral microbial community through co-evolution of genes encoding these adherence-relevant molecules. Sharing of genetic information critical to bacterial colonization of oral surfaces may have occurred through cell-to-cell contact like that observed with coaggregating partners. The potent effect of adherence-relevant molecules on colonization is reflected in the temporal relationship of the species of bacteria isolated at different times after teeth are cleaned and the coaggregation partners of these bacteria. Pioneer species are predominantly streptococci that exhibit strong intrageneric coaggregations (Figure 1). Secondary colonizers coaggregate with the streptococci and among themselves (Figure 2). And, finally, those that are late colonizers coaggregate most strongly with fusobacteria, which become the dominant gram-negative bacteria in subgingival dental plaque (Figure 3). Thus, although there is a shift in the balance of resident oral bacteria as dental plaque ages, the bacteria that populate these changing communities exhibit functionally similar surface molecules.

References

Andersen, R. N., Ganeshkumar, N. & Kolenbrander, P. E. (1998). *Helicobacter pylori* adheres selectively to *Fusobacterium* spp. *Oral Microbiol. Immunol.* **13**, 51-54.

Bos, R., van der Mei, H. C. & Busscher, H. J. (1995). A quantitative method to study co-adhesion of microorganisms in a parallel plate flow chamber. II: Analysis of the kinetics of co-adhesion. *J. Microbiol. Meth.* **23**, 169-182.

Cassels, F. J., Fales, H. M., London, J., Carlson, R. W. & Halbeek, H. v. (1990). Structure of a streptococcal adhesin carbohydrate receptor. *J. Biol. Chem.* **265**, 14127-14135.

Ciardi, J. E., McCray, G. F., Kolenbrander, P. E. & Lau, A. (1987). Cell-to-cell interaction of *Streptococcus sanguis* and *Propionibacterium acnes* on saliva-coated hydroxyapatite. *Infect Immun* **55**, 1441-6.

Cisar, J. O. (1986). Fimbrial lectins of the oral actinomyces. In *Microbial lectins and agglutinins: properties and biological activity*, pp. 183-196. Edited by D. Mirelman. New York: John Wiley & Sons, Inc.

Cisar, J. O., Barsumian, E. L., Siraganian, R. P., Clark, W. B., Yeung, M. K., Hsu, S. D., Curl, S. H., Vatter, A. E. & Sandberg, A. L. (1991). Immunochemical and functional studies of *Actinomyces viscosus* T14V type 1 fimbriae with monoclonal and polyclonal antibodies directed against the fimbrial subunit. *J. Gen. Microbiol.* **137**, 1971-1979.

Cisar, J. O., Kolenbrander, P. E. & McIntire, F. C. (1979). Specificity of coaggregation reactions between human oral streptococci and strains of *Actinomyces viscosus* or *Actinomyces naeslundii*. *Infect Immun* **24**, 742-52.

Cisar, J. O., Sandberg, A. L., Abeygunawardana, C., Reddy, G. P. & Bush, C. A. (1995). Lectin recognition of host-like saccharide motifs in streptococcal cell wall polysaccharides.

Glycobiology **5**, 655-662.

Clemans, D. L. & Kolenbrander, P. E. (1995). Identification of a 100-kilodalton putative coaggregation-mediating adhesin of *Streptococcus gordonii* DL1 (Challis). *Infect Immun* **63**, 4890-3.

Clemans, D. L. & Kolenbrander, P. E. (1995). Isolation and characterization of coaggregation-defective (Cog-) mutants of Streptococcus gordonii DL1 (Challis). *J Ind Microbiol* **15**, 193-7.

Clemans, D. L., Kolenbrander, P. E., Debabov, D. V., Zhang, Q., Lunsford, R. D., Sakone, H., Whittaker, C. J., Heaton, M. P. & Neuhaus, F. C. (1999). Insertional inactivation of genes responsible for the D-alanylation of lipoteichoic acid in *Streptococcus gordonii* DL1 (Challis) affects intrageneric coaggregations. *Infect. Immun.* **67**, 2464-2474.

Ellen, R. P., Veisman, H., Buivids, I. A. & Rosenberg, M. (1994). Kinetics of lactose-reversible coadhesion of *Actinomyces naeslundii* WVU398A and *Streptococcus oralis* 34 on the surface of hexadecane droplets. *Oral Microbiol. Immunol.* **9**, 364-371.

George, K. S. & Falkler, W. A., Jr. (1992). Coaggregation studies of the *Eubacterium* species. *Oral Microbiol. Immunol.* **7**, 285-290.

Gibbons, R. J. & Hay, D. I. (1988). Adsorbed salivary proline-rich proteins as bacterial receptors on apatitic surfaces. In *Molecular mechanisms of microbial adhesion*, pp. 143-163. Edited by L. Switalski, M. Hook & E. Beachey. New York: Springer-Verlag.

Gibbons, R. J., Hay, D. I., Cisar, J. O. & Clark, W. B. (1988). Adsorbed salivary proline-rich protein 1 and statherin: receptors for type 1 fimbriae of *Actinomyces viscosus* T14V-J1 on apatitic surfaces. *Infect. Immun.* **56**, 2990-2993.

Gibbons, R. J., Hay, D. I. & Schlesinger, D. H. (1991). Delincation of a segment of adsorbed salivary acidic proline-rich proteins which promotes adhesion of *Streptococcus gordonii* to apatitic surfaces. *Infect. Immun.* **59**, 2948-2954.

Gibbons, R. J. & Nygaard, M. (1970). Interbacterial aggregation of plaque bacteria. *Arch. Oral. Biol.* **15**, 1397-1400.

Gillece-Castro, B. L., Prakobphol, A., Burlingame, A. L., Leffler, H. & Fisher, S. J. (1991). Structure and bacterial receptor activity of a human salivary proline-rich glycoprotein. *J. Biol. Chem.* **266**, 17358-17368.

Hannig, M. (1997). Transmission electron microscopic study of *in vivo* pellicle formation on dental restorative materials. *Eur. J. Oral Sci.* **105**, 422-433.

Hogg, S. D., Whiley, R. A. & DeSoet, J. J. (1997). Occurrence of lipoteichoic acid in oral streptococci. *Int J Syst Bacteriol* **47**, 62-66.

Hsu, S. D., Cisar, J. O., Sandberg, A. L. & Kilian, M. (1994). Adhesive properties of viridans streptococcal species. *Microb. Ecol. Health Dis.* **7**, 125-137.

Hughes, C. V., Andersen, R. N. & Kolenbrander, P. E. (1992). Characterization of Veillonella atypica PK1910 adhesin-mediated coaggregation with oral Streptococcus spp. *Infect Immun* **60**, 1178-86.

Hughes, C. V., Kolenbrander, P. E., Andersen, R. N. & Moore, L. V. (1988). Coaggregation properties of human oral Veillonella spp.: relationship to colonization site and oral ecology. *Appl Environ Microbiol* **54**, 1957-63.

Hughes, C. V., Roseberry, C. A. & Kolenbrander, P. E. (1990). Isolation and characterization of coaggregation-defective mutants of Veillonella atypica. *Arch Oral Biol* **35**, 123S-125S.

Jenkinson, H. F., Terry, S. D., McNab, R. & Tannock, G. W. (1993). Inactivation of the gene encoding surface protein SspA in *Streptococcus gordonii* DL1 affects cell interactions with human salivary agglutinin and oral actinomyces. *Infect. Immun.* **61**, 3199-3208.

Kilian, M., Mikkelsen, L. & Henrichsen, J. (1989). Taxonomic study of viridans streptococci: description of *Streptococcus gordonii* sp. nov. and emended descriptions of *Streptococcus sanguis* (White and Niven, 1946), *Streptococcus oralis* (Bridge and Sneath, 1982), and *Streptococcus mitis* (Andrewes and Horder, 1906). *Int. J. Syst. Bacteriol.* **39**, 471-484.

Kilian, M. & Nyvad, B. (1990). Ability to bind salivary a-amylase discrimminates certain viridans group streptococcal species. *J. Clin. Microbiol.* **28**, 2576-2577.

Klier, C. M., Kolenbrander, P. E., Roble, A. G., Marco, M. L., Cross, S. & Handley, P. S. (1997). Identification of a 95 kDa putative adhesin from *Actinomyces* serovar WVA963 strain PK1259 that is distinct from type 2 fimbrial subunits. *Microbiology* **143**, 835-46.

Klier, C. M., Roble, A. G. & Kolenbrander, P. E. (1998). *Actinomyces* serovar WVA963 coaggregation-defective mutant strain PK2407 secretes lactose-sensitive adhesin that binds to coaggregation partner *Streptococcus oralis* 34. *Oral Microbiol Immunol* **13**, 337-40.

Kolenbrander, P. E. (1988). Intergeneric coaggregation among human oral bacteria and ecology of dental plaque. *Annu Rev Microbiol* **42**, 627-56.

Kolenbrander, P. E. & Andersen, R. N. (1990). Characterization of *Streptococcus gordonii* (*S. sanguis*) PK488 adhesin-mediated coaggregation with *Actinomyces naeslundii* PK606. *Infect. Immun.* **58**, 3064-3072.

Kolenbrander, P. E., Andersen, R. N. & Moore, L. V. H. (1989). Coaggregation of *Fusobacterium nucleatum, Selenomonas flueggei, Selenomonas infelix, Selenomonas noxia*, and *Selenomonas sputigena* with strains from 11 genera of oral bacteria. *Infect. Immun.* **57**, 3194-3203.

Kolenbrander, P. E., Andersen, R. N. & Moore, L. V. H. (1990). Intrageneric coaggregation among strains of human oral bacteria: potential role in primary colonization of the tooth surface. *Appl. Environ. Microbiol.* **56**, 3890-3894.

Kolenbrander, P. E., Parrish, K. D., Andersen, R. N. & Greenberg, E. P. (1995). Intergeneric coaggregation of oral *Treponema* spp. with *Fusobacterium* spp. and intrageneric coaggregation among *Fusobacterium* spp. *Infect. Immun.* **63**, 4584-4588.

Lai, C.-H., Bloomquist, C. & Liljemark, W. F. (1990). Purification and characterization of an outer membrane protein adhesin from *Haemophilus parainfluenzae* HP-28. *Infect. Immun.* **58**, 3833-3839.

Lamont, R. J., Demuth, D. R., Davis, C. A., Malamud, D. & Rosan, B. (1991). Salivary-agglutinin-mediated adherence of *Streptococcus mutans* to early plaque bacteria. *Infect. Immun.* **59**, 3446-3450.

Liljemark, W. F., Bloomquist, C. G. & Fenner, L. J. (1985). Characteristics of the adherence of oral *Haemophilus* species to an experimental salivary pellicle and to other oral bacteria. In *Molecular Basis of Oral Microbial Adhesion*, pp. 94-102. Edited by S. E. Mergenhagen & B. Rosan. Washington, D.C.: American Society for Microbiology.

McCabe, R. M. & Donkersloot, J. A. (1977). Adherence of *Veillonella* species mediated by extracellular glucosyltransferase from *Streptococcus salivarius*. *Infect Immun* **18**, 726-34.

McIntire, F. C., Vatter, A. E., Baros, J. & Arnold, J. (1978). Mechanism of coaggregation between *Actinomyces viscosus* T14V and *Streptococcus sanguis* 34. *Infect Immun* **21**, 978-988.

Moore, W. E. C. & Moore, L. V. H. (1994). The bacteria of periodontal diseases. *Periodontol. 2000* **5**, 66-77.

Murray, P. A., Prakobphol, A., Lee, T., Hoover, C. I. & Fisher, S. J. (1992). Adherence of oral streptococci to salivary glycoproteins. *Infect. Immun.* **60**, 31-38.

Nesbitt, W. E., Beem, J. E., Leung, K.-P. & Clark, W. B. (1992). Isolation and characterization of *Actinomyces viscosus* mutants defective in binding salivary proline-rich proteins. *Infect. Immun.* **60**, 1095-1100.

Nyvad, B. & Kilian, M. (1987). Microbiology of the early colonization of human enamel and root surfaces in vivo. *Scand. J. Dent. Res.* **95**, 369-380.

Palmer, R. J., Jr. & Caldwell, D. E. (1995). A flowcell for the study of plaque removal and regrowth. *J. Microbiol. Meth.* **24**, 171-182.

Scannapieco, F. A., Torres, G. I. & Levine, M. J. (1995). Salivary amylase promotes adhesion of oral streptococci to hydroxyapatite. *J. Dent. Res.* **74**, 1360-1366.

Schilling, K. M. & Bowen, W. H. (1992). Glucans synthesized in situ in experimental salivary pellicle function as specific binding sites for *Streptococcus mutans*. *Infect. Immun.* **60**, 284-295.

Skopek, R. J. & Liljemark, W. F. (1994). The influence of saliva on interbacterial adherence. *Oral Microbiol. Immunol.* **9**, 19-24.

Socransky, S. S., Haffajee, A. D., M. A., C., Smith, C. & Kent, R. L., Jr. (1998). Microbial complexes in subgingival plaque. *J. Clin. Periodontol.* **25**, 134-144.

Vickerman, M. M. & Jones, G. W. (1992). Adhesion of glucosyltransferase phase variants to *Streptococcus gordonii* bacterium-glucan substrata may involve lipoteichoic acid. *Infect Immun* **60**, 4301-4308.

Weiss, E. I., Eli, I., Shenitzki, B. & Smorodinsky, N. (1990). Identification of the rhamnose-sensitive adhesin of *Capnocytophaga ochracea* ATCC 33596. *Archs Oral Biol.* **35**, 127s-130s.

Weiss, E. I., Kolenbrander, P. E., London, J., Hand, A. R. & Andersen, R. N. (1987). Fimbria-associated proteins of Bacteroides loescheii PK1295 mediate intergeneric coaggregations. *J*

Bacteriol **169**, 4215-22.

Weiss, E. I., London, J., Kolenbrander, P. E., Andersen, R. N., Fischler, C. & Siraganian, R. P. (1988). Characterization of monoclonal antibodies to fimbria-associated adhesins of Bacteroides loescheii PK1295. *Infect Immun* **56**, 219-24.

Weiss, E. I., London, J., Kolenbrander, P. E., Kagermeier, A. S. & Andersen, R. N. (1987). Characterization of lectinlike surface components on *Capnocytophaga ochracea* ATCC33596 that mediate coaggregation with gram-positive oral bacteria. *Infect. Immun.* **55**, 1198-1202.

Whittaker, C. J., Clemans, D. L. & Kolenbrander, P. E. (1996). Insertional inactivation of an intrageneric coaggregation-relevant adhesin locus from *Streptococcus gordonii* DL1 (Challis). *Infect Immun* **64**, 4137-42.

Whittaker, C. J., Klier, C. M. & Kolenbrander, P. E. (1996). Mechanisms of adhesion by oral bacteria. *Annu. Rev. Microbiol.* **50**, 513-552.

FORMATION OF DENTAL PLAQUE AND OTHER ORAL BIOFILMS

Max A. Listgarten

Of all biofilms in nature, dental plaque is one of the most accessible. Starting with van Leeuwenhoek in the 17th century, it has been studied on and off for the last 300 years. This tooth-associated biofilm is among the most complex in nature and is home to over 300 species of microorganisms. Oral biofilms can also be found on the soft tissue surfaces as well as the various restorative and prosthetic materials introduced in the oral cavity in the course of dental treatment. Because of the constant desquamation of surface cells, bacteria colonizing the soft tissues do not form substantial accumulations on the mucosal lining of the mouth. By contrast, bacterial deposits on teeth and assorted dental materials can accumulate undisturbed as long as the surface is protected from frictional forces due to mastication and oral hygiene procedures. Since oral biofilms play a primary role in the etiology of dental caries and periodontal diseases, their development and biological properties are basic to the prevention and treatment of these diseases. This article summarizes the features of the oral environment that modulate the formation of oral biofilms. The development of oral biofilms in supra- and subgingival locations on teeth and artificial substrates is reviewed, as are the biological properties of these biofilms in relation to the prevention and treatment of infectious forms of periodontal disease.

Introduction

In 1898, Black was the first to refer to the dense accumulation of bacteria reported earlier by Williams (1897) over carious enamel as dental plaque (Bowen, 1975). The term was later extended to include bacterial deposits on other hard surfaces, including other dental tissues, and prosthetic materials, including dental implants. Since these early reports, a number of comprehensive reviews have been published on the development, structure and pathogenic potential of dental plaque (Genco *et al.*, 1969; Schroeder, 1969; Schroeder and de Boever, 1970; Socransky, 1970, 1977; Socransky and Manganiello, 1971; Bowen, 1975; Theilade and Theilade, 1975; 1981; Smith, 1977; Tanzer, 1977; Russell and Melville, 1979; Lie, 1979; Slots, 1979; van Palenstein-Helderman, 1981; Listgarten, 1994; Shibly *et al.*, 1995; Zambon, 1996; Darveau *et al.* 1997). Much less information is available on microbial colonizers of the oral soft tissues.

Costerton (1978) was first to introduce the term *biofilm*. A biofilm is defined as bacterial aggregates, usually existing as closely associated communities, that adhere to assorted natural or artificial surfaces, usually in an aqueous environment that contains a sufficient concentration of nutrients to sustain the metabolic needs of the microbiota. Examples of the wide diversity of such biofilms can be found in a number of previously published reviews (Costerton *et al.*, 1987;

1995; 1999; Marshall *et al.*, 1992). They range from naturally occurring aquatic environments (Geesey *et al.*, 1977; Marshall *et al.*, 1971, 1992), to industrial aquatic systems (Costerton, 1984; Costerton *et al.*, 1987), assorted external and internal body surfaces, as well as various medical devices and prostheses (Costerton *et al.*, 1987, 1995; 1999). Dental plaque is a naturally occurring biofilm that has been under investigation for over 300 years, in all likelihood for much longer than most other types of biofilm. It is readily accessible for various types of investigation. It is somewhat surprising, therefore, that the literature on dental plaque is so seldom referenced in reviews dealing with biofilms in general. Perhaps, the proceedings of this conference will contribute to rectifying this omission.

By virtue of their inclusion in complex bacterial communities, bacterial cells in biofilms exhibit biological characteristics that differ markedly from their isolated counterparts in planktonic suspensions. Some of the differences may be due, in part, to the diffusion barriers that are created by the interbacterial matrices that play a key role in the cohesion and adhesion of the bacterial mass to the substrate. These matrices interfere with the free diffusion of nutrients, gases and metabolic products, thereby modifying the immediate environment of the cells in the biofilm. However, there is evidence that bacterial cells in biofilms may also undergo phenotypic alterations, due to changes in gene expression (Davies *et al.*, 1993). These and other factors may account for the marked differences, including increased resistance to antibiotics, expressed by biofilm-associated versus planktonic microorganisms (Gilbert *et al.*, 1997). The biofilm environment may also explain the ability of certain bacterial species to persist under the constantly changing conditions in dental plaque. Bowden and Hamilton (1998) have recently reviewed the various mechanisms that allow oral bacteria to survive in their human hosts despite the many stresses to which they are subjected. Their incorporation into dental plaque is but one of these mechanisms.

The purpose of this symposium is to revisit the subject of dental plaque. This review will focus primarily on the formation of dental plaque or, as one might refer to it in a more contemporary context, tooth-associated biofilms. Other oral biofilms, namely those found on biomaterials and soft tissue surfaces will also be briefly discussed. In order to keep the bibliography within reasonable limits, references will emphasize reviews rather than original reports. The author wishes to apologize in advance to authors whose publications are not quoted directly, but have been included in one of the cited reviews.

Development of oral biofilms
The Oral Environment
The oral cavity contains hard as well as soft tissue surfaces, all of which are potentially available as substrates for the development of oral biofilms. Substantial accumulations of bacteria on the surfaces of the masticatory mucosa (gingiva and hard palate) and lining mucosa (cheeks, floor of the mouth, soft palate) are rare, primarily because of rapid rates of epithelial cell turnover and

desquamation of surface cells. The specialized mucosa of the dorsum of the tongue provides a much more protected environment for the sequestration of bacteria and fungi and harbors a significant bacterial population. All surfaces are kept lubricated by major and minor salivary glands that provide a nutritious aqueous environment suitable for the maintenance of a resident bacterial population. The saliva itself contains approximately $10^7 - 10^8$ bacteria/ml, mostly derived from colonized intraoral surfaces. Some salivary components, including various glycoproteins, lysozyme, β2-microglobulin, proline-rich proteins, statherin, fibronectin and a-amylase promote the adherence of bacterial cells to surfaces coated by these salivary constituents. On the other hand, salivary histatins and cystatins, lactoferrin, thiocyanate ions, peroxidases, as well as antibodies of the IgA type may play a defensive role because of their antimicrobial properties or their ability to interfere with the colonization of oral surfaces (Williams and Gibbons, 1972; McNabb and Tomasi, 1981; Scannapieco, 1994; Marcotte and Lavoie, 1998). By contrast to the constantly shedding soft tissue surfaces, the hard surfaces, consisting of natural teeth as well as assorted prosthetic materials, provide a stable substrate for colonization by bacteria. Notwithstanding the shearing forces of mastication and the constant friction of soft tissues, such surfaces are able to serve as suitable supports for the growth of adherent bacterial communities.

Unlike most prosthetic materials, teeth are composed of mineralized organic matrices (enamel, dentin, and cementum). Although dentin and cementum surfaces are not generally exposed to the intraoral environment, they may become exposed as a result of gingival recession, periodontal diseases or their treatment. The hydroxyapatite-rich mineral phase results in surface free energy that has been implicated as a factor in the rate of colonization of tooth surfaces by bacteria (Quirynen *et al.*, 1989; Weerkamp *et al.* 1989). Surfaces charges may influence the rate of adsorption of salivary proteins which in turn play a role in the early phase of bacterial colonization (Jenkins, 1968). The formation of these organic films, or acquired pellicles, precedes the actual colonization of the tooth surface by bacteria (Lie, 1978) and may enhance the rate of adhesion of certain species to the tooth surface (Kraus *et al.*, 1976). Notwithstanding the differences in surface charges and other characteristics between teeth and various biomaterials, the latter are also capable of adsorbing organic molecules from tissue fluids that can serve as receptors for the various adhesins found on bacterial cell surfaces (Gristina, 1987). The different mechanisms that mediate the adhesion of bacterial cells to salivary components of the acquired pellicle during the early stages of dental plaque formation have been the subject of some recent reviews (Scannapieco, 1994; Liljemark and Blomquist, 1996; Jenkinson and Lamont, 1997) and will not be discussed further in this presentation.

Whereas Lie (1978) reported detectable pellicles on hydroxyapatite surfaces after a 2-hour exposure to saliva, he found little evidence of pellicle formation on epoxy resin. After 24-48 hours, however, pellicles were detected with equal frequency on both types of surface (Lie, 1977a). Berthold *et al.* (1971) compared the growth of dental plaque on different substrates and found similarities between plaque formation on enamel and polished vestopal (a type of epoxy resin), but differences with plaques formed on mylar films and sandblasted vestopal. These observations suggest that the nature of the substrate may influence plaque formation, at least in the early phases. Surface roughness appears to have more influence on the rate of bacterial colonization than surface free energy (Quirynen and Bollen, 1995). However, surface roughness does not appear to affect plaque composition (Quirynen *et al.*, 1993).

Gatewood *et al.* (1993) inserted different substrates into deep periodontal pockets of human volunteers. The substrates consisted of small slabs of enamel-cementum and of smooth and plasma-sprayed titanium. They were left in the pockets to collect dental plaque for periods of 1 to 10 days. The recovered specimens were processed for scanning electron microscopy. No differences in the rate or pattern of plaque formation could be detected among the various substrates. These findings indicate that while the earliest stages of plaque formation may be influenced by surface charges and other physical and chemical properties of the substrate, there is little residual influence of these factors on subgingival plaque formation beyond 24 hours.

One factor that seems to influence the rate of plaque formation over a longer period of time is the inflammatory state of the tissues adjacent to the tooth surface. In the Gatewood (1993) study, the rates of plaque growth and maturation seen within inflamed periodontal pockets was much greater than that observed on surfaces adjacent to less diseased areas. Similar observations have been reported by Goh *et al.* (1986), Quirynen *et al.*, 1991; Ramberg *et al.* (1995) and Daly and Highfield (1996). The increased rate of plaque formation and maturation may be associated with the increased concentration of nutrients available in the inflammatory exudate as compared to that of the normal sulcus environment. It may also be due to anatomic changes in the sulcus region caused by inflammation, namely the formation of pseudopockets that provide a more anaerobic and protected environment suitable for the growth of the predominantly anaerobic species found in mature dental plaque.

Supragingival Plaque Formation on Teeth

The earliest bacterial colonizers of a freshly cleaned tooth surface or a plastic substrate appear within minutes (Saxton, 1973; Rönström *et al.* 1975) and tend to favor surface irregularities (Lie, 1977b; Berthold, 1979). In time, the adhesion of some of these initial colonizers becomes irreversible so that their proliferation gives rise to sessile colonies. Microcolonies produced by in situ bacterial cell division are detectable after 2-4 hours (Saxton, 1973; Rönström *et al.* 1975) and consist primarily of gram-positive coccoid cells (Theilade *et al.* 1982). Some of these early colonizers may be essential for the subsequent colonization of the surface by later arrivals. For example, Cook *et al.* (1998) reported that in a simple in vitro system, limited to 2 species, *Streptococcus gordonii* constituted an essential substrate for the establishment of *Porphyromonas gingivalis*. However, the major growth of dental plaque mass does not take place by co-aggregation at the surface of the developing biofilm, but rather by bacterial cell

Figure 1 One-week-old supragingival dental plaque. Note the dense packing of columnar microcolonies consisting largely of coccoid bacteria. The substrate is located along the bottom edge of the illustration (asterisks). Light micrograph of toluidine blue-methylene blue-stained epoxy resin section. x 1850.

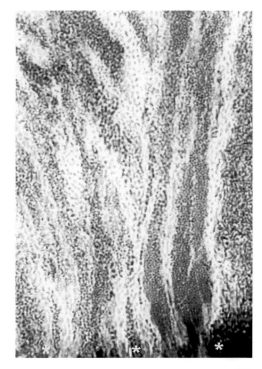

Figure 2 Higher magnification of a serial section of the specimen in Figure 1. The substrate is located along the bottom edge of the illustration (asterisks). Light micrograph of toluidine blue-methylene blue-stained epoxy resin section. x 3200.

division within the biofilm.

Brecx *et al.* (1983) allowed dental plaque to form for a 4-hour period on artificial substrates *in vivo* and then prevented further apposition by covering the plaque with a barrier. They harvested these samples after 8 and 24 hours and compared them with samples that were left uncovered for the same amount of time. In this manner, Brecx *et al.* (1983) were able to ascertain that most of the early plaque growth took place by cell division within the existing plaque mass, rather than by apposition of bacteria on the surface. This is confirmed by the structural characteristics of up to one-week-old supragingival dental plaques (Figures 1 and 2). These bacterial deposits are composed of densely packed columnar microcolonies that appear to grow as distinct bacterial communities, competing for space and nutrients with adjacent bacterial colonies (Listgarten *et al.*, 1975; Listgarten, 1994). Cook *et al.* (1998) reported a similar growth pattern for *Porphyromonas gingivalis* grown in vitro.

The adhesion of the initial colonizers to their substrate is mediated through a variety of structures that include bacterial capsules, pili and fimbriae. The molecular components of these structures responsible for adhesion are referred to as adhesins (Scannapieco, 1994; Liljemark and Bloomquist, 1996; Jenkinson and Lamont, 1997). They include sticky, predominantly carbohydrate coatings (Costerton, 1978), lipotechoic acid, glucosyltransferases and carbohydrate-binding proteins or lectins. These interact with a variety of receptors on the tooth surface, many of which are derived from salivary components (Liljemark and Bloomquist, 1996; Jenkinson and Lamont, 1997). They may also interact with receptors on bacterial surfaces, thereby providing the cohesiveness required for the formation of dental plaque as well as co-aggregation with other bacterial species (Scannapieco, 1994; Jenkinson and Lamont, 1997). Microorganisms may express several adhesins, each specific for a particular receptor.

The rate of plaque growth appears to proceed exponentially for the first few days, with a decreased rate thereafter (Quirynen and van Steenberghe, 1989). The stage of rapid growth appears to correspond to bacterial proliferation within the microcolonies that cover the colonized surface. Nutrients originate from saliva as well as metabolic products of adjacent bacterial colonies (Gilbert *et al.*, 1997). As the bacterial layer becomes thicker, compromised diffusion of nutrients and waste products may result in a slowing down of the rate of growth within the microcolonies. The decreased rate of growth has also been attributed to quorum-sensing, or density-dependent growth (Bowden and Hamilton, 1998). According to Bowden and Hamilton (1998), this sophisticated mechanism of cell growth regulation is dependent on cell-to-cell communication involving an auto-induced diffusible effector molecule that triggers the expression of various regulating genes. Davies *et al.* (1998) demonstrated in a *Pseudomonas aeruginosa* in vitro model that a mutation that blocks the signaling molecule interferes with the formation of the biofilm.

Gibbons and Nygaard (1970) and Gibbons and Spinell (1970) were among the first to suggest that bacterial co-aggregation, that is the aggregation of bacteria of different species, could play a significant role in plaque formation.

BACTERIAL SUCCESSIONS IN THE DEVELOPING DENTAL PLAQUE

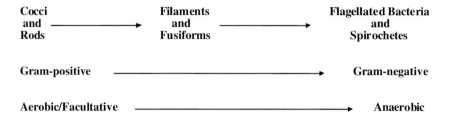

Figure 3 Bacterial successions in the developing dental plaque. Early plaque consists predominantly of Gram-positive, facultative coccoid cells, located supragingivally . As the biofilm matures, filamentous bacteria displace the coccoid cells. The supragingival dental plaque creates an ecological environment favorable to the subsequent establishment of the predominantly Gram-negative, anaerobic subgingival microbiota.

Their findings were confirmed and extended by Hay *et al.* (1971), Kelstrup and Funder-Nielsen (1974) and Cisar *et al.* (1979). It appears, however, that bacterial adhesion to the substrate and cohesion of cells within a homogeneous bacterial community (Ellen and Gibbons, 1972; Saxton, 1973; Long and Swenson, 1976; Socransky *et al.*, 1977; Clergeau-Guérithault, 1986) play a more important role in the early stages of bacterial plaque growth. Co-aggregation enables newly arrived species to colonize the surface of the preexisting bacterial layer, an event that becomes more apparent after a few days of dental plaque growth.

Initially, co-aggregated bacteria, i.e. those attached to the surface of the developing dental plaque, account for but a relatively small proportion of the total plaque mass. The newly attached species are composed primarily of filamentous morphotypes. Some of these filamentous bacteria form corncob-shaped aggregates with coccoid cells attached to their surface (Listgarten *et al.*, 1973,1975; Lancy *et al.*, 1980; Mouton *et al.*, 1980). Co-aggregation is fundamental to the development of these unique bacterial formations as well as those that resemble test-tube brushes (Listgarten, 1976). These result from the specific aggregation of two or more morphotypes, usually filaments and filaments or filaments and rods, to form unique structures that are attached to and extend above the bacterial biofilm, particularly in subgingival dental plaque.

As the bacterial layer increases in thickness, the initial, predominantly coccoid, gram-positive colonizers in the deeper parts of the bacterial mass are faced with an increasingly anaerobic environment and a diminished supply of nutrients. Assorted metabolites which cannot readily diffuse out may also contribute to changes in pH and eH and the accumulation of toxic products. This changing environment favors the eventual replacement of the initial colonizing bacteria by others better suited to the new conditions, namely the filamentous species that have colonized the surface of the coccoid plaque, beginning ap-

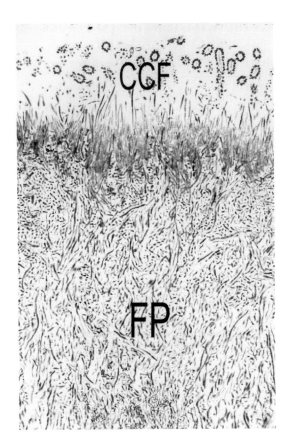

Figure 4 Two-month-old supragingival dental plaque. Filamentous bacteria are the predominant constituents of the mature biofilm (FP). Corncob formations (CCF) frequently occupy the surface. They consist of coccoid cells adhering to a centrally located filamentous microorganism. The substrate is located along the bottom edge of the illustration. Light micrograph of toluidine blue-methylene blue-stained epoxy resin section. x 1850.

proximately on day 3. After about one week, the biofilm undergoes significant internal remodeling that lasts approximately 3 weeks. The surface cells begin to invade and replace the underlying, predominantly coccoid bacterial communities, with a primarily filamentous mass of bacteria aligned more or less perpendicularly to the tooth surface (Listgarten *et al.*, 1975). While some of the initial colonizers may persist, they may be expressing different phenotypic characteristics more suitable to the altered environment (Davies *et al.* 1993; Bowden *et al.*, 1998).

Thus the initial growth phase, characterized by adhesion of bacterial cells and their proliferation, gives way to a secondary growth phase characterized by bacterial successions, that is the replacement of existing bacterial species and genera by others (Figure 3). Eventually the initial coccoid bacterial population of supragingival plaque is replaced by a stable population of filamentous bacteria, a process that may take 2 or more weeks, depending on how well the site is protected from frictional disturbances (Figure 4). The developmental process that leads to the establishment of this stable or climax community of filamentous bacteria is frequently interrupted on exposed tooth surfaces by

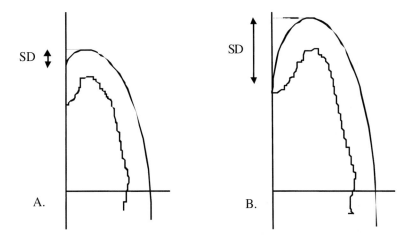

Figure 5 Diagrammatic illustration of (A) a healthy gingiva with a shallow sulcus depth (SD) and (B) an inflamed gingiva with increased sulcus depth (SD) due to tissue swelling. The deeper sulcus favors the establishment of an anaerobic microbiota.

shearing forces due to mastication, oral hygiene procedures or friction by the tongue and cheeks. These events disrupt the coccoid microcolonies to varying degrees, thereby forcing them to start again with their competitive growth at the affected site. On such surfaces, the coccoid cells may continue to form the predominant microbiota for an indefinite period of time, as filamentous bacteria are unable to gain a sufficient ecological advantage to replace the coccoid microbiota.

It is by no means clear that the convective fluid flow through water channels, described by Costerton *et al.* (1995) for a variety of biofilms, also exists in supragingival dental plaque. Dental plaque has not been examined for the existence of these channels with the techniques of confocal scanning electron microscopy and fluorescent probes (Lawrence *et al.*, 1991; Caldwell *et al.*, 1992). However, the dense packing of microbial colonies in immature supragingival dental plaque and of the filamentous bacteria in mature dental plaque would argue against the existence of such channels, at least in supragingival dental plaque.

Subgingival Plaque Formation on Teeth

In response to the supragingival bacterial mass adjacent to it, the marginal gingiva eventually develops an inflammatory response which results in tissue swelling and the formation of a deeper sulcus that provides a more suitable environment for anaerobic bacteria (Figure 5). The accompanying inflammatory exudate, that originates in the highly vascular gingival connective tissue and percolates into the sulcus, is rich in nutrients that also favor the establishment of a predominantly gram-negative, anaerobic subgingival microbiota. The presence of a distinct subgingival microbiota becomes evident after approximately three

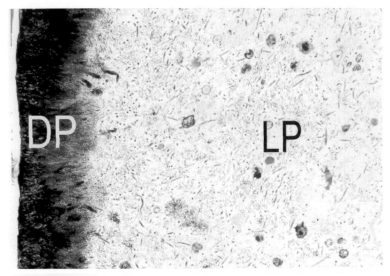

Figure 6 Subgingival dental plaque in a 7 mm periodontal pocket of a 50-year-old patient. Densely packed microorganisms (DP) mediate the attachment of the biofilm to the root surface (left border of the illustration). The bulk of the subgingival microbiota consists of loosely packed, frequently motile bacteria (LP). Light micrograph of toluidine blue-methylene blue-stained epoxy resin section. x 1200.

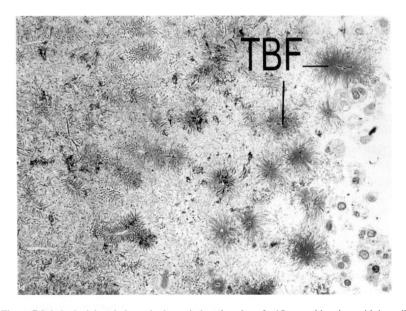

Figure 7 Subgingival dental plaque in the periodontal pocket of a 15-year-old patient with juvenile periodontitis. The surface of the biofilm facing the tissues (located toward the right border of the illustration) has numerous test-tube brush formations (TBF). These consist of one or more axially located filamentous bacteria covered by thin bristle-like bacteria. Light micrograph of toluidine blue-methylene blue-stained epoxy resin section. x 1200.

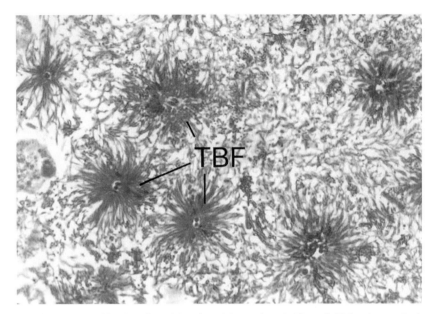

Figure 8 Higher magnification of a serial section of the specimen in Figure 7. Light micrograph of toluidine blue-methylene blue-stained epoxy resin section. TBF, test-tube brush formations. x 3200

weeks of plaque development (Listgarten *et al.* 1975). In contrast to the densely packed, adherent supragingival dental plaque, the subgingival microbiota is composed of a distinctive population of predominantly gram-negative, predominantly anaerobic species. Many of these microorganisms are motile. Because of their motility they do not form distinct microcolonies such as those found in immature supragingival dental plaque.

The subgingival microbiota may consist in part of a thin adherent bacterial layer similar in structure to the adherent bacterial layer in supragingival plaque (Figure 6). The bulk of the more loosely structured microbiota is located between the adherent microbial layer and the epithelial lining of the gingival sulcus or pocket (Listgarten *et al.* 1975; Listgarten, 1976). Despite the more open structure of the subgingival microbiota, it is a highly organized bacterial community. The deeper layers may contain commensal bacterial aggregates that consist of sessile filamentous bacteria to which are attached other bacterial species, often rod-shaped or filamentous bacteria, in formations resembling test-tube brushes (Figures 7 and 8).

Interspersed among these sessile formations are many gram-negative, motile species (Figures 9 and 10). Spirochetes predominate on the outer surface of the bacterial mass (Figure 11). They are usually separated from the gingival tissue *per se* by a polymorphonuclear leukocyte-rich inflammatory exudate. Although spirochetes are actively motile, they are capable of adhering to a variety of host cells (Thomas, 1996), including assorted coatings on tooth surfaces. The

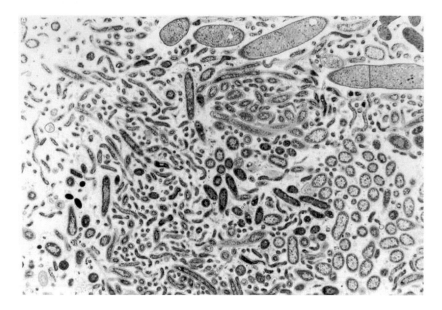

Figure 9 Subgingival dental plaque in the periodontal pocket of a 42-year-old patient with adult periodontitis. The bulk of the microbiota consists of anaerobic, Gram-negative, frequently motile species. Transmission electron micrograph. x 10,000.

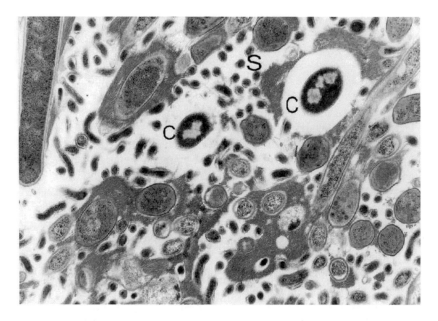

Figure 10 Subgingival 10-week-old dental plaque. The bulk of the microbiota consists of anaerobic, Gram-negative, frequently motile species. C, electronlucent capsule surrounding filamentous bacteria; S, spirochetes. Transmission electron micrograph. x 20,000.

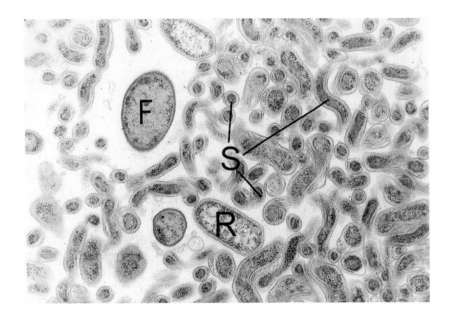

Figure 11 Subgingival dental plaque in the periodontal pocket of a 24-year-old patient with post-juvenile periodontitis. The bulk of the subgingival microbiota consists of small and medium-size spirochetes (S). F, Large Gram-negative filament; R, Gram-negative rod. Light micrograph of toluidine blue-methylene blue-stained epoxy resin section. x 30,000.

adhesion appears to be mediated through adhesins on the bacterial surface. The tendency for spirochetes to adhere through their cell tips is probably due to the high fluidity of the surface membrane and their motility pattern which tends to displace and cluster the adhesins near the cell ends (Charon *et al.*, 1981). As a result, adherent spirochetes often assume a palisading arrangement with the cell bodies parallel to one another and perpendicular to the substrate to which they are attached (Theilade and Attström, 1985).

The subgingival microbiota is bathed in crevicular fluid, an inflammatory exudate that originates from within the adjacent sulcus or pocket wall and differs in composition from the salivary secretions that bathe the supragingival environment (Cimasoni, 1974). As it diffuses from the tissue into the sulcus or pocket, the crevicular fluid picks up assorted constituents derived from the lysis of polymorphonuclear leukocytes as well as metabolic products from the subgingival microbiota. The components of crevicular fluid provide a complex source of nutrients to the subgingival microbiota. Unlike the dense supragingival plaque, which may have few if any diffusion channels within its structure, the more open structure of the subgingival microbiota allows most of the bacterial cells ready access to the crevicular fluid that slowly percolates through the sulcus or pocket toward the oral cavity.

Bacterial Biofilms on Artificial Substrates

In addition to the natural dentition, most individuals with access to modern dentistry display artificial intraoral hard surfaces that can serve as suitable, non-shedding substrates for the formation of bacterial biofilms. These include assorted restorations and prostheses composed of various metal alloys as well as plastics and ceramics. Some of these, such as fillings and crowns, serve to restore the continuity of individual teeth damaged by caries or trauma. Others, such as fixed partial dentures or bridges, are permanently secured to some of the remaining teeth and contain artificial dental units to replace missing teeth. Still others, namely removable full and partial dentures, are made of plastic and metal alloys in contact with mucosal surfaces. In recent years, dental implants have become increasingly popular as artificial replacements for missing teeth. Although a number of materials have been tried, titanium is by far the most successful and widely used of these for the manufacture of modern dental implants. Dental implants essentially serve as artificial tooth roots that are in intimate contact with the bone of the jaw and the overlying mucosa. They can serve as supports for assorted fixed and removable prostheses as well as for individual crowns.

All of these biomaterials, with surfaces open to the oral cavity, are potential substrates for bacterial biofilms. If the artificial surface is located at a site where dental plaque would usually form on natural tooth surface, a similar biofilm will also form on the restorative material. Relatively few studies have compared dental plaque development on teeth with that on various dental materials (Nassar *et al.*, 1995; Leonhardt *et al.*, 1995). Quirynen *et al.* (1989) have shown that the rate of plaque accumulation on a hydrophobic teflon strip is considerably less than on an adjacent hydrophylic enamel surface, even after 9 days of plaque accumulation. Although the adhesion of the initial bacterial layer may have been slower on teflon than enamel, it is likely that shearing forces due to mucosal friction were much more effective in removing accumulated bacteria on teflon than on enamel. As a result plaque composition probably did not mature beyond its early coccoid character. Based on this study, and others (Busscher and van der Mei, 1997), it is clear, indeed, that some artificial surfaces, such as Teflon, are less favorable to dental plaque formation than natural tooth surfaces. However, Teflon is not currently used in the construction of intraoral appliances or restorations. On more commonly used materials, the salivary pellicle eventually produces a uniform coating that allows plaque to accumulate in a similar manner on various materials (Nakazato *et al.*, 1989; Leonhardt *et al.*, 1995).

The microbiology of dental implants has received special attention in the past decade (Rosenberg, *et al.* 1991; Mombelli and Lang, 1994; Papaioannou *et al.*, 1995; Mombelli, 1998). In general, the composition of the microbiota around implants and teeth resemble one another, with plaque around healthy implants resembling that of periodontally healthy teeth and the microbiota of periimplantitis lesions resembling that of periodontitis lesions (Sanz *et al.*, 1990; Leonhardt *et al.* 1993; Papaioannou *et al.*, 1996; Augthun and Conrads, 1997; Salcetti *et al.*, 1998; Listgarten and Lai, 1999). Colonization of dental implants is markedly influenced by the prevalent microbiota in the oral cavity of the implant recipient (Papaioannou *et al.*, 1995). In edentulous mouths, the microbiota on exposed implant surfaces is initially derived from microorganisms able to survive on soft tissues and existing prostheses. In the presence of remaining healthy or minimally inflamed teeth, the tooth-associated microbiota will eventually colonize comparable surfaces on the implants (Danser, *et al.*, 1997). Likewise, periodontal pathogens from existing periodontitis lesions, are also likely to colonize implants inserted in periodontitis-affected mouths where they may predispose the implants to periimplantitis (George *et al.*, 1994; Mombelli *et al.* 1995; Papaioannou *et al.*, 1996). It has been reported that bacterial transmission from teeth to implants is more likely within the same dental arch than from one dental arch to the other (Quirynen *et al.*, 1996).

Certain types of dental implants may also become infected on their internal surfaces during insertion of the implant or during the later stages of abutment and prosthetic part installation (Quirynen and van Steenberghe, 1993; Quirynen *et al.*, 1994; Persson *et al.*, 1996). The presence of a persistent microbiota in this location may predispose to inflammatory changes in the tissues immediately adjacent to the mechanical junction of the implant and screw-retained restorations. It is not clear at this time to what extent, if any, the presence of these bacteria affects the long-term success of dental implants.

The Microbiota of Soft Tissue Surfaces

The microbial colonization of the oral mucosa of edentulous infants, 1-7 months of age, was described by Könönen *et al.* (1992a, 1992b). Interestingly, even in the absence of teeth, 27 of 30 subjects tested harbored some anaerobic species. However, none of the subjects had any detectable species considered as major periodontal pathogens. The composition of the resident microbiota on oral mucosal surfaces in older subjects has been reviewed by Dahlén *et al.* (1992). The major microorganisms found on the lining and masticatory mucosa consist of viridans streptococci (including *S. mutans, S. milleri,* and *S. salivarius)*, *Neisseria* sp., *Haemophilus* sp., *Staphylococcus* sp., *Veillonella* sp., and assorted gram-positive rods. Occasionally, *Candida albicans* and enterococci can also be recovered in low numbers. In addition to the above, the dorsum of the tongue and the tonsillar crypts also harbor a significant population of gram-negative anaerobic rods that include potential periodontal pathogens, including *Bacteroides* sp., *Fusobacterium* sp. and spirochetes. Therefore, the dorsum of the tongue and the tonsils may serve as reservoirs for the repopulation of treated periodontal lesions by pathogens. Danser *et al.* (1994) have reported that *Actinobacillus actinomycetemcomitans* and *Porphyromonas gingivalis* may not survive in saliva or on mucosal surfaces for up to 3 months following the extraction of periodontally diseased teeth, although *Prevotella* species do persist. On the other hand, Könönen *et al.* (1991) have reported that in patients wearing dentures many oral pathogens may still be detected. However, periodontal treatment alone does not eliminate mucosal surfaces as reservoirs for *Actinobacillus actinomycetemcomitans* and *Porphyromonas gingivalis* (Danser *et al.*, 1996).

Although most of the above microorganisms can adhere to the epithelial cells on the lining and masticatory mucosal surfaces and proliferate to form small microbial colonies, the normal rate of desquamation of the surface cells prevents substantial accumulations of bacteria from forming on these surfaces. Secretory immunoglobulins and other antibacterial substances in saliva may also interfere to varying degrees with the colonization and proliferation of these species. No comprehensive morphological studies have addressed the formation and structure of biofilms on the soft tissues of the oral cavity. Some published scanning electron micrographs indicate the presence of isolated bacteria as well as some bacterial clumps resembling small colonies on the surface of desquamating cells.

Clinical implications

As was the case for supragingival plaque, the development of the subgingival microbiota may be interrupted or prevented by events that disturb the environment of the gingival sulcus. For example, brushing or flossing may not only interfere with supragingival plaque formation, but indirectly with the establishment and maturation of the subgingival microbiota. By controlling the supragingival bacterial mass, effective oral hygiene measures coupled with periodic professional cleaning will prevent the inflammatory tissue changes that would favor the establishment of anaerobic species in the subgingival region and the subsequent development of an abundant subgingival microbiota. Even in the presence of periodontal pockets with a well established subgingival microbiota, supragingival plaque removal may affect the composition of the subgingival microbiota (Katsanoulas *et al.*, 1992; Al-Yahfoufi, *et al.*, 1995; Hellström, *et al.*, 1996), although this is not a universal finding (Kho *et al.*, 1985; Beltrami *et al.*, 1987). The effect on the subgingival microbiota may be due in part to inadvertent subgingival debridement. However, supragingival plaque control could also deprive the subgingival environment of nutrients and other metabolites that contribute to its ecological characteristics. Supragingival plaque control also decreases the intensity of the associated gingival inflammation and, consequently, the volume of the inflammatory exudate that serves as a nutrient source to the subgingival microorganisms.

Most species considered to be periodontal pathogens tend to be gram-negative anaerobes. Consequently, their preferred ecological niche is the subgingival area (Zambon, 1996). Because the establishment of the subgingival microbiota is dependent on the initial development of a supragingival plaque, periodontal pathogens do not readily colonize mouths with good oral hygiene, where supragingival plaque formation is minimal. Even if potential pathogens become established, the interaction with other bacterial species, as well as assorted host factors, may not necessarily result in the onset of periodontitis Baehni and Guggenheim, 1996). Since many known periodontal pathogens can be recovered, albeit infrequently and in small numbers, from healthy mouths, it is likely that most forms of periodontitis represent endogenous or opportunistic infections (Gmür and Guggenheim, 1994).

Some periodontal pathogens, for example *A. actinomycetemcomitans*, do not require a strict anaerobic environment to become established. *A. actinomycetemcomitans* is considered an important pathogen in early-onset forms of periodontitis and some cases of refractory periodontitis. It tends to be diffusely distributed throughout the oral cavity and is not readily eliminated by non-surgical mechanical debridement. This may be due, in part, to its ability to persist within the gingival tissues (Christersson *et al.* 1987). Consequently, the use of systemic antibiotics is justified in trying to control potential pathogens such as *A. actinomycetemcomitans* and others in early-onset and refractory forms of periodontitis (Zambon, 1996). Localization studies of *A. actinomycetemcomitans* using cytochemical methods have shown that the organisms is closely associated with dental plaque deposits (Berthold and Listgarten, 1986). Therefore, the strategy for eliminating *A. actinomycetemcomitans* should include mechanical debridement to eliminate the protective effect of the dental plaque biofilm, and systemic administration of an appropriate antibiotic for a sufficient length of time and at an appropriate dosage to kill microbial cells in the tissues as well as other soft tissue reservoirs in the oral cavity.

Because most periodontal pathogens, including *A. actinomycetemcomitans*, are opportunistic pathogens, their permanent eradication from the oral cavity is somewhat of a challenge. The strategy consists in suppressing the growth of the undesirable species long enough to allow other members of the resident microbiota to occupy the ecological niches favored by opportunistic pathogens. Once this is achieved, reestablishment of the displaced species becomes more difficult, particularly if potential foci of reinfection have been eliminated.

In addition to the dental surfaces and subgingival region, intraoral locations harboring *A. actinomycetemcomitans* and other pathogens may include tonsillar crypts, the cheek mucosa and the dorsum of the tongue (Müller *et al.*, 1993; 1996). Pathogenic species may also colonize assorted restorative and prosthetic materials. All these sites may serve as reservoirs for potential pathogens and foci of reinfection. There is a distinct possibility that residual foci of infection will persist in the oral cavity, following conventional mechanical debridement, particularly if the treatment is aimed at localized lesions rather than at all the infected sites. Reinfection from close friends and relatives is another risk, particularly for *A. actinomycetemcomitans* (von Troil-Linden *et al.*, 1995, 1996; Zambon, 1996; Asikainen *et al.*, 1997a).

The strategy is to create an ecological environment that is unfriendly to recolonization by the targeted bacteria. It is known that *A. actinomycetemcomitans* and certain streptococci have an antagonistic relationship (Hillman and Socransky, 1982; Hillman *et al.*, 1985; Stevens *et al.*, 1987; Hillman and Shivers, 1988). Following elimination of *A. actinomycetemcomitans*, good oral hygiene will favor the establishment of a streptococci-enriched microbiota, thereby making it more difficult for *A. actinomycetemcomitans* to become reestablished. It has also been recognized that for anyone species, some clonal derivatives are much more pathogenic than others are (Asikainen *et al.*, 1995, 1997b; Haubek *et al.*, 1995). Therefore, another approach toward establishing a health-compatible microbiota would be the replacement of potentially patho-genic clones by others of the same species that would readily occupy the available niches without endangering the host. At this time, this approach is still only hypothetical.

Mechanical debridement has been the main approach to controlling peri-odontal pathogens and, in the process, maintain a health-compatible periodontal microbiota. The rationale for mechanical debridement has been the reduction of plaque mass and the elimination of plaque retentive calculus deposits. The consequent reduction in inflammation and tissue shrinkage results in shallower pockets and sulci. Further reduction in pocket depth can be achieved through surgical therapy. There are, nevertheless, some periodontal diseases that are not readily controlled through mechanical debridement alone. These diseases, namely early-onset forms of periodontitis and refractory periodontitis, are most likely the result of specific infections by a limited number of bacterial pathogens.

The use of adjunctive antibiotic therapy may be indicated for these types of periodontitis. However, prior to the administration of antibiotics, it is desirable to obtain a baseline profile of the resident microbiota to determine if putative pathogens are present and whether they are likely targets for this type of therapy. This information can be obtained through specialized laboratories that analyze the composition of the microbiota in subgingival samples sent to them. Some laboratories also provide information about the antibiotic susceptibility profile of selected cultivable species. The results of subsequent microbial analyses of the treated lesions can then be compared to the baseline data to verify that the targeted pathogens have been eliminated or reduced to non-detectable levels.

Because antibiotics do not readily diffuse into bacterial biofilms (Gilbert *et al.*, 1997; Kleinfelder *et al.*, 1999), it is necessary to insure that mechanical disruption or removal of bacterial deposits are completed prior to the start of antibiotic therapy. Indeed, clinical studies suggest that patients with heavier dental plaque deposits do not respond as well to antibiotic treatment as those with lesser deposits (Kornman *et al.*, 1994).

The complex microbiota of the oral cavity tends to colonize exposed sur-faces as adherent biofilms. Left unchecked, the growth of these bacterial deposits may lead to caries and periodontal disease. The control of these biofilms provides a challenge for individuals interested in maintaining a health-compatible oral microbiota. The challenge consists first in minimizing the bacterial deposits on intra-oral surfaces, primarily by mechanical cleansing procedures, and secondly in maintaining a low bacterial load over time. The successful achievement of these objectives also results in a qualitative shift of the oral microbiota. Regular, thorough oral hygiene in the absence of anaerobic ecological niches interferes with the maturation of dental plaque and the shift toward an increasingly anaerobic, Gram-negative microbiota. Gram-negative, anaerobic species, which account for the majority of the periodontal pathogens, will be suppressed or eliminated. Regular oral hygiene also tends to gradually reduce the rate of plaque regrowth by suppressing inflammation and favoring the persistence of health-compatible bacterial species.

References

Al-Yahfoufi, Z., Mombelli, A., Wicki, A. and Lang, N.P. 1995. The effect of plaque control in subjects with shallow pockets and high prevalence of periodontal pathogens. *J. Clin. Periodontol.,* **22,** 78-84.

Asikainen, S., Chen, C., Alaluusua, S. and Slots, J. 1997a. Can one acquire periodontal bacteria and periodontitis from a family member? *J. Am. Dent. Assn,* **128,** 1263-1271.

Asikainen, S., Chen, C., Saarela, M., Saxén, L. and Slots, J. 1997b. Clonal specificity of *Actinobacillus actinomycetemcomitans* in destructive periodontal disease. *Clin. Inf. Dis.,* **25 suppl. 2,** S227-S229.

Asikainen, S., Chen, C. and Slots, J. 1995. *Actinobacillus actinomycetemcomitans* genotypes in relation to serotypes and periodontal status. *Oral Microbiol. Immunol.,* **10,** 65-68.

Augthun, M. and Conrads, G. 1997. Microbial findings of deep peri-implant bone defects. *Int. J. Oral Maxillofac. Implants,* **12,** 106-112.

Baehni, P.C. and Guggenheim, B. 1996. Potential of diagnostic microbiology for treatment and prognosis of dental caries and periodontal diseases. *Crit. Rev. Oral Biol. Med.,* **7,** 259-277.

Beltrami, M., Bickel, M. and Baehni, P.C. 1987. The effect of supragingival plaque control on the composition of the subgingival microflora in human periodontitis. *J. Clin. Periodontol.,* **14,** 161-164.

Berthold, P. 1979. Formation of salivary coating and dental plaque on two different supporting materials. An electron microscopic study. *J. Periodontol.,* **50,** 397-405.

Berthold, P., Berthold, C.-H. and Söder, P.-Ö. 1971. The growth of dental plaque on different materials. *Swed. Dent. J.,* **64,** 863-877.

Berthold, P. and Listgarten, M.A. 1982. Distribution of *Actinobacillus actinomycetemcomitans* in localized juvenile periodontitis plaque: an electron immunocytochemical study. *J. Periodont. Res.,* **21,** 473-485.

Black, G.V. (1898) Dr. Black's conclusions reviewed again. *Dent. Cosmos,* **40,** 440. (Quoted by Bowen, 1975).

Bowden, G.H.W. and Hamilton, I.R. 1998. Survival of oral bacteria. *Crit. Rev. Oral Biol. Med.,* **9,** 54-85.

Bowen, W.H. 1975. Nature of plaque. In: Melcher, A.H. and Zarb, G.A. (eds), Preventive dentistry: nature, pathogenicity, and clinical control of plaque. *Oral Sci. Rev.,* **9,** 3-22.

Brecx, M., Theilade, J. and Attström, R. (1983). An ultrastructural quantitative study of the significance of microbial multiplication during early dental plaque growth. *J. Periodont. Res.,* **18,** 177-186.

Busscher, H.J. and van der Mei, H.C. 1997. Physico-chemical interactions in initial microbial adhesion and relevance for biofilm formation. *Adv. Dent. Res.,* **11,** 24-32.

Caldwell, D.E., Korber, D.R. and Lawrence, J.R. 1992. Imaging of bacterial cells by fluorescence exclusion using scanning confocal laser microscopy. *J. Microbiol. Methods,* **15,** 249-261.

Charon, N.W., Lawrence, C.W. and O'Brien, S. 1981. Movement of antibody-coated latex beads attached to the spirochete *Leptospira interrogans. Proc. Natl Acad. Sci. U.S.A.,* **78,** 7166-7170.

Christersson, L.A., Albini, B., Zambon, J.J., Wikesjö, U.M.E. and Genco, R.J. 1987. Tissue localization of *Actinobacillus actinomycetemcomitans* in human periodontitis. I. Light, immunofluorescence and electron microscopic studies. *J. Periodontol,* **58,** 529-539.

Cimasoni, G. 1974. The crevicular fluid. In: Myers, H.M. (ed), *Monographs in Oral Science,* vol. 3, S. Karger, New York.

Cisar, J.D., Kolenbrander, P.E. and McIntire, F. 1979. Specificity of coaggregation reactions between human oral streptococci and strains of *Actinomyces viscosus* and *Actinomyces naeslundii. Infect. Immun.,* **24,** 742-752.

Clergeau-Guérithault, S. 1986. La plaque bactérienne. Mécanismes d'adhérence des microorganismes. *J. Parodontol.,* **5,** 295-1986.

Cook, G.S., Costerton, J.W. and Lamont, R.J. 1998. Biofilm formation by *Porphyromonas gingivalis* and *Streptococcus gordonii. J. Periodont. Res.,* **33,**323-327.

Costerton, J.W. 1978. How bacteria stick. *Sci. American,* **238,** 86-95.

Costerton, J.W. 1984. The formation of biocide-resistant biofilms in industrial, natural and medical systems. *Dev. Ind. Microbiol.,* **25,** 363-372.

Costerton, J.W., Cheng, K.-J., Geesey, G.G., Ladd, T.I., Nickel, J.C., Dasgupta, M. and Marrie, T.J.

1987. Bacterial biofilms in nature and disease. *Ann. Rev. Microbiol.*, **41**, 435-464.

Costerton, J.W., Lewandowski, Z., Caldwell, D.E., Korber, D.R. and Lappin-Scott, H.M. 1995. Microbial biofilms. *Ann. Rev. Microbiol.*, **49**, 711-745.

Costerton, J.W., Stewart, P.S. and Greenberg, E.P. 1999. Bacterial biofilms: A common cause of persistent infections. *Science*, **284**, 1318-1322.

Dahlén, G., Jonsson, R., Ohman, S.-C., Nielsen, R. and Möller, A.J.R. 1992. Infections of oral mucosa and submucosa. In: Slots, J. and Taubman, M.A. (eds), *Contemporary Oral Microbiology and Immunology*, pp. 476-499, Mosby, Saint Louis.

Daly, C.G. and Highfield, J.E. 1996. Effect of localized experimental gingivitis on early supragingival plaque accumulation. *J. Clin. Periodontol.*, **23**, 160-164.

Danser, M.M., Timmerman, M.F., van Winkelhoff, A.J. and van der Velden, U. 1996. The effect of periodontal treatment on periodontal bacteria on the oral mucous membranes. *J. Periodontol.*, **67**, 478-485.

Danser, M.M., van Winkelhoff, A.J., de Graaff, J., Loos, B.G. and van der Velden, U. 1994. Short-term effect of full-mouth extraction on periodontal pathogens colonizing the oral mucous membranes. *J. Clin. Periodontol.*, **21**, 484-489.

Danser, M.M., van Winkelhoff, A.J. and van der Velden, U. 1997. Periodontal bacteria colonizing oral mucous membranes in edentulous patients wearing dental implants. *J. Periodontol.*, **68**, 209-216.

Darveau, R.P., Tanner, A. and Page, R.C. 1997. The microbial challenge in periodontitis. In: Page, R.C. and Kornman, K.S. (eds), *The Pathogenesis of Periodontitis. Periodontology 2000*, **14**, 12-32.

Davies, D.G., Chakrabarty, A.M. and Geesey, G.G. 1993. Exopolysaccharide production in biofilms: substratum activation of alginate gene expression by *Pseudomonas aeruginosa*. *Appl. Environ. Microbiol.*, **59**, 1181-1186.

Davies, D.G., Parsek, M.R., Pearson, J.P., Iglewski, B.H., Costerton, J.W. and Greenberg, E.P. 1998. The involvement of cell-to-cell signals in the development of a bacterial biofilm. *Science*, **280**, 295-298.

Ellen, R.P. and Gibbons, R.J. 1972. M protein-associated adherence of *Streptococcus pyogenes* to epithelial surfaces prerequisite for virulence. *Infect. Immun.*, **5**, 826-830.

Galil, K. and Gwinnett, A. 1973. Scanning electron microscopy: observations on occlusal human dental plaque. *J. Can. Dent. Assoc.*, **39**, 472-.

Gatewood, R.R., Cobb, C.M. and Killoy, W.J. 1993. Microbial colonization on natural tooth structure compared with smooth and plasma-sprayed dental implant surfaces. *Clin. Oral Impl. Res.*, **4**, 53-64.

Geesey, G.G., Richardson, W.T., Yeomans, H.G. Irvin, R.T. and Costerton, J.W. 1977. Microscopic examination of natural sessile bacterial populations from an alpine stream. *Can. J. Microbiol.*, **23**, 1733-1736.

Genco, R.J., Evans, R.T. and Ellison, S.A. 1969. Dental research in microbiology with emphasis on periodontal disease. J. Am. Dent. Assoc., **78**, 1016-1036.

George, K., Zafiropoulos, G.-G., Murat, Y., Hubertus, S. and Nisengard, R.J. 1994. Clinical and microbiological status of osseointegrated implants. *J. Periodontol.*, **65**, 766-770.

Gibbons, R.J. and Nygaard,M. 1970. Interbacterial aggregation of plaque bacteria. *Arch. Oral Biol.*, **15**, 1397-1400.

Gibbons, R.J. and Spinell, D.M. 1970. Salivary induced aggregation of plaque bacteria. In: McHugh, W.D. (ed.), *Dental Plaque*, pp.207-215, Livingstone, Edinburg.

Gilbert, P., Das, J. and Foley, I. 1997. Biofilm susceptibility to antimicrobials. In: Novak, M.J. (ed), *Biofilms on Oral Surfaces: Implications for Health and Disease. Adv. Dent. Res.*, **11**, 160-167.

Gmür, R. and Guggenheim, B.1994. Interdental supragingival plaque - A natural habitat of *Actinobacillus actinomycetemcomitans, Bacteroides forsythus, Campylobacter rectus*, and *Prevotella nigrescens. J. Dent. Res.*, **73**, 1421-1428.

Goh, C.J.W., Waite, I.M., Groves, B.J. and Cornick, D.E.R. 1986. The influence of gingival inflammation and pocketing on the rate of plaque formation during non-surgical periodontal treatment. *Brit. Dent. J.*, **161**, 165-169.

Gristina, A.G. 1987. Biomaterial-centered infection: Microbial adhesion versus tissue integration. *Science*, **237**, 1588-1595.

Haubek, D., Poulsen, K., Asikainen, S. and Kilian, M. 1995. Evidence for absence in northern Europe of especially virulent clonal types of *Actinobacillus actinomycetemcomitans. J. Clin. Microbiol.,* **33,** 395-401.

Hay, D.I., Gibbons, R.J. and Spinell, D.M. 1971. Characteristics of some high molecular weight constituents with bacterial aggregating activity from whole saliva and dental plaque. *Caries Res.,* **5,** 111-123.

Hellström, M.-K., Ramberg, P., Krok, L. and Lindhe, J. 1996. The effect of supragingival plaque control on the subgingival microflora in human periodontitis. *J. Clin. Periodontol.,* **23,** 934-940.

Hillman, J.D. and Socransky, S.S. 1982. Bacterial interference in the oral ecology of *Actinobacillus actinomycetemcomitans* and its relationship to human periodontosis. *Arch. Oral Biol.,* **27,** 75-77.

Hillman, J.D., Socransky, S.S. and Shivers, M. 1985. The relationship between streptococcal species and periodontopathic bacteria in human dental plaque. *Arch. Oral Biol.,* **30,** 791-796.

Hillman, J.D. and Shivers, M. 1988. Interaction between wild-type, mutant and revertant forms of the bacterium *Actinobacillus actinomycetemcomitans* in vitro and in the gnotobiotic rat. *Arch. Oral Biol.,* **33,** 395-401.

Jenkins, G.N. 1968. The mode of formation of dental plaque. *Caries Res.,* **2,** 130-138.

Jenkinson, H.F. and Lamont, R.J. 1997. Streptococcal adhesion and colonization. *Crit. Rev. Oral Biol. Med.,* **8,** 175-200.

Katsanoulas, T., Reneè, I. and Attström, R. 1992. The effect of supragingival plaque control on the composition of the subgingival flora in periodontal pockets. *J. Clin. Periodontol.,***19,** 760-765.

Kelstrup, J. and Funder-Nielsen, T.D. 1974. Aggregation of oral streptococci with fusobacterium and actinomyces. *J. Biol. Buccale,* **2,** 347-362.

Kho, P,. Smales, F.C. and Hardie, J.M. 1985. The effect of supragingival plaque control on the subgingival microflora. *J. Clin. Periodontol.,* **12,** 676-686.

Kleinfelder, J.W., Müller, R.F. and Lange, D.E. 1999. Antibiotic susceptibility of putative periodontal pathogens in advanced periodontitis. *J. Clin. Periodontol.,* **26,** 347-351.

Könönen, E., Asikainen, S. and Jousimies-Somer, H. 1992. The early colonization of gram-negative anaerobic bacteria in edentulous infants. *Oral Microbiol. Immunol.,* **7,** 28-31.

Könönen, E., Asikainen, S., Alaluusua, S., Könönen, M., Summanen, P,. Kanervo, A. and Jousimies-Somer, H. 1991. Are certain oral pathogens part of normal oral flora in denture-wearing edentulous subjects? *Oral Microbiol. Immunol.,* **6,** 119-122.

Könönen, E., Jousimies-Somer, H. and Asikainen, S. 1992. Relationship between oral gram-negative anaerobic bacteria in saliva of the mother and the colonization of her edentulous infant. *Oral Microbiol. Immunol.,* **7,** 273-276.

Kornman, K.S., Newman, M.G., Moore, D.J. and Singer, R.E. 1994. The influence of supragingival plaque control on clinical and microbial outcomes following the use of antibiotics for the treatment of periodontitis. *J. Periodontol.,* **65,** 848-854.

Kraus, F.W. and Mestecky, J. 1976. Salivary proteins and the development of dental plaque. *J. Dent. Res.,* **55 special issue,** C141-C152.

Lancy, Jr., P., Appelbaum, B., Holt, S.C. and Rosan, B. 1980. Quantitative in vitro assay for "corncob" formation. *Infect. Immun.,* **29,** 663-670.

Lawrence, J.R., Korber, D.R., Hoyle, B.D., Costerton, J.W. and Caldwell, D.E. 1991. Optical sectioning of microbial films. *J. Bacteriol.,* **173,** 6558-6567.

Leonhardt, Å., Adolfsson, B., Lekholm, U., Wikström, M. and Dahlén, G. 1993. A longitudinal microbiological study on osseointegrated titanium implants in partially edentulous patients. *Clin. Oral Impl. Res.,* **4,** 113-120.

Leonhardt, Å., Olsson, J. and Dahlén, G. 1995. Bacterial colonization on titanium, hydroxyapatite, and amalgam surfaces in vivo. *J. Dent. Res.,* **74,** 1607-1612.

Lie, T. 1977a. Scanning and transmission electron microscopic study of pellicle morphogenesis. *Scand. J. Dent. Res.,* **85,** 217-231.

Lie, T. 1977b. Early dental plaque morphogenesis. A scanning electron microscope study using the hydroxyapatite splint model and a low-sucrose diet. *J. Periodont. Res.,* **12,** 73-89.

Lie, T. 1978. Ultrastructural study of early dental plaque formation. *J. Periodont. Res.,* **13,** 391-409.

Lie, T. 1979. Morphologic studies on dental plaque formation. Thesis. University of Bergen.

Liljemark, W.F. and Bloomquist,C. 1996. Human oral microbial ecology and dental caries and periodontal diseases. *Crit. Rev. Oral Biol. Med.,* **7,** 180-198.

Listgarten, M.A. 1976. Structure of the microbial flora associated with periodontal health and disease in man. A light and electron microscopic study. *J. Periodontol.*, **47**, 1-18.

Listgarten, M.A. 1994. The structure of dental plaque. In: Socransky, S.S. and Haffajee, A.D. (eds), *Microbiology and Immunology of Periodontal Diseases. Periodontology 2000*, **5**, 52-65.

Listgarten, M.A. and Lai, C-H. 1999. Comparative microbiological characteristics of failing implants and periodontally diseased teeth. *J. Periodontol.*, **70**, 431-437.

Listgarten, M.A., Mayo, H. and Amsterdam, M. 1973. Ultrastructure of the attachment device between coccal and filamentous microorganisms in "corncob" formations of dental plaque. *Arch. Oral Biol.*, **18**, 651-656.

Listgarten, M.A., Mayo, H.E. and Tremblay, R. 1975. Development of dental plaque on epoxy resin crowns in man. A light and electron microscopic study. *J. Periodontol.*, **46**, 10-26.

Long, S.S. and Swenson, R.M. 1976. Determinants of the developing oral flora in normal newborns. *Environ. Microbiol.*, **32**, 494-497.

Marcotte, H. and Lavoie, M.C. 1998. Oral microbial ecology and the role of salivary immunoglobulin A. *Microbiol. Mol. Biol. Rev.*, **62**, 71-109.

Marshall, K.C. 1992. Biofilms: an overview of bacterial adhesion activity and control at surfaces. *Am. Soc. Microbiol. News*, **58**, 202-207.

Marshall, K.C., Stout, R. and Mitchell, R. 1971. Mechanisms of the initial events in the sorption of marine bacteria to surfaces. *J. Gen. Microbiol.*, **68**, 337-348.

McNabb, P.C. and Tomasi, T.B. 1981. Host defense mechanisms at mucosal surfaces. *Annu. Rev. Microbiol.*, **35**, 477-496.

Mombelli, A. 1998. Aging and the periodontal and peri-implant microbiota. In: Ellcn, R.P. (ed.), *Periodontal Disease among Older Adults. Periodontology 2000*, **16**, 44-52.

Mombelli, A. and Lang, N.P. 1994. Microbial aspects of implant dentistry. In: Lang, N.P. and Nyman, S.R. (eds), *Implant and Crown and Bridge Therapy in the Periodontally Compromised Patient. Periodontology 2000*, **4**, 74-80.

Mombelli, A., Marxer, M., Gaberthüel, T., Grunder, U. and Lang, N.P. 1995. The microbiota of osseointegrated implants in patients with a history of periodontal disease. *J. Clin. Periodontol.*, **22**, 124-130.

Mouton, C., Reynolds, H.S. and Genco, R.J. 1980. Characterization of tufted streptococci isolated from "corn cob" configuration of human dental plaque. *Infect. Immun.*, **27**, 235-245.

Müller, H.-P., Lange, D.E. and Müller, R.F. 1993. *Actinobacillus actinomycetemcomitans* recovery from extracrevicular locations in the mouth. *Oral Microbiol. Immunol.*, **8**, 344-348.

Müller, H.-P., Zöller, L., Eger, T., Hoffmann, S. and Lobinsky, D. 1996. Natural distribution of oral *Actinobacillus actinomycetemcomitans* in young men with minimal periodontal disease. *J. Periodont. Res.*, **31**, 373-380.

Nakazato, G., Tsuchiya, H. and Sato, M. 1989. *In vivo* plaque formation on implant materials. *Int. J. Oral Maxillofac. Implants*, **4**, 321-326.

Nassar, U., Meyer, A.E., Ogle, R.E. and Baier, R.E. 1995. The effect of restorative and prosthetic materials on dental plaque. In: Ciancio, S. (ed), *Mechanical and Chemical Supragingival Plaque Control. Periodontology 2000*, **8**, 114-124.

Papaioannou, W., Quirynen, M., Nys, M. and van Steenberghe, D. 1995. The effect of periodontal parameters on the subgingival microbiota around implants. *Clin. Oral Impl. Res.*, **6**, 197-204.

Papaioannou, W., Quirynen, M. and van Steenberghe, D. 1996. The influence of periodontitis on the subgingival flora around implants in partially edentulous patients. *Clin. Oral Impl. Res.*, **7**, 405-409.

Persson, L.G., Lekholm, U., Leonhardt, Å., Dahlén, G. and Lindhe, J. 1996. Bacterial colonization on internal surfaces of Brånemark system implant components. *Clin. Oral Implants Res.*, **7**, 90-95.

Quirynen, M. and Bollen, C.M.L. 1995. The influence of surface roughness and surface-free energy on supra- and subgingival plaque formation in man. A review of the literature. *J. Clin. Periodontol.*, **22**, 1-14.

Quirynen, M., Bollen, C.M.L., Eyssen, H. and van Steenberghe, D. 1994. Microbial penetration along the implant components of the Brånemark system. An *in vitro* study. *Clin. Oral Implants Res.*, **5**, 239-244.

Quirynen, M., Dekeyser, C. and van Steenberghe, D. 1991. The influence of gingival inflammation, tooth type and timing on the rate of plaque formation. *J. Periodontol.*, **62**, 219-222.

Quirynen, M., Maréchal, M., Busscher, H.J., Weerkamp, A.H., Arends, J., Darius, P.L. and van Steenberghe, D. 1989. The influence of surface-free energy on planimetric plaque growth in man. *J. Dent. Res.*, **68**, 796-799.

Quirynen, M., Papaioannou, W. and van Steenberghe, D. 1996. Intraoral transmission and the colonization of oral hard surfaces. *J. Periodontol.*, **67**, 986-993.

Quirynen, M., van der Mei, H.C., Bollen, C.M.L., Schotte, A., Maréchal, M., Doornbusch, G.I., Naert, I., Busscher, H.J. and van Steenberghe, D. 1993. An *in vivo* study of the influence of the surface roughness of implants on the microbiology of supra- and subgingival plaque. *J. Dent. Res.*, **72**, 1304-1309.

Quirynen, M. and van Steenberghe, D. 1989. Is early plaque growth rate constant with time? *J. Clin. Periodontol.*, **16**, 278-283.

Quirynen, M. and van Steenberghe, D. 1993. Bacterial colonization of the internal part of two-stage implants. An *in vivo* study. *Clin. Oral Implants Res.*, **4**, 158-161.

Ramberg, P., Axelsson, P and Lindhe, J. 1995. Plaque formation at healthy and inflamed gingival sites in young individuals. *J. Clin. Periodontol.*, **22**, 85-88.

Rönström, A., Attström, R. and Egelberg, J. 1975. Early formation of dental plaque on plastic films. 1. Light microscopic observations. *J. Periodont. Res.*, **10**, 28-35.

Rosenberg, E.S., Torosian, J.P. and Slots, J. 1991. Microbial differences in 2 clinically distinct types of failures of osseointegrated implants. *Clin. Oral Impl. Res.*, **2**, 135-144.

Russell, C. and Melville, T.H. 1978. A review. Bacteria in the human mouth. *J. Appl. Microbiol.*, **44**, 163-181.

Salcetti, J.M., Moriarty, J.D., Cooper, L.F., Smith, F.W., Collins, J.G., Socransky, S.S. and Offenbacher, S. 1998 . The clinical, microbial, and host response characteristics of the failing implant. *Int. J. Oral Maxillofac. Implants, 12*, 32-42.

Sanz, M., Newman, M.G., Nachnani, S., Holt, R., Stewart, R. and Flemmig, I. 1990. Characterization of the subgingival microbial flora around endosteal sapphire dental implants in partially edentulous patients. *Int. J. Oral Maxillofac. Implants, 5*, 247-253.

Saxton, C.A. 1973. Scanning electron microscope study of the formation of dental plaque. *Caries Res.*, **7**, 102-119.

Scannapieco, F.A. 1994. Saliva-bacterium interactions in oral microbial ecology. *Crit. Rev. Oral Biol. Med.*, **5**, 203-248.

Schroeder, H.E. 1969. The structure and relationship of plaque to the hard and soft tissues. Electron microscopic interpretation. *Internat. Dent. J.*, **20**, 353-381.

Schroeder, H.E. and de Boever, J. 1970. The structure of microbial dental plaque. In: McHugh, W.D. (ed.), *Dental Plaque*, pp. 49-74, Livingstone, Edinburgh.

Shibly, O., Rifai, S. and Zambon, J.J. 1995. Supragingival dental plaque in the etiology of oral diseases. In: Ciancio, S.G. (ed), *Mechanical and Chemical Supragingival Plaque Control. Periodontology 2000*, **8**, 42-59.

Slots, J. 1979. Subgingival microflora and periodontal disease. *J. Clin. Periodontol.*, **6**, 351-382.

Smith, H. 1977. Microbial surfaces in relation to pathogenicity. *Bact. Rev.*, **41**, 475-500.

Socransky, S.S. 1970. Relationship of bacteria to the etiology of periodontal disease. *J. Dent. Res.*, **49**, 203-222.

Socransky, S.S. 1977. Microbiology of periodontal disease - Present status and future considerations. *J. Periodontol.*, **48**, 497-504.

Socransky, S.S. and Manganiello, S.D. 1971. The oral microbiota of man from birth to senility. *J. Periodontol.*, **42**, 485-496.

Socransky, S.S., Manganiello, A.D., Propas, D., Oram, V. and van Houte, J. 1977. Bacteriological studies of developing supragingival dental plaque. *J. Periodont. Res.*, **12**, 90-106.

Stevens, R.H., Lillard, S.E. and Hammond, B.F. 1987. Purification and biochemical properties of a bacteriocin from *Actinobacillus actinomycetemcomitans*. *Infect. Immun.*, **55**, 692-697.

Tanzer, J.M. 1977. Microbiology of periodontal disease. In: Klavan, B. *et al.* (eds), *International Conference on Research in the Biology of Periodontal Disease*, pp. 153-182, College of Dentistry, University of Illinois, Chicago.

Theilade, E. and Theilade, J. 1975. Role of plaque in the etiology of periodontal disease and caries. In: Melcher, A.H. and Zarb, G.A. (eds), *Preventive Dentistry: Nature, Pathogenicity, and*

Clinical Control of Plaque. Oral Sci. Rev., **9,** 23-64.

Theilade, E. and Theilade, J. 1981. Microbiology of periodontal disease. *Bull. Indian Soc. Periodontol.,* **5,** 3-8.

Theilade, E., Theilade, J. and Mikkelsen, L. 1982. Microbiological studies on early dento-gingival plaque on teeth and Mylar strips in humans. *J. Periodont. Res.,* **17,** 12-25.

Theilade, J. and Attström, R. 1985. Distribution and ultrastructure of subgingival plaque in beagle dogs with gingival inflammation. *J. Periodontol. Res.,* **20,** 131-145.

Thomas, D.D. 1996. Aspects of adherence of oral spirochetes. *Crit. Rev. Oral Biol. Med.,* **7,** 4-11.

van Palenstein-Helderman, W.H. 1981. Microbial etiology of periodontal disease. *J. Clin. Periodontol.,* **8,** 261-280.

von Troil-Lindén, B., Torkko, H., Alaluusua, S., Wolf, J., Jousimies-Somer, H. and Asikainen, S. 1995. Periodontal findings in spouses. A clinical, radiographic and microbiological study. *J. Clin. Periodontol.,* **22,** 93-99.

von Troil-Lindén, B., Saarela, M., Mättö, J., Alaluusua, S., Jousimies-Somer, H. and Asikainen, S. 1996. *J. Clin. Periodontol.,* **23,** 601-607.

Weerkamp, A.H., Quirynen, M., Marechal, M., van der Mei, H.C., van Steenberghe, D. and Busscher, H.J. 1989. The role of surface free energy in the early *in vivo* formation of dental plaque on human enamel and polymeric substrata. *Micr. Ecol. Health Dis.,* **2,** 11-18.

Williams, J.L. 1897. A contribution to the study of pathology of enamel. *Dent. Cosmos,* **39,** 169, 269, 353. (quoted by Bowen, 1975).

Williams, R.C. and Gibbons, R.J. 1972. Inhibition of bacterial adherence by secretory immunoglobulin A : a mechanism of antigen disposal. *Science,* **177,** 697-699.

Zambon, J.J. 1996. Periodontal diseases; microbial factors. *Ann. Periodontol.,* **1**:879-925.

Plaque in Health and Disease

ORAL BIOFILM AN ARCHIVE OF PAST EVENTS?

George H. W. Bowden

*Oral biofilms are reservoirs of numerous bacterial species and the composition of the biofilm is governed by factors which include cell adhesion, co-aggregation, growth and survival in the environment. Survival of species depends on their intrinsic characteristics, including their ability to adapt. Most resident oral bacterial species tested have been shown to include numerous genetic variants and several genetic variants (clones) of a species can be isolated from the same individual. In some pathogenic bacteria specific clones can be associated with causing disease. Generally, little is known of the association of specific, significant, phenotypic characters with clones of resident bacteria, although antigenic variation and resistance to chlorhexidine has been shown to be related to clonal variation. If clones of resident oral species express significant phenotypic characters involved in survival, then species with wide clonal diversity could be expected to be more stable during environmental fluctuations. In this case the biofilm could act as a reservoir for clones selected over time by different environments, enhancing the survival of the species. In order for biofilms to act as such a reservoir at least four criteria should be met; 1 the biofilm should be protective; 2 clones should express significant phenotypic characters; 3 clones should persist over time; 4 mechanisms to generate clonal variation should exist. Evidence suggests that biofilms fulfill these requirements. Initial studies of ribotypes of **A. naeslundii** gsp. 2 from a single person have confirmed significant phenotypic differences among them and competition of 5 ribotypes in a continuous culture biofilm model has shown dominance of the planktonic phase by one ribotype 'best suited' to the test environment and survival of the other ribotypes in the associated biofilm.*

Introduction

Dental plaque is a complex bacterial biofilm community which acts as a protective habitat and reservoir for many different resident bacterial species (Bowden *et al.*, 1979; Theilade, 1990; Bowden and Li, 1997, Bowden and Hamilton, 1998). Accumulation as a biofilm on non-shedding tooth surfaces and the tongue allows the resident bacteria to survive removal forces and also contributes to their protection against host specific and non-specific defence mechanisms and harmful agents from environments external to the mouth. The ecological survival of bacteria which make up the human resident oral flora is, then, influenced by the formation of oral biofilms, particularly those accumulating on the dentition. Although the biofilm provides physical protection, other related factors which contribute to survival of the component populations have

to be considered. These include,
1. cell growth, and
2. survival of autogenic and allogenic stresses (Bowden and Hamilton, 1998).

Growth of bacteria within the biofilm community is directly related to the availability of suitable niches and the intrinsic capacity for individual bacterial cells to resist being killed by autogenic and allogenic environmental changes. The exploitation of suitable niches during succession will increase the numbers of viable cells of strains of species in the biofilm community, often with concomitant increases in saliva, promoting the chance of salivary transmission to new hosts.

Survival against allogenic and autogenic stresses depends on the ability of a strain either to have intrinsic resistance or to adapt to a specific stress. Consequently, it could be proposed that the wider the range of stresses that strains of a species can tolerate the better are the chances of the species surviving in a habitat.

Although phenotypic (antigenic and biochemical) variation among strains of a species has been demonstrated for almost 100 years, more extensive strain diversity has been shown by the analysis of genomic DNA. Generally, individual strains of bacteria can be described as clones and daughter cells carry the same characteristics as their parent strain. However, this concept of identical cells arising from a parent has to be modified. During descent from an ancestral cell bacterial DNA may undergo mutation, or individual cells may incorporate 'foreign' DNA from other bacteria in the habitat. These cells may express different phenotypes from the ancestral strain. Therefore, clones of a species within an oral habitat may express significant phenotypic characters related to tolerance of specific environmental stresses, beyond those intrinsic to all strains of the species e. g. acid tolerance (Svensäter *et al.*, 1997), antibiotic resistance (Bennett, 1995) or the ability to degrade complex polymers (e.g. inulin, Table 1) for nutrient.

If this is the case, then a species that exhibits extensive clonal diversity in a habitat could also have a concomitant ability to survive a wider range of stresses, compared to a species showing less diversity. This aspect of clonal polymorphism within bacterial species in relation to survival has been discussed in detail by Rainey *et al.*, (1993) who have presented a hypothesis and a model that addresses some outcomes of intraclonal polymorphism among bacteria.

Once such relationships between genetic (clonal) diversity and expression of significant phenotypes has been established for strains of a species in oral biofilms it could be proposed that the biofilm acts as a reservoir for clones that enhance the survival of the species during environmental fluctuations. This would mean that under stresses that exert a selective pressure, a single clone 'best suited' to the stressing environment would predominate in the species population. Fluctuations in environmental stresses over time coupled to the generation of clonal diversity could result in incorporation of a range of clones of different phenotypes into oral biofilm communities. Thus, the biofilm may act as an archive of genetic variants of a species, each of which can survive in the

Table 1 Differential characteristics of *A. naeslundii* genospecies 2 ribotypes isolated from a single person.

CHARACTERS	RIBOTYPES				
	HNG 124	HNG 145	HNG 189	HNG 231	HNG 232
ACID FROM					
Inulin	+	-	-	+	-
Melezitose	-	+	+	+	-
Ribose	+	+	-	+	-
Trehalose	V	+	+	+	-
ENZYME ELECTROMORPHS [a]					
Malic enzyme	1	1	1	1	1
Malate dehyd.	1	1	1	1	1
6-phosphogluconate dehyd.	1	1	1	1	1
Glucose phosphate isomerase	1	1	1	1	1
Carboxyl esterase	2	2	2	3	1
Glutamate dehyd.	3	2	2	3	1
Glycerol phosphate dehyd.	2	3	1	4	1
Isocitrate dehyd.	3	2	3	1	ND
Acid phosphatase	1	2	ND	1	1

a. Numbers identify different electromorphs. ND = not detected.

habitat but also including those with phenotypes best suited to grow under specific environmental stresses. Such a biofilm could be seen as a simple 'memory system', incorporating a diversity of clones, enhancing the survival of resident oral species of bacteria and reflective of previous environments. In order for the biofilm to act as a long-term reservoir of significant clones of oral species, several criteria should be met:

1. the biofilm should be a protective reservoir for oral bacteria;

2. specific clones of resident bacterial species should be shown to express phenotypes significant to survival under different environments;

3. mechanisms to generate and select clones significant to survival should exist and

4. clones should persist over time, surviving normal fluctuations in oral habitats.

The current paper discusses aspects of these criteria and presents some initial data on phenotypic variation among strains of *Actinomyces naeslundii* genospecies 2 genetic variants (ribotypes) from the same host and demonstration of selection of a ribotype best suited to a given environment during competition in a continuous culture biofilm model.

The biofilm as a protective reservoir for strains of a bacterial species
Incorporation into the Biofilm
The mechanisms of incorporation of specific bacterial species into the biofilm on tooth surfaces have been described in detail. They involve specific adherence

to the tooth pellicle (conditioning film), and interbacterial co-aggregation (Kolenbrander and London, 1992), coupled to the ability either to survive stresses and remain viable as single cells, (Bowden and Hamilton, 1998), or to grow and increase their population (Bowden and Li, 1997). Specific adhesion and coaggregation have been studied in detail to the molecular level (Cisar, *et al.*, 1997; Jenkinson and Lamont, 1997; London, 1999) and the fundamental importance of both mechanisms in colonization of the tooth surface is very well established. However, bacteria in culture or suspension may adhere to any available solid surface, without obvious involvement of specific chemical receptors (Busscher *et al.*, 1992). Therefore, it is possible that any organism present in the mouth could adhere to the tooth surface. Consequently, although specific mechanisms involving known chemical adhesins contribute a major component of initial adhesion and coaggregation by pioneer bacteria on tooth surfaces, the possibility of adhesion by cells of bacteria other than the species regarded as 'pioneers' has to be accepted.

Adhesion and coaggregation represent the earliest stages in biofilm accumulation and determine the species that have the opportunity to contribute to the early stages of development of the biofilm community (Kolenbrander and London, 1992; Bos *et al.*, 1996a,b,c; Busscher and van der Mei, 1997; Cisar *et al.*, 1997). However, a third stage of biofilm accumulation involves growth (Brecx *et al.*, 1983; Li and Bowden, 1994a; Bowden and Li, 1997; Liljemark *et al.*, 1997). The growth phase, like adhesion and coaggregation, is also fundamental to the composition of the biofilm community and represents a dynamic process during which populations interact and respond to local autogenic and allogenic stresses, resulting in succession of bacterial populations in the biofilm (Bowden *et al.*, 1979; Milnes and Bowden, 1985; Bowden and Li, 1997; Marsh and Bradshaw, 1997). Although the outcome of succession in biofilms in any given oral habitat cannot be precisely predicted, oral biofilms in mouths with similar environments generally support a community comprised of similar bacterial genera and species. Thus, *Streptococcus* and *Actinomyces* are consistently present in supragingival dental plaque and include *S. sanguis*, *S. mitis*, *S. oralis*, *S. gordonii* and *A. naeslundii*, *A. odontolyticus*, *A. gerencsereae* and *A. israelii*. Cells of these species reach easily detectable levels in the biofilm community by being well adapted to the various environments within the supragingival plaque biofilm, while cells of other species may be present in low or even undetectable numbers. However, significant changes in the environment in the mouth, such as xerostomia or high sucrose intake can introduce new niches appropriate for different species which can then dominate the biofilm community (Bowden 1991; Marsh, 1994; Scheie, 1994; Van Houte, 1994). These fluctuations of populations and the impact of changing environments on oral biofilm communities have been detected *in vivo* (Milnes and Bowden, 1985; Lange *et al.*, 1987; Bowden, 1991) and modeled both *in vivo* and *in vitro* (Beckers and Van der Hoeven, 1982; de Jong *et al.*, 1985; Beighton and Hayday, 1986; Bowden, 1995; Marsh 1995; Bowden and Li, 1997; Marsh and Bradshaw, 1997; Sissons, 1997)

214

Survival in the Biofilm

Protection afforded by the biofilm

It is now well accepted that generally, bacteria within biofilms are better able to survive stressful environments than those in suspended culture (Brown and Gilbert, 1993; Larsen and Fiehn, 1996; Wilson, 1996; Gilbert *et al.*, 1997). Protection by biofilms can be physical, providing a sequestered habitat or avoiding shear forces; chemical, through binding and inactivating of antibacterials (Dibdin *et al.*, 1996), or related to the slow growth rate and different physiology of biofilm cells. Also, the mass and structure of the biofilm influences the resistance of some biofilm cells to harmful agents and stressful environments. Adherent cells and early accumulations (24 hours) of biofilms of oral bacteria have similar sensitivities to fluoride as those in the planktonic phase (Li and Bowden, 1994b), while the time of accumulation can affect the sensitivity of biofilm cells to acid (Bowden and Li, 1997) and antibiotics, when seven day accumulations are more resistant than those at four days (Wilson, *et al.*, 1996).

Adaptation and tolerance

One can add to the protection provided as a result of the physical nature of the biofilm and its localized environment the adaptive capacities of individual strains of oral bacteria within the biofilm community. Once bacteria have been incorporated into the biofilm community maintaining cell viability is obviously fundamental to survival of a strain. Cell growth may not be an absolute require-ment for survival but growth is closely linked to transmission within and among hosts and, significantly, with expression of the virulence of opportunist patho-gens. However, survival of low numbers of quiescent cells (Koch, 1997) of a species within the biofilm is a possibility that has to be considered.

Some of the responses by bacteria to a variety of stresses, including starva-tion (Kjelleberg 1993; Kolter *et al.*, 1993; Huisman and Kolter, 1994; Finkel and Kolter, 1999) and other environmental stresses are known (Gilbert *et al.*, 1990; Cheville *et al.*, 1996; Serano, 1996; Britton *et al.*, 1998). Generally, the re-sponses involve structural and physiological changes of cells, often mediated through the expression of stress related proteins. These responses may be common among strains of a species, being 'ancestral' mechanisms resulting from previous exposure to a given stress or 'novel' to a single strain as a result of gene transfer or mutation (Maynard Smith, 1991; Rainey *et al.*, 1993). They can be included under a general heading of adaptive responses, usually, but not always (Leroi *et al.*, 1994), resulting increased tolerance and survival of bacte-rial cells in environments that may cause their death. In common with other bacteria, strains of species of the resident oral flora adapt to and survive stress (Belli and Marquis, 1991; Lu and McBride 1994; Marquis, 1995; Svensäter *et al.*, 1997; Gouhlen *et al.*, 1998; Hamilton and Bowden, 1998; Hamilton and Svensäter, 1998). Adaptation to low pH, (Sissons *et al.*, 1990; Hamilton and Buckley 1991; Svensäter *et al.*, 1997, Morou-Bermudez and Burne, 1999) and fluoride (Bowden 1990; van Loveren *et al.*, 1991), has been described.

Relatively little is known of the responses of oral bacteria to other stresses such as heat (Stamm *et al.*, 1991; Lu and McBride, 1994; Goulhen *et al.* 1998; Hinode *et al.* 1998) and low nutrient levels (Park *et al.* 1997) or during starvation. However, it seems likely that oral bacteria will exhibit mechanisms for accommodating to stress equivalent to those used by bacteria from other habitats. Although adaptation is usually viewed as a characteristic of a species, both the intrinsic ability of strains to exist in harsh environments and their ability to adapt may vary (Rainey *et al.*, 1993, Svensäter *et al.*, 1997; Lenski *et al.*, 1998; Finkel and Kolter, 1999,).

It can be proposed, therefore, that strains of oral bacteria respond to stressful environments and the degree to which they can survive influences the composition of the biofilm community. Also, suitably adapted bacterial cells may grow, and if they are opportunist pathogens contribute towards oral disease. However, it is important to re-emphasize that the possibility of survival of very few cells of an organism under unfavourable biofilm environments exists (Koch, 1997). Significantly, these few cells may not be detected by cultural analyses, which generally isolate strains of the predominant species. Although the more sensitive methods employing detection of specific bacterial DNA will detect low numbers of cells they cannot confirm that the DNA was, in fact, from viable cells. Also, microscopic methods employing specific probes and dyes which enter living cells may 'miss' a few viable cells in a biofilm.

Diversity among strains of bacterial species

If individual strains of a species can exhibit variation in phenotypic characters, including physiology, adaptive responses and intrinsic resistance to harmful agents, then such variation must impact on the ability of strains to survive and consequently, affect the survival of the species. It has been known for years that strains of a species can express relatively stable phenotypic differences, including for example, variations in antigenic structure, production of toxins and sensitivity to phage, dyes and antibacterial chemicals. Such differences are used to identify groups of strains of a species in infectious diseases and also generally in microbiology.

The extent of diversity among strains of a bacterial species can also be shown by use of techniques applied to the study of genetic relationships among species of animals and plants. In particular, multi-locus enzyme electrophoresis (MLEE) has proved to be particularly useful in this respect (Selander and Musser, 1990). This method has been used extensively to show presence of clones of bacterial species and their relationships to human infections (Ørskov *et al.*, 1990; Loos *et al.*, 1993; Johnson *et al.*, 1994; Poulsen *et al.*, 1994; Maiden and Feavers, 1995; Musser *et al.*, 1995). In addition, a wide range of molecular microbiological methods have been developed to identify strains of species and demonstrate the genetic relationships among them (Bruneau *et al.*, 1994; Musser *et al.*, 1995; Stanley *et al.*, 1995; Bowden and Hamilton, 1998). These techniques have revealed limited clonal diversity within some bacterial species and extensive diversity among others. Significantly, in some cases, relatively few

216

clones may be responsible for the majority of infections caused by some bacterial pathogens.and often pathogens show less clonal diversity than opportunist pathogens and commensal bacteria (Selander and Musser 1990, Loos *et al.*, 1993; Musser *et al.*, 1995). The majority of organisms causing caries and periodontal disease are generally considered as opportunist pathogens within the resident flora although there may be exceptions (Haubek *et al.*, 1997), one might, therefore, expect to see considerable clonal diversity among strains of these opportunist pathogens

It is important to recognize that the degree of discrimination varies among the different methods to identify strains within a species. Consequently, changes in the genome may not always be detected by a given typing method. As an example, with *Streptococcus pyogenes* RFLP patterns will subdivide MLEE electromorphic types (Musser *et al.*, 1995), and M serotypes may include several ribotypes (Bruneau *et al.*, 1994; Stanley *et al*, 1995). Therefore, when changes in bacterial genomes are considered it must be accepted that intra-strain genomic variation could occur within isolates of the same ribotype. This means that even when isolates of species of the same ribotype persist over time, variations in the genome may, nevertheless, have occurred. The most discriminating of the methods for detecting variations in the genome is comparisons of the RFLP patterns, where a change in a single band can be detected (Hohwy and Kilian, 1995; Musser *et al.*, 1995).

Diversity Among Strains of Species of Oral Bacteria Within a Host
Species of bacteria among the resident flora and opportunist pathogens usually show wide genetic diversity with a large number of clones. This is true of members of the resident flora where, for example, *S. mitis*, and *S. oralis*, (which may be included among the 'low pH streptococci' Sansone *et al.*, 1993), *S. mutans*, *A. naeslundii*, *Porphyromonas gingivalis, Actinobacillus actinomycetemcomitans*, *Prevotella nigrescens* and *Prevotella intermedia* have been shown to be genetically diverse (Poulsen *et al.*, 1994; Hohwy and Kilian, 1995, Fitzsimmons *et al.*, 1996; Saarela *et al.*, 1996; Bowden and Hamilton, 1998; Suchett-Kaye *et al.*, 1998; Bowden *et al.*, 1999; Sims *et al.*, 1999). Although these species are all composed of a relatively large number of clones there are distinct differences in the distribution of clones of some species compared to others. In some cases such as with *A. naeslundii*, *S. mitis* and *S. mutans* a human host may be colonized by several clones, while in others, such as *P. gingivalis* despite wide clonal diversity within the species individuals are, apparently, only colonized by a single clone (Loos *et al.*, 1992; Saarela *et al.*, 1996). The former authors caution however that definitive demonstration that an individual is colonized by a single clone requires detailed examination of the flora with at least 29 isolates from 29 oral sites. Demonstration of the colonization of an individual site by a single clone in a host can be done more easily from the point of view of the workload.

It is relatively easy to appreciate that a single clone of a species may colonize and grow in a localized and protected habitat like a root canal (Loos *et. al.*,

1992). However, it is more difficult to explain the extensive clonal diversity of species like *S. mitis* and *A. naeslundii* within an individual, compared to the limited diversity of *P. gingivalis*. It may be that *P. gingivalis* has a 'narrow' niche and a limited number of habitats in the mouth, which causes reduced colonization and less growth, resulting in reduced genetic interchange and mutation *in vivo*. This contrasts to other oral species, which colonize easily, grow well in the oral cavity and possibly undergo clonal replacement, mutation and genetic exchange within the population.

Generation of Clonal Diversity Among Strains of a Species in a Habitat
Genetic exchange
Genetic exchange among bacteria is fairly common and of obvious significance in human pathogens, where transfer of characters can influence patterns of disease and virulence (Poulsen *et al.*, 1994; Maiden and Feavers,. 1995; Spratt *et al.*,1995; Haubeck *et al.*, 1997; Morelli *et al.*, 1997) and promote resistance to antibiotics (Maynard Smith *et al.*, 1991; Bennett, 1995; Reichmann *et al.*, 1997; Hakenbeck, *et al.*, 1998). Although such exchange is also likely to occur among the commensal resident microbiota of humans and animals it may be seen as less important. However, transfer of DNA between strains of resident commensal bacteria may result in different phenotypes, better suited a given environment. Milkman and McKane (1995), have used the name 'meroclone' to describe strains containing 'foreign' DNA which has been transferred during descent from an ancestral cell.

Genetic exchange may result from conjugation (Wilkins, 1995) transduction or transformation (Lorenz and Wakernagel, 1994). In particular, close association of cells is necessary for plasmid transfer during conjugation. The mechanisms of pheromone-inducible plasmid transfer in *Enterococcus faecalis* which includes cell aggregation is an excellent example of conjugation in Gram-positive cells (Dunny, 1990; Rhufel *et al.*, 1997). Such mechanisms may be promoted by the close cell association in biofilms. There is also evidence that plasmids can exchange from planktonic to biofilm phases (Angles, *et al.*, 1993; Beaudoin, *et al.*, 1998) and within biofilms (Christensen, *et al.* 1998; Goodman, *et al.*, 1993). In addition, surfaces may enhance transfer of DNA from one organism to another (Stotzky and Babich, 1984).

Little is known of the possibilities of genetic exchange among cells in biofilm communities of oral bacteria, although gene transfer among strains and species of oral bacteria has been shown to have occured (Reichmann *et al.*, 1997; Hakenbeck *et al.*, 1998; Poulsen *et al.*, 1998; Hanley *et al.*, 1999).

Mutation
Rainey *et al.* (1993) have discussed the basic mechanisms and role of intraclonal polymorphism in adaptation and survival of bacterial strains in varying environments. They point out that adaptive mechanisms involving coordinated gene expression have evolved and may be viewed as 'ancestral' and limited to those stimuli that an organism has been exposed to previously.

'Ancestral' adaptive mechanisms may not be effective when the organism is exposed to novel stresses.

Aspects of selection and the evolution of bacteria have been studied during chemostat and batch culture growth (Dykhuizen and Hartl, 1983; Dykhuizen, 1993; Elena *et al.*, 1995; Foster, 1995; Lenski, 1995; Travisano and Lenski, 1996; Lenski *et al.*, 1998; Papadopoulos *et al.*, 1999;). During growth bacterial genomes change (Bergthorsson and Ochman, 1999) and even in the absence of obvious growth mutations may occur (Foster, 1995). Studies of populations of *E. coli* have confirmed that mutations result in phenotypes 'best fitted' to the environment and that these phenotypes can predominate in the population in chemostat and transferred batch culture. During starvation in batch culture *E. coli* populations also exhibit evolution of mutant forms best fitted to the environment, however several mutant forms co-exist in the culture (Finkel and Kolter, 1999). This result suggests that mutants produced during growth of several generations of bacteria may not die or be eliminated by the mutant best suited to a specific environment. Moreover, structured habitats like biofilms with microcolonies of bacteria, may promote genetic polymorphism within populations (Korona *et al.*, 1994). Aspects of the diversity and interactions among cells of bacteria within colonies on surfaces are described in the volume edited by Shapiro and Dworkin (1997).

Clonal replacement
Transmission of different clones among various habitats in the host or transmission from other hosts may contribute to increased diversity among strains of a resident species (Caufield *et al.*, 1993; Alaluusua *et al.*, 1996; Fitzsimmons *et al.*, 1996; Mättö *et al.*, 1996; Saarela *et al.*, 1996; Suchett-Kaye *et al.*, 1999). Very often, the proportions of clones within a species population can change, such that one or more clones predominates and others are 'replaced'. It must be borne in mind that while true replacement may occur it is not inconceivable that the 'excluded' clones may remain below the level of detection. Clonal replacement, based on the inability to detect specific clones and the isolation of new clones, has been shown on several occasions, including during oral colonization of infants by *Streptococcus mitis* (Fitzsimmons *et al.*, 1996) It may be difficult to distinguish between clonal replacement resulting from colonization from the external environment and the emergence of a dominant clonal type generated from within the habitat. The reasons why one clone of a species should be 'replaced' by another are not clear, although selection by the environment seems a possibility. In pathogens, antigenic variation can be seen as the reason for the emergence of different clones selected by the host immune response (Brunham *et al.*, 1993). It is not known whether this or other subtle mechanisms promote clonal replacement in the human oral cavity. However, it is important to recognize that small changes in the genome, which would be detected by RFLP patterns, show clonal replacement which might not be detected by less discriminatory methods such as ribotyping. Thus, in some cases the word replacement may be too strong, inferring elimination of a strain rather than a small change in

its genome. The 'replacing' clone may be closely similar to that previously dominant, having the same array of intrinsic housekeeping characteristics.

Considering the above, genetic interchange among strains of bacteria within the habitat, mutation of the genome, and the possibility of introduction of new clones by transmission from other hosts are significant factors which could increase the genetic diversity among strains of a species within an oral biofilm community. Inclusion of clonal types which express character/s related to survival of stresses into the biofilm, contributes to the survival of the species.

Persistence of clones of oral bacteria in the mouth.

Although extensive studies have not been made there is evidence that clones of some oral bacteria such as *Streptococcus mutans* and *Actinomyces* spp. and *Prevotella* survive for several months in the mouth (Barsotti *et al.*, 1993; Alaluusua *et al.*, 1994; Mättö *et al.*, 1996; Grönroos *et al.*, 1998), even after treatment with antibacterials (Grönroos *et al.*, 1995; Kozai *et al.*, 1991; von Troil-Linden *et al.*, 1996). These limited results suggest that biofilms that are formed following normal ecological perturbation include clones present before the environmental change. Resident clones recolonizing following more extreme ecological upsets such as chlorhexidine treatment may have been resistant to the stress or survived in protected oral habitats or in associated tissues, such as the tonsils In contrast to those species which exhibit persistent clones, other species such as *S. mitis* appear to undergo clonal replacement with only an occasional persistent clone (Fitzsimmons *et al.*, 1996). Clonal replacement may be related to the presence of a species in a biofilm on shedding mucosal surfaces rather than one on the dentition.

A role for genetic diversity and biofilm in survival of *A. naeslundii* in the mouth

Given the above, supragingival dental plaque could play a role both as a protective reservoir and as a site for the development of genetic variants of oral species. Moreover, organization into structured communities could promote genetic exchange and enhance diversity. Variants may arise from genetic transfer and mutation and generally experiments have shown that variants 'best fitted' will predominate in a given environment. However, evidence exists that less successful variants are not eliminated and their inclusion into a biofilm should increase their chances of retention in the habitat.

In a recent study of ribotypes of *A. naeslundii* genospecies 1 and 2 in patients with root caries (Bowden *et al.*, 1999) it was shown that the distribution of ribotypes was closely similar or the same in different habitats, suggesting that all of the ribotypes possessed characters that enabled them to colonize and persist in the different localized environments. However, study of different ribotypes from a single individual revealed distinct phenotypic differences.

The expression of different phenotypes by the individual ribotypes made them ideal to test whether one was 'best suited' to a specific defined environment. The hypothesis was, 'that among the ribotypes from a single individual
220

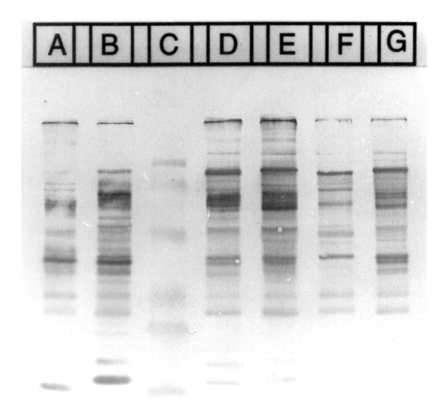

Figure 1 An example of a Western Blot of supernatant extracts of ribotypes from the same person, including those used in the competition experiment, developed with rabbit antiserum against HNG 128. **Lanes:** 5 µg of supernatant extracts of ribotypes in lanes, **A**. HNG 124; **B**. HNG 128; **D**. HNG 145; **E**. HNG 189; **F**. HNG 231; **G**. HNG 232.
Lane **C**. BioRad low molecular weight pre-stained standard.

would be one which was best suited to a specific environment' This hypothesis was tested by competing the five ribotypes in a continuous culture biofilm model.

Demonstration of Phenotypic Diversity Among *A. Naeslundii* Genospecies 2 Ribotypes from a Single Subject.

Five ribotypes (HNG 124, 145, 189, 231 and 232), from one subject (Bowden *et al.*, 1999) were examined for biochemical, antigenic and enzyme electromorph variation.

Carbohydrate fermentation was tested on bromophenol purple agar with 0.5% carbohydrate sterilised by heat or filtration. Antigenic analysis was made by testing dialysed supernatant extracts of whole cells following cell wall

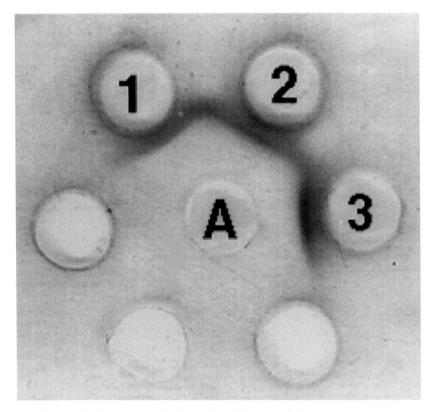

Figure 2 Example of cell wall carbohydrate antigen of Serogroup B ribotypes.
Wells, **Well A.** 30 μl of HNG 189 wall carbohydrate 0.1μg/ml. **Wells 1, 2, and 3**, rabbit antisera
against ribotypes HNG 128, HNG 145 and HNG 189 respectively.

preparation (Bowden and Fillery, 1978), and cell wall carbohydrate extracted
with 5% trichloracetic acid from pronase treated cell walls (Bowden and Fillery,
1978) against rabbit antisera. Supernatant extracts were examined by Western
Blotting and and wall carbohydrate by double diffusion in agarose gel. The
electrophoretic mobility of selected enzymes was determined in 2% agarose gels
(Agarose LE, Roche Biochemicals, Montreal, Quebec) prepared on GelBond
film (Amersham Pharmacia Biotech., Montreal, Quebec). Gels were run at 5^0C
on a Multiphor 1 (Amersham Pharmacia Biotech) at 8 volts/cm. The electrophoresis buffers and techniques for cell extracts and stains followed those
described by Zahner *et al.* (1989). Some initial results of these analyses are
shown in Figures 1 and 2 and Table 1.

All ribotypes fermented glucose, glycogen, maltose, melibiose, raffinose and
sucrose, while adonitol, amygdalin, arabinose, cellobiose, erythritol, aesculin,
glycerol mannose mannitol rhamnose salicin, sorbitol and xylose were negative.
Inulin, melezitose, ribose, and trehalose fermentation varied among the

ribotypes. Analysis of cell extracts by Western Blotting showed extensive antigenic relationships among the ribotypes (Figure 1), however, analysis of cell wall carbohydrate (Figure 2) showed two distinct antigens (A and B) dividing the five ribotypes into two groups. Group A antigen HNG 124 and 231, Group B antigen HNG 145, 189 and 232. Significantly, Group A included the two ribotypes that fermented inulin, while the other variations in fermentation were seen in both groups. Further analysis of whole cell extracts using sera absorbed with whole cells (Cole *et al.*, 1999) suggested that individual ribotypes could carry unique protein antigens.

Multilocus enzyme analysis has showed polymorphism of glutamate dehy-drogenase, glycerol phosphate dehydrogenase, isocitrate dehydrogenase, carboxyl-esterase and acid phosphatase among the ribotypes.

Competition among ribotypes of *a. naeslundii* genospecies 2 from a single subject
Methods
Chemostats provide a useful system for analysing the physiology of bacteria, including the influence of the environment on growth and competition between strains. Modified chemostats have also been used to measure the accumulation of biofilms of oral bacteria under controlled environmental conditions. A model of this type (Li and Bowden 1994a,b; Bowden, 1999) was used to determine the outcome of growth of the five ribotypes (Table 1) in a controlled environment. The conditions in the vessel were: X4 diluted basal medium (Li and Bowden, 1994a) with limiting (1.25mM, glucose) at pH 7.0, and 37^0 C with a dilution rate of D=0.1 h^{-1}. The gas phase above the culture in the fermenter was aerobic. Epon-hydroxy apatite rods were included in the model as substrata for biofilm accumulation (Li and Bowden, 1994b).

Inoculation of the Vessel
The strains (HNG 124, 145, 189, 231 and 232) were grown overnight in undiluted basal medium and the concentration of cells was measured by optical density. One ml of the least dense culture was taken and one ml of each of the other cultures, suitably diluted in basal medium to give the same optical density as the first were added. The total 5 ml was then inoculated into the culture vessel. Controls of the total viable counts of each of the individual cultures of the ribotypes were made.

Sampling the Planktonic and Biofilm Phases
A sample from the planktonic phase was taken 5 minutes after inoculation, to calculate total viable cells. After 2 h both the planktonic and biofilm (2 rods) phases were sampled (Li and Bowden, 1994a,b) and after suitable dilution spiral plated (Spiral systems, Cincinnati, Ohio) on to blood agar (Blood agar base No 2 Oxoid, Inc., Nepean, Ontario) supplemented with 5% w/w sheeps blood (Atlas Lab. Winnipeg, Manitoba) and incubated for 48 h in a candle jar. Further samples from the planktonic and biofilm phases were taken at 24, 48 and 96 or 120 h.

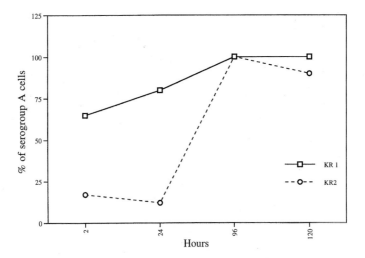

Figure 3 Proportions of Serogroup A ribotypes in the planktonic phases of experiments KR1 and KR 2.

Selection of Isolates

Colonies were selected randomly from the spiral plated culture plates. Twenty isolates were taken from each of the planktonic samples and 60 from the biofilm samples. Each isolate was stored freeze dried and cells for isolation of genomic DNA were stored at -80^0C.

Initial Serological Screening of Isolates

Antigenic analysis had shown that the 5 ribotypes could be divided into two groups on the basis of cell wall carbohydrate antigens. Initial studies using cross absorbed rabbit anti-sera (Putnins and Bowden, 1993) allowed identification of these groups by whole cell agglutination. Consequently, isolates could be assigned to Group A or B by whole cell agglutination with absorbed anti-sera.

Ribotyping Isolates

Ribotyping was carried out following the method described by Bowden *et al.*, (1993) with minor modification (Bowden *et al.*, 1999). In the initial study described here all isolates from 2, 24, 48 and 120h were ribotyped. In repeat experiments (selected data shown here) ribotyping has been limited to 2, 24 and 120 h.

Results

Proportion of Serogroup A and B Ribotypes in the Planktonic and Biofilm Phases over Time

The data in Figure 3 show that Serogroup A ribotypes dominated the planktonic phase of two experiments KR1 and 2 after 120 h. It should be noted that dominance by Serogroup A was apparently independent of the initial proportion of

224

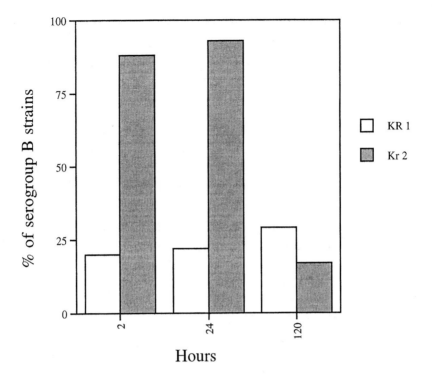

Figure 4 Proportions of Serogroup B ribotypes in the biofilm phases of experiments KR 1 and KR 2.

these strains in the vessel. In run KR1 the 2 h planktonic sample included 65% Serogroup A strains, however in KR2 serogroup A only accounted 17% of the 2 h sample. Figure 4 shows the proportions of Serogroup B ribotypes present in the biofilms over time. Serogroup B ribotypes contributed 29% (KR1) and 17% (KR2) to the biofilm population after 120h, despite dominance of both the planktonic and biofilm phases by Serogroup A ribotypes.

Proportions of Individual Ribotypes in the Planktonic and Biofilm Phases over Time in Experiment KR1

The data in Figure 5 show the proportions of the five ribotypes detected in the planktonic and biofilm phases of experiment KR1. Five minutes after inoculation isolates of HNG 124, 189 and 232 were cultured from the 20 planktonic isolates, cells of HNG 145 and 231 were not detected. In contrast, the 60 biofilm isolates from the epon-hydroxyapatite rods after two hours included representatives of each ribotype. At each time period the biofilm, like the planktonic phase, was dominated by cells of HNG 124, however, at 24, 48 and 120 hours 5, 3 and 4 of the ribotypes were detected respectively. The proportions of the ribotypes in the biofilms varied over time.

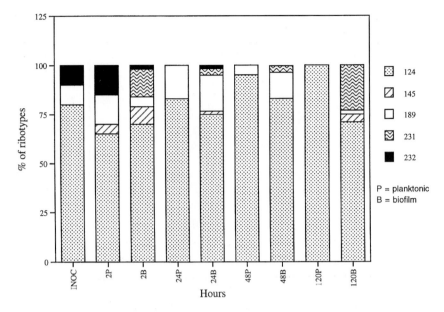

Figure 5 Proportions of individual ribotypes in the biofilm and planktonic phases of experiment KR1 during 120 hours.

Increases in Numbers of Ribotypes in Biofilms over Time in Experiment KR 1
The numbers of cells of each ribotype in the biofilms at 2 and 120 hours, calculated from the proportions of the ribotypes against total counts of viable cells X $10^6/cm^2$ of surface are shown in Table 2. Although HNG 124 dominated the biofilm, HNG 231, also a Serogroup A strain grew well in the biofilm, increasing its numbers 173 times compared to 101 times by HNG 124. The other two ribotypes detected both increased their cell numbers, indicating that they grew within the biofilm. HNG 232, the strain with the lowest numbers at 2h was not detected at 120h, suggesting that it had either not grown, or grown to numbers too low to be detected.

Discussion
The results of these initial experiments support the hypothesis that one of the ribotypes (HNG 124) of *A. naeslundii* genospecies 2 from a single patient was 'best suited' to the test environment. Also, in a relatively short term (5 days) the biofilm acted as a reservoir for the other less successful ribotypes, which in three cases were shown to increase their biofilm populations. It is important to recognize that ribotypes could only be reported as 'not detected' recognizing the limitation emphasized by Loos *et al.*, (1992) of the need to examine large numbers of isolates before deciding that a specific clone (ribotype) was absent from a sample. However, 60 isolates from a biofilm sample exceeded the number suggested by these authors to give 95% confidence level of detecting

226

Table 2 Numbers of viable biofilm cells of ribotypes Hng 124, 145, 189, 231 and 232 x $10^6/cm^2$ at 2 and 120 hours in experiment KR1.

RIBOTYPES	VIABLE CELLS X $10^6/cm^2$		RATIO OF COUNTS 120/2 HOURS
	2 hours	**120 hours**	
124	0.48	48.3	101
145	0.057	2.7	47
189	0.035	1.36	39
231	0.09	15.64	174
232	0.01	ND	-

ND = Not detected

ribotypes. Although 60 isolates were taken we could not assume that the ribotypes were equally distributed among the rods in the fermenter and this may also have influenced the isolation of ribotypes. The data presented and more recent data (not shown) show that cells of the ribotypes adhered to the rods at 2 hours before cell growth occurred in similar proportions to those in the planktonic phase. These data suggest that the ability to adhere to the hog gastric mucin conditioning film (Li and Bowden, 1994a) in this model is a common characteristic of the ribotypes tested. A related observation has been made by Hallberg *et al.* (1998) who demonstrated ribotype diversity among isolates of *A. naeslundii* genospecies 2 with GalNAcb-dependent and acidic proline-rich protein binding specificities.

Subsequent to adherence, cells of ribotype HNG 124 dominated the planktonic and biofilm phases. Increases of cells of HNG 124 in the biofilm could result both from growth on the surface and aggregation between biofilm cells and cells from the planktonic phase. In contrast, growth of cells of the other ribotypes (Table 2) must have taken place within the biofilm, because aggregation from the plantonic phase would be negligible. Growth of cells of ribotypes excluded from the planktonic phase within biofilms suggests that biofilms can play a significant role in survival of genetic variants.

Despite these encouraging initial data they are hardly sufficient to provide strong support for the concept that the biofilm acts both as a reservoir of previously selected phenotypes of a species best suited to specific environments and also, as a site where genetic and phenotypic diversity is generated. Further, and essential support would be the demonstration of outgrowth of a second 'best suited' ribotype, when changes are made in the experimental environment. An early continuous culture study of competition between *Lactobacillus* and *Streptococcus mutans* at low pH and in the presence of fluoride (Bowden and Hamilton, 1989) showed that *S. mutans* was apparently 'eliminated' from the culture at 20mM fluoride. However, on removal of the fluoride, cells of *S. mutans* were again detected in the culture. It is most likely that adherent cells of *S. mutans* survived on the surfaces of the vessel. Cells adherent to the vessel walls are a common feature of continuous culture, even when surface accumulations are not visible macroscopically. The next stage in exploring the ability of the biofilm to act as a reservoir for significant genetic variants is to attempt to reproduce this result with the 5 ribotype culture under different environments.

Among those environments which could be suggested for testing would be changes in nutrient, in particular, leaving mucin as the sole carbon source, providing complex carbohydrates such as starch, or removing the carbon source entirely. Increased dilution of the medium to give generalized nutrient stress could also be considered. Variation in pH to pH 5.5 would also place stress on the cells, generally *A. naeslundii* genospecies 2 grows optimally at pH 6.5. The current experiments have been made in an aerobic environment with CO_2 provided from carbonate in the medium, changing to an anaerobic gas phase (Hamilton *et al.*, 1989) could also promote the outgrowth of a ribotype other than HNG 124. In addition, changes in the dilution rate to modify cell generation times could influence the 'most successful' ribotype. Whole cell agglutination provides a rapid screen to show dominance of either Seroroup A or B ribotypes. Selection for dominance by a Serogroup B ribotype would be the initial objective of these studies.

Another limitation of these initial studies is the time period that was tested. Certainly, dominance by a single ribotype was demonstrated, but 120h only allowed approximately 17 generations of cells, vastly less than the thousands of generations used in studies of the evolution of different phenotypes of *E. coli*. The relatively few generations may have avoided the chance of significant variation within the ribotypes and to date (not shown) we have not seen evidence for the generation of new ribotypes among the hundreds of isolates that have been typed. However, as mentioned earlier, changes in the genomes of these isolates may have been detected had we used a more discriminating typing method. Also, data on the phenotypes of these ribotypes has only been tested on the five selected for study (Table 1). All of our isolates are stored, so that testing, for example, for enzyme polymorphism among a given ribotype from a person or from experiments KR1 and KR2 is feasible. In any event, running the biofilm model for longer periods (weeks), including testing for variation in the genome and phenotype is important to test whether a given ribotype will adapt over time to the test environment.

When the possibility that oral biofilms can act as archives, storing clones of bacteria which have been selected by previous environments is considered there is little doubt that the biofilm is protective habitat; that mechanisms of adaptation and generation of genetic variants are common among bacteria; and that it has been demonstrated phenotypes 'best suited' to a specific environment are selected. Areas which are less clear in terms of oral biofilms are the persistence and stability of specific clonal variants within the biofilm. In particular, testing persistence of predominant clones *in vivo* after excessive perturbation with antibacterials would give an idea of the robustness of the archive. A more difficult aspect to test is the persistence of a specific clonal variant *in vivo* when it is present at 'non-detectable' levels. Also, it may be that variation in the genome is a continuous process and that only those variants expressing

228

significant advantageous phenotypes in a given environment reach numbers that ensure their persistence within the biofilm. Given the potential for diverse environments within the biofilm each clonal variant may occupy its best 'realized niche', and this may explain the finding od several ribotypes in the spatially diverse communities in a caries lesion (Bowden *et al.*, 1999). Recolonization of re-forming biofilms by specific clonal variants after perturbation may require that the strains are sequestered at sites on the host other than where the biofilm is accumulating. These sites could be regarded as 'fugitive habitats' and such habitats may play a role in recolonization be *S. mutans* and *P. intermedia* and *P. nigrescens*. Little is known of such habitats for the oral flora but the tongue, pharynx and tonsils seem possibilities.

Does the possibility that oral biofilms act to some extent as an archive, storing clonal variants with important phenotypic characters have significance in the mouth? During initial and subsequent colonization of the human oral cavity following birth it seems possible that the host establishes an immune relationship with its resident organisms (Cole *et al.*, 1998, 1999). These and other unknown resident flora-host interactions probably continue during the life of the host. In health the established resident flora which has co-evolved with the host (Brunham *et al.*, 1993) can provide protection against colonization by pathogens. The persistence of host specific strains which play a commensal role can, therefore, contribute to oral health and possibly to the general health of a host. If the biofilm incorporates clonal types best suited to characters of specific environments the stability of a biofilm generally related to health, would be enhanced. This concept of a co-evolved 'healthy biofilm' would not be out of keeping with the converse, that is, a biofilm where significant and perhaps unnatural changes in the environment promote emergence of opportunist pathogens. Thus, if the bacterial clonal variant composition of oral biofilms does, indeed, reflect normal past environmental events it could be proposed to be associated with the health of the host. Unfortunately, the biofilm may also harbour strains of opportunist oral pathogens, generated in previous environments conducive to disease. Microbiological control of dental disease remains, therefore, in the realm of manipulation of the ecosystems, to encourage a stable healthy biofilm community, resistant to pertubation by opportunist pathogens.

Acknowledgements

G. H. W. Bowden is supported by MRC. Canada, Grant MT 7611. Data on the antigenic structure of the ribotypes was from a thesis presented by Dr. A. Cholakis, as part of a Diploma in Periodontology. Data from KR1 and 2 were taken from studies for a B.Sc. (Dent) by Ms. K. Eggertson.

References

Alaluusua, S., Alaluusua, S. J., Karjalainen, J., Saarela, M. Holttinen, T., Kallio, M., Hölttä, P., Torkko, H., Relander, P. and Asikainen, S. 1994. The demonstration by ribotyping of the stability of oral *Streptococcus mutans* infection over 5 to 7 years in children. *Archs. Oral Biol.* **39**, 467-471.

Alaluusua, S., Mättö, J., Grönroos, L., Innila, S, Torkko, H., Asikainem S. *et al*., 1996. Oral colonization by more than one clonal type of mutans streptococcus in children with nursing bottle dental caries. *Arch. Oral Biol.* **41**, 167-173.

Angles, M. L., Marshall, K. C. and Goodman, A. E. 1993. Plasmid transfer between marine bacteria in the aqueous phase and biofilms in reactor microcosms. *Appl. Environ. Microbiol.* **59**, 843-850.

Barsotti, O. Morrier, J. J., Decoret., Benay, G. and Rocca, J. P. 1993. An investigation into the use of restriction endonuclease analysis for the study of transmission of *Actinomyces. J. Clin Periodontol.* **20**, 436-442.

Beaudoin, D. L., Bryers, J. D., Cunningham, A. B. and Peretti, S. W. 1998. Mobilization of broad host range plasmid from *Pseudomonas putida* to established biofilm of *Bacillus azotoformans*. 1. experiments. *Biotechnol. Bioeng.* **57**, 272-279.

Beckers, H. J. A., and van Der Hoeven, J. S. 1982. Growth rates of *Actinomyces viscosus* and *Streptococcus mutans* during early colonization of tooth surfaces in gnotobiotic rats. *Infect Immun* **35**, 583-587.

Beighton, D. and Hayday, H. 1986. the influence of diet on the growth of streptococcal bacteria on the molar teeth of monkeys (*Macaca fascicularis*). *Arch. Oral Biol.* **31**, 449-454.

Belli, W. A. and Marquis, R. E. 1991. Adaptation of *Streptococcus mutans* and *Enterococcus hirae* to acid stress in continuous culture. *Appl. Environ. Microbiol.* **57**, 1134-1138.

Bennett, P. M. 1995. The spread of drug resistance. In:Baumberg, S., Young, J. P. W., Wellington, E. M. H. and Saunders, J. R. (eds.) *Population genetics of bacteria*, pp. 317-344, Society for General Microbiology, Symposium 52, University Press, Cambridge

Bergthorsson, U. and Ochman, H. 1999. Chromosomal changes during experimental evolution in laboratory populations of *Escherichia coli. J. Bacteriol.* **181**, 1360-1363.

Bos, R., van der Mei, H. C. and Busscher, H. J. 1996a. Co-adhesion of oral microbial pairs under flow in the presence of saliva and lactose. *J. Dent. Res.* **75**, 809-815.

Bos, R., van der Mei, H. C. and Busscher, H. J. 1996b. Influence of temperature on the co-adhesion of oral microbial pairs in saliva. *Eur. J. Oral Sci.* **104**, 372-377.

Bos, R., van der Mei, H. C. and Busscher, H. J. 1996c. Influence of ionic strength and substratum hydrophobicity on the co-adhesion of oral microbial pairs. *Microbiology* **142**, 2355-2361.

Bowden, G. H. W. 1990. Effects of fluoride on the microbial ecology of dental plaque. *J. Dent. Res.* **69 (Spec. Iss.)**, 653-659.

Bowden, G. H. W. 1991. Which bacteria are cariogenic in humans? In: Johnson, N. W. (ed.) *Risk markers for oral disease, Dental caries* Vol 1, pp. 266-286, Cambridge University Press, Cambridge.

Bowden, G. H. W. 1995. The role of microbiology in models of dental caries: reaction paper. *Adv. Dent. Res.* **9**,255-269.

Bowden, G. H. W. 1999. A controlled environment model for the accumulation of biofilms of oral bacteria . In: Doyle, R. J. (ed). *Biofilms, Methods in Enzymology,* Vol. 310, pp. 216-224, Academic Press, New York (in press).

Bowden, G. H. W., Ellwood, D. C. and Hamilton, I. R. 1979. Microbial ecology of the oral cavity. In: Alexander, K (ed.) *Advances in Microbial Ecology.* Vol 3, pp. 135-217, Plenum Press, New York.

Bowden, G. H. and Fillery, E. D. 1978. Wall carbohydrate antigens of *A. israelii.* In:McGhee, J. R., Mestecky, J. and Babb, J. L. (eds). *Advances in Experimental Medicine and Biology.* Vol 107, pp. 685-693 Plenum Press, New York.

Bowden, G. H. W. and Hamilton, I. R. 1989. Competition between *Streptococcus mutans* and *Lactobacillus casei* in mixed continuous culture. *Oral Microbiol Immunol.* **4**, 57-64.

Bowden, G. H. W. and Hamilton, I. R. 1998. Survival of oral bacteria. *Crit. Rev. Oral Biol. Med.* **9**, 54-85

Bowden, G. H., Johnson, J. and Schachtele, C. 1993. Characterization of *Actinomyces* with genomic DNA fingerprints and rRNA gene probes. *J. Dent. Res.* **72**, 1171-1179.

Bowden, G. H. W. and Li Y. H. 1997. Nutritional influences on biofilm development. *Adv. Dent. Res.* **11**, 81-99.

Bowden, G., H., Nolette, N., Ryding, H. A. and Cleghorn B. M 1999. The diversity and distribution of the predominant ribotypes of *Actinomyces naeslundii* genospecies 1 and 2 in samples from enamel and healthy and carious root surfaces of teeth. *J. Dent. Res.* (in press).

Brecx, M., Theilade, J. and Attstrom, R. 1983. An ultra-structural quantitative study of the significance of microbial multiplication during early plaque growth. *J. Periodont. Res.* **18**, 177-186.

Britton, K. L., Stillman, T. J., Yip, K. S. P., Forterre, P., Engel, P. C. and Rice, D. W. 1998. Insights into the molecular basis of salt tolerance from the study of glutamate dehydrogenase from *Halobacterium salinarium. J. Biol. Chem.* **273**, 9023-9030.

Brown, M. R. W. and Gilbert, P.1993. Sensitivity of biofilms to antimicrobial agents. *J. Appl. Bact. Symp. supple.*, **74**, 87S-97S.

Bruneau, S., de Montclos, H., Drouet, E. and Denoyel, G. A. 1994. rRNA gene restriction patterns of *Streptococcus pyogenes*: Epidemiological applications and relation to serotypes. *J. Clin. Microbiol.* **32**, 2953-2958.

Brunham, R. C., Plummer, F. A. and Stephens, R. S. 1993. Bacterial antigenic variation, host immune response, and pathogen-host coevolution. *Infect. Immun.* **61**, 2273-2276.

Busscher, H. J., Cowan, M.M. and van der Mei, H. C. 1992. On the relative importance of specific and non-specific approaches to oral microbial adhesion. *FEMS Microbiol. Rev.* **88**, 192-210.

Busscher, H. J. and van der Mei, H. C. 1997. Physico-chemical interactions in initial microbial adhesion and relevance for biofilm formation. *Adv. Dent. Res.* **11**, 24-32.

Caufield, P. W., Cutter, G. R. and Dasanayake, A. P. 1993. Initial acquisition of mutans streptococci by infants: evidence for a discrete window of infectivity. *J. Dent. Res.* **72**, 37-45.

Cheville, A. M., Arnold, K. W., Buchrieser, C., Cheng, C-M. and Kaspar, C. W. 1996. rpoS regulation of acid, heat and salt tolerance in *Escherichia coli. App. Environ. Microbiol.* **62**, 1822-1824

Cisar, J. O, Takahashi, Y., Ruhl, S., Donkersloot, J. A. and Sandberg, A. L. 1997. Specific inhibitors of bacterial adhesion: Observations from the study of Gram-positive bacteria that initiate biofilm formation on the tooth surface. *Adv. Dent. Res.* **11**, 168-175.

Christensen, B. B., Sternberg, C., Andersen, J., Eberl, L., Möller, S., Givskov, M. and Molin, S. 1998. Establishment of new genetic traits in a microbial biofilm community. *Appl. Environ. Microbiol.* **64**, 2247-2255.

Cole, M. F., Bryan, S., Evans, M. K., Pearce, C. L., Sheridan, M. J., Sura, P. A., Wientzen, R. and Bowden, G. H. W. 1998. Mucosal immunity to commensal oral bacteria in human infants: salivary antibodies reactive with *Actinomyces naeslundi* genospecies 1 and 2 during colonization. *Infect. Immun.* **66**, 4283-4289.

Cole, M. F., Bryan, S., Evans, M. K., Pearce, C. L., Sheridan, M. J., Sura, P. A., Wientzen, R. and Bowden, G. H. W. 1998. Mucosal immunity to commensal oral bacteria in human infants: Salivary secretory immunoglobulin A antibodies reactive with *Streptococcus mitis* biovar 1, *Streptococcus oralis*, *Streptococcus mutans* and *Enterococcus faecalis* during the first two years of life. *Infect. Immun.* 67, 1878-1886.

Cole, M., F., Cholakis, A. and Bowden, G. H. 1999. Antigenic differences among ribotypes of A. naeslundii gsp. 2 from a patient. *J. Dent. Res.* **78 spec. iss.**, 345, abstract 1913.

de Jong, M. H., van den Kieboom C. W. A., Lukassen, J. A. M. and van der Hoeven, J. S. 1985. Effects of dietary carbohydrates on the numbers of *Streptococcus mutans* and *Actinomyces viscosus* in dental plaque of mono-infected gnotobiotic rats. *J. Dent. Res.* **64**, 1134-1137.

Dibdin, G. H., Assinder, S. J., Nichols, W. W. and Lambert, P. A. 1996. Mathematical model of b-lactam penetration into a biofilm of *Pseudomonas aeruginosa* while undergoing simultaneous inactivation by released b-lactamases. *J. Antimicrobial Chemother.* **38**, 757-769.

Dunny, G. M. 1990. Genetic functions and cell-cell interactions in the pheromone-inducible plasmid transfer system of *Enterococcus faecalis. Mol. Microbiol.* **4**, 689-696.

Dykhuizen, D, E. 1993. Chemostats used for studying natural selection and adaptive evolution. *Methods Enzymology*, **224**, 613-631.

Dykhuizen, D. E. and Hartl, D. L. 1983. Selection in chemostats. *Microbiol. Rev.* **47**, 150-168.

Elena, S. F., Cooper, V. S. and Lenski, R. E. 1996. Punctuated evolution caused by selection of rare beneficial mutations. *Science* **272**, 1802-1804.

Finkel, S. E. and Kolter, R. (1999). Evolution of microbial diversity during prolonged starvation. *Proc. Natl. Acad. Sci. USA*, **96**, 4023-4027.

Fitzsimmons, S., Evans, M., Pearce, C., Sheridan, M., Weitzen, R., Bowden G. H. W. *et al.* 1996.

231

Clonal diversity of *Streptococcus mitis* biovar 1 isolates from the oral cavity of human neonates. *Clin. Diag. Lab. Immunol.* **3**, 517-522.

Foster, P. C. 1995. Adaptive mutation. In:Baumberg, S., Young, J. P. W., Wellington, E. M. H. and Saunders, J. R. (eds.) *Population genetics of bacteria*, pp. 13-30, Society for General Microbiology, Symposium 52, University Press, Cambridge

Gilbert, P., Collier, P. J. and Brown, M. R. W. 1990. Influence of growth rate on susceptibility to antimicrobial agents: biofilms, cell cycle, dormancy and stringent response. *Antimicrob. Agents Chemother.* **34**, 1865-1868.

Gilbert, P., Das, J. and Foley, I. 1997. Biofilm susceptibility to antimicrobials. *Adv. Dent. Res.* **11**, 160-167.

Goodman, A. E., Hild, E., Marshall, K. C. and Hermansson, M. 1993. Conjugative plasmid transfer between bacteria under simulated marine oligotrophic conditions. *Appl. Environ. Microbiol.* **59**, 1035-1040.

Goulhen, F., Hafezi, A., Uitto, V-J., Nakamura, R., Grenier, D. and Mayrand, D. 1998. Subcellular localization and cytotoxic activity of the groEL-like protein isolated from *Actinobacillus actinomycetemcomitans*. *Infect. Immun.* **66**, 5307-5313.

Grönroos, L., Mättö, J., Saarela, M, Luoma, A. R., Luoma, H., Jousimies-Somer, H. Pyhälä, L., Asikainen, S. and Alauusua, S. 1995. Chlorhexidine susceptibilities of mutans streptococcal serotypes and ribotypes. *Antimicrob. Agents Chemother.* **39**, 894-898.

Grönroos, L., Saarela, M., Mättö, J., Tanner-Salo, U., Vuorela, A. and Alaluusua, S. 1998. Mutacin production by *Streptococcus mutans* may promote transmission of bacteria from mother to child. *Infect. Immun.* **66**, 2595-2600.

Hakenbeck, R., König, A., Kern, I., van der Linden, M., Keck, W., Billot-Klein, D., Legrand, R., Scoot, B. and Gutman, L. 1998. Acquisition of five high Mr penicillin-binding protein variants of high level b- lactam resistance from *Streptococcus mitis* to *Streptococcus pneumoniae*. *J. Bacteriol.* **180**, 1831-1840.

Hallberg K., Holm, C., Hammarström, K-J., Kalfas, S. and Strömberg N. 1998. Ribotype diversity of *Actinomyces* with similar intraoral tropism but different types of *N*-acetyl-b-D-galactosamine binding specificity. *Oral Microbiol. Immunol.* **13**, 188-192.

Hamilton, I. R. and Buckley, N. D. 1991. Adaptation by Streptococcus mutans to acid tolerance. *Oral Microbiol. Immunol.* **6**, 65-71.

Hamilton, I. R., McKee, A. S. and Bowden, G. H. W. 1989. Growth and metabolic properties of *Bacteroides intermedius* in anaerobic continuous culture. *Oral Microbiol. Immunol.* **4**, 89-97.

Hamilton, I. R. and Svensäter, G. 1998. Acid-regulated proteins induced by *Streptococcus mutans* and other oral bacteria during acid shock. *Oral Microbiol. Immunol.* **13**, 292-300.

Hanley, S. A., Aduse-Opoku, J. and Curtis, M. 1999. A 55-Kilodalton immunodominant antigen of *Porphyromonas gingivalis* W50 has arisen via horizontal gene transfer. *Infect. Immun.* **67**, 1157-1171.

Haubek, D., Dirienzo, J. M., Tinoco, E. M. B., Westergaard, J., López, N. J., Chung, C. P., Poulsen, K. and Kilian, M. 1997. Racial tropism of a highly toxic clone of *Actinobacillus actinomycetemcomitans* associated with juvenile periodontitis. *J. Clin. Microbiol.* **35**, 3037-3042.

Hinode, D., Nakamura, R., Grenier, D., and Mayrand, D. 1998. Cross reactivity of specific antibodies directed to heat shock proteins from periodontopathogenic bacteria of human origin. *Oral Microbiol. Immunol.* **13**, 55-58.

Hohwy, J. and Kilian, M. 1995. Clonal diversity of the *Streptococcus mitis* biovar 1 population in the human oral cavity and pharynx. *Oral Microbiol. Immunol.* **10**, 19-25.

Huisman, G. W. and Kolter, R. 1994. Sensing starvation: a homoserine lactone dependent signaling pathway in *Escherichia coli*. *Science* **265**, 537-539.

Jenkison, H. F. and Lamont, R. J. 1997. Streptococcal adhesion and colonization. *Crit. Rev. Oral Biol. Med.* **8**, 175-200.

Johnson, W. M., Tyler, S. D. and Rozee, K. R. 1994. Linkage analysis of geographic and clinical clusters in *Pseudomonas cepacia* infections by multilocus enzyme electrophoresis and ribotyping. *J. Clin. Microbiol.* **32**, 924-930.

Kjelleberg, S. 1993. (ed.) *Starvation in bacteria*. Plenum Press, New York.

Koch, A. L. 1997. Microbial physiology and ecology at slow growth. *Micro. Mol. Biol. Rev.* **61**, 305-

318.

Kolenbrander, P. E. and London, J. 1992. Ecological significance of coaggregation among oral bacteria. In: Marshall, K. C. (ed.), *Advances in Microbial Ecology*. Vol 12, pp. 183-217, Plenum, New York.

Kolter, R., Siegele, D. A. and Tormo, A. 1993, The stationary phase of the bacterial life cycle. In: Ornston, L. N., Balows, A. and Greenberg, E. P. (eds). *Annual Review of Microbiology*, Vol. 47, pp. 855-874, Annual Reviews Inc. Palo Alto.

Korona, R., Nakatsu, C. H., Forney, L. J. and Lenski, R. E. 1994. Evidence for multiple adaptive peaks from populations of bacteria evolving in a structured habitat. *Proc. Natl. Acad. Sci. USA*. **91**, 9037-9041.

Kozai, K., Wang, D. S., Sandham, H. J. and Philips H. I. 1991. Changes in strains of mutans streptococci induced by treatment with chlorhexidine varnish. *J. Dent. Res.* **70**, 1252-1257.

Lange, K. P., Hotz, P. R., Gusberti, F. and Joss, A. 1987. Longitudinal, clinical and microbiological study on the relationship between infection with *Streptococcus mutans* and the development of caries in humans. *Oral Microbiol. Immunol.* **2**, 39-47.

Larsen, T. and Fiehn, N-E. 1996. Resistance of *Streptococcus sanguis* biofilms to antimicrobial agents. *APMIS* **104**, 280-284.

Lenski, R. E. 1995. Evolution in experimental populations of bacteria. In:Baumberg, S., Young, J. P. W., Wellington, E. M. H. and Saunders, J. R. (eds.) *Population genetics of bacteria*, pp. 193-215, Society for General Microbiology, Symposium 52, University Press, Cambridge

Lenski, R. E., Mongold, J. A., Sniegowski, P. D., Travissano, M., Vasi, F., Gerrish, P. J. and Schmidt, T. M. 1998. Evolution of competitive fitness in experimental populations of *E. coli*: what makes one genotype a better competitor than another? *Anton. van. Leeuwenhoek* **73**, 35-47.

Leroi, A. M., Bennet, A. F. and Lenski, R. E. 1994. temperature acclimation and competitive fitness: an experimental test of the beneficial acclimation assumption. *Proc. Natl. Acad. Sci. USA*, **91**, 1917-1921.

Li, Y-H. and Bowden, G. H. W. 1994a. Characteristics of accumulation of oral Gram-positive bacteria on mucin-conditioned glass surfaces in a model system. *Oral Microbiol. Immunol.* **9**, 1-11.

Li, Y-H. and Bowden, G. H. W. 1994b. The effect of environmental fluoride from the substratum on the development of biofilms of selected oral bacteria. *J. Dent. Res.* **73**, 1615-162

Liljemark, W. F., Bloomquist, C. G., Reilly, B. E., Bernards, C. J., Townsend, D. W. Pennock, A. T. and LeMoine, J. L. 1997. Growth dynamics in a natural biofilm and its impact on oral disease management. *Adv. Dent. Res.* **11**, 14-23.

London, J. 1999. From dental plaque to oral biofilm: A molecular odyssey. In: Rosenberg, E. (ed.), *Microbial Ecology and Infectious Disease*, pp. 53-65, American Society for Microbiology, Washington, D.C.

Loos, B. G., Dyer, D. W. Whittam, T. S. and Selander, R. K. 1993. Genetic structure of populations of *Porphyromonas gingivalis* associated with periodontitis and other oral infections. *Infect. Immun.* **61**, 204-212.

Loos, B. G., van Winkelhof, A. J., Dunford, R. G., Genco, R. J., De Graaff, J., Dickinson, D. P. and Dyer, D. W. 1992. A statistical approach to the ecology of *Porphyromonas gingivalis. J. Dent. Res.* **71**, 353-358.

Lorenz, M. G. and Wakernagel. W. 1994. Bacterial gene transfer by natural genetic transformation in the environment. *Microbiol. Rev.* **58**, 563-602.

Lu, B. and McBride, B. C. 1994. Stress response of *Porphyromonas gingivalis*. *Oral Microbiol. Immunol.* **9**, 166-173.

Maiden, M. C. J. and Feavers I. M. 1995. Population genetics and global epidemiology of the human pathogen *Neisseria meningitidis*. In:Baumberg, S., Young, J. P. W., Wellington, E. M. H. and Saunders, J. R. (eds.) *Population genetics of bacteria*, pp. 267-293, Society for General Microbiology, Symposium 52, University Press, Cambridge.

Marquis, R. E. 1995. Oxygen metabolism, oxidative stress and acid-base physiology of dental plaque biofilms. *J. Indust. Microbiol.* **15**, 198-207.

Marsh, P. D. 1994. Microbiology of dental plaque and its significance in health and disease. *Adv. Dent. Res.* **8**,263-271.

Marsh, P. D. 1995. the role of microbiology in models of dental caries. *Adv. Dent. Res.* **9**,244-254.

Marsh, P. D. and Bradshaw, D. J. 1997. Physiological approaches to the control of oral biofilms. *Adv. Dent. Res.* **11**, 176-185.

Mättö J., Saarela, M., von Troil-Lindén B, Jousimies-Somer H,. Torkko, H., Alaluusua, S. *et al.*, 1996. Distribution and genetic analysis of oral *Prevotella intermedia* and *Prevotella nigrescens*. *Oral Microbiol. Immunol.* **11**, 96-102.

Maynard Smith, J., Dowson, C. G., and Spratt, B. G. 1991. Localized sex in bacteria. *Nature,* **349**, 29-31.

Milkman, R. and McKane, M. 1995. DNA sequence variation and recombination in *E. coli*. In:Baumberg, S., Young, J. P. W., Wellington, E. M. H. and Saunders, J. R. (eds.) *Population Genetics of Bacteria*, pp. 127-142, Society for General Microbiology, Symposium 52, University Press, Cambridge.

Milnes, A. R. and Bowden, G. H. W. 1985. The microflora associated with developing lesions of nursing caries. *Caries Res.* **19**, 289-297.

Morelli, G., Malorny, B., Müller, K. Seiler, A., Wang, J-F., de Valle, J. and Achtman, M. 1997. Clonal descent and microevolution of *Neisseria meningitidis* during 30 years of epidemic spread. *Mol. Microbiol.* **25**, 1047-1064.

Morou-Bermudez, E. and Burne, R. A. 1999. Genetic and physiologic characterization of urease of *Actinomyces naeslundii*. *Infect. Immun.* **67**, 504-512.

Musser, J. M., Kapur, V., Szeto, J., Pan, X., Swanson, D. S. and Martin, D. R. 1995. Genetic diversity and relationships among *Streptococcus pyogenes* strains expressing serotype M1 protein: recent intercontinental spread of a subclone causing episodes of invasive disease. *Infect. Immun.* 63, 994-1003.

Ørskov, F., Whittam, T. S., Cravioto, A. and Øskov, I. 1990. Clonal relationships among classic enteropathogenic *Escherichia coli* (EPEC) belonging to different O groups. *J. Infect. Dis.* **162**, 76-81.

Park, Y., Lu, B., Mazur, C. and McBride, B. C. 1997. Inducible expression of a *Porphyromonas gingivalis* W83 membrane-associated protease. *Infect. Immun.* **65**, 1101-1104.

Papadopoulos, D., Schneider, D., Meier-Eiss, J., Arber, W., Lenski, R. E. and Blot, M. 1999. genomic evolution during a 10,000-generation experiment with bacteria. *Proc. Natl. Acad. Sci. USA* **96**, 3807-3812.

Poulsen, K., Theilade, E., Lally, E. T., Demuth, D. R. and Kilian, M. 1994. Population structure of *Actinobacillus actinomycetemcomitans*: a framework for studies of disease associated properties. *Microbiology*, **140,** 2049-2060.

Poulsen, K., Reinholdt, J., Jespersgaard, C., Boye, K., Brown, T. A. Hauge, M. and Kilian, M. 1998. A comprehensive genetic study of streptococcal immunoglobulin A1 proteases: evidence for recombination within and between species. *Inf. Immun.* **66**, 181-190.

Putnins, E. E. and Bowden G. H. 1993. Antigenic relationships among oral *Actinomyces* isolates, *Actinomyces naeslundii* genospecies 1 and 2, *Actinomyces howellii, Actinomyces denticolens*, and *Actinomyces slackii*. *J. Dent. Res.* **72**, 1374-1385.

Rainey, P. B., Moxon, E. R. and Thompson, I. P. 1993. Intraclonal polymorphism in bacteria. In: Gwynfryn Jones, J. (ed.) *Advances in Microbial Ecology*, Vol. **13**, pp. 263-300, Plenum Press, New York.

Reichmann, P., König, A., Liñares, J., Alcaide, F., Tenover, F. C., McDougal, L., Swidsinski, S. and Hakenbeck, R. 1997. A global gene pool for high-level cephalosporin resistance in commensal *Streptococcus* species and *Streptococcus pneumoniae*. *J. Infect. Dis.* **176**,1001-1012.

Rhufel, R. E., Leonard, B. A. B. and Dunny, G. M. 1997. Pheromone-inducible conjugation in *Enterococcus faecalis*. In: Shapiro, J. A. and Dworkin, M. (eds.) *Bacteria as Multicellular Organisms*. pp. 53-68. Oxford University Press, New York.

Saarela, M., Mättö, J., Asikainen, S., Jousimies-Somer, H., Torkko H., Pyhälä, L., *et al.*, 1996. Clonal diversity of *Actinobacillus actinomycetemcommitans, Porphyromonas gingivalis* and *Prevotella intermedia/nigrescens* in two families. *Anaerobe* **2**, 19-27.

Sansone, C., van Houte, J., Joshipura, K., Kent, R. and Margolis, H. C. 1993. The association of mutans streptococci and non-mutans streptococci capable of acidogenesis at a low pH with dental caries on enamel and root surfaces. *J. Dent. Res.* **72**, 508-516.

Scheie, A. A. 1994. Mechanisms of dental plaque formation. *Adv. Dent. Res.* **8**, 246-253.

Selander, R. K. and Musser, J. M. 1990. Population genetics of bacterial pathogenesis. In: Iglewski,

B. H. and Clark, V. L. (eds.) *Molecular Basis of Bacterial Pathogenesis*. pp. 11-36, Academic Press Inc., New York.

Serano, R. 1996. Salt tolerance in plants and microorganisms: toxicity targets and defence responses. *Int. Rev. Cytol*. **165**, 1-52.

Shapiro, J. A. and Dworkin, M. 1997. Editors. *Bacteria as Multicellular Organisms*. Oxford University Press, New York. 1997

Sims, T. J., Ali, R. W., Brockman, E. S., Skaug, N. and Page, R. C. 1999. Antigenic variation in *Porphyromonas gingivalis* ribotypes recognized by serum immunoglobulin G of adult periodontitis patients. *Oral Microbiol. Immunol*. **14**, 73-85.

Sissons, C. H. 1997. Artificial dental plaque biofilm model systems. *Adv. Dent. Res*. **11**, 110-126.

Sissons, C. H., Perinpanayagam, H. E. R., Hancock, E. M. and Cutress, T. W. 1990. pH regulation of urease levels in *Streptococcus salivarius*. *J. Dent. Res*. **69**, 1131-1137.

Spratt,B. G., Smith, N. H., Zhou, J., O'Rourke, M. and Feil, E. 1995. The population genetics of pathogenic *Neisseria*. In:Baumberg, S., Young, J. P. W., Wellington, E. M. H. and Saunders, J. R. (eds.) *Population Genetics of Bacteria*, pp. 141-160., Society for General Microbiology, Symposium 52, University Press, Cambridge

Stamm, L. V., Gherardini, F. C., Parrish, E. A. and Moomaw, C. R. 1991. Heat shock response of spirochetes. *Infect. Immun*. **59**, 1572-1575.

Stanley, J., Linton, D., Desai, M., Efstatiou, A. and George, R. 1995. Molecular subtyping of prevalent M serotypes of *Streptococcus pyogenes* causing invasive disease. *J. Clin. Microbiol*. **33**, 2850-2855.

Stotzky, G and Babich, H. 1984. Fate of genetically-engineered microbes in natural environments. *Recomb. DNA Tech. bull*. **7**, 163-188.

Suchett-Kaye, G., Décoret, D. and Barsotti, O. 1998. Clonal analysis by ribotyping of *Fusobacterium nucleatum* isolates obtained from healthy young adults with optimal plaque control. *J. Periodontal. Res*. **33**, 179-186.

Svensäter, G., Larson, U-B., Greif, E. C. G., Cvitcovich, D. G. and Hamilton, I. R. 1997. Acid tolerance response and survival by oral bacteria. *Oral Microbiol. Immunol*. **12**, 266-273.

Theilade, E. 1990. Factors controlling the microflora of the healthy mouth. In:Hill, M. J. and Marsh, P. D. (eds.), *Human Microbial Ecology*, pp. 1-56, CRC Press Inc., Boca Raton, Florida.

Travisano, M. and Lenski, R. E. 1996. Long -term experimental evolution in *Escherichia coli*. IV targets of selection and the specificity of adaptation. *Genetics* **143**, 15-26.

Van Houte, J. 1994. Role of microorganisms in caries etiology. *J. Dent. Res*. **73**, 672-681.

Van Loveren, C., Spitz L. M. Buijs, J. F., Ten Cate, J. M. and Eisenberg A. D. 1991. *In vitro* demineralization of enamel by F-sensitive and F-resistant mutans streptococci in the presence of 0, 0.05, or 0.5 mmol/L NaF. *J. Dent. Res*. **70**, 1491-1496.

Von Troil-Lindén, B., Saarela, M., Mättö, J., Alaluusua, S., Jousimies-Somer, H. and Asikainen, S. 1996. Source of suspected periodontal pathogens re-emerging after periodontal treatment. *J. Clin. Periodontol*. **23**, 601-607.

Wilkins, B. M. 1995. Gene transfer by bacterial conjugation: diversity of systems and functional specializations. In:Baumberg, S., Young, J. P. W., Wellington, E. M. H. and Saunders, J. R. (eds.) *Population Genetics of Bacteria*, pp. 59-88, Society for General Microbiology, Symposium 52, University Press, Cambridge

Wilson, M. 1996. Susceptibility of oral biofilms to antimicrobial agents. *J. Med. Microbiol*. **44**, 79-87.

Wilson M., Patel. H. and Fletcher, J. 1996. Susceptibility of biofilms of *Streptococcus sanguis* to chlorhexidine gluconate and cetylpyridinium chloride. *Oral Microbiol. Immunol*. **11**, 188-192.

Zahner, V., Momen, H., Salles, C. A. and Rabinovitch, L. 1989 A comparative study of enzyme variation in *Bacillus cereus* and *Bacillus thuringiensis*. *J. Appl. Bacteriol*. **67**, 275-282.

MICROBIAL COMMUNITY ASPECTS OF DENTAL PLAQUE

Philip D. Marsh and David J. Bradshaw

*The microbial composition of plaque is diverse, comprising up to 300 bacterial species. Plaque formation involves an ordered accumulation of organisms, with a limited number of pioneer species attaching by specific molecular mechanisms to pellicle-coated tooth surfaces. The microflora then increases in complexity by interactions between secondary colonisers and the already attached bacteria (co-aggregation). The metabolism of these organisms generates gradients in key parameters (oxygen, redox, pH, substrate, metabolic end products) over short distances, creating a biofilm with a mosaic of micro-environments. This hetero-geneity enables the co-existence of organisms with conflicting properties. Bacteria in biofilms may also persist because of mutual protection from hostile external factors (e.g. host defences, antimicrobial agents, oxygen, pH shock). Once established, the microbial composition of plaque remains relatively stable with time (microbial homeostasis). This stability is not due to metabolic indiffer-ence but is a result of a dynamic balance among the component species. This balance involves both antagonistic and synergistic inter-bacterial interactions, where certain organisms are dependent for their persistence on the activity of neighbouring species. Thus, obligate anaerobes grow in plaque by deploying appropriate protective metabolic strategies and by interacting with oxygen-consuming bacteria, such as **Neisseria** spp.. Likewise, the catabolism of complex endogenous nutrients (e.g. glycoproteins) by the resident microflora requires the concerted action of multiple species with complementary patterns of glycosidase and peptidase activities. Complex substrates are also cycled efficiently to simpler products by the development of food chains. Such interactions may require organisms to be spatially-organised for optimal efficiency. Evidence suggests that co-aggregation can promote such close physical contact between interacting cells. Thus, plaque communities display "emergent properties" where their overall metabolic capabilities are greater than the sum of their component parts.*

Introduction

Dental plaque has been defined as the community of micro-organisms found on the tooth surface as a biofilm, embedded in a matrix of polymers of salivary and bacterial origin (Marsh and Martin, 1999). Such a definition would induce little scientific curiosity if biofilm bacteria were merely planktonic cells attached to a surface, and microbial communities displayed properties that were simply the sum of those of the component species. However, studies over recent years have clearly established that bacteria growing as a biofilm can display a phenotype distinct to that expressed by the same cells cultured planktonically in conven-tional liquid culture (Costerton *et al.*, 1987, 1994, 1995, this volume). For example, in the context of plaque, genes associated with extracellular

polysaccharide synthesis are up-regulated on a surface (Burne, 1998), while oral
bacteria are more resistant to antimicrobial agents when growing as a biofilm
(Wilson, 1996). Similarly, microbial communities display "emergent properties", that is, the properties of the community are generally greater than the sum
of its component populations (Odum, 1986). A community can be defined as a
group of interacting micro-organisms growing in association with one another,
usually on a surface. As a consequence of this, growth in a community allows
bacterial species to display (a) a broader habitat range, (b) enhanced resistance
to environmental stresses, and (c) an increased metabolic efficiency and versatil-
ity than when individual species are grown in isolation (Caldwell *et al.*, 1997).

In this chapter, some of the implications for both the host and the oral
bacteria of a "community" life-style for plaque biofilms will be described. An
understanding of the way in which individual species contribute to the functioning of plaque as a microbial community can help explain the role of this biofilm
in health and disease, and identify novel strategies for control.

Plaque formation and structure

The formation and structure of dental plaque has been described previously
(Listgarten, 1994, this volume; Marsh, 1995; Marsh and Bradshaw, 1995). Some
of the key stages that are critical to our understanding of plaque as a microbial
community will be re-emphasised here.

The development of dental plaque can be divided into several arbitrary
stages, although it should be appreciated that biofilm formation is a dynamic
process, and that the attachment, growth, removal and re-attachment of bacteria
is continuous. These stages are:

1. the adsorption of host and bacterial polymers to the tooth to form a surface
   conditioning film (the acquired pellicle),
2. the transport of micro-organisms to the polymer-coated tooth surface;
   generally, this is a passive process facilitated by the flow of oral secretions
   as very few oral bacteria are motile,
3. long-range physico-chemical interactions between the microbial cell surface
   and the pellicle-coated tooth (Busscher *et al.*, 1992; Busscher and van der
   Mei, 1997). The interplay of van der Waals attractive forces and electrostatic
   repulsion due to the interaction of charged molecules on the bacterial cell
   surface and in the conditioning film produces a weak area of net attraction
   that facilitates reversible adhesion,
4. short-range interactions involving specific, stereo-chemical interactions
   between adhesins on the microbial surface and receptors in the acquired
   pellicle; these interactions usually result in irreversible adhesion,
5. the co-aggregation of micro-organisms to already attached cells; this stage
   results in an increased diversity of the plaque microflora. Thus, many late
   colonisers, such as obligately anaerobic bacteria, bind not to the acquired
   pellicle but to already attached species such as streptococci and *Actinomyces*
   spp. (Kolenbrander and London, 1993; Kolenbrander, this volume). In
   addition, co-aggregation can provide the mechanism that facilitates a range

Table 1 Bacterial genera found in dental plaque.

GRAM-POSITIVE	GRAM-NEGATIVE
COCCI	
Abiotrophia	*Neisseria*
Peptostreptococcus	*Veillonella*
Streptococcus	
Staphylococcus	
RODS	
Actinomyces	*Actinobacillus*
Bifidobacterium	*(Bacteroides)**
Corynebacterium	*Campylobacter*
Eubacterium	*Cantonella*
Lactobacillus	*Capnocytophaga*
Propionibacterium	*Centipeda*
Pseudoramibacter	*Desulfovibrio*
Rothia	*Desulfobacter Eikenella*
	Fusobacterium
	Haemophilus
	Johnsonii
	Leptotrichia
	Porphyromonas
	Prevotella
	Selenomonas
	Treponema
	Wolinella

*The genus *"Bacteroides"* has been redefined. In time, the remaining oral bacteria still placed in this genus will be reclassified.
Mycoplasmas are also isolated from the mouth

of physical and metabolic synergistic interactions.
6. the multiplication of the attached organisms to produce confluent growth and a biofilm (Marsh, 1995; Marsh and Bradshaw, 1995).

Biofilms provide the physical opportunities for close range cell-to-cell interactions, such as quorum sensing (Bloomquist *et al.*, 1996; Liljemark *et al.*, 1997) and gene transfer (Hanley *et al.*, 1999), although there is only limited evidence at present for this occurring in plaque. Extracellular polymer synthesis also occurs, especially from the metabolism of sucrose, and the resultant glucans and fructans contribute to the plaque matrix, and will help determine the architecture of the biofilm. Recent studies of the structure of smooth surface plaque using confocal scanning laser microscopy have shown it to have a more open architecture than previously suggested from studies using conventional electron microscopy. Channels are present that can traverse the depth of the biofilm (Wood *et al.*, 1999), in an analogous manner to that seen in environmental biofilms (Costerton *et al.*, 1994). It remains to be determined whether a similar open architecture will develop at more stagnant sites where compaction may occur.

Table 2 The predominant bacteria found in plaque at three distinct sites.

Bacterium	Percentage viable count (range)		
	Fissures	**Approximal surfaces**	**Gingival crevice**
Streptococcus	8-86	<1-70	2-73
Actinomyces	0-46	4-81	10-63
AnGPR*	0-21	0-6	0-37
Neisseria	+**	0-44	0-2
Veillonella	0-44	0-59	0-5
AnG-R*	+**	0-66	8-20

Environment			
Nutrient source	saliva & diet,	saliva & GCF***	GCF
pH	Neutral low pH	neutral-low pH	neutral-high pH
Eh	positive	slight negative	negative

*AnG+R, AnG-R: obligately anaerobic Gram positive and anaerobic Gram negative rods, respectively
**+:   detected occasionally
***GCF, gingival crevicular fluid

Microbial composition of dental plaque

Microscopic and cultural studies of plaque have shown the microflora to be diverse, and up to 300 different species, from a broad range of genera have been isolated (Table 1); however, only around 50% of the organisms present can currently be cultivated. The application of molecular techniques to identify micro-organisms without the need for culture (e.g. by the determination of 16S rRNA sequences) is leading to the identification of an ever more diverse plaque microflora (Wade, this symposium). The microflora of dental plaque also displays site-specific differences in composition when sampled from distinct sites (Table 2). These microbial variations are a result of differences in the local supply of nutrients (e.g. fissure plaque is influenced more by saliva and the diet, while organisms in the gingival crevice are dependent on the proteins and glycoproteins in gingival crevicular fluid, GCF), pH and redox potential at particular sites.

As will be discussed in detail later, the ability of individual organisms to catabolise complex host substrates, and survive fluctuating environmental conditions, is dependent on their co-operative role when part of a microbial community (Caldwell *et al.*, 1997). The microbial heterogeneity within a site is also facilitated by the development of gradients in key environmental parameters within the plaque biofilm. The microbial consumption of oxygen and sugars, and the concomitant production of carbon dioxide and acidic fermentation products results in horizontal and vertical stratification in these and other factors, thus creating a mosaic of micro-environments. These micro-environments permit the growth of bacteria with quite diverse, and often conflicting, needs. Thus, obligate anaerobes are recovered from overtly aerobic sites between teeth (approximal), and are also present in samples that contain facultatively anaerobic or capnophilic (CO_2-requiring) bacteria. In sub-gingival samples, saccharolytic species co-exist with asaccharolytic but proteolytic organisms (Table 2). Similarly, aciduric species like mutans streptococci can be recovered in close proximity to acid-sensitive bacteria, such as *Streptococcus sanguis*. Thus, plaque becomes spatially-organised over time, with organisms occupying particular positions defined by the biological and physical properties of that site.

Until recently, the existence of such environmental heterogeneity in biofilms has been deduced from relatively crude measurements, for example, by using micro-electrodes, or fluorescence-intensity-based methods to measure changes in redox potential or pH over time and at different sites. Two novel techniques have been combined recently in order to demonstrate and map pH gradients in model biofilms. Two-photon excitation microscopy (Denk *et al.*, 1990) (TPEM) relies on the simultaneous absorption of two (infra) red photons to excite fluorescence. This allows greater depth penetration into highly scattering samples such as biofilms, compared with conventional confocal microscopy. TPEM has been combined with fluorescence lifetime imaging (FLIM) using pH-sensitive dyes, for three-dimensional observation of unprocessed samples. FLIM utilises the differences in fluorescence lifetimes of the variously protonated forms of the fluorescent probes to generate contrast in images proportional to pH. The fluorescence lifetimes are determined by a ratiometric determination in sequential time gates. Thus, FLIM determination of pH offers the significant advantage of measurements independent of probe concentrations. As expected, biofilms comprising complex mixtures of oral bacteria with distinct pH optima for growth were found to have pH gradients; however, these gradients were not linear (Vroom *et al.*, 1999). Rather, micro-zones of pH developed, so that discrete areas of low pH could be surrounded by biofilm maintained around neutrality (Figure 1); such gradients were more apparent in the *x-z* rather than the *x-y* plane (Vroom *et al.*, 1999). These pH gradients developed over relatively short distances (few cell diameters), on much the same scale as observed for oxygen levels in microcolonies of pure cultures of a non-oral microbe (Costerton *et al.*, 1987, 1994). In the future, these techniques could be applied to studies of pH gradients in plaque allowed to develop *in situ* on removable enamel slices worn by human volunteers, or on extracted teeth. Such approaches may eventually also be used to study gradients in other significant ions in plaque.

Thus, as plaque develops, the composition of the microflora increases in diversity due to waves of bacterial succession. Bacterial metabolism can modify

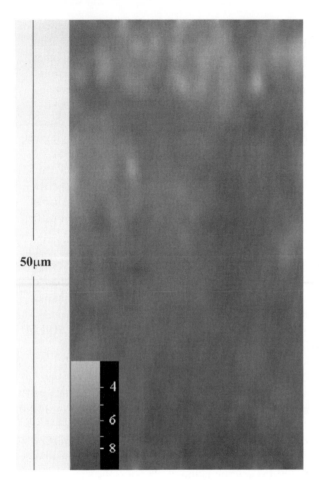

50μm

Figure 1 Demonstration of environmental heterogeneity (in terms of pH) in oral microbial communities growing on a hydroxyapatite surface. A mixed culture of oral bacteria has been visualised using two photon excitation microscopy after staining with carboxyfluorescein (Vroom *et al.*, 1999; reproduced with permission of American Society for Microbiology).

the local environment, so that a complex microflora develops. Eventually, a climax community is achieved at a site, the microbial composition of which remains relatively stable over time (Marsh, 1989).

Dental plaque as a microbial community

A key feature of a microbial community is the maintenance of a stable microflora in a variable environment. Such stability has been termed "microbial homeostasis" (Alexander, 1971; Marsh, 1989), and does not imply any meta-bolic indifference among the constituent microbial populations. Rather, this stability is a result of a dynamic balance, held by a series of interactions (both synergistic and antagonistic; Table 3) between groups of microbes. These interactions enhance the catabolism of endogenous nutrients, and provide protection from stressful environments by maintaining a favourable local environment during periodic unfavourable fluctuations in the macro-environment

242

Table 3 Microbial interactions in dental plaque.

BENEFICIAL	ANTAGONISTIC
Enzyme complementation Food chains/food webs Co-aggregation Inactivation of inhibitors Subversion of host defences	Bacteriocins Hydrogen peroxide Organic acids Low pH Nutrient competition

(Caldwell *et al.*, 1997; Marsh and Bradshaw, 1998). These interactions allow organisms within a community to persist and grow over a broader habitat range, and to display synergy in the recycling of nutrients, which would not be possible in monocultures. Thus, the overall metabolic efficiency of the community is increased. The following sections will describe how dental plaque displays many of these features, and functions, therefore, as a true microbial community.

(A) Nutrient Acquisition
Catabolism of complex host nutrients
In order to proliferate at a site, micro-organisms need to acquire nutrients and modify the local environment to make conditions more favourable. In the mouth, proteins and glycoproteins present in saliva and GCF are used as primary sources of carbon and nitrogen, and are more responsible for maintaining the diversity of the resident microflora than are the substrates provided by the diet. These endogenous nutrients are biochemically complex and, in the case of glycoproteins such as mucins, their degradation requires the concerted action of a range of proteases, peptidases and glycosidases (see Figures 2 & 3). Individual oral bacterial species have limited capabilities to degrade these molecules, and studies using peptides, mucin and albumin as model substrates have shown that bacteria can grow only poorly in the presence of these complex molecules in pure culture. However, higher cell densities were achieved when species with complementary enzyme profiles were grown in binary or triplet culture (for examples, see Gharbia and Shah, 1989; Homer and Beighton, 1992; van der Hoeven and Camp, 1991).

Similar trends have been observed in studies using more diverse mixtures of plaque micro-organisms (ter Steeg and van der Hoeven, 1989; ter Steeg *et al.*, 1987, 1988). Three phases of metabolism were recognised when consortia derived from sub-gingival plaque were grown on human serum (used to simulate growth on GCF). Firstly, saccharolytic bacteria such as *Streptococcus* spp., *Bifidobacterium* spp. and *Eubacterium* spp. predominated, and utilised the oligosaccharide side chains. Secondly, proteolysis occurred and any remaining carbohydrates were consumed; finally, amino acid fermentations predominated (ter Steeg and van der Hoeven, 1989). As a consequence of this community action, serum glycoproteins, including immunoglobulins, were extensively degraded. Thus, the utilisation of these complex molecules involves not only a

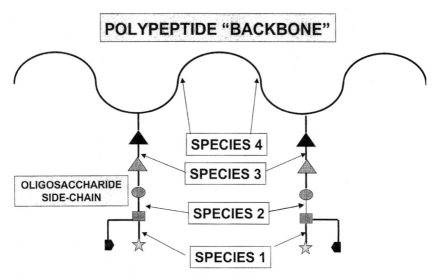

Figure 2 Microbial co-operation during the degradation of host glycoproteins. Species 1 is able to cleave the terminal sugar of the oligosaccharide side-chain, which enables species 2 to cleave the penultimate residue, etc. In this way, interacting groups of micro-organism are mutually dependent on each other for nutrient acquisition (Marsh and Martin, 1999; reproduced with permission).

concerted metabolic attack but also the sequential catabolism of the breakdown products of earlier reactions, yielding much simpler end products, and thereby increasing the energetic yields from the original substrate.

Similar studies were undertaken using defined communities of oral bacteria, with pre-selected biochemical attributes, growing on hog gastric mucin (HGM) as a model glycoprotein (Bradshaw *et al.*, 1994). The terminal carbohydrates in the oligosaccharide side chains of HGM are sialic acid and fucose, and members of the communities for study were selected on the basis of their ability or inability to remove these terminal sugars. Initially, five plaque species were selected (*F. nucleatum, Neisseria subflava, Veillonella dispar, Streptococccus gordonii* and *S. mutans*) with minimal glycosidase activity to be grown together on HGM at pH 7.0. These organisms established as a stable community but at relatively low population levels. Subsequently, species with additional and relevant glycosidase (*Actinomyces naeslundii* and *S. oralis*: sialidase ; *Lactobacillus rhamnosus*: fucosidase) and protease (*Porphyromonas gingivalis* and *Prevotella nigrescens*: endopeptidase) activities were added sequentially, and stable communities were allowed to establish comprising seven, eight, nine, and eventually, ten species, respectively. Increasing the metabolic diversity of the communities resulted in step-wise increases in the biomass of the culture. Significantly, the increase in total viable count of the community was made up not only of the numbers of the newly-added species, but also from an increase in the extant populations (Bradshaw *et al.*, 1994). As with serum the catabolism of

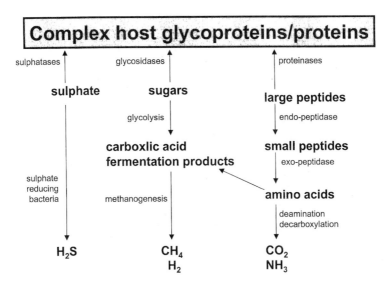

Figure 3 Concerted and sequential breakdown of complex host substrates by communities of oral bacteria with complementary enzyme activities.
(Marsh and Martin, 1999; reproduced with permission).

a glycoprotein such as HGM involves the concerted and synergistic action of several species with complementary patterns of enzyme activity. The rise in biomass from a five to a nine-membered community was due to the step-wise increase in novel degradative activity, which exposed additional sugars or novel peptides that acted as fresh substrates for other community members. Notably, there was no increase in bacterial numbers following the addition of *P. nigrescens* to the nine-species community suggesting that the introduction of this species did not provide any new degradative activity, and the subsequent ten-member bacterial community was derived merely from competitive interactions.

Such interactions also lead to the establishment of simple food-chains, or more complex food webs, whereby the product of one organism (primary feeder) becomes the substrate for another (secondary feeder). Such interactions contribute significantly to homeostasis in microbial communities because the component species become mutually dependent on each other for nutrient acquisition. A potential increase by one species could be held in check by the lack of a response by a co-dependent organism. Many of these large and complex host molecules can be regarded as providing an array of discrete nutrient niches which can be exploited only by particular species or consortia.

Catabolism of dietary components
Concerted efforts are also needed to break down complex molecules delivered to the mouth via the diet, e.g. as starches, casein or plant macromolecules, although much less is known about the role of individual species in these

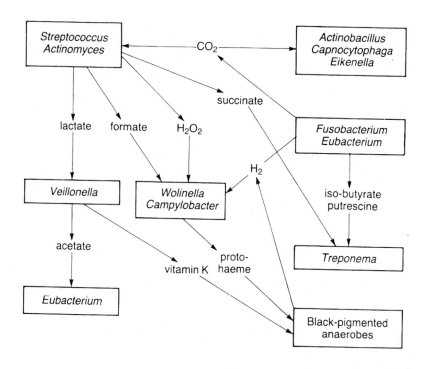

Figure 4 A schematic representation of some nutritional interactions among plaque bacteria; these numerous food-chains form a complex food web. Such interdependencies contribute to the stability of community composition. (Marsh and Martin, 1999; reproduced with permission).

degradative processes. Dietary sugars are avidly catabolised by a range of saccharolytic bacteria, but food chains develop in order to completely metabolise these sugars. In the presence of an excess of carbohydrate, streptococci and a range of Gram positive rods produce lactate as a metabolic end product. Lactate can then be cycled to simpler fermentation products (e.g. propionic and acetic acids) by Veillonella spp (Mikx and van der Hoeven, 1975), and in turn, such acids can be further catabolised by other bacteria to CO_2, CH_4, H_2, etc (see later; Figures 3 and 4) (Carlsson, 1997). These types of food chain may have significance for the host since lactic acid has the lowest pKa of the acids produced in quantity in plaque, and its utilisation to weaker acids by Veillonella has been shown to reduce the incidence of caries in an animal model (Mikx *et al.*, 1972). Strains of Neisseria, *Corynebacterium*, and *Eubacterium* are also able to metabolize lactate.

Bacterial nutritional interactions
Bacterial polymers are also targets for degradation. Some extracellular polysaccharides can be metabolized by other bacteria in the absence of exogenous (dietary) carbohydrates. The fructan of *S. salivarius* and other streptococci,

246

Table 4 pH range for growth of selected oral bacteria in pure and mixed culture.

Bacterium	Pure culture			Mixed culture	
	pH 7.0	5.0	4.5	5.0	4.5
S. mutans	+++	+++	+++	++++	++++
S. sanguis	++++	++	-	+++	++
S. mitis/oralis	++++	+++	+/-	++++	+++
A. naeslundii	++++	+/-	-	++	++
L. casei	+++	+++	++++	++++	++++
N. subflava	++++	+	-	+++	-
V. dispar	+++	+++	++	++++	++++
P. intermedia	++++	++	++	+++	+++
F. nucleatum	++++	+	+	+++	+++

Data taken from (Bradshaw and Marsh, 1998; Bradshaw, McKee, andMarsh, 1989; Harper and Loesche, 1984).

and the glycogen-like polymer of *Neisseria*, are particularly labile (Parker and Creamer, 1971; van Houte and Jansen, 1968), and only low levels of fructan are detected in plaque. In addition, mutans streptococci, members of the *S. mitis*-group, *S. salivarius*, *A. israelii*, *Capnocytophaga* spp., and *Fusobacterium* spp. possess exo- and/or endo-hydrolytic activity (Schachtele *et al.*, 1976) and metabolize streptococcal glucans.

Other examples of nutritional interactions between oral bacteria are shown in Figure 4 (Marsh and Martin, 1999). Oral spirochaetes can be dependent on the production of iso-butyrate and putrescine or spermine by fusobacteria, and on succinate produced by various Gram-positive rods. Similarly, *Fusobacterium* and *Prevotella* species provide hydrogen and formate for the growth of *Wolinella* spp., while the metabolism of some black-pigmented anaerobes is dependent on the synthesis of vitamin K by other bacteria in the gingival crevice. Also, *S. sanguis* can provide *p*-aminobenzoic acid for the growth of *S. mutans*.

Recently, both sulphate reducing bacteria and methanogens have been detected in plaque. These bacteria gain energy from the utilisation of end products of other organisms, converting them to terminal products of the community (e.g. hydrogen sulphide, hydrogen, methane) (Figure 3). Their presence provides further evidence that plaque functions as a true community (Wimpenny, 1994), in which complex substrates are cycled efficiently to their simplest products, with the maximum energy gain. Thus, dental plaque can be considered to be a complete ecosystem (Carlsson, 1997).

(B) Reponse To Environmental Stress

Many of the bacteria listed in Tables 1 and 2 persist and grow successfully in plaque under macro-environmental conditions that are apparently hostile. For example, the mouth is an essentially overtly aerobic environment and yet many of the predominant bacteria in plaque are obligately anaerobic (Table 1).

Similarly, several bacterial species in plaque are sensitive to low pH and yet survive repeated exposure to pH values below 5.0 following the intake of fermentable carbohydrates in the diet. Studies of the properties of plaque as a biofilm and as a microbial community have shown that bacterial interactions play a critical role in the persistence of species under such hostile conditions. Some key examples of these interactions will now be described.

(i) pH

The pH range for growth of many species has been determined in the laboratory in pure culture (Table 4). Species associated with sound enamel have pH optima for growth around neutrality, whereas cariogenic species such as mutans streptococci grow preferentially under acidic conditions (Harper and Loesche, 1984); in contrast some periodontal pathogens prefer a slightly alkaline environment (McDermid *et al.*, 1988). In laboratory studies of mixed cultures, bacteria have persisted for prolonged periods at pH values they could not tolerate in pure culture (Bradshaw *et al.*, 1989; McDermid *et al.*, 1986). Their survival is probably due to several features of plaque as a surface-associated microbial community. Firstly, the studies described earlier with two photon excitation microscopy coupled with FLIM and pH-sensitive dyes have confirmed conditions of environmental heterogeneity in terms of pH over short distances (Fig 1; Vroom *et al.*, 1999). Secondly, bacteria in plaque are able to modulate the local pH by up-regulating genes involved with acid or base production. Urease and arginine deiminase activity by *S. salivarius* (Chen *et al.*, 1996) and *S. sanguis* (Casiano-Colon and Marquis, 1988; Rogers *et al.*, 1987) is maintained and even enhanced at low pH, liberating ammonia and raising the pH. These enzymes can be active at pH values lower than those at which the bacteria can grow. The local pH could also be modulated by deamination and decarboxylation reactions. Aciduric plaque bacteria also possess specific molecular strategies which enable them to adapt rapidly to sudden changes in pH (Bowden and Hamilton, 1998).

(ii) Oxygen

Direct evidence that microbial communities of oral bacteria can provide protection for obligate anaerobes from the toxic effects of oxygen has been obtained from studies using laboratory models (Bradshaw *et al.*, 1996, 1997, 1998). A two stage, mixed culture, biofilm model system was established; the inoculum consisted of an aerobe (*N. subflava*), facultative anaerobes (*S. oralis, S. gordonii, S. mutans, L. rhamnosus, A. naeslundii*) and obligate anaerobes (*V. dispar, F. nucleatum, P. nigrescens, P. gingivalis*). A stable microbial community was established in the anaerobic first stage fermenter, and this was then passed continuously into an aerated vessel containing hydroxyapatite surfaces for biofilm formation. Surprisingly, the obligate anerobes grew both in the biofilm and in the planktonic culture, even under these actively aerated conditions. The predominant species, however, was *N subflava*, which had been present at barely detectable levels in the community grown anaerobically. No dissolved

248

oxygen could be detected in the planktonic phase (this was attributed to the metabolism of the aerobe, *N. subflava*), and the redox potential remained reduced (*ca.* -250 mV). In a subsequent experiment, in which *N. subflava* was deliberately omitted from the inoculum, the anaerobes still persisted, but the loss of the aerobe was compensated for by an increase in the levels of facultatively anaerobic species, especially the streptococci (Bradshaw *et al.*, 1996). The data suggested that close cell-to-cell contact between oxygen-consuming and oxygen-sensitive species must be required if the obligate anaerobes are to survive, especially in the planktonic phase. As stated earlier, co-aggregation is a key process during plaque formation, facilitating intra- and inter-generic attachment (Kolenbrander, 1988; Kolenbrander *et al.*, 1990; Kolenbrander and London, 1993). Studies subsequently showed that the oxygen-consumer (*N. subflava*) co-aggregated only poorly with the obligate anaerobes, but that this interaction could be markedly enhanced in the presence of *F. nucleatum*, which could act as a bridging organism between otherwise weakly-coaggregating pairs of strains (Bradshaw *et al.*, 1998). The key role for this co-aggregation came when consortia lacking *F. nucleatum* were re-introduced into the aerated biofilm vessel. The proportions of the anaerobes in the resultant community fell by ten-fold, and the viable counts of the black-pigmenting anaerobes fell by three orders of magnitude (Bradshaw *et al.*, 1998). It is probable that similar physical interactions will occur to ensure that organisms that need to interact for nutritional or environmental-modifying purposes are appropriately spatially-organised.

(iii) Antimicrobial tolerance and resistance.
Cells are more resistant to antimicrobial agents when growing as a biofilm, and plaque bacteria are no exception (Costerton *et al.*, 1987; Marsh and Bradshaw, 1993; Kinniment *et al.*, 1996; Wilson, 1996; Gilbert *et al.*, 1997). This may be due to the relatively slow growth rate of cells on a surface or the expression of a novel surface-associated phenotype; both responses may result in cells being more resistant to antimicrobials. In addition, community-mediated effects may contribute; cells can be protected by the restricted penetration of an antimicrobial into the biofilm due to selective binding to the extracellular matrix, or to the inactivation of the agent by enzymes (e.g. β-lactamases; (Rams *et al.*, 1992; van Winkelhoff *et al.*, 1997)) concentrated within the biofilm. Similarly, organisms could be protected from components of the host defences by being physically-close to neighbours producing a neutralising enzyme, such as sIgA protease (Kilian *et al.*, 1996) and other immunoglobulin- and complement-degrading proteases (Sundqvist *et al.*, 1985).

Antagonism among micro-organisms is a major contributing factor in the determination of the composition of microbial communities such as dental plaque. The production of antagonistic compounds (such as bacteriocins or bacteriocin-like inhibitory substances (BLIS) can give an organism a competitive advantage when interacting with other microbes. Bacteriocins are produced by most species of oral streptococci (e.g. mutacin by *S. mutans* (Alaluusua *et al.*,

1991) and sanguicin (Fujimura and Nakamura, 1979) by *S. sanguis*), as well as by *Corynebacterium matruchotii*, black-pigmented anaerobes, and *Actinobacillus actinomycetemcomitans*. In contrast, *Actinomyces* species are not generally bacteriocinogenic. In studies using either gnotobiotic animals (van der Hoeven and Rogers, 1979) or human volunteers (Hillman *et al.*,1987), the degree of colonization was proportional to the level of *in vitro* bacteriocin activity.

Other inhibitory factors produced by plaque bacteria include organic acids, hydrogen peroxide, and enzymes (Table 3; Marsh and Martin, 1999). The production of hydrogen peroxide by members of the *S. mitis*-group has been proposed as a mechanism whereby the numbers of periodontal pathogens are reduced in plaque to levels at which they are incapable of initiating disease (Hillman *et al.*, 1985). Some periodontal pathogens (e.g. *A. actinomycetemcomitans*) also produce factors inhibitory to oral streptococci, so that certain periodontal diseases might result from an ecological imbalance between dynamically-interacting groups of bacteria (Hillman *et al.*, 1985).

Despite the production of such a range of inhibitory factors, the existence of discrete micro-habitats within a biofilm such as plaque results in bacteria being spatially-organised, and therefore bacteria can co-exist that would be incompatible with one another in a homogeneous environment.

The production of antagonistic factors will also be a mechanism whereby exogenous species are prevented from colonizing the oral cavity. For example, some *S. salivarius* strains can produce an inhibitor (enocin or salivaricin) active against Lancefield Group A streptococci. It has been claimed that *S. salivarius* is more frequently isolated from the throats of children who do not become colonized following exposure to Group A streptococci than from those who do become infected (Sanders and Sanders, 1982). Thus, microbial interactions will play a major role in determining both the final composition and the pattern of development of the plaque microbial community at any site.

Implications for defining the role of a micro-organism

It is now recognised that micro-organisms inhabiting a wide range of habitats preferentially grow as microbial communities. However, for over a century, microbiologists have adopted an approach in which the properties of bacteria are defined from studies of the particular organism growing in pure culture. Now that bacteria are being studied in mixed cultures as part of interacting communities, it is clear that their behaviour and properties cannot always be predicted from such studies. Thus, in mixed culture, an organism may be able to utilise substrates that are normally recalcitrant, grow over a wider pH range, and survive challenges by antimicrobials or immunoglobulins, depending on the properties of other cells in close proximity.

The studies of plaque communities reviewed here are consistent with the features of microbial communities found elsewhere in diverse ecosystems (Caldwell *et al.*, 1997). Features in common to micro-organisms in all of these communities include an enhanced stability (homeostasis) despite regular perturbations to their habitat, a broader habitat range, enhanced resistance to host and environmental stress, and increased metabolic efficiency. A greater understanding of the role of individual organisms in spatially- and functionally-organised communities such as plaque can offer insights into novel approaches for control (Marsh and Bradshaw, 1997).

References

Alaluusua, S., Takei, T., Ooshima, T., and Hamada, S. 1991. Mutacin activity of strains isolated from children with varying levels of mutans streptococci and caries. *Arch. Oral Biol.* **36,** 251-255.

Alexander, M. 1971. *Microbial Ecology.* John Wiley, New York.

Bloomquist, C. G., Reilly, B. E., and Liljemark, W. F. 1996. Adherence, accumulation, and cell division of a natural adherent bacterial population. *J. Bacteriol.* **178,** 1172-1177.

Bowden, G. H. W., and Hamilton, I. R. 1998. Survival of oral bacteria. *Crit. Rev. Oral Biol. Med.* **9,** 54-85.

Bradshaw, D. J., Homer, K. A., Marsh, P. D., and Beighton, D. 1994. Metabolic cooperation in oral microbial communities during growth on mucin. *Microbiol* **140,** 3407-3412.

Bradshaw, D. J., and Marsh, P. D. 1998. Analysis of pH-driven disruption of oral microbial communities *in vitro. Caries Res.* **32,** 456-462.

Bradshaw, D. J., Marsh, P. D., Allison, C., and Schilling, K. M. 1996. Effect of oxygen, inoculum composition and flow rate on development of mixed culture oral biofilms. *Microbiol* **142,** 623-629.

Bradshaw, D. J., Marsh, P. D., Watson, G. K., and Allison, C. 1997. Oral anaerobes cannot survive oxygen stress without interacting with aerobic / facultative species as a microbial community. *Lett. Appl. Microbiol.* **25,** 385-387.

Bradshaw, D. J., Marsh, P. D., Watson, G. K., and Allison, C. 1998. Role of *Fusobacterium nucleatum* and coaggregation in anaerobe survival in planktonic and biofilm oral microbial communities during aeration. *Infect. Immun.* **66,** 4729-4732.

Bradshaw, D. J., McKee, A. S., and Marsh, P. D. 1989. Effects of carbohydrate pulses and pH on population shifts within oral microbial communities *in vitro. J. Dent. Res.* **68,** 1298-1302.

Burne, R. A. 1998. Regulation of gene expression in adherent populations of oral streptococci. In: LeBlanc, D. J., Lantz, M. S., and Switalski, L. M. (Ed.), *Microbial pathogenesis: Current and Emerging Issues.*, pp. 41-53, Indiana University, Indianapolis.

Busscher, H. J., Cowan, M. M., and van der Mei, H. C. 1992. On the relative importance of specific and non-specific approaches to oral microbial adhesion. *FEMS Microbiol. Rev.* **88,** 199-210.

Busscher, H. J., and van der Mei, H. C. 1997. Physico-chemical interactions in initial microbial adhesion and relevance for biofilm formation. *Adv. Dent. Res.* **11,** 24-32.

Caldwell, D. E., Wolfaardt, G. M., Korber, D. R., and Lawrence, J. R. 1997. Do bacterial communities transcend Darwinism? In: Jones, J. G. (Ed.), *Advances in Microbial Ecology*, pp. 105-191, Plenum, New York.

Carlsson, J. 1997. Bacterial metabolism in dental biofilms. *Adv. Dent. Res.* **11,** 75-80.

Casiano-Colon, A., and Marquis, R. E. 1988. Role of the arginine deiminase system in protecting oral bacteria and an enzymatic basis for acid tolerance. *Appl. Environ. Microbiol.* **54,** 1318-1324.

Chen, Y. Y., Clancy, K. A., and Burne, R. A. 1996. *Streptococcus salivarius* urease: genetic and biochemical characterization and expression in a dental plaque streptococcus. *Infect. Immun.* **64,** 585-592.

Costerton, J. W., Cheng, K. J., Geesey, G. G., Ladd, T. I., Nickel, J. C., Dasgupta, M., and Marrie, T. J. 1987. Bacterial biofilms in nature and disease. *Ann Rev Microbiol* **41,** 435-464.

Costerton, J. W., Lewandowski, Z., Caldwell, D. E., Korber, D. R., and Lappin-Scott, H. M. 1995. Microbial biofilms. *Ann Rev Microbio* **49,** 711-745.

Costerton, J. W., Lewandowski, Z., DeBeer, D., Caldwell, D. E., Korber, D. R., and James, G. 1994. Biofilms, the customized microniche. *J. Bacteriol.* **176,** 2137-2142.

Denk, W., Strickler, J., and Webb, W. W. 1990. Two-photon laser scanning fluorescence microscopy. *Science* **248,** 73-76.

Fujimura, S., and Nakamura, T. 1979. Sanguicin, a bacteriocin of oral *Streptococcus sanguis.*

Antimicrob. Agents Chemother. **16,** 262-265.

Gharbia, S. E., and Shah, H. N. 1989. The influence of peptides on the uptake of amino acids in *Fusobacterium*; predicted interactions with *Porphyromonas gingivalis. Curr. Microbiol.* **19,** 231-235.

Gilbert, P., Das, J., and Foley, I. 1997. Biofilm susceptibility to antimicrobials. *Adv. Dent. Res.* **11,** 160-167.

Hanley, S. A., Aduse-Opoku, J., and Curtis, M. A. 1999. A 55-kilodalton immunodominant antigen of *Porphyromonas gingivalis* W50 has arisen via horizontal gene transfer. *Infect. Immun.* **67,** 1157-1171.

Harper, D. S., and Loesche, W. J. 1984. Growth and acid tolerance of human dental plaque bacteria. *Arch. Oral Biol.* **29,** 843-848.

Hillman, J. D., Dzuback, A. L., and Andrews, S. W. 1987. Colonization of the human oral cavity by a *Streptococcus mutans* mutant producing increased bacteriocin. *J. Dent. Res.* **66,** 1092-1094.

Hillman, J. D., Socransky, S. S., and Shivers, M. 1985. The relationships between streptococcal species and periodontopathic bacteria in human dental plaque. *Arch. Oral Biol.* **30,** 791-795.

Homer, K. A., and Beighton, D. 1992. Synergistic degradation of bovine serum albumin by mutans streptococci and other dental plaque bacteria. *FEMS Microbiol. Lett.* **90,** 259-262.

Kilian, M., Reinholdt, J., Lomholt, H., Poulsen, K., and Frandsen, E. V. G. 1996. Biological significance of IgA1 proteases in bacterial colonisation and pathogenesis: critical evaluation of experimental evidence. *APMIS* **104,** 321-338.

Kinniment, S. L., Wimpenny, J. W. T., Adams, D., and Marsh, P. D. 1996. The effect of chlorhexidine on defined, mixed culture oral biofilms grown in a novel model system. *J. Appl. Bacteriol.* **81,** 120-125.

Kolenbrander, P. E. 1988. Intergeneric coaggregation among human oral bacteria and ecology of dental plaque. *Ann Rev Microbiol* **42,** 627-656.

Kolenbrander, P. E., Andersen, R. N., and Moore, L. V. 1990. Intrageneric coaggregation among strains of human oral bacteria: potential role in primary colonization of the tooth surface. *Appl. Environ. Microbiol.* **56,** 3890-3894.

Kolenbrander, P. E., and London, J. 1993. Adhere today, here tomorrow: oral bacterial adherence. *J. Bacteriol.* **175,** 3247-3252.

Liljemark, W. F., Bloomquist, C. G., Reilly, B. E., Bernards, C. J., Townsend, D. W., Pennock, A. T., and LeMoine, J. L. 1997. Growth dynamics in a natural biofilm and its impact on oral disease management. *Adv. Dent. Res.* **11,** 14-23.

Listgarten, M. A. 1994. The structure of dental plaque. *Periodontol. 2000.* **5,** 52-65.

Marsh, P. D. 1989. Host defenses and microbial homeostasis: role of microbial interactions. *J. Dent. Res.* **68,** 1567-1575.

Marsh, P. D. 1995. Dental plaque. In: Lappin-Scott, H. M., and Costerton, J. W. (Ed.), *Microbial biofilms*, pp. 282-300, Cambridge University Press, Cambridge.

Marsh, P. D., and Bradshaw, D. J. 1993. Microbiological effects of new agents in dentifrices for plaque control. *Int. Dent. J.* **43,** 399-406.

Marsh, P. D., and Bradshaw, D. J. 1995. Dental plaque as a biofilm. *J. Ind. Microbiol.* **15,** 169-175.

Marsh, P. D., and Bradshaw, D. J. 1997. Physiological approaches to plaque control. *Adv. Dent. Res.* **11,** 176-185.

Marsh, P. D., and Bradshaw, D. J. 1998. Dental plaque: community spirit in action. In: LeBlanc, D.J., Lanz, M.S., and Switalski, L.M.. (Eds.), *Microbial Pathogenesis: Current and Emerging Issues*, pp. 41-53. University of Indiana, Indianapolis.

Marsh, P. D., and Martin, M. V. 1999. *Oral microbiology.* Wright, Bristol.

McDermid, A. S., McKee, A. S., Ellwood, D. C., and Marsh, P. D. 1986. The effect of lowering the pH on the composition and metabolism of a community of nine oral bacteria grown in a chemostat. *J. Gen. Microbiol.* **132,** 1205-1214.

McDermid, A. S., McKee, A. S., and Marsh, P. D. 1988. Effect of environmental pH on enzyme activity and growth of *Bacteroides gingivalis* W50. *Infect. Immun.* **56,** 1096-1100.

Mikx, F. H. M., and van der Hoeven, J. S. 1975. Symbiosis of *Streptococcus mutans* and *Veillonella alcalescens* in mixed continuous culture. *Arch. Oral Biol.* **20,** 407-410.

Mikx, F. H. M., van der Hoeven, J. S., Konig, K. G., Plasschaert, A. J. M., and Guggenheim, B. 1972. Establishment of defined microbial ecosystems in germ-free rats. I. the effect of the interaction of *Streptococcus mutans* or *Streptococcus sanguis* with *Veillonella alcalescens* on plaque formation and caries activity. *Caries Res.* **6**, 211-223.

Odum, E. P. 1986. Introductory review: perspective of ecosystem theory and application. In: Polunin, N. (Ed.), *Ecosystem Theory and Application*, pp. 1-11, John Wiley & Sons, Chichester.

Parker, R. B., and Creamer, H. R. 1971. Contribution of plaque polysaccharides to growth of cariogenic bacteria. *Arch. Oral Biol.* **16**, 855-862.

Rams, T. E., Feik, D., Young, V., Hammond, B. F., and Slots, J. 1992. Enterococci in human periodontitis. *Oral Microbiol. Immunol.* **7**, 249-252.

Rogers, A. H., Zilm, P. S., Gully, N. J., and Pfennig, A. L. 1987. Chlorhexidine affects arginine metabolism as well as glycolysis in a strain of *Streptococcus sanguis*. *Oral Microbiol. Immunol.* **2**, 172-182.

Sanders, C. C., and Sanders, W. E. 1982. Enocin: an antibiotic produced by *Streptococcus salivarius* that may contribute to protection against infections due to group A streptococci. *J Infect Dis* **146**, 683-690.

Schachtele, C. F., Harlander, S. K., Fuller, D. W., Zolinder, P. K., and Leung, W.-L. S. 1976. Bacterial interference with sucrose-dependent adhesion of oral streptococci. In: Stiles, H. M., Loesche, W. J., and O'Brien, T. C. (Ed.), *Proceedings, Microbial Aspects of Dental Caries*, pp. 401-412, Information Retrieval, New York.

Sundqvist, G., Carlsson, J., Herrmann, B., and Tarnvik, A. 1985. Degradation of human immunoglobulins G and M and complement factors C3 and C5 by black-pigmented *Bacteroides*. *J. Med. Microbiol.* **19**, 85-94.

ter Steeg, P. F., and van der Hoeven, J. S. 1989. Development of periodontal microflora on human serum. *Microb. Ecol. Hlth Dis.* **2**, 1-10.

ter Steeg, P. F., van der Hoeven, J. S., de Jong, M. H., van Munster, P. J. J., and Jansen, M. J. H. 1987. Enrichment of subgingival microflora on human serum leading to accumulation of *Bacteroides* species, peptostreptococci and fusobacteria. *Antonie van Leeuwenhoek* **53**, 261-272.

ter Steeg, P. F., van der Hoeven, J. S., de Jong, M. H., van Munster, P. J. J., and Jansen, M. J. H. 1988. Modelling the gingival pocket by enrichment of subgingival microflora in human serum in chemostats. *Microb. Ecol. Hlth Dis.* **1**, 73-84.

van der Hoeven, J. S., and Camp, P. J. M. 1991. Synergistic degradation of mucin by *Streptococcus oralis* and *Streptococcus sanguis* in mixed chemostat cultures. *J. Dent. Res.* **68**, 1041-1044.

van der Hoeven, J. S., and Rogers, A. H. 1979. Stability of the resident microflora and bacteriocinogeny of *Streptococcus mutans* as factors affecting its establishment in specific pathogen free rats. *Infect. Immun.* **23**, 206-212.

van Houte, J., and Jansen, H. M. 1968. Levan degradation by streptococci isolated from human dental plaque. *Arch. Oral Biol.* **13**, 827-830.

van Winkelhoff, A. J., Winkel, E. G., Barendregt, D., Dellemijn-Kippuw, N., Stijne, A., and van der Velden, U. 1997. Beta-lactamase producing bacteria in adult periodontitis. *J. Clin. Periodontol.* **24**, 538-543.

Vroom, J. M., de Grauw, K. J., Gerritsen, H. C., Bradshaw, D. J., Marsh, P. D., Watson, G. K., Allison, C., and Birmingham, J. J. 1999. Depth penetration and detection of pH gradients in biofilms using two-photon excitation microscopy. *Appl. Environ. Microbiol.* **65**, in press.

Wilson, M. 1996. Susceptibility of oral bacterial biofilms to antimicrobial agents. *J. Med. Microbiol.* **44**, 79-87.

Wimpenny, J. W. T. 1994. The spatial organisation of biofilm. In: Wimpenny, J., Nichols, W., Stickler, D., and Lappin-Scott, H. (Ed.), *Bacterial Biofilms and their Control in Medicine and Industry*, pp. 1-6, Bioline, School of Pure & Applied Biology, University of Wales College of Cardiff, Cardiff.

Wood, S. R., Kirkham, J., Marsh, P. D., Shore, R. C., Nattress, B., and Robinson, C. 1999. Architecture of intact natural human plaque biofilms studied by confocal laser scanning microscopy. *J. Dent. Res.* in press.

PLAQUE MICROBIOLOGY IN HEALTH AND DISEASE

A. D. Haffajee, S. S. Socransky, M. Feres and
L. A. Ximenez-Fyvie

*In order to understand the role of plaque species in maintaining periodontal health or initiating disease, it is necessary to determine plaque composition in different clinical states. Studies using whole genomic DNA probes and checkerboard DNA-DNA hybridization have indicated some of the associations that occur among subgingival species. For example, species such as **Bacteroides forsythus**, **Porphyromonas gingivalis** and **T. denticola** (red complex) frequently occur together and are more prevalent in periodontally diseased subjects than healthy controls. These species relate strongly to measures of gingival inflammation and probing pocket depth. The checkerboard technique has also allowed the comparison of supra and subgingival plaque composition on the same tooth surfaces in both periodontal health and disease. **Actinomyces** species predominated in healthy supragingival plaque, but declined in proportions in diseased and subgingival sites. In contrast, **Fusobacterium**, **Prevotella**, **Campylobacter** and red complex species increased in counts and proportions in disease and subgingivally. All 40 species examined could be detected in both health and disease and in supra or subgingival sites, although proportions were significantly different among sample locations. The effect of different periodontal therapies including SRP, systemically administered antibiotics and professional supragingival plaque removal, on the composition of the subgingival microbiota was examined. Metronidazole had a profound clinical and microbiological effect. Levels and proportions of red complex species were significantly reduced by 3 days and remained at low levels up to 180 days post-therapy. Disruption of plaque by weekly professional supragingival plaque removal led to decreases in many subgingival species. At 3 months post therapy the microbial profile was similar to that found in periodontal health. Improved microbiological techniques provide a clearer picture of the levels and proportions of species in supra and subgingival plaque in health and disease, their ecological relationships and the effects of periodontal therapies on this ecosystem.*

Introduction

Oral biofilms consist of complex communities of bacterial species that reside on tooth surfaces or soft tissues. These biofilms are important, because some resident species have the potential to cause local or systemic disease, and because other species contribute to the maintenance of oral health. The study of oral biofilms has been slowed by a number of difficulties. One of the most important has been the complexity of the microbial communities. It has been estimated that between 400 and 1,000 species may, at some time, colonize oral biofilms. Many of these species are difficult to cultivate or even uncultivable. Once isolated, strains are frequently difficult to identify using conventional phenotypic tests. Detection of 20 to 30 species in a sample from a single tooth surface is common and one suspects that many more species may reside in individual biofilm samples. Early studies of biofilm composition employed light microscopy, but this method was incapable of distinguishing the wide array of resident species and has been largely discarded. Cultural techniques, while useful for many investigations, had serious limitations. Difficulty in recovering all or the majority of species in samples and failure to adequately recover even cultivable species were major concerns. On a practical level, the enormous labor and cost involved in evaluating hundreds or thousands of samples precluded major studies of biofilm ecology or its relationship to local and systemic diseases. Comprehensive study of the complex communities of oral biofilms required a major technological shift. One example of this frame shift has been the use of the checkerboard DNA-DNA hybridization technique employed in all the studies described in this manuscript. This method overcomes many of the limitations of culture and is more rapid and cost-effective than antibody-based techniques.

In this meeting, plaque is being revisited, in part, because of technical improvements in our ability to examine plaque, and in part, because of cognitive changes in our understanding of biofilm development, biology and ecology. The examination of the composition of dental plaque in periodontal health serves as a logical point of departure to understand the changes that occur leading to periodontal disease. Comparison of the microbiota found in diseased and non diseased subjects should indicate the species that initiate or contribute to disease progression. In addition, the composition of the microbiota found in health provides a desired endpoint for periodontal disease prevention and treatment procedures. Thus, in this manuscript, data will be presented that indicate the nature of plaque composition in health, the nature of changes in disease, outline some of the factors that affect plaque composition and examine the effects of treatments attempting to change plaque composition.

Checkerboard DNA-DNA Hybridization

Microbiologists were slowed in earlier investigations by the need to culture microorganisms in order to provide identification to a species level. For example, Figure 1 indicates the number of subgingival plaque samples enumerated at Forsyth Dental Center between the years 1969 to 1999. From 1969 to 1979, 135 samples were examined culturally to evaluate the microbiota in localized juvenile periodontitis and adult periodontitis lesions. Cultural techniques were also employed between 1982 and 1988 to examine 300 plaque samples that included actively progressing lesions and the microbiota after treatment of these lesions. From 1988 to 1993, a colony lift method that utilized DNA probes, was employed to evaluate 9,600 plaque samples. The checkerboard DNA-DNA hybridization technique was introduced in 1993 and was used to evaluate 34,400 plaque samples, to date, for their content of 40 bacterial species.

The technique involves the deposition of the bacterial DNA from 28 plaque samples and sets of standards in parallel lanes on a nylon membrane (Socransky

256

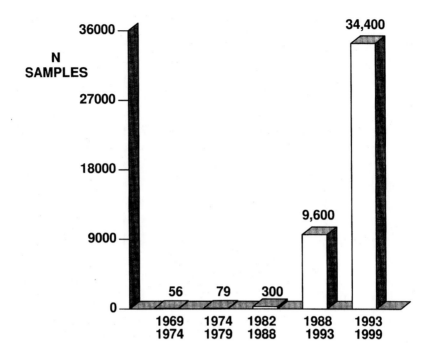

Figure 1 Bar chart of the number of plaque samples examined using different microbiological identification techniques at different time periods.

et al., 1994). Forty digoxigenin-labelled whole genomic DNA probes are run at right angles to the lanes of the samples. After stringency washing, signals are detected by using antibody to digoxigenin conjugated with alkaline phosphatase and substrates that provide either chemiluminescent or fluorescent signals. The images can be captured by film or computer linked detection systems. Signals can be converted to ranks or counts by comparison with the 10^5 and 10^6 standards on the same membrane. Figure 2 is an example of a checkerboard from one subject for one visit. The intensity of the signals relates to the number of cells of a given species in the samples from the individual sites. This single membrane provides 1,120 bacterial counts. The advantages of this technique include the speed of identification of bacteria, the low cost per sample and the ability to identify uncultivable or difficult to grow species. Disadvantages include the fact that detection is limited to species for which probes are available, the need for precise quality control and the possibility of cross reactions. The last concern can be virtually eliminated by appropriate control of stringency of hybridization and washing and the use of competitive hybridization or improved probes.

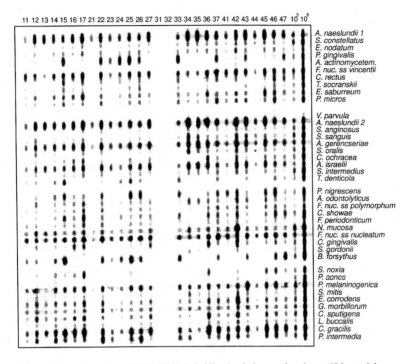

Figure 2 Example of checkerboard DNA-DNA hybridization being used to detect 40 bacterial species in 28 subgingival plaque samples from a single patient. The vertical lanes are the plaque samples numbered from 11 (upper right central incisor) to 47 (lower right second molar). The 2 vertical lanes on the right are standards containing either 10^5 or 10^6 cells of each test species. The horizontal lanes contained the indicated DNA probes in hybridization buffer. A signal at the intersection of the vertical and horizontal lanes indicates the presence of a species. The intensity of the signal is related to the number of organisms of that species in the sample. In brief, samples of plaque were placed into individual Eppendorf tubes and the DNA released from the microorganisms by boiling in NaOH. After neutralization, the released DNA was transferred to the surface of a nylon membrane using the 30 channels of a Minislot device (Immunetics, Cambridge MA). The DNA was fixed to the membrane by UV light and baking and placed in a Miniblotter 45 (Immunetics) with the lanes of DNA at right angles to the 45 channels of the Miniblotter device. Whole genomic DNA probes labelled with digoxigenin were placed in hybridization buffer into 40 of the lanes and hybridized overnight. After stringency washing, the signals were detected using phosphatase-conjugated antibody to digoxigenin and chemifluorescent substrates. Signals were read using a Storm Fluorimager (Molecular Dynamics). The empty vertical lanes, 31 and 32 were due to missing teeth.

Microbial complexes in dental plaque

Bacterial species rarely exist in pure culture in supra or subgingival plaque samples. Indeed, in most microbial communities, there are observable associations between specific species due in part to synergistic or antagonistic relationships and in part due to the nature of available surfaces for colonization or nutrient availability. The nature of the complexes that occur within dental plaque are poorly understood. Knowledge of these bacterial associations may be

Table 1 2 x 2 contingency table of the association between *P. gingivalis* and *B. forsythus* in subgingival plaque samples.

P. gingivalis

B. forsythus		-	+	
	-	9024	311	9335
	+	1,991	1,727	2,146
		11,015	2,038	13,053

important in determining optimal (to the host) ecosystems for long-term periodontal health.

The associations between species in subgingival plaque samples from subjects with different levels of periodontal disease were examined. 13,261 subgingival plaque samples from 185 subjects were evaluated for the presence of 40 subgingival species using the checkerboard DNA-DNA hybridization technique (Socransky *et al.,* 1998). The associations between pairs of microbial species in plaque samples were assessed by preparing 2 X 2 contingency tables for all possible pairs of the 40 species. An example of such a table for *B. forsythus* and *P. gingivalis* is presented in Table 1. The computed phi coefficient was 0.536. The strength of the associations between all possible pairs was assessed using this coefficient which was scaled to range from 0 to 100% similarity. The similarities were used in a cluster analysis using an average unweighted linkage sort. In the analyses to follow, species that were detected in < 5% of sites were omitted, providing a total of 32 taxa.

The dendrogram in Figure 3 depicts the five clusters that were formed with > 60% similarity. The red complex was comprised of 3 suspected periodontal pathogens, *Bacteroides forsythus, Porphyromonas gingivalis* and *Treponema denticola.* This combination was found more frequently at deeper periodontal pocket depths. The orange complex was comprised of a tightly related central group consisting of *Fusobacterium* species and subspecies, *Peptostreptococcus micros, Prevotella nigrescens* and *Prevotella intermedia.* These were joined by *Campylobacter rectus, Campylobacter gracilis, Campylobacter showae, Eubacterium nodatum* and *Streptococcus constellatus.* Many of the species in this complex are suspected periodontal pathogens and like the red complex species, this complex was detected more often at deeper periodontal pockets, possibly reflecting the selective pressures of such pockets. The yellow complex was comprised solely of members of the genus *Streptococcus,* while the green complex consisted of members of the genus *Capnocytophaga, Actinobacillus actinomycetemcomitans* serotype a, *Campylobacter concisus* and *Eikenella corrodens. Actinomyces odontolyticus* and *Veillonella parvula* made up the purple complex. Three species did not fall into any of the cluster groups. Species of the yellow, green and purple complexes together with *Actinomyces*

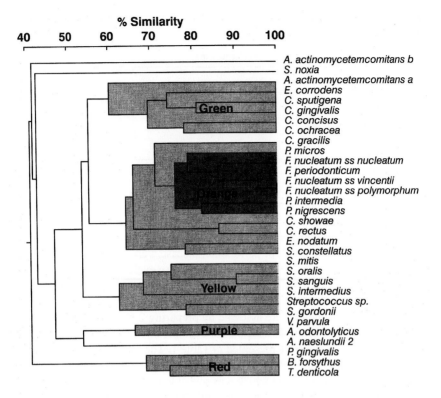

% Similarity

A. actinomycetemcomitans b
S. noxia
A. actinomycetemcomitans a
E. corrodens
C. sputigena
C. gingivalis
C. concisus
C. ochracea
C. gracilis
P. micros
F. nucleatum ss nucleatum
F. periodonticum
F. nucleatum ss vincentii
F. nucleatum ss polymorphum
P. intermedia
P. nigrescens
C. showae
C. rectus
E. nodatum
S. constellatus
S. mitis
S. oralis
S. sanguis
S. intermedius
Streptococcus sp.
S. gordonii
V. parvula
A. odontolyticus
A. naeslundii 2
P. gingivalis
B. forsythus
T. denticola

Figure 3 Dendrogram of a cluster analysis of 32 subgingival taxa. The similarity between pairs of species was computed using a phi coefficient, the coefficients were scaled and then sorted using an average unweighted linkage sort. 29 of the taxa fit into 5 clusters that were formed using a threshold level of 60% similarity. *A. naeslundii* genospecies 2, *A. actinomycetemcomitans* serotype b and *S. noxia* were not part of any complex. Colors are used to designate different microbial complexes. (Adapted from Socransky *et al.*, 1998).

naeslundii genospecies 2, are for the most part considered to be host compatible or beneficial species. *A. naeslundii* genospecies 2, for example, was detected more frequently at sites with shallow pockets.

Community ordination was used as a second approach to examine the data. This procedure attempted to indicate closely related species within a community and then demonstrate the relatedness among different communities of species within the ecosystem of interest. Figure 4 is a correspondence analysis of the data from the 13,261 samples from 185 subjects. The x and y axes indicate the first and second components respectively. A third component was plotted in 3-dimensional plots (data not shown). The Figure reinforces groupings observed using the cluster analyses and also relates communities of species to each other. For example, the red complex of *B. forsythus*, *P. gingivalis* and *T. denticola* is most closely related to the orange complex consisting of species of the genera

260

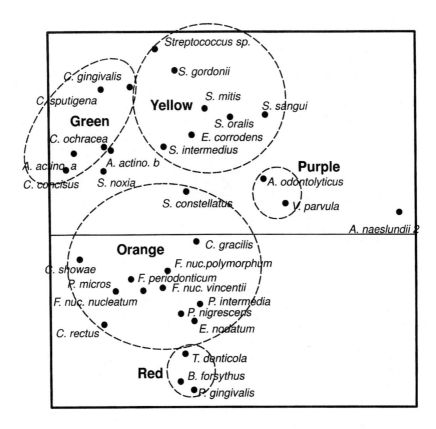

Figure 4 Community ordination of 32 subgingival taxa using correspondence analysis. The relationships among species were evaluated using the levels of the species at each of the sampled sites. Correspondence analysis was performed as described by Ludwig & Reynolds (1988) and the species were plotted along the first (x-axis) and second (y-axis) axes. The dotted circles represent the different microbial complexes indicated in Figure 3.

Fusobacterium, Prevotella, Campylobacter, P. micros, E. nodatum and *S. constellatus*. This complex in turn related to 3 other groups observed in the cluster analysis. The data indicated that bacterial species were not randomly distributed but occurred in distinct complexes. The large number of plaque samples from 185 subjects used in this analysis suggested that these groupings occur in more than a handful of subjects. Cluster analysis using different similarity coefficients (e.g. Bray-Curtis, Mahalanobis d^2) and different subsets of the data as well as community ordination using correspondence analysis and principal components analysis showed quite consistent grouping of species and relationships among the groups. These are depicted in Figure 5.

These data suggest the nature of some of the microbial complexes in subgingival plaque. Although the number of plaque samples was large and the number of species evaluated was reasonably extensive, the results represent an initial

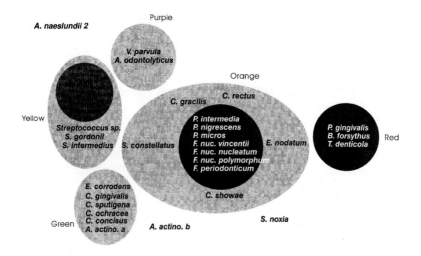

Figure 5 Diagrammatic representation of the relationships of species within microbial complexes and between the microbial complexes. This diagram was based on the results of multiple cluster and community ordination analyses using the entire data base as well as subsets of data. (Adapted from Socransky *et al.,* 1998).

attempt at evaluating inter-relationships among subgingival species. While some of the associations depicted may require refinement, certain associations were seen repeatedly using different analytical techniques and were in accord with data in the literature. Further, certain complexes, and members within the complexes, related strongly to clinical parameters of inflammation and periodontal destruction. It was concluded that these data provide a framework for understanding the complex ecology observed in plaque and may be used to guide approaches to diagnosis and therapy of periodontal diseases.

Subgingival microbiota in periodontally healthy and periodontitis subjects

Few studies have comprehensively examined the composition of subgingival plaque samples in periodontal health. Further, studies comparing the composition of plaque in periodontitis and periodontal health are limited. The studies of Moore and Moore (1994), to date, have provided some of the most complete data on plaque composition in health and various states of periodontal disease. These studies employed cultural techniques to examine over 17,000 isolates from over 600 periodontal sites in healthy subjects and subjects with different periodontal diseases. The most commonly detected species in both health and disease were *A. naeslundii,* including all of its genotypes, and *F. nucleatum.* With increasing levels of disease, the proportions of the *Actinomyces* and *Streptococci* decreased while proportions of members of the genera *Actinobacillus, Campylobacter, Eubacterium, Fusobacterium, Prevotella, Porphyromonas*

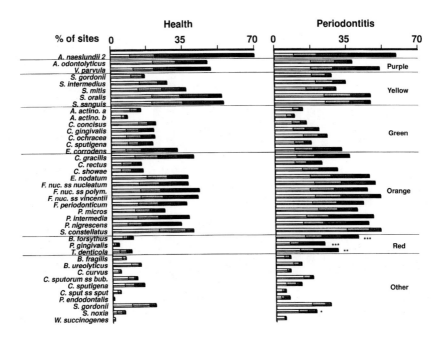

Figure 6 . Stacked bar charts of the mean prevalence and levels of the 40 subgingival species evaluated in 30 periodontally healthy and 138 periodontitis subjects. 791 and 3,398 subgingival plaque samples were obtained from the periodontally healthy and periodontitis subjects respectively. The % of sites colonized by each of the 40 species examined was computed for each subject and then averaged across subjects in the 2 groups. Significance of differences in prevalence between groups was evaluated using the Mann-Whitney test. * = p <0.05, ** = p < 0.01 and *** = p < 0.001 after adjusting for multiple comparisons (Haffajee *et al.,* 1998). Mean levels of each species were determined by averaging the levels of the species within a subject and then across subjects in the 2 groups. Significance of differences in mean levels was computed as described for the prevalence data. The same taxa were found to differ.

and *Selenomonas* increased. While the microbiological identifications were precise, the results were based on a relatively small number of samples for each periodontal disease category.

Other studies have evaluated the composition of subgingival plaque from periodontally diseased sites (Haffajee & Socransky 1994). However, few studies have examined the microbiota of subgingival plaque in periodontally healthy individuals. The species that predominate the subgingival microbiota in peri-odontal health and disease were somewhat similar (Dahlen *et al.,*, 1992b, 1995, Tanner *et al.,* 1996, Ali *et al.,* 1997). However, a number of studies have indicated that periodontal pathogens can be found in the dental plaque of healthy individuals (Ashimoto *et al.,* 1996, Christopher *et al.,* 1996, Riviere *et al.,* 1996, Tuite-McDonnell *et al.,* 1997). *A. actinomycetemcomitans* was found in supra and subgingival plaque samples of both periodontally healthy and diseased

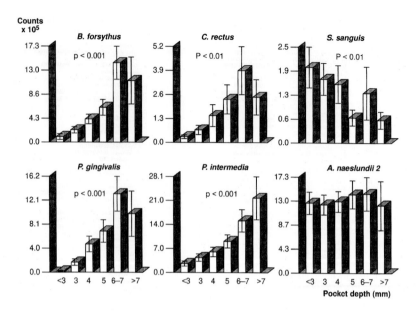

Figure 7 Bar charts of the mean counts (x 10^5 ± SEM) of 6 subgingival species at selected pocket depths. The mean counts of each species at each pocket depth category was computed for each subject and then averaged across subjects. Significance of differences among pocket depth categories was tested using the Kruskal-Wallis test. The total number of subjects was 138.

subjects (Asikainen *et al.*, 1991, Zimmer *et al.*, 1991), while *B. forsythus* has been detected at periodontally healthy sites (Lai *et al.*, 1987, Gmur *et al.*, 1989). Gmur & Guggenheim (1994) evaluated the prevalence of 4 periodontal pathogens in the supragingival plaque of periodontally healthy subjects. *A. actinomycetemcomitans*, *B. forsythus* and *C. rectus* were detected at > 30% of sampled sites, while *P. nigrescens* was found in all samples.

The development of reliable and rapid techniques for the identification of bacteria in dental plaque coupled with a better understanding of relationships among bacterial species in dental plaque have widened the scope of previous studies. The composition of subgingival plaque was examined in 30 periodontally healthy and 138 adult periodontitis subjects (Haffajee *et al.*, 1998). Periodontally healthy subjects had no probing pocket depths and no attachment level measurements > 4 mm. However, subjects in this group could exhibit gingival inflammation. The periodontitis subjects had at least 4 sites with pocket depth > 4 mm and 4 sites with attachment loss > 4 mm. Clinical measurements of gingival inflammation, pocket depth and attachment level were made at 6 sites per tooth in each subject. In addition, a total of 4,189 subgingival plaque samples (mean 24.9 per subject) from the mesio-buccal aspect of each tooth in each subject were analyzed for their content of 40 bacterial taxa using checkerboard DNA-DNA hybridization.

Examination of up to 28 sites in a subject using checkerboard DNA-DNA

264

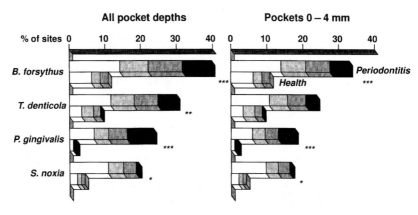

Figure 8 Stacked bar charts of the prevalence and levels of species that differed significantly in plaque samples from periodontally healthy and periodontitis subjects. The length of the bars represents the mean prevalence, while the shadings in the bars represent the proportion of sites colonized by different levels of the species. The top bar in each pair represents the periodontitis subjects. The left panel presents data from all sites, while the right panel presents data from pockets of 0 - 4 mm only. Significance of differences between health and periodontitis for each species was sought using the Mann Whitney test; * = p <0.05, ** = p < 0.01 and *** = p < 0.001 after adjusting for multiple comparisons.

hybridization allowed a more robust estimate of mean counts for each species in a subject and in the different groups. Further, a meaningful estimation of the prevalence (% of sites colonized) of the test species within the oral cavity could be performed; a parameter not measured previously when only a few sites were sampled within a subject. Figure 6 presents the mean prevalence and levels of the 40 test species, ordered to reflect the microbial complexes outlined above, in 4,189 subgingival plaque samples obtained from subjects in the 2 groups. The more commonly detected species and those thought to be beneficial, such as *A. naeslundii* genospecies 2, *S. sanguis, S. oralis, V. parvula* and *A. odontolyticus* were comparable in the 2 groups, although the counts and prevalences were higher in the healthy subjects. This was particularly noticeable for *Actinomyces odontolyticus* which was found significantly more frequently in the healthy subjects. Many of the orange complex species including the *F. nucleatum* subspecies, *C. rectus, P. intermedia, P. nigrescens* and *P. micros* were found more frequently in the periodontitis subjects. Most notable, however, were the elevated levels and prevalence of *B. forsythus, P. gingivalis, T. denticola* and *Selenomonas noxia* in the periodontitis group.

It has been recognized for some time that certain species, particularly those of the red and orange complexes, are positively related to increasing pocket depth. This is illustrated in Figure 7 which presents the mean counts of 2 red (*B. forsythus, P. gingivalis*), 2 orange complex (*C. rectus, P. intermedia*), *Streptococcus sanguis* and *A. naeslundii* genospecies 2 at sites with different pocket depths. The red and orange complex species showed a significant positive

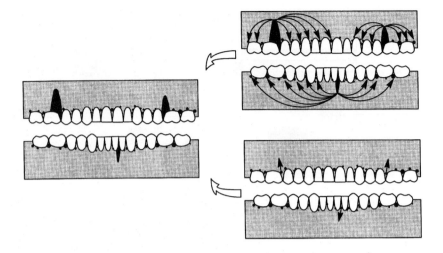

Figure 9 Diagrammatic representation of hypotheses explaining the presence of red complex species in multiple shallow pockets of periodontitis subjects. The left panel depicts the possible distribution of red complex species detected at deep and shallow sites. The representations on the right represent alternative hypotheses explaining this distribution. The top panel suggests that species may have spread from infected deep periodontal pockets to shallow sites in the same oral cavity. The lower panel suggests that many sites in healthy subjects might have to be colonized by periodontal pathogens before some sites exhibit disease progression.

association with increasing pocket depth while *S. sanguis* showed a negative association and no significant relationship was observed for *A. naeslundii*.

The prevalence and levels of the 4 species that differed in the 2 subject groups for all pocket depths is presented in the left panel of Figure 8. The data indicated that mean counts of the 4 species were significantly higher in the periodontitis subjects when compared with the healthy subjects. This finding was not unexpected given the data of Figure 6 and the relationship between increasing pocket depth and increased counts of certain species described above. However, when the data were subset into sites with pockets 0 - 4 mm in the 2 groups and the analysis repeated (Figure 8, right panel), it was found that the periodontitis subjects had significantly elevated mean counts and prevalences of the 4 species at shallow periodontal pockets compared with shallow sites in the periodontally healthy subjects. These data have therapeutic and preventive ramifications. The colonization of a "typical" adult periodontitis patient by members of the red complex is depicted in the left panel of Figure 9. The Figure is in accord with the detection of a large number of shallow pockets colonized by the pathogenic complex. It also depicts higher levels in deep periodontal pockets. This situation could have been due to spread of the complex from deep periodontal pockets as depicted in the upper right panel or it may have been due to the requirement that many shallow sites be colonized before a subset progresses to more advanced disease. The clinical implication of the first

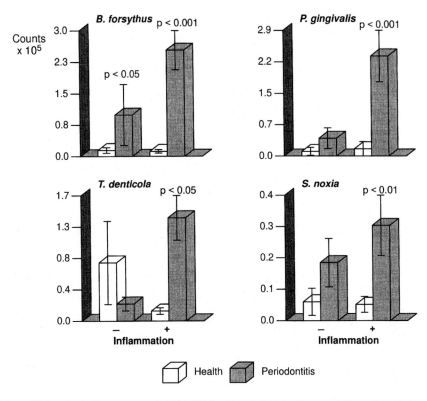

Figure 10 Bar charts of mean counts (x 10^5 ± SEM) of 4 periodontal pathogens at sites with pockets of 0 - 4 mm in periodontally healthy (open bars) and periodontitis subjects (shaded bars). The right pair of bars in each panel represent sites that exhibited gingival redness and/or bleeding on probing. The left pair of bars represents sites that did not exhibit either parameter. Significance of differences between samples from periodontally healthy and periodontitis subjects was tested using the Mann Whitney test.

hypothesis would be that pocket elimination should reduce pathogen load throughout the mouth. The implication of the second hypothesis is that suppression of pathogens in heavily colonized, periodontally healthy subjects prior to disease initiation would be imperative to prevent disease onset.

Since differences existed in counts of certain species at shallow periodontal pockets of healthy and periodontitis subjects, it was of interest to determine if other clinical parameters might be related to these differences. Sites in the 0 - 4 mm pocket depth category in the 2 subject groups were further subset into those that exhibited signs of gingival inflammation (gingival erythema and/or bleeding on probing) or were clinically healthy. Figure 10 presents the mean counts for *B. forsythus*, *P. gingivalis*, *T. denticola* and *S. noxia* at sites with or without signs of gingival inflammation in the periodontally healthy and periodontitis subjects. In general, counts of these species were higher at both the inflamed

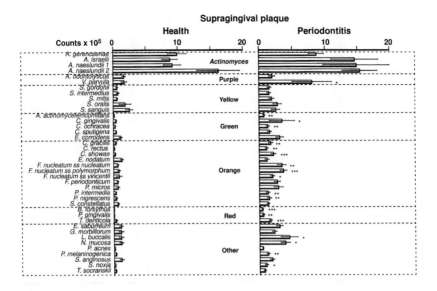

Figure 11 Mean counts x 10^5 ($\pm$ SEM) of individual species in supragingival plaque samples from 22 healthy and 23 periodontitis subjects. The mean count was computed for each species, for each subject and then averaged across subjects in each clinical group. The significance of differences between health and periodontitis counts was tested using the Mann-Whitney test. * $p < 0.05$, ** $p < 0.01$, *** $p < 0.001$ after adjusting for multiple comparisons.

and non inflamed sites of the periodontitis subjects than at similar sites in the healthy subjects. Further, sites exhibiting gingival inflammation in the periodontitis subjects harbored significantly higher mean counts of *B. forsythus, P. gingivalis* and *T. denticola* than non inflamed sites in the same subjects.

The data of this investigation indicated that the majority of species detected in periodontally healthy subjects were also detected in periodontally diseased subjects. There were differences in total numbers of organisms between health and disease and in the levels of specific subgingival species. Many of these differences related to the clinical status of the sampled sites in terms of both pocket depth and gingival inflammation. Deeper pockets and sites exhibiting gingival redness and/or bleeding on probing harbored higher mean counts of specific subgingival species. However, samples from sites with similar clinical characteristics in the 2 subject groups, differed in mean counts and prevalences of red complex species and *S. noxia*.

Composition of supra and subgingival plaque in periodontal health and disease

The nature and relationship of supragingival plaque to subgingival plaque and to periodontal health and disease have received little attention. In this series of studies, the composition of both supra and subgingival plaque was examined in

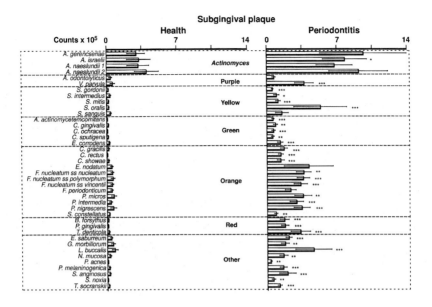

Figure 12 Mean counts x 10^5 ($\pm$ SEM) of individual species in subgingival plaque samples from 22 healthy and 23 periodontitis subjects. The mean count was computed for each species, for each subject and then averaged across subjects in each clinical group. The significance of differences between health and periodontitis counts was tested using the Mann-Whitney test. * $p < 0.05$, ** $p < 0.01$, *** $p < 0.001$ after adjusting for multiple comparisons.

22 periodontally healthy and 23 periodontitis subjects (Ximenez-Fyvie *et al.,* 1998,1999). Samples of supra and separately subgingival plaque were taken from the mesial aspect of each tooth in each subject providing a total of 1,179 supragingival and 1,179 subgingival samples. These samples were individually evaluated for their content of 40 species as described earlier. 32 of the DNA probes were the same as those employed in the previous section, while DNA probes to 8 infrequently detected species were replaced by probes to different species, particularly to members of the genus *Actinomyces*. In addition, chemifluorescent detection and a fluorimager replaced chemiluminescent detection and X ray film.

Figure 11 presents the mean counts ($\times 10^5$) of the test species in supragingival plaque samples obtained from the periodontally healthy and periodontitis subjects. The *Actinomyces* species were in the highest numbers in samples from both subject groups. Major differences, however, were observed between subject groups in counts of species in the other complexes. In particular, counts of the red and orange complex species were markedly higher in samples from the periodontitis subjects. Figure 12 presents similar data for the subgingival plaque samples. The difference between health and disease in plaque composition at subgingival sites was more pronounced than in the supragingival plaque

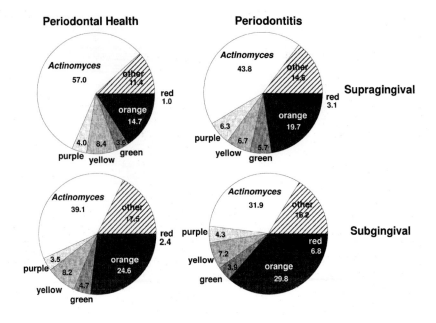

Figure 13 Mean % DNA probe count of microbial groups in supra and subgingival plaque samples from 22 periodontally healthy and 23 periodontitis subjects. The grouping of species was described in Figure 5. The category "other" represents DNA probes to different species whose relationships with other species have not yet been determined.

samples from the same subjects. Mean counts of the majority of the species in the subgingival samples were much higher in the diseased subjects than in the healthy subjects. Once more the red and orange complex species were markedly elevated in the diseased individuals, but other species such as *V. parvula, Streptococcus oralis, E. nodatum* and *Leptotrichia buccalis* were also significantly higher in the periodontitis subjects.

The proportions that each complex comprised of the total DNA probe count in the supra and subgingival plaque samples from the healthy and periodontitis subjects are presented in Figure 13. This Figure describes the shift in proportions of species from the supragingival samples obtained from periodontally healthy subjects to the subgingival samples obtained from periodontally diseased subjects. The major changes appeared to be an increase in proportions of red and orange complex species as the sampling proceeded from health to disease and from supra to subgingival locations. For example, these 2 complexes averaged 15.7% of the samples from supragingival plaque in healthy subjects but were more than doubled to 36.6% in subgingival samples from periodontitis subjects. The increase in these 2 complexes appeared to occur at the expense of the *Actinomyces* species. The remaining complexes and species were in comparable proportions at all sample locations. Figure 14 presents the

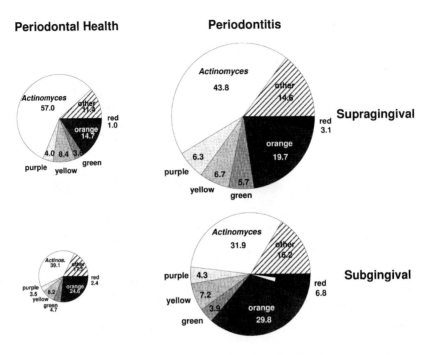

Figure 14 Data of Figure 13 with the area of the pies adjusted to reflect the relative mean total counts at each sample location. The white segment included in the red complex segment of the subgingival periodontitis samples reflects the proportion and levels of the red complex species found in subgingival plaque samples from periodontally healthy subjects.

same data but the areas of the pies have been adjusted to reflect the mean total DNA probe counts at the different sample locations. The highest total counts were for supragingival samples from periodontitis subjects, while the lowest total counts were seen at subgingival sites in the periodontally healthy individuals. The most striking feature of the data was the 6 fold greater total numbers of bacteria detected in subgingival plaque samples of periodontitis subjects when compared with subgingival samples from periodontally healthy subjects. The difference in red complex species was even more marked in the 2 sample locations. For example, there was an approximately 18 fold increase in red complex species in the subgingival samples from periodontitis subjects compared with samples from healthy individuals.

Modification of plaque composition by periodontal therapy

The major reason for determining the microbial composition of dental plaque in health is that the prevention and control of periodontal infections is dependent on creating and maintaining a subgingival plaque microbiota that approximates that observed in health. Many periodontal therapies are available to the therapist including mechanical debridement procedures such as SRP and surgery as well

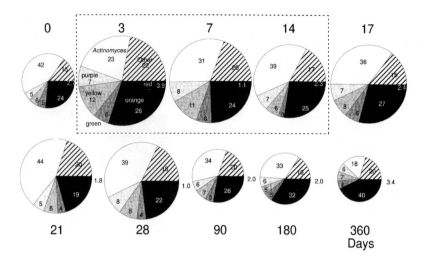

Figure 15 Mean proportion of microbial complexes at different time points in the 10 subjects receiving SRP only. % DNA probe counts for each species were determined at each site. The proportions were then averaged across subjects at each time point. Species in the complexes were summed and the proportion that each complex comprised was determined. The area of each pie was adjusted to reflect its size relative to the baseline total count. The dashed boxed area represents the time of antibiotic therapy for the other treatment groups.

as systemically and locally administered antimicrobial agents. In addition, supragingival plaque control can play a major role in maintaining the desired microbial changes. Each therapy is likely to produce somewhat different microbiological effects. Thus, in order to select the most appropriate therapy for a specific periodontal infection, it is important to understand the microbial effects of different therapies and to determine whether the resulting microbial profile is compatible with periodontal stability. In this section, the effect of selected mechanical and antibiotic therapies on the subgingival microbiota will be described.

The clinical and microbiological effects of SRP alone or in combination with either systemically administered doxycycline or metronidazole were evaluated (Feres *et al.*, 1999ab). The novel aspect of this study was that microbiological parameters were assessed during administration, immediately after completion of antibiotic therapy as well as at 3, 6 and 12 months post therapy. 29 adult periodontitis subjects were assigned to the 3 treatment groups. Full mouth clinical measurements and microbial sampling were performed at baseline, 3, 6 and 12 months. In addition, subgingival plaque samples were taken at 3, 7 and 14 days during and at 3, 7 and 14 days after antibiotic administration. All subjects received SRP at baseline; 9 subjects received doxycycline (100 mg / day) for 14 days and 10 subjects received metronidazole (250 mg 3 times a day) for 14 days.

Figure 15 presents the proportions of species in the microbial complexes at

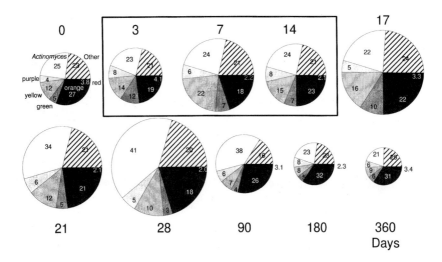

Figure 16 Mean proportion of microbial complexes at different time points in the 10 subjects receiving SRP and systemically administered doxycycline. % DNA probe counts for each species were determined at each site. The proportions were then averaged across subjects at each time point. Species in the complexes were summed and the proportion that each complex comprised was determined. The area of each pie was adjusted to reflect its size relative to the baseline total count. The boxed area represents the time of antibiotic therapy.

each of the time points for the 10 subjects receiving SRP only. The areas of the pies have been adjusted to reflect the total DNA probe counts at each of the visits. Total counts increased at days 3, 7 and 14 as indicated by an increase in the size of the pies. However, counts decreased over time so that at 360 days, counts were comparable to those found at baseline. Proportions of the different complexes were modestly affected by SRP.

In contrast, microbiological changes were more pronounced in the antibiotic treated subjects. Figure 16 presents similar data for the 9 subjects treated with doxycycline. Total counts were comparable to baseline levels during antibiotic administration but increased once the agent had been withdrawn. Counts returned to baseline levels or lower between 90 and 360 days. Proportions of organisms were also affected by this therapy. The proportions of the yellow complex species (streptococci) increased during doxycycline administration, but declined shortly after its withdrawal. This increase may have be due to the fact that many of the streptococci were resistant to doxycycline. *Actinomyces* species increased in proportion after completion of antibiotic administration, but returned to baseline levels by 180 days. This agent had little effect on the proportions of red and orange complex species.

The effect of metronidazole on the subgingival microbiota was more profound (Figure 17). The total counts were markedly decreased during antibiotic administration, but increased once the subjects stopped taking the agent. Nonetheless, at 180 days, counts were somewhat lower than those detected at base-

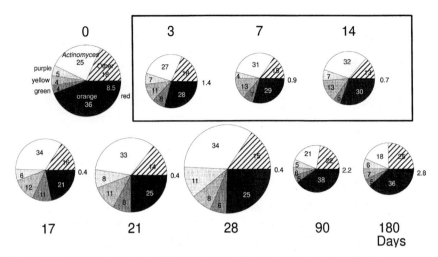

Figure 17 Mean proportion of microbial complexes at different time points in the 10 subjects receiving SRP and systemically administered metronidazole. % DNA probe counts for each species were determined at each site. The proportions were then averaged across subjects at each time point. Species in the complexes were summed and the proportion that each complex comprised was determined. The area of each pie was adjusted to reflect its size relative to the baseline total count. The boxed area represents the time of antibiotic therapy.

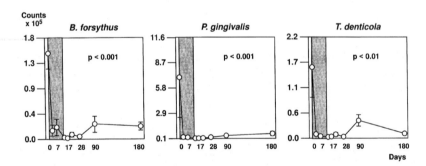

Figure 18 Mean counts (x 10^5, $\pm$ SEM) at all time points of red complex species (*B. forsythus* and *P. gingivalis, T. denticola*) in the 10 subjects who received scaling and root planing in combination with systemically administered metronidazole. Data were averaged within a subject at each time point and then across subjects. The circles represent the mean and the whiskers the standard error of the mean. The shaded area represents the period of metronidazole administration. Significance of differences over time were sought using the Quade test.

line. The most striking effect of this agent was on members of the orange and particularly the red complex. The red complex species were reduced to almost undetectable levels during and immediately after metronidazole administration. Figure 18 highlights the decrease in absolute numbers of these 3 species at each time point. The decrease in red and orange complex species during and immediately after antibiotic therapy was accompanied by an increase in the proportions

274

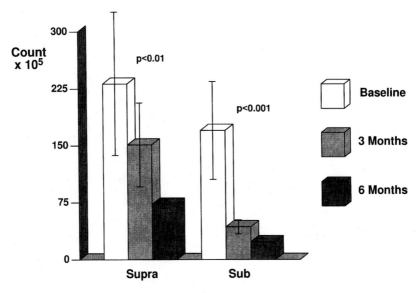

Figure 19 Mean total DNA probe counts (x 10^5, ± SEM) in supra and subgingival plaque samples taken at baseline, 3 and 6 months. Professional supragingival plaque control was performed between baseline and 3 months. Mean counts were computed for a subject for each visit and then values averaged across the 19 subjects at each time point. The whiskers indicate the standard error of the mean. Significance of differences were sought using the Quade test.

of the *Actinomyces* and *Streptococcus* species (Figure 17). Red complex species continued to be reduced at 90 and 180 days although their proportions began to increase during this time period (Figure 18).

Of the 3 therapies examined, metronidazole administration had the greatest effect on the levels and proportions of the subgingival species examined. Indeed, the increase in beneficial species such as members of the genera *Actinomyces* and *Streptococcus*, at least short term, and the significant decrease in periodontal pathogens in the red and orange complexes, produced a subgingival microbiota more similar to that found in periodontal health. Further, the most impressive clinical improvements in terms of reduction of signs of gingival inflammation, pocket depth reduction and gain in attachment level were seen in the metronidazole treated subjects.

Effect of supragingival plaque removal on subgingival plaque composition

Supragingival plaque provides a continuous biofilm structure with subgingival plaque on the same tooth surface. Both are bordered on one side by the tooth. On the other side, supragingival plaque is exposed to saliva, while subgingival plaque is bordered by the gingival sulcus or periodontal pocket wall. Given the continuity between the supra and subgingival biofilms it was of interest to determine what effect removal of the supragingival portion would have on the

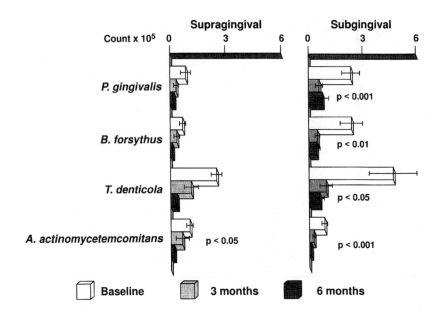

Figure 20 Mean counts (x 10^5, $\pm$ SEM) of selected species in supra and subgingival plaque samples taken at baseline, 3 and 6 months. Professional supragingival plaque control was performed between baseline and 3 months. Mean counts for each species were computed for a subject for each visit and then values averaged across the 19 subjects at each time point. The whiskers indicate the standard error of the mean. Significance of differences were sought using the Quade test and were adjusted for multiple comparisons.

biofilm composition remaining below the gingival margin. In more practical terms, the above studies indicated that therapies could affect the composition of subgingival plaque but that the beneficial changes were not maintained. The question was whether additional procedures that involve the systematic disruption of the supragingival biofilm would further affect the subgingival biofilm. A number of studies have been performed to determine the effect of regular professional cleaning on subgingival plaque composition (Tabita *et al.,* 1981, Smulow *et al.,* 1983, Magnusson *et al.,* 1984, Kho *et al.,* 1985, Muller *et al.,* 1986, Beltrami *et al.,* 1987, Dahlen *et al.,* 1992a, McNabb *et al.,* 1992, Al-Yahfoufi *et al.,* 1995, Hellstrom *et al.,* 1996). While, some studies found no effect, others suggested that regular, meticulous supragingival plaque removal decreased the amount of subgingival plaque and/or the levels of specific subgingival species or morphotypes. Nonetheless, the microbiological assessment in these studies was limited in terms of the number of subjects, samples and species examined. Thus, a more extensive study was initiated to determine the effect of regular professional supragingival plaque removal on the composition of the subgingival microbiota.

Nineteen adult periodontitis subjects who had been previously treated and

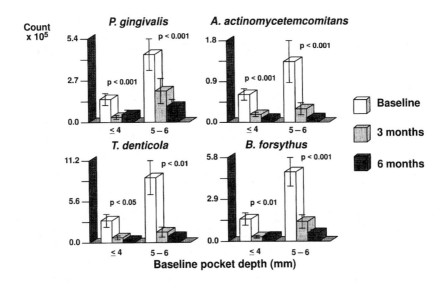

Figure 21 Mean counts (x 10^5, ± SEM) of selected species in subgingival plaque samples taken at baseline, 3 and 6 months from sites with different pocket depth. Professional supragingival plaque control was performed between baseline and 3 months. Sites were subset into those with initial pocket depths of ≤ 4 mm and > 4 mm. Mean counts for each species were computed for each initial pocket depth category for a subject for each visit and then values averaged across the 19 subjects at each time point. The whiskers indicate the standard error of the mean. Significance of differences were sought using the Quade test and adjusted for multiple comparisons.

were in a maintenance program were selected for the study (Haffajee *et al.*, 1999). All subjects were monitored clinically and microbiologically at baseline, 90 and 180 days. Supra and subgingival plaque samples were taken separately from the mesial aspect of each tooth in each subject providing 469 supra and 469 subgingival samples at each time point. The samples were individually analyzed for their content of 40 subgingival species using checkerboard DNA-DNA hybridization. The subjects received SRP at baseline and full mouth professional supragingival plaque removal at weekly intervals for a period of 3 months. Figure 19 presents the mean total DNA probe counts for both supra and subgingival plaques at the 3 time points. Total counts were reduced in both the supra and subgingival plaque samples over time. It was of interest that the counts continued to decline from the 3 to 6 month monitoring period even though the subjects had ceased to receive professional plaque removal 3 months earlier. The effects on individual species was also quite striking. Figure 20 presents mean counts of 4 periodontal pathogens in supra and subgingival plaque samples prior to and at 3 and 6 months post professional cleaning. All 4 species were significantly reduced in the subgingival plaque samples and *A. actinomycetemcomitans* was significantly reduced in the supragingival plaque samples over time. These reductions occurred at both shallow (≤ 4 mm) and

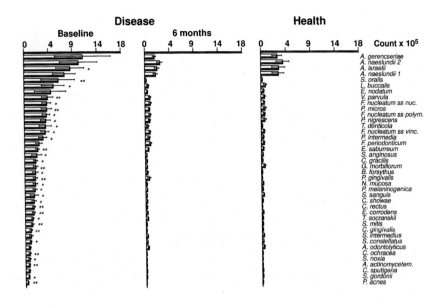

Figure 22 Bar chart of mean counts (x 10⁵, ± SEM) of individual species in subgingival plaque samples taken from 19 periodontitis subjects at baseline and 6 months as well as from 22 periodontally healthy subjects at baseline. The bars represent the mean counts and the whiskers indicate the standard error of the mean. Professional supragingival plaque control was performed between baseline and 3 months in the periodontitis group. Mean counts for each species were computed for a subject for each visit and then values averaged across the subjects at each time point. Significance of differences between baseline and 6 months were sought using the Wilcoxon Signed Ranks test. * p < 0.05, ** p < 0.01, *** p < 0.001 after adjusting for multiple comparisons. Significance of differences between the healthy and 6 month periodontitis samples were sought using the Mann-Whitney test. No significant differences were observed after adjusting for multiple comparisons.

deeper periodontal pockets (5-6 mm) (Figure 21).

It was of interest to compare the microbial profiles in this group of subjects at baseline and at 6 months with that observed in periodontally healthy subjects. Figure 22 presents the mean counts for the 40 test species in subgingival plaque samples in the 19 professionally cleaned subjects and 22 periodontally healthy individuals. While there were multiple significant differences between the baseline and 6 month samples of the professionally cleaned subjects, there were no significant differences in mean counts for any species between the 6 month data and that of the healthy subjects. Similar effects were found in supragingival plaque as illustrated in Figure 23. These data indicated that regular professional supragingival plaque removal can profoundly affect the composition of both supra and subgingival plaque and that these effects are maintained for at least 3 months after cessation of professional cleaning. Further, the microbial profiles established are almost identical to those found in periodontal health.

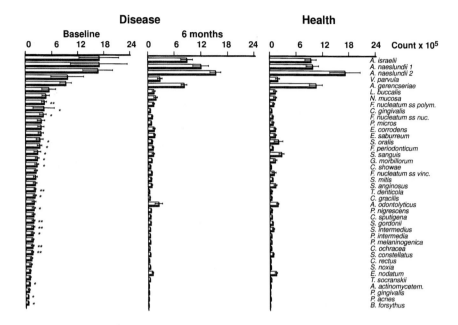

Figure 23 Bar chart of mean counts (x 10⁵, ± SEM) of individual species in supragingival plaque samples taken from 19 periodontitis subjects at baseline and 6 months as well as from 22 periodontally healthy subjects at baseline. The bars represent the mean counts and the whiskers indicate the standard error of the mean. Professional supragingival plaque control was performed between baseline and 3 months in the periodontitis group. Mean counts for each species were computed for a subject for each visit and then values averaged across the subjects at each time point. Significance of differences between baseline and 6 months were sought using the Wilcoxon Signed Ranks test. * p < 0.05, ** p < 0.01, *** p < 0.001 after adjusting for multiple comparisons. Significance of differences between the healthy and 6 month periodontitis samples were sought using the Mann-Whitney test. No significant differences were observed after adjusting for multiple comparisons.

Summary and discussion

The data presented in this manuscript indicated that differences exist in the composition of subgingival plaque samples obtained from periodontally healthy individuals and subjects with adult periodontitis. Indeed, levels of species in the genera *Actinomyces* and *Streptococcus* predominated in the subgingival plaque of healthy individuals. Further, species thought to be important in the etiology of periodontal infections, such as members of the red and orange complexes were at low levels and proportions in the plaque of healthy individuals compared with samples from periodontitis subjects. However, most of the species examined could be found in both health and disease. Indeed, there appeared to be a core group of organisms that constituted the "backbone" of dental plaque in both diseased and healthy subjects. These included members of the genera *Actinomyces*, *Streptococcus*, *Capnocytophaga*, *Fusobacterium*, *Veillonella*, *Campylobacter* and *Prevotella*. Disease seemed to be associated with an increase in proportions and levels of certain species such as *B. forsythus, P. gingivalis* and spirochetes such as *T. denticola.* Part of this increase may have been due to a second "domain" contributed by the lateral wall of the periodontal pocket. Organisms of this group may be able to adhere to or invade epithelial cells of this wall and also derive nutrients from the underlying host tissues. Thus, the change in the local environment might account for the differences observed between health and disease and between deep and shallow periodontal pockets. However, this might not be the entire picture because clinically healthy sites in subjects with periodontitis differed in plaque composition from similar sites in healthy subjects. In addition, differences were seen in the plaque composition of supragingival plaque of healthy and periodontally diseased subjects. Reasons for this difference include a possible overgrowth of pathogenic species from the subgingival area, an overgrowth of existing species in supragingival plaque and a changed local environment brought about by alterations in the periodontal tissues. The importance of detection of anaerobic species in supragingival plaque must be recognized. On a clinical level such findings indicate a potential reservoir for attack on the periodontal tissues or re-colonization after therapy. On a biological level the findings suggest that anaerobic organisms can adhere to supragingival plaque, survive and multiply when the environment has shifted to one compatible with their growth. Although the supragingival area might be considered to be aerobic, especially in those who talk a lot, anaerobic environments must be created in discrete areas.

Clearly, there is a progression from a microbiota compatible with health to one that initiates and maintains periodontal disease. The steps in this progression are not completely understood. However, acquisition of the appropriate periodontal pathogens, individually or in combination, along with a change in the local environment appear to be essential. These changes must be set against a background of an appropriately susceptible host due to either genetic factors or pernicious life style choices. Examination of the natural history of periodontal disease suggests that the cumulative effect of these changes takes place over a long period of time. The reversal of these changes by therapy or preventive procedures may provide some hint as to the nature of the changes that occur and the time scale for their correction. The treatments described in this manuscript indicated that, for the most part, it is not easy to alter the composition of dental plaque. This is fortunate, because in general the species compatible with health are also prominent in disease. There is a subset of species that is associated with disease which should be eliminated or suppressed to host-compatible levels. Certain therapies such as metronidazole appeared to have a rapid and profound effect on some members of the subgingival microbiota. However, even this agent did not eliminate susceptible species and over time there was a slow return towards the pre-therapy climax community. Professional supragingival plaque control also had a profound effect on the subgingival microbiota. This may have been due to an effect on the supra-subgingival biofilm continuum and a beneficial effect on the clinical status of the adjacent tissues. These 2 studies suggest that "active" therapies can modify the subgingival microbiota quite markedly,

280

but that the return to long-term stability, as seen in health, may require change in the local environment and the establishment of a group of species that are compatible with health in that individual.

The data presented in this manuscript have described the composition of plaque in periodontal health and its similarities and differences with plaque samples from adult periodontitis subjects. Further, the relation of clinical features such as pocket depth and gingival inflammation to plaque composition was presented. Of particular interest was the difference in microbial composition between samples from sites with comparable clinical characteristics in periodontally diseased and healthy subjects. Finally, examination of the effects of periodontal therapy on plaque composition revealed that treatment can affect plaque composition but that the effects differed depending on the therapy employed. Ongoing studies in our and other laboratories, employing improved microbiological techniques, provide basic knowledge of plaque composition in health and disease and factors that affect plaque composition. This information can be used to design improved therapies and preventive approaches to control human periodontal infections.

Acknowledgments

This work was supported in part by research grants DE-04881, DE-10977 and DE-12108 from the National Institute of Dental and Craniofacial Research.

References

Ali, R. W., Johannessen, A. C., Dahlén, G., Socransky, S. S. and Skaug, N. 1997. Comparison of the subgingival microbiota of periodontally healthy and diseased adults in Northern Cameroon. *J. Clin. Periodontol.* **24**, 830-835.

Al-Yahfoufi, Z., Mombelli, A., Wicki, A. and Lang, N.P. 1995. The effect of plaque control in subjects with shallow pockets and high prevalence of periodontal pathogens. *J. Clin. Periodontol.* **22**, 78-84.

Ashimoto, A., Chen, C., Bakker, I. and Slots, J. 1996. Polymerase chain reaction detection of 8 putative periodontal pathogens in subgingival plaque of gingivitis and advanced periodontitis patients. *Oral Microbiol. Immunol.* **11**, 266-273.

Asikainen, S., Alaluusua, S. and Saxén, L. 1991. Recovery of *A. actinomycetemcomitans* from teeth, tongue, and saliva. *J. Periodontol.* **62**, 203-206.

Beltrami, M., Bickel, M. and Baehni, P.C. 1987. The effect of supragingival plaque control on the composition of the subgingival microflora in human periodontitis. *J. Clin. Periodontol.* **14**, 161-164.

Christopher, L.A., Griffen, A.L. & Leys, E.J. 1996. Low incidence of colonization of *Porphyromonas gingivalis* among dental students. *J. Dent. Res.* **75**, Special issue, 354, Abstract #2694.

Dahlen, G., Lindhe, J., Sato, K., Hanamura, H. and Okamoto, H. 1992a. The effect of supragingival plaque control on the subgingival microbiota in subjects with periodontal disease. *J. Clin. Periodontol.* **19**, 802-809.

Dahlén, G., Manji, F., Baelum, V. and Fejerskov, O. 1992b. Putative periodontophathogens in "diseased" and "non-diseased" persons exhibiting poor oral hygiene. *J. Clin. Periodontol.* **19**, 35-42.

Dahlén, G., Luan, W-M., Baelum, V., Fejerskov, O. and Chen, X. 1995. Periodontophathogens in elderly Chinese with different periodontal disease experience. *J. Clin. Periodontol.* **22**, 188-200.

Feres, M., Haffajee, A.D., Allard, K., Som, S. and Socransky, S.S. 1999a. Effect of systemically administered metronidazole on subgingival plaque composition. *J. Dent. Res.* **78**, Abstract 3494.

Feres, M., Haffajee, A.D., Goncalves, C., Allard, K.A., Som, S., Smith, C., Goodson, J.M, and Socransky, S.S. 1999b. Systemic doxycycline administration in the treatment of periodontal infections. I. Effect on the subgingival microbiota. *J. Clin. Periodontol.* in press.

Gmur, R., Strub, J.R. and Guggenheim, B. 1989. Prevalence of *Bacteroides forsythus* and *Bacteroides gingivalis* in subgingival plaque of prosthodontically treated patients on short recall. *J. Periodont. Res.* **24**, 113-120.

Gmür, R. and Guggenheim, B. 1994. Interdental supragingival plaque-A natural habitat of *Actinobacillus actinomycetemcomitans, Bacteroides forsythus, Campylobacter rectus* and *Prevotella nigrescens. J. Dent. Res.* **73**, 1421-1428.

Haffajee, A. D., Cugini, M. A., Tanner, A., Pollack, R. P., Smith, C., Kent, Jr. R. L. and Socransky, S. S. 1998. Subgingival microbiota in healthy, well-maintained elder and periodontitis subjects. *J. Clin. Periodontol.* **25**, 346-353.

Haffajee, A.D. and Socransky, S.S. 1994. Microbial etiological agents of destructive periodontal diseases. *Periodontology 2000,* **5,** 78-111.

Haffajee, A.D., Ximenez-Fyvie, L.A., Som, S. and Socransky, S.S. 1999. Effect of supragingival plaque control on supra and subgingival species. *J. Dent. Res.* **78**, Abstract 235.

Hellstrom, M-K., Ramberg, P., Krok, L. and Lindhe, J. 1996. The effect of supragingival plaque control on the subgingival microflora in human periodontitis. *J. Clin. Periodontol.* **23**, 934-940.

Kho, P., Smales, F.C. and Hardie, J.M. 1985. The effect of supragingival plaque control on the subgingival microflora. *J. Clin. Periodontol.* **12,** 676-686.

Lai, C-H., Listgarten, M. A., Shirakawa, M. and Slots, J. 1987. *Bacteroides forsythus* in adult gingivitis and periodontitis. *Oral Microbiol. Immunol.* **2**, 152-157.

Ludwig, J.A. and Reynolds, J.F. 1988. Statistical ecology. A primer on methods and computing. John Wiley & Sons New York. pp 223-256.

Magnusson, I., Lindhe, J., Yoneyama, T. and Liljenberg, B. 1984. Recolonization of a subgingival microbiota following scaling in deep pockets. *J. Clin. Periodontol.* **11,** 193-207.

McNabb, H., Mombelli, A. and Lang, N.P. 1992. Supragingival cleaning 3 times a week. The microbiological effects in moderately deep pockets. *J. Clin. Periodontol.* **19,** 348-356.

Moore, W.E.C and Moore, L.V.H. 1994. The bacteria of periodontal diseases. *Periodontology 2000* **5**, 66-77.

Muller, H-P., Hartmann, J. and Flores-de-Jacoby, L. 1986. Clinical alterations in relation to the morphological composition of the subgingival microflora following scaling and root planing. *J. Clin. Periodontol.* **13,** 825-832.

Riviere, G.R., Smith, K.S., Tzagaroulaki, E., Kay, S.L., Zhu, X., DeRouen, T.A. and Adams, D.F. 1996. Periodontal status and detection frequency of bacteria at sites of periodontal health and gingivitis. *J. Periodontol.* **67,** 109-115.

Socransky, S.S., Haffajee, A.D., Cugini, M.A., Smith, C. and Kent, R.L. Jr. 1998. Microbial complexes in subgingival plaque. *J. Clin. Periodontol.* **25,** 134-144.

Socransky, S.S., Smith, C., Martin, L., Paster, B.J., Dewhirst, F.E. and Levin, A.E. 1994. Checkerboard DNA-DNA hybridization. *Biotechniques,* **17,** 788-792.

Smulow, J., Turesky, S.S. and Hill, R.G. 1983. The effect of supragingival plaque removal on anaerobic bacteria in deep periodontal pockets. *J. Amer. Dent. Assoc.* **107,** 737-742.

Tabita, P.V., Bissada, N.F. and Mayberry, J.E. 1981. Effectiveness of supragingival plaque control on the development of subgingival plaque and gingival inflammation in patients with moderate pocket depth. *J. Periodontol.* **52,** 88-93.

Tanner, A., Kent, R., Maiden, M. F. J. and Taubman, M. A. 1996. Clinical, microbiological and immunological profile of healthy, gingivitis and putative active periodontal subjects. *J. Periodont. Res.* **31**, 195-204.

Tuite-McDonnell, M., Griffen, A.L., Moeschberger, M.L., Dalton, R.E., Fuerst, P.A. and Leys, E.J. 1997. Concordance of *Porphyromonas gingivalis* colonization in families. *J. Clin. Microbiol.* **35**, 455-461.

Ximenez-Fyvie, L.A, Haffajee, A.D. and Socransky, S.S. 1998. Comparison of the microbial composition of supra- and subgingival plaque. *J. Dent. Res.* **77**, Abstract 150.

Ximenez-Fyvie, L.A, Haffajee, A.D., Som, S and Socransky, S.S. 1999. Supra and subgingival plaque composition in health and periodontitis. *J. Dent. Res.* **78**, Abstract 1517.

Zimmer, W., Wilson, M., Marsh, P. D., Newman, N. H. and Bulman, J. 1991. *Porphyromonas gingivalis, Prevotella intermedia* and *Actinobacillus actinomycetemcomitans* in the plaque of children without periodontitis. *Microbial Ecology in Health and Disease* **4**, 329-336.

PLAQUE MICROBIOLOGY OF CROWN CARIES

Jeremy M. Hardie and Robert A. Whiley

*Supragingival dental plaque is a highly complex microbial biofilm which, under appropriate conditions, is associated with the initiation of coronal dental caries. Within this complex microbiota is a wide variety of bacterial species which are capable of producing sufficient amounts of acid from carbohydrates to demineralise tooth enamel, even though the acidogenic bacteria co-exist with other species which may counteract such potentially damaging metabolic activity. Specific attention has been paid to the caries-inducing capabilities of the mutans streptococci, particularly **Streptococcus mutans** and **S. sorbinus** in humans, and, to a lesser extent, the lactobacilli, although other genera and species have been shown to have some cariogenic potential in gnotobiotic animals. Epidemiological studies on caries have often been limited to the consideration of only a small proportion of the total cultivable microflora and have usually been cross-sectional rather than longitudinal in design. Despite such limitations there is a strong association between the presence of mutans streptococci and the initiation of caries, even though lesions sometimes appear to develop without these streptococci being detected. Application of molecular methods allows more detailed analysis of clonal variation amongst mutans streptococci, and this approach has been of particular value in colonisation/ transmission studies. Many investigators have concentrated on the levels of cariogenic bacteria in saliva rather than plaque, but the relationship between salivary and plaque numbers is not usually known. What is clear is that plaque containing high concentrations of mutans streptococci in an individual with frequent intakes of dietary sucrose is more likely to lead to the development of coronal caries than plaque lacking these bacteria. The dynamic equilibrium between the various bacteria which colonise the exposed tooth surface and the many environmental factors which operate at the tooth-plaque interface, is central to the maintenance of health. When this equilibrium is disturbed, dental caries is one of the possible consequences.*

Introduction

The complex microbial biofilm which forms on exposed tooth surfaces in the mouth, known as dental plaque, was first described towards the end of the last century. The vast amount of research carried out on the development, structure, biochemistry, bacteriology and control of dental plaque between then and the late 1960s was conveniently reviewed and summarised in the proceedings of the 1969 symposium in Dundee (McHugh, 1970). More recent work has seen the application of increasingly sophisticated methods of study, but many of the basic concepts described in 1969 - whilst undergoing continued refinement and development - remain pertinent and valid to this day.

Dental plaque which forms on the crowns of the teeth above the gingival margin is referred to as supragingival plaque, as distinct from subgingival plaque which is found below the gingival margin, within the gingival crevice or periodontal pocket. It is supragingival plaque which is associated with coronal or crown caries and is the subject of this brief review.

Caries affecting the crowns of the teeth can occur in pits and fissures, at approximal sites (mesial and distal) between adjacent teeth, and on buccal or lingual smooth surfaces, usually near to the gingival margin. In these situations, the initial lesions occur in enamel but may progress to involve dentine and pulp tissues if allowed to develop unchecked (Silverstone *et al.*, 1981). Studies on the microbiology of crown caries have generally been concerned with initiation of the lesions in enamel rather than their progression through the deeper tissues. However, one of the problems with research in this field is determining the point in time when the disease process actually starts. As pointed out by Fejerskov (1997), diagnosis of caries usually reflects the signs and symptoms of both ongoing and past disease, particularly where cavitation has occurred, so it is important to improve methods for early detection of mineral loss at the tooth surface.

A significant trend in dental plaque research in recent years has been that of a more ecological approach, so that interactions between different microorganisms and their responses to environmental changes can be evaluated. One productive aspect of this approach has been the use of laboratory models, such as the chemostat, in which environmental conditions can be controlled and the effects of varying individual parameters on mixed microbial communities can be monitored (Marsh, 1995; Marsh and Bradshaw, 1997; Bradshaw and Marsh, 1998).

It has long been recognised that dental caries is a multifactorial condition, only produced when there is an appropriate combination of plaque bacteria, dietary sugar and susceptible tooth surfaces in a susceptible individual (Keyes,1968). Of special interest in the context of this review is the question of microbial specificity with respect to the aetiology of dental caries ; in other words, is the condition caused by one or more particular bacterial species or can it be the end result of the metabolic activities of any combination of bacteria on the tooth?

Because the published literature on the microbiology of dental plaque and dental caries is very extensive, reference will, where possible, be made to reviews rather than to an extensive list of original articles. As pointed out recently (Bowen, 1999), dental caries is a 'dietobacterial disease' about which a considerable amount is known, but which continues to be a public health problem in many parts of the world and for which there is still a need for continuing research.

Microbial composition of supragingival plaque
Formation
Much attention was given to the development, biochemistry and structure of dental plaque during the 1969 Dundee Symposium (McHugh, 1970). Studies

Table 1 Genera found in dental plaque.

Gram positive		Gram negative		
cocci	**rods and filaments**	**cocci**	**rods and filaments**	**Spirals**
Abiotrophia	*Actinomyces*	*Branhamella*	*Actinobacillus*	*Treponema*
Enterococcus	*Arachnia*	*Neisseria*	*Campylobacter*	
Peptostreptococcus	*Bifidobacterium*	*Veillonella*	*Capnocytophaga*	
(Staphylococcus)	*Corynebacterium*		*Centipeda*	
Stomatococcus	*Eubacterium*		*Eikenella*	
Streptococcus	*Lactobacillus*		*Fusobacterium*	
	Propionibacterium		*Haemophilus*	
	Rothia		*Leptotrichia*	
			Mitsuokella	
			Prevatella	
			Porphyromonas	
			Selenomonas	
			Simansiella	
			Wolinella	

reported at that time, and much subsequent work, have shown that the formation of plaque on clean tooth surfaces follows a recognizable sequence of events (Addy *et al.*, 1992; Gibbons and van Houte, 1973; Hardie and Bowden, 1976). After rapid initial deposition of organic material derived from saliva (pellicle) on to the exposed enamel surface, early 'pioneer' colonizing bacteria become attached to form the initial layer of plaque (Nyvad and Kilian, 1987). Thereafter, by a combination of growth of these initial colonizers and attachment of other species to them, the plaque increases in both thickness and complexity until it reaches equilibrium (Kolenbrander and London, 1993). By about 10 days of development, supragingival plaque contains a wide range of bacterial species of different morphological forms and physiological properties, including aerobes, facultatives and obligate anaerobes. The whole process of plaque formation and changes with time is a classic example of bacterial succession (Loesche, 1975; Marsh and Martin, 1999).

Range of Genera and Species

The number of cultivable bacterial species which may be present in dental plaque is thought to exceed 300, and these fall into at least 30 different genera (Table 1). In addition, many currently non-cultivable taxa, which can be detected by molecular methods, are also thought to be present (Harper-Owen *et al.*, 1999) .

Considerable progress has been made in understanding the taxonomy of some of these previously poorly characterised genera, notably the genus *Streptococcus*, which is now divided into several 'species groups; as shown in Table 2. Although the changing nomenclature can be confusing, developments with the classification of the streptococci represent a considerable advance on the situation 30 years or so ago (Hardie and Whiley, 1994 ; 1995 ; Whiley and Beighton, 1998). Much of the impetus for this work has come from dental researchers around the world, stimulated by the desire to gain a better understanding of dental caries and other oral diseases. Similarly, in the case of the many Gram-negative species present in subgingival plaque that are associated with periodontal disease, there has been extensive taxonomic revision (Marsh and Martin, 1999; Shah *et al.*, 1993).

Variations in Composition of Plaque

Although established dental plaque from different sites has a number of similarities in microbial composition, both qualitative and quantitative differences can be detected by cultural and immunofluorescence studies (Bowden *et al.*, 1975 ; Babaahmady *et al.*, 1998). Early studies on freshly extracted teeth showed that samples of plaque from three adjacent sites on the same tooth, at or around the contact area, could have considerable quantitative variations at the generic level of identification (Hardie and Bowden, 1974) and such preliminary observations have been extended considerably by Babaahmady *et al.* (1998) in an ecological study of selected cariogenic bacteria in 274 approximal samples from 90 teeth from 60 11-14 year-old children. Here it was observed that mutans streptococci preferentially colonized the site immediately below the contact area, being found in low proportions at the two other sites examined, and established that there were clear variations in the relative frequency of detection of difference cariogenic species (*S. mutans*, *S. sobrinus* and *Lactobacillus* spp.) within approximal plaque. In view of the detectable variations in plaque composition at different sites, as well as at comparable sites from different teeth and from different individuals, it would seem that the exact composition of plaque at any particular site (caries-prone or otherwise) is probably unique (Bowden *et al.*, 1975). However, this does not preclude the possibility that one or a number of common microbial attributes may be necessary in order to initiate dental caries at such sites.

Theories of caries aetiology

Since ancient times, several theories have been advanced in an attempt to explain the aetiology of dental caries (Silverstone *et al.*; 1981). However, since the latter part of the 19th century it has been widely acknowledged that caries results from the demineralisation of dental hard tissues following production of acid by oral bacteria when they ferment dietary carbohydrates (Miller, 1890). Throughout the 20th century there has been increasing understanding of the importance of dental plaque as an essential prerequisite of both dental caries and periodontal diseases, and these almost ubiquitous conditions have come to be regarded, collectively, as 'plaque-related infections' McHugh, 1970; MacFarlane, 1989; Shibley *et al.*, 1995).

There has been some debate in the literature about whether plaque-related conditions, including caries, are caused specifically by individual components of the complex polymicrobial biofilm which makes up dental plaque, or whether

286

plaque as a whole is the culprit, regardless of the particular species present at different sites (Theilade and Theilade, 1976: Theilade, 1986; Loesche, 1976). The apparently conflicting claims of the "Non-Specific Plaque Hypothesis" and the "Specific Plaque Hypothesis" have effectively been reconciled in a series of papers by Marsh in which he has outlined the "Ecological Plaque Hypothesis" (Marsh 1991, 1994). According to this hypothesis, it is suggested that environmental changes (at the tooth surface) trigger shifts in the balance of the resident plaque microflora which may then predispose the local site to disease. An obvious example relevant to the initiation and development of caries would be the increased availability of fermentable carbohydrate, leading to acid production and lowering of the local plaque pH. Such a change in environmental conditions (i.e. low pH) would then favour an ecological shift towards more acid-tolerant species, such as mutans streptococci and lactobacilli. Thus, the dental plaque in a particular situation may contain low numbers of potentially cariogenic bacteria which are weakly competitive and in equilibrium with other components of the tooth surface microflora under normal conditions and of little or no clinical signifance at that time. Under changed environmental conditions, however, such bacteria may proliferate and become dominant within the plaque, increasing their harmful metabolic activities and eventually leading to demineralisation of the tooth. The net outcome of such ecological shifts will depend not only on the relative numbers of different bacteria but also on their metabolic interactions (Liljemark and Bloomquist, 1996; Tanzer, 1989).

A number of local or systemic factors could give rise to such ecological shifts in the plaque microflora, including dietary influences (particularly sugar intake) and alterations to the flow of saliva. The attraction of this ecological explanation of events within dental plaque is that it does appear to encompass known experimental observations from many laboratory and epidemiological studies, and it also allows a theoretical basis on which to design rational approaches to plaque control (Marsh and Bradshaw, 1997). The concept that ecological perturbations affect the stability of the resident microbial community and lead to shifts in their composition is supported by examples from many other ecosystems (Marsh, 1994).

Cariogenicity of plaque bacteria

Although dental caries is known to be multifactorial, it is invariably associated with the presence of dental plaque bacteria at the sites where the initial lesions occur. Evidence for the role of bacteria in the process and for the potential cariogenicity of specific genera and species has been derived from *in vitro* studies, experimental animal studies and epidemiological observations on humans (Silverstone *et al.*, 1981; Loesche, 1976; van Houte, 1994). In order to be involved in the process of caries initiation, the cariogenic species need to be able to establish themselves and survive on the tooth surface as part of the plaque microflora, to produce sufficient acid from carbohydrate fermentation to lower the plaque pH below the threshold for enamel solubility (around pH 5.5), and to withstand the low pH conditions thus produced.

Several genera and species have been judged to have cariogenic potential over the last 100 years or so, but the development of gnotobiotic animal model systems for testing individual strains has produced the most convincing experimental evidence for this pathogenic ability (Orland *et al.*, 1954; Fitzgerald and Keyes, 1960; Tanzer, 1981). The fascinating history of how caries was shown to be a transmissible infectious disease, experimentally satisfying Koch's Postulates, has been reviewed extensively by Tanzer (1995). Most of the bacterial strains tested have been streptococci, particularly mutans streptococci, but some *Lactobacillus* and *Actinomyces* species have also yielded positive results (Table 3) (Edwardsson, 1986).

Although these experiments have shown that the ability to induce dental caries in animals is not confined to a single species, it is also clear that the mutans streptococci are the most aggressively cariogenic bacteria. More strains of these streptococci have caries-producing potential, compared to other species, and the number and extent of the lesions they produce is greater.

Lactobacilli

Lactobacilli, because of their acidogenicity and acid tolerance, have long been regarded as potential aetiological agents in dental caries. Indeed for much of the first half of this century (notwithstanding the first description of *S. mutans* by Clarke in 1924), they were considered to be the prime suspect and enumeration of lactobacilli in saliva was recommended as a useful method of assessing caries susceptibility in humans. *Lactobacillus* counts were also used as an indirect means of monitoring the effect of dietary restriction of carbohydrate intake (Jay, 1947).

Established carious lesions have been found to contain high numbers of lactobacilli in some studies, and several authors have suggested that they may be more significant in the progression, rather than initiation of caries (Bowden, 1991; Hardie, 1992). Studies on the lactobacilli isolated from active dentinal lesions have reported the presence of both homofermentative species, predominantly *Lactobacillus paracasei* and *L. rhamnosus*, and heterofermentative species, such as *L. fermentum* (Botha *et al.*, 1998).

Lactobacilli have not generally been found to be present in high numbers in supragingival plaque, although some studies have suggested a positive correlation between plaque and salivary lactobacilli and caries initiation in humans (van Houte, 1980). However, the value of estimating either lactobacillus or mutans streptococci levels in dental plaque or saliva as a means of predicting caries is open to question (Beighton, 1991; Sullivan *et al.*, 1996).

At present, as pointed out by van Houte (1994), it is difficult to assess the true aetiological significance of lactobacilli in coronal dental caries. The suspicion is that they may be the prime caries initiating bacteria in a relatively small number of lesions, but that they are probably more important in the progression of established lesions (Loesche, 1986; van Houte, 1980; 1994).

Table 2 Current classification of oral streptococci.

Species Group[a]	Species
Salivarius	*S. salivarius*
	S. vestibularis
	(S. thermophilus)[c]
Mutans	*S. mutans*
	S. rattus[b]
	S. sobrinus
	S. cricetus[b]
	S. downei[b]
	S. macacae[b]
	S. ferus[b]
Anginosus ("milleri")	*S. anginosus*
	S. constellatus
	S. intermedius
Mitis	*S. mitis*
	S. oralis
	S. sanguis
	S. gordonii
	S. parasanguis
	S. crista
	(S. pneumoniae)[c]

[a]species groups defined by Kawamura *et al.*, 1995
[b]species not normally found in humans
[c]species not normally found in dental plaque

Mutans Streptococci

Streptococcus mutans was first described by Clarke (1924) but subsequently almost disappeared from sight in the published literature until the mid -1960s. Since then the mutans streptococci have been the subject of an enormous number of papers, covering many aspects of their biological and cariogenic properties, which have been comprehensively reviewed by several authors (Hamada and Slade, 1980; Loesche, 1986; De Soet *et al.*, 1992; Van Houte, 1994).

Taxonomic and serological studies by a number of workers eventually led to the recognition of the mutans streptococci as a species group comprising *S.mutans* and several other clearly distinct species, as listed in Table 2 (Hardie and Whiley, 1994; Hardie and Whiley, 1995; Kawamura *et al.*, 1995; Whiley and Beighton, 1998). Of the seven species included in this group, only *S.mutans* and *S. sobrinus* are regularly isolated from humans and thought to be significant in human caries, although the others can induce caries in experimental animals.

There are two main groups of virulence factors which contribute to the cariogenicity of the mutans streptococci, those related to acid production and others concerned with adherence (Hamada *et al.*, 1984; Van Houte, 1994). The ability to produce acids from carbohydrates is a characteristic of many plaque bacteria, including all species of streptococci, but the mutans streptococci are able both to drop the pH to low levels (e.g. pH 4.5 and below) and to survive under such acid conditions which inhibit many other plaque bacteria. Similarly, the ability to adhere to oral surfaces and to produce extracellular polysaccharides from sucrose is not exclusively confined to the mutans strepto-cocci. There is some evidence that within individual species, such as *S. mutans*, there may be specific clones which have higher levels of virulence than other clones (Bowden, 1997).

Epidemiological studies on the relationship of mutans streptococci to caries have provided strong evidence of an association between the presence of the bacteria and the initiation of coronal caries, although it is difficult to establish an absolutely clear-cut cause and effect relationship from such studies. Even with the relatively uncommon longitudinal studies, which are conceptually preferable to cross-sectional studies, difficulties arise because of the imprecise diagnostic criteria currently available for initial lesions and from the choice of appropriate samples and sampling frequency. Some studies have shown that mutans strepto-cocci are apparently not invariably present at sites where enamel caries develops (Hardie *et al.*, 1972), but the weight of evidence does support a strong degree of association between these streptococci and the sites of many early lesions (Roetgers *et al.* 1995; Sigurjons *et al.*, 1995). It is also interesting to note studies on some populations, such as in rural Sudan, where high levels of mutans streptococci in the mouth are not accompanied by correspondingly high caries prevalence (Carlsson *et al.*, 1987).

Transmission of mutans streptococci to infants in the early years of life appears to be most commonly from the mother, the median age for acquisition being 26 months in one study of 46 mother-child pairs in the USA (Caufield *et al.*, 1993). However, not all children become colonised with mutans streptococci by the age of five years. Recent studies have shown that production of the bacteriocin-like inhibitory substances, known as mutacins, by strains of *S.mutans* may be an important determining factor in transmission from mother to child (Gronroos *et al.*, 1998).

It is apparent that appropriate preventive measures in mothers can markedly influence the establishment of mutans streptococci in their new-born children (Kÿhler *et al.*, 1983) and, also, that early colonisation results in higher preva-lence of caries in four-year-olds (Kÿhler *et al.*, 1988). Thus, current knowledge of transmission of mutans streptococci within family groups underlines the potential value of caries preventive measures and advice in pregnant and nursing mothers.

Other Organisms

As mentioned previously, several other species of streptococci, in addition to mutans streptococci, have been shown to have some cariogenic potential in experimental animal studies (Table 3). The finding of non-mutans, low pH streptococci capable of acid production at low pH in association with some carious lesions in humans indicates that other species are, on occasions, in-volved in the disease process (van Houte, 1994; Sansone *et al.*, 1993; Bowden,

Table 3 Cariogenic bacteria in experimental animals.

Streptococcus		Lactobacillus	Actinomyces
Mutans streptococci	Other streptococci		
S. mutans[1]	"S. faecalis"[3]	L. acidophilus	A. naeslundii
S. sobrinus[1]	"S. milleri"[4]	L. casei[7]	A. viscosus[8]
S. rattus[2]	S. oralis[5]	L. salivarius	A. israelii
S. ferus[2]	S. salivarius	L. fermentum	
S. cricetus[2]	S. sanguis[6]		

[1]species commonly found in humans
[2]species not normally associated with humans
[3]now called Enterococcus faecalis
[4]now called S. enginosus, S. intermedius or S. constellatus
[5]some strains previously called "S. mitior"
[6]may include some strains of S. gordonii
[7]may include some strains now called L. rhamnosus
[8]species now called A. naeslundii genospecies II

1997). Such observations lend further support to the idea that, whilst mutans streptococci are the group most commonly found at the site of early carious lesions, other streptococci should not be discounted as potential aetiological agents on occasions.

The role of other bacterial genera, such as *Actinomyces*, in enamel caries is not clear at present, although they may be significant in root surface lesions (Bowden, 1990; Beighton and Lynch, 1995).

Conclusions

The available evidence relating to the various theories on the aetiology of dental caries and the role of dental plaque would seem to favour the "Ecological Hypothesis". This hypothesis acknowledges the dynamic situation at the tooth surface in which the equilibrium between the the various components of the complex microflora can be disturbed by changes in the local environmental conditions, allowing different species or sub-clones within a species to become dominant at different times. A common precipitating cause of such ecological shifts is the frequent availability of fermentable sugars in the mouth.

It seems probable that several different combinations of bacteria within plaque may be capable of initiating the caries process at susceptible tooth sites. Once the initial lesion has been formed in the enamel, subsequent progression of the disease into the deeper dental tissues is accompanied by successional changes in the microflora present in the resulting cavity.

There are several groups of bacteria in supragingival dental plaque which have the necessary acid-producing capability to initiate caries under appropriate conditions. Of these, the mutans streptococci appear to be the most common and effective cariogenic bacteria from *in vitro*, experimental animal and human studies. However, other streptococci, lactobacilli and, possibly, *Actinomyces* species may play a significant role in some situations. Within individual species, clonal variation may give rise to more or less cariogenic strains.

Although much is known about dental plaque and caries, there is still a need for continuing research in order to determine more accurately what goes on at the dental plaque-tooth enamel interface during the earliest stages of caries initiation. Such information should help to facilitate the development of improved preventive methods in the future.

References

Addy, M., Slayne, M.A. and Wade, W.G. 1992. The formation and control of dental plaque - an overview. *J. Appl. Bacteriol.*, **73**, 269-278.

Babaahmady, K.G., Challacombe, S.J., Marsh, P.D. and Newman, N.H. 1988. Ecological study of *Streptococcus mutans*, *Streptococcus sobrinus* and *Lactobacillus* spp. at sub-sites from approximal dental plaque from children. *Caries Res.*, **32**, 51.58.

Beighton, D. 1991. The value of salivary bacterial counts in the prediction of caries activity. In: Johnson, N.W. (cd.) *Dental Caries. Markers of high and low risk groups and individuals*. pp. 313-326, Cambridge: Cambridge University Press.

Beighton, D. and Lynch, E. 1995. Comparison of selected microflora of plaque and underlying carious dentine associated with primary root caries lesions. *Caries Res.*, **29**, 154-158.

Botha, S.J., Boy, S.C., Botha, F.S. and Senekal, R. 1998. *Lactobacillus* species associated with active caries lesions. *J. Dent. Assoc. South Africa*, 53, 3-6.

Bowden, G.H., Hardie, J.M. and Slack, G.L. 1975. Microbial variations in approximal dental plaque. *Caries Res.*, **9**, 253-277.

Bowden, G.H.W. 1990. Microbiology of root surface caries in humans. *J. Dent. Res.*, **69**, 1205-1210.

Bowden, G.H. 1997. Does assessment of microbial composition of plaque/saliva allow for diagnosis of disease activity of individuals ? *Commun. Dent. Oral Epidemiol.*, **25**, 76-81.

Bowden, G.H.W. 1991. Which bacteria are cariogenic in humans ? In: Johnson, N.W. (ed.), *Risk Markers for Oral Diseases, Volume 1, Dental Caries*. pp. 266-286, Cambridge University Press, Cambridge.

Bowen, W.H. 1999. Wither or whither caries research ? *Caries Res.*, **33**, 1-3.

Bradshaw, D.J. and Marsh, P.D. 1998. Analysis of pH-driven disruption of oral microbial communities *in vitro*. *Caries Res.*, **32**, 456-462.

Carlsson, P, Gandour, I.A., Olsson, B., Rickardsson, B. and Abbas, K. 1987. High prevalence of mutans streptococci in a population with extremely low prevalence of dental caries. *Oral Microbiol. Immunol.* **2**, 121-124.

Caufield, P.W., Cutter, G.R. and Dasanayake, A.P. 1993. Initial acquisition of mutans streptococci by infants: evidence for a discrete window of infectivity. *J. Dent. Res.* **72**, 37-45.

Clarke, J.K. 1924. On the bacterial factor in the aetiology of dental caries. *Brit. J. Exp. Path.* **5**, 141-147.

De Soet, J.J., van Steenbergen, T.J.M. and de Graaff, J. 1992. *Streptococcus sobrinus* : taxonomy, virulence and pathogenicity. *Alpe Adria Microbiol. J.*, **3**, 127-145.

Edwardsson, S. 1986. Microorganisms associated with dental caries. In : Thylstrup, A. and Fejerskov, O. (eds.) *Textbook of Cariology*, pp. 107-130, Munksgaard, Copenhagen.

Fejerskov, O. 1997. Concepts of dental caries and their consequences for understanding the disease. *Commun. Dent. Oral Epidemiol.*, **25**, 5-12.

Fitzgerald, R.J. and Keyes, P.H. 1960. Demonstration of the etiologic role of streptococci in experimental caries in the hamster. *J. Am. Dent Assoc.* **61**, 9-19.

Gibbons, R.J. and van Houte, J. 1973. On the formation of dental plaques. *J.Periodontol.* **44**, 347-360.

Gronroos, L., Saarela, M., Matto, J., Tanner-Salo, U. and Alaluusua, S. 1998. Mutacin production by

Streptococcus mutans may promote transmission from mother to child. *Infection and Immunity,* 66, 2595-2600.

Hamada, S., Koga, T. and Ooshima, T. 1984. Virulence factors of *Streptococcus mutans* and dental caries prevention. *J. Dent. Res.* 63, 407-411.

Hamada, S. and Slade, H.D. 1980. Biology, immunology and cariogenicity of *Streptococcus mutans*. *Microbiol. Revs.*, 44, 331-384.

Hardie, J.M. 1992. Oral Microbiology: current concepts in the microbiology of dental caries and periodontal disease. *Brit. Dent. J.*, 172, 271-278.

Hardie, J.M. and Bowden, G.H. 1974. The normal microbial flora of the mouth. In: Skinner, F.A. and Carr, J.G. (eds.), *The Normal Microbial Flora of Man*, pp. 47-83, Academic Press, London.

Hardie, J.M. and Bowden, G.H. 1976. The microbial flora of dental plaque: bacterial succession and isolation considerations. In: Stiles, H.M., Loesche, W.J. and O'Brien, T.C. (eds.), Microbial Aspects of Dental Caries, Special Supplement, Microbiology Abstracts, 1.
pp. 63-87.

Hardie, J.M., Thomson, P.L., South, R.J., Marsh, P.D., Bowden, G.H., McKee, A.S., Fillery, E.D. and Slack, G.L. 1977. A longitudinal epidemiological study on dental plaque and the development of dental caries – interim results after two years. *J. Dent. Res., Special Issue C*, 56, C90-C98.

Hardie, J.M. and Whiley, R.A. 1994. Recent developments in streptococcal taxonomy: their relation to infection. *Rev. Med. Microbiol.*, 5, 151-162.

Hardie, J.M. and Whiley, R.A. 1995. The genus *Streptococcus*. In: Wood, B.J.B. and Holzapfel, W. H. (eds.) *The Lactic Acid Bacteria, Volume 2. The Genera of Lactic Acid Bacteria*, pp. 55-124, Blackie Academic and Professional, London.

Harper-Owen, R., Dymock, D., Booth, V., Weightman, A.J. and Wade, W.G. 1999. Detection of unculturable bacteria in periodontal health and disease by PCR. *J.Clin.Microbiol.* 37, 1469-1473.

Jay, P. 1947. The reduction of oral lactobacillus counts by the periodic restriction of carbohydrate. Am. J. Orthod. 33, 162-169.

Kawamura, Y., Hou, X., Sultana, F., Miura, H. and Ezaki, T. 1995. Determination of 16S rRNA sequences of *Streptococcus mitis* and *Streptococcus gordonii* and phylogenetic relationships among members of the genus *Streptococcus*. *Int. J. Syst. Bacteriol.* 45, 406-408.

Keyes, P. 1968. Research in dental caries. *J.Am.Dent.Assoc.*, 76, 1357-1373.

Kÿhler, B., Bratthall, D. and Krasse, B. 1983. Preventive measures in mothers influence the establishment of the bacterium *Streptococcus mutans* in their infants. *Arch.Oral Biol.* 28, 225-231.

Kÿhler, B., Andreen, I. and Johnsson, B. 1988. The earlier colonisation of mutans streptococci, the higher the caries prevalence at 4 years of age. *Oral Microbiol. Immunol.* 3, 14-17.

Kolenbrander, P.E. and London, J. 1993. Adhere today , here tomorrow: oral bacterial adherence. *J. Bacteriol.* 175, 3247-3252.

Liljemark, W.F. and Bloomquist, C. 1996. Human oral microbial ecology and dental caries and periodontal diseases. *Crit. Rev. Oral Biol. Med.*, 7, 180-198.

Loesche, W.J. 1975. Bacterial succession in dental plaque: role in dental disease. *Microbiology*, 132-1136.

Loesche, W.J. 1976. Chemotherapy of dental plaque infections. *Oral Sci. Rev.* 9, 63-107.

Loesche, W.J. 1986. Role of *Streptococcus mutans* in human dental decay. *Microbiol. Rev.*, 50, 353-380.

Marsh, P.D. 1994. Microbial ecology of dental plaque and its significance in health and disease. *Adv. Dent. Res.*, 8, 263-271.

Marsh, P.D. 1995. The role of microbiology in models of dental caries. *Adv. Dent. Res.*, 9, 244-254.

Marsh, P.D. and Bradshaw, D.J. 1997. Physiological approaches to the control of oral biofilms. *Adv. Dent. Res.*, 11, 176-185.

Marsh , P.D. and Martin, M.V. 1999. *Oral Microbiology*. 4th Edition. Wright, Oxford.

MacFarlane, T.W. 1989. Plaque-related infections. *J. Med. Microbiol.*, 29, 161-170.

Miller, W.D. 1890. *The microorganisms of the human mouth*. Originally published in Philadelphia by S.S.White Manufacturing Co., reprinted by S.Karger, Basel in 1973.

McHugh, W-D. (ed.). 1970. *Dental Plaque*. E. & S. Livingstone, Edinburgh and London.

Nyvad, B. and Kilian, M. 1987. Microbiology of the early colonization of human enamel and root surfaces in vivo. *Scand. J. Dent. Res.*, **95**, 369-380.

Orland, F.J., Blayney, J.R., Harrison, R.W., Reyniers, J.A., Trexler, P.C., Wagner, M. *et al*. 1954. Use of the germfree animal technic in the study of experimental dental caries. I. Basic observations on rats reared free of all micro-organisms. *J.Dent. Res.* **33**, 147-174.

Roeters, F.J., van der Hoeven, J.S., Burgersdijk, R.C. and Schaeken, M.J. 1995. Lactobacilli, mutans streptococci and dental caries: a longitudinal study in 2-year-old children up to the age of 5 years. *Caries Res.* **29**, 272-279.

Sansone, C., van Houte, J., Joshipura, K., Kent, R. and Margolis, H.C. 1993. The association of mutans streptococci and non-mutans streptococci capable of acidogenesis at a low pH with dental caries on enamel and root surfaces. *J. Dent. Res.* **72**, 508-516.

Shah, H.N., Mayrand, D. and Genco, R.J. (eds.) 1993. *Biology of the species* Porphyromonas gingivalis. CRC Press, Boca Raton, Fla.

Shibly, O., Rifai, S. and Zambon, J.J. 1995. Supragingival dental plaque in the etiology of oral diseases. *Periodontol. 2000.*, **8,** 42-59.

Sigurjons, H., Magnusdottir, M.O. and Holbrook, W.P. 1995. Cariogenic bacteria in a longitudinal study of approximal caries. *Caries Res.* **29**, 42-45.

Silverstone,L.M., Johnson, N.W., Hardie, J.M. and Williams, R.A.D. 1981. *Dental caries, aetiology, pathology and prevention.* Macmillan Press.

Sullivan, Å., Borgström, M.K., Granath, L. and Nilsson, G. 1996. Number of mutans streptococci or lactobacilli in a total dental plaque sample does not explain the variation in caries better than the numbers in stimulated whole saliva. *Commun. Dent. Oral Epidemiol.*, **24,** 159-163.

Tanzer, J.M. (ed.) 1981. *Animal models in cariology.* Information Retrieval Inc., Washington DC.

Tanzer, J.M. 1989. On changing the cariogenic chemistry of dental plaque. *J. Dent. Res.*, **68** (Special Issue), 1576-1587.

Tanzer, J.M. 1995. Dental caries is a transmissible infectious disease : the Keyes and Fitzgerald revolution. *J. Dent. Res.*, **74**, 1536-1542.

Theilade, E. 1986. The non-specific theory in microbial etiology of inflammatory periodontal diseases. *J. Clin. Periodontol.* **13**, 905-911.

Theilade, E. and Theilade, J. 1976. Role of plaque in the etiology of periodontal disease and caries. *Oral Sci. Rev.* **9**, 23-63.

van Houte, J. 1980. Bacterial specificity in the etiology of dental caries. *Internat. Dent. J.*, **30,** 305-326.

van Houte, J. 1994. Role of micro-organisms in caries etiology. *J. Dent. Res.*, **73**, 672-681.

van Houte, J., Lopman J. and Kent, R. 1994. The predominant cultivable flora of sound and carious human root surfaces. *J. Dent. Res.*, **73,** 1727-1734.

van Houte, J., Lopman, J. and Kent, R. 1996. The final pH of bacteria comprising the predominant flora on sound and carious human root and enamel surfaces. *J. Dent. Res.*, **75**, 1008-104.

Whiley, R.A. and Beighton, D. 1998. Current classification of the oral streptococci. *Oral Microbiol. Immunol.*, **13,** 195-216.

PLAQUE MICROBIOLOGY OF ROOT CARIES

David Beighton and Susan R. Brailsford

Root caries describes dental caries which is initiated in the dentine of exposed root surfaces and usually in association with supra-gingival plaque accumulation at the gingival margin. Longitudinal studies have indicated that exposed root surface sites which become carious are more likely to harbour **Streptococcus mutans** *and lactobacilli. The clinical status of individual root lesions, and the management requirement, may be ascertained by determination of the degree of root dentine infection. The microbiology of root caries lesions must be considered in relation to the clinical status of individual lesions. The predominant flora of infected dentine are streptococci, actinomyces and lactobacilli. Yeasts, primarily* **Candida albicans** *and* **Candida glabrata**, *are isolated more frequently from active lesions.* **Actinomyces** *spp. are the largest component of the microflora of infected dentine with* **A. naeslundii, A. gerencseriae** *and* **A. israelii** *being the most frequently isolated species and together forming approximately 40 per cent of the cultivable flora.* **A. naeslundii** *genospecies 2 is more frequently isolated than A. naeslundii genospecies 1. The predominant streptococci are* **S. mutans, S. oralis** *and* **S. parasanguis.** **Veillonella** *spp. are frequently isolated from root caries lesions as from all carious sites. In our experience anaerobic Gram negative rods are only isolated in significant numbers if the lesion is so extensive as to involve the pulp. Examination of the microflora at different depths, into the lesion, indicates that each sample has a different flora suggestive of microbial succession. Analysis of the predominant microflora of root caries lesions indicates that the microflora of each lesion is different supporting the hypothesis that varied microbial populations, have the same metabolic potential, and may be associated with the same clinical presentation. The mechanisms of tissue destruction involve both demineralisation and protein destruction. The role of bacteria in these processes has been demonstrated but recently a role for matrix metalloproteinases in tissue destruction has been proposed. The microflora mediating the destruction of exposed root surfaces requires further study and the mechanisms of tissue destruction remain to be fully elucidated.*

Root caries, particularly its diagnosis, management, treatment and prevention, is of increasing clinical concern for the dental profession in industrialised countries with the ever-increasing number of elderly people. This is especially so since not only is the proportion of these populations aged over 65 years increasing but so is the proportion retaining some or most of their natural teeth. This increase in the number of dentate elderly is also coupled with an expectation amongst many elderly people that they will continue to have good oral health, retain their teeth and that their teeth will continue to function adequately throughout their lives. In England, for the first time since records have been kept over half the population aged over 65 years are dentate (Steel *et al.*, 1998). However, the reality is that the oral health of the elderly is depressingly poor and in particular is the increase in coronal and root caries.

Root caries occurs on the exposed roots of the teeth and although it may occur in adults of any age it is most often diagnosed in the frail, socially disadvantaged and institutionalised elderly (Simons *et al.*, 1999). National surveys have indicated that the prevalence of root caries is around 60-70 per cent. In these surveys it was also found that the majority of the teeth retained by the elderly also exhibit exposed root surfaces so that the number of sites at risk of root caries is very great indeed. The treatment of this disease is very expensive and in the future this will impose an increasing cost burden on the health expenditure of all industrialised countries. Failure to adequately prevent or treat root caries may result in a reduced sense of well being and, due to reduced functionality, malnutrition or dietary deficiencies may be a particularly insidious consequence. Understanding the aetiology and pathology of root caries may enable strategies, simple and complex, to be formulated to reduce the rate of disease initiation and progression leading to an improvement in the quality of life amongst the older members of our communities.

Diagnosis of root caries

The diagnosis of root caries has for many years been subject to much controversy due to the wide range of clinical appearance of root caries lesions. These criteria are usually used to determine the severity of individual lesions in order to decide the most appropriate treatment or management. It is not the purpose of this paper to describe the many diverse studies which have used these varied diagnostic criteria; this has been described in considerable detail by others (Galan *et al.*, 1993). However, it is important to consider certain of these criteria in order that the microbiological studies later to be described may be understood in the light of the clinical manifestation of root lesions. Not all root lesions are the same and not all root lesions require the same treatment or management. The simplest, most useful and probably the most sensible way to regard root lesions, since it reflects their pathological status, is to use the criteria described by Nyvad and Fejerskov 1987. Root lesions were classified as soft, leathery or hard. Soft lesions permit the easy entry of a probe, leathery lesions may also be probed but there is some resistance felt on withdrawal of the probe while hard lesions are as hard as the surrounding, exposed but unaffected root dentine. The colour of the lesion is not at all useful in determining the clinical severity or treatment requirements of a lesion Lynch and Beighton, 1994.

The appropriateness of this simple method may be seen when root lesions classified in this way are examined electron-microscopically and microbiologically. When viewed under the electronmicroscope the root dentine of soft lesions is extensively demineralised, the structure apparent in the uninfected dentine is completely destroyed and bacteria are visualised infiltrating and demineralised organic component of the root (Nyvad and Fejerskov, 1987; Schupbach *et al.*, 1990). The dentine of root caries lesions classified as soft

296

represents dentine, extensively demineralised and infected by bacteria, active caries. Root lesions classified as hard when viewed using an electronmicroscope display a very different appearance (Schupbach *et al.*, 1992). The lesions are fully mineralised but the mineral exhibits an amorphous mineral formation indicative of remineralised tissue and within the remineralised tissue may be seen bacterial cell wall ghosts. Thus the hardness of these lesions is again a reflection of their degree of mineralisation, inactive lesions. Leathery lesions may display a range of microscopic appearances, intermediate between those of the soft and hard lesions (Nyvad and Fejerskov, 1987). They are lesions, which show a transition from the appearance of soft lesions towards the fully remineralised appearance of hard lesions and may display increased amorphous mineralisation, a remineralising surface layer and disrupted and mineralised bacteria within the tissue. Since the category "leathery" represents root lesions in a variety of stages of remineralisation the range of treatments and management regimens available for this type of lesion may also be quite varied.

Implicit in the above is that root lesions are active when soft, inactive when hard and undergoing repair remineralising when leathery. This progression, with no identification of an enamel "white spot" equivalent for a root lesion, arises from a consideration of the anatomical positioning of root caries lesions with respect to the gingival margin. Thus, irrespective of colour, soft lesions were significantly closer to the gingival margin than leathery lesions, which in turn are significantly closer than hard lesions. In a study of 395 root caries lesions the mean distance from the gingival margin to the gingival border of the lesions were approximately 0.4, 2.0 and 2.7 mm for the soft, leathery and hard lesions, respectively (Lynch and Beighton, 1994).

The need for a diagnostic method to identify the "white spot" equivalent of root caries is overwhelming. At the moment the earliest clinical sign of a root lesion is its most clinically severe-the soft root lesion. To properly understand the aetiology of root caries lesions technologies need to be developed which permit the detection of demineralised dentine before the formation of a clinically detectable lesion. Identification of "white spot" equivalents will permit the characterisation of the microflora associated directly with root caries initiation.

Microbial examination of soft, leathery and hard root caries lesions

The electronmicroscopic appearance of lesions classified as soft, leathery or hard should be mirrored in the microbiology of these lesions. In order to examine the dentine associated with root caries lesions it is necessary to remove the overlying dental plaque. The presence of plaque overlying the lesion may significantly modify the number of micro-organisms recovered from a lesion and perhaps the microbial composition of the sample of infected dentine if the plaque is not first removed. Unfortunately, in many earlier microbiological studies of root caries the samples obtained from lesions were collected by simply sampling all the biofilm above the uninfected dentine. This type of sampling protocol has resulted in the accumulation of data which are in part unreliable since it has since been demonstrated that the microbial composition

Table 1 Comparison of the percentage composition of the microflora of overlying plaque and underlying carious dentine (Beighton and Lynch, 1995).

Microorganism	Mean CFU as percentage of total CFU $\pm$S.E.	
	Overlying plaque	**Carious Dentine**
Lactobacilli *	8.0 ± 2.0	15.0 ± 2.0
Mutans streptococci	7.5 ± 2.0	5.0 ± 1.0
Gram-positive pleomorphic rods *	18.0 ± 2.5	35.0 ± 3.0
Streptococci *	22.0 ± 3.0	15.0 ± 2.0

CFU= colony forming units
* Means are significantly different ($p<0.05$)

of the overlying dental plaque is significantly different to that associated with the infected underlying dentine. Thus in a cross-sectional study the composition of the microflora recovered from superficial dental plaque sampled from 81 primary root caries lesions requiring restoration was compared with the microflora of the underlying, infected carious dentine (Beighton and Lynch, 1995). The frequency of recovery of mutans streptococci, streptococci, lactobacilli, gram-positive pleomorphic rods primarily *Actinomyces* spp., and yeasts was not significantly different between the paired samples. However, the proportion of lactobacilli and gram-positive pleomorphic rods was significantly greater in the dentine, while the proportions of streptococci and yeasts did not differ significantly Table 1. Of particular interest was the finding that the proportions of mutans streptococci were similar in both samples. It was apparent that the method of sampling and culturing the microflora of root caries lesions must, therefore, discriminate between the microflora of the superficial supragingival plaque and the microflora associated with destruction of the infected underlying dentine.

The samples taken for microbiological study should be taken under standardised conditions, at least with the overlying dental plaque removed, otherwise the reported composition of the microflora of a lesion will be a reflection of the microflora of both the overlying plaque and the underlying dentine which, in the case of hard lesions, may be reported as infected when in fact they are not. Removal of overlying dental plaque and the subsequent sampling of the dentine produces a better sample but if the purpose of a study is to determine whether there are particular microbiota associated with different parts or levels of the lesion, for example with the advancing front of the lesion, then more precise sampling protocols are essential to permit the precise sampling. Such sampling procedures should enable both the microbiological status of sample sites to be determined and the mineralisation/organic status of the dentine sampled to be ascertained. Such protocols are difficult and time-consuming but potentially offer considerable rewards in permitting a better understanding of the progression of lesions to be determined (Schupbach *et al.*, 1996).

Examination of the microbiota of root caries lesions from which the overlying dental plaque was removed enabled the expected association between the texture of the lesion and the degree of infection of the dentine and between the texture of the lesion and the frequency of isolation of individual taxa and the percentage composition of the flora to be demonstrated (Beighton *et al.*, 1993). The lesions were sampled by passing a sterile dental excavator through the vertical dimension of the lesion and the total number of micro-organisms in the sample and its composition were determined using conventional bacteriological methods.

In a study of 501 lesions in 59 patients it was found that soft lesions yielded significantly more bacteria than leathery lesions which in turn yielded significantly more bacteria than hard lesions. The mean number of bacteria per sample as log10[colony-forming-units per sample] was 6.8, 4.3 and 1.9 for the soft, leathery and hard lesions, respectively. Thus the soft lesions yielded over 100 times more bacteria than the leathery lesions with all lesions prepared and sampled as described. In a similar fashion the numbers of gram-positive pleomorphic rods primarily *Actinomyces* spp., lactobacilli, mutans streptococci and yeasts recovered from lesions exhibiting these different textures were also significantly reduced between soft and hard lesions. Failure to remove the overlying plaque did not permit these clear differences to be detected since the volume/amount of plaque overlying individual lesions, irrespective of its degree of mineralisation, was highly variable. The interpretation of these differences in the recovery of bacteria from lesions of varying texture is greatly simplified in the light of the available electronmicroscopic data described above. In particular, once the plaque is removed from above the hard lesions, which are fully mineralised with only bacteria cell wall ghosts embedded in amorphous crystal, it is to be expected that it is not possible to sample viable bacteria from such lesions. This was found to be the case with only small numbers of bacteria being recovered from hard lesions once the overlying plaque was removed and these small numbers no doubt represented the residual bacteria not successfully removed during the clean-up procedure.

At a slightly subtler level the leathery lesions could be categorised into three types of lesions which required different types of treatment, 1. caries debridement and restoration, 2. caries debridement but no restoration and 3. chemotherapeutic treatment (Beighton *et al.*, 1993). When the microflora of these were considered it was found that the more severe the proposed treatment the greater was the number of bacteria recovered so that the numbers of bacteria and of individual taxa recovered from these three different categories of leathery lesions were significantly different. Such a clinical classification of root carious lesions must therefore use, quite fortuitously, the level of infection of the dentine as a major determination of the required treatment. However, it must be remembered that even soft root caries lesions may be managed without recourse to restorative procedures by use of improved oral hygiene and topical application of fluoride to facilitate the remineralisation of infected dentine (Nyvad and Fejerskov, 1986).

Colonisation of exposed root dentine

The most extensive study of the microflora of exposed root dentine was reported by Nyvad and Kilian (1987) although the colonising flora of only four subjects was investigated. In all, 1742 fresh isolates from amongst the predominant early microflora on human teeth were identified from the surfaces of both enamel and dentine test pieces placed in the oral cavity for 4, 8, 12, and 24 hours during which times oral hygiene was discontinued. Root surfaces were more heavily colonised than were enamel surfaces. However, the composition of the microbiota was the same. Within the first 24 hours streptococci and gram-positive pleomorphic rods dominated the microflora. *S. sanguis* contributed only 6-18% of the early colonisers whereas *S. mitis* and *S. oralis* varied between 24-42% and 1-27%, respectively. The relative proportion of *S. oralis* increased significantly within the observation period while the proportion of *S. salivarius* and arginine-positive *S. mitis* biotype 1 showed a declining tendency. *Actinomyces* spp. adsorbed to the tooth surfaces within the first 4 h but did not increase their relative proportions until after 8-12 h, possibly due to a long doubling time. The time-dependent shifts in the bacterial populations within 24 hours corroborate parallelled ultrastructural findings. While these findings are of great interest it is not the microflora in plaque at this early stage of development which initiates root caries. This occurs in association with voluminous plaque accumulation, which will have remained relatively undisturbed for a long, but unknown, period of time sufficient to permit clinically significant demineralisation of the underlying exposed root dentine.

The changes which occur in the microbial composition during the extended period of plaque accumulation at the dentine/gingival margin interface are not known. To determine the changes in the composition of the plaque microflora and perhaps in the physiological status of species present throughout the accumulation period will require considerable expertise and will be a costly undertaking. However, this is an area of great clinical importance and must become known if a better understanding of the microbial aetiology of root caries is to be gained and if the prevention and management of root caries lesions, based on anti-microbial regimens, are to be appropriately formulated and not empirically applied.

Microflora associated with the initiation of root caries

Few longitudinal studies have been undertaken to investigate the microflora of sound surfaces, which eventually become carious. The most significant study was that of Ellen and colleagues (1985a,b) who followed the microflora of exposed root surfaces for up to 24 months. In that study the bacteria investigated were primarily mutans streptococci, veillonella, lactobacilli and *Actinomyces* spp. *Actinomyces viscosus* [catalase positive] and *Actinomyces naeslundii* [catalase negative]. No significant associations between the root caries and any of these components of the microflora were demonstrated. They were able to demonstrate that root surfaces from which *S.mutans* and lactobacilli were isolated were at greater risk of becoming carious and that individuals harbouring

300

both of these taxa in their plaque were at a higher risk of developing root caries. Although *A.viscosus* was regularly isolated from all exposed root surfaces no differences were detected between the frequency of isolation or numbers of this species from sound or carious root surfaces. Of course the taxonomic status of the genus *Actinomyces* has been revised extensively by Johnson *et al.* (1990) and bacteria classified by Ellen and colleagues as *A.viscosus* would now be classified as *A.naeslundii*.

It is perhaps worthwhile just considering the taxonomic position of these two species which have been for many years associated very closely with root caries and there are numerous studies which have reported on the prevalence and proportion of these two species in human dental plaque. Gerencser and Slack 1976 described four serotypes of *A. naeslundii* I, II, III and IV. Serotype IV as later renamed *Actinomyces* serotype WVA 963 Gerencser, 1979. Firtel and Fillery 1988 investigated the distribution of antigenic determinants between *A. viscosus* and *A. naeslundii* using 18 monoclonal antibodies raised against *A. viscosus* and *A. naeslundii*. The antibodies recognised 11 different antigenic determinants. *A. viscosus* serotype II appeared to lie between *A. viscosus* animal and *A. naeslundii* strains, with the *A. naeslundii* clusters being more similar to *A. viscosus* human than to each other. Fillery *et al.* 1978 studied the A. naeslundii/ A. viscosus group using a collection of serologically well-defined organisms to determine the phenotypic relatedness of these two similar species. *A. viscosus* and *A. naeslundii* strains n=43 were examined using cultural, morphological, biochemical and serological tests in combination with cell wall composition analyses. Unit characters of growth and morphology were found to be irreproducible although colony consistency was not affected by growth conditions. All strains of *A. naeslundii* and *A. viscosus* produced acid from dextrin, galactose, glucose, inulin, maltose, mannose, starch and sucrose, reduced nitrate to nitrite and the urease reaction was variable 67% positive as was acid production from lactose, melezitose, ribose, salicin and sorbitol.

Schofield and Schaal 1981 studied a large collection of 222 type and reference strains from the *Actinomycetaceae* using 124 unit characters. *A. viscosus* and *A. naeslundii* clustered together but within this cluster one large subcluster contained only *A. naeslundii* strains and the *A. viscosus* strains were divided into subgroups relating to serotype I from animals, serotype II strains from humans, and atypical human *A. viscosus* strains. *A. viscosus* serotype I and serotype II isolates were phenotypically different with serotype II fermenting ribose, whereas no animal strains did. The studies of Holmberg and Hallander (1973) clustered *Actinomyces* on the basis of biochemical and physiological tests, they found *A. naeslundii* and *A. viscosus* type strains to be 92.5% similar. *A. viscosus* was considered to be a catalase positive variant of *A. naeslundii*.

In all of the forgoing studies the taxonomic status of the species was determined by chemotaxonomic studies in conjunction with cell wall and serological studies. In no instance was the status of these species established using more appropriate genetic methods. The first report of genetic studies was by Coykendall and Munzenmaier (1979) who used a membrane method of DNA-DNA hybridisation and found that *A. viscosus* serotype I animal strain showed only 53% and 54% homology with *A. viscosus* serotype II human strain and *A. naeslundii* isolates respectively. Stackebrandt and Charfreitag (1990) compared partial sequences of the 16S rRNA gene of *A. viscosus* and *A. naeslundii* genospecies 1 and found homology of only 95.4% indicating that these strains belonged to different species. These observations were confirmed and extended by Johnson *et al.* 1990 who used the S1 nuclease method for DNA-DNA hybridisation again finding low levels of DNA homology 36% between the type strain of *A. viscosus* serotype I and *A. naeslundii*. In this extensive study Johnson et al 1990 proposed that *A. naeslundii* serotypes I II, III and NV together with *A. viscosus* serotype II should be reclassified as *A. naeslundii* genospecies. A genospecies is established when organisms are significantly different at the genetic level but there are no phenotypic tests that can differentiate between the organisms. The genospecies were described as *A. naeslundii* genospecies 1 *A. naeslundii* serotype I and *A. naeslundii* genospecies 2 *A. viscosus* serotype II, *A. naeslundii* serotype III, *A. naeslundii* serotype II and *Actinomyces* serotype NV. *Actinomyces* serotype WVA 963 was found to be more distantly related and it was proposed that it should be termed *Actinomyces* genospecies WVA 963, the former *A. viscosus* serotype I retained the name *A. viscosus* and is now used to describe *A. viscosus* strains isolated from rats.

We now have a considerably greater understanding of the ecology of *A. naeslundii* in relation to human root caries. Brailsford *et al.* (1998) studied the isolation of *A.naeslundii* from sound, exposed root surfaces n = 56 and soft and leathery root carious lesions n = 71. The microbiological samples of supragingival plaque or carious dentine were obtained using a sterile excavator, the samples were disaggregated and cultured on both selective and non-selective media. *A. naeslundii* isolates were identified to the genospecies using specific antisera (Putnins and Bowden, 1993). Genospecies 1 and 2 were isolated from 16 and 48 per cent of sound exposed root surfaces while they were isolated from 16 and 47 per cent of leathery lesions and 4 and 42 per cent of soft lesions, respectively. Genospecies 1 constituted 0.8 per cent, 0.96 and 0.99 per cent of the flora of sound surfaces, leathery lesions and soft lesions, respectively while the respective proportions of genospecies 2 were 9.8, 8.1 and 5.2 per cent. A negative association was found between the presence of *A.naeslundii* and specific acidogenic bacteria. Thus those sound exposed root surfaces from which *A. naeslundii* genospecies 1 and/or 2 were isolated yielded significantly lower numbers of lactobacilli and yeasts than the surfaces from which *A. naeslundii* were not isolated. It was also found in this study that the microflora of soft root carious lesions was comprised of primarily gram-positive pleomorphic rods which formed 70+/-7.8% of the flora. It is therefore apparent that the relative proportion of *A.naeslundii* in active carious lesions is not predominant. Other species of *Actinomyces*, in particular *A.israelii* and *A. gerencseriae*, are predominant Brailsford *et al.*, 1999.

However, these considerations do not alter the overall findings of the longitudinal studies of Ellen (1995a,b). In addition to this extensive longitudinal study there have been many cross-sectional studies which have determined the composition of the microflora of carious lesions, classified using a wide variety of diagnostic criteria, and of sound root surfaces see Bowden, 1990 and these have all tended to show the same associations as were found by Ellen *et al.* (1985a,b) although the consistent finding is that the numbers or proportion of *S.mutans* is greater in carious lesions than on sound surfaces or on hard carious lesions (Keltjens *et al.*, 1987).

Acid production and root surface plaque composition

Despite the finding of significantly raised levels of mutans streptococci in root carious lesions and an increased risk of developing root caries if an exposed root surface harbours mutans streptococci it is not a convincing argument that these bacteria initiate and progress root lesions either on their own or even in collaboration with other bacteria. Mutans streptococci constitute only a small proportion of the flora of the biofilm from any intra-oral site, including infected and demineralising dentine associated with root caries. Root caries like all caries is mediated in great part by the production of acid in restricted defined sites and measurement of the production of acid in biofilms in vivo provides a very accurate indication as to the potential of the plaque at that site to initiate or progress caries. In an excellent study Aamdal-Scheie *et al.* (1996)0 measured the change in pH of plaque on exposed root surfaces, which possessed detectable levels of mutans streptococci or non-detectable levels of mutans streptococci. Consideration of the mean responses from 53 sites harbouring mutans streptococci and the 13 sites not harbouring detectable levels of mutans streptococci found that there was no significant difference between the responses of the two types of biofilms to a one-minute exposure to 10 ml of 10% sucrose solution. In both cases the terminal pH values were approximately 4.7 and these were achieved 5-7 minutes following the rinse. Clearly mutans streptococci are not necessary or essential for the production of acid on exposed root surfaces and neither is the amount of acid or the rate of acid production significantly affected by the presence of mutans streptococci in the plaque biofilm. The question remains, as yet unanswered, what is the role of mutans streptococci in the initiation of dental caries.

Non-specific plaque hypothesis of root caries initiation and progression

The number of studies investigating the associations between root caries activity and the presence of a specific microflora, in particular mutans streptococci and lactobacilli, is quite numerous. These studies have not successfully managed to come near to demonstrating consistently significant relationships between the clinical indices and the composition of the associated microflora/biofilm. It may be of course that there is no single aetiological association but rather the disease in all its clinically defined stages is associated with microflora which exhibit a specific range of physiological characteristics rather than a particular set of specific micro-organisms. That is to say that the presence of any particular species is not essential or even necessary for the initiation or progression of root caries lesions and that the clinical severity of an individual lesion does not prescribe the composition of the infecting microflora.

Root caries lesions are most often initiated at the gingival margin in association with the accumulation of dental plaque at that site. The gingival margin must therefore be regarded as a stagnation site for root caries much as interproximal sites and pits and fissures are for coronal caries. As was discussed above soft lesions are most likely to be found at or close to the gingival margin. It may be that it is the accumulation of dental plaque that is responsible for the initiation of root caries and that the mass of plaque inhibiting acid diffusion from the exposed root surface and the exposure of the underlying demineralised root dentine to the remineralising properties of the saliva mediates caries development with no specific microbial taxa necessary or essential for the disease initiation. The hypothesis would therefore be that the initiation of root caries has a non-specific microbial origin. However it must be that if this hypothesis is to be fully acceptable then the microflora initiating root caries must have particular properties, it must be acidogenic and aciduric. A range of genera including streptococci, Actinomyces, lactobacilli and bifidobacteria also possesses these features.

van Houte and colleagues Sansone *et al.* (1993) have addressed directly the question of the potential role of acidogenic bacteria other than mutans streptococci and lactobacilli and yeasts in the caries process and have also demonstrated that other dental plaque bacteria are heterogeneous with respect to their acidogenicity. That is, not all non-mutans streptococci are equivalent. In these studies is was assumed, quite correctly that acidogenesis at low pH appears to be an important bacterial cariogenic trait but that most information is known of only a few of the acidogenic dental plaque bacteria. Therefore, the 'final' pH in sugar broth was determined for a wide variety of oral bacteria obtained from carious dentine from advanced root lesions n=389 and plaque from sound root surfaces n=358 of root-caries-free subjects. All strains were placed in one of 4 final pH categories, < 4.2, 4.2-4.4, 4.4-4.6, and > or = 4.6. The dentine samples from advanced root lesions contained many strains with a final pH < 4.2 mean percentage of 25.7 and included all strains of Lactobacillus and mutans streptococci, most Bifidobacterium strains and non-mutans streptococci non-MS, and about 20% of the Actinomyces strains Table 2. By contrast, sound root surface plaque samples contained far fewer strains with a final pH < 4.2 mean percentage of 8.4 which were nearly all non-mutans streptococci. The bacteria with a final pH < 4.4 constituted mean percentages of 41.5 and 32.1 for the advanced root lesion samples and sound root surface samples, respectively. They concluded that their findings furthered the concept that increased cariogenic conditions are associated with increased proportions of organisms capable of acidogenesis at a low pH and that this shift involves organisms other than the mutans streptococci and lactobacilli. These observations provided for the first time a strong suggestion that the non-mutans streptococci and *Actinomyces* spp. were heterogeneous with respect to acidogenicity and that there may be a

Table 2 Comparison of the percentage distribution of lactobacilli, mutans streptococci, bifidibacterium and non mutans streptococci, isolated from root caries lesions n=84 and sound tooth surfaces n=223 on the basis of their terminal pH values in 1 percent glucose broth.

| | Terminal pH in 1 percent glucose broth | | | | | |
| | Advanced root caries lesions | | | Sound root surfaces | | |
Organism	<4.2	4.2 -4.4	>4.4	<4.2	4.2 -4.4	>4.4
Lactobacillus	100	0	0	0	0	0
Mutans streptococci	100	0	0	100	0	0
Bifidobacterium	68	11	21	0	0	0
Non mutans streptococci	78	18	4	16	51	33

selection for bacteria able to produce more acid in lesions compared to those bacteria from sound root surfaces. The identity of these bacteria was not precisely ascertained since the methods of microbial identification were not necessarily appropriate.

We have investigated the aciduricity of individual species isolated from root caries lesions and from sound root surfaces in subjects with no root caries. Samples of infected dentine are taken as described above and plaque is removed from exposed roots using excavators, dispersed and the predominant aciduric bacteria re isolated by culturing the samples in media adjusted to pH 4.8 or 5.2. From the sound root surface samples the predominant aciduric bacteria isolated are *S. oralis, S. intermedius* and *S. salivarius* while from soft root caries lesions the predominant bacteria include lactobacilli, *Actinomyces* spp., *S. oralis, S. intermedius* and *S. mutans*. *Actinomyces* capable of growth in media at pH 4.8 are routinely isolated from root caries lesions. It is also of interest that when S.oralis strains in interproximal plaque were isolated at pH 5.2 and pH 7.0 and compared using a genotyping method REP-PCR (Alam *et al.*, 1999), the strains in most subjects represented two distinct populations. This suggests that *S. oralis*, and therefore perhaps other non-mutans streptococci, are also heterogeneous with respect to aciduricity as well as with respect to acidogenicity. The genetic basis for this heterogeneity within the non-mutans streptococci is not known. The finding that *Actinomyces* spp. are capable of growth at low pH and that they are predominate amongst the microflora of carious root dentine is novel and quite unexpected since in in vitro model systems this genus is not reported to persist if the pH becomes acidic, usually below pH 5.5. The genetic basis for the persistence and proliferation of these strains within root carious lesions remains unknown and warrants further study.

The acidogenicity and aciduricity of the microflora, and of individual species, associated with the initiation of root caries has not been reported. Consideration of these properties should form part of any microbiological study of the accumulation of plaque at the gingival margin on exposed root surfaces and of the initiation and progression of root caries. It may be these properties, rather than the presence of any specific flora, which are necessary for root caries initiation and progression.

Nyvad and Kilian (1990) reported a study in which they established an experimental root caries model in humans. The microflora from actively progressing root surface caries lesions, in which mineral loss had been determined by quantitative microradiography was determined. The caries lesions were produced experimentally in root surface specimens from human molars inserted in lower partial dentures carried for 3 months by six elderly individuals. A total of 780 bacterial isolates were identified from 13 plaque samples. The composition of the microflora showed distinct individual differences with the microflora from plaque samples associated with the highest mineral loss the most simple dominated by either *A. viscosus naeslundii* or a combination of mutans streptococci *S. mutans* and *S. sobrinus* and *Lactobacillus* spp. Plaque from root surfaces with less pronounced mineral loss harboured a more complex microflora comprising gram-positive rods, mutans streptococci, *S. mitis* biovar 1, *Veillonella* spp., gram-negative rods and low numbers of lactobacilli. The authors suggested that these findings suggest that certain species or combinations of species are more cariogenic than others are and that dominance of single acidogenic species in particular is conducive to high caries activity. These results were obtained in this model system while in studies of true root lesions the flora appears to be more complex but no clear and unequivocal associations between the presence of individual species and caries activity or severity have been demonstrated.

van Houte *et al.* (1994) determined the predominant cultivable flora of plaque from sound root surfaces in eight subjects without root caries, plaque from incipient root lesions in eight subjects with root caries, and carious material from advanced root lesions in nine other subjects with root caries. In excess of 1100 isolates were identified using standard methods, primarily commercial identification kits and it was found that collectively streptococci, *Actinomyces*, and veillonellae constituted 84.2, 57.8, and 65.7 per cent of the flora of samples taken from sound root surfaces, incipient root lesions and advanced root lesions samples, respectively. Of particular interest is the finding that in many samples the predominant cultivable flora was often dominated by few organisms, the identity of which differed from sample to sample. Further, mutans streptococci and lactobacilli were not always isolated from either the incipient or advanced root lesion as has been discussed above although non-mutans streptococci were isolated from most lesions and *Actinomyces* spp. were always isolated. It was concluded that while the flora associated with different lesions was highly varied the data supported a role for other bacteria, other than mutans streptococci and lactobacilli, in the development and progression of root caries. Somewhat similar findings were reported by Schupbach *et al.* (1995) who studied, in great detail, the plaque microbiota covering sound or carious root surfaces and compared this to the flora covering arrested root caries lesions. Underlining the complexity of the microbial analysis undertaken in this investigation only five extracted teeth were examined in each category. The experimental design of the study allowed the qualitative and quantitative microbial composition of the microbial samples to be related to the degree of integrity of the root surface. In this study the microbiota on all surfaces, regardless of its state of mineralisation, resembled marginal plaque associated with gingivitis. In addition to the gram-positive predominant facultative anaerobic genera *Strepto-coccus, Staphylococcus, Lactobacillus and Actinomyces*, gram-negative anaerobes, predominantly *Bacteroides, Prevotella, Selenomonas, Fusobacte-rium, Leptotrichia, and Capnocytophaga,* showed the highest isolation frequencies. On all surfaces *Actinomyces* spp. predominated, with streptococci and lactobacilli forming a minor part of the microbiota. With respect to the detected proportions of anaerobes, microaerophiles, *Actinomyces naeslundii, Prevotella buccae* and *Selenomonas dianae*, significant differences were observed between the three categories of root surfaces. The authors suggested that the results supported a polymicrobial aetiology for caries initiation on root surfaces, with *A. naeslundii, Capnocytophaga spp.*, and *Prevotella spp.* making specific contributions to the processes of cementum and dentine breakdown. However the evidence that these taxa were capable of, *in vivo*, contributing to the destruction of dentine was only by association.

Similar conclusions were drawn by Aamdal-Scheie *et al.* (1996) who studied the microbial composition of plaque from carious and non-carious root surfaces in 17 elderly Chinese with poor oral hygiene. Plaque samples for microbiological analyses were collected from 2 sound and 2 or 3 carious sites in each subject. The prevalence of *Prevotella intermedia, Prevotella melaninogenica, Fusobacterium nucleatum, Campylobacter rectus, Capnocytophaga* spp., *A. viscosus naeslundii, A. naeslundii, S. sanguis, S. mitis, S. mutans, S. sobrinus, Lactobacillus* spp., and *Candida* spp. was determined. As would be expected, there was no difference in the composition of the plaque microflora on sound and carious root surfaces since the sound surfaces examined were in the same subjects as the carious surfaces, examination of sound surfaces in subjects with no root caries may have enabled differences in composition to be demonstrated. The authors conclude that their results thus do not readily support the traditional concept of caries formation but instead support a polymicrobial aetiology.

We (Brailsford *et al.*, 1999) have recently examined in detail the composition of the flora of active soft root caries lesions with particular emphasis on the gram-positive rods present in the lesions n=9. Many studies have focused on *A. naeslundii* and *A.viscosus* in root caries lesions but few reports have documented other members of the genus *Actinomyces*. The organisms were isolated under both aerobic and anaerobic conditions and identified using biochemical and physiological tests to the species level according to the new taxonomy. Of 654 isolates identified as pleomorphic gram-positive rods by gram staining 607 were identified as belonging to the genus *Actinomyces*, of these 242 were identified as *A. israelii*, 225 as *A. gerencseriae* 109 as *A. naeslundii*, 15 as *A. odontolyticus* and 13 as *A. georgiae*. A significantly greater proportion of *A. gerencseriae* were isolated from the aerobic plates p<0.05 while the proportion of *A. israelii* was significantly p<0.05 greater from anaerobic plates. The role of individual *Actinomyces* spp. in the root caries process remains unclear since

Table 3 Proportion of *Actinomyces* spp. and aciduiric microorganisms isolated aerobically and anaerobically and expressed as a percentage of the anaerobic total colony count

Subject Microorganism	Percentage of total count[a]								
	1	2	3	4	5	6	7	8	9
mutans streptococci	0.06	0.83	ND	ND	1.18	5.23	5.49	ND	ND
lactobacilli	0.03	<0.01	0.33	0.04	2.21	3.84	29.67	11.63	9.99
Candida spp.	<0.01	ND	0.11	<0.01	0.17	0.08	0.11	0.72	0.58
anaerobic *A. israelii*	5.01	ND	44.44	42.14	ND	1.38	6.87	63.30	0.78
aerobic *A. gerencseriae*	35.30	60.61	30.16	35.76	2.15	12.52	12.09	0.80	1.50
aerobic *A. naeslundii*	ND	7.09	ND	0.82	19.29	0.69	6.04	1.83	0.21
anaerobic *A. naeslundii*	0.49	2.41	22.22	ND	33.87	0.08	ND	5.75	ND
anaerobic *A. georgiae*	ND	2.41	ND	ND	ND	ND	ND	ND	ND
anaerobic *A. odontolyticus*	ND	ND	ND	ND	15.48	ND	ND	ND	ND

[a] total count = anaerobic total count-anaerobic *A. gerencseriae* count + *A. gerencseriae* aerobic count
ND = not detected

varied populations of were isolated from individual active root carious lesions Table 3. Again this phenomenon of great diversity in the flora associated with demineralised dentine supports the hypothesis that it is the physiological properties of the plaque and not necessarily the presence of an individual species which determines the pathogenicity of the infecting microflora.

To ascertain the genotypic homogeneity of the actinomyces populations PCR methods were developed which enabled the genotypes of the different actinomyces species to be determined. Individual strains of *A. israelii* n = 56 and *A. gerencseriae* n = 46 were also investigated at the DNA level using Repetitive Extragenic Palindromic polymerase chain reactions REP-PCR to study clonal diversity. The REP-PCRs showed that genotypes of both *A. gerencseriae* and *A. israelii* populations were heterogeneous within individual root caries lesions and that *A. gerencseriae* and *A. israelii* strains from the same lesions did not share the same REP-PCR patterns showing the robustness of the identification scheme. This study demonstrated that the actinomyces populations are heterogeneous at the strain level within a given lesion but whether the genotypes exhibit different level of pathogenicity is not known.

The data collectively provide support for the non-specific plaque hypothesis to explain, at least the progression of the lesions through the dentine. Presumably the demineralisation is mediated by the production of acids by the flora from dietary carbohydrates. However the mechanism by which the organic component of the demineralised dentine is destroyed is not yet clear despite considerable in vitro work which has been undertaken over many years. However recent studies suggest that host-derived matrix-metaloproteinases may be primarily responsible for the destruction of the dentine component and consequently these enzymes may play a significant role in the progression of lesions, and penetration of bacteria, through the dentine.

Mechanisms of destruction of dentine

Over the years many investigators have determined the effects of proteases on the organism components of dentine. To degrade the organic component, principally acid-denatured collagen, the proteases must have the ability to degrade gelatine or collagen. Many bacteria, including *Actinomyces* spp., many species of oral streptococci, lactobacilli and bifidiobacteria, produce proteases detectable using gelatine as the substrate but few produce collagenase activity. These assays may be performed using a variety of in vitro test systems with substrates labelled so that low molecular weight degradation products are detected or by zymograms in which activity of individual proteins are detected on SDS-PAGE gels. However production of an activity in such a system does not necessarily mean that the same activity is produced in vivo, in the demineralised dentine resulting in the loss of organic matrix. van Strijp *et al.* (1994) established an in vivo model which enabled decalcified dentine matrix, placed in the oral cavity for long periods, and the microflora colonising the device to be isolated and their gelatinolytic activity to be demonstrated. The predominant bacteria isolated from these dentine samples were *S. mitis*, *Peptostreptococcus productus*, *Lactobacillus casei*, *Propionibacterium* spp. and *Veillonella parvula*. Individuals varied greatly with respect to the composition of the microflora and although the microflora possessed gelatinolytic activity, although no correlation was found with the severity of dentine matrix degradation and the production of gelatinolytic activity in vitro. Such observations are difficult to tie together. Perhaps the conditions for protease production in vitro were not the same as those encountered in vivo, this is highly likely. Therefore these results are not unexpected. However, it may be that the collagen degradation that occurs in vivo is mediated by non-bacterial protease activity. The most likely candidates for degrading human tissue are the matrix metalloproteinases. Matrix metalloproteinases MMPs are a family of enzymes which, in concert, are capable of degrading collagen. Tjaderhane *et al.* (1998) investigated the hypothesis that human MMPs participated in the degradation of dentine organic matrix after demineralisation. They were extremely successful in their search for the presence of these activities in carious dentine. Western blot analyses using MMP-specific antibodies were used to identify MMPs in human dental caries lesions and 125I-labelled gelatine or type I collagen were used to determine the activity of purified and salivary gelatinolytic MMP-2 and MMP-9 and collagenolytic MMP-8 enzymes with and without acid-activation in pHs relevant to caries. Human MMP-2, MMP-8, and MMP-9 were identified in demineralised dentinal lesions. Incubation of human saliva at low pH 4.5 followed by neutralisation resulted in a four-fold increase in the gelatinolytic activity. No gelatinolytic or collagenolytic activity was observed in bacterial samples although it should be pointed out that using similar species many other investigators have demonstrated protease, including gelatinase, activity, amongst these bacteria. The low pH-activated MMP in saliva degraded demineralised dentine organic matrix in vitro. These are significant observations which may have an important role in our understanding of the pathology of root caries and of especial interest is the observation of the pH-dependent activation mechanism of MMPs, which may have a distinct role in different physiological and pathological conditions, in the carious lesion or on a plaque covered root surface. While it remains difficult to exclude completely the role of bacterial proteases in the destruction of the organic component of demineralised dentine this particular study has demonstrated quite clearly that host MMPs, activated by bacterial acids, have a crucial role in the destruction of dentine during the progression of carious lesions.

Conclusions

This brief summary of the current position regarding microbiological investigations into the microflora involved in the initiation and progression of root caries has highlighted that root caries is associated with plaque accumulation at the gingival margin. The microflora associated with the initiation of demineralisation is not well characterised but it may be that mutans streptococci are not essential for the initiation of disease. Studies of the changes in plaque composition and physiology, especially in relation to acidogenicity and aciduricity, are urgently required. The microflora associated with the progression of disease appears to be primarily associated with gram positive rods, *Actinomyces* spp. and lactobacilli in particular, but the studies reviewed are consistent with the message that the microflora is highly heterogeneous between lesions in different individuals and that no one taxon is essential for root caries progression. Future work should endeavour to localise bacteria within lesions and to determine the physiological properties required for bacterial growth and survival under the adverse conditions of root caries lesions. Understanding the microbial initiation and progression of root caries may enable targeted protocols to be formulated to better prevent the onset and progression of this widespread disease.

References

Aamdal-Scheie, A., Luan, W.M., Dahlen. G. and Fejerskov, O. 1996. Plaque pH and microflora of dental plaque on sound and carious root surfaces. *J Dent Res* **75**, 1901-1908.

Alam, S., Brailsford, S.R., Whiley, R.A. and Beighton D. 1999. PCR-based Methods for Genotyping Viridans Streptococci. *J Clin Microbiol.* **37**, 2772-2776.

Beighton, D. and Lynch, E 1995. Comparison of selected microflora of plaque and underlying carious dentine associated with primary root caries lesions. *Caries Res* **29**, 154-158.

Beighton, D., Lynch, E. and Heath, M.R. 1993. A microbiological study of primary root-caries lesions with different treatment needs. *J Dent Res* **72**, 623-629.

Bowden, G.H.W. 1990. Microbiology of root surface caries in humans. *J Dent Res* **69**, 1205-1210.

Brailsford, S,R,, Lynch, E. and Beighton, D. 1998. The isolation of *Actinomyces naeslundii* from sound root surfaces and root carious lesions. *Caries Res.* **32,** 100-106.

Brailsford, S.R., Leftwich, H., Tregaskis, R. and Beighton, D. 1999. The predominant *Actinomyces* spp. isolated from infected dentine of active root caries lesions. *J Dent Res.* **78**, in press.

Coykendall, A.L. and Munzenmaier, A.J. 1979. Deoxyribonucleic acid hybridization among strains of *Actinomyces viscosus* and *Actinomyces naeslundii. Int J Syst Bacteriol.* **29**, 234-240.

Ellen, R.P., Banting, D.W. and Fillery, E.D. 1985a. *Streptococcus mutans* and Lactobacillus detection in the assessment of dental root surface caries risk. *J Dent Res* **64**, 1245-1249.

Ellen, R.P., Banting, D.W.and Fillery, E, D. 1985b. Longitudinal microbiological investigation of a hospitalised population of older adults with a high root surface caries risk. *J Dent Res* **64**, 1377-1381.

Fillery, E,D., Bowden, G.H. and Hardie, J.M. 1978, A comparison of strains of bacteria designated *Actinomyces viscosus* and *Actinomyces naeslundii. Caries Res.* **12,** 299-312.

Firtel, M. and Fillery, E.D. 1988, Distribution of antigenic determinants between *Actinomyces viscosus* and *Actinomyces naeslundii. J Dent Res.* **67,** 15-20.

Galan. D. and Lynch, E. 1993. Epidemiology of root caries. *Gerodontology* **10,** 59-71

Gerencser, M. A. 1979. The application of fluorescent antibody techniques to the identification of Actinomyces and Arachnia. In Bergan and Norris Editors. Methods in Microbiology. 13, Academic Press. London-New York-San Franscisco. 287-321.

Gerencser, M. A. and Slack, J.M. 1976, Serological identification of Actinomyces using fluorescent antibody techniques. *J Dent Res.* **55A,** A184-A191.

Holmberg, K. and Hallander, H.O. 1973, Numerical taxonomy and laboratory identification of *Bacterionema matruchotii, Rothia denticariosa, Actinomyces naeslundii, Actinomyces viscosus,* and some related bacteria. *J Gen Microbiol.* **76,** 43-63.

Johnson, J.L., Moore, L.V.H., Kaneko, B. and Moore, W.E.C. 1990, *Actinomyces georgiae* sp. nov., *Actinomyces gerencseriae* sp. nov., designation of two genospecies of *Actinomyces naeslundii* and inclusion of *A. naeslundii* serotypes II and III and *Actinomyces viscosus* serotype II in *A. naeslundii* genospecies 2. *Int J System Bacteriol* **40,** 273-286.

Keltjens, H.M.A., Schaeken, M.J.M., van der Hoeven, J.S. and Hendricks, J.C.M. 1987. Microflora of plaque from sound and carious root surfaces. *Caries Res* **21,** 193-199.

Lynch, E. and Beighton, D. 1994. A comparison of primary root caries lesions classified according to colour. *Caries Res* **28,** 233-239.

Nyvad, B. and Fejerskov, O. 1986. Active root surface caries converted into inactive caries as a response to oral hygiene. *Scand J Dent Res* **94,** 281-284

Nyvad, B, Fejerskov, O. 1987. Active and inactive root surface caries-structural entities? In: Thylstrup, A., Leach, S.A. and Qvist, V. editors. Dentine and dentine reactions in the oral cavity. Oxford (United Kingdom:IRL Press) pp165-179.

Nyvad, B. and Kilian, M. 1987. Microbiology of the early colonization of human enamel and root surfaces in vivo. *Scand J Dent Res* **95,** 369-380.

Nyvad, B. and Kilian, M. 1990. Microflora associated with experimental root surfaces caries in humans. *Infect Immun* **58,** 1628-1633.

Putnins, E.E. and Bowden, G.H. 1993, Antigenic relationships among oral *Actinomyces* isolates, *Actinomyces naeslundii* genospecies 1 and 2, *Actinomyces howellii, Actinomyces denticolens* and *Actinomyces slackii. J Dent Res.* **72,** 1374-1385.

Sansone, C., van Houte, J., Joshipura, K., Kent, R. and Margolis, H.C. 1993. The association of mutans streptococci and non-mutans streptococci capable of acidogenesis at a low pH with dental caries on enamel and root surfaces. *J Dent Res* **72,** 508-516.

Schofield, G.M. and Schaal, K.P. 1981, A numerical taxonomic study of members of the *Actinomycetaceae* and related taxa. *J Gen Microbiol.* **127,** 237-259.

Schupbach, P., Lutz, F. and Guggenheim, B. 1992. Human root caries, histopathology of arrested lesions. *Caries Res* **26,** 153-164.

Schupbach, P., Guggenheim, B and Lutz, F. 1990. Human root caries, histopathology of advanced lesions. *Caries Res* **24,** 145-158.

Schüpbach, P., Osterwalder, V. and Guggenheim, B, 1995. Human root caries, microbiota in plaque covering sound, carious and arrested root surfaces. *Caries Res* **29,** 382-395.

Schüpbach, P., Osterwalder, V. and Guggenheim, B. 1996. Human root caries, microbiota of a limited number of root caries lesions. *Caries Res* **30,** 52-64.

Simons, D., Kidd, E.A.M. and Beighton, D. 1999. Oral health of elderly occupants in residential homes. *Lancet* **353,** 1761.

Stackebrandt, E. and Charfreitag, O. 1990, Partial 16S rRNA primary structure of five *Actinomyces* species, phylogenetic implications and development of an *Actinomyces israelii*-specific oligonucleotide probe. *J Gen Microbiol.* **136,** 37-43.

Steele, J.G., Walls, A.W., Ayatollahi, S.M. and Murray, J.J. 1996. Major clinical findings from a dental survey of elderly people in three different English communities. *Br Dent J* **180,** 17-23.

Tjaderhane, L., Larjava, H., Sorsa, T., Uitto, V.J., Larmas, M. and Salo, T. 1998. The activation and function of host matrix metalloproteinases in dentin matrix breakdown in caries lesions. *J Dent Res* **77,** 1622-1629.

311

van Houte, J., Lopman, J. and Kent, R. 1994. The predominant cultivable flora of sound and carious human root surfaces. *J Dent Res* **73,** 1727-1734.

van Strijp, A.J., van Steenbergen, T.J., de Graaff. J. and ten Cate, J.M. 1994. Bacterial colonization and degradation of demineralized dentin matrix in situ. *Caries Res* **28,** 21-27.

UNCULTURABLE BACTERIA IN ORAL BIOFILMS

William Wade

*Artificial culture media, developed at the end of the last century, have been remarkably successful in supporting the growth **in vitro** of a wide range of pathogens of man. Given this success, it is easy to forget that 98% of bacteria on the earth as a whole, and around 50% in the mouth, cannot be cultured. On numerical grounds alone, it is likely that as yet uncharacterised bacteria play an active role in oral infections. Recently developed molecular methods have made it possible to characterise the bacterial communities present in oral biofilms in their entirety. In studies of the microflora associated with oral infections, biomass was collected from periodontal, endodontic and dentoalveolar infections. Samples were cultured using non-selective media and DNA was extracted both from the isolates and the original samples. 16S rRNA genes were amplified by PCR, cloned from the direct amplification, and partially sequenced. Sequences from the isolates and the clones were then compared. In this way, a number of novel lines of descent (phylotypes) have been identified. Interestingly, these are predominantly found in two divisions of the phylogenetic tree: the Cytophagales and the Low G+C Gram Positive. DNA probes have been prepared to selected phylotypes and significant associations with disease have been found. For example, phylotype PUS9.170 has been detected in advanced periodontitis lesions but not from healthy sites. Molecular analysis allows culture-independent characterisation of the complex microflora found in oral biofilms. Novel as yet uncultured organisms have been discovered which may be of value as disease markers.*

Introduction

Frau Hesse was very good at making jam. One day, her husband returned from the lab again frustrated that the gelatin that he was using to solidify his bacterial plate cultures had been dissolved by the organisms themselves. His wife suggested that he try agar-agar, an extract of Japanese seaweed, which possessed some unusual properties. She had noticed that although it had to be boiled before it melted, on cooling it remained liquid to around 45°C. Herr Hesse was of course one of the assistants of Robert Koch and the adoption of agar for the solidification of bacterial cultures revolutionised the new scientific discipline of bacteriology (Foster, 1970; Collard, 1976). In the golden age that ensued, in the last quarter of the last century, the ability to purify bacterial cultures by streaking them on agar plates led to the identification of the majority of the bacterial pathogens of man. Pure cultures also allowed the preparation of vaccines for use in the prevention of disease.

The nutrients included in early culture media, and indeed still used today, were principally enzymatic digests of animal tissues often enriched with blood or serum. It is remarkable, and perhaps fortuitous, that so many important organisms could be grown in what were quite artificial conditions. It is perhaps this good fortune that led microbiologists to be somewhat complacent and even conclude that if an organism could not be grown it was not important. However, from the earliest days it was recognised that some bacteria associated with disease could not be cultured using the agar plate method. Perhaps the most important of these is *Treponema pallidum*, the cause of syphilis. However, the distinctive spiral shape of this organism allowed it to be easily recognised by microscopic methods.

In fact, if we look at the microflora of the earth as a whole, culturability is very much the exception. It is estimated that less than 2% of the bacteria on earth can be cultured using artificial media. In the human mouth, we can do rather better and that approximately 50% of the human oral flora is culturable (Wilson *et al.*, 1997). Even so, this means that on numerical grounds alone, it is likely that unculturable, and therefore as yet uncharacterised organisms, play a role in oral disease processes.

Molecular Phylogeny

If an organism cannot be cultured then obviously its biological properties cannot be determined. Therefore, methods for the study of unculturable bacteria have long been sought. The key to the development of techniques for the investigation of unculturable organisms came from the realisation that the sequence information contained in biological macromolecules could be deciphered and would include regions specific to the whole organism itself. This was first suggested by Zuckerandel and Pauling (1965) who realised that sequence data could be used to elucidate evolutionary relationships and that differences in sequence in genes of common ancestry would reflect the evolutionary history of the parent organisms.

In order to compare organisms across divergent lineages it is obviously important that the genes used for these studies are widely distributed. The most appropriate are therefore housekeeping genes which encode for fundamentally important functional molecules. Genes encoding proteins essential for function evolve slowly because mutations which interfere with function are lethal. The most widely used gene to date has been that encoding the small sub-unit ribosomal RNA gene. In prokaryotes. this is the 16S rRNA gene which, at around 1500 bases in length, is an ideal size for molecular evolution studies because it is both long enough to provide useful discriminatory information and also short enough for rapid sequencing. Within the gene itself some stretches of sequence that are important for function are highly conserved, being identical in the most primitive of bacteria and man (Olsen and Woese, 1993). Other regions are more variable and reflect evolutionary divergence with "signatures" left behind at evolutionary branch points. The conserved regions are extremely useful for the design of PCR primers as will be discussed later, while the variable regions contain the information useful for strain discrimination. It was in environmental studies that 16S rRNA was first used as a tool for dissecting complex bacterial communities and which gave rise to the sub-speciality of molecular microbial ecology (Woese, 1987).

314

Environmental molecular microbial ecology

Ward *et al.* (1990) isolated 16S rRNA from the cyanobacterial mat at Octopus Spring. Using this as a template, complementary cDNA was synthesised and recombinant libraries constructed by cloning. Sequencing of the cloned 16S rcDNA revealed 8 distinct sequence types, none of which were related to 16S rRNA sequences of any organism isolated from the mat or any other similar habitat. Giovannoni *et al.* (1990) amplified and cloned the gene encoding 16S rRNA directly from bacterioplankton collected from the Sargasso Sea. Twelve of the cloned genes were selected at random and sequenced and found to constitute two novel groups, one related to the cyanobacteria and the other two the α-proteobacteria. These studies illustrated the tremendous potential for molecular ecology and the methods described Giovannoni *et al.* (1990) have since been widely adopted.

The primary amplification step is clearly crucial since the specificity of the primers used will determine the organisms whose 16S rRNA genes are amplified. Lane (1991) described a selection of primers of varying specificities which proved extremely useful and have been widely adopted. For the bacterial domain, 27F and either 1492R or 1525R (*E. coli* base numbering) are widely used. However, 16S rRNA genes from not all organisms are amplified by these primers and other universal primer sets have been described, such as 63F and 1386R (Marchesi *et al.,* 1998).

Although, as described above, the methods of molecular ecology were developed to study the environment, there were immediate applications to medical microbiology. For example, Whipple's Disease, a chronic systemic infection causing mal-absorption, sometimes complicated by arthritis, fever and CNS involvement, had been recognised for around 100 years and known to be associated with a gram positive bacillus which could not be cultured. By direct application of 16S rRNA from biopsy material this organism, now named *Tropheryma whippelii*, has been identified as belonging to a distinct genus among the actinomycetes (Relman *et al.*, 1992).

Oral biofilms

The mouth harbours an extraordinary number and diversity of bacteria. Each ml of saliva contains approximately 100 million organisms and over 350 different bacterial species have been isolated. All of the surfaces of the mouth are covered in bacteria from the soft shedding tissues of the buccal mucosa to the hard non-shedding surfaces of the teeth. The biofilms are complex, harbouring a wide variety of organisms, including both obligate aerobes and facultative and obligate anaerobes. The microflora associated with disease are also complex, with mono-infections rare. In chronic periodontitis, the periodontal pocket is colonised with an extremely complex flora consisting predominantly of anaerobic, asaccharolytic species. Moore *et al.* (1982, 1983, 1985, 1987) have comprehensively described the culturable flora associated with the different periodontal diseases. However, in recent years there has been considerable focus on a restricted number of species such as *Porphyromonas gingivalis, Prevotella*

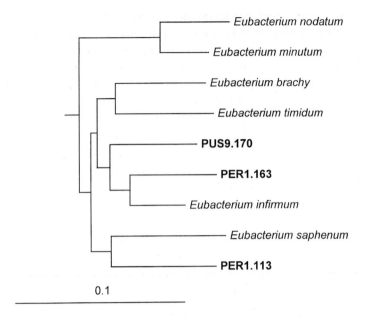

Figure 1 Dendrogram showing phylogenetic placement of novel sequences representing unculturable phylotypes isolated from dentoalveolar abscesses (PUS prefix) and periodontitis (PER prefix) within the Low G+C Gram Positive Division.

intermedia and others, because of studies linking these taxa with progressive disease (Sockransky *et al.*, 1998). Although these organisms are undoubtedly useful as markers of disease activity and may play a role in aetiology, it is unfortunate that the diversity of the sub-gingival microflora has largely remained unexplored.

In contrast to the complexity of the periodontal flora, acute infections such as dento-alveolar abscesses are associated with a more restricted microflora. In cultural studies, approximately three species were associated with each abscess (Lewis *et al.,* 1986). For this reason, dentoalveolar abscesses were chosen for molecular analysis because the restricted flora would make the detection of unculturable species present in the lesions more easy.

Molecular Analysis of Dentoalveolar Abscesses

The aim of this study (Dymock *et al.*, 1996; Wade *et al.*, 1997) was to compare cultural and molecular analyses of the microflora associated with dentoalveolar abscesses. Samples of pus were obtained from acute abscesses by means of a needle and syringe. DNA was extracted from the whole sample and the 16S rRNA genes amplified. These were then singularised by cloning, re-amplified and digested with restriction endonucleases to give a RFLP profile. These profiles were then compared with similar profiles obtained from isolates

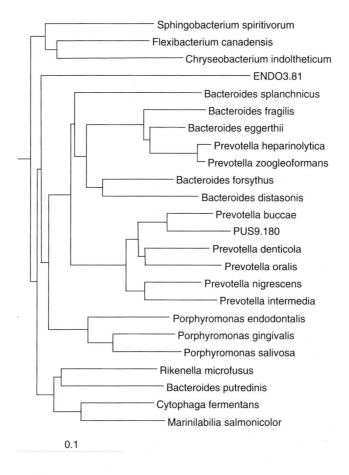

Figure 2 Dendrogram showing phylogenetic placement of novel sequences representing unculturable phylotypes isolated from dentoalveolar abscesses (PUS prefix) and endodontic infections (ENDO prefix) within the Cytophagales Division.

cultured from the sample. In this way cloned genes isolated from organisms not represented in the culturable portion were identified. These genes were fully sequenced and subjected to phylogenetic analysis. In every sample studied a major component of the abscess microflora was a previously uncharacterised organism and a novel line of descent. Novel taxa identified in this way are termed phylotypes and examples detected with the Cytophagales and low G+C Gram Positive Divisions are shown in Figures 1 and 2. In addition, a common finding was that the numbers of some culturable and well-characterised organisms were consistently under-estimated by culture. These included *Porphyromonas endodontalis* and *Fusobacterium nucleatum*. It is likely that these species include unculturable biotypes.

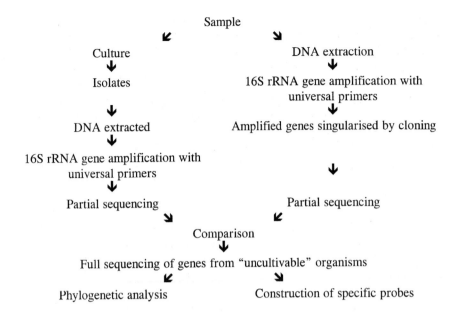

Figure 3 Outline of methodology for detection of unculturable organisms.

In a similar way the flora associated with endodontic infections has been studied. A modification of the method outlined above has been to perform partial sequencing on all of the cloned genes in the library. This is now possible with the advent of rapid-throughput automated DNA sequencers and overcomes the limitations of RFLP profiling. Sequences representing unculturable lineages from endodontic infections have been detected (Figure 2). A general overview of the method is shown in Figure 3.

Molecular Analysis of Specific Oral Microbial Sub-populations

The approach outlined in Figure 3 uses universal primers to attempt to identify the predominant organisms in a sample. Given the enormous complexity of the oral flora, an alternative approach would be to focus in on particular groups of organisms suspected to be important in oral disease. Spirochaetes have been long associated with periodontitis (Listgarten *et al.*, 1978) but because the majority of species cannot be cultured, which spirochaete taxa are important in disease is unknown. This makes these organisms prime candidates for molecular analysis.

Choi *et al.* (1994) used a *Treponema*-specific oligonucleotide probe to screen a 16S rRNA gene library generated from a periodontal pocket with universal PCR primers. By this process they identified 81 spirochaetal clones and by sequencing found 23 different taxa to be present. This level of diversity from a single sample suggests that there is enormous diversity in oral spirochaete populations. Some spirochaetes have been particularly associated with active disease and have thus been named the pathogen-related oral spirochaetes (PROS, Riviere *et al.*,1991). This group is in fact a heterogeneous group of organisms (Choi *et al.*, 1996) and Moter *et al.* (1998) have shown that among the PROS the only culturable species is *Treponema vincentii*. Furthermore this species was found to make up only 9% of PROS with the remaining organisms being unculturable. Clearly, further work is required to characterise the spirochaete populations associated with oral health and disease. Molecular methodology provides the tools to do this.

Another important group of organisms in oral infections are the oral asaccharolytic Eubacterium species. These are present in large number in periodontitis (Moore *et al.*, 1982; 1983, Wade, 1997), but are rarely found in gingival health. However, they are difficult organisms to cultivate being highly sensitive to oxygen and also difficult to identify because of their general un-reactivity in biochemical tests. The indifferent growth of culturable members of the group suggests the presence of a substantial unculturable population. A reverse primer specific for the oral asaccharolytic Eubacterium was therefore designed and synthesised and used in conjunction with the universal forward primer 27F to amplify fragments of 16S rRNA genes from a deep pocket in a patient with chronic periodontitis. From this single sample, four Eubacterium taxa were detected two of which corresponded to uncharacterised, presumed unculturable, phylotypes (Figure 1, Spratt *et al.*, 1999). As with the spirochaetes, there is likely to be considerable diversity within the as yet uncultured organisms within this group.

DNA Probes for Detection and Visualisation of Unculturable Bacteria In Oral Biofilms

Once an unculturable phylotype has been identified, the sequence data can be used to design DNA probes to enable its detection in clinical samples and thereby assess its numerical importance in disease. DNA probes specific for novel phylotypes, PUS3.42, PUS9.170 and PUS 9.180, identified in dentoalveolar abscesses were constructed and validate. These were then used to determine the prevalence of the phylotypes in samples collected from periodon-tal health and disease (Harper-Owen *et al.*, 1999). Two specific reverse primers were devised for each phylotype and these were used in duplex PCR reactions with universal forward and reverse primers. All three phylotypes were detected in periodontal samples and PUS9.170, related to oral asaccharolytic *Eubacterium* was significantly associated with disease. This study demonstrates the possibility of using unculturable, and therefore uncharacterised, organisms as markers of disease.

The molecular methods described thus far yield a sequence as the end-result. PCR reactions are easily contaminated and it is important to prove that a novel sequence identified in a sample is genuine. Confirmation of the presence of unculturable bacteria in biofilms can be achieved via their visualisation. The sequence data can be used to design specific DNA probes which can then be labelled with a fluorescent chromophore. Such probes can then be used in conjunction with in-situ hybridisation protocols (Amann, 1995). Smears of biofilms prepared on slides can be viewed under conventional UV microscopes. Alternatively confocal microscopy can be used to determine spatial relationships of organisms contained within the biofilm in-situ.

Reasons for microbial unculturability

Molecular methods are now available which allow the characterisation of the unculturable portion of bacterial communities. But why are so many bacteria unculturable? The failure to grow an organism on artificial culture media obviously means that the correct environment for growth has not been provided. There are a number of possible reasons for this. Artificial culture media may lack the nutrients required by the organism or incubation atmosphere or temperature may be sub-optimal. Alternatively, media may contain substances toxic for growth or other bacteria in the sample may produce inhibitory substances. There is evidence that each of these possibilities apply for certain species/medium combinations.

An alternative reason for unculturability relates to the evolution of the oral flora as a biofilm over millions of years. Because bacteria *in vivo* are always in close contact with other species, should an individual cell acquire a mutation in an essential synthetic pathway, it may be able to obtain a pre-formed metabolite further down the pathway from the mutation from another organism in the biofilm. An example of this is *Bacteroides forsythus* which is unable to synthesise N-acetyl muramic acid (NAM), an essential component of cell wall peptidoglycan (Wyss, 1989). *B. forsythus* grows extremely poorly in pure culture but growth can be markedly stimulated either by addition of NAM to the medium or by co-culture with another organism.

In order to increase the recovery of isolates from clinical samples, it is common practice to streak a feeder organism, such as *S. aureus,* across the streaks of subcultured organisms from the primary plate. The growth of approximately 10-20% of isolates from oral infections can be stimulated by the feeder organism. These interactions have been presumed to be nutritional. However, Mukamolova *et al.* (1998) have shown that growth promoting substances produced by bacteria, termed bacterial cytokines, can be proteins which only need to be present in picomolar amounts. It may be that such bacterial cytokines operate in oral biofilms and indeed may be signals responding to environmental pressures on the biofilm. It may be that by separating bacteria *in vitro* we are depriving them of the cytokine networks which they use *in vivo* to regulate the growth of the whole community.

Viable but non-culturable

There has been considerable controversy over the concept that certain organisms may, under certain conditions, go into a dormant state, whereby they may not be recoverable *in vitro,* but remaining infectious *in vivo* (Huq and Colwell,

1996). This is of particular concern to the food industry, where pathogens such as *Campylobacter* and *Salmonella* may be undetectable by conventional culture methods, but may be present in infectious doses within food for human consumption. This phenomenon, although it may exist among organisms present in the mouth, is not thought to be responsible for the principal groups of unculturable bacteria found in oral biofilms. Although, as mentioned previously, it is thought that some organisms, although detectable, remain largely unculturable such as *Porphyromonas endodontalis*, most of the unculturable organisms detected to date have represented novel lineages.

Conclusions

There is now no doubt that uncultivable, or perhaps better-termed not-yet-cultivable, organisms are commonly found in oral biofilms in health and disease. We clearly need to understand better whether their lack of culturability is nutritional or results from interruption of a communications network. The molecular methods described here will allow a far better understanding of the composition of oral biofilms. The use of oligonucleotide probes in conjunction with flow cytometers and cell sorters should allow physical isolation of unculturable organisms. This in turn will permit molecular dissection of functional and pathogenic aspects of these organisms. We are entering a new and exciting era for microbial ecology.

Acknowledgements

Dr A.J. Weightman has been a long-standing collaborator in studies in this area. Dr M.J. Wilson, Dr D. Dymock, Dr D.A. Spratt, Dr R. Harper-Owen and Dr M. Munson are thanked for their contributions to the work described in this chapter.

References

Amann, R.I., Ludwig, W. and Schliefer, K-H. 1995. Phylogenetic identification and in-situ detection of individual microbial cells without cultivation. *Microbiol. Rev.* **59**, 143-169.

Choi, B.K., Paster, B.J., Dewhirst, F.E. and Gobel, U.B. 1994. Diversity of cultivable and uncultivable oral spirochaetes from a patient with severe destructive periodontitis. *Infect. Immun.* **62**, 1889-1895.

Choi B.K., Wyss C. and Gobel U.B. 1996. Phylogenetic analysis of pathogen-related oral spirochaetes (PROS). *J. Clin. Microbiol.* **34**, 1922-1925.

Collard, P. 1976. *The Development of Microbiology.* Cambridge University Press, Cambridge.

Dymock, D., Weightman, A.J., Scully, C., Wade, W.G. 1996. Molecular analysis of microflora associated with dentoalveolar abscess. *Journal of Clinical Microbiology* **34**: 537-542.

Foster, W.D. 1970. *A History of Medical Bacteriology and Immunology.* William Heinemann, London.

Giovannoni, S.J., Britschgi, T.B., Moyer, C.L. and Field, G. 1990. Genetic diversity in Sargasso Sea bacterioplankton. *Nature* **345**, 60-62.

Harper-Owen, R., Dymock, D., Booth, V., Weightman, A.J. and Wade, W.G. 1999. Detection of unculturable bacteria in periodontal health and disease by PCR. *J. Clin. Microbiol.* **37**, 1469-1473.

Huq, A. and Colwell, R.R. 1996. A microbiological paradox: Viable but nonculturable bacteria with special reference to *Vibrio cholerae. J. Food Protect.* **59**, 96-101.

Lane, D. J. 1991. 16S/23S rRNA sequencing, p. 249-276. In: Stackebrandt, E. and Goodfellow, M.

(ed.), *Nucleic Acid Techniques in Bacterial Systematics*, pp. 148-163, Wiley and Sons Ltd, Chichester, UK.

Lewis, M.A.O., MacFarlane, T.W. and McGowan, D.A. 1986. Quantitative bacteriology of acute dentoalveolar abscesses. *J. Med. Microbiol.* 21, 101-104.

Listgarten, M.A. and Hellden, L. 1978. Relative distribution of bacteria at clinically healthy and periodontally diseased sites in humans. *J. Clin. Periodontol.* 5, 115-132.

Marchesi, J.R., Sato, T., Weightman, A.J., Martin, T.A., Fry, J.C., Hiom, S.J. and Wade W.G. 1998. Design and evaluation of useful bacterium-specific PCR primers that amplify genes coding for bacterial 16S rRNA genes. *Appl. Env. Microbiol.* 64, 795-799.

Moore, W.E.C., Holdeman, L.V., Cato, E.P., Smibert, R.M., Burmeister, J.A., Palcanis, K.G. and Ranney, R.R. 1985. Comparative bacteriology of juvenile periodontitis. *Infect. Immun.* 48, 507-519.

Moore, W.E.C., Holdeman, L.V., Cato, E.P., Smibert, R.M., Burmeister, J.A. and Ranney, R.R. 1983. Bacteriology of moderate (chronic) periodontitis mature adult humans. *Infect. Immun.* 42, 510-515.

Moore, W.E.C, Holdeman, L.V., Smibert, R.M., Hash, D.E., Burmeister, J.A. and Ranney RR. 1982. Bacteriology of severe periodontitis in young adult humans. *Infect. Immun.* 38, 1137-1148.

Moore, L.V.H., Moore, W.E.C., Cato, E.P., Smibert, R.M., Burmeister, J.A., Best, A.M. and Ranney, R.R. 1987. Bacteriology of human gingivitis. *J. Dent. Res.* 66; 989-995.

Moter, A., Hoenig, C., Choi, B.K., Riep, B. and Gobel, U.B. 1998. Molecular epidemiology of oral treponemes associated with periodontal disease. *J. Clin. Microbiol.* 36, 1399-1403.

Mukamolova, G.V., Kaprelyants, A.S., Young, D.I., Young, M. and Kell, D.B. 1998. A bacterial cytokine. *Proc. Natl. Acad. Sci. USA.* 95, 8916-8921.

Olsen, G.J. and Woese, C.R. 1993. Ribosomal RNA: a key to phylogeny. *FASEB* 7, 113-123.

Relman, D.A., Schmidt, T.M., MacDermott, R.P. and Falkow, S. 1992. Identification of the uncultured bacillus of Whipple's disease. *N. Engl. J. Med.* 327, 293-301.

Riviere, G.R., Wagoner M.A., Baker-Zander S.A., Weisz K.S., Adams D.F., Simonson L. and Lukehart S.A. 1991. Identification of spirochaetes related to Treponema pallidum in necrotising ulcerative gingivitis and chronic periodontitis. *New. Engl. J. Med.* 325, 539-543.

Socransky, S.S., Haffajee, A.D., Cugini, M.A., Smith, C. and Kent, R.L. 1998. Microbial complexes in subgingival plaque. *J. Clin. Periodontol.* 25, 134-144.

Spratt, D.A., Weightman, A.J. and Wade, W.G. 1999. Diversity of oral asaccharolytic Eubacterium species in periodontitis - identification of novel phylotypes representing uncultivated taxa. *Oral Microbiol. Immunol.* 14, 56-59.

Wade, W.G. 1997. The role of Eubacterium species in periodontal disease and other oral infections. *Microb. Ecol. Health Dis.* 9, 367-370.

Wade, W.G., Spratt, D.A., Dymock, D. and Weightman, A.J. 1997. Molecular detection of novel anaerobic species in dentoalveolar abscesses. *Clin. Infect. Dis.* 25, S235-S236.

Ward, D.M., Weller, R. and Bateson, M.M. 1990. 16S rRNA sequences reveal numerous uncultured micro-organisms in a natural community. *Nature* 345, 63-65.

Wilson, M.J., Weightman, A.J. and Wade, W.G. 1997. Applications of molecular ecology in the characterisation of uncultured microorganisms associated with human disease. *Rev. Med. Microbiol.* 8, 91-101.

Woese, C.R. 1987. Bacterial evolution. *Microbiol. Rev.* 51, 221-271.

Wyss, C. 1989. Dependence of proliferation of Bacteroides forsythus on exogenous N-acetylmuramic acid. *Infect. Immun.* 57, 1757-1759.

Zuckerkandl, E. and Pauling, L. 1965. Molecules as documents of evolutionary history. *J. Theoret. Biol.* 8, 357-366.

EARLY ONSET PERIODONTITIS: A TALE OF TWO INFECTIONS

Walter J. Loesche, James R. Giordano and Janice K. Stoll

Early onset periodontitis (EOP) is a descriptive term for the presence of attachment and bone loss about many teeth in individuals less ≤ 35 years of age. The syndrome occurs with a high frequency in families across generations, implying that a genetic predisposition and/or environmental factors, or both are involved.. Bacteriologically the plaques from these individuals exhibit the presence and/or overgrowth of many of the periodontopathic anaerobic species associated with adult periodontitis, with the important exception that the microaerophilic species, A. actinomycetemcomitans, can be associated with the noninflammatory forms of the syndrome called LJP, and can be present along with the anaerobes in some cases of inflammatory EOP. LJP can be successfully treated by conventional periodontal therapy, as it appears to be stable and nonprogressive. The other forms of EOP are unstable when treated by these conventional means, but appear to be treatable by various antimicrobial regimens that include metronidazole, an antimicrobial agent specific for anaerobes. It is possible that EOP results from the early acquisition of a periodontopathic flora by an infant/child from infected individuals in his/her environment.

I. Introduction

In periodontal disease the pathophysiological response of the host to the bacterial accumulations on the teeth results in a slow and intermittent loss of attachment of the teeth to the alveolar bone. While this is the dominant pattern, important exceptions occur. A small percentage of tooth sites may show a burst of 2 to 3 mm attachment loss (Goodson *et al.*, 1982), and a small percentage of individuals may show such rapid deterioration that they lose many of their teeth at an early age. These *rapidly* progressing forms often occur in families raising the possibility that there is genetic component (Novak and Novak, 1996). Indeed for some rare inherited and chromosomal disorders, such as Papillon-Lefevre syndrome, Ehlers-Danlos syndromes and Chediak-Higashi syndrome among others, severe early onset forms of periodontal disease are often characteristic of the syndrome, and reflect a fundamental defect in epithelial cell, connective tissue or leukocyte function (Sofaer, 1990; Hart, 1994).

In the majority of these rapidly progressing forms, the genetic component is subtle and presumably manifests as an altered host response(s) to the bacterial flora (Hart, 1994). In one scenario the host monocytes would over-react to a small level of bacterial challenge and produce large amounts of inflammatory mediators such as prostaglandin or cytokines (Offenbacher *et al.,* 1993). In another scenario, defects in leukocyte mobility and/or adhesion would cause a sluggish host response in the gingival environment which results in bacterial overgrowth in the plaque and persistence in the tissue. This mechanism is supported by the in vitro finding that about 66 to 85% of the patients with rapidly progressing periodontitis have neutrophils and/or monocytes that exhibit various chemotactic defects (Page *et al.,* 1985, Astemborski *et al.,* 1989).

Yet even with these genetic predispositions, a trigger or bacterial challenge from the plaque flora may be needed to cause the tissues loss. This is most dramatically demonstrated by the observation that in the Papillon-Lefevre syndrome, a protocol involving systemic antibiotics and extraction of the primary teeth prior to the eruption of the permanent teeth, can result in maintenance of the permanent dentition for at least six years (French *et al.,* 1995, Kleinfelder *et al.* 1996). This protocol would be successful only if a true periodontopathic bacterial flora had been eliminated from the plaque. Preus (1988) has suggested that infections with periodontopathic bacterial species such as *A. actinomycetemcomitans* are necessary for periodontal destruction to occur in the Papillon-Lefevre syndrome. If this be the case for this genetically linked clinical syndrome, then it is possible that it is also the situation in the other forms of severe, early onset periodontitis. A specific infection hypothesis would provide treatment options that offer clinical improvement and possibly restoration of periodontal health, as periodontal infections can be successfully managed (Loesche, 1999). The rational for the antimicrobial management of early onset forms of periodontitis will be the subject of this report.

II. Classification schemes for early onset periodontitis

Periodontal disease(s) consists of a multiplicity of clinical entities with different etiologies and responses to treatment. The American Academy of Periodontology (AAP) recommended a classification scheme which contained five primary forms of periodontitis, one of which was called Early-onset Periodontitis (EOP) (American Academy Periodontology 1989, Caton 1989). EOP was further subdivided into three types, Prepupertal Periodontitis (PP), Juvenile periodontitis (JP) and Rapidly Progressive Periodontitis (RPP) (Table 1), based upon the age of onset of clinical disease with juvenile beginning at about the time of puberty and rapidly progressive at approximately 20 to 35 years of age. A localized form that is mainly confined to the first molars and incisors, and a generalized form that includes all the teeth was recognized within the prepuberty and juvenile classifications. This distinction in the case of JP is supported by the observations that in the local form (LJP), *A. actinomycetemcomitans* is frequently associated with the initial lesion, and there is a characteristic IgG2 antibody response to this organism. In the generalized form (GJP), *A. actinomycetemcomitans* is not obviously involved and there is a tendency for black-pigmented species, especially *Porphyromonas gingivalis* to be associated with the lesions. The JP form could be distinguished from RPP by an abnormality of leukocyte chemotaxis, a reduced number of cell-surface receptors for chemo-attractants ligands and an abnormal amount of a cell-surface glycoprotein designated GP-110.

These distinctions between the JP and RPP forms were challenged as not being mutual exclusive as there is considerable overlap between the LJP, GJP

324

Table 1 Classification schemes for early-onset periodontitis.

AAP 1989	Host Response (Ranney,1991)	NIDR (Loe & Brown,1991)	Bacterial

Prepubertal
    Localized
    Generalized
	Systemic-disease-related		Microaerophilic
			Anaerobic
			Undiagnosable

Juvenile
    Localized
    Generalized
	Localized (LJP)
	Neutrophil functional abnormality
	Systemic deficiency uncertain
		IAL
		LJP
		GJP
			Microaerophilic
			Anaerobic
			Undiagnosable

Rapidly Progressive	Generalized (GJP) Neutrophil functional abnormality Immunodeficient Systemic deficiency uncertain	GEOP	Microaerophilic Anaerobic Undiagnosable

and RPP forms (Ranney, 1991). Also as PP, LJP, GJP and RRP are relatively rare and can occur in the same families (for review see Hart, 1994), it would seem likely that they are differing manifestations of the same disease. As PP forms are usually associated with systemic diseases it was suggested that this category with its localized and generalized subgroups be replaced by a grouping called "Systemic-disease-related". This alternate classification proposed by Ranney was based upon a mixed infection etiology with modifications based upon specific systemic determinants such as neutrophil function and immuno-competence (Table 1).

A clinical classification of EOP was proposed by Loe and Brown (1991) based on the extent of attachment loss observed in a random sampling of 11,007 school children, aged from 14 to 17 years, during the National Institute of Dental Research national survey of the oral health of US children. This classifi-cation recognized LJP based on the involvement of at least one first molar and at least one incisor or second molar and two or fewer cuspids or premolars having ≥ 3 mm loss of attachment". If this "criteria were not met and if four or more teeth had ≥ 3 mm loss of attachment and at least two affected teeth were second molars, cuspids or premolars" the subjects were classified as GJP. "Individuals who did not meet the first two criteria, but had one or more teeth with ≥ 3 mm loss of attachment" were classified as having incidental loss of attachment (IAL) (Table 1).

These descriptive schemes offer no guidance for the treatment of individuals with EOP. We have found that individuals with EOP of the type referred to as RPP, GJP, or SP have an anaerobic bacterial flora similar to those with adult forms of periodontitis (AP) (Loesche *et al.*, 1985), and that they respond to scaling and root planning and the unsupervised usage of systemic metronidazole (Loesche *et al.*, 1984). We have recruited these individuals into double blind clinical trials of metronidazole, based on the clinical needs for periodontal surgery and extractions, and the diagnosis of an anaerobic periodontal infection (Loesche and Giordano, 1997). This anaerobic diagnosis is supported by the DNA probe findings in the EOP patients followed longitudinally by Albandar *et al.* (1997). In that investigation the anaerobic species, *P. gingivalis*, *Treponema denticola* and *Prevotella intermedia* were significantly associated with the generalized and/or rapidly progressing disease. Thus in the bacterial classification scheme, the individuals presenting with EOP are diagnosed as having either an anaerobic infection, a microaerophilic infection such as seen in LJP with *A. actinomycetemcomitans*, or as being bacteriologically undiagnosable (Table 1).

III. Epidemiology

The prevalence of EOP is in the range of 0.1% to 0.2% for Norwegian, Finnish, Danish, English and Dutch children; 0.75 to 0.8% in Nigeria adolescents, and 3.7% in Brazilian teenagers (Loe and Brown, 1991, Papapanou, 1996). In a large randomly chosen sample of American children classified according to the NIDR scheme (Table 1), 0.53% of the adolescents had LJP, 0.13% had GJP and 1.61 % had incidental loss of attachment (IAL). Blacks were at greater risk to have all forms of EOP compared to whites. In a subsequent analysis of 18-34 year old Americans examined in the NIDR Adult Survey, 3.6% of 5,849 subjects were classified as having generalized EOP involving at least 8 teeth (Oliver *et al.,* 1998). Kowashi (1988) reported a prevalence rate of 0.47% for Japanese University students aged 19 to 28 years.

While these prevalences indicate how uncommon EOP is among these populations in terms of actual numbers of individuals affected the numbers can be quite high. The 3.6% of GEOP in the US subjects translates to 1,781,756 people (Oliver *et al.*, 1998). As periodontal disease and loss of teeth at an early age have been identified as significant risk factors for coronary heart disease and death at an early age (De Stefano *et al,.* 1993, Mattila *et al.,* 1995), untreated EOP could constitute a health burden of considerable magnitude.

There are anecdotal reports of individuals with prepuberty periodontitis subsequently developing LJP and/or GJP, and LJP patients developing GJP, suggesting that these clinical entities are in reality the same disease, which some patients progress through as they age (Ranney, 1991). This possibility was investigated in the NIDR study by reexamining 91 subjects with EOP after six years to determine their subsequent clinical status (Brown *et al.,* 1996). Most subjects showed an increase in the number of tooth sites with attachment loss with only one LJP subject and 14 IAL subjects showing no loss of attachment. Of the 34 subjects with LJP, 12 had progressed to GJP, and 21 remained classified as LJP. Of the 46 patients classified initially as IAL, 7 were now classified as LJP and 6 as GJP. Thus 27% of the subjects had deteriorated in the 6 year period to the extent that they had changed to a classification with a more dire prognosis. The authors concluded that "the difference between LJP and GJP is in the number and type of teeth involved", and speculate as to what extent time is the important factor. Would all LJP cases convert to GJP given enough time and

326

without treatment?

The low prevalence of EOP discourages prospective studies, as is illustrated by an attempt to document changes in the bacterial flora that preceded the loss of attachment (Ashley *et al.*, 1989). Subgingival plaque samples were collected from mesial and distal surfaces of permanent molars in 100 14- year old school children, and the 800 plaque samples were stored in liquid nitrogen. The children were examined at 6 month intervals over a 24 month period. When a site showed ≥ 1 mm attachment loss additional subgingival plaque samples were obtained from the diseased site and a contralateral control site in the same person, as well as from similar sites in a randomly chosen unaffected subject. This excellent clinical design was frustrated by the fact that only 6 subjects, each with only one site, developed attachment loss, so that the study was not sufficiently powered to show anything but very obvious differences. The site with loss of attachment had a higher proportion of *spirochetes* than the control site in the same subject and the equivalent sites in the control subject. There was a tendency for the proportions of black-pigmented species and *P. intermedia* to be higher, and for *A. actinomycetemcomitans* to be more frequently encountered at the site that loss attachment. As these six subjects might have been classified as IAL by the NIDR scheme (Table 1), and as about 25% of IAL subjects go on to develop EOP (Brown *et al.*, 1996), this suggests that a prospective bacteriology study in a IAL group among 14 to 17 year olds would be a suitable high risk group to monitor for the development of EOP.

IV. Familial tendency

The tendency for EOP to cluster in families across several generations has suggested a common cause or predisposition. Most investigators have proposed a genetic link, but some controversies exist as to the mode of transmission (Hart 1994). In one large study involving 100 families a mixed model segregation analysis was applied to test major locus and multifactorial hypothesis about the inheritance of EOP (Marazita *et al.*, 1994). The findings were consistent with an autosomal major locus being sufficient to explain the data in both Black and non-Black kindreds. The higher prevalence of EOP among Blacks could be explained by the higher frequency estimate of the EOP allele in Blacks vs. non-Blacks, i.e. 0.016 vs. 0.001. The most likely mode of inheritance was dominant for both Blacks and non-Blacks with an estimated penetrance of 0.7 to 0.73.

This genetic predilection does not rule out environmental and behavior factors as contributors to EOP. In this context it is likely that infants in an EOP family become colonized by the periodontopathic flora at an earlier age than infants in non-EOP families. The infant's oral flora is acquired from humans in his/her environment with the mother being the most important source. Mother to infant transmission has been most frequently studied in regards to the mutans streptococci, where the importance of teeth for the colonization of the mutans streptococci is well established (Loesche, 1985, Caufield *et al.*, 1993).

One might think that teeth and their associated gingival sulci would be necessary for the colonization of the anaerobic members of the plaque flora.

However *Prevotella melaninogenica* was found in 70% of 30 edentulous infants (1 to 7 months of age) and as many as 6 other anaerobic species such as *F. nucleatum*, could be recovered from the saliva and mucosa surfaces. In contrast *A. actinomycetemcomitans* could not be detected in 51 edentulous infants (Kononen *et al.*, 1992a). All mothers of these infants harbored *F. nucleatum*, and 29 of 30 had *P. melaninogenica* in their saliva. A positive correlation between maternal salivary concentrations of *P. melaninogenica* and colonization of the infant with this organism was demonstrated (Kononen *et al,.* 1992b). Isolates of *P. melaninogenica* from 11 mother-child pairs were ribotyped, and in 6 pairs, identical ribotypes were found suggesting the transmission of *P. melaninogenica* from mother to child (Kononen *et al.*, 1994a). The presence of non-maternal ribotypes in the infants indicated that other sources, such as siblings, the father and other humans contributed to the flora of the infant. When the primary teeth erupted, *P. melaninogenica*, *F. nucleatum*, non-pigmented *Prevotella* spp. and *Capnocytophaga* spp. were found in all mouths and previously undetected species such as *P. denticola*, Fusobacterium spp. and Selenomonas spp. were present in most children (Kononen *et al,.* 1994b).

This sequence of events demonstrated in a small number of Finnish mother-infant pairs probably reflects the dominant pattern by which the anaerobic flora is acquired at the infant-toddler stage. Other investigators have found the periodontopathic anaerobes such as *spirochetes* (Mikx *et al.*, 1986), and *P. gingivalis* (Sweeney *et al.*, 1987, Frisken *et al.*, 1987) in the mouths of young children. The occurrence of *P. gingivalis* in saliva, as detected by a polymerase chain reaction (PCR) procedure increased with age, being present in 5% of subjects between 5 and 10 years of age, and 13.8 % of subjects between 11 and 20 years of age (Matto *et al.*, 1998). No evidence of parent to child transmission of *P. gingivalis* could be demonstrated among families in which a parent was positive for *P. gingivalis* , whereas the transmission of *A. actinomycetem-comitans* took place in 6 of 19 studied families (Asikainen *et al.*, 1996). In another study, when a child was positive for *A. actinomycetemcomitans*, the parent always harbored the same serotype (Alaluusa *et al.,*1991). In a sample of 5 families with members with LJP, all *A. actinomycetemcomitans* isolates from family members were of the same biotype and serotype (Zambon *et al.*, 1983). *A. actinomycetemcomitans* can be found in more than half of the subjects with no periodontal attachment loss who are in the same family as an EOP patient, which would suggest inter-familial transmission (Gunsolley *et al.*, 1990). However when genomic DNA from *A. actinomycetemcomitans* strains isolated from probands and family members were amplified and characterized, the generated amplitypes showed a wide distribution among the probands and family members with no clear transmission paths observed (Tinoco *et al.*, 1998).

These data collectively indicate that some children have, even at the stage of the primary dentition, acquired the flora associated with periodontal disease, and that this flora most likely came from the parent. What is not known is whether children of periodontally diseased parents are more likely to acquire the flora sooner than children of periodontally healthy parents, and whether children who

Table 2 Relationship between parents' periodontal and BANA status and the BANA status of the child.

		Presence of Periodontitis in Parent			
Plaque	BANA Test	No	Yes	Total	Significance Fisher exact test
Parent	Negative	3	1	4	
	Positive	11	19	30	
		14	20	34	p = 0.28
Child	Negative	8	2	10	
	Positive	6	18	24	
		4	20	34	p = 0.006

from Watson *et al.* 1994. *J Dent Res.* **73**:1636-1640.

acquire this flora at an early age are more likely to develop EOP. The frequent occurrence of both of these events could explain the familial nature of EOP.

A partial answer to the question as to whether children of periodontally diseased parents are more likely to be colonized by periodontal pathogens was obtained by surveying young children for the presence of the BANA positive species in plaque samples (Watson *et al.*, 1991). A positive BANA test reflects the presence in the plaque of *P. gingivalis*, *T. denticola*, and *B. forsythus* either singularly or collectively (Loesche *et al.*, 1992a). Fifty-six percent of 157 children tested positive and/or weak positive in one or more of four plaque samples. Black children were significantly more likely to have a BANA positive plaque that White children (55% Vs 37%, chi square =0.02). Forty percent of the children whose parents had a documented history of periodontal disease, as determined by evaluation of their dental records, had BANA positive plaques, compared to 16% of the children whose parents' periodontal status was not documented (Chi square = 15.3, p <0.001).

All parents and children were invited to participate in a follow-up study in which the parents were given a periodontal examination and four plaque samples from each parent and child were evaluated with the BANA test (Watson *et al.*, 1994). If the parent was colonized by the BANA positive species then the odds ratio that the child would be colonized was 9.8, but this ratio was not significant (95% confidence interval 0.7-293). If the parent had periodontitis (moderate and advanced forms were grouped together), then s/he was 5.2 times more likely to have at least one BANA positive plaque (not significant), but the child was 12 times more likely to have a BANA positive plaque (significant, 95% confidence interval 1.59 to 114) (Table 2). These data suggest that periodontal disease in the parent is a risk indicator for a child becoming colonized by one or more of the BANA positive species such as *P. gingivalis*, *T. denticola* and *B. forsythus*. Whether this early colonization is in turn a risk factor for the development of EOP in the child can only be determined by prospective longitudinal studies.

These findings suggest that the familial tendency of EOP could be partially explained by the early colonization of the child by periodontopathic members of the parents' plaque flora, especially when the parents have periodontal disease. The higher prevalence of EOP among Black children could be explained by the greater frequency by which Black children harbored the BANA positive species. It could be that the nurturing of a Black child by his/her significant caregiver, most likely a mother/grandmother, provides more opportunities for transmission of the periodontopathic flora than occurs with the nurturing of a White child.

V. A tale of two infections: microaerophilic *vs* anaerobic

The microbial composition of dental plaque is complex as more than 400 bacterial species are estimated to be present in various mouths (Moore and Moore, 1994). Most of these species have not been identified; many have never been isolated, and some, such as the *spirochetes*, can be lysed by the various procedures used to disperse plaque samples for quantitative culturing procedures (Salvador *et al.,* 1987). Various detection procedures which use DNA probes, immunological reagents and culturing on selective and nonselective agar media often yield different isolation outcomes with culturing probably being the most unreliable of these procedures (Loesche *et al.,*1992b). Important cultivable species such as *B. forsythus* and *T. denticola* are difficult to identify on primary isolation, if they indeed grow, and accordingly are often omitted from data analysis. Some species such as *A. actinomycetemcomitans* have a highly effective selective medium for their cultivation (Slots, 1982), and others like the black pigmented species, which would include *P. gingivalis* and *P. intermedia*, can be easily identified on agar media containing blood, and accordingly are usually accounted for in cultural studies, possibly leading to an over interpretation of their importance in EOP.

Some investigators have shown that serum antibody levels to *A. actinomycetemcomitans* (Cappelli *et al.*, 1994; Ebersole *et al.*, 1995) and *P. gingivalis* (Kojima *et al.,* 1997) correspond to the number of tooth sites colonized with these organisms and with their levels in these sites. This has suggested that serum antibody levels could be used as markers of infection with these and possibly other periodontopathic organisms (Ebersole *et al.*, 1992). This approach has limitations when a suspected periodontopathic species such as *B. forsythus* is poorly immunogenic (Califano *et al.*, 1997a). Also, as immunological responses to these species can be influenced by smoking and race (Quinn *et al.*, 1996), these factors need to be accounted for in the interpretation of immunological data obtained from periodontal patients. For example in LJP patients when the independent variables included age, gender, race, plaque index, gingival index and serum antibody concentration for *A. actinomycetemcomitans* leukotoxin, there was no evidence that antibody concentration was related to attachment loss (Califano *et al.*, 1997b).

This bacterial complexity would imply that it is presumptuous to think that simple interpretations can be made of the bacteriological data obtained from EOP patients. Yet patterns can be discerned that should allow a clinician to decide if s/he is dealing with a microaerophilic infection that can be detected by monitoring for *A. actinomycetemcomitans*, or an anaerobic infection that can be detected by monitoring for *P. gingivalis, P. intermedia, B. forsythus T. denticola* or spirochetes. For example when 8th grade teenagers were encountered who had a molar-incisor pattern of attachment loss in the presence of plaque, gingival inflammation, bleeding on probing and calculus (Cappelli *et al.,* 1994), should they be classified as LJP or GJP? These 8th grade subjects had high levels of *A. actinomycetemcomitans* in their plaques and high levels of antibody to *A. actinomycetemcomitans,* so that they should be treated as if they have an *A. actinomycetemcomitans* infection. This microbiological approach, if it results in successful choices of treatment, should then overcome the confusion associated with the overlapping criteria of the existing classification schemes (Table 1).

A. Microaerophilic Infection vs Anaerobic Infection

A. actinomycetemcomitans is uniquely involved with LJP (for review see Zambon, 1985), and has been linked with the inflammatory forms of EOP (Tanner *et al.,* 1979). However other putative periodontopathogens, most notably *P. gingivalis,* were also prominent in these plaques, so that the un-equivocal involvement of *A. actinomycetemcomitans* with inflammatory forms of EOP has not been determined. For example even though 90% of a subset of 27 8th grade students who presented with an inflammatory form of LJP, had *A. actinomycetemcomitans* colonizing (infecting) a mean of 14.2 teeth per child, because no other periodontopathic species was sought for, the uniqueness of *A. actinomycetemcomitans* as a periodontopathogen in these patients could not be established.

In a rare prospective study, Ebersole *et al.* (1995) followed for three years 28 AP patients, 11 EOP patients and 12 control subjects for the loss of periodontal attachment. The EOP patients and 16 of the AP patients had elevated serum IgG antibody to *A. actinomycetemcomitans,* whereas the other 12 AP patients and the controls had normal antibody levels. The patients with the elevated antibodies also had more teeth infected with *A. actinomycetemcomitans* and higher propor-tions of *A. actinomycetemcomitans* in the plaques of these infected teeth. *A. actinomycetemcomitans* significantly increased in certain plaques 2 to 6 months prior to attachment loss in that site. The levels of serum IgG antibody also increased in 2/3s of these periodontally active patients, again about 2 to 4 months prior to the detection of the attachment loss.

This report provided convincing evidence that *A. actinomycetemcomitans* infections can contribute to progressive loss of attachment in certain EOP and AP patients and that the antibody response to this organism coincides with the increased levels of *A. actinomycetemcomitans* in the plaque. However, as noted by the authors, this was a "closed" format study in which patients were selected on the basis of having high serum IgG titers to *A. actinomycetemcomitans* and no other periodontopathic species was sought for. Consequently it is not possi-ble to infer that other periodontopathic species were not involved in the ob-served pathology.

Table 3 Prevalence of putative periodontopathic species in patients with early onset periodontitis (EOP), localized juvenile periodontitis (LJP) and adult periodontitis (AP).

Periodonto-pathic spp	Loesche *et al.*, 1985			Van Winkelhoff *et al.*,1992			Kamma *et al.* 1994
	EOP(23)	LJP(4)	AP(80)	EOP(40	LJP(28	AP(50)	EOP(10)
Spirochetes	100%	75%	100%	——— not sought for ———			
A.actinomy.	——— not detected ———			100%	100%	100%	20%
P. gingivalis	65	0	46	23	18	40	100
P. intermedia	78	100	98	48	47	72	100
T. denticola	——— not sought for ———			——— not sought for ———			
B. forsythus	——— not sought for ———			——— not sought for ———			100

number of patients in each clinical category shown in parenthesis.

This is the great problem with bacteriological studies of EOP as the complexity of the flora encourages the usage of selective media which permit the detection of a limited number of species such as *A. actinomycetemcomitans*. In fact when other periodontopathic members of the flora are sought for in EOP patients, they usually outnumber *A. actinomycetemcomitans*. In 23 EOP and 4 LJP patients *spirochetes* averaged 27% of the microscopic count and *A. actinomycetemcomitans* could not be detected (Loesche *et al.*, 1985). There was no difference in the monitored flora between EOP and AP as spirochetes and black- pigmented species were ubiquitous in both types of patients (Table 3). In another study *A. actinomycetemcomitans* was found in only 2 of 10 EOP patients, whereas *P. gingivalis* was present in 92% of the plaques and accounted for 26.7% of the cultivable flora (Table 3) (Kamma *et al.*, 1994). *B. forsythus*, a more recently described species, was found in 53% of the plaques and accounted for 23.6% of the cultivable flora. Van der Velden *et al.*, (1989) culturing only for *A. actinomycetemcomitans* found this organism in only 17 of 105 Dutch adolescents with EOP, and Han *et al.* (1991) could not associate *A. actinomycetemcomitans* with EOP among Chinese teenagers. Kuru *et al.*, (1999), in a study involving 15 EOP patients, could isolate *P. gingivalis* , *P. intermedia* and *A. actinomycetemcomitans* from 93%, 80% and 50% of inflamed sites that also were positive for the presence of aspartate aminotransferase (AST) in the gingival crevicular fluid. AST is released when there is cell damage and correlates with gingival inflammation (Persson *et al.*, 1990). None of these reports would support a role for *A. actinomycetemcomitans* in EOP. But Van Winkelhoff *et al.*, (1992) found *A. actinomycetemcomitans* in all EOP, LJP and AP patients(Table 3), at levels in which it accounted for 19% of the cultivable flora in the EOP patients, 16% in the LJP patients and 7% of the AP patients. This is by far the most convincing data for an important role of *A. actinomycetemcomitans* in EOP.

Most investigators did not look for spirochetes, and *T. denticola* was not sought for in these studies. The inclusion of the "not sought for" label in Table 3

332

Table 4 Relationship between levels of periodontopathic species and disease progression in early onset periodontitis.

	Levels in Individuals with		
Bacterial Species	**Disease progression**	**No Disease progression**	**Significance**
A. actinomycetemcomitans	4,000	2,200	p=0.2
P. gingivalis	77,000	22,900	=0.0001
T. denticola	159,900	53,200	=0.0001
P. intermedia	60,900	38,100	=0.03
C. rectus	23,400	12,600	=0.08

adapted from Albandar *et al.* (1997). *J Periodontol.* **68**: 973-981.

is meant to underscore that almost all studies that rely upon culturing methods fail, through cost and manpower limitations, to account for all the important members of the periodontopathic flora. This situation is changing as more investigators use DNA probes to detect these organisms. Commercially available DNA probes to 8 putative periodontal pathogens were used to examine the plaque flora of 10 Downs Syndrome(average age = 26.3 years) and 11 cerebral palsy patients (average age =36 years) (Cichon *et al.,* 1998). The Downs Syndrome patients exhibit an EOP that is superimposed upon various immunological deficiencies. Their plaque flora had high proportions of *P. intermedia, T. denticola, F. nucleatum* and *P. gingivalis,* lower proportions *of E. corrodens, C. rectus* and *B. forsythus,* whereas *A. actinomycetemcomitans* could be detected in only one patient. This anaerobic pattern was also found in the cerebral palsy patients, so that in these individuals an anaerobic plaque infection could be diagnosed.

DNA probes were used to assess the relationship between the plaque flora and EOP in a population of 248 US adolescents who were reexamined after 6 years as part of the NIDR study on the incidence of EOP in representative US adolescents (Albandar *et al.,* 1997). The subjects were classified as General-EOP(n=64), LJP (n=26), incidental-EOP(n=58) and as periodontally healthy (n=100), and also according to the rate of attachment loss which the subjects had experienced during the 6 year interval. The level of *P. gingivalis* was 3-fold higher in the G-EOP group than in the LJP, 5-fold higher than in the incidental-EOP group and 16-fold higher than in the periodontally healthy group. The level of *T. denticola* was 3 to 5 times higher in the EOP groups compared to the healthy control, whereas the levels of the other monitored species did not show any correlation with disease classification. The individuals showing disease progression had significantly higher levels of *P. gingivalis, T. denticola,* and *P. intermedia* than the group with no progression, whereas there was no evidence that *A. actinomycetemcomitans* could be associated with disease progression (Table 4).

Sites with high numbers of *P. gingivalis, P. intermedia* or *T. denticola* had the highest levels of beta-glucuronidase activity (Albandar *et al.* 1998). A previous study in AP patients had shown significant correlations between beta glucuronidase activity and the level of *P. gingivalis*, *P. intermedia* and *spirochetes* in the subgingival plaque flora (Harper *et al.* 1989). These findings suggest that the interactions between beta-glucuronidase and the subgingival plaque is similar in EOP and AP, and that in both, the host is responding to an anaerobic infection in the plaque. There is supported by the observation that there was no relationship between *A. actinomycetemcomitans* and disease progression as it was found in only 21% of the EOP subjects and 14% of the healthy subjects (Albandar *et al.,* 1997).

These bacteriological studies strongly indicate that most forms of EOP can be considered as anaerobic infections, with the important exception that in the non-inflammatory forms of LJP, *A. actinomycetemcomitans* should be suspected as the etiologic agent.

B. Treatment of EOP

Shortly after LJP was identified as being associated with *A. actinomycetem-comitans*, several investigators reported dramatic improvement in the bone and attachment levels about the involved teeth, when rigorous debridement of the teeth was combined with systemic usage of tetracycline (Lindhe and Liljenberg, 1984, Novak *et al.,* 1991). The degree of improvement could be correlated with the elimination of *A. actinomycetemcomitans* from the plaque (Christersson and Zambon, 1993), but the complete elimination of *A. actinomycetemcomitans* from the plaques proved difficult (Slots and Rosling, 1983, Zambo,n 1985). These studies used an open clinical design and usually had no control groups that received only the debridement treatment. Subsequently Saxen *et al.* (1986) reported that good periodontal health could be maintained for at least 6 to 12 years in 20 LJP patients treated with oral hygiene instructions, scaling and root planing, flap surgery if necessary, but with no antibiotics.

A double blind study involving doxycycline showed no advantage of doxycycline plus debridement over the placebo plus debridement in the treat-ment of LJP patients (Asikainen *et al.*, 1990). But in a double blind study involving 38 EOP patients, tetracycline reduced the need for surgery in 42% of the affected teeth, while the placebo reduced the surgical needs of 25% of the affected teeth (Palmer *et al.*, 1996). In an open study in which metronidazole was compared to doxycycline, or placebo treatments, all 27 LJP patients im-proved, and there was no significance differences between the treatment groups (Saxen and Asikainen 1993). The improvements tended to be better in the metronidazole treated group, and metronidazole treatment was the most success-ful in eliminating *A. actinomycetemcomitans* from the plaques. Van Winkelhoff *et al.* (1992) found metronidazole plus amoxicillin to be effective in reducing *A. actinomycetemcomitans* from plaques in patients with LJP, EOP and AP, but the open design of the study didn't permit the determination of how much of the reduction was due to metronidazole and how much was due to the amoxicillin. Given the proven efficacy of metronidazole to improve periodontal health (Loesche, 1999), and to reduce *A. actinomycetemcomitans* levels in the plaque (Saxen and Asikainen, 1993), it is possible that all the improvements noted could have been due to the metronidazole, and that the treatment with amoxicillin was not necessary.

These findings suggest that LJP patients can be successfully managed by traditional periodontal procedures without systemic antimicrobial agents. This issue was addressed by Gunsolley *et al.* (1995) in their summary of the long term results of treatment of 40 LJP and 48 EOP (called severe periodontitis or SP in their report) patients who had been treated by scaling and root planing and open flap curettage as necessary. The patients were re-examined approximately 3 years after their most recent dental visit in the case of the LJP patients, and almost 4 years in the case of the EOP patients. There were no differences in clinical outcomes between patients who had received root planing and scaling and those who had received root planing and scaling plus open flap curettage. Patients who had received some form of periodontal therapy differed from those who had not received any therapy.

The treated LJP patients had more sites that gained attachment than sites that lost attachment (p <0.02), whereas the untreated LJP patients had significantly more sites that lost attachment (p <0.05). There was no effect of treatment in the EOP patients! More sites broke down than gained attachment, regardless of whether or not the patient had received treatment. The authors concluded that LJP is a stable disease that responds to mechanical periodontal therapy, whereas EOP is an unstable disease that does not respond to conventional periodontal treatment. They suggest that the usage of antibiotics should be investigated in these EOP patients.

We interpreted the results of our 1985 study (Table 3) as Indicating that EOP and AP were both anaerobic infections. We have entered both types of patients into our clinical trials of metronidazole based on their clinical need for periodontal surgery and the presence of an anaerobic infection in ≥ 3 of the 4 most diseased appearing pocket sites in the dentition. We diagnosed an anaerobic infection by the presence of ≥ 20 % *spirochetes* in the microscopic examination of each plaque sample, or by the presence of a BANA positive reaction in the plaque sample (Loesche and Giordano, 1997). About 90% of the initially recommended surgical needs of patients so diagnosed, can be prevented by a regimen consisting of scaling and root planing and the short term usage of systemic metronidazole or doxycycline, followed, as needed, by the usage of delivery systems which released either metronidazole or chlorhexidine into the pocket (Loesche *et al.* 1996).

It was of interest to determine *post facto* whether the patients periodontal classification as either an EOP or AP patient affected the treatment outcome. About 15 % of the patients initially recruited into the study could be considered as EOP patients based upon being ≤ 35 years of age. The EOP patients were significantly younger, had significantly more teeth in need of surgical treatment (12.2 Vs 8.2), had more current smokers, and tended to be non-White compared to the AP patients (Table 5). They had more teeth, probably reflecting their younger age. But there was no difference between the two groups in terms of their average BANA score. Ninety-eight percent of over 350 tested plaques were

Table 5 Characteristics of patients with early onset periodontitis (EOP) and adult periodontitis(AP) at the entry into clinical trial of antimicrobial therapy.

		EOP (n=15)	AP (n=81)
Age in years		31.7 (26-35)	51.9 (36-77)
Gender	Female	9 (60%)	41 (51%)
	Male	6 (40%)	40 (49%)
Race	White	5 (33%)	43 (53%)
	Black	7 (47%)	34 (42%)
	Other	3 (20%)	4 (5%)
Smoking	History		
	Never smoked	4 (27%)	17 (21%)
	Quit	2 (13%)	24 (30%)
	Current <1 pack/day	3 (20%)	10 (12%)
	Current ≥1 pack/day	6 (40%)	29 (36%)
Number of Teeth		26.3≠3.6	23.3≠3.6
Criteria Used to Diagnose an Anaerobic Infection			
Number of Teeth needing Periodontal surgery		10.5≠8.0 (ave.≠stand. dev.)	6.8≠4.1
Extractions		1.7≠1.3	1.4≠1.7
	Total	12.2	8.2
Average BANA Score		2.9≠0.1	2.9≠0.1

BANA positive with the remaining 2 % being weakly BANA positive.

Both types of patients were randomly assigned to metronidazole, doxycycline or placebo medication in the first round of treatment, and then were retreated based upon their continued need for periodontal surgery (for protocol see Loesche *et al.*, 1996). After the patients entered the maintenance phase they were scheduled for maintenance therapy at 3 month intervals and for an annual periodontal evaluation. Eleven EOP and 70 AP patients were seen at the first annual evaluation (1.2 years after completion of treatment) and 8 EOP patients and 55 AP patients were seen at the second annual evaluation (2.4 years after completion of treatment).

The EOP patients had 9 teeth in need of surgery and 1.9 needing extractions at the baseline examination (Table 6). The combined systemic/local/debridement therapy reduced the surgical needs by 88% immediately after the completion of these treatments, and this effect was still apparent 1.1 to 2.4 years later. These EOP patients had 1.7 missing teeth prior to the start of the study and 2.6 missing teeth some 2.4 years later. This 0.9 increment was less than the 1.9 teeth that initially had been considered "hopeless" and recommended for extraction. Thus

Table 6 Effects of antimicrobial treatments on need for periodontal surgery and extractions.

Number of Teeth Needing		EOP Patients n= 11 Ave.≠sd (range)		AP Patients n=70 Ave.≠sd (range)
Periodontal Surgery				
Before Treatments		9.0≠8.0 (2-25)		6.8≠ 4.2 (2-23)
After Treatments		0.7 ≠1.7 (0-5)		0.3≠0.6 (0-3)
After 1.1 years		0.5 ≠0.8 (0-2)		0.3≠1.0 (0-6)
After 2.4 years	(n=8)	0.9≠0.2.1(0-6)	(n=55)	0.2≠0.7 (0-4)
Extractions				
Before Treatments		1.9≠ 1.8 (0-6)		1.6≠1.8 (0-8)
After Treatments		0.6≠1.7 (0-4)		0.4≠1.0(0-5)
After 1.1 years		0.0≠0.0 (0) 0.		2≠0.8 (0-5)
After 2.4 years		0.3≠0.7 (0-2)		0.1≠0.3 (0-2)
Missing Teeth				
Before Treatments		1.7≠ 2.5 (0-8)		4.7≠3.6 (0-16)
After Treatments		2.1≠2.3 (0-8)		5.1≠3.6(0-16)
After 1.1 years		2.6≠2.4 (0-8)		5.5≠3.8 (0-16)
After 2.4 years		2.6≠11.5 (1-4)		5.9≠3.8 (0-18)

in these EOP patients the antimicrobial approach not only spared most patients from having surgery, but actually saved some teeth from extraction. The AP patients has 6.8 teeth in need of surgery and 1.6 teeth in need of extractions at the baseline examination. The antimicrobial treatment reduced the surgical needs by 91%, and this effect was still apparent some 2.4 years later (Table 6).

Both EOP and AP patients responded in the same positive way to antimicrobial treatments based upon a diagnosis of an anaerobic infection. The surgery that was initially prevented has remained prevented for at least 2.4 years , and some teeth that were scheduled for extraction because of a hopeless prognosis remained in the mouth. These data, while on a limited number of patients, indicate that many, if not most, EOP patients can be successfully treated using antimicrobial agents that are effective against the anaerobic bacteria species such as spirochetes (*T. denticola*), black-pigmented species (*P. gingivalis* and *P. intermedia*) and *B. forsythus*, among others. They suggest that *A. actinomycetemcomitans* is not an important periodontopathic species in those EOP patients who present with inflammatory lesions. And as the findings of Saxen and Asikainen (1986) and Gunsolley *et al.* (1995) indicate, the LJP patients in whom *A. actinomycetemcomitans* is a putative periodontal pathogen can be successfully managed without the use of antimicrobial agents. These findings suggest that patients who present with most, if not all, forms of EOP can be successfully managed by the clinician who applies an antimicrobial strategy to their treatments.

Acknowledgements

This research was supported by USPHS grant DE-06030 from the National Institute of Dental Research. Drs. Steven Soehren, Charles Rau and Rowland Hutchinson assisted in the clinical examinations of the patien

References

Alaluusua S. Asikainen S. and Lai CH. 1991. Intrafamilial transmission of *Actinobacillus actinomycetemcomitans. J of Periodontology* **62**(3): 207-10.

Albandar JM. Brown LJ. and Loe H. 1997. Putative periodontal pathogens in subgingival plaque of young adults with and without early-onset periodontitis. *Journal of Periodontology* **68**(10): 973-81.

Albandar JM. Kingman A. and Lamster IB. 1998. Crevicular fluid level of beta-glucuronidase in relation to clinical periodontal parameters and putative periodontal pathogens in early-onset periodontitis. *J of Clin Periodontology.* **25**(8): 630-9.

American Academy of Periodontology 1989. Consensus Report, Discussion Section I. Periodontal diagnosis and diagnostic aids. Chicago: *The American of Periodontology* I23-I31.

Ashley FP, Gallagher J and Wilson RF. 1989. The occurrence of *A. actinomycetemcomitans, Bacteroides gingivalis, Bacteroides intermedius* and spirochetes in the subgingival microflora in relation to the early onset of periodontitis in a group of adolescents. *Oral Microbiol Immunol* **4**: 236-238.

Asikainen S., Jousimies-Somer H., Kanervo A. and Saxen L. 1990. The immediate efficacy of adjunctive doxycycline in treatment of localized juvenile periodontitis. *Arch Oral Biol* **35** Suppl: 231S-234S.

Asikainen S. Chen C. and Slots J. 1996. Likelihood of transmitting *Actinobacillus actinomycetemcomitans* and *Porphyromonas gingivalis* in families with periodontitis. *Oral Microbiology & Immunology* **11**(6): 387-94.

Astemborski JA, Boughman JA, Myrick PO, Goodman SB, Wootem RK, Agarwal S, Vincent JW, and Suzuki JB. 1989. Clinical and laboratory characterization of early onset periodontitis. *J Periodontol* **60**: 557-563.

Brown LJ. Albandar JM. Brunelle JA. and Loe H. 1996. Early-onset periodontitis: progression of attachment loss during 6 years *J of Periodontology* **67**(10): 968-75.

Califano JV. Gunsolley JC. Schenkein HA. and Tew JG 1997a. A comparison of IgG antibody reactive with *Bacteroides forsythus* and *Porphyromonas gingivalis* in adult and early-onset periodontitis. *Journal of Periodontology* **68**(8): 734-8.

Califano JV. Pace BE. Gunsolley JC. Schenkein HA. Lally ET. and Tew JG. 1997b. Antibody reactive with *Actinobacillus actinomycetemcomitans* leukotoxin in early-onset periodontitis patients. *Oral Microbiology & Immunology* **12**(1): 20-6.

Cappelli DP. Ebersole JL. and Kornman KS. 1994. Early-onset periodontitis in Hispanic-American adolescents associated with *A. actinomycetemcomitans. Community Dentistry & Oral EPidemiology* **22**(2): 116-21.

Caton J. 1989. Periodontal diagnosis and diagnostic aids. In: M Nevins, W. Becker Kornman K. (eds.), *World Workshop in Clinical Periodontics*, pp. I23-I31. Princeton NJ: The American of Periodontology

Caufield PW, Cutter GR and Dasanayake AP. 1993. Initial acquisition of mutans streptococci by infants: Evidence for a discrete window of infectivity. *J Dent Res* **72**: 37-45.

Christersson L.A. and Zambon J.J. 1993. Suppression of subgingival *Actinobacillus actinomycetemcomitans* in localized juvenile periodontitis by systemic tetracycline. *J Clin Periodontol* **58**: 395-401.

Cichon P. Crawford L. and Grimm WD. 1998. Early-onset periodontitis associated with Down's syndrome-clinical interventional study. *Annals of Periodontology* **3**(1): 370-80.

DeStefano F., Anda R.F., Kahn H.S., Williamson D.F. and Russell C.M. 1993. Dental disease and risk of coronary heart disease and mortality. *Br Med J* **306**: 688-691.

Ebersole JL. Capelli D. and Steffen MJ. 1992. Characteristics and utilization of antibody measurements in clinical studies of periodontal disease. *J Periodontol.* **63**: 1110-1116.

Ebersole JL. Capelli D. and Steffen MJ. 1995. Longitudinal dynamics of infection and serum antibody *in A. actinomycetemcomitans* periodontitis. *Oral Diseases* **1**(3): 129-38.

French D. Scott H. and Overall CM. 1995, Papillon-Lefevre syndrome associated earlonset periodontitis: a review and case study. *J Canadian Dental Association* **61**(5): 432-8.

Goodson JM Tanner ACR, Haffajee AD, Sornberger GC and Socransky. 1982. Patterns of progression and regression of advance periodontal disease. *J Clin Periodontol* **9**: 472-481.

Gunsolley J.C., Califano J.V., Koertge T.E., Burmeister J.A., Cooper L.C. and Schenkein H.A. 1995. Longitudinal assessment of early onset periodontitis. *J Periodontol* **66**: 321-328.

Gunsolley JC. Ranney RR. Zambon JJ. Burmeister JA. and Schenkein HA. 1990. *Actinobacillus actinomycetemcomitans* in families afflicted with periodontitis. *J Periodontol.* **61**(10): 643-8.

Han N, Xial X, Zhang L, Zhang J, Tong Y Yang M and Xiao Z. 1991. Bacteriological study of juvenile periodontitis in China. *J Periodont Res* **26**: 409-414.

Harper DS, Lamster IB and Clenti R. 1989. Relationship of subgingival plaque flora to lysosomal and cytoplasmic enzyme activity in gingival crevicular fluid. *J. Clin Periodontology* **16**:164-169.

Hart TC. 1994. Genetic considerations of risk in human periodontal disease. *Current Opinion in Periodontology* 3-11.

Kamma J.J., Nakou M. and Manti F.A. 1994. Microbiota of rapidly progressive periodontitis lesions in association with clinical parameters. *J Periodontol* **65**: 1073-1078.

Kleinfelder JW. Topoll HH. Preus HR. Muller RF. Lange DE. and Bocker W. 1996. Microbiological and immunohistological findings in a patient with Papillon-Lefevre syndrome. *J Clin Periodontology* **23**(11): 1032-8.

Kojima T. Yano K. and Ishikawa I. 1997. Relationship between serum antibody levels and subgingival colonization of *Porphyromonas gingivalis* in patients with various types of periodontitis. *J Periodontology* **68**(7): 618-25.

Kononen E. Asikainen S. and Jousimies-Somer H. 1992a. The early colonization of gram-negative anaerobic bacteria in edentulous infants. *Oral Microbiology & Immunology* **7**(1): 28-31.

Kononen E. Jousimies-Somer H. and Asikainen S. 1992b. Relationship between oral gram-negative anaerobic bacteria in saliva of the mother and the colonization of her edentulous infant. *Oral Microbiology & Immunology* **7**(5): 273-6.

Kononen E. Asikainen S. Saarela M. Karjalainen J. and Jousimies-Somer H. 1994b . The oral gram-negative anaerobic microflora in young children: longitudinal changes from edentulous to dentate mouth. *Oral Microbiology & Immunology* **9**(3): 136-41.

Kononen E. Saarela M. Karjalainen J. Jousimies-Somer H. Alaluusua S. and Asikainen S. 1994a. Transmission of oral *Prevotella melaninogenica* between a mother and her young child. *Oral Microbiology & Immunology* **9**(5): 310-4.

Kowashi Y. 1988. Prevalence of juvenile periodontitis among students at Nagasaki University. *Adv Dent Res.* **2**: 395-398.

Kuru B. Yilmaz S. Noyan U. Acar O. and Kadir T. 1999. Microbiological features and crevicular fluid aspartate aminotransferase enzyme activity in early onset periodontitis patients. *J Clin Periodontology* **26**(1): 19-25.

Lindhe J. and Liljenberg B. 1984. Treatment of localized juvenile periodontitis. Results after 5 years. *J Clin Periodontol* **11**: 399-410.

Loe H. and Brown LJ. 1991. Early onset periodontitis in the United States of America. *J Periodont* **62**: 608-16.

Loesche, W.J. 1985.*Streptococcus mutans* and dental decay in infants. Ch. in Introduction of Food to Infants: Why, When, Which. F.A. Falkner and N. Kretchmer eds., Sp. Iss. *AMER. J. CLINICAL NUTRITION* **41**: 423-435.

Loesche WJ. 1999. The antimicrobial treatment of periodontal disease: Changing the treatment paradigm. Adv Dent Res Aug in press.

Loesche W.J., Syed S.A., Morrison E.C., Kerry G.A., Higgins T. and Stoll J. 1984. Metronidazole in periodontitis. I. Clinical and bacteriological results after 15 to 30 weeks. *J Periodontol* **55**:325-335.

Loesche W.J., Syed S.A., Schmidt E. and Morrison EC. 1985. Bacterial profiles of subgingival plaques in periodontitis. *J Periodontol* **56**: 447-456.

Loesche W.J., Lopatin D.E., Giordano J., Alcoforado G. and Hujoel P. 1992a. Comparison of the benzoyl-DL-arginine-naphthylamide (BANA) test, DNA probes, and immunological reagents for ability to detect anaerobic periodontal infections due to *Porphyromonas gingivalis*, *Treponema denticola*, and *Bacteroides forsythus*. *J Clin Microbiol* **30**: 427-433.

Loesche W.J., Lopatin D.E., Stoll J., van Poperin N. and Hujoel P.P. 1992b. Comparison of various detection methods for periodontopathic bacteria: can culture be considered the primary reference standard? *J Clin Microbiol* **30**: 418-426.

Loesche W.J., Giordano J., Soehren S., *et al.* 1996. Nonsurgical treatment of patients with periodontal disease. *Oral Surg Oral Med Oral Pathol Oral Radiol Endod* **81**: 533-543.

Loesche WJ, and Giordano JR. 1997. Treatment Paradigms in Periodontal Disease. *Compendium for Dental Education* **18**(3): 221-232.

Marazita ML. Burmeister JA. Gunsolley JC. Koertge TE. Lake K. and Schenkein HA. 1994. Evidence for autosomal dominant inheritance and race-specific heterogeneity in early-onset periodontitis. *J Periodontology* **65**(6): 623-30.

Mattila K.J., Valtonen V.V.., Nieminen M.S and Huttunen J.K. 1995. Dental infection and the risk of new coronary events: prospective study of patients with documented coronary artery disease. *Clin Infect Dis* **20**: 588-592.

Matto J, Saarela M, Alaluusua S. Oja V, Jousimies-Somer H, and Asikainen S. 1998. Detection of *Porphyromonas gingivalis* from saliva by PCR by using a simple sample-processing method. *J Clin Microbiol.* **36**: 157-60.

Mikx FHM, Matee MI and Schaeken MJM. 1986. The prevalence of spirochetes in the subgingival microbiota of Tanzanian and Dutch children. *J Clin Periodontol* **13**: 289-293.

Moore W.E.C. and Moore L.V.H. 1994. The bacteria of periodontal diseases. *Periodontol 2000* **5**: 66-77.

Novak MJ. and Novak KF. 1996. Early-onset periodontitis. *Current Opinion in Periodontology* **3**: 45-58

Novak M.J., Stamatelakys C. and Adair S.M. 1991. Resolution of early lesions of juvenile periodontitis with tetracycline therapy alone: long-term observations of 4 cases. *J Periodontol* **62**: 628-633.

Offenbacher S. Heasman PA, Collins JG. 1993. Modulation of host PGE2 secretion as a determinant of periodontal disease expression.. J Periodontol 64: 432-444.

Oliver RC. Brown LJ. and Loe H. 1998. Periodontal diseases in the United States population. *Journal of Periodontology* **69**(2): 269-78.

Quinn SM. Zhang JB. Gunsolley JC. Schenkein JG. Schenkein HA. and Tew JG. 1996. Influence of smoking and race on immunoglobulin G subclass concentrations in early-onset periodontitis patients. *Infection & Immunit.* **64**(7): 2500-5.

Page RC, Sims TJ, Geissler F and Altman LC. 1985. Defective neutrophil and monocyte motility in patients with early onset periodontitis. *Infection Immunity* **47**: 169-175.

Palmer R.M., Watts T.L. and Wilson R.F. 1996. A double-blind trial of tetracycline in the management of early onset periodontitis. *J Clin Periodontol* **23**: 670-674.

Papapanou PN. 1996. Periodontal diseases: epidemiology. *Annals of Periodontology* **1**(1): 1-36.

Persson GR, DeRouen TA and Page RC. 1990. Relationship between levels of aspartate aminotransferase in gingival crevicular fluid and gingival inflammation. *J Periodon Res* **25**: 17-24.

Preus HR. 1988. Treatment of rapidly destructive periodontitis in PaPillon-Lefevre syndrome. Laboratory and clinical observations. *J Clin Periodontology* **15**(10): 639-43.

Ranney RR. 1991. Diagnosis of periodontal diseases. *Advances in Dent Res* **5**: 21-36.

Salvador, S.L., Syed S.A. and Loesche, W.J. 1987. Comparison of three dispersion procedures for the quantitative recovery of cultivable species of subgingival spirochetes. *J. Clin. Microbiol.* **25**: 2230-2232.

Saxen L. Asikainen S. Sandholm L. and Kari K. 1986. Treatment of juvenile periodontitis without antibiotics. A follow-up study. *J Clin Periodontology* **13**(7): 714-9.

Saxen L. and Asikainen S. 1993. Metronidazole in the treatment of localized juvenile periodontitis. *J Clin Periodontol* **20**: 166-171.

Slots J. 1982. Selective medium for isolation of *Actinobacillus actinomycetemcomitans. J Clin Microbiol* **15**: 606-609.

Slots J. and Rosling B.G. 1983. Suppression of the periodontopathic microflora in localized juvenile periodontitis by systemic tetracycline. *J Clin Periodontol* **10**: 465-486.

Sofaer JA. 1990. Genetic approaches in the study of periodontal diseses. *J Clin Periodontol* **17**: 401-408.

Sweeney EA, Alcoforado GAP,Nyman S and Slots J. 1987. Prevalence and microbiology of local prepubertal periodontitis. *Oral Microbiol. Immunol* **2**: 65-70

Tanner A.C.R., Haffer C., Brattthall C. and Socransky S.S. 1979. A study of the bacteria associated with advancing periodontitis in man. *J Clin Periodontol* **6**: 278-307.

Tinoco EM. Sivakumar M. and Preus HR. 1998. The distribution and transmission *of Actinobacillus actinomycetemcomitans* in families with localized juvenile Periodontitis. *J Clinical Periodontology* **25**(2): 99-105.

van der Velden U, Abbas F, van Steenbergen TJ, *et al.* 1989. Prevalence of periodontal breakdown in adolescents and presence of *A. actinomycetemcomitans* in subjects with attachment loss. *J Periodontol* **60**: 604-610.

van Winkelhoff A.J. and Tijhof C.J.. 1992. Microbiological and clinical results of metronidazole plus amoxicillin therapy in *Actinobacillus actinomycetemcomitans*- associated periodontitis. *J Periodontol* **63**: 52-57.

Watson MR, Lopatin DE, Bretz WA, Ertel IJ and Loesche WJ. 1991. Detection of two anaerobic periodontopathogens in children by means of the BANA and ELISA assays. *J. Dent. Res.* **70**: 1052-1056.

Watson MR, Bretz WA and Loesche WJ. 1994. Presence of *Treponema denticola* and *Porphyromonas gingivalis* in children correlated with periodontal disease of their parents. *J. Dent Res* **73**: 1636-1640.

Zambon J.J. 1985. *Actinobacillus actinomycetemcomitans* in human periodontal disease. *J Clin Periodontol* **12**: 1-20.

Zambon JJ. Christersson LA and Slots J. 1983. *A. actinomycetemcomitans* in human periodontal disease; prevalence in patient groups and distribution of biotypes and serotypes within families. *J Periodontol.* **54**: 707-711.

THE APICAL PLAQUE BORDER IN HEALTH AND DISEASE

Nicola Jane Mordan, Hubert Neil Newman, Jennifer Mable Slaney and Michael Anthony Curtis

Microbial biofilms are widespread in nature and have existed for millions of years. The human body is host to many biofilms and plaque biofilm which forms on teeth is part of the natural organic tooth tegument and as such is consistent with health. However there is ample evidence that the plaque accumulation associated with modern diet results in an increase in the prevalence of oral diseases.

Much modern research concerning the aetiology and progression of chronic inflammatory periodontal disease is based upon the characteristics of individual cells whether microbes or host cells and their reaction products. Whilst there is undeniable evidence of an increasing variety of individual plaque organisms in disease this is based on samples removed from specific sites. Relatively little attention is paid to plaque as a microbial community on the tooth surface and on the impact of the intact biofilm on the periodontal tissues. There is a need to understand the precise location of individual plaque members and the composition and behaviour of plaque and its metabolic products in 'at risk' sites.

We have established a protocol for the identification of bacteria and their products in situ using immunocytochemical techniques and electron microscopy. This research has confirmed the presence of implicated Gram negative bacteria at the apical plaque border, that is in the portion of dental plaque closest to the advancing front of the periodontal lesion. Our continuing programme of identification of bacteria in situ in plaque aims to relate laboratory studies of plaque bacteria in isolation to plaque as a living entity on the tooth surface.

Introduction

The majority of surfaces whether biological or abiological, are covered by micro-organisms and each such surface has its own associated individual microbial biofilm (Newman, 1974). In biological systems, the microflora is normally in a state of symbiotic, dynamic equilibrium with its host surface and it is usually as a result of an imbalance in this equilibrium that a pathologic assault may be initiated. The human body is host to many microbial communities including the dental plaque on the tooth surface. Plaque is part of the natural dental organic integument, and as with many other such biofilms, its ubiquitous presence is not necessarily associated with disease. However it is well documented that the various common infectious inflammatory diseases of the gingivae and teeth coincide with changes in the composition of the plaque microflora (Löe, *et al.,* 1965, Newman, 1990).

The origins of the organic covering of the tooth, of which the microflora is a part, have been the subject of some debate, particularly the protective role, if any, of the enamel organ during and after tooth eruption. The present view is that the enamel organ remains and becomes incorporated into the organic tooth integument (Newman, 1973b). This natural organic integument of the enamel surface is not a homogenous structure, and comprises three components - plaque bacteria, acquired pellicle of salivary origin and vestigial enamel organ. It has been proposed that the first bacterial attachment to the tooth is therefore to the original enamel cuticle or salivary pellicle and not directly to the enamel surface. This is also the case with many other natural biofilms, the attachment of which to a mineral surface is mediated by such an acellular organic layer (Newman, 1974). Of these three components only the bacterial component is considered capable of sufficient alteration as to cause injury to the tissues. It is, therefore, on the composition and inter-relationships of the bacteria in plaque that attention has focused in the investigations of disease aetiology in this area.

Several reviews have considered the prevelance of different plaque bacteria in oral health and disease (Newman, 1990, Christersson, 1991), the majority of the data being derived from removed plaque samples. It is now appropriate to review available information concerning the location of periodontopathic bacteria *in situ*, with specific reference to the apical plaque border (APB), as the advancing lesions of both approximal caries and chronic inflammatory peri-odontal disease (CIPD) are in direct relation to this portion of the plaque.

Techniques for examinining apical border plaque
Culture Studies
Culture and histology methodologies employed to identify the constituent bacteria and their products within plaque have utilised mainly plaque isolates, chemostat cultures and clinical biopsies of plaque or host tissue. Information gained from conventional cultural studies has been paramount in relation to the general identification of bacteria, both in the healthy gingival crevice or sulcus and, in particular, in the periodontal pocket. Estimates of the total numbers of species found in the plaque have been given as around 350 (Moore and Moore, 1994) though only the identity of cultivable species can be ascertained in this way. There have been accounts that the proportion of the plaque comprising Gram +ve cocci and rods can range from 70-92% in healthy sites, with spirochaetes and fusiforms rarely observed (Gibbons *et al.*, 1963, Theilade *et al.*, 1966, Slots, 1977). Such reports have also demonstrated an increase in Gram -ve facultative anaerobic rods and spirochaetes at the expense of Gram +ve anaerobic coccoid species with disease progression (Slots, 1977, Moore *et al.*, 1983). This may imply a reduction in the variety of species since there are estimated to be as few as 10 - 30 species of the 300-400 identified in health that may be capable of initiating chronic periodontitis (Socransky and Haffajee, 1994).

Recently there have been assessments of the accuracy with which culture methods detect presumed periodontopathogens when compared with other techniques - DNA probe, indirect immunofluorescence and some commercial kits (Loesche *et al.*, 1992, Aass *et al.*, 1994, Listgarten *et al.*, 1995, van Steenbergen *et al.*, 1996, Papapanou *et al.*, 1997, Tanner *et al.*, 1998). Culture

344

methods appear to be more accurate than the comercial kits but similar to or less accurate than DNA and immunofluorescence techniques, although van Steenbergen (1996) reported that detection with DNA provided many false negatives and false positives. The principal limitations of culture studies are that they do not recover non-viable organisms or those that require fastidious growth conditions, and that they provide little specific location data for organisms *in situ* on the tooth surface. In order to acquire this information, other methodologies may be considered.

Immunofluorescence Studies

As recently as 1990, assays utilising monoclonal antibodies visualised by immunofluorescence were being proposed as highly reliable, accurate probes to oral bacteria (Gmur and Guggenheim, 1990). In the last 10 years data from indirect immunofluorescence combined with light microscopy (LM) have confirmed the identity of several periodontopathic bacteria. However the majority of such studies have involved plaque samples removed from the tooth with little *in situ* data. This basic methodology is very adaptable for *in situ* detection and one *in situ* study has identified periodontopathic bacteria on sections from extracted teeth (Noiri *et al.*, 1997). The study demonstrated the relative localisation of *Porphyromonas gingivalis*, *Campylobacter rectus* and *Actinomyces viscosus* on the tooth surface and also indicated the presence of bacteria in the gingival tissues. As this report illustrates, because sectioned material is used, the method provides the possibility of applying different staining techniques to serial sections. By employing antibodies with various fluorescent markers, it would be possible to distinguish more than 1 species in each *in situ* section. In comparison studies, indirect immunofluorescence has been shown to be more accurate than culture (Listgarten *et al.*, 1995) although this can vary depending on the species in question (Tanner *et al.*, 1998). The limitations of this type of fluorescence detection combined with LM rest principally in the short duration of the fluorescence itself and inadequate resolution by LM.

DNA Probes and Polymerase Chain Reaction (PCR) Studies

DNA probes utilise a hybridisation technique in which hybrid DNA is usually tagged with a radio-labelled marker so that the location of the hybridisation can be visualised on suitably sensitive film. Several studies have used DNA probes to species from removed plaque samples or paper points (Lippke *et al.*, 1991, Haffajee *et al.*, 1992, 1997, Loesche *et al.*, 1992, Soder *et al.*, 1993, Papaponou *et al.*, 1997). This technique appears to be as, if not more, accurate than culture (Papapanou *et al.*, 1997, Tanner *et al.*, 1998). In general DNA probes have confirmed the information gained from many years of culture studies with the advantage that this is a rapid technique which can detect both viable and non-viable organisms. However it is not suited to *in situ* studies since the methodology may require cell lysis and immobilisation onto a suitable substrate for visualisation.

Studies specifically combining DNA and PCR have demonstrated the increased accuracy of the combined technique to detect *Bacteroides forsythus* (Chandad *et al.,* 1997) and *P. gingivalis* (Watanabe and Frommel, 1993). However, this combined methodology is also only suitable for removed specimens.

Enzyme Linked Immunoabsorbant Assay (ELISA) Studies

ELISA involves using known antibodies to screen unknown samples, often detected by colour change and there have been reports on the use of ELISA techniques for analysing plaque samples (Saxen *et al.,* 1989, Clerehugh *et al.,* 1997, Ellwood *et al.,* 1997, Kojima *et al.,* 1997). This technique is not suitable for *in situ* studies since removed samples are required, however, many specimens can be rapidly analysed in this way.

Probe Microscopies

Bacteria have been imaged using the newer probe microscopies in studies specifically aimed at examining bacterial adhesion, bacterial cell coats and, to some extent, biofilms (Razatos *et al.,* 1998, Ridout *et al.,* 1998). However these microscopies, including atomic force and scanning probe, are designed to examine surfaces and 3D architecture at a very high resolution giving maximum working distances of up to only $10\mu m$. This yields a limited number of cells to provide new information concerning the types of bacteria at the advancing front of the plaque in health and disease, or detail of relevant interactions with the host tissues. Although these techniques are feasible for application to the most apical plaque, there is currently no data concerning the application of probe microscopies to bacteria *in situ.*

Confocal Laser Scanning Microscopy (CLSM)

CLSM, a technique for providing 3-dimensional data from immunofluorescent labeled specimens, has been applied to both *in vitro* biofilms of oral bacteria, *P. gingivalis* and *Streptococcus gordonii* (Cook *et al.*, 1998) and organisms *in situ*, such as *P. gingivalis,* (Assmus *et al.,* 1997). This instrumentation is potentially capable of identifying up to 3-4 different species by visualisation with different fluorochromes within the bulk of plaque, and can retrieve information from large areas. However, CLSM may be less accurate at providing the exact location of individual organisms, particularly close to the tooth surface, bearing in mind the autofluorescence of tooth structures, and since bulk specimens are examined and the instrumentation only detects fluorescent probes, information gained from using different types of stains on similar adjacent areas is not available.

Scanning Electron Microscopy (SEM) and Transmission Electron Microscopy (TEM) Studies

Since the realisation that the constituent members of the apical plaque border are possible causative agents in chronic inflammatory periodontal disease

(CIPD), several SEM and TEM studies have examined the plaque *in situ* on the tooth surface, with the aim of identifying the offending specific organisms comprising the apical plaque. In particular, the identity is sought of those bacteria at the most apical border and within the so-called plaque-free zone (PFZ) and therefore closest to the advancing front of the periodontal lesion. In one pilot *in vitro* SEM study, suspensions of pure *Actinobacillus actinomycetemcomitans* were treated with antibodies conjugated to gold probes and visualised with a back-scatter detector in the SEM (Carassi *et al.,* 1990). Although useful for identification of layers of bacteria a few deep at the most apical tip of the plaque, such methodologies would not be appropriate for more bulky plaques, as organisms within deep plaque could not be visualised. An advance in SEM technology has led to the Environmental SEM (ESEM) which examines wet specimens without prior preparation. This novel instrumentation would be effective in verifying that previously reported spatial arrangements are not preparation artefacts, but has the same limitation as traditional SEM of only being capable of examining surface structures. Specimens can be immunolabeled and examined with the ESEM but they cannot be kept without further preservation. This methodology has been used to study exopolymers in biofilms (Allison *et al.,* 1998) but not bacteria *in situ*.

The combination of resin embedded material and TEM has proved very successful at verifying the Gram nature of organisms in apical border plaque and localising their position in relation to the tooth surface *in situ* (Newman, 1973c, 1976). This method of specimen preparation also provides the possibility of using electron-histochemical staining techniques including stains for the pres- ence of intra- and extra-cellular polysaccharides (Newman, 1979a, Vrahopoulos, 1992). Autoradiography, where the specimens are treated with radioactive- labeled precursors and then processed for LM and TEM, can be applied to *in situ* plaque. This has provided information concerning the metabolism and viability of plaque organisms on the tooth surface (Saxton, 1975, Newman and Wilson, 1975).

With careful selection of fixative procedure and embedding resin (Maunsbach and Afzelius, 1999), TEM can be used for immuno-labelling specific bacteria *in situ*. None of the identification techniques mentioned previously provides the high-resolution of TEM, and therefore, the application of immunology to resin-embedded material is particularly relevant to the study of species at the advancing front of plaque. Rosen *et al.* as early as 1976, had immunolabelled *Streptococcus sanguis* in plaques grown on resin strips attached to teeth. The label was visualised with horseradish peroxidase or heavy metal stains, a method which has been superseded by visualisation with gold probes. Few studies have adopted this immunogold technique but it has been used sucessfully to identify *P.gingivalis* and *Treponema denticola* in subgingival plaque (Kigure *et al.,* 1995) and *A. actinomycetemcomitans* in the apical plaque border *in situ* on the tooth surface (Vrahopoulos, 1989). The principal limitation of this methodology is the length of time for specimen preparation however, once labeled, the sections can be kept and re-examined for years.

It is important to bear in mind with all of the techniques mentioned here for the detection and identification of oral bacteria, whether from removed samples or *in situ* specimens, we can only locate that which we have set out to find. Research which uses immunological markers or DNA probes can only detect those species which the respective markers or probes have been directed at. Culture techniques may employ selective media, although non-selective methods give the greatest possibility of yielding many species. There is always the possibility that species as yet uncultivated will prove to be important pathogens in the oral environment. However, a recent study described previously unknown species in removed plaque samples, using molecular methods and PCR, one of which was identified as related to oral asaccharolytic *Eubacterium* spp (Harper-Owen *et al.,* 1999).

In situ plaque

The earliest plaque formation on the natural tooth surface appears to consist predominantly of streptococcal forms with *Streptococcus sanguis* probably one of the most important organisms in early tooth colonisation (Carlsson, 1968). Extensive LM, SEM and TEM studies have characterised the spatial arrangements of plaque organisms on the tooth, both in health and disease. Such studies have also shown specific structural differences relating to the onset of disease, apart from an increase in plaque bulk. In health, and even throughout the CIPD process, plaque normally follows the highest margin of the gingiva, and can be demonstrated in both LM and SEM surface views to be separated from the attached tissues by a macroscopically plaque-free zone (Newman, 1973a, 1976). In health the apical border is well defined by the gingival margin, but with the initiation of disease the plaque usually extends into the gingival crevice (Newman, 1976, 1992). As the disease progresses, the most apical plaque remains some distance from the periodontitis lesion as it advances apically (Newman, 1976).

The 'healthy' plaque comprises many bacteria and other microorganisms and the arrangement of bacterial morphotypes has been demonstrated in topographical and structural studies *in situ* on the tooth surface. LM and TEM studies have demonstrated that the spatial order of these organisms varies from highly organised at the tooth surface of established plaque, where the plaque bacteria are often arranged in palisades with little intermicrobial matrix, to loosely associated at the interface with the oral cavity, where the bacteria are randomly arranged with relatively more intermicrobial matrix (Newman, 1973c). The most apical plaque also comprises randomly associated organisms and an increased number of lysed bacteria (Newman 1979a, Vrahopoulos *et al.*, 1992). The palisade arrangement of microorganisms may simply be a consequence of cell division in a limited space, but its significance is possibly that of nutrition for organisms in deeper plaque (Poole and Newman, 1971, Newman and Poole, 1974). TEM studies have verified Gram stains of plaque and shown that the organisms present on the tooth surface in health are predominantly Gram +ve cocci and rods (Listgarten, 1976).

348

There is evidence from TEM electron-histochemical staining that the large Gram +ve cells associated with health are polysaccharide producers and that the intercellular matrix within the dense plaque at the tooth surface contains a higher proportion of polysaccharides than that of the superficial plaque especially at the subcontact area apical border, where both approximal caries and CIPD are initiated (Newman, 1977, 1979b). *In situ* electronhistochemistry has demonstrated that even bacteria deep within the healthy plaque at the tooth surface are capable of metabolising carbohydrates (Newman, 1976). Autoradiography has also been applied to investigate the viability of plaque organisms *in situ* and has demonstrated that even the deep plaque organisms are capable of cell division although most labelling was in the more superficial layers. We may assume that the whole of the structurally apparently intact plaque microbiota is active and thus capable of interacting with the host tissues, while viability may vary depending on growth conditions at different loci within a given plaque (Newman and Wilson, 1975).

In general terms, the two most common groups of healthy plaque bacteria are *Streptococcus* spp and Gram +ve rods mainly *Actinomyces* spp. There are few spirochaetes and other Gram -ve organisms associated with healthy plaque.

In relation to both caries and gingivitis initiation there are shifts in proportions of organisms in the apical border plaque subjacent to the sub-contact area, with a notable increase in the numbers of Gram -ve rods and spirochaetes present, as demonstrated with both SEM and TEM (Listgarten, 1976, Newman, 1976, 1979a). This progression from predominantly Gram +ve cocci, rods and filaments to more Gram -ve cocci, filaments, vibrios and spirochaetes is well documented to be associated with CIPD progression (Newman, 1976, Vrahopoulos *et al.*, 1995). The transition occurs principally in the most apical plaque, that is, the portion of plaque associated most directly with onset and progression of disease, (approximal) dental caries, or the CIPDs.

Although the exact progression of organisms in transition from health to disease is unknown, studies have indicated that no single bacterium or group of bacteria are specific pathogens, as stated above, but rather that shifts in plaque microflora underlie the relationship of plaque to CIPDs and dental caries (Newman and Poole, 1974, Newman, 1990, Zimmer *et al.*, 1991, Babaahmady *et al.*, 1997). More recent evidence from plaque samples and some *in situ* specimens confirms that many of the species present in disease are also present in health, and that there are few direct correlations between the mere presence of a single species and the state of oral health or disease. *P. gingivalis* is one of the few species still proposed as having a greater frequency in diseased sites (Ali *et al.*, 1996, Albander *et al.*, 1997, Clerehugh *et al.*, 1997, Papapanou *et al.*, 1997, Schliegel-Bregenzer *et al.*, 1998). However this species was not isolated in a study by Rawlinson (1993) of subgingival plaque samples from adult periodontitis patients.

As mentioned earlier, attention should be directed specifically to the apical border of the plaque as the advancing lesions of (approximal and cervical) caries and of chronic gingivitis and periodontitis are in direct relation to this portion of the plaque throughout the course of these diseases. There are sparse data on the precise *in situ* location of specific periodontopathogens at the apical border of plaque but, despite the wealth of information concerning the inhabitants of the subgingival plaque, we do not know which are present at the critical locus. Reference has been made to the carbohydrate metabolism of plaque organisms in this location and it has been shown that mutans streptococci and other caries-related species predominate in this location and are related to the initiation of chronic gingivitis as well as (approximal) caries (Newman, 1977, Babaahmady *et al.,* 1997). Our studies continue to be directed at the apical plaque border with reference to its involvement in the common oral infections, dental caries and the CIPDs. We have been particularly concerned with the identification of important metabolic features and with the identification (*in situ* where possible) of organisms, as these relate to disease. Since caries data have been reported elsewhere, in this paper we have concentrated on CIPDs and the significance of the apical plaque border zone and its bacteria, with special emphasis on their *in situ* identification.

In this report are presented our latest data relating to the localisation of 3 potential periodontopathic species *in situ* in the apical border plaque relating to CIPD.

Materials and methods

Although the primary aim was the *in situ* identification of bacteria at the advancing front of the apical border plaque and in the so-called PFZ, since many previous bacterial population studies have concentrated on removed plaque samples, such plaque aliquots were included for comparison. Specimens therefore comprised pure cultures of bacteria as immunological controls, natural dental plaque samples removed from the bottom of the peridontal pocket and apical border plaque *in situ* on extracted teeth.

Specimen Origination

P. gingivalis (strain W50), *Capnocytophaga ochracea* (*ATCC27872*) and *Campylobacter rectus* (FDC285) were obtained from 3-5day blood agar culture and inocula of each strain were grown in brain-heart infusion broth under anaerobic conditions for 48 hours at 37 °C. Cells were harvested by centrifugation at 10,000g.

Subgingival plaque samples from the apical border were carefully removed with a curette from patients (4 male, 2 female) with diagnosed routine chronic adult periodontitis and placed directly in fixative.

Teeth from patients with routine chronic adult periodontitis (1 male, 3 female) were carefully removed with minimal disturbance to the subgingival plaque and gently rinsed in sterile normal saline before immersion in fixative.

Polyclonal Antibody Production *(Curtis **et al.,** 1990)*

Inoculae of *P. gingivalis*, *C. ochracea* and *C. rectus* prepared as before were grown in pre-reduced BM broth (Shah *et al.*, 1976) and incubated in an anaerobic

Table 1 List of antibody concentrations used for labelling specimens.

Antibody	Type	Concentration
Rabbit anti-*Porphyromonas gingivalis*	primary	1 in 200
Rabbit anti-*Capnocytophaga ochracea*	primary	1 in 20
Rabbit anti-*Campylobacter rectus*	primary	1 in 50
Goat-anti-rabbit 10nm gold (Biocell, UK)	secondary	1 in 50

chamber at 37°C for 48 hours. Cells were harvested by centrifugation at 10,000g at 4°C for 20 minutes, washed in sterile tris HCl (50mM pH7.2) at 4°C, formalin fixed and washed again in tris HCl. Hybrid lop Dutch rabbits were immunised weekly for 10 weeks.

Specimen Preparation

Suspensions of bacteria from control cultures were centrifuged to form a pellet, the supernatant removed and the bacteria resuspended in fixative. After fixation, the bacteria were further centrifuged to form a pellet which was maintained entire for the remainder of the processing. Plaque samples and extracted teeth were treated as whole specimens and handled with caution in order to maintain their integrity. Reagents for processing were added and removed with great care. The methodology was adapted from Marshall *et al.* (1990).

All specimens were fixed in 0.5% glutaraldehyde in 0.1M cacodylic acid buffer (CAB), pH 7.4, 30 minutes for cultures and plaque samples and 1-2 hours for teeth at 4°C. All specimens were dehydrated in a graded series of ethanols from 20% to 90% only and then embedded in LR White resin at 0°C. After embedding, teeth were sliced bucco-lingually and corono-apically using a high-speed diamond saw (Exakt, UK) and briefly stored in 0.1M CAB. Slices were taken from the approximal region of each tooth. Where possible the so-called plaque-free zone was used as a reference to establish the location of the apical border of the plaque but for specimens without osmium tetroxide post-fixation this was not always easy and larger lengths of tooth were processed. The slices were decalcified in sodium hydroxide-buffered EDTA pH7.4 for 3-4 weeks at room temperature, re-dehydrated and re-embedded in LR White. Semi-thin sections of 0.5μm were taken and stained with toluidine blue for orientation. Ultra-thin sections were then cut at 90 - 100nm and collected on either copper 200 or carbon-formvar-coated copper 200 grids for immunocytochemistry.

Ultrastructure

Sections on both uncoated and carbon-formvar-coated 200 mesh copper grids were stained with 1% ethanolic uranyl acetate and Reynolds' lead citrate (Reynolds, 1963) and viewed in a JEOL 100CX (JEOL, UK) transmission electron microscope operating at 60-80kV.

Nicola Jane Mordan, Hubert Neil Newman, Jennifer Mable Slaney & Michael Anthony Curtis

Table 2 Array to show the results of antibody reaction with pure cultures.

Antibody	*P. gingivalis*	*C. ochracea*	*C. rectus*
anti-*P. gingivalis*	+++	-	-
anti-*C. ochracea*	-	+++	-
anti-*C. rectus*	-	-	+++

Key:
0 no reaction   - very slight reaction   ++ average labelling

Immunocytochemistry

Sections on carbon-formvar-coated 200 mesh copper grids were placed section side down on drops of reagent on dental wax. Phosphate-buffered saline (PBS) was prepared as a 10mM solution using 1 tablet in 500ml distilled water (Sigma Chemicals Ltd, UK). Tris buffer was prepared as a 50mM solution using 1 tablet in 15ml distilled water (Sigma Chemicals Ltd, UK). All buffer solutions and the distilled water were sterilised and filtered prior to use. The dilutions of the primary and secondary antibodies used are shown in Table 1. As each copper grid was moved from one solution to another, the drop of liquid on the grid was tapped off so that there was minimal dilution and contamination from one reagent to the next. Also the forceps were wiped between handling each grid throughout the process. The immunocytochemical methodology was adapted from Mordan *et al.* (1992).

Immunocytochemical Protocol

Sections on carbon-formvar-coated grids were rehydrated on drops of distilled water for 10 minutes. They were then placed on drops of 2% powdered fat-free milk in 10 mM PBS for 30 minutes to block non-immune groups. The grids were incubated in the relevant 1° antibody in 10mM PBS for 1 hour before washing in drops of 10mM PBS for 2 x 1 minute and 1 longer 5 minute washes. They were then washed in drops of 50mM TRIS with 0.1% Tween 20 for 2 rapid 1 minute and 1 longer 5 minute washes. The grids were further incubated in 2° antibody at 1 in 50 in 50mM Tris for 1 hour and then washed in drops of 50 mM TRIS for 2 rapid 1 minute and 1 longer 5 minute washes. All grids were given a final wash in distilled water for similar time periods to previous washes. The grids were blotted dry and stained with ethanolic uranyl acetate and Reynolds' lead citrate for 1 minute each.

All antibodies were applied against pure cultures of their own species or genus and the pure cultures of the other species used in the study.

Results

Pure Cultures

In all the cultures examined there was a positive labelling of the pure cultures by the appropriate specific antibody and only sparse labelling with other species (Table 2). The immunolabelling of pure cultures of *P. gingivalis* treated with

352

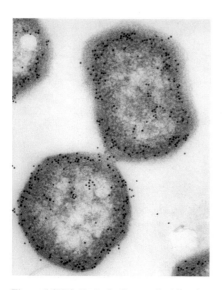

Figure 1 TEM. *P. gingivalis* treated with anti-*P. gingivalis* showing the predominant distribution of gold probes within the cell membrane/wall complex.   x81,000

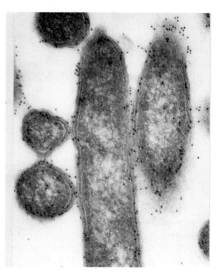

Figure 2 TEM. *C. ochracea* treated with anti-*C. ochracea* showing the distribution of gold probes mostly within the cell wall/cell coat complex.   x75,000

anti-*P. gingivalis* serum revealed a pattern of labelling such that the probes were mainly confined to the cell wall and cytoplasmic membrane with less in the cytoplasm and cell coat (Figure 1). Cultures of *C. ochracea* treated with anti-*C. ochracea* serum showed little cytoplasmic staining and the majority of probes were found in the cell wall and coat (Figure 2). When sections from cultures of *C. rectus* were treated with anti-*C. rectus* serum the labelling was also located at the cytoplasmic membrane and cell wall (Figure 3).

Subgingival Plaque

Six specimens of apical border samples from periodontitis cases have been immunolabeled, and there were several distinct bacterial arrangements within the plaque which seemed to

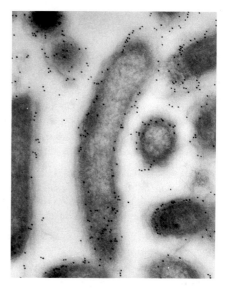

Figure 3 TEM. *C. rectus* treated with anti- *C. rectus* showing the distribution of gold probes within the cell membrane/cell wall complex. x61,000

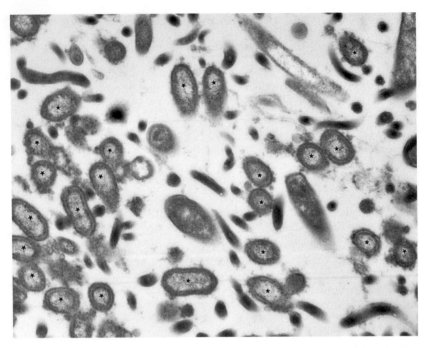

Figure 4 TEM of a portion of loosely associated bacteria from a plaque sample demonstrating the positive *P. gingivalis* organisms (asterisks). There are unlabeled Gram -ve cells present, the majority of which are spirochaetes.   x21,000

possess differing labelling properties. There were areas of loosely associated plaque bacteria with some intermicrobial matrix and, usually adjacent, areas of more densely packed organisms. These two types of arrangement of plaque cells were both readily immunolabeled. Three other types of plaque arrangement were observed in these samples which did not appear to immunolabel successfully. There was an electron-dense type of plaque where the bacteria were generally unrecognisable, often surrounded by lysed organisms and other areas where calcification appeared to be taking place.

Two of the plaque samples contained abundant *P. gingivalis* (asterisks) (Figure 4) in areas where the biofilm was loosely associated. The intermicrobial matrix in these areas, particularly between the *P. gingivalis* cells, also labeled positive for *P. gingivalis*. There were several large 'bristle' formations in one of the specimens and many smaller 'corn-cob' arrangements in the other. No *P. gingivalis*-positive bacteria labeled in the centre or among the bacteria close to the centre of the large 'bristle' formations. However in the small 'corn-cob' associations where a single layer of cells was observed surrounding a central bacterium, the former were found to label positively for *P. gingivalis* (Figure 5). Many of these *P. gingivalis* labeled 'corn-cobs' were observed in areas of densely packed organisms. *P. gingivalis* was not observed in the remaining four

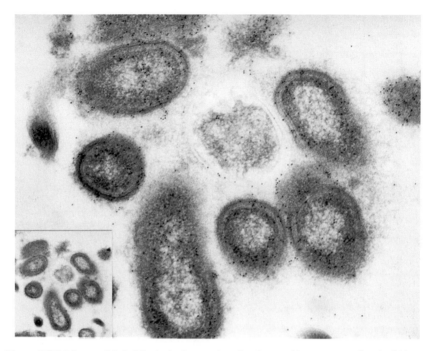

Figure 5 TEM. Immunolabeled *P. gingivalis* organisms in a 'corn-cob' arrangement (inset) within loosely associated removed plaque. Note that the central bacterium also has some immuno-probes at its surface.   x56,000

plaques, even after extensive searching and immunostaining further sections. It was noted that these four plaques differed from those containing *P. gingivalis* in that a large proportion comprised primarily electron-dense plaque surrounded by debris and bacterial ghosts (Figure 6).

    C. ochracea was found in five of the six subgingival plaque samples though it was not abundant. Bacteria stained positive in the loosely associated and more dense areas of plaque and occasional specimens were found among the lysed bacteria surrounding the electron-dense plaque (Figure 7). There were also organisms which stained positive for *C. ochracea* in the layer of cells surrounding the central bacteria of the 'bristle' associations (Figure 8). It was noted that the two samples which stained immuno-positive for *C. ochracea* but which had indicated a total lack of *P. gingivalis* comprised mainly dense plaque, electron-dense plaque and calculus, and one of these samples had only a few *C. ochracea* cells present.

    No bacteria stained positive for *C. rectus* in any of the six samples of subgingival plaque.

    One of the subgingival plaque samples generally did not label for any of the three organisms immunolocalised in this study. It was, however, noticeable that there were many large filamentous Gram -ve organisms present which stained prolifically with each of the three primary antibodies (Figure 9). This appeared

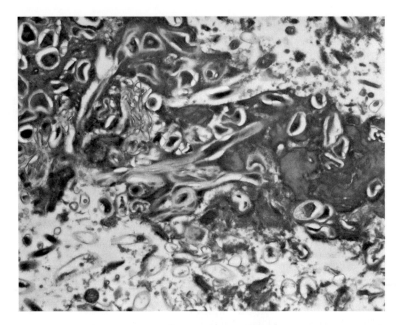

Figure 6 TEM illustrating the electron-dense areas frequently observed in the plaque samples. The bacteria within the electron-dense area reveal little ultrastructure whilst the majority of the surrounding bacteria are lysed.   x14,000

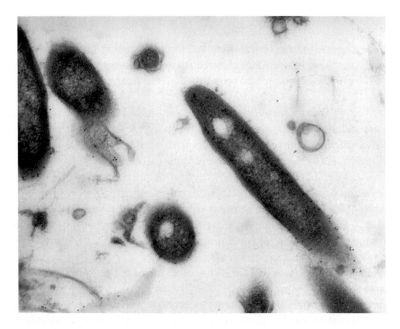

Figure 7 TEM of an area close to the electron-dense plaque observed in samples where several organisms identified as *C. ochracea* were located. x42,000

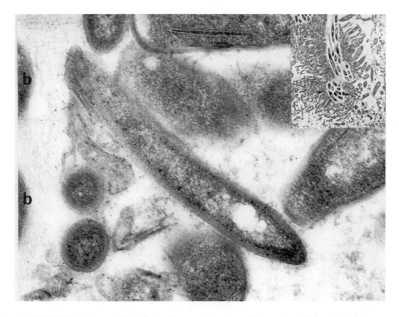

Figure 8 TEM of *C. ochracea* identified adjacent to the central bacterium (b) in a 'bristle' association (inset) from the loosely associated removed plaque. The labeled organism is aligned with one end attached to the central core and there is also some labeled cell debris.   x52,000

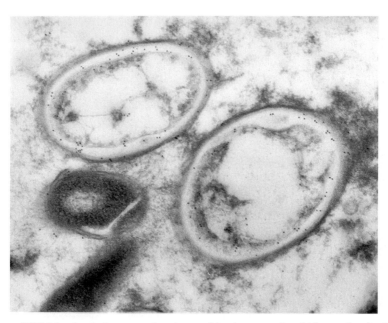

Figure 9 TEM showing the large organisms in one of the plaque samples which were found to label with all three antisera used in the study. They were similar to the bacteria at the central core of the 'corn-cob' and 'bristle' associations.   x58,000

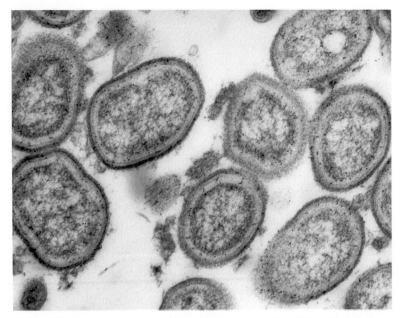

Figure 10 TEM of *P. gingivalis* organisms from an area of outer plaque at the APB. This area was remarkable for the numbers of *P. gingivalis* present and the intermicrobial matrix which was also immunolabeled. x52,000

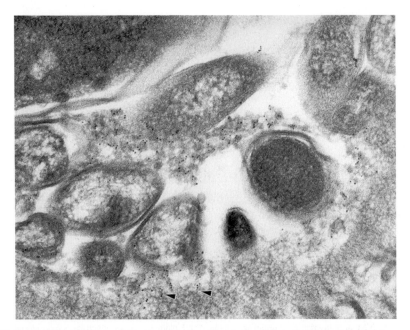

Figure 11 TEM of an area adjacent to the tooth surface in the APB region where cell debris/ intercellular matrix is immunolabeled for *P. gingivalis* as are some areas of the dental cuticle (arrows). x44,000

similar to the organism at the centre of the 'corn-cob' and 'bristle' structures which also labeled for each of the three bacterial species on consecutive sections.

Apical Plaque Border

Four specimens immunostained for *P. gingivalis*, *C. ochracea* and *C. rectus*. The semi-thin sections of these specimens were stained with toluidine blue and photographed to aid orientation of the apical border for TEM. The principal aim of this part of the study was to characterise the most apical plaque and the bacteria in the so-called PFZ. However, where possible the established plaque and the remains of any gingival tissue were also examined, although the constraints of specimen size for TEM resulted in these areas not always being present.

P. gingivalis

P. gingivalis was identified in three of the four apical plaque border specimens and was fairly abundant. Organisms staining positive for *P. gingivalis* were observed in the outer, less dense areas of the established plaque where they occurred as single cells or small colonies. In one apical border plaque (Figure 10) there were outer areas where the majority of organisms labeled for *P. gingivalis*. No cells were identified as *P. gingivalis* at the tooth interface. However, there was cell debris/intermicrobial matrix which labeled with the *P. gingivalis* antibody within the apical border plaque and, in particular, between the organisms in the dense plaque at the tooth surface (Figure 11). There was also immuno-labelling in the outer layer of the dental cuticle (Figure 11) in the area of attachment of plaque to tooth.

At the apical plaque border where the plaque was generally less organised, *P. gingivalis* was often amongst the most apical organisms (Figure 12). It was located in the so-called PFZ in two of the four specimens, where it was observed either alone or associated with small groups of other morphotypes (Figure 13) and appeared viable, or at least structurally intact. In the sections examined, no organism labelling for *P. gingivalis* was observed attached to the dental cuticle in the PFZ although some cells were less than 1μm away (Figure 13). On one of the specimens, which both labeled for *P. gingivalis* and contained some gingival remnants removed with the tooth, the organism was observed next to the tissue, near the small 'bristle' associations in that location, where it appeared viable (Figure 14).

As with the removed plaque samples, where 'corn-cob' associations were observed, usually in the outer plaque of the apical border, the attached cells often labeled for *P. gingivalis* (Figure 15), whereas there was no such labelling in the attached cells of the 'bristle' structures in the apical plaque border.

C. ochracea

C. ochracea was detected in all four apical plaque border specimens, in both the dense plaque at the tooth interface and in the less dense outer plaque, in the

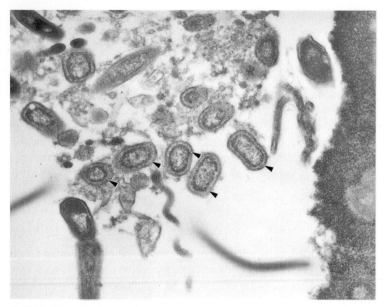

Figure 12 TEM of *P. gingivalis* organisms (arrows) at the most apical border of the plaque where they appear viable. x21,000

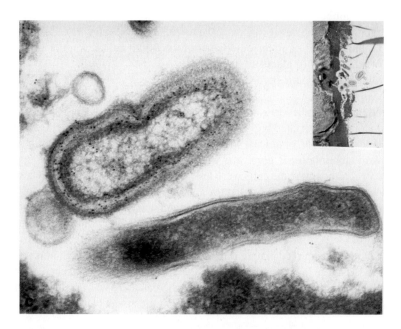

Figure 13 TEM of a *P. gingivalis* cell in the so-called PFZ (inset). This organism appears healthy at this location and may be dividing. Note that although not directly attached to the dental cuticle (C) it is close to it. x71,000

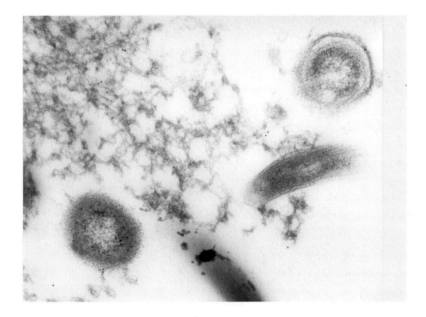

Figure 14 TEM of *P. gingivalis* identified adjacent to the gingival tissue remnants removed with the tooth.   x72,000

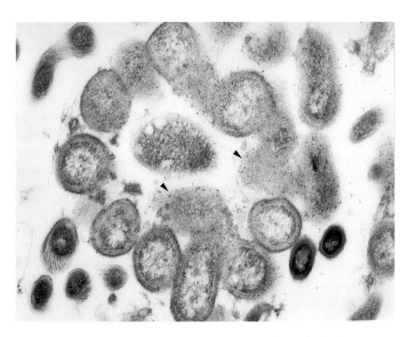

Figure 15 TEM of a 'corn-cob' arrangement from the outer loosely associated apical border plaque. The attached organisms have labeled for *P. gingivalis* but note the degeneration of the organisms where the structure becomes two cells thick (arrows).   x35,500

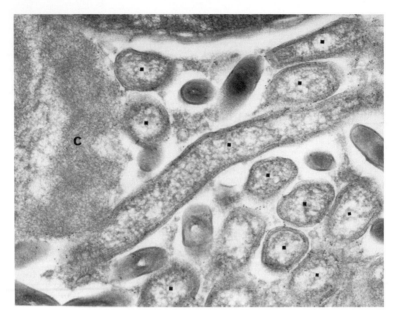

Figure 16 TEM showing a group of organisms labeled as *C. ochracea* (boxes) directly adjacent to the dental cuticle (C) in the apical border plaque. Only one of the cells is attached, at one end, to the cuticle and aligned perpendicular to it.   x49,000

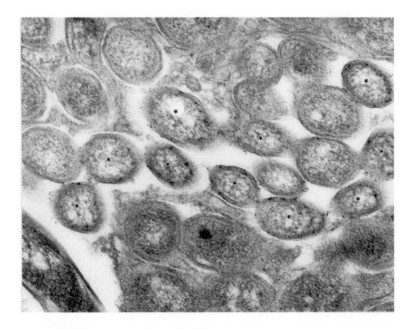

Figure 17 TEM of an area of loosely associated organisms at the outer region of the apical plaque border. Note microcolony immunolabeled as *C ochracea* (asterisks).   x50,000

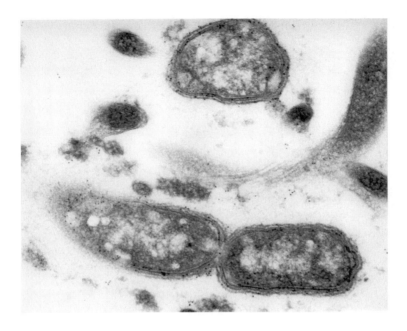

Figure 18 TEM of *C. ochracea* located at the most apical region of the plaque where it is apparently dividing.   x60,000

apical plaque border, the so-called PFZ and the tissue remnants.

In both the apical border and the more organised plaque, *C. ochracea* was often observed in small colonies at the tooth interface (asterisks) but cells were only occasionally aligned at right angles to the dental cuticle in these locations (Figure 16). In the outer plaque (Figure 17) *C. ochracea* was found both as single cells and in small colonies (asterisks). *C. ochracea* was often identified at the advancing plaque border and comprised some of the most apical organisms, where they appeared structurally intact (Figure 18). *C. ochracea* was also located in the small groups of organisms in the PFZ and within the islands of bacteria below the advancing front of the plaque (Figure 19). One of the specimens contained many inflammatory cells both around the plaque and covering the PFZ and *C. ochracea* was observed apparently within large vacuoles of the inflammatory cells, although serial sections were not performed to confirm this, and amongst the inflammatory cells in the PFZ.

In one of the two specimens which included remains of gingival tissue, *C. ochracea* was identified associated with the bristle formations found next to the gingival tissue (Figure 20). There were some separate cells which may have become detached from the 'bristle' but *C. ochracea* was not found within the tissue itself.

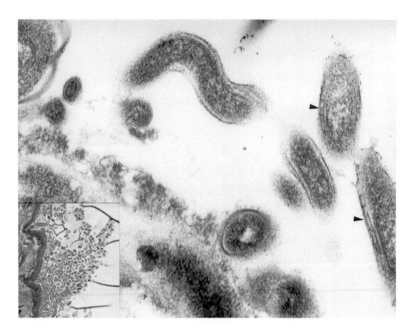

Figure 19 TEM of several cells of *C. ochracea* (arrows) in the so-called PFZ. The cells were part of a small island (inset) and of some distance from the apical plaque border.   x50,000

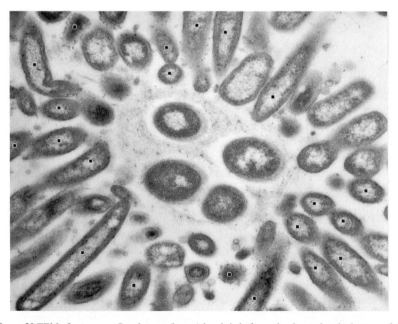

Figure 20 TEM of numerous *C. ochracea* (boxes) in a bristle formation located at the bottom of the pocket adjacent to gingival tissue residues. Note the extensive labelling of the interbacterial matrix of the core bacteria.   x25,000

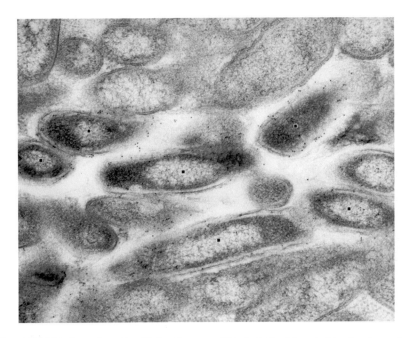

Figure 21 TEM of organisms identified as *C. rectus* within the bulk of the apical border plaque close to the tooth interface. The cytoplasm appears slightly more electron-dense than in adjacent cells. x50,000

C. rectus

C. rectus was identified significantly in only one of the apical plaque border specimens although a single organism and some labeled cell debris/intercellular matrix were found in a second specimen. *C. rectus* was observed in the deeper layers of the plaque and at the tooth interface, but not in great numbers. Small colonies were identified in the deep plaque (asterisk) and these organisms appeared more electron-dense than the surrounding unidentified cells (Figure 21). Very few cells labeled for *C. rectus* in the less dense outer plaque (Figure 22). This organism was also identified at the bottom of the pocket where it was associated with two 'bristle' formations (Figure 23)

Few organisms attached to the dental cuticle in the so-called PFZ with the exception of unidentified coccoid forms sometimes observed within the cuticle. However, there was an area of cuticle which was apparently being undermined by spirochaete and filamentous organisms and a cell of *P. gingivalis* was observed adjacent to this group (Figure 24).

Discussion

Conventional microbiology and microscopy studies of the healthy gingival sulcus or crevice have shown the presence of strict but mainly facultative anaerobes. Gram +ve cocci and rods account for 70-92% of all cultivable flora (Gibbons *et al.,* 1963, Theilade *et al.,* 1966, Slots, 1977), whilst Gram -ve

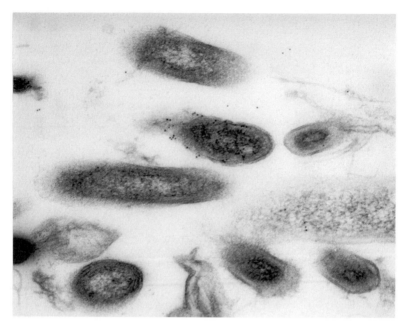

Figure 22 TEM of a single cell of *C. rectus* located in the loosely associated outer apical border plaque.   x66,000

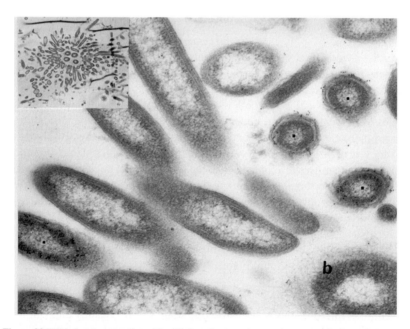

Figure 23 TEM showing organisms identified as *C. rectus* (squares) amongst the bacteria surrounding the central core bacteria (b) of a 'bristle' formation (inset) located adjacent to the gingival tissue residue. x48,000

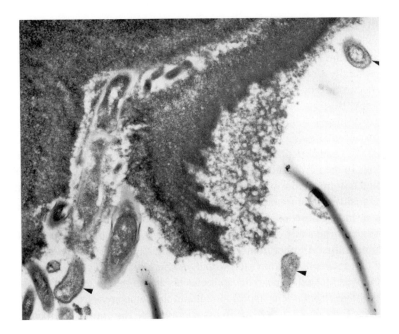

Figure 24 TEM of an area of the so-called PFZ with several bacteria within the dental cuticle. None have been immunolabeled, but *P. gingivalis* cells are close to the group.   x17,000

organisms make up the remainder, with spirochaetes and fusiforms rarely observed. Again one may emphasise in relation to biofilm studies in general and dental plaque in particular, that many biofilm organisms have not yet been cultivated, and studies of plaque based on cultivable counts alone may be misleading. TEM studies have shown that in health there are mostly Gram +ve cocci at the tooth interface with few Gram -ve organisms. Spirochaetes are rare in the healthy sulcus. The change from health to disease has been documented with a shift from Gram +ve cocci, rods and filaments to more Gram -ve cocci, filaments, vibrios and spirochaetes. Most relevant are the changes in the bacterial population at the sites of disease onset and progression if we are to elucidate the direct and indirect pathogenic mechanisms of concern.

From the few previous *in situ* studies there is evidence that a change in the frequency and location of bacteria occurs both within the bulk of the plaque and with increasing proximity to the apical border of plaque in routine chronic adult periodontitis. There have been various accounts of the zonation of the bulk plaque ranging from 2 - 4 layers (Listgarten, 1976, Vrahopoulos *et al.*, 1992) but this is probably dependent on many factors such as age, location and composition of the plaque and may not, of itself, be significant in the progression of disease, especially as there is no such zonation at the apical plaque border. Vrahopoulos *et al.* (1992) found that the most apical intact organisms, either in isolation or in bacterial islands in the so-called PFZ, were Gram -ve cocci and rods with only occasional other morphotypes observed. The present study has also shown that there are many fewer morphotypes at the advancing front of the plaque and in the PFZ, again mainly coccoid, with *P. gingivalis, C. ochracea* and occasionally *C. rectus* identified using immunocytochemistry.

The occurrence of *P. gingivalis* in both the removed plaque samples and *in situ* at the APB is not unexpected. This species is well documented as a common inhabitant of plaque in both health and disease. In an *in situ* study Noiri *et al.* (1997) observed *P. gingivalis* throughout subgingival plaque in advanced adult periodontitis. Using streptavidin-biotin-linked probes, *P. gingivalis* was located at all levels in the periodontal pocket in 9/12 samples. However other immuno-logical and culture studies have noted that, even in diseased sites, there was not always a positive identification for *P. gingivalis* in removed subgingival plaque samples, a finding observed in 2/6 of our plaque samples. Indeed Rawlinson (1993) in a cultural study did not detect *P. gingivalis* in any of 21 subjects with adult periodontitis. Another immunogold labelling study (Kigure *et al.,* 1995) reported that *P. gingivalis* coexisted with *T. denticola* in the deeper levels of the plaque but was located beneath the spirochaetes and higher in the pocket. We have found that *P. gingivalis* appears to inhabit the same areas as the spirochaetes throughout the plaque in association with the chronic periodontitis lesion, except obviously where this organism is apparently absent from the sample.

P. gingivalis, was observed to adhere around the central filament in the small 'corn-cob' formations of chronic periodontitis-related subgingival plaque but was not identified internally in large 'bristle' formations. If the larger 'bristle' formations develop from the smaller associations, it would appear that cells of *P. gingivalis* do not remain viable in the innermost location. We have demonstated that where the layer around a 'corn-cob' becomes as little as two cells thick, the innermost cells lose their structural integrity. Cell/cell and cell/surface interac-tions have been reported to alter the surface coat of *P. gingivalis* cells (Xie *et al.,* 1997) If the 'bristle' formations have a separate development from the smaller type, this specific localisation of *P. gingivalis* may be a manifestation of some of the microbial complexes which have been identified in previous *in vitro* studies (Kornman *et al.,* 1991, Socransky *et al.,* 1998).

In 3/4 *in situ* specimens which were found to contain abundant *P. gingivalis,* the organism was identified at the advancing front of the plaque and in the PFZ, where it appeared to be structurally intact and therefore, possibly, viable. However, *P. gingivalis* was not identified within the deep plaque adjacent to the tooth, though there was much labeled cell debris in this region, including within the dental cuticle. It is possible that *P. gingivalis* cells, initially adjacent to the dental cuticle, lysed in this area as the plaque density increased. It may be proposed that, if these organisms had originally attached to or been close to the dental cuticle at the advancing front, they do not appear to survive or propagate to any great extent in the plaque interior. The intercellular labelled material may also comprise surface associated material dislodged from *P. gingivalis* cells elsewhere in the plaque. However, there were large areas in the outer plaque layer of one specimen that comprised, almost exclusively, *P. gingivalis* cells which appeared viable and, therefore, there may be two mechanisms at work, one of micro-colony formation and one contributing to overall biofilm formation. There is *in vitro* evidence that *P. gingivalis* may have only a limited capacity for forming a biofilm on a saliva-treated surface without the presence of specific coaggregating pre-attached cells (Cook *et al.,* 1998). The relatively abundant localisation of P. gingivalis in the PFZ combined with a possible stagnant environment could imply a more important role in initial colonisation *in vivo.* Bearing in mind the reported presence of this organism in healthy sites (Zimmer *et al.,* 1991), these observations may indicate that *P. gingivalis,* when present, is a potential colonising organism without necessarily initiating disease, but may increase in proportion with disease (Newman, 1990).

To date, no studies have identified *Capnocytophaga* species and, in particular *C. ochracea, in situ* on the tooth surface. Most information about *C. ochracea* in plaque has been gained from removed plaque samples. However, members of the *Capnocytophaga* genus have been identified in healthy sulcus fluid from children (Conrads *et al.,* 1996) and in relation to a range of diseases (Ali *et al.*, 1996, Muller *et al.,* 1997, Kamma *et al.,* 1998). Using DNA probes, Ali (1996) found *Capnocytophaga* spp. in almost all 36 adult periodontitis patients, although data for *C. ochracea* in similar studies are not so consistent (Dahlen *et al.*, 1992, Conrads *et al.,* 1996). In the present study, *C. ochracea* was identified in 4/5 plaque samples and in all *in situ* specimens, at the tooth/plaque interface, within the bulk plaque, at the oral interface, in the 'bristle' associations and in the so-called PFZ and its associated bacterial islands. It appears to be a prolific, common member of the apical plaque border, where it is found at all levels. The identification of colonies of *C. ochracea,* some cells of which were localised at the tooth surface, may be an indication of the potential of this organism for longer term plaque proliferation.

There have been few immunology studies aimed at identifying *C. rectus* in subgingival plaque and one *in situ* study. Most information on the prevalence of this organism in plaque has been obtained from culture. *C. rectus* has been associated with a range of inflammatory periodontal diseases and detection varies from 81% of diseased sites, when localised using DNA probes (Lippke, 1991), to 26% of diseased sites examined in a culture study (Steinlein *et al.,* 1989). Although *C. rectus* has been associated with periodontally-active sites and has been correlated with tissue breakdown (Steinlein *et al.,* 1989), bleeding on probing (Tanner and Bouldin, 1989) and insulin dependent diabetes (Mandell, 1992), it has also been shown not to be a unique indicator of CIPD (Lippke *et al.,* 1991). Dahlen (1992) found no significant differences in the prevalence of *C. rectus* between diseased and non-diseased subjects or between test and control sites within individual subjects. However, considering the frequent identification of this organism in such studies, the lack of *C. rectus* in the subgingival plaque samples and in 3/4 apical border plaque specimens in this study was somewhat unexpected. Throughout the study, pure cultures of *C. rectus* were used as positive controls and were always labeled. It may be that *C.*

369

rectus is not as prevalent as has been reported and Papapanou *et al.* (1997) in a comparison study found a much higher prevelence for *C. rectus* from culture than DNA probe methodology. However, within the apical border in which it was identified, it was found at all levels within the plaque, in the so-called PFZ and at the bottom of the pocket.

The presence of bacteria within the cuticle on the tooth surface of periodontitis-involved teeth has been noted previously (Friedman *et al.,* 1992). It may suggest the ready availability of nutrient sources from extracellular factors derived from elements of the host response and the contiguous soft periodontal tissues. There are many accounts of bacteria observed within cells (inflammatory, epithelial and osteoblasts) and the internalisation process is usually assumed to be due to phagocytosis while the cell remains viable. However such mechanisms cannot be supposed for the dental cuticle, and therefore it is possible that these organisms play a more active role in cuticle formation, and that this ability of specific bacteria to firmly embed themselves on or in the cuticle is an important step in colonisation.

Although, at present, this pilot *in situ* immunolabelling research has evaluated only 6 removed plaque samples and 4 *in situ* specimens, several conclusions can be drawn. There is confirmation of the variability of the presence of *P. gingivalis* from both removed samples and at the *in situ* apical plaque border. Very careful examination of the immunogold-labeled sections has revealed that there are sites at which there are absolutely no cells of *P. gingivalis* although this is a common species in the oral environment even in health. Though there are reports that it may be present at some sites and not others within the same patient (Wikstrom *et al.*, 1993) it is surprising that there were sites at which not a single organism was observed close to the advancing front of the lesion, especially since the species has been located on the tongue (Dahlen *et al.,* 1992) and there is always the possibility of translocation by saliva flow or toothbrushing. We have observed that *P. gingivalis,* when present, is generally found at the advancing front of the apical plaque and, indeed, is among the most apical organisms where it appears to remain viable or at least structurally intact. However, even here growth conditions appear to be limiting, and only presumed cell debris was detected in the deeper layers of established plaque.

C. ochracea was identified in all the specimens examined in this study and may be more common in the periodontitis patient than previously reported. It is also located at all regions throughout the plaque, notably at the advancing/colonising region of the apical plaque border.

There was little evidence of *C. rectus* in the samples examined thus far, in contradiction to much previous culture data. Although this organism is reported to be particularly prevalent in relation to diabetes-associated periodontitis (Ciontar) such specimens were not within the scope of this study. When present, it was observed at all levels throughout the plaque, but particularly at the tooth interface and it is possible that at this locus it is not removed when subgingival plaque samples are taken. There is also the possibility that it may be more readily cultivable than some plaque species, so that low numbers *in vivo*

370

may give rise to larger numbers in the total cultivable count.

Concerning the potential for immunolocalisation of bacterial species in subgingival plaque, both removed and *in situ*, this research to date has highlighted a discrepancy between the frequency of detection of *P. gingivalis*, *C. ochracea* and *C. rectus* in both types of specimen. The *in situ* border reveals a more complete picture than the removed samples, so that in the latter few or no organisms were identified. Most of such removed specimens contained electron-dense material, lysed cells and many large unidentified bacteria which cross-reacted with all the antibodies used. Although great care was taken throughout the processing, more loosely associated areas of removed plaque samples may have been lost. The finding of organisms in removed plaque samples which show non-specific labeling has been noted in a previous immunofluorescence study where a large filamentous bacterium was found to label with anti-*Streptococcus mutans* antibody (Bush *et al.*, 1990). However few such cross-reacting bacteria were identified at the apical plaque border of *in situ* samples. It must be borne in mind that this methodology examines only a few sections from the APB and it is conceivable that there may have been cells elsewhere within the plaque.

To date, it may be concluded that *P. gingivalis* and *C. ochracea* are common close to the advancing front of the lesion in chronic periodontitis. The immunoelectron microscopy technique employed has been shown to be both highly specific and highly sensitive for major disease-associated species with polyclonal antisera particularly useful. The technique is to be recommended for any locus where biofilm research is required, in health and disease.

References

Aass, A.M. Preus, H.R. Zambon, J.J. and Gjermo, P. 1994. Microbiologic tests in epidemiologic studies: are they reproducible? *Scand. J. Dent. Res.*, **102**, 355-360.

Albander, J.M. Brown, L.J. and Löe, H. 1997. Putative periodontal pathogens in subgingival plaque of young adults with and without early-onset periodontitis. *J. Periodontol.*, **68**, 973-981.

Ali, R.W. Velcescu, C. Jivanescu, M.C. Lofthus, B. and Skaug, N. 1996. Prevalence of 6 putative periodontal pathogens in subgingival plaque samples from Romanian adult periodontitis patients. *J. Clin. Periodontol.*, **23**, 113-119.

Allison, D.G. Ruiz, B. SanJose, C. Jaspe, A. and Gilbert, P. 1998. Extracellular products as mediators of the formation and detachment of *Pseudomonas fluorescens* biofilms. *FEMS. Microbiol. Lett.*, **167**, 179-184.

Assmus, B. Hausner, M. Grenier, D. Schloter, M. Hartmann, A. and Goldner, M. 1997. Direct examination of subgingival plaque from a diseased periodontal site using confocal laser scanning microscopy (CLSM). *New Microbiol.*, **20**, 155-159.

Babaahmady, K.G. Marsh, P.D. Challacombe, S.J. and Newman, H.N. 1997. Variations in the predominant cultivable microflora of dental plaque at defined subsites on approximal tooth surfaces in children. *Arch. Oral Biol.*, **42**, 101-111.

Bush, M.S. Challacombe, S.J. and Newman, H.N. 1990. A method for the identification of *Streptococcus mutans* in gingival margin plaque by immunofluorescence. *Caries Res.*, **24**, 23-29.

Carassi, A. Soligo, D. Vogel, G. Lambertenghi-Deliliers, G and Zambon, J.J. 1990. Identification of *Actinobacillus actinomycetemcomitans* by gold immunolabeling and scanning electron microscopy. *J. Periodontol.*, **61**, 249-254.

Carlsson, J. 1968. Plaque formation and streptococcal colonisation on teeth. *Odont. Revy*, **19**, suppl 14.

Chandad, F. Guillot, E. and Mouton, C. 1997. Detection of *Bacteroides forsythus* by immunomagnetic capture and a polymerase chain reaction-DNA probe assay. *Oral Microbiol. Immunol.*, **12**, 311-317.

Christersson, L.A. Zambon, J.J. and Genco R.J. 1991. Dental bacterial plaques. Nature and role in periodontal disease. *J. Clin. Periodontol.*, **18**, 441-446.

Clerehugh, V. Seymour, G.J. Bird, P.S. Cullinan, M. Drucker, D.B. and Worthington, H.V. 1997. The detection of *Actinobacillus actinomycetemcomitans*, *Porphyromonas gingivalis* and *Prevotella intermedia* using an ELISA in an adolescent population with early periodontitis. *J. Clin. Periodontol.*, **24**, 57-64.

Conrads, G. Mutters, R. Fischer, J. Brauner, A. Lutticken, R. and Lampert, F. 1996. PCR reaction and dot-blot hybridization to monitor the distribution of oral pathogens within plaque samples of periodontally healthy individuals. *J. Periodontol.*, **67**, 994-1003.

Cook, G.S. Costerton, J.W. and Lamont, R.J. 1998. Biofilm formation by *Porphyromonas gingivalis* and *Streptococcus gordonii*. *J. Periodontal. Res.*, **33**, 323-327.

Curtis, M.A. Slaney, J.M. Carmen, R.J. Harper, F.H. Wilton, J.M.A. Griffiths, G.S. and Johnson, N.A. 1990. Serum IgG antibody response to antigens of presumed periodontal pathogens: a case control study using ELISA and western blot analysis. *Microb. Ecol. Health and Dis.*, **3**, 251-258.

Dahlen, G. Manji, F. Baelum, V. and Fejerskov, O. 1992. Putative periodonto-pathogens in "diseased" and "non-diseased persons exhibiting poor oral hygiene. *J. Clin. Periodontol.*, **19**, 35-42.

Ellwood, R. Worthington, H.V. Cullinan, M.P. Hamlet, S. Clerehugh, V. and Davies, R. 1997. Prevelance of suspected periodontal pathogens identified using ELISA in adolescents of differing ethnic origins. *J. Clin. Periodontol.*, **24**, 141-145.

Friedman, M.T. Barber, P.M. Mordan, N.J. and Newman, H.N. 1992. The "plaque free zone" in health and disease: a scanning electron microscope study. *J. Periodontol.,* **63**, 890-896.

Gibbons, R.J. Socransky, S.S. Sawyer, S. Kapsimalis, B. and Macdonald, J.B. 1963. The microbiota of the gingival crevice area in man. II. The predominant cultivable organisms. *Archs. Oral Biol.*, 8, 281-289.

Gmur, R. and Guggenheim, B. 1990. Monoclonal antibodies for the detection of 'periodontopathic' bacteria. *Arch. Oral Biol.*, **35**, 145S-151S.

Haffajee, A.D. Socransky, S.S. Smith, C. and Dibart, S. 1992. The use of DNA probes to examine the distribution of subgingival species in subjects with different levels of periodontal destruction. *J. Clin. Periodontol.*, **19**, 84-91.

Haffajee, A.D, Cugini, M.A. Dibart, S. Smith, C. Kent, R.L. Jr. and Socransky, S.S. 1997. Clinical and microbiological features of subjects with adult periodontitis who responded poorly to scaling and root planing. *J. Clin. Periodontol.*, **24**, 767-776.

Harper-Owen, R. Dymock, D. Booth, V. Weightman, A.J. and Wade, W.G. 1999. Detection of unculturable bacteria in periodontal health and disease by PCR. *J. Clin. Microbiol.*, **37**, 1469-1473.

Hutchins, D.W. Parker, W.A. and Johnson, R.M. 1971. *J. Dent. Res.*, **50**, 224.

Kamma, J.J. Lygidakis, N.A. and Nakou, M. 1998. Subgingival microflora and treatment in prepubertal periodontitis associated with chronic idiopathic neutropenia. *J. Clin. Periodontol.*, **25**, 759-765.

Kigure, T. Saito, A. Seida, K. Yamada, S. Ishihara, K. and Okuda, K. 1995. Distribution of *Porphyromonas gingivalis* and *Treponema denticola* in human subgingival plaque at different periodontal pocket depths examined by immunohistochemical methods. *J. Periodontal. Res.*, **30**, 332-341.

Kojima, T. Yano, K. and Ishikawa, I. 1997. Relationship between serum antibody levels and subgingival colonisation of *Porphyromonas gingivalis* in patients with various types of periodontitis. *J. Periodontol.*, **68**, 618-625.

Kornman, K.S. Newman, M.G. Alvarado, R. Flemming, T.F. Nachnani, S. and Tumbusch J. 1991. Clinical and microbiological patterns of adults with periodontitis. *J. Periodontol.*, **62**, 634-642.

Lippke, J.A. Peros, W.J. Keville, M.W. Savitt, E.D. and French, C.K. 1991. DNA probe detection of *Eikenella corrodens*, *Wolinella recta* and *Fusobacterium nucleatum* in subgingival plaque. *Oral Microbiol. Immunol.*, **6**, 81-87.

Listgarten, M.A. 1976. Structure of the microbial flora associated with periodontal health and disease in man. A light and electron microscopic study. *J. Periodontol.*, **47**, 1-18.

Listgarten, M.A. Wong, M.Y. and Lai, C.H. 1995. Detection of *Actinobacillus actinomycetemcomitans*, *Porphyromonas gingivalis*, and *Bacteroides forsythus* in an *A. actinomycetemcomitans*-positive patient population. *J. Periodontol.*, **66**, 158-164.

Löe, H. Theilade, E. and Borglum Jensen, S. 1965. Experimental gingivitis in man. *J. Periodontol.*, **36**, 177-187.

Loesche, W.J. Lopatin, D.E. Stoll, J. van Paperin, N. and Hujoel, P.P. 1992. Comparison of various detection methods for periodontopathic bacteria: can culture be considered the primary reference standard? *J. Clin. Microbiol.*, **30**, 418-426.

Mandell, R.L. Dirienzo, J. Kent, R. Joshipura, K. and Haber, J. 1992. Microbiology of healthy and diseased periodontal sites in poorly controlled insulin dependant diabetics. *J. Periodontol.*, **63**, 274-279.

Marshall, G.E. Konstas, A.G. and Lee, W.R. 1990. Ultrastructural distribution of collagen types I-VI in aging human retinal vessels. *Br. J. Opthalmol.*, **74**, 228-232.

Maunsbach, A.B. and Afzelius, B.A. 1999. Biomedical electron microscopy. Academinc Press, USA.

Mordan, N.J. Hill, T.R. and Barber, P. 1992. Immunogold labelling of types I and III collagen in normal keratinised porcine skin. *J. Dent. Res.*, **71**, 72.

Moore, W.E.C. and Moore, L.V.H. 1994. The bacteria of periodontal diseases. *Periodontol. 2000*, **5**, 66-77.

Moore, W.E.C. Holdeman, L.V. Cato, E.P. Smibert, R.M. Burmeister, J.A. and Ranney, R.R. 1983. Bacteriology of moderate (chronic) periodontitis in mature adult humans. *Infect. Immunol.*, **42**, 510-515.

Muller, H.P. Heinecke, A. Borneff, M. Knopf, A. Kiencke, C. and Pohl, S. 1997. Microbial ecology of *Actinobacillus actinomycetemcomitans*, *Eikenella corrodens* and *Capnocytophaga spp.* in adult periodontitis. *J. Periodont. Res.*, **32**, 530-542.

Newman, H.N. 1973a. Zone demarcation of organic films present on human enamel surfaces. *Br. Dent. J.*, **134**, 273-278.

Newman, H.N. 1973b. The organic films on enamel surfaces. 1. The vestigial enamel organ. *Br. Dent. J.*, **135**, 64-67.

Newman, H.N.1973c. The organic films on enamel surfaces. 2. The dental plaque. *Br. Dent. J.*, **135**, 106-111.

Newman, H.N. 1974. Microbial films in nature. *Microbios.*, **9**, 247-257.

Newman, H.N. 1976. The apical border of plaque in chronic inflammatory periodontal disease. *Br. Dent. J.*, **141**, 105-113.

Newman, H.N. 1977. Ultrastructure of the apical border of dental plaque. *The Borderland between Caries and Periodontal Research.* Academic Press, London., 79-103.

Newman, H.N. 1979a. The approximal apical border of plaque on children's teeth. 1. Morphology, structure and cell content. *J. Periodontol.*, **50**, 561-567.

Newman, H.N. 1979b. The approximal apical border of plaque on children's teeth. 2. Adhesion, interbacterial connections and carbohydrate metabolism. *J. Periodontol.*, **50**, 568-576.

Newman, H.N. 1990. Plaque and chronic inflammatory periodontal disease. A question of ecology. *J. Clin. Periodontol.*, **17**, 533-541.

Newman, H.N. and Poole, D.F. 1974. Structural and ecological aspects of dental plaque. *The Normal Microbial Flora of Man*, Academic Press, London.

Newman, H.N. and Wilson, C.M. 1975. Thymidine and thymine uptake in human dental plaque: an autoradiographic study. *Caries Res.*, **9**, 405-417.

Noiri, Y. Ozaki, K. Nakae, H. Matsuo, T. and Ebisu, S. 1997. An immunohistochemical study on the localisation of *Porphoromonas gingivalis*, *Campylobacter rectus* and *Actinomyces viscosus* in human periodontal pockets. *J. Periodontal. Res.*, **32**, 598-607.

Papapanou, P.N. Madianios, P.N. Dahlen, G. and Sandros, J. 1997. "Checkerboard" versus culture: a comparison between two methods for identification of subgingival microbiota. *Eur. J. Oral Sci.*, **105**, 389-396.

Poole, D.F.G. and Newman, H.N. 1971. Dental plaque and oral health. *Nature*, **234**, 329-331.

Rawlinson, A. Duerden, B.I. and Goodwin, L. 1993. New findings on the microbial flora associated with adult periodontitis. *J. Dent.*, **21**, 179-184.

Razatos, A. Ong, Y.L. Sharma, M.M. and Georgiou, G. 1998. Molecular determinants of bacterial adhesion monitored by atomic force microscopy. *Proc. Natl. Acad. Sci. USA.*, **95**, 11059-11064.

Reynolds, E.S. 1963. The use of lead citrate at high pH as an electron-opaque stain in electron microscopy. *J. Cell Biol.*, **17**, 208-212.

Ridout, M.J. Brownsey, G.J. Gunning, A.P. and Morris, V.J. 1998. Characterisation of the polysaccharide produced by *Acetobacter xylinum* strain CR1/4 by light scattering and atomic force microscopy. *Int. J. Biol. Macromol.*, **23**, 287-293.

Rosen, B. Lai, C.H. and Listgarten, M.A. 1976. *Streptococcus sanguis*: A model in the application in immunochemical analysis for the *in situ* localisation in dental plaque. *J. Dent. Res.*, **55**, A124-A141.

Saxen, L. Jousimies-Somer, H. Kaisla, A. Kanervo, A. Summanen, P. and Sipila, I. 1989. Subgingival microflora, dental and periodontal conditions in patients with hereditary fructose intolerance. *Scand. J. Dent Res.*, **97**, 150-158.

Saxton, C.A. 1975. Determination by electron microscope autoradiography of the distribution of plaque organisms that synthesise intracellular polysaccharide *in situ*. *Caries Res.*, **9**, 418-437.

Schlegel-Bregenzer, B. Persson, R.E. Lukehart, S. Braham, P. Oswald, T. and Persson G.R. 1998. Clinical and microbiological findings in elderly subjects with gingivitis or periodontitis. *J. Clin. Periodontol.*, **25**, 897-907.

Shah, H.N. Williams, R.A. Bowden, G.H. and Hardie, J.M. 1976. Comparison of the biochemical properties of *Bacteroides melaninogenicus* from human dental plaque and other sites. *J. Appl. Bacteriol.*, **41**, 473-95.

Slots, J. 1977. Microflora in the healthy gingival sulcus in man. *Scand. J. Dent. Res.*, **85**, 247-254.

Socransky, S.S. and Haffajee, A.D. 1994. Evidence of bacterial etiology: a historical perspective. *Periodontol 2000*, **5**, 7-25

Socransky, S.S. Haffajee, A.D. Cugini, M.A. Smith, C. and Kent, R.L. Jr. 1998. Microbial complexes in subgingival plaque. *J. Clin. Periodontol.*, **25**, 134-144.

Soder, P.O. Jin, L.J. and Soder, B. 1993. DNA probe detection of periodontopathogens in advanced periodontitis. *Scand. J. Dent. Res.*, **101**, 363-370.

Steinlein, T. Nessier, M.C. Mombelli, A. and Lang, N.P. 1989. *Wolinella recta* and spirochaetes in relation to alteration of probing depth in a population without regular dental care. *Schweiz. Monatsschr. Zahnmed.*, **99**, 993-997.

Tanner, A. and Bouldin, H. 1989. The microbiota of early periodontitis lesions in adults. *J. Clin. Periodontol.*, **16**, 467-471.

Tanner, A. Maiden, M.F. Macuch, P.J. Murray, L.L. and Kent, R.L. Jr. 1998. Microbiota of health, gingivitis and initial periodontitis. *J. Clin. Periodontol.*, **25**, 85-98.

Theilade, E. Wright, W.H. Jensen, S.B. and Löe, H. 1966. Experimental gingivitis in man. II. A longitudinal clinical and microbiological investigation. *J. Periodontal. Res.*, **17**, 1-13.

van Steenberger, T.J. Timmerman, M.F. Mikx, F.H. de Quincey, G. van der Weijden, G.A. van der Velden, U. and de Graaff, J. 1996. Discrepancy between culture and DNA probe analysis for the detection of periodontal bacteria. *J. Clin. Periodontol.*, **23**, 955-959.

Vrahopoulos, T.P. 1989. An ultrastructural study of the apical border plaque. PhD thesis, University of London.

Vrahopoulos, T.P. Barber, P.M. and Newman, H.N. 1992. The apical border plaque in chronic adult periodontitis. An ultrastructural study. II. Adhesion, matrix, and carbohydrate metabolism. *J. Periodontol.*, **63**, 253-261.

Vrahopolous, T.P. Barber, P.M. and Newman, H.N. 1995. The apical border in severe periodontitis. An ultrastructural study. *J. Periodontol.*, **66**, 113-124.

Watanabe, K. and Frommel, T.O. 1993. Detection of *Porphyromonas gingivalis* in oral plaque samples by use of polymerase chain reaction. *J. Dent. Res.*, **72**, 1040-1044.

Wikstrom, M. Fenvert, S. Johnsson, T. and Dahlen, G. 1993. Microbial associations in periodontitis sites before and after treatement. *Oral Microbiol. Immunol.*, **8**, 213-218.

Xie, H. Cai, S. and Lamont, R.J. 1997. Environmental regulation of fimbrial gene expression in *Porphyromonas gingivalis*. *Infect. Immun.*, **65**, 2265-2271.

Zimmer, W. Wilson, M. Marsh, P.D. Newman, H.N. and Bulman, J. 1991. *Porphyromonas gingivalis*, *Prevotella intermedia* and *Actinobacillus actinomycetemcomitans* in the plaque of children without periodontitis. *Microb. Ecol. Health and Dis.*, **4**, 329 - 336.

Medical Implications of Oral Biofilms

ORAL INFECTION AND SYSTEMIC DISEASE: INITIAL EVIDENCE FOR SYSTEMIC INVASION OF ORAL PATHOGENS

S Offenbacher, RC Williams, CME Champagne, PN Madianos, HJ Chung, Y Liu, S Geva and JD Beck

*In the present manuscript we provide an overview of some preliminary data that demonstrate that a low-grade chronic **P. gingivalis** infection can result in activation of the hepatic acute phase response (APR) in an animal model of infection. Bacterial-induced cytokines result in metabolic changes in the animal and elevations in blood cholesterol and triglycerides. The long-term persistence of organisms within the liver suggests that the normal hepatic clearance mechanisms that remove bacteria from the bloodstream are less than fully effective in clearing **P. gingivalis**. Finally, challenge with certain strains of **P. gingivalis** in murine models of atherosclerosis (ApoE $^{+/-}$) result in accelerated atheroma formation and calcification of major arteries. Other lines of preliminary evidence from prospective human epidemiology studies in progress demonstrate that oral infections in pregnant mothers can result in direct fetal exposure **in utero**. This is suggested by data that indicate that at birth, certain fetal cord blood samples contain high-titer fetal IgM specific for maternal oral pathogens. Thus, increasing evidence suggests that periodontitis is associated with systemic dissemination of oral organisms that are capable of contributing to the acute phase response and translocate to distant anatomical sites, perhaps as a consequence of specific tropisms. The data presented summarize work-in-progress to serve as examples of experimental approaches rather than definitive studies.*

Introduction

Inflammation that occurs in the systemic blood compartment can occur as a non-specific response to stress, injury or infection and represents the activation of the innate immune response at a systemic level. In septic states the synthesis and release of inflammatory mediators into the circulation, such as Interleukin-6 (IL-6) and tumor necrosis factor alpha (TNFa), is referred to as the systemic inflammatory response syndrome (SIRS). Once initiated the pathophysiology and clinical sequelae of SIRS can be explained largely by the quality and magnitude of the host innate inflammatory response, rather than the nature of the initiating stimuli. Activation of the hepatic acute phase response (APR) can occur by circulating endotoxin, bacteria, reactive oxygen species, or cytokines such as TNFα or IL-6. These stimuli trigger the release of acute phase proteins (APP), including C-reactive protein (CRP), serum amyloid A, α-1 antitrypsin (α1-AT), fibrinogen, haptoglobin and others that mediate the APR. Most of these molecules provide non-specific protection from outside stressors by scavenging unchecked proteases or reactive oxygen species and by facilitating the clearance of foreign agents and damaged host tissues by non-antibody mediated processes. However, in many acute and chronic diseases and conditions including cardiovascular disease, type 2 diabetes and preterm delivery, there is a mild activation of the APR, usually in the absence of any identifiable initiating factors (Duncan, Schmidt *et al.,* 1999; Schmidt, Duncan *et al.,* 1999). In an attempt to understand the observed associations between periodontitis, and these other systemic conditions, the question arises as to whether there is any direct evidence that periodontal infection can serve as a trigger for inflammation at a systemic level. In order to establish a causal pathway, it is of interest to determine what attributable fraction periodontitis contributes to the known associations between markers of the APR and these systemic conditions. The underlying mechanism for these associations might involve a common inflammatory trait that is simultaneously a risk factor for both periodontitis and these systemic conditions. In this capacity periodontitis may simply serve as a marker for this underlying trait. Alternatively, the sphere of influence of the oral microbial and inflammatory challenge may gain systemic proportions and directly enhance the pathogenesis of these "distant" maladies. Finally, both components might be active in that the more severe forms of periodontitis, which affect 7-20% of the adult population, are more likely to occur in individuals with a propensity towards an exaggerated innate immune responsiveness and that this also provides a permissive environment for systemic involvement for these oral pathogens.

In the present manuscript we discuss the concept that the oral biofilm may have a greater sphere of influence than the adjacent periodontal tissues. Little experimental evidence is available regarding this new line of scientific inquiry. Issues regarding organism invasion, translocation, tropism and clearance at a systemic level are discussed to outline key questions and present examples of specific experimental approaches for future and on-going investigations in this emerging area.

Microbial clearance

Earlier studies have indicated that individuals with periodontitis experience transient bacteremias and that the level, the duration and the microbial diversity of the bacteremia increases with periodontal disease severity. Serum antibody levels to oral microbes provide compelling testament to this systemic involvement. However, the tissue distribution and disposition of these oral microbes following these blood-born exposures, and the mechanisms of final bacterial clearance from the circulation are unknown. Although certain periodontal pathogens are capable of invading host cells and tissues, the mechanisms by which these organisms gain access to the blood circulation have not been fully

376

characterized. The relative contributions of potential portals of entry–venous, arterial, lymphatic or the tissue interstitial compartment have not been examined. Anatomically, infection in the head and neck area has both venous and lymphatic drainage directly into the mediastinum at the base of the neck with relatively short anatomic pathways to major blood vessels. There are differences in the blood supply with greater perfusion in the maxillae as compared to the mandible, but it is not known whether these anatomical considerations are relevant to providing systemic egress. It has often been cited that approximately 80-90% of any blood-born challenge, whether particulate, microbial or macromolecular aggregates such as endotoxin, are cleared during the first pass through the liver by the Kupffer cells, the hepatic tissue-resident macrophages. These cells constitute 80-90% of the total fixed macrophage population in the body. New research by Gregory and colleagues (Gregory and Wing, 1998) have emphasized the key role of the neutrophil in assisting in the hepatic clearance of bacteria. These investigators describe hepatic bacterial clearance as a three step process; 1) microbial binding to the surface of hepatic Kupffer cells, 2) microbial-stimulated expression of adhesion molecules and cytokines that recruit and activate neutrophils and local inflammation and 3) neutrophil-mediated phagocytosis, killing and the secretion of additional proinflammatory molecules. Thus, the Kupffer cell serves to trap the organism that is subsequently cleared by the action of newly recruited neutrophils. The experimental evidence for this dual phagocyte interactivity includes demonstrating that inhibiting Kuffer cell adhesion blocks microbial trapping; similarly blocking neutrophil clearance leads to microbial persistence within the liver (Gregory and Wing 1998). These observations raise some relevant questions with regard to the clearance of oral microbes. First, are oral microbes being trapped by tissue resident macrophages, principally in the liver, and is this resulting in activation of the hepatic acute phase response (APR). Since many oral microbes are capable of evading neutrophil clearance, is this virulence trait playing a role in delaying hepatic clearance and thereby exacerbating the APR in a manner disproportionate with the level of systemic exposure?. Furthermore, the presence of other extra-hepatic tissue-resident macrophages, such as those in atheromatous plaques in major arteries and coronary vessels, or in the placental membranes may play a special role in processing oral microbes. In this capacity oral microbes might contribute to the local inflammatory response and thereby promote inflammatory-mediated pathology at distant sites.

Activation of the APR

Data by Ebersole (Ebersole, Machen *et al.*, 1997), Slade and Loos (both in press)all point to periodontal infection as an activator of the APR. These investigators indicate that periodontitis results in elevated in serum levels of activators of the APR, such as IL-6 (Loos, in press), as well as modest increases in acute phase proteins such as C-reactive protein and haptoglobin. When considered in combination with observed decreases in serum albumin and mild increases in white blood cell counts, two additional key clinical features of the APR, there is

S Offenbacher, R Williams, C Champagne, P Madianos, H Chung, Y Liu, S Geva & J Beck

Table 1 Effects of *P. gingivalis* infection on murine acute phase proteins.

	CRP (ng/ml) mean±SE	Serum Amyloid A (mg/ml) mean±SE
Non-Challenged (n = 6)	6.73 ± 0.87	14.11 ± 0.50
P. gingivalis-Challenged (n = 7)	31.50 ± 1.73	55.04 ± 2.64
P values (non-paired *t* test)	0.0381	0.0261

Heterozygous ApoE$^{+/-}$ mice (strain C57B6) were primed at week 8 with an intra-peritoneal injection of saline or heat-killed *P. gingivalis* strain A7436 (10^9 CFU equivalents). Subcutaneous chambers (stainless steel coil) were implanted dorsally at week 10 on each side of each animal. Mice were challenged at weeks 12 and 15 with an intra-chamber injection of saline or live *P. gingivalis* strain A7436 (10^8 CFU equivalents). Finally, mice were sacrificed at week 18. Serum samples were collected at weeks 12, 15, and 18. C reactive protein (CRP) and serum amyloid A (SAA) levels were determined by ELISA, using sheep anti-human CRP (American Research Products, Inc, Belmont, MA) and rat anti-human SAA (Biosource International, Camarillo, CA) respectively. Results are expressed as mean ± SE of the average values obtained at weeks 15 and 18 for each animal and for each group of animals (n = 6 for non-challenged and n = 7 for *P. gingivalis*-challenged animals). Serum levels of both acute phase reactants CRP and SAA were significantly increased in *P. gingivalis*-challenged animals compared to the non-challenged animals ($P < 0.05$, non-paired *t* test).

now little doubt that periodontal infections are mild activators of the acute phase response. Since periodontal disease is a chronic, albeit low-grade microbial threat, the level of activation of the APR is not of the same magnitude as with an acute infection or a septic challenge. The underlying mechanism whereby periodontal organisms trigger the hepatic APR is unknown, but we have begun to explore this mechanism in animal models.

We have begun to examine the role of *P. gingivalis* in activating the APR using the subcutaneous tissue chamber model in C57BJ6 mice, as described earlier (Collins, Smith *et al.,* 1994; Collins, Windley *et al.,* 1994). The benefits of this model include the ability to standardized the infectious load at a localized site and monitor local cytokine and host inflammatory cell responses. Most importantly, we have superimposed this infection model on knock-out mice models of systemic disease, such as using APOE knockouts (+/- and -/-) as models of atherosclerosis, to facilitate understanding how exogenous infection modulates the systemic condition. In this model *P. gingivalis* challenge results in increases in serum Amyloid A (SAA) and CRP (Table 1). The *P. gingivalis* infection in the subcutaneous chamber not only activates the hepatic APR, but it also results in an increase in the atheroma lesion scores (data not shown). In mice SAA is the dominant acute phase protein that is comparable to the CRP response in humans. Activation of the hepatic APR in response to a hematogenously disseminating infection is usually a consequence of increased serum levels of either LPS (lipopolysaccharide) or blood-born bacteria that target the liver directly. However, distant infections that result in increases of serum IL-1, IL-6 and/or TNFa can also act in the liver to induce synthesis and release of acute phase proteins. Interestingly, infection also results in a shift in

Table 2 Effects of *P. gingivalis* infection on murine serum lipid levels.

	Cholesterol (mg/dl) mean±SE	Triglycerides (mg/dl) mean±SE
Non-Challenged (n = 6)	50.88 ± 0.68	55.91 ± 1.06
P. gingivalis-Challenged (n = 7)	60.55 ± 0.43	92.48 ± 2.26
P values (non-paired *t* test)	0.0403	0.0226

Heterozygous ApoE[+/-] mice (strain C57B6) were primed at week 8 with an intra-peritoneal injection of saline or heat-killed *P. gingivalis* strain A7436 (10^9 CFU equivalents). Subcutaneous chambers (stainless steel coil) were implanted dorsally at week 10 on each side of each animal. Mice were challenged at weeks 12 and 15 with an intra-chamber injection of saline or live *P. gingivalis* strain A7436 (10^8 CFU equivalents). Finally, mice were sacrificed at week 18. Serum samples were collected at weeks 12, 15, and 18. Serum levels of total cholesterol and triglycerides were determined using diagnostic kits (Wako Pure Chemical Industries, Ltd., Osaka, Japan, and SigmaDiagnostics, Inc., St. Louis, MO, respectively). Results are expressed as mean ± SE of the average values obtained at weeks 15 and 18 for each animal and for each group of animals (n = 6 for non-challenged and n = 7 for *P. gingivalis*-challenged animals). Serum levels of both total cholesterol and triglycerides were significantly increased in *P. gingivalis*-challenged animals compared to the non-challenged animals ($P < 0.05$, non-paired *t* test).

serum lipid profiles with an increase in serum cholesterol and triglycerides, perhaps as a result of the lipogenic and lipemic properties of IL-1, IL-6 and TNFα (Table 2). To determine whether blood-born cytokines or microbes were responsible for the observed increase in serum acute phase proteins, we examined tissue biopsy samples of liver for the presence of *P. gingivalis* by RT-PCR. This method is very sensitive (i.e. can detect $<10^3$ organisms) and does not require viable bacteria to provide a signal. As can be seen in Figure 1, *P. gingivalis* DNA can be detected within the liver, even 3 weeks following the last subcutaneous challenge in this model. Normally, hepatic clearance of organisms occurs within hours. However, additional experiments with other strains of *P. gingivalis* and other organisms need to be tested in this model to confirm and explore what appears to be an abnormally long survival of *P. gingivalis* within the liver. It is enticing to surmise as to whether certain oral organisms, such as *P.gingivalis* or *Actinobacillus actinomycetemcomitans* that can evade neutrophil clearance in the oral compartment might also persist in the hepatic compartment for an extended period of time. Clearly, further experiments need to be performed to characterize what appears to be hepatic sequestering of *P. gingivalis* in this infection model, but this oral-hepatic pathway may represent a possible explanation of how a low-grade infectious challenge might serve as an activator of the APR.

Tropism

Tropism represents the guided translocation of organisms from areas of infection to specific distant homing sites. Certainly, hepatic sequestering might represent one form of tropism for oral organisms, but this is probably a

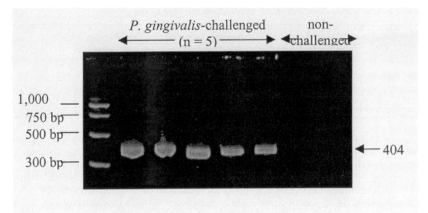

Figure 1 Detection of *P. gingivalis* in murine liver extracts.

Heterozygous female ApoE[+/-] mice (strain C57B6) were fed a high-fat diet at week 8, and two subcutaneous chambers (stainless steel coil) were implanted on each side on the back of each animal. Mice were primed at week 10 with an intraperitoneal injection of heat-killed *P. gingivalis* strain A7436 (10^9 CFU equivalents). Mice were regularly challenged over a 3-month period, with an intra-chamber injection of culture media (non-challenged animals, n = 2) or live *P. gingivalis* strain A7436 (5×10^7 or 10^8 CFU equivalents), at weeks 13, 14, 15, 18, 20, 22, and 24 (*P. gingivalis*-challenged animals, n = 5). Mice were sacrificed at week 27, and livers were collected. Livers were homogenized with a Pellet Pestle homogenizer (Kontes Glass Company, Vinelang, NJ). Homogenates were treated with 2 cycles of freeze/thaw and centrifuged. Supernatants of homogenates were used to detect the presence of *P. gingivalis* DNA by PCR, with PCR primers corresponding to *P. gingivalis* specific sequences on 16S ribosomal RNA gene (Slots *et al.*, 1995 and 1996). *P. gingivalis*-specific DNA was amplified from liver extracts from *P. gingivalis*-challenged animals, but not from non-challenged animals.

References

Slots J, Ashimoto A, Flynn MJ, Li G and Chen C. (1995) Detection of putative periodontal pathogens in subgingival specimens by 16S ribosomal DNA amplification with the polymerase chain reaction. *Clin Infect Dis* Jun; **20** Suppl 2: S304-7.

Ashimoto A, Chen C, Bakker I and Slots J. (1996) Polymerase chain reaction detection of 8 putative periodontal pathogens in subgingival plaque of gingivitis and advanced periodontitis lesions. *Oral Microbiol Immunol* Aug; **11**(4): 266-73.

relatively hostile environment for these microbes. Usually tropism results in microbial translocation to an ecological niche that promotes survival of the microbe. Bacteria that display tropism often possess unique homing receptors that bind to specific ligands expressed by targeted areas of host tissue. The specificity of the host tissue ligand-microbial-receptor results in localized binding and colonization or sequestering. This tropism is often quite species-specific, from a microbial and host tissue stand-point, so microbial tropism patterns in animal models may not be applicable to tropic responses in human disease. Nonetheless, examining microbial tropism in animal models can provide insight into potential analogous mechanisms in humans. It remains to be seen as to whether animal models can mimic the tissue distribution patterns

380

of oral microbes reported in humans. Studies have demonstrated oral pathogens including *P. gingivalis* and *B. forsythus* in atheromatous plaques present within carotid and coronary arteries. It is unclear as to whether the co-localization of these organisms within these atheromas reflects surface adsorption of organisms, tissue-specific tropism or invasion and incorporation into the plaque. Studies by Deshpande and others demonstrating the ability of *P.gingivalis* to invade endothelial cells suggest the capacity for atheroma invasion (Deshpande, Khan *et al.,* 1998). If these organisms are inhabitants of the atheroma for prolonged periods, then the potential role of matrix-metalloproteinase production as a plaque de-stabilizer gains potential importance. Plaque de-stabilization that results in plaque rupture, thrombi and emboli formation are the principle steps leading to myocardial infarction and stroke. Thus, microbial presence within the atheroma may have special significance regarding cardiovascular events. Since the techniques used to identify these organisms within arterial plaques do not require viable organisms (e.g. PCR or immunocytochemistry) it is not clear as to whether this represents ectopic colonization of viable organisms. Clearly, additional research is needed to understand the biological significance of colocalization of oral microbes within atheromatous plaques.

Invasion of fetal tissues

Preterm birth (PTB) is the major cause of neonatal mortality, and morbidity and can lead to long-term neurodevelopmental deficits such as cerebral palsy and respiratory conditions such as bronchopulmonary dysplasia. There is increasing evidence that infection may play a role in PTB. Numerous studies have demonstrated significantly increased risks for preterm labor (PTL), premature rupture of membranes (PROM) and PTB among women with genitourinary tract infections. Further evidence to link prematurity with infection comes from studies reporting that 10-20% of women with intact membranes in preterm labor have positive amniotic fluid cultures. In addition, histologic chorioamnionitis defined as inflammation of the extraplacental membrane has been consistently linked with PTB. Microorganisms have been recovered in 51% to 71% of these cases. However, the fact that 19% to 49% of placentas with histologic evidence of chorioamnionitis are culture negative has prompted investigators to propose that PTB occurring as a result of infection is mediated indirectly, by the translocation of bacteria or their products, such as lipopolysaccharide (LPS) and by the action of locally produced inflammatory mediators. Indeed, strong evidence exists implicating such molecules, including prostaglandin E_2 (PGE_2), interleukin-1 (IL-1) and tumor necrosis factor-α (TNF-α) as the biochemical mediators of parturition. Furthermore, these mediators have been shown to be produced by macrophages, amnion and decidua in response to bacteria or LPS (see Offenbacher, Jared *et al.,* 1998, for review)

It is our hypothesis that periodontal infections, which serve as reservoirs for Gram-negative anaerobic organisms, LPS and inflammatory mediators including PGE_2, IL-1 and TNF-α, may pose a threat to the fetal-placental unit and have a bearing on pregnancy outcome. Evidence to support this concept first came from experimental studies in the pregnant hamster model, which demonstrated that experimental periodontitis, as well as localized non-disseminating subcutaneous infections with *Porphyromonas gingivalis*, could significantly retard fetal weight (Collins, Windley *et al.,* 1994). Two human case-control studies conducted in the University of North Carolina provided further support to our hypothesis. In the first study, mothers with periodontal disease were found to be at significantly greater risk for preterm low birth weight delivery (PLBW), in comparison to periodontaly healthy ones (odds ratio 7.9) (Offenbacher, Katz *et al.,* 1996). In the second study, levels of gingival crevicular fluid PGE$_2$ as well as levels of periodontal pathogens (*P. gingivalis, Bacteroides forsythus, Treponema denticola, Actinobacillus actinomycetemcomitans*) were found to be significantly elevated in PLBW mothers as compared with normal birth weight (NBW) controls (Offenbacher, Beck *et al.,* 1998).

We recently employed the checkerboard immunoblotting technology to probe the fetal immunologic response, which consists primarily of IgM class antibody, to determine whether it could be triggered by periodontal organisms during gestation. Since maternal IgM (in contrast to IgG) cannot cross the placental barrier, the presence of IgM antibody against periodontal organisms in the fetal serum would serve as direct evidence of fetal exposure to these organisms or their products *in utero*. Fetal cord blood was collected at the time of delivery from 60 babies and after centrifugation, serum samples were stored for the analysis. In order to avoid potential interference from maternal IgG present in the fetal serum, the IgM fraction was separated by molecular exclusion gel chromatography. Bacterial antigens (whole bacterial suspensions in PBS, O.D.=1) from 13 bacterial species were deposited in parallel lanes on a nitrocellulose membrane, with the help of a minislot device. The serum IgM samples were then layed on the membrane in lanes running perpendicularly to the antigen lanes. Each serum sample could, thereby, react with all 13 species. After extensive washing, membrane-bound IgM was detected by incubation with an anti-human IgM antibody and enhanced chemiluminescence. 23.3% of the fetal serum samples contained IgM reactive with at least one periodontal organism. As shown in Table 3, IgM against *Campylobacter rectus* was the most frequently detected antibody, followed by *P. gingivalis* and *Fusobacterium nucleatum*, which were detected in 18.3% of the samples. Interestingly, *F. nucleatum* has been reported to be one of the most frequently recovered organisms in positive amniotic fluid cultures from women in preterm labor with intact membranes. These findings provide direct evidence that periodontal organisms or their products may reach the fetal-placental unit and cross the placental barrier to challenge the fetus *in utero*.

Based on the above findings we propose the following model of periodontal infection associated prematurity. Periodontitis serves as a remote infection that seeds bacteria, LPS and mediators into the systemic circulation. Certain bacteria may show tropism for the fetal-placental unit, where they may reside and even invade placental tissues to directly challenge the fetus *in utero*. This would not be particularly surprising since pathogens like *P. gingivalis* and

382

Table 3 Prevalence of specific IgM antibody in fetal cord blood samples[1]

Bacterial species[2]	% positive[3]
Campylobacter rectus	23.3
Porphyromonas gingivalis	18.3
Fusobacterium nucleatum	18.3
Eikenella corrodens	15.0
Actinobacillus actinomycetemcomitans	13.3
Veillonella parvula	13.3
Capnocytophaga gingivalis	11.6
Prevotella intermedia	10.0
Capnocytophaga ochracea	8.3
Bacteroides forsythus	8.3
Prevotella nigrescens	3.3
Streptococcus sanguis	1.6
Peptostreptococcus micros	0.0

[1] The IgM fraction from fetal cord blood serum samples was separated by molecular exclusion gel chromatography and analyzed for the presence of specific IgM against 13 periodontal organisms by checkerboard immunoblotting
[2] Whole bacterial suspensions in PBS (O.D.=1) were used as antigens in the assay
[3] A total of 60 fetal cord blood samples were analyzed

A. actinomycetemcomitans have been shown capable of invading a number of different host cell types in vitro. Alternatively, bacterial products, such as LPS may cross the placenta to provoke a fetal immunologic and inflammatory response. In any event circulating mediators, bacteria and bacterial products trigger the local release of inflammatory mediators, like PGE_2, IL-1 and TNF-α, by maternal and fetal tissues (decidua, chorioamnion) causing uterine contraction, cervical dilation, cervical effacement and premature delivery.

Microbial stealth, biomimicry and evolutionary persistence

Skulls from early man show evidence of periodontal disease. Non-human primates experience periodontitis and have virtually an identical flora to man at a genus and species level. The oral cavity appears to be the sole ecological niche for periodontal organisms and no extraoral reservoir or vector has been identified. It appears likely that selective evolutionary pressures on the commensual oral flora that co-evolved with our species have resulted in the careful selection of organisms that can persist. Considering the constant egress of neutrophils into the gingival sulcus or pocket, it appears unlikely that these organisms could persist in the oral cavity if these organisms had not evolved mechanisms to evade neutrophil phagocytosis and killing. *P. gingivalis* is a case in point. Evading neutrophil clearance and activating the innate immune response is a potential survival strategy for an organism. This would avoid clearance and provide an inflammatory, nutrient-rich environment for organism growth. Activation of the acquired immune response would not be a selective advantage for a bacterial species, as it would ultimately facilitate clearance and suppress colonization and growth. Thus, the same selective pressures that have resulted in the guided evolution of *P. gingivalis* would by design result in an organism that would elicit a mild inflammatory response, but remain as a "stealth" organism that avoids wholesale activation of the acquired immune response. With this conceptual framework it is not surprising that *P. gingivalis* has a unique genome that includes genes encoding molecules that emulate certain host enzymes or proteins that regulate the innate immune response. Or perhaps a better descriptor is the selective interference with normal cell-to-cell communication that is often interleukin mediated. This "biomimicry" extends to an extensive array of molecules that regulate the clotting cascade, platelet aggregation, chemotactic stimuli, tissue protease activity, and even host acute phase proteins such as CRP (Travis, Pike *et al.,* 1994; Discipio, Daffern *et al.,* 1996; Jagels, Travis *et al.,* 1996; Travis, Pike *et al.,* 1997). Although the function of these molecules is not fully understood, the apparently unique expression of these molecules by oral organisms suggest that these molecules are necessary for survival in the oral compartment. If however, the organisms have evolved to elegantly titrate the host inflammatory response to achieve a delicate balance that results in clearance avoidance and the selective activation of the innate host response, the potential for systemic dissemination appears quite plausible. It would seem that evolutionary pressures that would enable the organism to persist in the hostile oral environment would also simultaneously empower the organism with unprecedented stealth capabilities to permit host dissemination. Why then does not *P. gingivalis* kill us? Evolutionary microbiologists (Ewald 1995; Ewald, Sussman *et al.,* 1998) provide data and arguments that this is not a desirable trait for a pathogen. Slow, mildly debilitating diseases are acceptable from a microbial virulence standpoint, as this permits host mobility and transmission opportunity and secures a long-term environment for the organism. Indeed, studies of HIV variants, or variants of dysentery, demonstrate that the less virulent the strain, the greater the penetration into the susceptible population at risk. This line of reasoning has lead some scientists to suggest that many chronic conditions of humans that are sufficiently widespread probably can not have a major or dominant genetic component, but are more likely to be a consequence of infectious origin, albeit infections of unknown origin or identity. Thus, evolutionary microbiologists might argue that the biofilm that grows in household plumbing that is there for decades without any consequence, but can under certain circumstances eventually lead to plumbing failure, may have analogies to the role of microbes in the vascular system. It remains to be seen as to whether those properties, which enable oral organisms to persist within the oral biofilm and invade into tissues, may also enable systemic dissemination and distant sequestering. Nonetheless, it is clear that oral biology has entered into a new domain where the biological significance of oral organisms has gained a much larger sphere of influence. This poses new questions and exciting investigative opportunities for dental scientists.

References

Collins, J. G., M. A. Smith, *et al.* (1994). Effects of Escherichia coli and *Porphyromonas gingivalis* lipopolysaccharide on pregnancy outcome in the golden hamster.*"Infect Immun* **62**(10): 4652-5.

Collins, J. G., H. W. Windley, 3rd, *et al.* (1994). Effects of a Porphyromonas gingivalis infection on inflammatory mediator response and pregnancy outcome in hamsters. *Infect Immun* **62**(10): 4356-61.

Deshpande, R. G., M. B. Khan, *et al.* (1998). Invasion of aortic and heart endothelial cells by *Porphyromonas gingivalis. Infect Immun* **66**(11): 5337-43.

Discipio, R. G., P. J. Daffern, *et al.* (1996). Cleavage of human complement component C5 by cysteine proteinases from *Porphyromonas (Bacteroides) gingivalis.* Prior oxidation of C5 augments proteinase digestion of C5 [published erratum appears in Immunology 1996 Aug;88(4):657]. *Immunology* **87**(4): 660-7.

Duncan, B. B., M. I. Schmidt, *et al.* (1999). Factor VIII and other hemostasis variables are related to incident diabetes in adults. The Atherosclerosis Risk in Communities (ARIC) Study. *Diabetes Care* **22**(5): 767-72.

Ebersole, J. L., R. L. Machen, *et al.* (1997). Systemic acute-phase reactants, C-reactive protein and haptoglobin, in adult periodontitis. *Clin Exp Immunol* **107**(2): 347-52.

Ewald, P. W. (1995). The evolution of virulence: a unifying link between parasitology and ecology. *J Parasitol* **81**(5): 659-69.

Ewald, P. W., J. B. Sussman, *et al.* (1998). Evolutionary control of infectious disease: prospects for vectorborne and waterborne pathogens. *Mem Inst Oswaldo Cruz* **93**(5): 567-76.

Gregory, S. H. and E. J. Wing (1998). Neutrophil-Kupffer-cell interaction in host defenses to systemic infections.*"Immunol Today* **19**(11): 507-10.

Jagels, M. A., J. Travis, *et al.* (1996). Proteolytic inactivation of the leukocyte C5a receptor by proteinases derived from Porphyromonas gingivalis.*"Infect Immun* **64** (6): 1984-91.

Offenbacher, S., J. D. Beck, *et al.* (1998). Role of periodontitis in systemic health: spontaneous preterm birth. *J Dent Educ* **62**(10): 852-8.

Offenbacher, S., H. L. Jared, *et al.* (1998). Potential pathogenic mechanisms of periodontitis associated pregnancy complications. *Ann Periodontol* **3**(1): 233-50.

Offenbacher, S., V. Katz, *et al.* (1996). Periodontal infection as a possible risk factor for preterm low birth weight. *J Periodontol* **67**(10 Suppl): 1103-13.

Schmidt, M. I., B. B. Duncan, *et al.* (1999). Markers of inflammation and prediction of diabetes mellitus in adults (Atherosclerosis Risk in Communities study): a cohort study. *Lancet* **353**(9165): 1649-52.

Travis, J., R. Pike, *et al.,* (1994). The role of proteolytic enzymes in the development of pulmonary emphysema and periodontal disease [published erratum appears in Am J Respir Crit Care Med 1995 Mar;151(3 Pt 1):926]. *Am J Respir Crit Care Med* **150**(6 Pt 2): S143-6.

Travis, J., R. Pike, *et al.* (1997). *Porphyromonas gingivalis* proteinases as virulence factors in the development of periodontitis. *J Periodontal Res* **32**(1 Pt 2): 120-5.

FUNGI AND OTHER OPPORTUNISTIC PATHOGENS IN PLAQUE

Andrew Smith and T. Wallace MacFarlane

Introduction

Although the microbiology of dental plaque has been studied intensively during the past 50 years, it is only in the last 10-15 years that detailed information about the presence of Candida and other opportunistic micro-organisms has become available. Generally, the reasons for this discrepancy are linked to the technical difficulties involved in isolating and enumerating micro-organisms which are present only in small numbers from plaque. Conventional culture techniques to investigate plaque involve disaggregation of plaque followed by dilution of the sample before inoculation and culture. Species that occur in small numbers are usually eliminated during the dilution step and therefore are rarely recovered. Selective culture media are traditionally employed to overcome this difficulty but due to the complexity of the species present in dental plaque, relatively few media are truly selective, and for many species, the problem cannot be easily and consistently resolved by this means.

The literature dealing with the oral carriage of Candida, enteric-gram negative rods, staphylococci and other opportunistic pathogens has increased substantially over recent years. However, much of the data relates to non-dental plaque, samples (e.g. mucosal swabs and salivary rinses) and there is relatively little information linked specifically to plaque samples that have been both carefully collected and subsequently investigated by appropriate laboratory techniques. There is increasing interest in the oral ecology of opportunistic micro-organism, and since many grow in a biofilm such as plaque tend to be less susceptible to a range of antimicrobial agents, this could have important implications in diseases caused by these organisms, with regard to the creation of reservoirs of infection, re-infection and treatment failure due to antimicrobial resistance. The aim of this chapter is to review current knowledge in relation to the above mentioned groups of micro-organisms in dental plaque, and to discuss the clinical significance of the data.

Fungi

Introduction

Individuals colonised with *Candida spp.* possess numerous interdependent mechanisms to prevent establishment of infection. Efficient protection involves components of the non-specific and specific humoral and cell mediated immunological mechanisms (Challacombe 1990). Impairments of these defences are sufficient to allow *C. albicans,* the most pathogenic member of the species, to establish infection. *Candida spp.* are common members of the oral micro-flora; the oral carriage rate has been estimated at 40-60% of the population. The prevalence and concentration of Candida varies in different oral sites and is affected by the presence or absence of intra-oral appliances (Berdicevsky *et al.,*

1980; Addy *et al.,* 1982). In healthy dentate carriers, yeast's are most commonly isolated from the dorsum of the tongue (Arendorf and Walker, 1980), whilst in healthy denture-wearing carriers, similar prevalence rates are found for the tongue, fitting surface of the upper denture and in some cases the palate (Arendorf and Walker, 1979).

Ecology of Fungi in Plaque

There is some confusion concerning the relationship of Candida and dental plaque. In the oral cavity of volunteers widely colonised by yeasts, use of an impression culture technique by Arendorf and Walker (1980), revealed that Candida preferentially colonised the plaque coated surfaces of teeth. However, there are few data in the very extensive literature of plaque microbiology, both in relation to dental caries and periodontitis, to support this view (Krasse, 1954; Hodson and Craig, 1972; Slots, Rams and Listgarten, 1988). The reason for this discrepancy is unclear although it is possible that Candida was detected in some samples but not reported. Another possible explanation is that yeasts were present in small numbers and due to sample dilution before culture, their presence was undetected.

Oral Carriage

The oral carriage rate for Candida in healthy individuals is approximately 40% when saliva/mouthwash techniques are used (Odds, 1988) with consistently higher rates for hospitalised patients (median 55%). The number of yeasts isolated from the healthy carrier are usually low, 10-20 cfu/cm^2 (imprint culture method), 200-500 cfu/ml in mixed saliva and 600 cfu/ml from an oral rinse technique (Arendorf and Walker, 1980). *C. albicans* is the single most commonly isolated species from oral samples, (Shipman, 1979; Wright *et al.,* 1985), other species such as, *C. glabrata* and *C. tropicalis* account for about 7% of oral isolates with *C. krusei, C. parasilosis, C. guilliermondii, Rhodotorula* species and other yeasts being infrequently found (Odds, 1988).

Although *C. albicans* is the most frequent clinical isolate there is considerable geographic and patient group variation over time (Knoke *et al.,* 1997). In the 1970's *C. tropicalis* emerged as an important pathogen in neutropenic patients and *C. parasilosis* infection was more common in patients receiving parenteral nutrition. More recently, changes in anti-fungal usage have led to higher rate of colonisation and infection with *C. glabrata* and *C. krusei* which are less susceptible to antifungal treatment. Of further interest is the emergence of *C. lusitaniae* as a nosocomial pathogen (Sanchez *et al.,* 1992), and *C. dubliniensis* in HIV positive patients (Kirkpatrick *et al.,* 1998).

Many workers have observed the changes in the oral flora in patients undergoing treatment for both solid and haematological malignancies (Dreizen *et al.,* 1983, 1986; Wahlin and Holm, 1988; Makkonen *et al.,* 1989; Peterson *et al.,* 1990; Bergman *et al.,* 1991) using oral rinse techniques. These changes are induced by the combined effects of anti-neoplastic therapy and antibiotic treatment, suppressing the normal oral flora which become replaced by potential

388

pathogens such as *Candida spp.* and Gram negative bacilli. The frequency of yeasts recovered depends on the type of malignancies, for example, solid tumours are less than one third as liable to oral infections than those with leukaemia (Driezen *et al.,* 1983). Approximately 80% of patients (from a cohort of 1,000 with variable malignant diseases) had oral infections caused by fungi (Driezen *et al.,* 1983). In a study on the oral flora during bouts of radiation mucositis the counts of fungi (and Gram negative bacilli) increased from 20 to 80% of patients colonised with yeasts (Makkonen *et al.,* 1989).

Opportunism
Caries and Root Caries

There are several reports indicating a relationship between *C. albicans* and/or denture plaque and enamel and root caries (Arendorf and Walker, 1980; Samaranayake *et al.,* 1983 and 1986; Pienihakkinen *et al.,* 1987; Russel *et al.,* 1991; Schneinin *et al.,* 1992 and 1994; Coulter *et al.,* 1993; Ainamo *et al.,* 1993). It is often assumed that such a relationship reflects the acidogenicity of *Candida spp.* since Candida are not usually considered to play a major role in caries development. Beighton *et al.,* (1995) reported the recovery of *Candida spp.* from dental plaque samples and highlighted the relatively high prevalence of *Candida spp.* (59%) from 81 root caries lesions. Recently, Sen *et al.* (1997), have shown that *C. albicans* can colonise cleaned human enamel, cementum and dentine. Once colonisation has taken place collagenolytic enzymes are produced (Kaminishi *et al.,* 1986; Hagihara *et al.,* 1988), that may degrade dentinal collagen fibres. Proteinases are secreted by virtually all isolates of *C. albicans* and *C. tropicalis* to varying degrees (Ruchel, 1990). The enzymic effects of candidal proteinases require a lowered pH; enzymic activity is minimal at pH 6.5 but near to the pH maximum of 3.0-3.5, candidal proteinases act in an indiscriminate manner.

Candida and Periodontal Disease

There are several reports indicating severe periodontitis in relation to Candida isolation. Slots *et al.,* (1988) reported recovery of high numbers of *C. albicans* organisms from the sub-gingival flora of severe periodontitis in adult patients. Rams and Slots (1991) also reported patients with severe periodontitis and Candida in subgingival plaque. In a more recent study Dahlén *et al.* (1995), fungi were recovered from 7.3% of samples from 19.6% of patients undergoing various forms of periodontal treatment; a similar frequency to that of Slots *et al.* (1988). Candida was not found to exceed 10% of the total viable count in any of the samples with no relationship between the presence of Candida and type of periodontal treatment.

Oral Mucosal Infections

The well known presentations of oral candidal infection includes pseudomembranous, erythematous and hyperplastic forms which may be accompanied by angular chelitis and glossitis (Samaranayake and MacFarlane, 1990). It is possible that Candida in plaque acts as a reservoir for infection in these sites, or vice versa. Candida like organisms in gingival plaque samples were observed by transmission electron microscopy in 12 of 17 AIDS patients (CD4 count <100/ mm³). However, clinical signs of oral candidosis were absent in 6 of these 12 patients; the values for the oral rinses ranged from 0-100,000 cfu/ml, demonstrating that dental plaque may be a reservoir of Candida organisms in the immunocompromised (Berthold *et al.,* 1994). Over 80% of HIV positive individuals develop oral candidosis at some time during their illness. This infection is an important AIDS defining diagnosis and is used in many countries as a surrogate marker for clinically significant decreases in the CD4 counts. Of interest is the recent report of a new species of Candida, *C. dubliniensis* from HIV positive individuals with oropharyngeal candidosis, some of which were resistant to fluconazole (Kirkpatrick *et al.,* 1998).

Gastrointestinal and Pulmonary Infections

Oral infection with Candida often spreads to the oesophagus in HIV infected individuals and although oesophagitis can occur without oral involvement, this is rare. There are several reports indicating that aspiration of oral bacteria into the respiratory tract may occur (Worthington, 1983; Martin *et al.,* 1994; Cannon *et al.,* 1995) it seems feasable then that fungal infection of the lower respiratory tract may originate from the oral cavity.

In the European Prevalence of Infection in Intensive Care (EPIC) study it was reported that *Candida spp.* were the causative agent of 14% of intensive care unit (ICU)-acquired pneumonia's on the day of the study, but this relatively high figure almost certainly included many patients with asymptomatic colonisation (Vincent *et al.,* 1995). Furthermore, candidal pneumonia is extremely uncommon in ventilated patients and requires bronchial biopsy for diagnosis (Fraser *et al.,* 1992).

The incidence of *Candida spp.* bacteraemia has increased since the 1980's and is now the fourth most common bloodstream pathogen in North American hospitals, accounting for 8-15% of nosocomial septicaemias in the USA (Pfaller, 1992.) with *C. albicans* causing 60% of all infections. (Beck-Sague, 1993). Risk factors include prolonged vascular catheterisation, tracheal intubation, parenteral nutrition, broad spectrum antibiotics and acute pancreatitis (Flanagan and Barnes, 1998). Non-albicans *Candida spp.* have emerged recently as significant pathogens in ICU environments, especially *C. tropicalis, C. glabrata* and *C. parasilosis.* In one study non-albicans *Candida spp.* accounted for 15% of candidaemias in 1991 and 56% in 1994 (Beck-Sague, 1993; Voss, 1997). Invasive mycoses are especially problematic in critically ill patients as they are difficult to diagnose and there is a narrow range of anti-fungal agents available, with limited anti-fungal spectrum or dose limiting side effects. Deep fungal infection is also an increasing problem in patients treated for haematological malignancies and organ transplants, although the exact contribution oropharanygeal candidosis makes to fungal infections in the compromised host is unclear, despite the frequency of candidal isolation from respiratory secretions

Table 1 Oral carriage of staphylococci in different patient groups.

Study Group	N tested	S. aureus	S. epidermidis	S. warneri	S. haemolyticus	S. schleiferi	S. lugdunensis
Healthy adults	50	12(24%)	44(88%)	14(28%)	7(14%)	2(4%)	1(2%)
Healthy elderly	25	9(36%)	23(92%)	9(36%)	10(40%)	2(8%)	ND
Rheumatoid arthritis patients	25	14(56%)	21(84%)	4(16%)	7(28%)	ND	2(8%)
Healthy children	25	16(64%)	16(64%)	5(20%)	ND	ND	ND
Children with malignancies	120	6(5%)	42(35%)	3(3%)	ND	1(0.8%)	ND

(ND = not detected). Data from Jackson MS (1999).

in ICU patients (Petri *et al.*, 1997). However, in one study infection in most patients, infection appeared to be derived from the individual's own endogenous flora (Voss *et al.*, 1994).

Spread of Candida from the Mouth

Using biotyping techniques, yeast's from the mouth have been shown to colonise the skin in some cancer patients (McCreight *et al.*, 1985). Transmission of organisms from person to person can occur and outbreaks of candidosis in neonatal and surgical intensive care units have sometimes been attributed to carriage of organisms on the hands of hospital staff (Strasbaugh *et al.*, 1994). There is also some evidence that the mouth is the likely source or organisms in candida paronchyia (Ganor and Pumpianski, 1970 and 1974), in chronic vaginal candidosis (Pumpianski *et al.*, 1968, Soll *et al.*, 1991) and in burns patients (Smith *et al.*, 1975).

Gram positives

Staphylococci in Dental Plaque
Introduction

The presence of Staphylococci in the oral cavity is controversial, since they are frequently considered not part of the normal oral flora although both coagulase positive and negative Staphylococci have been isolated from the healthy mouth and also from endodontic infections, osteomyelitis of the jaw, parotitis (Goldberg, 1981) and several other oral conditions. Whilst there is an increasing amount of data regarding the oral ecology and pathogenesis of staphylococci in the mouth much of the information is collected from samples such as oral rinses, saliva and mucosal lesions. Recent studies have shown that Staphylococci can be frequently isolated from the mouths of children (Miyake *et al.*, 1991), the elderly (Bagg *et al.*, 1995) and some groups with systemic disease such as the terminally ill (Jobbins *et al.*, 1992), rheumatoid arthritis (Jacobson *et al.*,1997) and haematological malignancies (Jackson, 1998) (See Table 1).

Ecology of Staphylococci in Plaque
Staphylococci have been isolated from supragingival plaque (Gibbons *et al.*, 1964, Piochi and Zelante, 1975 and Percival *et al.*, 1991) and from subgingival plaque (Gibbons *et al.*, 1963, Sanchez-Cordero *et al.*, 1979, Moore *et al.*, 1985, Rams *et al.*, 1990, Dahlen and Wikström 1995 and Kamma *et al.*, 1999). Few plaque samples have been collected from non-diseased sites, and therefore no definitive interpretation of the available qualitative and quantitative data for Staphylococci in health is possible. Percival *et al.* (1991) reported the isolation of Staphylococci from about 12% of supragingival plaque samples in 79 healthy individuals, all with low mean percentage counts. Also, there were no clear age related trends in the isolation frequency or proportions of staphylococci. The species of Staphylococci most frequently reported from oral samples are *S.epidermidis* and *S.aureus*, but *S.haemolyticus, S.hominus, S.warneri, S.capilis, S.saprophyticus, S.xylosus* and *S.simulans* have also been described (Rams, Fick and Slots, 1990; Jackson, 1998).

Staphylococci in Plaque-related Diseases
A study of subgingival plaque from 658 individuals with various forms of periodontal disease reported that up to 50% of plaque samples from periodontitis, gingivitis, local juvenile periodontitis and early onset periodontitis patients contained low levels of *Staphylococcus species* which accounted for about 1% of the total cultivable flora, with much higher values occurring in a few sites(Rams *et al.*, 1990). In another study involving subgingival plaque samples from 3,075 'refractory' periodontitis patients, staphylococci were isolated from about 28% of patients (Slots *et al.*, 1990). In a more recent study (Dahlén and Wikström, 1995) Staphylococci constituted only a small percentage of the total microbial counts ($\geq 1\%$); *S.epidermidis* was most frequently isolated and was detected in 41% of samples from 54% of patients, whereas *S.aureus* was found in only 3 samples. Finally, *S.aureus* was one of a number of bacterial species that was isolated in statistically significant higher numbers and significantly more frequently from subgingival plaque collected from smokers compared to non-smokers who were diagnosed with early onset periodontitis (Kamma *et al.*, 1999). The precise involvement of *Staphylococcus species* in plaque related infections is unknown, and may represent colonisation rather than superinfection. However, in cases of failing dental implants, a significant proportion (69%) of the affected sites had high proportions of *Staphylococcus species* (15% - 100% of the total flora) in associated plaque (Slots *et al* 1990a*). However, this association has not been confirmed in other studies (Listgarten and Lai, 1999).

Staphylococci in Oral Mucosal Infections
In addition, to the well described association with angular cheilitis, oral mucosal infection with *S. aureus* has recently been incriminated in a severe form of

mucositis seen among elderly patients receiving parenteral nutrition (Bagg *et al.,* 1995).

Oral Staphylococci as a Source for Systemic Infection

Recently there has been debate over the role of oral micro-organisms in prosthetic joint infections (Bartzokas *et al.,* 1994) and the possible need for antibiotic prophylaxis in such patients during dental treatment. Staphylococci are the
most important cause of prosthetic joint infections. *S. aureus* is a significant
pathogen in acute septic arthritis, affecting both native and prosthetic joints
whilst *S. epidermidis* is responsible for a large percentage of late or chronic
infections (An and Friedman, 1996). Such joints are frequently placed in
patients with rheumatoid arthritis and the possibility of a bacteraemia from an
oral source resulting in a prosthetic joint infection should be of considerable
interest. At present, the source of staphylococcal joint sepsis cannot be identified
in up to 30% of cases (Kaandorp *et al.,* 1997). Recent work by Jackson *et al.,*
(1999) investigated oral carriage of Staphylococci in patients with rheumatoid
arthritis (Table 1). The study found that a significantly higher proportion (56%)
of the patients with rheumatoid arthritis carried oral *S. aureus* than controls
(24%) ($P < 0.05$). This is unlikely to be an age-related effect, since there was no
significant difference between colonisation rates for the two adult control groups
($P > 0.05$) and the rheumatoid arthritis patients were significantly younger than
the healthy elderly individuals. It is well recognised that many patients with
rheumatoid arthritis have a reduced salivary flow rate (Sullivan *et al.,* 1978),
and the dry mouth may result in significant changes to the oral flora
(MacFarlane, 1984). The drug regimens used in the treatment of rheumatoid
arthritis, many of which are immunosuppressive or cytotoxic will also affect the
mucosal immunity in the mouth and some, for example methotrexate, can cause
oral ulceration further enhancing the possibility of an oral source for staphylococcal joint sepsis.

Coagulase negative staphylococci are frequently isolated from blood cultures
among patients receiving treatment for malignant disease (Bergmann, 1988). It
is commonly a result of colonisation of venous access devices, but in some
cases no such source of infection is present. The mouth has not been generally
considered to play a role in such infections, but many patients receiving chemotherapeutic drug regimens develop severe oral ulceration (mucositis) as a result
of the effect of these drugs on the oral mucosa (Rosenberg, 1986). Such ulceration provides a portal of entry for organisms in the oral flora, and has already
been identified in relation to septicaemia caused by oral streptococci in children
receiving treatment for leukaemia. This has been demonstrated more recently by
a *S. epidemidis* and *S. oralis* bacteraemia in a bone marrow transplant patient
(Kennedy, personal communication). Identical isolates by pulsed field gel
electrophoresis (PFGE) were found in the mouth and bloodstream (Figure 1). In
the study by Jackson (1999) (Table 1) children with haematologic malignancy
were investigated by oral rinses for levels of staphylococci and compared to
healthy child controls. Only 6 (5%) of the 120 children with haematologic

malignancy carried *S. aureus* compared with 64% of the healthy children. It is likely that the lower levels of *S. aureus* are a result of frequent antibiotic treatment. In the same study a significantly smaller proportion of the children with malignant disease (37%) carried coagulase negative staphylococci compared with the healthy control children (64%) but levels of carriage are higher than previously noted.

Streptococci
Introduction

Oral streptococci form a major part of supra-gingival plaque and the oro-pharyngeal flora. They are described in more detail in earlier chapters and following major reclassifications that have taken place in recent years they have been placed into a series of species groups; mutans group, mitis group, salivarius group and an anginosis group (for review see Whiley and Beighton 1998).

In addition to their role in the formation of dental caries they have had a well recognised etiological role in bacterial endocarditis. Also oral streptococci frequently cause asymptomatic bacteraemia, especially after dental treatment or endoscopic procedures. Generally, there is a reluctance to ascribe clinical significance to these organisms in blood cultures, which is probably due to their low virulence and the transient nature of the bacteraemia. On the other hand they have been considered to be truly significant pathogens in rare infections. Since the last decade has seen a considerable increase in systemic infections with oral streptococci and with potentially fatal complications in the neonate and in oncology patients (Oppenheim 1998) their role in systemic disease requires careful consideration.

Changes in the Oral Streptococcal flora in the Compromised Host

It is important to understand the changes that occur in the oral micro-flora of patients who are susceptible to opportunistic disease. However, there are conflicting reports in the literature which probably reflects differences in cytotoxic drug therapy and antibiotic treatment. In addition the recent nomenclature changes in oral streptococci makes comparisons between reports difficult. In a detailed study using oral rinses, from 20 children undergoing allogeneic bone marrow transplantation a significant increase in aerobic , and anaerobic counts and in the proportion of the *S. oralis* group organisms between baseline and 7 days post transplant was reported. However, this returned to baseline levels by the end of the study (119 days later) (Lucas *et al.*, 1997). Interestingly this group of children had a 20% incidence of "oralis group" bacteraemia. A study by Richard *et al.* (1995) provides additional evidence for the role of oral streptococcal septicaemia in leukaemic patients by demonstrating similar ribotypes in oral isolates and subsequent blood culture isolates. More recently (Kennedy H, Personal Communication), similar relationships have been described for oral and blood culture isolates of coagulase negative staphylococci and *S. oralis* (Figure 1).

394

Systemic Disease
Bacteraemia

Again, the recent changes in nomenclature makes the comparison of different reports difficult and some papers simply report "viridans streptococci" with no attempt at detailed identification. Oral streptococci accounted for 2.6% of positive blood cultures in one study (Swenson and Rubin, 1982) and of these only 21% were considered clinically significant. The remainder were attributed to contamination as part of the normal skin flora, despite the fact that the viridans streptococci are rarely isolated from this site.

Interestingly streptococcal bacteria has been considered as an emerging pathogen in patients undergoing intensive chemotherapy (Oppenheim 1998). Successive data from the European Organisation for Research and Treatment of Cancer (EORTC) (Cometta *et al.*, 1996) demonstratesd an increasing incidence of "viridans" streptococcal bacteraemia (Figure 2). The decline in some centers due to changes in empirical antibiotic regimens. A mortality rate of 6-30% has been reported for an "alpha-strep shock syndrome" from a number of centres (for review see Bochud, Cometta and Francioli, 1997). Risk factors for bacteraemia are the presence of profound

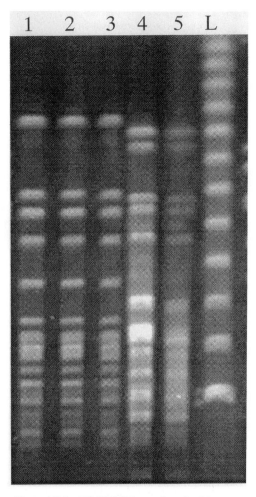

Figure 1 Pulsed Field Gel Electrophoresis of *S. epidermidis* and *S. oralis* isolates from oral cavity and bloodstream in a bone marrow transplant patient.

Lane 1: *S. epidermidis* PFGE from blood
Lane 2: *S. epidermidis* PFGE from blood.
Lane 3: *S. epidermidis* PFGE from mouth.
Lane 4:. : *S. oralis* from blood.
Lane 5: *S. oralis* from mouth.
Lane L: DNA molecular weight marker (48.5 kb Lambda ladder).

(PFGE courtesy of Dr H. Kennedy Dept. of Microbiology, Royal Hospital for Sick Children, Yorkhill NHS Trust, Glasgow and Dr D. Morrison, Scottish MRSA Reference Laboratory and University Department of Bacteriology, Glasgow Royal Infirmary, Glasgow, UK.)

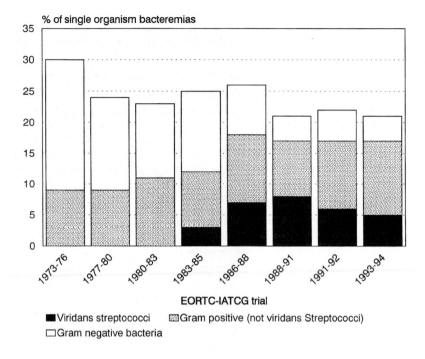

Figure 2 Incidence of "viridans streptococcus" bacteraemias among neutropenic patients in eight consecutive EORTC-IATCG trials

neutropenia, antibiotic prophylaxis with quinolones or co-trimoxazole, administration of cytosine arabinoside in large doses and oropharyngeal mucositis. However, more recently the incidence of oral streptococcal bacteraemia has declined, probably due to changes in empiric antimicrobial regimens.

Endocarditis

In the pre-antibiotic era oral streptococci accounted for approximately 75% of the cases of infective endocarditis (Kaye *et al.,* 1962). Latterly this has declined to 30-40 % (Roberts 1992, Dyson *et al.,* 1999). Although many different species have been reported to cause endocarditis, it is unfortunate that a significant correlation between specific streptococcal species and the clinical manifestations or outcome of the disease will be not achieved due to changes in taxonomy and methods used for speciation. A detailed analysis of species was performed by Douglas *et al.* (1993), who identified 47 strains of oral streptococci from 42 confirmed cases of endocarditis, the most common species being *Streptococcus sanguis sensu stricto* (32%), *S. oralis* (30%) and *S. gordonii* (13%); other related species such as *S. mitis* were less common. Unfortunately few clinical details were presented probably due to the retrospective nature of the study.

Meningitis

Although the oral streptococci frequently cause bacteraemia, they are an infrequent cause of community acquired meningitis, representing<2% of the total number of cases in adults. Oral streptococcal meningitis occurs in patients of all ages including neonates. Patients with streptococcal meningitis (other than pneumococci) usually have an identifiable source of infection, which in most cases is related to traumatic CSF leaks or to neurosurgical procedures. In the review by Cabellos *et al.* (1999), most cases were due to *S. mitis* (6/20) and four of these strains demonstrated decreased susceptibility to penicillin (MIC 0.5-2.0 μg/ml). Streptococci from the "milleri" group are frequently isolated from brain abscesses and are a frequent cause of secondary meningitis, a complication that occurs in 15% of cases of brain abscess.

Pneumonia

Oral streptococci are commonly isolated from cultures of expectorated sputum and are rarely ascribed clinical significance since they are regarded as part of the normal oral flora. They are also isolated frequently from cultures of lower respiratory tract specimens obtained via protected bronchial brush or broncho-alveolar lavage. They can be cultured in samples from patients with aspiration pneumonia syndrome and are very rarely isolated in pure culture, usually being recovered in association with other oral organisms, such as anaerobes (Gonzalez and Calia, 1975; Brook and Finegold, 1980; Rose, 1981). Despite the consistent appearance of oral streptococci from respiratory tract culture specimens, they are not often recognised as pulmonary pathogens, which is probably linked to their reputation as having low pathogenicty and their usual in-vitro susceptibil-ity to beta-lactams, agents normally prescribed in the treatment of pneumonia.

Miscellaneous Infections

Oral streptococci are associated with a variety of other infections, which are usually reported as single case reports. Pathogenicity in these cases has been confirmed by recovery of the organism in pure culture and often by the concur-rent presence of bacteraemia. Excluding localised purulent collections associ-ated with the milleri group, oral streptococci have been identified in patients with pericarditis, peritonitis, acute bacterial sialadenitis, odontogenic abscesses, endopthalmitis, otitis media and sinusitis (Gaudreau *et al.*, 1981; Catto *et al.*, 1987; Raad *et al.*, 1990; Lewis *et al.*, 1990)

Some centres have reported an increase in invasive *S. mitis* in neonates (Adams and Fairfax 1994). Most infants infected with *S. mitis* are <3 days of age and mothers have identifiable perinatal risk factors for neonatal sepsis such as premature onset of labour, UTI, peripartum fever or prolonged rupture of membranes. Of interest is the observation that "viridans streptococci" are the second most frequent isolate (10% of cultures (Mercer *et al.*, 1996) from preterm premature rupture of membranes. Whether these organisms originate in the genitourinary tract or are secondary to an oral focus of infection remains to be concluded.

Antimicrobial Susceptibility

Recent studies of the antimicrobial susceptibility pattern of oral streptococci have demonstrated the emergence of resistance to an increasing number of antibiotics (Doern *et al.,* 1996; Alcaide *et al.,* 1996; Renneberg *et al.,* 1997; Teng *et al.,*1998). Susceptibility to b-lactam agents often with MIC's >2 µg/ml have been described especially in *S. mitis* isolates. Such levels are worrying since this limits the use of oral penicillins and cephalosporins. Resistance is due to the development of altered forms of high molecular mass penicillin binding proteins (PBP's) that have greatly decreased affinity for β-lactam antibiotics (Quinn *et al.,* 1988).

There is an intriguing link between members of the oro-pharyngeal flora, in particular members of the oral streptococci, such as *S. mitis* and *S. pneumoniae.* It has been suggested that the low-affinity PBP's of penicillin-resistant pneumo-cocci have arisen by inter-species recombination events that replace part of the pneumococcal PBP genes with the corresponding regions from oral streptococci (Dowson *et al.,* 1993).

If the resistance to antibiotics among oral streptococci continues to increase, then the efficacy of certain antibiotics, not only for prophylaxis but also for treatment especially in the immunocompromised host, will need to be reassessed.

Actinomyces

Introduction

The *Actinomyces species* are commensals and normal inhabitants of the oropharynx, gastrointestinal tract and female genital tract.. Of the 14 *Actinomyces species* six may cause disease in humans; *A. israelii, A. naeslundii, A. odontolyticus, A viscosus, A. meyeri* and *A. gerencseriae. Actinomyces spp.* form a major portion of the microflora of dental plaque, particularly at interproximal sites and have been implicated in plaque related disease (see earlier chapters).

Opportunistic Infections

Classically, actinomycosis is a relatively rare chronic disease characterised by abscess formation, multiple draining sinuses and tissue fibrosis. *Actinomyces spp.* are generally of low pathogenicity and cause disease only in the setting of antecedent tissue injury and are frequently isolated as part of a mixed flora. Four clinical forms of actinomycosis ,i.e., cervicofacial, thoracic, abdominopelvic and cerebral account for the majority of infections in humans (Smego and Foglia, 1998). The face and neck are the most common sites of actinomycosis. The frequency of this location among cases of actinomycosis averages about 55% of cases. *Actinomyces spp.* are normally present in high concentrations in tonsillar crypts and gingival crevices and many actinomyces infections are odontogenic in origin. In addition to poor dentition and recent dental manipulation, chronic tonsillitis, otitis and mastoiditis are important risk factors. Cervicofacial actino-mycosis may take the form of acute, pyogenic abscesses or indolent disease characterised by abscess formation, tissue fibrosis and multiple draining sinuses. Lesions are frequently located at the angle of the mandible which may extend to

Table 2 Detection of *H. pylori* from dental plaque in patients with/without abdominal complaints by means of culture and PCR

	No. cases	H. pylori +ve culture	No. cases	H. pylori +ve PCR
Detection of *H. pylori* in pts with abdominal complaints	448	33(7.1%)	236	73(30.9%)
Detection of *H. pylori* in pts without abdominal complaints	284	52(18.3%)	479	23(4.8%)

Data extracted from Madinier *et al.* (1997).

the underlying facial bones leading to periostitis or osteomyelitis.

Of interest is the fact that other bacteria are frequently isolated from clinical specimens such as, *Actinobacillus actinomycetemcomitans, Eikonella corrodens, Fusobacterium spp., Bacteroides spp., Capnocytophaga,* and *Streptococci* organisms frequently found in dental plaque (Smego and Foglia, 1998).

Gram negatives
Helicobacter pylori and Dental Plaque
Introduction
Helicobacter pylori a microaerophilic Gram-negative rod is widely recognised as an aetiologic agent of chronic active gastritis and peptic ulcer disease (Andersen *et al.,* 1987; Taylor and Blaser, 1991; Lee *et al.,* 1993), and has also been associated with gastric cancer (Forman *et al.,* 1991; Parsonnet *et al.,* 1991). The average *H. pylori* infection rates in healthy adults in the Western world are estimated to be between 10 and 40%, whereas patients with gastritis or gastric and duodenal ulceration have infection rates of between 80 and 100% (Megraud, 1993). The prevalence of *H. pylori* infection has been shown to increase with age, with an estimated 50-60% of people over the age of 55 being infected compared to only 10-20% of young adults (Kosunen *et al.,* 1989; Veldhuyzen van Zanten *et al.,*1994). In developing countries, where sanitation is poor, up to 50% of children are infected by 5 years of age (Mitchell *et al.,* 1992; Holcombe, 1992). The natural reservoir for *H. pylori* is unknown, although the oral cavity has been the focus of much attention in this respect (Madinier *et al.,* 1997).

Ecology of H. pylori
The presence of *H. pylori* in dental plaque of patients both with and without stomach disorders has been investigated by culture and polymerase chain reaction (PCR) methods (Table 2). Most studies have failed to isolate *H. pylori* by culture from dental plaque of patients undergoing endoscopy (Banatvala *et al.,* 1994; Bickley *et al.,* 1993; Krajden *et al.,* 1989; Bernander *et al.,* 1993; Khandaker *et al.,* 1993). PCR analysis of dental plaque from endoscopy patients has yielded more conflicting data, with *H. pylori* found frequently in some studies (Banatvala *et al.,* 1994; Nguyen *et al.,* 1993; Yang, 1993) but is absent or

found extremely rarely in others (Bickley *et al.,* 1993; Hardo *et al.,* 1995). In the dental plaque of healthy subjects, culture methods have detected *H. pylori* at high frequency in a single study (Majmudar *et al.,* 1990), while PCR has detected the organism at high frequency in only one study (Banatvala *et al.,* 1994). In symptomatic individuals, PCR has detected *H. pylori* in saliva (Hammar *et al.,* 1992; Shimada *et al.,* 1994; Li *et al.,* 1995) whereas culture methods have very rarely isolated *H. pylori* from saliva (Ferguson *et al.,* 1993).

H. pylori and Sub-gingival Plaque

The vast majority of published studies have examined dental plaque of subjects without periodontitis i.e. supragingival plaque or subgingival plaque from the gingival crevice. A single study has been carried out in which 336 subgingival plaque samples from adult periodontitis in the USA (Asikainen *et al.,* 1994); none of the samples analysed were positive for *H. pylori*. These results are clearly at odds with the results of a more recent study by Riggio and Lennon (1999) who found *H. pylori* in the subgingival plaque of approximately one third of the adult periodontitis patients examined. This difference may be attributable to variations in the population groups examined and also in the plaque sampling methods employed, for example, paper point versus sampling by currette.

A potentially important factor in explaining the wide variation in results obtained by different workers in relation to *H. pylori* and dental plaque are the primers and PCR conditions employed. A recent study (Song *et al.,* 1999) used 4 different primers to detect *H. pylori* in plaque samples and reported a substantial variation in detection which was directly related to the primers employed. The primer pair EHC-4/EHC-1 directed to the 860 bp fragment of *H. pylori* produced a high sensitivity and specificity and detected *H. pylori* in 100% of plaque samples. In the only other published study that employed this primer (Li *et al.,* 1995), *H. pylori* was detected in 58.9% of saliva samples.

Opportunistic Infection

Helicobacter pylori is widely recognised as an aetiologic agent of chronic active gastritis and peptic ulcer disease (Anderson *et al.,* 1987; Taylor and Blaser 1991; Lee *et al.,* 1993), and has also been associated with gastric cancer. Genetic typing studies on isolates obtained both from the oral cavity and stomach of patients have shown that strains from these two sites tend to be identical, although different strains are harboured by different individuals (Shames *et al.,* 1989; Khandaker *et al.,* 1993). The identification of identical strains of *H. pylori* in stomach and oral samples of individuals can be interpreted in two ways. Firstly, such observations could lend credence to the theory that *H. pylori* may only be a transient member of the oral cavity as it may be present in the oral cavity as a direct result of gastric reflux. Alternatively it can be speculated that oral sites such as dental plaque may be a reservoir for gastric re-infection by *H. pylori*. PCR has demonstrated the presence of *H. pylori* in the saliva of patients whose gastric biopsies are negative for *H. pylori* and lack of

400

correlation between gastric symptoms and the presence of *H. pylori* in the oral cavity was also observed (Li *et al.,* 1995). These observations led the authors (Li *et al.,* 1995) to suggest that oral colonisation by *H. pylori* may precede gastric infection and that saliva may also be a reservoir for gastric re-infection by *H. pylori*. Claims that *H. pylori* is a permanent member of the oral cavity that can cause gastric re-infection, and inevitably person-to-person transmission, can only be substantiated by recovery of viable *H. pylori* from the oral cavity, which has rarely been accomplished. Reasons for the general inability to culture *H. pylori* from the oral cavity are difficult to assign with any certainty but could include the presence of the organism in a coccoid form that is viable but non-culturable *in vitro* (Cellini *et al.,* 1994 a and b; Hua *et al.,* 1996). It has been postulated that *H. pylori* may exist in the environment in a non-culturable coccoid form that can revert to a replicative form *in vivo* following ingestion by a mammalian host (Fox 1995), but no conclusive evidence exists to support this hypothesis. If this hypothesis could be proven it would strengthen the notion of water and food as important reservoirs of *H. pylori*.

Transmission

The exact mode of transmission of *H. pylori* is poorly understood, although it appears that oral-oral and faecal-oral routes are possible (Goodman and Correa, 1995). Evidence exists for possible oral transmission from person-to-person (Drumm *et al.,* 1990; Li *et al.,* 1996) and faecal-oral transmission is thought to be particularly prevalent in developing countries, although the organism is rarely isolated from faeces (Li *et al.,* 1996). Transmission of *H. pylori* via gastric juice as a result of epidemic childhood vomiting has also been proposed (Axon 1996). However, overall controversy still surrounds the hypothesis that the oral cavity may be a permanent reservoir for *H. pylori*.

Enteric Gram negative rods

Introduction

Enteric Gram negative rods include bacteria belonging to the families Entero-bacteriaceae and Pseudomonaceae which are non-spore forming, aerobic and facultatively anaerobic bacilli that can be found in the gastrointestinal tract of humans and animals, on plants, and in soil or aquatic habitats.

There is an increasing volume of information about the presence of a wide range of enteric species in the oral cavity (Sedgley and Samaranayake, 1994), but most of the data is derived from non-plaque samples (e.g. oral rinses, saliva or mucosal swabs). However, since most studies have largely been cross-sectional, there is little definitive evidence to confirm or dispute the general impression that enteric species are transitory members of the oral microflora.

Ecology

There is virtually no data concerning enteric bacteria in either supra or subgin-gival plaque from healthy sites, but there are a number of reports dealing with their presence in subgingival plaque from patients with periodontitis (Table 3).

Table 3 'Enteric' microorganisms in subgingival dental plaque.

Predominant species	No. of patients	No. positive(%)	No. of species	Reference
E.cloacae	500	51 (10)	12	Slots *et al.* (1988)
E.agglomerans				
K.pneumoniae				
K.oxytoca				
Pse.aeruginosa				
E.cloacae	3050	427 (14)	42	Slots *et al.* (1990b)
K.oxytoca				
K.pneumoniae				
Pse.aeruginosa				
E.cloacae	535	244 (27)	20	Dahlén & Wikström (1995)
K.oxytoca				
K.pneumoniae				

Although a wide range of genera have been reported the three most common were Enterobacter (especially *E.cloacae* and *E.agglomerans)*; Klebsiella (especially *K.oxytoca* and *K. pneumoniae)* and Pseudomonas (especially *P. aeruguniosa)*. Generally, enteric organisms have been found in relatively small numbers in a low percentage of patients. Although Dahlén and Wikström (1995) reported almost double the number of enteric positive patients compared with other workers (Table 3), the majority of subjects in their study had a light microbial load, and when results were confined to those samples with levels >1% of total viable counts, the percentage dropped to 9.5%.

There is little information concerning the mechanisms by which enteric organisms colonise the oral cavity, but attachment to dental plaque perhaps by means of fimbriae or to receptors on the oral mucosal surface (Johansen *et al.*, 1980) seems likely. In particular fibronectin appears to play an intergral role in the attachment of enteric Gram negative organisms. Woods *et al.* (1981 and 1987) have suggested that the loss of mucosal fibronectin may be due t enzymes found in saliva that may unmask surface receptors allowing enhanced binding for these organisms.

Localised Disease

The role of enteric micro-organisms in periodontal disease is uncertain. There is evidence in a few patients that antimicrobial therapy e.g. ciprofloxacin can eradicate enteric rods from subgingival sites in periodontitis patients, with an associated reduction in probing depth (Slots *et al.*, 1990b). However, the evidence is slight and longitudinal data is required from both healthy and diseased sites before definitive assessments can be made. The carriage rate of coliforms, usually assessed by oral rinse or denture imprint culture techniques in terminally ill cancer patients has varied from 11-19% (Driezen *et al.*, 1983 and 1986; Bagg *et al.*, 1992). Risk factors for the acquisition and subsequent oral carriage of aerobic Gram negative bacilli include malignancies, xerostomia,

Table 4 Bacterial causes of pneumonia.

Community acquired pneumonia		Hospital acquired pneumonia	
Streptococcus pneumoniae	30-75%	*Enterobactericaea*	37%
Haemophilus influenzae	4-5%	*Pseudomonas aeruginosa*	17%
Mycoplasma pneumoniae	5-18%	*S. aureus*	13%
Chlamydia spp	2-3%	*fungi*	6%
Legionella spp	2-5%	*Anaerobes*	2%
S. aureus	1-5%	*S. pneumoniae*	<3%
Gram negative enteric bacilli	Rare	*H. influenzae*	<3%
Anaerobes	Rare		

Adapted from Brown and Lerner (1998) & Dal Nogare (1994).

hospitalisation and broad spectrum antibiotic therapy. Whilst endotoxin release from coliforms has been suggested as an aetiological factor in mucositis induced by radiotherapy or chemotherapy, there is no recognised causal link with other forms of oral mucosal disease (Leenstra *et al.,* 1996).

Systemic Disease
Pneumonia

Pneumonia is a common and potentially fatal condition that can affect all age groups. Practically it is useful to divide pneumonia into community acquired and hospital acquired (nosocomial). Community acquired pneumonia has a different pattern of pathogens to hospital acquired (Table 4). However, the elderly are an important and increasing population sub-group and in pneumonia in the over 65's, *S. pneumoniae* was the most common cause followed by *H. influenzae* but Gram negative bacilli, *S. aureus* and anaerobes are isolated in higher frequencies in the elderly than the general population (Woodhead, 1994). The higher levels of Gram negative bacilli and anaerobes are probably due to the increased risk of aspiration pneumonia in this group. Clinically important aspiration usually occurs in patients who have; i. a depressed level of consciousness; ii. dysphagia resulting from neurologic or oesophageal disorders and iii. an endotracheal tube or are receiving enteral feeding. It has been postulated that the source of these organisms is from the oral cavity (Limeback, 1988) and that there is a link between poor oral hygiene in the elderly and an increased risk of pneumonia (Scannapieco and Mylotte, 1996).

Of increasing interest is the microbiology of the respiratory flora from hospitalised patients especially in intensive care units, the prevalence of nosocomially acquired pneumonia (mortality may exceed 50%) and the possible spread of organisms from the oropharynx to the lung. The most frequently reported pathogens for ICU-acquired respiratory tract infection are members of the Enterobacteriaceae (34%) (Vincent *et al.*, 1995).

In general, hospital acquired pneumonia may develop either as a result of aspiration of upper airway flora or secondary to bactaeremia. Important risk factors are intubation, stay in an ICU, broad spectrum antibiotics, prolonged surgery, advanced age, chronic lung disease and decreased immune response. The majority of the organisms involved are probably from aspiration from the upper airway (Johanson, 1972; Reynolds, 1987) although the precise origin of these organisms is controversial. There are two main proposed sources;

a. The endogenous flora - The recent popularity of gastric alkalinisation to prevent stress ulcers and bleeding in ICU patients has resulted in large numbers of patients with extensive bacterial overgrowth in the upper gastrointestinal tract. This is often followed by passive oesophageal reflux and aspiration of gastric contents into the oropharynx and then along the endotracheal tube into the lower respiratory tact (DuMoulin *et al.,* 1982; Olson *et al.,* 1984; Murthy *et al.,* 1989; Cook *et al.,* 1991)

b. Environmental contamination - many of the organisms found in nosocomial pneumonia are frequently found in the hospital environment. Cross-contamination can occur leading to colonisation of the oro-pharynx and subsequent infection of the lower respiratory tract (Maki *et al.*, 1982)

Determination of the exact sources of enteric rods is vital if appropriate measures are to be introduced to reduce the infection rates. In an early study, culture of oral swabs from patients on an ICU unit , demonstrated that 45% were colonised with enteric Gram negative rods by the end of one week. Nosocomial pneumonia occurred in 22% of those colonised and only 3% of non-colonised patients (Johanson *et al.,* 1972). The presence of enteric organisms in supragingival plaque from a small number of patients in ICU's who had been hospitalised with a range of medical conditions has been investigated (Scannapieco *et al.,* 1992 and 1996). Enteric bacteria which included *P. aeruginosa, K. pneumoniae* and *E. aerogenes* were isolated from the supragingival plaque of about 30% of patients studied, and the authors speculated that oral colonisation may serve as a reservoir of potential respiratory pathogens in these patients. There has been considerable effort to reduce colonisation by enteric Gram negatives and yeasts in the oro-pharynx of ICU patients using a process of selective decontamination. This is a method designed to prevent infection by eradicating and preventing carriage of potentially pathogenic aerobic microorganisms from the oropharynx, stomach and gut but preserving the endogenous anaerobic flora. It consists of antibiotics applied topically to the oropharynx and through a nasogastric tube. Whilst reducing rates of infection the use of topical antibiotics has no effect on mortality rates (D'Amico *et al.,* 1998).

The existing data in this area is sparse and there is a need for well-planned, multi-centre longitudinal studies to clarify the role of oral colonisation by enteric bacteria, (especially in plaque), in the pathogenesis of pneumonia.

Other Gram negatives
The HACEK group
This group of fastidious Gram negative bacteria form part of the normal human oropharygeal and urogenital flora. They are comprised of *Haemophilus aphrophilus/paraphrophilus (H), Actinobacillus actinomycetemcomitans (A),*

Table 5 Opportunistic infections caused by the HACEK group.

Organism	Opportunistic infection
H. aphrophilus & H. paraphrophilus	Septic arthritis, osteomyelitis, dentoalveolar abscess, pneumonia, brain abscess, abdominal infections and endocarditis
A. actinomycetemcomitans	Localised juvenile periodontitis, dentoalveolar abscess, actinomycotic infections and endocarditis
C. hominis	Endocarditis
E. corrodens	Periodontal diseases, dentoalveolar abscess, sinusitis, otitis media, brain abscess, pleuropulmonary infections and endocarditis
Kingella spp	Osteomyelitis, septic arthritis and endocarditis

Adapted from Janda (1999)

Cardiobacterium hominis (C), Eikenella corrodens (E) and *Kingella spp (K)*.

They represent diverse genera that possess several common cultural characteristics, such as, slow growth on enriched media and are capnophilic. Some such as *H. aphrophilus and H. paraphrophilus* are frequently found in dental plaque and gingival crevices (Tempro and Slots, 1986), although the quantities of these organisms never exceeded 1%. Others such as *Kingellae spp* can be recovered from dental plaque (Dewhirst *et al.,* 1993) and *Cardiobacterium hominis* is found mostly in the upper respiratory tract, are frequently overlooked because of their slow rate of growth (48-72 hours) and small colony size. All members of this group are classically associated with bacteraemia and endocarditis and may be found in acute dento-alveolar infections (Table 5).

Anaerobes

Introduction

Earlier chapters have dealt with oral anaerobes which form a substantial component of the dental plaque flora. Although numerous anaerobic species have been recovered from dental plaque, the precise pathogenic roles for many remain unknown. This is probably due to the mixed nature of many oral infections, difficulties in sampling and suitable culture techniques. However, for others an accumulating body of evidence suggests that they are clearly important potential pathogens , for example, *P. gingivalis, Pr. intermedia* and *F. nucleatum*. It seems probable that many local oral infections involve multiple pathogens with a sequential role for each that are important steps in the ecology of the disease process.

The majority of anaerobic infections are polymicrobial and may involve multiple anaerobes as well as facultative aerobes, such as *Streptococcus spp.*. The members of the *B. fragilis* group, although important pathogens in other settings are not normally present in the oral flora. Two anaerobic genera that are often overlooked as opportunistic pathogens are the anaerobic streptococci and

Veillonella spp.. The anaerobic streptococci are present in the oral flora, the gastrointestinal tract and the urogenital system. These organisms have been relatively poorly studied to date but have been frequently detected in dental plaque and are associated with various oral infections including periodontal disease, carious dentine, infected pulp chambers and dental abscesses(Wren, 1996). They have also been isolated from abscess's at various deep body sites and have been increasingly associated with septic joint infections and other implants (Wren, 1996). *Veillonella spp.* are strictly anaerobic Gram negative cocci that have been isolated from most surfaces of the oral cavity although they occur in highest numbers in dental plaque. They can also be found in the upper respiratory tact, intestine and vagina. In a review of 2, 033 specimens submitted for anaerobic bacteriology from paediatric patients 4% yielded *Veillonella spp.* Most *Veillonella spp.* were recovered from abscesses, aspiration pneumonia, burns, bites and sinusitis and were frequently recovered with mixed oral or bowel flora (Brook, 1996).

Dento-alveolar Infection

Most infections are polymicrobial. Infections may be localised or spread to involve the tissue spaces of the head and neck which may be potentially life threatening (Lewis *et al.,* 1990). Anaerobic head and neck infections are usually related to untreated dental caries or are preceded by events that impair the integrity of the normal oral mucosa or other anatomic barriers such as, trauma, malignancy and surgery.

Ear, Nose and Throat Infections

The possibility that oral anaerobes may be primary pathogens in acute tonsillitis has been suggested by the recovery of pigmented oral anaerobes from the tonsils of 23 of 25 children with acute tonsillitis (Brook and Gober, 1983). A more serious form of anaerobic oro-pharyngeal infection is that caused by *F. necrophorum* (Lemierres diease or post angina sepsis) comprising an initial pharyngitis followed by sepsis with metastatic foci of infection frequently pulmonary or rheumatologic (Moore-Gillan *et al.,* 1994)

Although rarely found in acute sinusitis, a large proportion of chronic maxillary sinusitis cases are secondary to dental infections. Most due to direct extension of infection from root apices or the periodontium. There have been several case reports of CNS abscess following sinusitis secondary to odon-togenic infection. The frequent isolation of *Prevotella spp., Bacteroides spp., Fusobacterium spp.* often in association with other anaerobes (Busc 1984). and streptococcal species such as *S. intermedius* would support a potential oro-pharyngeal source.

Respiratory Tract Infections

These include community acquired aspiration pneumonia, necrotising pneumo-nia, lung abscess and empyema and are thought to follow aspiration of the oro-pharyngeal flora. The bacteriology of these infections is similar to that found in

Table 6 Anaerobic bacteria from blood culture isolates over a 10 year period.

Isolate	% of total number anaerobes isolated
B. fragilis	56
Clostridium spp	12
Bacteroides spp.	9
C. perfringens	6.5
Peptosteptococcus spp.	6
Fusobacterium spp	3
F. nucleatum	3
Eubacterium spp	3
Veillonella spp	1
B. melaninogenicus	0.8
Bifidobacterium spp.	0.3

Data compiled from Dorsher et al. (1989)

odontogenic infections; being poly microbial with three to four anaerobes together with facultative organisms such as an oral streptocci. *Pr. melaningenica, Pr. intermedia, F. nucleatum* and *B. ureolyticus* are the most commonly isolated species. These organisms may occur more frequently than generally acknowledged, due to difficulties with the diagnostic techniques.

Anaerobic Bacteraemia and Cardiovascular Infection

Detection of anaerobic bacteraemia has improved with the advent of more reliable blood culture techniques and account for some 13% of all bacteraemia episodes over a 10 year period (Dorscher *et al.*, 1989). The majority of anaerobic isolates from blood cultures are unlikely to be from an oral source (see Table 6). The role of oral anaerobic bacteria in the remainder is uncertain to determine, since an oral source is frequently overlooked and other sites may also play a significant role such as the female genital tract for anaerobic streptococci and the respiratory tract for *Prevotella spp.* and *Fusobacterium spp.*

The incidence of anaerobic endocarditis reportedly ranges from 0.8% to 11% of the total cases of endocarditis (Von Reyn *et al.*, 1981; Sapico and Sarma, 1982, Dyson *et al.*, 1999). It is difficult to elucidate the role of the oral flora in these cases but of interest is the large proportion of anaerobic streptococci isolated and more recently there has been an increase in polymicrobial endocarditis consisting of anaerobic streptococci, and anaerobic pigmented gram negative rods together with facultative streptococci in intra-venous drug users which presumably reflects contamination of the injecting equipment with saliva.

Other Opportunistic Infections with Anaerobes

Bite wounds are common injuries. Whilst some bite wounds are trivial, many lead to a variety of infectious complications including cellulitis, septic arthritis, osteomyelitis, abscesses and in some cases overwhelming fatal septicaemia. The organisms isolated from the culture of bite wounds will reflect the oral flora of the biting animal and may pose difficulties in identification especially veterinary isolates (Goldstein, 1978).

Human bite wounds or clenched fist injuries tend to have higher infection rates than other animal bites. Anaerobic bacteria may be isolated from more than 50% of human bite wounds, frequently these contain mixed cultures of *Porphyromonas spp*, *Prevotella spp.*, *Peptostreptococci spp* and *Fusobacteria*. Other frequent isolates include *Streptococcus spp*, *Staphylococci*, *Eikenella corrodens* and *Haemophilus* spp.

The most common bite wound is due to dog bites which are classically associated with *Pasteurella multicoda*, considered by many to be the primary dog bite wound pathogen but is present in only 20-30% of cases. *Staphylococcus intermedius* is a newly described pathogen found in the mouths of 39% of dogs (Talan *et al.,* 1989). Also of note from the canine flora is *Capnocytophaga canimorsus* occasionally associated with fatal sepsis following dog bites (Lion *et al.,* 1996).

Antimicrobial Susceptibility

Over the years antibiotic resistance has been increasingly reported. *Bacteroides spp.* have been shown to acquire resistance rapidly to most beta-lactam antibiotics (minimal inhibitory concentration usually exceeds 16 mg l^{-1}). This is associated with the production of broad spectrum beta-lactamases (Olsson, Dornbusch and Nord, 1979). Lower incidences of beta-lactamases (40-60%) have been reported for *Prevotella spp.* and *Fusobacterium spp.* (Konenen, 1997 and 1999). Both chromosomally mediated and plasmid mediated penicillin resistance have been described. Recent studies suggest that resistance to clindamycin is less than 5% in oral *Bacteroides spp.* and 10% for *Prevotella spp.* and *Porphyromonas spp.*. Resistance is due to the transfer of transposable elements (Shoemaker *et al.,* 1985). Tetracycline resistance in Bacteroides isolates was uncommon, but today most clinical isolates of *Bacteroides spp.* are resistant to tetracycline due to the spread of conjugative elements throughout *Bacteroides spp.* Increased use of topical tetracyclines may be responsible for the spread of resistance (via the tetQ and tetM determinants) among *Prevotella spp.* and *Porphyromonas spp.*

Other Organisms

The preceding micro-organisms are by no means an exhaustive list of the potential opportunistic pathogens present in dental plaque. However, it is clear that the oral cavity is not the sole source of many of these organisms and it is vital that good clinical information is available together with detailed typing of isolates (now made possible by molecular techniques) to determine the precise origins of these opportunistic micro-organisms. This is illustrated in the ecology of non-viral sexually transmitted infections, whereby, gonorrhoea, syphilis, *Chlamydia trachomatis*, chancroid, *Neisseria meningitidis* and *Mycoplasma pneumoniae* may all be transmitted via the oral route (Edwards and Carne, 1998). Whilst the role of atypical pathogens, such as *Chlamydia spp.* and *Mycoplamsa spp.* has been relatively well defined for respiratory tract infections,

408

relatively little has been done in the oral cavity. *C. pneumoniae* was not detected using PCR in the sub-gingival plaque of 50 patients (Tran *et al.,* 1997), in contrast, *M. fermentans* was detected using PCR in 55% of saliva samples from 201 individuals (Watanabe *et al.,* 1986). Other genera detected in the oral cavity, include parasites, such as, *Entamoeba gingivalis* recently detected in 77% of HIV positive patients with periodontal disease (Lucht *et al.,* 1998). There is also the issue of the role of uncultivable organisms (see chapter by Professor W. Wade) which awaits investigation.

Conclusion

Clearly further research remains to be done to elucidate the role of fungi and other opportunistic organisms from dental plaque in human disease. It is becoming increasingly apparent as appropriate investigations are performed that the oral cavity is ideally placed to disseminate micro-organisms to the external environment and also to the respiratory tract and gastrointestinal system. Furthermore, if one considers the frequency with which oral streptococcal bacteraemia occurs, access to the cardiovascular system by many other members of the plaque micro-flora must surely follow. These points are clearly highlighted by the emerging information on carriage of oral staphylococci and the potential for opportunism in infections of the joints. There is also a surprising lack of knowledge surrounding the oral carriage of methicillin resistant *S. aureus*, an organism that appears to be difficult to eradicate from the oral cavity.

Controversy surrounds the hypothesis that the oral cavity may be a permanent reservoir for *H. pylori*. Clearly the prevalence of *H. pylori* will vary amongst different population groups and this may account partly for the conflicting data presented in the literature on the presence of this organism in the oral cavity. As more information employing standard laboratory methods emerges hopefully this issue will be clarified.

With an increasing elderly population and the growing burden of hospital acquired infections there is a need for a greater understanding of the oral flora in compromised patients. The existing data in this area is sparse and there is a need for well-planned, multi-centre longitudinal studies to clarify the role of the carriage of potential pathogens such as, enteric bacteria in the oral cavity, (especially in plaque).

Finally, and perhaps more worrisome is the relentless advance of antimicrobial resistance in many genera of the oral flora. The dental plaque biofilm is an ideal environment to encourage this process but little information is available on the clinical significance of these interactions. The future then lies in a greater awareness of the potential of the oral flora and a greater interaction between bacteriologists and clinicians to understand the full clinical implications of this data.

References

Adams, J.T. and Fairfax, R.G. 1994. *Streptococcus mitis* infection in newborns. *J. Perinatal,* **14,** 473-478.

Addy, M., Shaw, W.C., Hansford, P. and Hopkins, M. 1982. The effect of orthodontic appliances on the distribution of Candida and plaque in adolescents. *Br. J. Ortho.*, **9**, 158-163.

Anamo, A., Narhi, T., Vehkalahti, M. and Schmidt-Kaunisaho K. 1993. Association between salivary micro-organisms and root caries in the elderly (Abstr 1870). *J. Dent. Res.*, **73**, 335.

Alcaide, F., Carratala, J., Linares, J., Gudiol, F., Martin, R. 1996. In vitro activities of eight macrolide antibiotics and RP-59500 (quinupristin-dalfopristin) against viridans group streptococci isolated from blood of neutropenic cancer patients. *Antimicrob. Agents Chemother.*, **40**, 2117-2120.

An, Y.H., and Friedman, R.J. 1996. Prevention of sepsis in total joint arthroplasty. *J. Hosp. Infect.*, **33**, 93-108.

Anderson, L.P., Holck, S., Povlsen, C.O., Elsborg, L., Justesen, T. 1987. *Campylobacter pyloridis* in peptic ulcer disease. I. Gastric and duodenal infection caused by *C. pyloridis*: histopathologic and microbiologic findings. *Scand. J. Gastroenterol.*, **22**, 219-224.

Arendorf, T.M. and Walker, D.M. 1980. The prevalence and intra-oral distribution of *Candida albicans* in man. *Archs Oral Biol.*, **25**, 1-10.

Arendorf, T.M. and Walker, D.M. 1979. Oral candidal populations in health and disease. *Br. Dent. J.* **147**, 267-272.

Asikainen, S., Chen, C., Slots, J. 1994. Absence of *Helicobacter pylori* in subgingival samples determined by polymerase chain reaction. *Oral Microbiol. Immunol.*, **9**, 318-320.

Axon, A.T.R. 1996. The transmission of *Helicobacter pylori*: which theory fits the facts? *Eur. J. Gastroenterol. Hepatol.*, **8**, 1-2.

Bagg, J., Parsons. K., Finlay, I. Addy, M. and Newcombe, R.G. 1992. Oral carriage of yeasts,coliforms and staphylococci in patients with advanced malignant disease. *J. Oral Path. Med.,* **21**, 305-308.

Bagg, J., Sweeney, M.P., Harvey Wood, K. and Wiggins, A. 1995. Possible role of *Staphylococcus aureus* in severe oral mucositis among elderly dehydrated patients. *Microb. Ecol. Health Dis.*, **8**, 51-56.

Banatvala, N., Romero Lopez, C., Owen, R.J. *et al.* 1994. Use of the polymerase chain reaction to detect *Helicobacter pylori* in the dental plaque of healthy and symptomatic individuals. *Microb. Ecol. Health Dis.*,7, 1-8.

Barthold, P., Stewart, J., Cumming, C., Decker, S., MacGragor, R. and Malmud, D. 1994. Candida organisms in dental plaque from AIDS patients. *J. Infect. Dis.*, **170**, 1053-1054.

Bartzokas, C.A., Johnson, R., Jane, M., Martin, M.V., Pearce, P.K. and Saw, Y. 1994. Relation between mouth and haematogenous infection in total joint replacements. *B.M.J.,* **309**, 506-508.

Beck-Sague, C.M., Jarvis, W.R. and the National Nosocomial Infections Surveillance System. 1993. Secular trends in the epidemiology of nosocomial fungal infections in the United States, 1980-1990. *J. Infect. Dis.*, **167**, 1247-1251.

Beighton, D., Lynch, E. 1995. Comparison of selected microflora of plaque and underlying carious dentine associated with primary root caries lesions. *Caries Res.*, 29, 154-158.

Berdicevsky, I., Ben-Aryeh, H., Szargel, R. and Gutman, D. 1980. Oral Candida in asymptomatic denture wearers. *Int. J. Oral Surg.*, **9**, 113-115.

Bergman, O.J. 1991. Alterations in oral microflora and pathogenesis of acute oral infections during remission-induction therapy on patients with acute myeloid leukaemia. *Scand. J. Infect. Dis.*, **23**, 355-366.

Bergmann, O.J. 1988. Oral infections and septicaemia in immunocompromised patients with haematologic malignancies. *J. Clin. Micro.*, **26**, 2105-2109.

Bernander, S., Dalen, J., Gastrin, B., Hedenborg, L., Lamke, L.O., Ohrn, R. 1993. Absence of *Helicobacter pylori* in dental plaques in *Helicobacter pylori* positive dyspeptic patients. *Eur. J. Clin. Microbiol. Infect. Dis.,* **12**, 282-285.

Berthold, P., Stewart, J., Cumming, C., Decker, S., MacGregor, R. and Malamud, D. 1994. Candida organisms in dental plaque from AIDS patients. *J. Infect. Dis.*, **170**, 1053-54.

Bickley, J., Owen, R.J., Fraser, A..G. and Pounder, R.E. 1993. Evaluation of the polymerase chain reaction for detecting the urease C gene of *Helicobacter pylori* in gastric biopsy samples and dental plaque. *J. Med. Microbiol.,* **39**, 338-344.

Bochud, P.Y., Cometta, A., Francioli, P. 1997. Virulent infections caused by alpha-haemolytic streptococci in cancer patients and their management. *Curr. Opin. Infect. Dis.,* **10**, 422-430.

Brook, I. and Gober, A.E. 1983. *Bacteroides melaninogenicus*. Its recovery from tonsils of children with acute tonsillitis. *Arch. Otolaryngeal.,* **109**, 818-820.

Brook, I., Finegold, S.M. 1980. Bacteriology of aspiration pneumonia in children. *Pediatrics,* **65**, 1115-1120.

Brook, I. 1996. Veillonella infections in children. *J. Clin. Microbiol.,* **34**, 1283-1285.

Brown, L.R., Mackler, B.F. Levy, B.M. *et al.* 1979. Comparison of the plaque microflora in immunodeficent and immunocompetent dental patients. *J. Dent Res.,* **58**, 2344-2352.

Brown, P.D. and Lerner, S.A. 1998. Community acquired pneumonia. *Lancet,* **352**, 1295-302.

Busch, D.F. 1984. Anaerobes in infections of the head and neck and ear, nose and throat. *Rev. Infect. Dis.,* **6**, S115-S122.

Cabellos, C., Viladrich, P.F., Corredoira, J., Verdaguer, R., Ariza, J., Gudiol, F. 1999. Streptococcal meningitis in Adult patients: Current epidemiology and clinical spectrum. *Clin. Infect. Dis.,* **28**, 1104-1108.

Cannon, R.D., Holmes, A.R., Mason, A.B., Monk, B.C. 1995. Oral candida - clearance, colonization, or candidiasis. *J. Dent Res.,* **74**, 1152-1161.

Catto, B.A., Jacobs, M.R., Shlaes, D.M. Streptococcus mitis: 1987. A cause of serious infection in adults. *Arch. Intern. Med.,* **147**, 885-888.

Cellini, L., Allocati, N., Dicampli, E, Dainelli, B. 1994a. *Helicobacter pylori* - a fickle germ. *Microbiol. Immunol.,* **38**, 25-30.

Cellini, L., Allocati, N., Angelucci, D. *et al.* 1994b. Coccoid *Helicobacter pylori* not culturable *in vitro* reverts in mice. *Microbiol. Immunol.,* **38**, 843-850.

Challacombe, S.J. 1990. Immunology of oral candidosis. In: L.P. Samaranayake, T.W. McFarlane (eds). *Oral Candidosis.* 104-124. Butterworth & Co. (publishers) Ltd, London.

Cometta, A., Viscoli, C., Castagnola, E. *et al.* 1996. Empirical treatment of fever in neutropenic children: the role of the carbapenems. International Antimicrobial therapy Cooperative Group of the European organisation for research and treatment of cancer and the Gimema infection program. *Pediatr. Infect. Dis. J.,* **15**, 744-748.

Cook, D.J., Laine, L.A., Guyatt, G.H. *et al.* 1991. Nosocomial pneumonia and the role of gastric pH. *Chest,* **100**, 7-13.

Coulter, W.A., Murray, S.D. and Kinirons, M.J. 1993. The use of a concentrated oral rinse culture technique to sample oral candida and lactobacilli levels and dental caries experience: a pilot study. *Int. J. Ped. Dent.,* **3**, 17-21.

D'Amico, R., Pifferi, S., Leonetti, C. *et al.* 1998. Effectiveness of antibiotic prophylaxis in critically ill adult patients: systematic review of randomised controlled trials. *B.M.J.,* **316**, 1275-85.

Dahlén, G., Wikström, M. 1995. Occurrence of enteric rods, staphylococci and Candida in subgingival samples. *Oral Microbiol. Immunol.,* **10,** 42-46.

Dal Nogare, A.R. 1994. *Nosocomial pneumonia outside the intensive care unit.* In: Niederman, M.S., Sarosi, G.A., Glassroth, J. (eds). Respiratory infections, a scientific basis for management. pp 139-146, W.B. Saunders Co., Philadelphia.

Dewhirst., F.E., Chen., C.K.C., Paster., B.J., Zambon., J.J. 1993. Phylogeny of species in the family *Neisseriaceae* isolated from human dental plaque and description of *Kingella orale sp. nov. Int. J. Syst. Bacteriol.* **43**, 490-499

Doern, G.V., Ferraro, M.J., Brueggemann, A.B., Ruoff, K.L. 1996. Emergence of high rates of antimicrobial resistance among viridans group streptococci in the United States. *Antimicrob. Chemother.,* **40**, 891-894.

Dorsher, C.W., Wilson, W.R., Rosenblatt, J.E. 1989. *Anaerobic bacteremia and cardiovascular infections.* Eds Finegold, S.M., George, W.L., pp. 289-310, Academic Press Inc.

Douglas, C.W.I., Heath, J., Hampton, K.K., Preston, F.E. 1993. Identity of viridans streptococci isolated from cases of infective endocarditis. *J. Med. Micro.,* **39**, 179-182.

Dowson, C.G., Coffey, T.J., Kell, C., Whiley. 1993. Evolution of penicillin resistance in streptococcus pneumoniae; the role of *Streptococcus mitis* in the formation of a low affinity PBP2B in *S. pneumoniae. Molecular Microbiol.,* **9**, 635-643.

Dreizen, S., Bodey, G.P. and Valdivieso, M. 1983. Chemotherapy associated oral infections in adults with solid tumours. *Oral Surg., Oral Med., Oral Path.,* **55**, 1113-1120.

Dreizen, S., McCredie, Bodie, G.P. and Keating M.J. 1986. Quantitative analysis of the oral complications of antileukaemia chemotherapy. *Oral Surg., Oral Med., Oral Path.,* **62**, 650-653.

Dreizen, S., Bodey, G.P. McCredie, K.B. Keating, M.J. 1985. Orofacial aspergillosis in acute leukemia. *Oral Surg., Oral Med., Oral Path.*, **59**, 499-504.

Drumm, B., Perez-Perez, G.I., Blaser, M.J., Sherman, P.M. 1990. Intrafamilial clustering of *Helicobacter pylori* infection. *New Engl. J. Med.*, **322**, 359-363.

DuMoulin, G.C., Paterson, D.G., Hedley-Whyte, J. *et al.* 1982. Aspiration of gastric bacteria in antacid treated patients: a frequent cause of postoperative colonisation of the airway. *Lancet*, **1**, 242-245.

Dyson, C., Barnes, R.A., Harrison, G.A.J. 1999. Infective endocarditis: an epidemiological review of 128 episodes. *J. Infect.*, **38**, 87-93.

Edwards, S., Carne C. Oral sex and the transmission of non-viral STI's. 1998. *Sex. Trans. Infect.* **74**, 95-100.

Ferguson, D.A., Li, C., Patel, N.R., Mayberry, W.R., Chi, D.S. and Thomas, E. 1993. Isolation of *Helicobacter pylori* from saliva. *J. Clin. Microbiol.*, **31**, 2802-2804.

Flanagan PG, Barnes RA. Fungal infection in the intensive care unit. *J. Hosp. Infect.* 1998, **38**, 163-177.

Forman, D., Newell, D.G., Fullerton, F. *et al.* 1991. Association between infection with *Helicobacter pylori* and risk of gastric cancer: evidence from a prospective investigation. *B.M.J.*, **302**, 1302-1305.

Fox, J.G. 1995. Nonhuman reservoirs of *Helicobacter pylori*. *Aliment. Pharmacol. Therap.*, **9**, 93-103.

Fraser, V.J., Jones. M., Duncel, J., *et al.* 1992. Candidaemia in a tertiary care hospital: epidemiology, risk factors and predictors of mortality. *Clin. Infect. Dis.*, **15**, 414-421.

Ganor, S. and Pumpianski, R. 1970. Chronic paronychiaand oral and vaginal candidal carriage. *Mykosen,* **13**, 537-542.

Ganor, S., and Pumpianski, R. 1974. Chronic Candida albicans paronychia in adult Isreali women. *B. J. Derm.,* **90**, 77-83.

Gaudreau, C., Delage, G., Rousseau, D., *et al.* 1981. Cacteraemia caused by viridans streptococci in 71 children. *Can. Med. Assoc. J.*, **125**, 1246-1249.

Gibbons, R. J., Socransky, S. S., Araujo, W. C., van Houte, J. 1964. Studies on the predominant cultivable microbiota of dental plaque. *Archs Oral Biol.,* **9**, 365-370

Gibbons, R. J., Socransky, S. S., Sawyer, S., Kapsimalis, B., MacDonald, J. B. 1963. The microbiology of the gingival crevice area of man. The predominant cultivable organisms. *Archs Oral Biol.*, **8**, 281-289.

Goldberg, M.H. 1981. Infections of the salivary glands. In *"Management of infections in the oral and maxillofacial regions.* R.G. Topazian & M.H. Gioldberg (eds) Ch 8 Saunders, Philadelphia.

Goldstein, E.J.C., Citron, D.M., Wield, *et al.* 1978. Bacteriology of human and animal bite wounds. *J. Clin. Microbiol.*, **8**, 667-672.

Gonzalez, C.L., Calia, F.M. 1975. Bacteriologic flora of aspiration indcuced pulmonary infections. *Arch. Intern. Med.*, **135**, 711-714.

Goodman, K.J., Correa, P. 1995. The transmission of *Helicobacter pylori*. A critical review of the evidence. *Int. J. Epidemiol.*, **24**, 875-887.

Hagihara, Y., Kaminishi. H, Cho, T., Tanaka, M. and Kaita, H. 1988. Degradation of human dentine collagen by an enzyme produced by the yeast *Candida albicans*. *Archs Oral Biol.*, **33**, 617-619.

Hammar, M., Tyszkiewicz, T., Wadström, T., O'Toole, P.W. 1992. Rapid detection of *Helicobacter pylori* in gastric biopsy material by polymerase chain reaction. *J. Clin. Microbiol.,* **30**, 54-58.

Hardo, P.G., Tugnait, A., Hassan, F. *et al.* 1995. *Helicobacter pylori* infection and dental care. *Gut,* **37**, 44-46.

Heimdahl, A. and Nord, C.E. 1990. Oral infections in immunocompromised patients. *J. Clin. Perio.,* **17**, 501-503.

Hodson, J.J. and Craig, G.T. 1972. The incidence of candida albicans in the plaques of teeth of children. *Dent. Pract. Dent. Rec.*, **22**, 296-301.

Holcombe, C. 1992. *Helicobacter pylori*: the African enigma. *Gut*, **33**, 429-431.

Hua, J., Ho, B. 1996. Is the coccoid form of *Helicobacter pylori* viable? *Microbios,* **87**, 103-112.

Jackson MS. Oral Staphylococci in Health and Disease. FIBMS thesis, 1998, University of Glasgow.

Jackson., M.S., Bagg., J., Gupta., M.N., Strurrock, R.D. 1999. Oral carriage of staphylococci in patients with rheumatoid arthritis. *Rheumatol.* **38**, 572-575.

Jacobson, J.J., Patel, B., Asher, G., Wooliscroft, J.O. and Schaberg, D. 1997. Oral staphylococcus in older subjects with rheumatoid arthritis. *J. Am. Ger. Soc.* **45**, 590-593.

Janda, W.M. 1999. The "HACEK" group: enigmatic fastidious Gram negative bacilli. *Rev. Med. Micro.*, **10**, 37-50.

Jobbins, J.M., Bagg, J., Parsons, K., Finlay, I., Addy, M. and Newcombe, R.G. 1992 Oral carriage of yeasts, coliforms and staphylococci in patients with advanced malignant disease. *J. Oral Path. Med.*, **21**, 305-308.

Johanson, W.G., Higuchi, J. H., Chaudhieri, T.R., Woods, D.E. 1980. Bacterial adherence to epithelial cells in bacillary colonization of the respiratory tract. *Am. Rev. Resp. Dis.*, **121**, 55-63.

Johanson, W.G., Pierce, A.K., Sanford, *et al.* 1972. Nosocomial respiratory infections with gram negative bacilli. *Ann. Intern. Med.*, **77**, 701-706.

Jordan, R.C.K., Diss, T.C., Millson, C., Wilson, M., Speight, P.M. 1997. Absence of *Helicobacter pylori* DNA in salivary lymphoepithelial lesions. *J. Oral Pathol. Med.*, **26**, 454-457.

Kaandorp, C.J.E., Dinant, H.J., van de Laar. M.A.F.J., Moens, H.J.B., Prins, A.P.A. and Dijkmans, B.A.C. 1997. Incidence and source of native and prosthetic joint infection: a community-based prospective survey. *Annals Rheum. Dis.*, **56**, 470-475.

Kamma, J.J., Nakou, M., Baehni, P.C. 1999. Clinical and microbiological characteristics of smokers with early onset periodontitis. *J. Perio. Res.*, **34**, 25-33.

Kaminishi, H., Hagihara, Y., Hayashi, S., Cho T. 1986. Isolation and characteristics of collagenolytic enzyme produced by *Candida albicans*. Infect. Immun. **53**, 312-316

.Kaye, D., McCormick, R.C., Hook, E.W. 1962. Bacterial endocarditis: The changing pattern since the introduction of penicillin therapy. *Antimicrob. Agents Chemother.*, **1**, 37-46.

Khandaker, K., Palmer, K.R., Eastwood. M.A., Scott, A.C., Desai, M., Owen, R.J. 1993. DNA fingerprints of *Helicobacter pylori* from mouth and antrum of patients with chronic ulcer dyspepsia. *Lancet*, **342**, 751.

Kirkpatrick, W.R., Revankar, S.G., McAtee, R.K. *et al.* 1998. Detection of Candida dubliniensis in oropharyngeal samples from HIV infected patients in North America by primary CHROMagar Candida screening and susceptibility testing of isolates. *J. Clin. Micro.*, **36**, 3007-3012.

Knoke, M., Schulz, K., Bernhardt, H. 1997. Dynamics of Candida isolations from humans from 1992-1995 in Greifswald, germany. *Mycoses,* **40**, 105-110.

Kononen, E., Nyfors, S., Matto, J., Asikainen, Jousimies-Somer H. 1997. Beta-lactamase production by oral pigmented Prevotella species isolated from young children. *Clin. Infect. Dis.*, **25**, S272-274.

Kononen, E., Nyfors, S., Matto, J., Asikainen, Jousimies-Somer, H. 1999. Beta-lactamase production and antimicrobial susceptibility of oral heterogenous Fusobacterium nucleatum populations in young children. *Antimicrob. Agents Chemother.*, **43**, 1270-1273.

Kosunen, T.U., Höök, J., Rautelin, H.I., Myllylä, G. 1989. Age-dependent increase of *Campylobacter pylori* antibodies in blood donors. *Scand. J. Gastroenterol.*, **24**, 110-114.

Krajden, S., Fuksa, M., Anderson, J. *et al.* 1989. Examination of human stomach biopsies, saliva, and dental plaque for *Campylobacter pylori*. *J. Clin. Microbiol.*, **27**, 1397-1398.

Kralovic, S.M., Melin-Aldana, H., Smith, K.K. and Linnemann, Jr., C.C. 1995. *Staphylococcus lugdunensis* endocarditis after tooth extraction. *Clin. Infect. Dis.*, **20**, 715-716.

Krasse, B. 1954. The relationship between lactobacilli, candida and streptococci and dental caries. *Odontol. Rev.,* **5**, 241-261.

Lee, A., Fox, J., Hazell, S. 1993. Pathogenicity of *Helicobacter pylori*: a perspective. *Infect. Immun.*, **61**, 1601-1610.

Leenstra TS, van Saene JJM, van Saene HKF, Martin MV. 1996. Oral endotoxin in healthy adults. *Oral Surg. Oral Med. Oral Pathol. Oral Radiol. Endod.* 82, 637-43.

Lewis, M.A., MacFarlane, T.W., McGowan, D.A. 1990. A microbiological and clinical review of the acute dentoalveolar abscess. *B. J Oral Max. Surg.*, **28**, 359-66.

Li, C. Ha, T., Ferguson, D.A. *et al.* 1996. A newly developed PCR assay of *H. pylori* in gastric biopsy, saliva, and feces. Evidence of high prevalence of *H. pylori* in saliva supports oral transmission. *Digest Dis. Sci.*, **41**, 2142-2149.

Li, C., Musich, P.R., Ha, T. *et al.* 1995. High prevalence of *Helicobacter pylori* in saliva demonstrated by a novel PCR assay. *J. Clin. Pathol.*, **48**, 662-666.

Limeback, H. 1988. The relationship between oral health and systemic infections among elderly residents of chronic care facilities: a review. *Gerodontol.*, **7**, 131-137.

413

Lion, C., Escande, F., Burdin, J.C. 1996. Capnocytophaga canimorsus infections in humans: a review of the literature and case report. *Eur. J. Epidemiol.*, **12**, 521-533.

Listgarten, M. and Lai, C.H. 1999. Comparitive microbiological characteristics of failing implants and periodontally diseased teeth. *J. Periodontol.*, **70**, 431-437.

Lucas, V.S., Beighton, D., Roberts, G.J., Challacombe, S.J. Changes in the oral streptococcal flora of children undergoing allogeneic bone marrow transplantation. *J. Infect.*, **35**, 135-141.

Lucht, E., Evengard, B., Skott, J., Pehrson, P. and Nord C.E. 1998. Entamoeba gingivalis in HIV type 1 infected patients with periodontal disease. *Clin. Infect. Dis.*, **27**, 47-473.

MacDonald, F. 1984. Secretion of inducible proteinase by pathogenic candida. *Sabouraudia*, **22**, 79-82

MacFarlane, T.W. and Helnarska, S. 1976. The microbiology of angular cheilitis. *Br. Dent. J.*, **140**, 403-406.

MacFarlane, T.W. 1984. The oral ecology of patients with severe Sjogren's syndrome. *Microbios*, **41**, 99-106.

Madinier, I.M., Fosse, T.M., Montiel, RA. 1997. Oral carriage of Helicobacter pylori: a review. *J. Periodontol,.* **68**, 2-6.

Majmudar, P., Shah, S.M., Dhunjibhoy, K.R., Desai, H.G. 1990. Incidence of *Helicobacter pylori* in dental plaques in healthy volunteers. *Ind. J. Gastroenterol.*, **9**, 271-272.

Maki, D.G., Alvarado, C.J., Hassemer, C.A. *et al.* 1982. Relation of the inanimate hospital environment to endemic nosocomial infection E. *N. Engl. J. Med.*, **25**, 1562-6.

Makkonen, T.A., Borthen, L., Heimdahl, A., Joensuu, H., Lehtonen, O.P. and Nord C.E. 1989. Oropharyngeal colonisation with fungi and gram negative rods in patients treated with radiotherapy of the head and neck. *B. J. Oral Max. Surg.*, **27**, 334-340.

Martin, B.L, Corlew, M.M., Wood, H., Olsen, D., Golopol, L.A., Wingo, M. and Kirmani, N. 1994. The association of swallowing dysfunction and aspiration pneomonia. *Dyspahgia*, **9**, 1-6.

McCreight, M.C., Warnock, D.W. and Martin M.V. 1985. Resistogram typing of Candida albicans isolates from oral and cutaneous sites in irradiated patients. *Sabouraudia J. Med. Vet. Mycol.*, **23**, 403-406.

Megraud, F. 1993. Epidemiology of *Helicobacter pylori* infection. *Gastroenterol. Clin. North Am.*, **22**, 73-88.

Mercer, B.M., Arheart, K.L. 1996. Antibiotic therapy for preterm premature rupture of the membranes. *Sem. Perinatol.*, **20**, 426-438 1996.

Mitchell, H.M., Li, Y.Y., Hu, P.J. *et al.* 1992. Epidemiology of *Helicobacter pylori* in Southern China: identification of early childhood as the critical period for acquisition. *J. Infect. Dis.*, **166**, 149-153.

Miyake, Y., Iwai, M., Sugai, M., Miura, K., Suginaka, H. and Nagasaka, N. 1991. Incidence and characterization of *Staphylococcus aureus* from the tongues of children. *J. Dent Res.*, **70**, 1045-1047.

Moore, W.E.C., Holdeman, L.U., Cato. E.P., Smibert, R.M., Burmeister, J.A., Palcanis, K. G., Ranney, R.R. 1985. Comparative bacteriology of juvenile periodontitis. *Infect. Immun.*, **48**, 507-519.

Moore-Gillon, J., Lee, T.H., Eykyn, S.J. and Philips I. 1984. Necrobacillosis: A forgotten disease. *B.M.J.*, **288**, 1526-1527.

Murthy, S.K., Baltch, A.L., Smith, R.P. *et al.* 1989. Oropharyngeal and fecal carriage of Pseudomonas aeruginosa in hospital patients. *J. Clin. Microbiol.*, **27**, 35-40.

Nguyen, A.M.H., Engstrand. L., Genta, R.M., Graham, D.Y., El Zaatari, F.A.K. 1993. Detection of *Helicobacter pylori* in dental plaque by reverse transcription polymerase chain reaction. *J. Clin. Microbiol.*, **31**, 783-787.

Odds, F.C. 1988. *Candida and Candidosis: A review and bibliography*, 2 edn. London, Bailliere Tindall.

Olson, B., Weinstein, R.A. Nathan, C. *et al.* 1984. Epidemiology of endemic *Pseudomonas aeruginosa*: Why infection control efforts have failed. *J. Infect. Dis.*,**150**, 808-16.

Olsson, B., Dornbusch, K., Nord, C.E., 1979. Factors contributing to resistance to beta-lactam antibiotics in Bacteroides fragilis. *Antimicrob. Agents Chemother.*, **15**, 263-8.

Oppenheim, B.A. 1988. The changing pattern of infection in neutropenic patients. *J. Antimicrob Chemother.*, **41**, suppl D, 7-11.

Parsonnet, J., Vandersteen, D., Goates, J., Sibley, R.K., Pritikin, J., Chang, Y. 1991. *Helicobacter pylori* infection in intestinal-and diffuse-type gastric adenocarcinomas. *J. Natl. Cancer Inst.,* **83**, 640-643.

Percival, R.S., Challacombe, S.J. and Marsh, L.P.D. 1991. Age-related microbiological changes in the salivary and plaque microflora of healthy adults. *J.of Med. Micro.*, **35**, 5-11.

Peterson, D.E., Minah, G.E., Reynolds, M.A. *et al.* 1990. Effect of granulocytopenia on oral microbial relationships in patients with acute leukaemia. *Oral Surg., Oral Med., Oral Path.*, **70**, 720-723.

Petri, M.G., Konig, J., Moecke, H.P. *et al.* 1997. Epidemiology of invasive mycoses in ICU patients: a prospective multicentre study in 435 non-neutropenic patients. *Intensive Care Med.*, **23**, 317-325.

Pfaller, M. Wenzel, R. 1992. Impact of the changing epidemiology of fungal infections in the 1990's. *Eur. J. Clin. Micriobiol. Infect. Di.s*, **11**, 287-291.

Pienihakkinen, K., Scheinin, A. and Bancoxy, J. 1987. Screening of caries in children through salivary Lactobacilli and yeasts. *Scand. J. Dent Res.,* **95**, 397-404.

Piochi, B.J.A., Zelante, F. 1975. Contribution to the study of *Staphylococcus* isolated from the mouth. III Staphylococcus isolated from dental plaque. *Rev. Fac. Odont. S paulo*, **B**, 91-98.

Pumpianski, R. and Ganor, S. 1968. Epidemiological significance of oral candida in recurrent candidal vaginitis. *Isr. J. Med. Sci.,* **4**, 1268-1269.

Quinn, J.P., DiVincenzo, C.A., Lucks, D.A., Luskin, R.L., Shatzer, K.L., Lerner, S.A. 1988. Serious infections due to penicillin resistant strains of viridans streptococci with altered penicillin binding proteins. *J. Infect. Dis.*, **157**, 764-769.

Raad, I.I., Sabbagh, M.F., Caranasos, G.J. 1990. Acute bacterial sialadenitis: A study of 29 cases and review. *Clin. Infect. Dis.,* **12**, 591-601.

Rams, T.E., Fick, D., Slots, J. 1990. Staphylococci in human periodontal diseases. *Oral Microbiol. Immunol.*, **5**, 29-32.

Rams, T.E., Slots, J. 1991. Candida biotypes in human adult periodontitis. *Oral Microbiol. Immunol.*, **6**, 191-192

Renneberg, J., Nieman, L.L., Gutschik, E. 1997. Antimicrobial susceptibility of 278 streptococcal blood isolates to seven antimicrobial agents. *J. Antimicrob. Chemother.*, **39**, 135-140.

Reynolds, H.Y. 1987. Bacterial adherence to respiratory tract mucosa - a dynamic interaction leading to colonisation. *Semin. Resp. Infect.*, **2**, 8-19.

Richard, P., Amador Del Valle, G., Moreau, P. *et al.* 1995. Viridans streptococci in patients with neutropenia. *Lancet*, **345**, 1607-1609.

Riggio, M.P., Lennon, A. 1999. Identification by PCR of Helicobacter pylori in sub-gingival plaque of adult periodontitis patients. *J. Med. Micro.*, **48**, 317-322.

Roberts, R.B. 1992. Streptococcal endocarditis: The viridans and beta heamolytic streptococci. In: *Kaye D ed; Infective endocarditis. 2ed New York*, pp. 191-208, Raven Press.

Rose H. 1981. Viridans streptococcal pneumonia (letter). *J.A.M.A.*, **245**, 32.

Rosenberg, S.W. 1986. Oral complications of cancer chemotherapy: a review of 398 patients. *J. Oral Med.*, **41**, 93-97

Ruechel R. 1990. Virulence factors of *Candida* species. In: L.P. Samaranayake, T.W. McFarlane (eds). *Oral Candidosis.*47-66. Butterworth & Co. (publishers) Ltd, London.

Russel, J.I., MacFarlane, T.W., Aichison, T.C., Stephen, K.W. and Burchell, C.K. 1991. Prediction of caries increment in Scottish adolescents. *Comm. Dent. Oral Epidemiol.,* **19**, 74-77.

Samaranayake L.P.,Geddes, D.A.M., Weetman, D.A. and MacFarlane, T.W. 1983. Growth and acid production of *Candida albicans* in carbohydrate supplemented media. *Microbios* **37**, 105-115.

Samaranayake L.P., Hughes, A., Weetman, D.A. and MacFarlane, T.W. 1986. Growth and acid production of Candida species in human saliva supplemented with glucose. *J Oral Pathol.* **15**, 251-254.

Samaranayake L.P. 1990. Host factors and oral candidosis. In: L.P. Samaranayake, T.W. McFarlane (eds), *Oral Candidosis.* 66-104. Butterworth & Co. (publishers) Ltd, London.

Sanchez, V. Vazquez, J.A. Barth-Jones, D., Dembry, L.. Sobel, J.D., Zervos, M.J. 1992. Epidemiology of nosocomial acquisition of Candida lusitaniae. *J. Clin. Micro.*, **30**, 3005-3008.

Sanchez-Cordero, S., Hoffman, H., Stahl, S.S. 1979. Occurrence of Staphylococcus in periodontal pockets of diabetic and non-diabetic adults. *J. Periodontol.*, **50**, 109-113.

Sapico, F.L. and Sarma, R.J. 1982. Infective endocarditis due to anaerobic and microaerophilic bacteria. *West J. Med.,* **137**, 18-23.

Scannapieco, F.A., Stewart, E.M., Mylotte, J.M. 1992. Colonisation of dental plaque by respiratory pathogens in medical intesive care patients. *Crit. Care Med.,* **20**, 740-745.

Scannpapieco, F.A., Mylotte, J.M. 1996. Relationships between periodontal disease and bacterial pneumonia. *J. Periodontol.,* **67**, 1114-1122.

Schneinin, A., Pienihakkinen, K., Tiekso, J. and Holmberg S. 1992. Multifactorial modelling for root caries prediction. *Comm. Dent. Oral Epidemiol.,* **20**, 35-37.

Schneinin, A., Pienihakkinen, K., Tiekso, J., Holmberg, S., Fakuda, M. and Suzuli A. 1994. Multifactorial modelling for root caries prediction: 3 year follow up results. *Comm. Dent. Oral Epidemiol.,* **22**, 126-129.

Sedgley, C.M., Samaranayake L.P. 1994. Oral and oropharyngeal prevalence of *Enterobacteriacea* in humans: a review. *J Oral Path. Med.,* **23**, 104-13.

Sen, B.H., Safavi, K.E., Spangberg, L.S.W. 1997. Colonization of *Candida albicans* on cleaned human dental hard tissues. *Archs Oral Biol.,* **42**, 513-520.

Shames, B., Krajden, S., Fuksa, M., Babida, C., Penner, J.L. 1989. Evidence for the occurrence of the same strain of *Campylobacter pylori* in the stomach and dental plaque. *J. Clin. Microbiol.,* **27**, 2849-2850.

Shimada, T., Ogura, K., Ota, S. *et al.* 1994. Identification of *Helicobacter pylori* in gastric specimens, gastric juice, saliva, and faeces of Japanese patients. *Lancet,* **343**, 1636-1637.

Shipman, B. 1979. Clinical evaluation of oral Candida in cancer chemotherapy patients. *J. Pros. Dent.,* **41**, 63-67.

Shoemaker, N.B., Guthrie, E.P., *et al.* 1985. Evidence that the clindamycin-erythromycin resistance gene of Bacteroides plasmid pBF4 is on a transposable element. *J. Bacteriol.,* **162**, 626-32.

Slots, J., Feik, D., Rams, T.E. 1990a. Age and sex relationships of superinfecting microorganisms in periodontitis patients. *Oral Microbiol. Immunol.,* **5**, 305-308.

Slots, J., Feik, D., Rams, T.E. 1990b. Prevalence and antimicrobial susceptibility of *Enterobacteriacea* and *Pseudomonadacae* and *Acinetobacter* in human periodontitis. *Oral Microbiol. Immunol.,* **5**, 149-154.

Slots, J., Ram, T.E. and Listgarten, M.A. 1988. Yeasts, enteric rods and pseudomonas in the sub-gingival flora of severe adult periodontitis. *Oral Microbiol. Immunol.,* **3**, 42-52.

Slots, J., Fick, D., Rams, T.E. 1990. Age and sex relationship of superinfecting microorganisms in periodontitis patients. *Oral Microbiol. Immunol.,* **5**, 305-308.

Smego, R.A. and Foglia, G. 1998. Actinomycosis. *Clin. Infect. Dis,.* **26**, 1255-1263.

Smith, R.F., Dayton, S.L., Blasi, D. and Chipps, D.D. 1975. Incidence of yeats and influence of nystatin on their control in a group of burned children. *Mycopath. Mycol. Appl.,* **55**,115-120.

Soll, D.R., Galask, R., Schmid, J., Hanna, C., Mac, K., Morrow, B. 1991. Genetic dissimilarity of commensal strains of *Candida spp* carried in different anatomical locations of the same healthy women. *J. Clin. Micro.,* **29**, 1702-1710.

Song, Q., Haller, B., Schmid, R.M., Adler, G., Bode, G. 1999. *Helicobacter pylori* in Dental plaque. A comparison of different PCR primer sets. *Digest. Dis. Sci.,* **44**, 3: 479-484.

Strange, P., Skov, L., Lisby, S., Nielsen, P. and Baadsgaard, O. 1996. Staphylococcal enterotoxin B applied on intact normal and intact atopic skin induces dermatitis. *Archs Dermatol.,* **132**, 27-33.

Strasbaugh, L.J., Sewell, D.L., Ward, T.T., Pfaller, M.A., Heitzman, T., Tjoelker, R. 1994. High frequency of yeast carriage on the hands of hospital personnel. *J. Clin. Microbiol.,* **32**, 2299-2300.

Sullivan, S., Fernandez, L., MacFarlane, I.G., Wojcicka, B., Eddleston, A.L., Doniach, D., *et al.* 1978. Impairment of lachrymal and salivary secretion and cellular immune responses to salivary antigens in rheuamtoid arthritis. *Annals Rheum. Dis.,* **37**, 164-167.

Swenson, F.J. and Rubin, S.J. 1982. Clinical significance of viridans streptococci isolated from blood cultures. *J. Clin. Microbiol.,* **15**, 725-727.

Talan, D.A., Staatz, D., Staatz, A., Goldstein, E.J.C., Singer, K., Overturf, G.D. 1989. *Staphylococcus intermedius* in canine gingiva and canine inflicted human wound infections: laboratory characterisation of a newly recongnised zoonotic pathogen. *J. Clin. Microbiol.,* **27**, 78-81.

Taylor, D.N., Blaser, MJ. 1991. The epidemiology of *Helicobacter pylori* infection. *Epidemiol Rev,*

13, 42-59.

Tempro., P.J., Slots., J. 1986. Selective medium for the isolation of *Haemophilus aphrophilus* from the human periodontium and other oral sites and the low proportion of the organism in the oral flora. *J. Clin. Micro.* **23**, 777-782.

Teng, L.J., Hsueh, P.R., Chen, Y.C., Ho, S.W., Luh, K.T. 1998. Antimicrobial susceptibility of viridans group streptococci in Taiwan with an emphasis on the high rates of resistance to penicillin and macrolides in *Streptococcus oralis. J. Antimicrob. Chemother.*, **41**, 621-627.

Tran, T., Flynn, M.J., Chen, M.J., Slots, J. 1997. Absence of *Porphyromonas asaccharolytica, Bacteroides fragilis* and *Chlamydia pnuemoniae* in human sub-gingival plaque. *Oral Microbiol. Immunol.* **12**, 377-378.

Veldhuyzen van Zanten, S.J.O., Pollak, P.T., Best, L.M., Bezanson, G.S., Marrie, T. 1994. Increasing prevalence of *Helicobacter pylori* infection with age: continuous risk of infection in adults rather than cohort effect. *J. Infect.Dis.*, **169**, 434-437.

Vincent, J.L., Bihari, D.J., Suter, P.M., Bruining, H.A. *et al.* 1995. The prevalence of Nosocomial Infection in Intensive Care units in Europe: Results of the European prevalence of infection in intensive care (EPIC) study. *J.A.M.A.*, **274**, 639-644.

Von Reyn, C.F., Levy, B.S., Arbeit, R.D., Friedland, G. and Crumpacker, C.S. 1981. Infective endocarditis: An analysis based on strict case definitions. *Ann. Intern. Med.*, **94**, 505-518.

Voss, A., Hollis, R.J., Pfaller, M.A., Wenzel, R.P., Doebbeling, B.N. 1994. Investigation of the sequence of colonisation and candidaemia in non-neutropenic patients. *J. Clin. Microbiol.*, **32**, 975-980.

Voss, A., Le Noble, J.L.M.L., Verduyn Lunel, F.M., Foudraine, N.A., Meis, J.F.G.M. 1997. Candidaemia in intensive care units: risk factors for mortality. *Infection*, **25**, 8-11.

Wahlin, Y.B. and Holm, A.K. 1988. Changes in the oral microflora in patients with acute leukaemia and related disorders during the period of induction therapy. *Oral Surg., Oral Med., Oral Path.*, **65**, 411-471.

Watanabe, T., Matsuura, M., Seto, K. 1986. Enumeration, isolation and species identification of mycoplasmas in saliva sampled from the normal and pathological human oral cavity and antibody response to an oral mycoplasma (*M. salivarium*). *J. Clin. Micro.* **23**, 1034-1038.

Whiley, R.A., Beighton., D. Current classification of the oral streptococci. 1998. *Oral Micro. Immunol.* **13**, 195-216.

Woodhead, M. 1994. Pneumonia in the elderly. *J.Antimicrob. Chemother.*, **34**, supl. A, 85-92.

Woods, D.E. 1987. Role of fibronectin in the pathogenesis of Gram negative bacillary pneumonia. *Rev. Infect. Dis.,* **9**, 386-390.

Woods, D.E., Strauss, D.C., Johansen, W.G., Bass, J.A. 1981. Role of fibronectin in the prevention of adherence of Pseudomonas aeruginosa to nuccal cells. *J. Infect. Dis.*, **143**, 784-90.

Worthington, M. 1983. Fetal candida pneumonia in a non-immunosuppressed host. *J. Infect.*, **7**, 159-161.

Wren, M.W.D. 1996. Anaerobic cocci of clinical importance. *Br. J. Biomedical Science*, **53**, 294-301.

Wright, P.S., Clark, P. and Hardie, J.M. 1985. The prevalence and significance of yeasts in persons wearing complete dentures with soft lining materials. *J. Dent Res.*, **64**, 122-125.

Yang, H.T. 1993. Nested polymerase chain reaction in detection of *Helicobacter pylori* in human dental plaque. *Chin. Med. J.*, **73**, 750-752.

MICROBIAL AETIOLOGY OF HALITOSIS

John Greenman

*Bad breath (halitosis) can arise from a number of oral and non-oral conditions, although most cases are due to odiferous volatile compounds (VC's), including volatile sulphur compounds (VSC's), being generated by the oral flora. **In vitro** studies suggest that the most important groups of organisms generating VC's and VSC's are anaerobes, particularly those Gram-negative anaerobes (GNA) isolated from the tongue biofilm. Studies on human volunteers have revealed a correlation between subjects' oral malodour scores and log numbers of anaerobes, GNA and sulphide producing organisms per unit area of tongue surface. This relationship is also observed following use of metronidazole mouthrinse to selectively target the anaerobes, where odour reduction and concomitant reduction of GNA and sulphide producing organisms is highly significant (p< 0.01 at 24 h post rinse).*

Modelling of oral malodour requires experimental data on many fronts: the nature, types and supply rates of VC/VSC substrates into the tongue biofilm; the affinities for these substrates by the tongue microflora and subsequent VC/VSC generation rate; the fugacity of the VC/VSC's in question (partitioning into the gas phase) and their p_{ol} values (olfactory power). Salivary flow rate, composition and pH may affect many of these processes.

*Data from a chemostat model as well as from using substrate mouthrinses on human volunteers suggest that substrate supply is a key 'rate-limiting' step. Therefore, conditions which can give rise to additional substrates **in vivo**, (periodontal disease; glossitis) may increase VC/VSC production immediately as well as induce longer term physiological and ecological shifts in the tongue biofilm.*

Introduction

Halitosis is a non-life threatening but distressing condition that is relatively common (Miyazaki et al., 1995) throughout the adult population. For some individuals it can be persistent and does not necessarily result from poor oral hygiene. Halitosis is caused by the presence in the breath of volatile compounds (VC's) whose odour is considered objectionable by others. In the majority of cases (>80%) the oral cavity itself is considered to be the main site of odour generation (Prinz, 1930; Tonzetich, 1977; Rosenberg, 1995), this being due to the production of VC's by various microbes present within the biofilms of the tongue and teeth. The dorsoposterior surface of the tongue is considered to be the principal generation site accounting for up to 60-70% of the VC's generated, with the teeth and periodontium contributing the rest (Yaegaki and Sanada, 1992; Rosenberg and Leib, 1995). A minority of cases (<20%) are due to non-oral aetiologies (Preti et al., 1992) where VC's are produced by the host. These may originate from gut absorption (of foods such as garlic) or follow an organ dysfunction or metabolic disorder of the host. In these cases the VC's are present in the circulatory system before being secreted in saliva or excreted by the lungs and exhaled.

Alternatively, VC's may be generated by microbes infecting the lung or respiratory tracts and are therefore present on the breath following exhalation. In this review, the term "oral malodour" will be used to mean breath odour arising from processes in the oral cavity itself as opposed to all other categories.

Fundamental early work established oral malodour to be the result of bacterial putrefaction by oral microbes (Miller, 1890; Sulser *et al.,* 1939; Berg and Fosdick, 1946; Tonzetich, 1971; McNamara *et al.,* 1972). The principal VC's in microbe-derived oral malodour are thought to be the VSC's, mainly hydrogen sulphide (H_2S) and methyl mercaptan ($CH_3.SH$) (Tonzetich, 1971; Yaegaki and Sanada, 1992). However, amines (e.g. cadaverine, putrescine, trimethylamine), indole and volatile acids (e.g. butyrate and isovalerate) and other VC's may also contribute to an unknown extent (Kostelc *et al.,* 1980; Goldberg *et al.,* 1994).

Methods of measuring VC/VSC

A number of methods have been employed in order to measure VC/VSC in breath and the headspace of bacterial cultures. For incubated saliva or tongue scrape suspensions, and microbial cultures grown in rich medium, there is usually a high build up of VC/VSC and analysis can be carried out without using particularly sensitive systems. However, to detect or analyse gases in human breath, a sensitivity of a just a few parts per billion (ppb) may be necessary. Table 1 compares a number of different methods employed to measure VC/VSC.

The trained human nose is sufficiently sensitive to detect hydrogen sulphide and methyl mercaptan at about 150 and 20 ppb respectively, and is capable of detecting other VC's when present above their threshold concentrations. Since oral malodour is a perceived olfactory stimulus, direct sampling and assessment by human judges (known as hedonic or organoleptic assessment) is an obvious logical approach (Rosenberg and McCulloch, 1992). The measurements are quick allowing a high throughput of samples to be taken over a relatively short time. However, the disadvantages include the considerable variation that occurs between judges in ranking the degree of odour and the psycho-physiological state of individual judges which may influence their sense of smell.

One commonly used system for organoleptic assessment of breath is that described by Rosenberg *et al.* (1991) where the degree of odour is scored on a one to five scale where, 0 = no odour, 1 = barely noticeable odour, 2 = slight odour, 3 = moderate odour, 4 = strong odour, 5 = extremely foul odour. Alternatively, a sample of mouth gas may be diluted to the point at which the odour disappears (the so-called osmoscope method; Sulser *et al.,* 1939). The end-point is taken as the last dilution where the odour is just discernible. In this method, the human nose is simply used to indicate whether the odour is present or not; a subjective assessment of odour strength is not required. A comparison of

Table 1 Comparison of measurement techniques for VC/VSC.

System	Principle	Advantages	Disasvantages	Sensitivity for VSC's
GC-FPD	Chromatographic separation and detection by a flame photometric device	Differentiates between different VSC's. Quantitative.	Only detects VSC's, not VC's. Expensive non-portable. Samples collected in tube/bag subject to deterioration	<100 ppb
GC-MS	Chromatographic separation and detection by mass-spectroscopy	Differentiates between all VC's.	Expensive, non-portable. Samples collected in tube/bag subject to deterioration	10-100 ppb
Organoleptic (hedonic)	Trained odour judges score levels of malodour	Convenient for screening. Detects all odour VC's	Cannot identify individual VC's. Only semi-quantitative. Inter-judge variation	~ 150 ppb for H_2S ~ 20 ppb for CH_3SH
Thin film gold electrode (eg. Jerome analyser, Arizona Instruments Corp.)	Concentration dependent changes in resistance of gold film sensor	Very sensitive, portable, convenient for screening	Only specific for H_2S	~ 1 ppb
Voltammetric sensor (eg. Halimeter, I nterscan Corp.)	Electrochemical detection using voltammetry	Portable, convenient for screening	Only detects VSC's. Does not discriminate between VSC's. Subject to breath interferents	~ 50-100 ppb
Amperometric screen printed sensor	Electrochemical oxidation of thiol groups	Inexpensive, portable, disposable. Unaffected by moisture, ETOH and other interferents	Only detects VSC's. Current prototype does not discriminate between VSC's	~ 50 ppb
Tin oxide electrodes (eg. BB-checker)	Concentration dependent changes in conductance	Portable, small, convenient for screening	Only detects VSC's. Does not discriminate between VSC's. Subject to breath interferents	~ 50-100 ppb
Chemical methods	H_2S + lead acetate CH_3SH + DTNB*	Inexpensive, response shown as colour change	Only semi-quantitative, not very sensitive	~ 10 ppm

*5',5'-dithio-bis-(2-nitrobenzoic acid)

organoleptic assessment with this dilution method (El-Maaytah, 1996) indicates that the 0 to 5 organoleptic scale is exponential in nature. A score of "3" is approximately five times greater than a score of "2" and twenty five times greater than a score of "1".

Objective instrumental methods of measuring VC/VSC include gas chromatography with sensitive detectors (flame photometric devices, sulphur chemiluminescence detectors, mass spectroscopy detectors). These instruments are often expensive and require technical maintenance and support. They are rarely portable which means that gas sampling is required in a tube, teflon bag or storage loop which can then be transported to the GC machine. Alternatively, the gas sample may be adsorbed on to an inert material or cryogenically "trapped" and later thermally desorbed into the GC inlet. Despite these problems, many workers have used GC to great advantage to identify and measure different molecular species. The methods which use FPD and SCD detectors are specific for sulphide gases. Gas chromatography in combination with an FPD has been used successfully to measure breath VSC (Tonzetich, 1971; Tonzetich, 1977; Yaegaki and Sanada, 1992). The advantage of GC with an MS detector is that it can potentially detect a whole range of VC and VSC. However, water, carbon dioxide and air can often mask detection and consequently, it has not been used to routinely measure bad breath.

In recent years a number of selective sensors have become available to detect one or more of the VSC found in breath. One such sensor is a gold film electrode (Jerome 631-X analyser, Arizona Instruments Corporation, Phoenix, Arizona, US.) that specifically detects hydrogen sulphide and is extremely sensitive down to 1ppb.

Another instrument widely used for measuring VSC on breath is the halimeter (Rosenberg *et al.,* 1991) which uses a sulphide sensitive voltammetric sensor. An instrument using a zinc oxide sensor has also been described (Shimura *et al.,* 1996). Unfortunately, these instruments are sensitive to moisture and require either pumps, traps or filters in order to draw mouth gas across the sensor and exclude it. Other interferents include alcohol, flavour oils or chlorine compounds that are commonly found in breath freshening mouthwashes. Both these instruments detect VSC but cannot discriminate between the levels of hydrogen sulphide and methyl mercaptan. The sensors are less sensitive to methyl mercaptan and yet this compound has a much higher odour power rating (p_{ol} value) than hydrogen sulphide.

An amperometric sensor based on a screen-printed carbon electrode, modified by inclusion of cobalt phthaocyanine as an electrocatalyst has recently been described which is not affected by moisture or commonly encountered interferent molecules (Napier and Hart, 1996; Hart and Abass, 1997; Spencer *et al.,* 1999). At their present stage of development these electrodes cannot discriminate between the different types of VSC although this limitation may be overcome with further development. However, the electrodes are small, sensitive, inexpensive and disposable.

Chemical methods for measuring hydrogen sulphide (lead acetate papers)

Table 2 Averaged olfactory threshold for putative malodour compounds in bad breath.

Compound	Synonym	[1]P.ol	[2]P.ol (exp)
Sulphides:			
Hydrogen sulphide	Hydrogen sulphide	7.75	-
Methanthiol	Methyl sulphide	8.98	-
Methylthiomethane	Dimethyl sulphide	8.60	8.44
Methyldithiomethane	Dimethyl disulphide	7.91	7.72
Indoles:			
Indole	Indole	10.50	10.32
3-methyl indole	Skatole	9.25	8.58
Acids:			
Acetic	Acetic (C2)	6.84	-
Propanoic	Propionic (C3)	7.45	7.39
Butanoic	Butyric (C4)	8.41	8.07
2-methylpropanoic	Isobutyric (C4)	7.71	-
Pentanoic	Valeric (C5)	8.32	-
3-methylbutanoic	Isovaleric (C5)	8.61	8.41
Hexanoic	Caproic (C6)	7.90	-
4-methylpentanoic	Isocaproic (C6)	7.81	-
Heptanoic	Oenanthic (C7)	7.56	-
Octanoic	Caprylic (C8)	8.40	-
Amines:			
Ammonia		5.24	-
Methylamine		7.73	-
Trimethylamine		8.60	-
1,4 diaminobutane	Putrecine	-	7.45
1,5 diaminopentane	Cadaverine	7.10	8.20
Pyrrolidine		6.82	7.50
Hexylamine		-	7.74
Butylamine		6.28	6.08

[1] obtained from published data (Devos *et al.*, 1990)
[2] mean p.ol values determined by experiment (El-Maaytah, 1996)

and methyl mercaptan (5',5'-dithio-bis-(2-nitrobenzoic acid; DTNB) have been described (Kleinberg and Westbay, 1992). These are suitable for measuring VSC produced by incubated salivary sediment or microbial cultures but are not sufficiently sensitive to detect these gases on breath.

The relative odour power of VC/VSC

To be significant in causing odour a VC must be present in breath at a concentration above the smell threshold. The relative "smell" of a compound can be determined by accurate dilution of the VC to the point where a panel of judges can just detect it. The degree of dilution necessary to reach this point is a measure of the olfactory or odour power (p_{ol} value) of the compound in question. The unit of measurement (p_{ol} by volume) is defined as the negative log of the threshold concentration expressed in volumic or molar fractions. For example, 1 ppm = p_{ol} 6, whilst 1 ppb = p_{ol} 9. Different authors have used different methods to measure thresholds, but approximate, averaged standardised thresholds (using weighting coefficients to reduce the differences due to different techniques) can be arrived at and have been published for many different types of compound (Devos *et al.*, 1990). The p_{ol} values of compounds of possible importance in oral malodour are shown in Table 2.

The data in Table 2 shows that indole, methyl mercaptan and trimethylamine are the most odiferous compounds, followed by isovaleric and butyric acids, cadaverine and hydrogen sulphide. The fact that hydrogen sulphide is thought to be the most important VSC in mouth gas suggests that other factors in addition to p_{ol} have a more important bearing on malodour. These include generation rates (and hence the concentrations of VC/VSC attained), and fugacity (volatility).

Fugacity

Fugacity (Lewis and Randall, 1961) is the true measure of the escaping tendency of a component in solution and can be thought of as an idealised partial vapour pressure. Under equilibrium conditions (which may be far from the case in the oral cavity) the fugacity of a component 'i' in the liquid (f_L^i) is equal to that of the gaseous phase (f_v^i):

$$f_L^i = f_v^i$$

The liquid fugacity is related to a standard state (f_i°) by a mole fraction (x_i) and activity coefficient (g_i):

$$f_L^i = x_i\, \gamma_i\, f_i^\circ$$

The gas fugacity is related to the pressure (P), mole fraction (y_i), and activity of the vapour (f_i):

$$f_v^i = y_i\, \phi_i\, P$$

For compounds that can exist as liquids, the standard fugacity is equal to the saturated pressure. For non-condensable compounds it is equal to Henry's constant for the compound in question. Data on standard fugacity would allow the concentrations in the gaseous phase to be calculated from knowledge of the liquid concentrations (or vice versa). In theory, fugacity is a useful concept for binary interactions (pure water plus pure, inert compound). In practice, VC's react with salivary components (giving molecular complexations) which could affect the predictions obtained from the theory. However, simulations of fugacity for different compounds at normal temperatures and pressures in water show that hydrogen sulphide has a very high escaping tendency whilst indole has a very low escape tendency. The order for some common odour compounds is $H_2S > CH_3SH >$ butyrate > cadaverine > indole. Experiments by Tonzetich *et al.* (1967) where VC/VSC were added to saliva suggested that the inability of certain amines and indole to increase the odour of saliva was mainly due to their low volatility (fugacity).

424

Table 3 Some possible microbial transformations giving VC's.

a. Generalised scheme for decomposition of amino acids

1. Oxidative deamination	$\rightarrow$	keto acid + NH_3
2. Hydrolytic deaminatio	$\rightarrow$	hydroxy acid + NH_3
3. Reductive deamination	$\rightarrow$	saturated fatty acid + NH_3
4. Dehydrogenation deamination	$\rightarrow$	unsaturated fatty acid + NH_3
5. Decarboxylation	$\rightarrow$	amine + CO_2
6. Hydrolytic deamination + decarboxylation	$\rightarrow$	primary alcohol + NH_3 + CO_2
7. Reductive deamination + decarboxylation	$\rightarrow$	hydrocarbon + NH_3 + CO_2
8. Oxidative deamination + decarboxylation	$\rightarrow$	fatty acid + NH_3 + CO_2

b. Normal end-products of carbon-energy metabolism by groups of oral organisms

eg. *Propionibacterium*	$\rightarrow$	propionate + acetate + CO_2
eg. *Fusobacterium*	$\rightarrow$	butyrate, propionate, acetate, formate, lactate, succinate
eg. *Bacteroides*	$\rightarrow$	valerate, isovalerate, butyrate, isobutyrate, propionate, acetate, formate, lactate, succinate, phenylacetate

c. VSC production

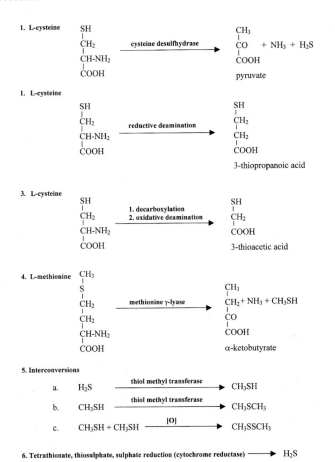

d. Indole, cadaverine and putrescine production

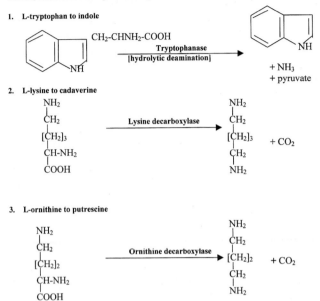

d. Indole, cadaverine and putrescine production

1. L-tryptophan to indole

CH$_2$-CHNH$_2$-COOH

Tryptophanase
[hydrolytic deamination]

+ NH$_3$
+ pyruvate

2. L-lysine to cadaverine

Lysine decarboxylase

+ CO$_2$

3. L-ornithine to putrescine

Ornithine decarboxylase

+ CO$_2$

(also L-arginine to citrulline to ornithine to putrescine)

It follows that in addition to odour power and fugacity, the concentrations of VC/VSC produced in the oral cavity by the oral flora (i.e. generation rate) is an important feature of oral malodour. The generation rate depends on the catalytic conversion of substrates into VC/VSC. This in turn depends on the types and numbers of VC/VSC producing microorganisms present (i.e. amount of enzyme) and/or the supply rate of substrates if it assumed that there is sufficient enzyme and that the limiting step is substrate availability.

Range of VC's produced by oral microorganisms

A number of transformations of substrates into potential malodour VC's are possible (Table 3). In general, little is known about which specific oral organisms can carry out which pathways. A subjective indication of the types of VC's produced by oral microbes can be obtained by organoleptic assessment where trained odour judges "smell" plates or broth culture samples of representative oral species. In this way, a tentative identification of dominant odours can be made (Table 4). This method assumes that the odour judges are able to recognise and distinguish the major categories of compounds present as sulphides, amines, acids, indoles and "other".

It is clear from previous work (McNamara *et al.,* 1972; Tonzetich, 1971; Tonzetich and McBride, 1981; Kleinberg and Codipilly, 1995) that anaerobes, and particularly the Gram negative anaerobes, tend to produce a higher degree

426

Table 4 Organoleptic assessment of oral microbial species grown on solid medium (plates).

Group	Examples	Dominant VC	Degree
Aerobes	*Neisseria*	Indole	+
	Micrococcus	Acids	+
	Stomatococcus	Acids	+
Micro-aerophillic	*Haemophilus*	Indole, other	+++
Facultative anaerobes	*Streptococcus*	None	-
	Lactobacillus	None	-
	Actinomyces	None	-
	Propionibacterium	Acids	+
Strict anaerobes	*Fusobacterium*	VSC, acids, amines	++++
	Bacteroides	VSC, acids, amines, indole	++++
	Veillonella	VSC, amines, indole	++
	Porphyromonas	VSC, acids, amines, indole, other	++++
	Peptostreptococcus	VSC, amines	+++
	Clostridium	VSC, acids, amines	++++

of malodourous VC/VSC in culture than other groups. By incubating species of oral microbes in liquid culture containing elevated levels of amino acid substrates, Kleinberg and Codipilly (1995) were able to demonstrate odour production by a range of species against a range of substrates. In general, Gram positive species were not particularly effective at producing odour whilst Gram negative species, particularly the anaerobic species *P. gingivalis* and *P. intermedia,* were effective odour producers. The most effective substrates to induce odour were cystine/cysteine, methionine, ornithine, lysine and tryptophan. *P. gingivalis* produced increased odour with all these substrates which implies that it may have the potential to produce hydrogen sulphide, methyl mercaptan, putrescine, cadaverine and indole from respective substrates.

A more objective analysis of VC and VSC production by oral species can be made using GC-MS measurements of culture headspace. Data obtained in our own laboratories from analysing a limited number of oral species as well as headspace analysis of mixed samples (incubated saliva and tongue-scrape material) show that a wide variety of volatile chemical species are produced (Table 5; see also Kostelc *et al.*, 1980). However, none of the cultures on plates or in broth produce an overall odour that may be comparable to that of bad breath.

Substrate availability

The amino acid substrates required for VSC production (cysteine, homocysteine and methionine) although found free in saliva and serum (and thus in gingival crevicular fluid) are at concentrations insufficient to account for malodour. The concentrations found are typically in the mM range (Stabler *et al.*, 1987). Tonzetich and Johnson (1977) analysed the thiol, disulphide and total sulphur content of human salivary fractions and studied the ability of different fractions to produce VSC when mixed with oral micro-organisms. These workers showed that salivary filtrate had a low capacity to serve as a VSC-substrate in contrast to whole saliva or salivary sediment which had a high capacity to serve as VSC substrate. They concluded that since neither thiocyanate, inorganic sulphate nor sulphate bound to salivary proteins could be converted into VSC by oral micro-organisms that the main substrates were the cellular elements (mainly leucocytes and exfoliated epithelial cells). These cells are mainly composed of structural proteins which implies an important role for cell disintegration and proteolysis in order for the microbial cells to be provided with membrane permeable substrates (amino acids or small peptides).

The total sulphur content of crevicular fluid is thought to match that of serum (29 mM). The levels of VSC's which have been detected after incubating mixed subgingival flora in serum is up to 7.0 mM (Persson *et al.,* 1989). Given the low levels of free amino acids in serum this implies that the sulphur-containing amino acids contained in the serum proteins are the main source of VSC substrates and that they are made available through proteolysis.

A correlation between the BANA test (for trypsin-like protease activity) and oral malodour parameters was made by Kozlovsky *et al.* (1994). These workers showed that the BANA scores from four loci (shallow pocket, deep pocket, tongue dorsum and saliva), were significantly associated with judged odour ratings. Hartley *et al.* (1996a) showed that high malodour subjects were shown to harbour a higher proportion of proteolytic species on their tongue (as measured by BAPNA, a similar substrate to BANA) than did low odour subjects. It is likely that many oral species possess amino- or carboxypeptidase activities which would also contribute to supplying amino acids from the N- or C- termini of proteins or peptides.

Experiments using human volunteers have shown that a rapid increase in organoleptic malodour scores (typically changing from a score of two to a score of four or more on a five point scale) occurs when subjects use certain amino acids as mouth-rinses. The effects occur between two to ten minutes following rinses with 10 ml of 0.1% w/v strength amino acid solution, held in the mouth for one minute and then fully expectorated. This effect occurs for cysteine, methionine, lysine, arginine, ornithine and tryptophan. The type of odour produced is compatible with the expected products of the bioconversions outlined in Table 3 (i.e. hydrogen sulphide, methyl mercaptan, cadaverine, putrescine and indole respectively (El-Maaytah and Greenman, unpublished observations). In a similar experiment using mouth-rinses on 12 healthy volunteers (none with a history of halitosis or periodontal disease) and measuring breath VSC using a halimeter, Wåler (1997) was able to demonstrate the conversion of cysteine and reduced glutathione into VSC within the oral cavity.

Key:
- = not detected
t = trace amounts (~10ppm)
+ = amounts between 10-100ppm
++ = major amounts (>100ppm)
† = H_2S detected using FPD
* Normal - isolated from low odour subjects;
Malodour - isolated from high odour subjects
BPPP = Black pigmenting *Porphyromonas/Prevotella* spp.

428

Table 5 GC-MS analysis of culture headspace of several oral species, incubated saliva and tongue scrape inoculated mixed culture of VC/VSC.

Compound	Porphyromonas gingivalis W50	BPPP (Normal)*	BPPP (Normal)*	BPPP (Malodour)*	Prevotella intermedia	Bacteroides (Malodour)*	Fusobacterium nucleatum ATCC 10953	Fusobacterium nucleatum (Normal)*	Veillonella dispar ATCC 17745	Veillonella spp (Normal)*	Veillonella spp. (Malodour)*	Campylobacter spp.	Peptostreptococcus micros ATCC 33270	Neisseria subflava A1078	Neisseria spp. (Malodour)*	Actinomyces naeslundii WW627	Actinomyces spp. (Malodour)*	Propionibacterium (Normal)*	Propionibacterium (Malodour)*	Incubated saliva	Incubated tongue scrape
hydrogen sulphide	+	†	†	†	†	†	+	+	-	-	-	+	+	-	-	-	-	-	-	+	++
methanethiol	+	-	-	-	-	-	+	+	-	-	-	+	+	-	-	-	-	-	-	+	++
trimethylamine	+	-	-	-	-	-	+	t	-	t	-	+	+	-	-	-	-	-	-	-	+
ethanethiol	-	-	-	-	-	-	-	-	-	-	-	-	-	-	-	-	-	-	-	-	-
ethanol	+	t	t	t	t	+	+	t	t	+	t	+	-	+	+	t	-	+	-	+	+
dimethyl sulphide	-	-	-	-	-	-	-	-	-	-	-	-	-	-	-	-	-	-	-	-	-
1 propanol	+	-	-	-	-	+	-	-	+	-	-	-	-	-	-	-	-	-	-	t/-	+
2 butanone	t	-	-	-	-	-	-	t	-	-	-	+	-	-	-	-	-	-	-	-	-
butanamine	+	-	-	-	-	-	+	+	-	+	-	-	-	-	-	-	-	-	-	-	-
acetic acid	+	++	++	+	++	+	+	+	+	+	+	+	+	+	+	t	t	+	+	t/+	+
butanal 3 methyl	-	-	-	-	-	-	-	-	-	-	-	-	+	-	-	-	-	-	-	-	-
butanal 2 methyl	-	-	-	-	-	-	-	-	-	-	-	-	+	-	-	-	-	-	-	-	-
1 butanol	+	t	t	t	t	-	+	-	-	-	-	+	-	t	-	t	-	-	-	t	+
pyrrolidine	?+	-	-	-	-	-	-	-	-	-	-	-	-	-	-	-	-	-	-	-	-
propionic acid	+	t	t	+	t	+	-	+	++	+	+	++	t	-	t	t	t	++	++	t/+	+
butanol 3 methyl	-	-	-	-	-	-	-	t	-	-	-	+	t	-	-	-	-	-	-	-	-
butanol 2 methyl	-	-	-	-	-	-	-	-	-	-	-	+	t	-	-	-	-	-	-	-	-
dimethyl disulphide	++	-	-	-	-	+	++	+	t	+	t	+	+	-	-	-	-	-	-	++	++
propionic acid 2 methyl	+	-	t	-	+	+	-	-	-	-	-	t	+	-	-	-	-	-	-	t	+
butanoic acid	++	t	-	-	-	-	++	++	-	+	-	t	t	+	-	-	+	-	-	t	+
hexanamine	++	-	-	-	-	-	+	++	-	+	t	+	+	-	-	-	-	-	+	+	+
butanoic acid 3 methyl	++	+	+	+	+	+	+	+	-	-	-	+	+	-	t	-	-	t	t	t	+
butanoic acid 2 methyl	++	+	++	+	+	+	-	+	-	-	-	t	+	-	-	-	-	-	-	t	+
pentanoic acid	t	-	-	-	-	-	-	-	-	-	-	-	t	-	-	-	-	-	-	t	+
pyrazine 2,5 dimethyl	+	-	-	-	-	-	-	-	-	-	-	-	-	-	-	-	-	+	-	-	-
1,4 butanediamine	+	-	-	-	-	-	-	-	-	-	-	-	-	-	-	-	-	-	-	-	+
1,5 pentanediamine	+	-	-	-	-	-	-	-	-	-	-	-	-	-	-	-	-	-	-	-	+
benzaldehyde	t	-	-	-	-	-	-	-	-	-	-	-	-	-	-	-	-	-	-	-	-
pentanoic acid 4 methyl	-	-	-	-	-	-	-	-	-	-	-	-	t	++	-	-	-	-	-	t	+
dimethyl trisulphide	+	-	-	-	-	-	-	+	-	+	-	t	+	-	-	-	-	-	-	+	+
phenol	-	-	-	-	-	-	-	t	-	-	-	-	-	-	-	-	-	-	-	-	+
hexanoic acid	-	-	-	-	-	-	-	-	-	-	-	-	-	-	-	-	-	-	-	t	+
pyrazine 3 ethyl 2,5 dimethyl	+	-	-	-	-	-	-	-	-	-	-	-	t	-	-	-	-	-	-	-	-
benzenamine n ethyl	-	-	-	-	-	-	-	-	-	+	-	+	-	-	-	-	-	-	-	-	-
dimethyl tetrasulphide	t	-	-	-	-	-	-	t	-	t	-	t	t/-	-	-	-	-	-	-	t	t
benzeneacetic acid	+	-	-	-	-	-	-	-	-	-	-	-	-	+	-	-	-	-	-	-	-
indole	+	-	-	-	-	+	+	-	-	-	t	-	+	-	+	-	-	-	-	+	+
benzenepropanoic acid	-	-	-	-	-	-	-	-	-	-	-	-	-	-	-	+	-	-	-	t	t
toluene	-	-	-	-	-	-	+	-	-	-	-	-	-	-	-	-	-	-	-	-	-

Experiments using substrate mouth-rinses demonstrate that the main rate-limiting step in the production of VC/VSC *in vivo* is the supply rate of substrates. It reinforces the view that in the absence of exogenous free amino acids as substrate, the proteolytic activity of the tongue flora is an important feature. Proteolytic activity by some microbes that produce little in the way of VC/VSC (e.g. *Stomatococcus* species) may nevertheless play an important role in the tongue biofilm by providing amino acid substrates for others species that can produce significant levels of odoriferous VC/VSC (Greenman *et al.*, 1995).

Microbial enzymes important in VC/VSC formation

Little is known about which specific oral organisms carry out which of the particular pathways outlined in Table 3. Even less information is available about the properties of any of the specific enzymes involved and whether or not enzyme synthesis is controlled by induction, repression or global regulation. Some features of L-cysteine desulphydrase and L-methionine-γ-lyase activity in cells of *Peptostreptococcus micros, Fusobacterium nucleatum* and *Porphyromonas gingivalis* have been described (Persson *et al.*, 1990; Tang-Larsen *et al.*, 1995; Carlsson, Larsen and Edlund, 1993). Studies regarding the ability of species to produce hydrogen sulphide and methyl mercaptan from peptides containing L-cysteine (glutathione, L-cysteinylglycine) or methionine, (N-methionyl-L-methionine) (Tang-Larsen *et al.*, 1995), showed that the various peptides were utilised by the cells and converted into VSC with K_m values between 5.0 and 720μM depending on both species and substrate. The K_m values for glutathione and L-cysteinylglycine were higher than those obtained from cysteine suggesting a specific high affinity uptake system for these peptides. In cell suspension assays using amperometric sensors to measure VSC, Spencer *et al.* (1999) determined K_m values of 1.80, 0.51 and 0.1 μM for conversion of cysteine to hydrogen sulphide for *P. gingivalis, Fusobacterium nucleatum* and *Peptostreptococcus micros* respectively.

The proportion of indole positive species isolated from the tongue biofilm of five human volunteers (unpublished results) has indicated that indole positive species are relatively common. Between 20 and 40% of the total isolates were shown to be indole positive when cultured in broth containing 0.1% (w/v) tryptophan. The enzyme responsible (tryptophanase) has been described for *E. coli* (Snell, 1975). However, the pH optima for tryptophanase activity in *E. coli* (pH 7.4 to 7.8) is markedly lower than that observed for *Porphyromonas gingivalis* (pH 8.5) (Greenman, unpublished work). It is interesting to note that the *E. coli* tryptophanase is induced by tryptophan (Yanofsky, Horn and Gollnick, 1991) and may catalyse several α,β-elimination and β-replacement reactions (Snell, 1975) including:

$$\text{Cysteine} + H_2O \rightarrow \text{pyruvate} + NH_3 + H_2S$$

and $\quad\quad$ $$\text{Cysteine} + \text{indole} \rightarrow \text{tryptophan} + H_2S$$

It is unknown to what extent these reactions are important in producing H_2S in the tongue biofilm.

430

Lysine decarboxylase and other decarboxylase enzymes have been described for *E. coli* (Gale, 1946) and oral species (Hayes and Hyatt, 1974). The inducible nature of VC/VSC forming enzymes (i.e. up-regulation of enzyme synthesis in the presence of respective substrates) has not been studied in detail. However, it seems likely that in explaining malodour the physiological state of the VC/VSC producing tongue biofilm cells as well as their absolute numbers is an important feature.

VC/VSC producing microorganisms *in situ*

A number of distinct oral biofilm environments can be identified in the mouth: hard tissue surfaces (supragingival plaque); hard tissue/soft tissue interface (subgingival plaque); smooth epithelial surfaces (e.g. buccal mucosa) and the dorsal tongue surface (tongue biofilm) (Marsh and Martin, 1992). The surface areas and biofilm densities suggest that dental plaque and tongue biofilm are both likely to be important sites for odour generation when compared to smooth epithelial surfaces since they harbour a much greater biomass of attached microbes, typically reaching 10^9 or 10^{10} cfu.cm^{-2}.

It is accepted that the oral microbiota is extremely diverse. It is estimated that 300 or more species of bacteria are present within the mouth, and that enormous variation exists between individuals (Moore, 1987). Most research in oral microbiology has been centered on the teeth, examining plaque formation and caries, with emphasis on the streptococci as primary colonisers. Periodontal disease has also been the subject of considerable attention, the focus here being on proteolytic anaerobes such as *Porphyromonas, Bacteroides, Treponema spp.* and other periodontopathogens. In contrast, the bacterial composition of the tongue biofilm is relatively unexplored; only a few groups have attempted comprehensive surveys (Gordon and Gibbons, 1966; Milnes *et al.,* 1993; De Boever and Loesche, 1995; Hartley *et al.,* 1996a). Other authors, (van Winklehoff *et al.,* 1988; Frisken *et al.,* 1987) have looked at a limited range of specific bacterial species. De Boever and Loesche (1995) surveyed the tongues of 16 malodorous individuals, but concluded that only 30 per cent of the isolates could be identified to species level using conventional methods.

The dorsum of the tongue can be divided into two symmetrical areas either side of the mid-line. It has a large surface area with a highly fissured papillary surface that allows it to harbour a large number of bacteria in a relatively anaerobic environment, ideal for the generation of odours.

One major problem when analysing the tongue flora is obtaining representative samples that relate to a given surface area of tongue. Traditionally a swab has been used for taking such samples. However, the tongue is highly convoluted and of an unknown fine surface area with relatively limited access. An alternative method has been devised (Hartley *et al.,* 1996b) using a toothbrush as a sampling tool. This has several advantages over the more conventional swab method since the size of the toothbrush head is fixed. As long as the toothbrush is firmly pressed against the tongue without touching or dragging along other surfaces, and provided the pressure is constant between samples, then so is the area. As the area is fixed, the brush can be used with confidence to access areas that cannot be demarcated with a clamp or other such device required to delineate the swab's contact area. The nylon bristles don't absorb saliva in the way a swab does, so the sample is relatively uncontaminated by salivary bacteria. Moreover the bristles may also penetrate the larger crypts towards the back of the tongue, where theoretically, microenvironments exist which are more anaerobic and therefore harbour a flora with a greater odour generating potential.

Results using the impressed toothbrush sampling method (Hartley *et al.* 1996b) showed that the biofilm on the dorsum of the tongue is composed of a much higher flora (from 10^7 to 10^9 cfu.cm^{-2}), than previously thought (Coykendall, 1995). Aerobes, anaerobes and Gram negative anaerobes were recovered with mean log counts of 6.79, 7.60 and 7.12 cfu cm^{-2} respectively. Moreover, Hartley *et al.* (1996b) demonstrated a bilateral symmetry in the distribution of microbes across the tongue, with bacterial numbers increasing towards the back (up to 5×10^9 cfu.cm^{-2}). Sequential sampling of the same area up to ten times (without salivary contamination) showed that a single sample only removed a fraction of the flora from that site suggesting that the flora may be significantly more numerous (perhaps by as much as one log-fold greater), than generally reported.

The tongue bacterial flora of 50 individuals without overt signs of periodontal disease was identified and enumerated to group or genus level by Hartley *et al.* (1996a). The relationship between these data and the oral malodour status of the individuals was also explored. When subjects were grouped into low or high odour producers, significant increases in the total bacterial load and key bacterial groups, namely Gram-negative anaerobes, were seen. These included *Porphyromonas/Prevotella* species and fusiforms, which relate to high odour. Furthermore, the importance of the anaerobes in oral malodour was demonstrated using metronidazole to selectively target the anaerobic types (Hartley *et al.*, 1999). Metronidazole (a single mouthwash used on 32 volunteers) significantly reduced total anaerobes and Gram-negative anaerobes. The decreases were associated with a concomitant reduction in the oral malodour status of subjects thus confirming the association between anaerobes and oral malodour production.

Measurements of sulphide producing colonies from tongue samples by use of an iron-containing culture medium also show a strong correlation between the counts of sulphide-producing organisms and oral malodour (Hartley *et al.*, 1996a; Hartley *et al.*, 1999).

Subjects with periodontal disease produce malodour with an increased ratio of methyl mercaptan to hydrogen sulphide (Yaegaki and Sanada, 1992), possibly reflecting the higher methionine content of crevicular fluid and/or a changed microbial composition. It is not known to what extent the tongue flora changes in individuals with periodontal disease. A few studies suggest that periodontal species that are normally absent or in very low numbers from the tongues of clinically healthy subjects (e.g. *Porphyromonas gingivalis*) can be isolated as significant transient flora from the tongues of periodontitis patients (Van

432

Winkelhoff *et al.*, 1988). It is also interesting to note that the amount of tongue coating (i.e. removable biofilm) that can be removed (measured as biomass) from periodontal subjects is approximately six times higher than that which can be removed from control subjects and that removal of the tongue coating decreased VSC levels by 75% compared with only a 25% reduction from tooth brushing alone (Yaegaki and Sanada, 1992).

In vitro models of VC/VSC formation by oral flora
Closed Systems
Cell suspension activity assays
Typically, in closed systems, cells are harvested from culture or in quantity from *in vivo* (e.g. tongue scraping). Cells are washed and resuspended in buffer and treated as "crude" enzyme. The substrate (e.g. cysteine, glutathione, methionine) is added in excess to the reaction mixture and rates of VSC formation determined by sequential sampling of the headspace and analysing for VSC using GC. In these types of "cell activity" assays, incubation is usually of short duration (cell growth is not desired) and attempts are made to determine initial reaction rates. Cells may be sonicated or otherwise treated to release enzyme or increase permeability of the cell membrane. By employing these types of assays, the pH optimum for the conversion of cysteine to hydrogen sulphide by *Fusobacterium nucleatum* and *Porphyromonas gingivalis* cells has been determined (Figure 1). A variation on this theme has been to insert an amperometric sensor into the assay headspace and monitor the evolution of VSC continuously over time. Such procedures are useful for determining K_m values against substrates (Spencer *et al.*, 1999) as well as studying pH optima and the effects of enzyme inhibitors. Figure 2 shows a comparison of two tongue-scrape samples, one taken from a low odour subject and the other from an individual with high odour. The amount of material taken was equivalent by dry weight. The rate of VSC production is clearly higher in the latter sample.

Incubated salivary sediment model
An *in vitro* model system to study the metabolic basis of pH and pO_2 changes occurring in plaque *in vivo* has been widely used (Kleinberg, 1967). In this system, salivary sediment is isolated from whole saliva and used to study metabolic transformations and pH changes when incubated mixtures are challenged with carbohydrate and/or amino acid substrates. More recently (Kleinberg and Codipilly, 1995) used this model to simulate some of the biological mechanisms involved in oral malodour generation. These authors were able to demonstrate a resultant reduction in odour formation and VSC due to the addition of glucose that subsequently caused a decrease in pH following incubation. However, the degree to which glucose alone or pH alone caused odour/VSC reduction was not ascertained.

Incubated whole saliva model
Studies attempting to relate breath odour scores with the VSC-potential of

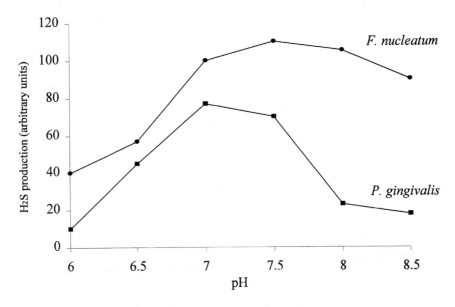

Figure 1 Effect of pH on cysteine desulphydrase activity in washed cell suspensions of *Fusobacterium nucleatum* (●) and *Porphyromonas gingivalis* (■). Rate of H_2S production measured by GC-FPD.

subjects incubated saliva showed no correlation (El-Maaytah *et al.*, 1996). As stated by these authors, once saliva is collected and incubated, a series of physicochemical shifts occur that will not occur *in vivo* to the same extent since the mouth is more likely to reflect a 'continuous open system' rather than a batch culture. In batch conditions the mixed microbial flora is subjected to batch growth conditions unlike those occurring *in vivo* where cells grow mainly as a biofilm on the tongue. In the mouth the microbial flora is subject to perturbations but the ratios of different groups one to another appears to remain relatively constant over time. The microbial flora occurring in salivary batch culture will be subjected to microbial succession whereby one group of organisms may become dominant and outgrow or out-compete the other groups. In particular, strictly anaerobic organisms may be inhibited by oxygen, and outcompeted by faster growing facultative or oxygen indifferent types such as the streptococci. These factors may explain the lack of strong correlation between salivary incubation tests and oral malodour.

In closed systems, too many of the parameters are shifting simultaneously to be able to easily ascertain cause and effect. For such a mixed culture system subjected to prolonged incubation the variables include; substrate concentration, pH, redox potential, oxygen tension, product formation, cell numbers and cell types.

434

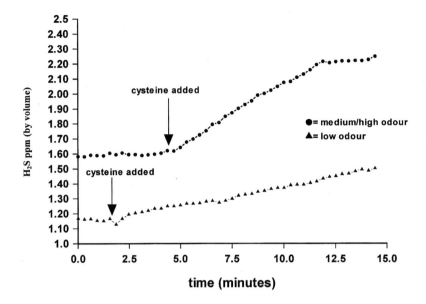

Figure 2 Hydrogen sulphide production from tongue scrape samples measured by amperometric gas sensor. The production follows addition of cysteine (0.01% w/v) to tongue scrape samples resuspended in tryptone broth (0.03% w/v/; OD_{540nm} = 0.28) from an individual with low odour and an individual with medium/high odour.

Open Systems

Continuous culture has been employed to study oral mixed culture ecological interactions and metabolic transformations, as models of both supragingival plaque (and its role in caries) and subgingival plaque (and its role in periodontal diseases) (Marsh *et al.*, 1983; McKee *et al.*, 1985; McDermid *et al.*, 1986; Glenister *et al.*, 1988; ter Steeg *et al.*, 1989). Recently, a mixed culture model of tongue flora species was employed in our own laboratories in order to study VSC production from pulsed additions of cysteine. The results (Table 6) describe the broad categories of genera isolated from both the inoculum (tongue scrape) and during steady state growth in a chemostat. The ecological profile of the chemostat culture showed higher proportions of *Actinomyces*, *Fusobacterium* species and *Veillonella* and lower proportions of streptococci and *Bacteroides* than were detected in the tongue scrape sample. Nevertheless, the proportions of different groups of species detected were not widely dissimilar to those of the inoculum and were within the overall range described for tongue flora by Hartley *et al.*, (1996a). The ability of the chemostat culture to transform cysteine substrate into hydrogen sulphide was studied by the addition of a single pulse of cysteine (final culture concentration of 0.01% w/v). Samples of culture were removed at various times and rapidly injected into gas tight GC vials. Hydrogen sulphide production was measured using GC-FPD (El-Maaytah *et al.*, 1996) and

Table 6 Tongue model chemostat: Composition of tongue inoculum and steady state flora.

Group	Tongue inoculum		Chemostat	
	Viable count (cm^{-2})	**%**	**Viable count (ml^{-1})**	**%**
Aerobic/facultative:				
Streptococcus spp.	8.318	34.49	6.110	1.67
Stomatococcus	4.699	0.01	4.127	0.02
Neisseria	6.780	0.99	5.544	0.45
Actinomyces	7.380	3.98	7.037	14.17
Anaerobic:				
Actinomyces spp.	7.599	6.60	6.950	11.61
Bacteroides	8.079	19.92	6.651	5.82
BPPP	4.699	0.01	3.690	0.006
Fusobacterium spp.	7.380	3.97	7.294	25.60
Curved rod	6.299	0.33	3.690	0.006
Anaerobic cocci	4.699	0.01	6.130	1.75
Veillonella	7.899	13.11	7.460	37.50
Unknown (G-ve rod)	8.000	16.50	5.690	0.60
Propionibacterium	4.699	0.01	5.690	0.60
Total aerobes/facultative	8.377	39.45	7.098	16.32
Total anaerobes	8.562	60.55	7.808	83.68
Total flora	8.780	100	7.690	100
Sulphide producers	-	4.20*	-	4.55*

* Given as a percent of total growing on sulphide detection medium

Chemostat conditions: D = 0.1h^{-1}, pH = 7.4, anaerobic gas sparge, 37°C.
Nutrient medium: Artificial saliva + BHI + haemin + dithiothreitol.

detected in samples 1 hour following the cysteine addition. A maximum was reached 3 hours following the start of the experiment (Figure 3). Hydrogen sulphide levels then dropped close to measured starting levels at 6 hours. After 6 hours a second pulse of cysteine at the same concentration as the first pulse was added. A second response was observed which also peaked at 3 hours. However, the second response was over 4 times higher than the initial response. Further sampling of the chemostat at the end of the 12 hour experiment showed no significant shifts in the types of microflora recovered. This suggests that the cysteine substrate is capable of inducing the synthesis of enzymes (cysteine desulphydrase) in some or all of the species that can produce it. When methionine was pulsed into the chemostat, methyl mercaptan generation was observed (data not shown) although the response following a second pulse was similar to the first suggesting that enzyme induction did not occur in this case.

Induction of the cysteine to hydrogen sulphide response can also be observed in human volunteers when a cysteine mouthrinse is given within an hour of an initial substrate rinse (Figure 4). This phenomenon has also been observed by others (Chang, 1998).

The main problems with using chemostats as model systems are that cells are in planktonic state whereas the majority of cells on the tongue surface are

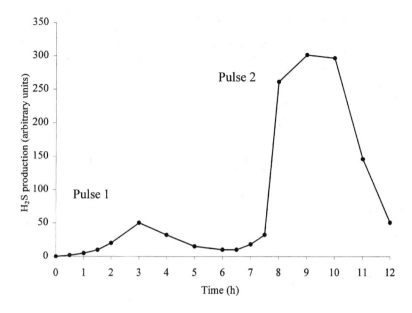

Figure 3 Effect of pulsing cysteine into a mixed culture chemostat (tongue flora). Each pulse was added to give a final concentration of 0.01% (w/v). First pulse added at zero time. Second pulse added at 6 hours.

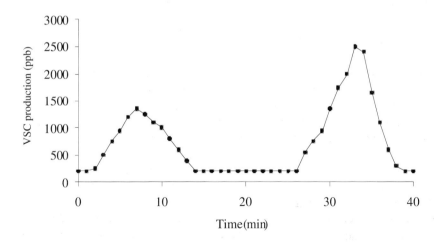

Figure 4 VSC production following cysteine (0.01% w/v) mouth rinses. Identical rinses administered at time zero and at time 25 minutes (data points represent averaged response).

immobilised in the biofilm. To the author's knowledge no one has yet tried to model tongue flora interactions (ecological or biochemical) using an *in vitro* biofilm system.

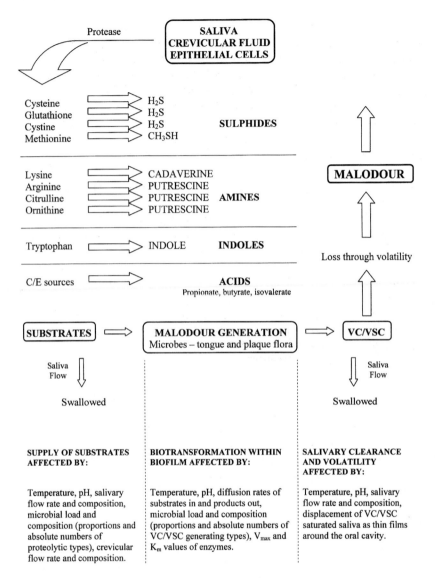

Figure 5 Model of oral malodour.

Overview

The factors and inter-relationships considered to be important in oral malodour are shown in Figure 5. Salivary flow rate, composition and pH may affect many of the main processes. Although the tongue biofilm may be the main VC/VSC generation site, the salivary film overlaying the tongue is displaced rapidly to other oral sites. Indeed, if the salivary displacement is as a thin film (e.g. over the buccal mucosa) its rate of VC/VSC production may be enhanced as it

BioLine © 1999

evaporates (Rosenberg, 1996).

In addition to being toxic to host cells, VSC may also be toxic to other microorganisms and it seems possible that VSC-producing species are less sensitive to VSC toxicity than are other types (however this hypothesis would need testing). It follows that any prolonged changes in the availability of sulphur-rich substrates (which may be envisaged to occur through periodontal disease, denture stomatitis, tongue glossitis and compacted food debris or cells) would have the effect of enrichment of the proteolytic/asaccharolytic types (ter Steeg *et al.*, 1989) and concomitant reduction of non-VSC producing types due to their sensitivity to VSC. This would have the effect of shifting the microbial ecology in favour of a VSC producing flora with full expression of VSC producing enzymes.

Potential points of intervention in oral malodour production (bad breath treatment) include: (a) gross removal of substrates by oral hygiene measures; (b) removal of substrates by chemical reaction (eg. oxidation of thiols); (c) reduction in the microbial flora (which produce VC/VSC generating enzymes); (d) inhibition of proteolysis; (e) inhibition of the microbial VC/VSC enzymes, and (f) changes in the physico-chemical environment which could affect the partition of VC/VSC into the gas phase. Therefore, oral malodour "treatments" (mouthrinses, lozenges, chewing gums) should be designed to interfere with one or more of the above processes.

Acknowledgements

The author would like to acknowledge Dr. Margaret Hartley, Dr. Mohammad El-Maaytah, Mr. Colin McKenzie and Mr. Paul Spencer for their help and contribution with regard to much of the experimental work at UWE described in this paper. The author would also like to thank Dr. Kay Saunders and Mr. Steven Jones for their assistance in preparation of the manuscript. Much of the investigative work was supported by a grant from Procter and Gamble, Cincinnati, Ohio, US.

References

Berg, M. and Fosdick, L.S. 1946. Studies in periodontal disease. II. Putrefactive organisms in the mouth. *J. Dent. Res.* **25**, 73-81.

Carlsson, J., Larsen, J.T. and Edlund, M-B. 1993. *Peptostreptococcus micros* has a uniquely high capacity to form hydrogen sulphide from glutathione. *Oral Microbiol. Immunol.* **8**, 42-45.

Chang, H. 1998. Reduction of oral malodour by a chlorine dioxide containing mouthrinse: Likely mechanisms of action *in vivo*. MSc thesis, University of London.

Coykendall, A.L. 1995. A method to quantitate the tongue flora. *J. Dent. Res.*, **74**, special issue, AADR abstract no. 924, 127.

De Boever, E.H. and Loesche, W.J. 1995. Strategies to identify the main microbial contributors to oral malodor. In: Rosenberg, M. (ed.), *Bad Breath: Research Perspectives,* pp. 41-54, Ramot Publishing, Tel Aviv.

Devos, M., Patte, F., Rouault, J., Laffort, P. and van Gemert, L.J. 1990. *Standardised human olfactory thresholds.* IRL Press at Oxford University Press, Oxford.

El-Maaytah, M. 1996. PhD Thesis, UWE, Bristol, UK.

El-Maaytah, M., Hartley, M.G., Greenman, J., Porter, S.R. and Scully, C. 1996. Relationship of the salivary incubation test with oral malodour levels. In: van Steenberghe, D. and Rosenberg, M.

(eds.), *Bad Breath: a Multidisciplinary Approach*. pp. 145-154, Leuven University Press, Belgium.

Frisken, K., Tagg, J., Laws, A. and Orr, M. 1987. Suspected periodontal microorganisms and their oral habitats in young children. *Oral Microbiol. Immunol*. **5**, 43-45.

Gale, E.F. 1946. The bacterial amino acid decarboxylases. *Adv. Enzymol*. **6**, 1-32.

Glenister, D.A., Salamon, K.E., Smith, K., Beighton, D. and Keevil, C.W. 1988. Enhanced growth of complex communities of dental plaque bacteria in mucin-limited continuous culture. *Micro. Ecol. Health Dis*. **1**, 31-38.

Goldberg, S., Kozlovsky, A., Gordon, D., Gelernter, I., Sintov, A. and Rosenberg, M. 1994. Cadaverine as a putative component of oral malodor. *J. Dent. Res*. **73**, 1168-1172.

Gordon, D.F. and Gibbons, R.J. 1966. Studies of the predominant cultivable micro-organisms from the human tongue. *Archs. Oral Biol*., **11**, 627-632.

Greenman, J., El-Maaytah, M.A., Hartley, M.G. and McKenzie, C. 1995. Proteolytic activity of *Stomatococcus mucilaginus*. In: van Steenberghe, D. and Rosenberg, M. (eds.), *Bad Breath: a Multidisciplinary Approach*. pp. 157-162, Leuven University Press, Belgium.

Hart, J.P. and Abass, A.K. 1997. A disposable amperometric gas sensor for sulphur-containing compounds based on a chemically modified screen printed carbon electrode coated with a hydrogel. *Analytica Chimica Acta*, **342**, 199-206.

Hartley, M.G., McKenzie, C., Greenman, J., El-Maaytah, M., Scully, C. and Porter, S. 1999. Effects of metronidazole mouthrinse on tongue microbiota and breath odour levels. *Micro. Ecol. Health Dis*. (Accepted for publication).

Hartley, M.G., El-Maaytah, M.A., McKenzie, C. and Greenman, J. 1996a. The tongue microbiota of low odour and malodorous individuals. *Micro. Ecol. Health Dis*. **9**, 215-223.

Hartley, M.G., El-Maaytah, M.A., McKenzie, C. and Greenman, J. 1996b. Assessment of an impressed toothbrush as a method of sampling tongue microbiota. In: van Steenberghe, D. and Rosenberg, M. (eds.), *Bad Breath: a Multidisciplinary Approach*. pp. 123-133, Leuven University Press, Belgium.

Hayes, M.L. and Hyatt, A.T. 1974. The decarboxylation of amino acids by bacteria derived from human dental plaque. *Arch. Oral Biol*., **19**, 361-369.

Kleinberg, I. 1967. Effect of varying sediment and glucose concentrations on the pH and acid production in human salivary sediment mixtures. *Arch. Oral Biol*., **12**, 1457-1473.

Kleinberg, I. and Codipilly, M. 1995. The biological basis of oral malodour formation. In: Rosenberg, M. (ed.), *Bad breath: Research perspectives*, pp. 13-39, Ramot Publishing, Tel Aviv.

Kleinberg, I. and Westbay, G. 1992. Salivary and metabolic factors involved in oral malodor formation. *J. Periodontol*. **63**, 768-775.

Kostelc, J.G., Preti, G., Zelson., Stoller, N. and Tonzetich, J. 1980. Salivary volatiles as indicators of periodontitis. *J. Periodont. Res*. **15**, 185-192.

Kozlovsky, A., Gordon, D., Gelernter, I., Loesche, W.J. and Rosenberg, M. 1994. Correlation between the BANA test and oral malodor parameters. *J. Dent. Res*, **73**, 1036-1042.

Lewis, G.N. and Randall, M. 1961. *Thermodynamics*. Revised by Pitzer, K.S. and Brewer, L. McGraw-Hill, New York, U.S.

Marsh, P.D., Hunter, J.R., Bowden, G.H., Hamilton, I.R., McKee, A.S., Hardie, J.M. and Ellwood, D.C. 1983. The influence of growth rate and nutrient limitation on the microbial composition and biochemical properties of a mixed culture of oral bacteria grown in a chemostat. *J. Gen. Microbiol*. **129**, 755-770.

Marsh, P.D. and Martin, M.V. 1992. *Oral Microbiology*, Chapman & Hall, London.

McDermid, A.S., McKee, A.S., Ellwood, D.C. and Marsh, P.D. 1986. The effect of lowering the pH on the composition and metabolism of a community of nine oral bacteria grown in a chemostat. *J. Gen. Microbiol*. **132**, 1205-1214.

McKee, A.S., McDermid, A.S., Ellwood, D.C. and Marsh, P.D. 1985. The establishment of reproducible, complex communities of oral bacteria in the chemostat using defined inocula. *J. Appl. Bact*. **59**, 263-275.

McNamara, T.F., Alexander, J.F., Lee, M. and Plains, M. 1972. The role of microorganisms in the production of oral malodor. *Oral Surg*. **34**, 41-48.

Miller, W.D. 1890. The micro-organisms of the human mouth. S.S. White, Philadelphia (reprinted in 1973 by Karger, Basel).

Milnes, A.R., Bowden, G.H., Gates, D. and Tate, R. 1993. Predominant cultivable microorganisms on the tongue of pre-school children. *Micro. Ecol. Health Dis.* **6**, 229-235.

Miyazaki, H., Sakao, S., Katoh, Y. and Takehara, T. 1995. Oral Malodour in the general population of Japan. In: Rosenberg, M. (ed.), *Bad breath: Research perspectives*, pp. 119-136, Ramot Publishing, Tel Aviv.

Moore, W.E.C. 1987. Microbiology of periodontal disease. *J. Periodont. Res* **22**, 335-341.

Napier, A. and Hart, J.P. 1996. Voltammetric and amperometric studies of selected thiols and dimethyldisulphide using a sreen-printed carbon electrode modified with cobalt phthalocyanine: Studies towards a gas sensor. *Electroanalysis*, **8**, 1006-1013.

Persson, S., Claesson, R. and Carlsson, J. 1989. The capacity of subgingival microbiotas to produce volatile sulfur compounds in human serum. *Oral Microbiol. Immunol.*, **4**, 169-172.

Persson, S., Edlund, M.B., Claesson, R. and Carlsson, J. 1990. The formation of hydrogen sulphide and methylmercaptan by oral bacteria. *Oral Microbiol. Immunol.*, **5**, 195-201

Preti, G., Clark, L., Cowart, B.J., Feldman, R.S., Lowry, L.D., Weber, E. and Young, I-M. 1992. Non-oral etiologies of oral malodour and altered chemosensation. *J. Periodontol.* **63**, 790-796.

Prinz, H. 1930. Offensive breath, its causes and its prevention. *Dent. Cosmos* **72**, 700-707.

Rosenberg, M. 1995. Bad breath: Research perspectives, pp. 1-12, Ramot Publishing, Tel Aviv.

Rosenberg, M. 1996. Clinical assessment of bad breath: Current concepts. *J. Amer. Dent. Ass.* **127**, 475-482.

Rosenberg, M. and Leib, E. 1995. Experiences of an Israeli malodour clinic. In: Rosenberg, M. (ed.), *Bad breath: Research perspectives*, pp. 137-148, Ramot Publishing, Tel Aviv.

Rosenberg, M. and McCulloch, C.A. 1992. Measurements of oral malodor: current methods and future prospects. *J. Periodontol.* **63**, 776-782.

Rosenberg, M., Kulkarni, G.V., Bosy, A. and McCulloch, C.A. 1991. Reproducibility and sensitivity of oral malodor measurements with a portable sulphide monitor. *J. Dent. Res.* **70**, 1436-1440.

Shimura, M., Yasuno, Y., Iwakura, M., Shimada, Y., Sakai, S., Suzuki, K. and Sakamoto, S. 1996. A new monitor with a zinc-oxide thin film semiconductor sensor for the measurement of volatile sulphur compounds in mouth air. *J. Periodontol.*, **67**, 396-402.

Snell, E. E. 1975. Tryptophanase: Structure, catalytic activities and mechanism of action. *Advances in Enzymology.*, **42**, 287-333.

Spencer, P., Greenman, J., Hart, J.P. and Abass, A.K. 1999. Amperometric sensors to measure biogenic VSC. 4th International Conference on Oral Malodour. Aug 20th-21st 1999. UCLA, CA, US.

Stabler, S.P., Marcell, P.D., Podell, E.R. and Allen, R.H. 1987. Quantitation of total homocysteine, total cysteine, and methionine in normal serum and urine using capillary gas chromatography-mass spectrometry. *Anal. Biochem.*, **162**, 185-196.

Sulser, G.F., Brening, R.H. and Fosdick, L.S. 1939. Some conditions that affect the odour concentration of breath. *J. Dent. Res.*, **18**, 355-359.

Tang-Larsen, J., Claesson, R., -B. Edlund, M., Carlsson J. 1995. Competition for peptides and amino acids among periodontal bacteria. *J. Periodont. Res.*, **30**, 390-395.

Ter Steeg, P.F. and van der Hoeven, J.S. 1989. Development of periodontal microflora on human serum. *Microbial Ecol. Health Dis.*, **2**, 1-10.

Tonzetich, J. 1971. Direct gas chromatographic analysis of sulphur compounds in mouth air in man. *Arch. Oral Biol.*, **16**, 587-597.

Tonzetich, J. 1977. Production and origin of oral malodor: a review of mechanisms and methods of analysis. *J. Periodontol.*, **48**, 13-20.

Tonzetich, J., Eigen, E., King, W.J. and Weiss, S. 1967. Volatility as a factor in the inability of certain amines and indole to increase the odor of saliva. *Arch. Oral Biol.*, **12**, 1167-1175.

Tonzetich, J. and Johnson, P.W. 1977. Chemical analysis of thiol, disulphide and total sulphur content of human saliva. *Arch. Oral Biol.*, **22**, 125-131.

Tonzetich, J. and McBride, B.C. 1981. Characterization of volatile sulphur production by pathogenic and non-pathogenic strains of oral *Bacteroides*. *Arch. Oral Biol.*, **26**, 963-969.

Van Winkelhoff, A.J., Van der Velden, U., Clement, M. and de Graaff, J. 1988. Intra-oral distribution of black-pigmented *Bacteroides* species in periodontitis patients. *Oral Microbiol. Immunol.*, **3**, 83-85.

Wåler, S.M. 1997. On the transformation of sulfur-containing amino acids and peptides to volatile sulfur compounds (VSC) in the human mouth. *Eur. J. Oral Sci.*, **105**, 534-537.

Yaegaki, K. and Sanada, K. 1992. Volatile sulfur compounds in mouth air from clinically healthy subjects and patients with periodontal disease. *J. Periodont. Res.,* **27**, 233-238.

Yanofsky, C., Horn, V., Gollnick, P. 1991. Physiological studies of tryptophan transport and tryptophanase operon induction in *E. coli. J. Bact.*, **173**, 6009-6017.

Treatment of Plaque-related Diseases

BACTERIA/HOST INTERACTIONS IN THE PERIODONTAL DISEASES: CLUES TO THE DEVELOPMENT OF NOVEL THERAPEUTICS FOR THE PERIODONTAL DISEASES

Brian Henderson

1. Introduction

Bacteriology as a science had been in relative decline during the period between the 1950s and the 1980s. It is only in the last decade or so that various factors have contributed to a renaissance in bacteriology. The major factor has, of course, been the increasing incidence of antibiotic resistance. This has led to the spectre of the *post-antibiotic age* with its appalling medical and social consequences. A contributory factor has been the realisation that bacteria are not simple cellular automata, but have complex intracellular and intercellular signalling systems similar to that of eukaryotic cells. These signalling systems are now recognised to be not only involved in communication between bacteria but in the communication that takes place between bacteria and host cells. Most of this communication is recognised in the context of bacterial virulence. Study of the interactions of bacteria with host cells has given rise to a new interdisciplinary science that has been called Cellular Microbiology (1). This new discipline is a combination of microbiology, cellular biology and, the ubiquitous, molecular biology. Most of the literature on Cellular Microbiology concerns a handful of pathogenic organisms such as enteropathogenic strains of *E. coli*, *Shigella* spp, *Salmonella* spp, *Listeria monocytogenes* and *Yersinia* spp. Little is known of the cellular microbiology of oral bacteria involved in the periodontal diseases. In this chapter the specific focus will be on the role of bacteria in the induction of inflammation and tissue destruction and the potential therapeutic targets that are emerging for the treatment of bacterially-induced inflammatory conditions.

2. Bacteria and the periodontal diseases

The starting point for the discussion of the pathology and therapy of the periodontal diseases is that: (i) a number of different oral commensal bacteria are implicated and (ii) in some way the interaction of these bacteria, in the form of a biofilm, with host tissues drives a process of periodontal inflammation and tissue destruction (2). The possibility that invasion of periodontal cells by oral bacteria may play a role in the pathogenesis of the periodontal diseases has been suggested (3) and there is increasing evidence that many bacteria can invade many human cell types in culture. Unfortunately, it is not clear that these finding are more than a laboratory artefact. As this is still somewhat controversial, it will not be discussed in this chapter.

In bacterial infection, the ability of a pathogenic bacterium to adhere to epithelial cells is the starting point in the disease. Once the bacterium has made contact with the target cell it can release toxic products and 'intoxicate' the cell thus causing pathology and/or it can invade the organism and create pathology. In the periodontal diseases the causative organisms are members of the oral microflora and the key events in disease induction are the interaction of the junctional epithelium with the oral bacteria in a manner that leads to the formation of a periodontal pocket, and the generation of a subgingival biofilm. The biofilm mode of bacterial growth and maintenance is a key factor in the periodontal diseases and sets up a new paradigm for the generation of pathology and for the creation of novel therapeutics.

2.1. The Bacterial Biofilm: An Unsolved Problem for Immunity

The evolution of the human immune system has been driven by the behaviour of the parasites that infect *Homo sapiens*. Parasites can either live within cells or in the extracellular spaces. Those parasites that live within non-myeloid cells (mainly viruses and a small number of bacteria) are targetted by CD8 T lymphocytes and NK cells. Those parasites (bacteria and protozoa) which have evolved to live within macrophages (much like finding a thief living in a police station) are attacked by Th1 CD4 T lymphocytes. Viruses, bacteria and protozoa which live in the 'open plains' of the body's intercellular spaces are prey to complement and antibodies. However, an obvious way of dealing with the immune system, and a manner favoured by the American pioneers when attacked by Native Americans, is to group together and seek safety in numbers. This, in a nutshell, is the biofilm. As an organised structure, in which the bacteria are firmly complexed, the immune system finds it difficult to deal with biofilms. It is relatively difficult to phagocytose cells from a biofilm and as biofilms are more resistant to synthetic antibiotics they are likely to be similarly resistant to our endogenous peptide antibiotics and to other host defences such as complement and antibacterial proteins such as BPI (bactericidal/permeability-increasing protein) (4).

If the argument is accepted that the biofilm is relatively resistant to exogenous therapies such as antibacterial agents and if augmentation of the immune response to the biofilm, for example by vaccination, may not provide sufficient 'immunological muscle' to remove the biofilm, then what are the options for treatment? The obvious therapeutic targets are the molecules which ultimately cause pathology. These can be divided into two groups: (i) bacterially-derived molecules which induce inflammation and (ii) host-derived molecules which produce inflammation. These two groups of molecules have a common focus – the large number of local signalling proteins known as cytokines (4).

Table 1 Cytokine families.

Family	Examples	Major Biological Functions
Interleukins*	IL-1 – IL-18	Many, but major function is lymphoid growth Factors
TNF family	TNFα	Many such family members – pro-inflammatory proteins with cytotoxic/apoptotic activity
Interferons	α, β, γ	Anti-viral and immunomodulatory
Colony-stimulating factors	IL-3, M-CSF	Myeloid growth and differentiation factors
Growth factors cells	EGF, TGFα	Growth factors for epithelial and mesenchymal
Chemokines	IL-8, MCP	Chemotactic proteins

* Also known as Haematopoiens

3. Cytokines: The pivotal proteins of health and disease

Homeostasis in multicellular organisms depends on communication (between organs, tissues and the cells which compose these organs and tissues) and three intercellular communication systems have evolved for this purpose: neural, endocrine and cytokine. Cytokines can be considered to be the dark matter of biology and have only been known about since the 1960s. At the time of writing there must be well over 100 cytokines described (5) and many more homologous genes are evident in the ESTs generated as part of the human genome project. Cytokines are generally subdivided into six groupings based on structure/function considerations, the receptors to which they bind and historical considerations (Table 1). Cytokines are intercellular messengers whose biological activity is dependent on binding to selected high affinity receptors on target cells and generating particular patterns of intracellular signalling resulting in selected gene transcription. The importance of cytokines to the periodontal diseases is their role in immune and inflammatory mechanisms.

Immunity can be subdivided into innate and acquired. The former evolved first and is the only means of defence for 95% of the multicellular organisms (the invertebrates) which live on our planet. It is often considered that innate immunity with its phagocytic cells and iron-binding molecules is an ancient, and not particularly important, defence mechanism for vertebrates. However, new research is uncovering the complexity and the importance of innate immunity and is revealing that this non-clonal form of immune defence is key in focusing the activity of acquired immunity (1,6). The key question, and one that has only been asked in recent years is – how does innate immunity, which does not have the complex recognition systems of acquired immunity, recognise bacteria. The importance of this question is obvious when one considers that it may take 7-14 days to mount an effective T and B lymphocyte response to an infectious agent.

One answer to this question has been proposed by Charles Janeway. He has introduced the concept that innate immunity can recognise bacteria (and other parasites) through non-clonal receptors that recognise bacterial molecules which are so important to the bacterium that they will not undergo substantial evolutionary change (6). These non-clonal receptors have been termed pattern-recognition receptors (PRRs) and they recognise pattern-associated molecular patterns (PAMPs) on parasites. The PAMPs include lipopolysaccharide (LPS) and related bacterial cell wall components (peptidoglycan, lipoarabinomannan) and bacterial DNA with a high CpG content. It is likely that many other PAMPs will be discovered. When these PAMPs bind to receptors on macrophages and dendritic cells they switch on the production of cytokines and also upregulate the production of two cell surface molecules, CD80 and CD86, that are known as co-stimulatory molecules. These are key proteins in the generation of T and B cell responses because they are required, along with MCH class II and the T cell receptor (TCR), to switch on the clonal proliferation of T and B lymphocytes (7). It is this upregulation of co-stimulatory molecules by bacterial factors which explains why antigens require to be administered in adjuvants composed of bacterial components (e.g. Freund's complete adjuvant) in order to develop a good immune response.

To recap, the immune system is now seen as a seamless complex of cells and mediators evolved to recognise particular patterns of molecules emanating from bacteria (and other parasites) and to produce particular populations of cells in order to deal with the infectious agent. The interactions between the leukocytes is controlled by cytokines. Thus cytokines are clearly homeostatic mediators required to defend us against infectious organisms. Unfortunately, and it is not clear if this is some grand fault in the design or if it has some deeper meaning in terms of evolutionary development, the response against infectious agents can often be so great that it leads to tissue pathology and even death. The mediators of this tissue pathology are the very one that help in our defences against infections – the cytokines.

4. Bacteria-cytokine interactions in health and disease

As has been described, bacteria contain molecules called PAMPs which, when recognised by eukaryotic cells, induce the production of cytokines. The major PAMP is lipopolysaccharide (LPS), which binds to cells via CD14 (4), a GPI-anchored protein which has no signalling function. It has recently been suggested that the true receptor for LPS is one (or more) of a group of proteins homologous to the protein Toll found in *Drosophila* and termed the Toll-like receptors (TLRs) (8). These, like CD14, are leucine-rich repeat (LRR)-containing proteins. The story has recently become more complex with the suggestion that a second protein, called MD-2, may be required for TLR signalling (9). In *Drosophila* Toll controls dorso-ventral patterning. Thus we see that the process of recognition of infectious agents is closely linked to key processes in embryogenesis.

Many of the complex carbohydrates of bacteria appear to stimulate cells via

Table 2 Cytokine-inducing bacterial molecules

CD14-dependent	CD14-independent
Lipopolysaccharide	Superantigens
Lipoarabinomannan	Chaperonins
Peptidoglycan	Heat shock proteins
Teichoic acids	Porins
Cell wall carbohydrates	Fimbrial proteins
Lipid A	Exotoxins
	DNA
	Lipoproteins
	LipidA-asoociated proteins

this CD14-TLR-MD-2 system. However, over the past decade or so it has become established that there are many other bacterial components, mainly proteins, which can stimulate host cell cytokine synthesis by binding to receptors other than CD14-TLR-MD-2 (10-13). The nature of the receptors to which these proteins bind is not established.

Table 2 shows the bacterial components which have been shown to stimulate human or rodent cells to produce cytokines. There appears to be an enormous amount of redundancy either in bacterial cytokine-inducing component or in the eukaryotic receptors able to recognise bacteria and induce cytokine synthesis. The obvious consequence of the recognition by host cells of these bacterial components is pathology and we have therefore suggested that these bacterial cytokine-inducing components are an additional form of bacterial virulence factor. The established bacterial virulence factors fall into four groupings: adhesins, invasins, impedins and aggressins with the names implying function. We have termed bacterial factors that stimulate cytokine synthesis, the modulins, as by inducing cells to produce cytokines these cytokines will feed-back onto the cell and *modulate* its function (10).

4.1. The Commensal Paradox

With the establishment that bacteria contain and secrete a very large number of cytokine-inducing components there arose a major problem. Our bodies, which on average are composed of 10^{13} cells contain 10^{14} bacteria. These are the normal microflora, sometimes commensal microflora, and it is members of this large group of bacterial species (possibly 1,000 species live in and on us) that cause the periodontal diseases. Now, all these bacteria which exist on epithelial and mucosal surfaces contain, and must constantly release, cytokine-inducing components. Thus our mucosal surfaces should be constantly inflamed. However, they are not. This is what we have termed the commensal paradox (13).

To explain why our mucosal surfaces are not constantly inflamed we have proposed that members of the normal microflora can synthesise proteins that inhibit the induction of pro-inflammatory cytokine networks. Thus we envisage that the interactions between commensal bacteria and mucosal surfaces is replete with mutual signals in which both Kingdoms of cells reach a mutually-beneficial equilibrium. Interference with this equilibrium (either by changing the bacteria or by changing host cells) should lead to pathology. An excellent example of this happerning in practice is found in mice in which the genes encoding the cytokines IL-2 or IL-10 have been inactivated by homologous recombination. In both cytokine knockout mice the major pathology is chronic intestinal inflammation (14.15). However, the pathology in both cytokine knockouts does not occur if the mice are bred under germ-free conditions establishing that the chronic intestinal inflammation is due to some form of mis-communication between the normal intestinal microflora and the mucosal immune system of the gut. Moreover, it has been claimed that the intestinal inflammation in the IL-10 knockout mice can be alleviated by 'administration' of the bacterium *Lactobacillus reuteri* (16).

These findings and recent reports of close signalling between *Bacteroides thetaiotaomicron* and gut epithelia (17) is rewriting the book on bacteria-host interactions which is important for our view of the periodontal diseases.

5. Therapeutic targets in the periodontal diseases

Returning to a consideration of the periodontal diseases it is clear that effective treatment of these conditions requires the identification of the key virulence mechanisms. The search for such mechanisms needs to encompass the panoply of pro-inflammatory bacterial molecules produced by subgingival biofilms, the particular patterns of cytokines induced in response to these bacterial moieties, which are likely to include inflammogens and molecules with other actions, including cytokine inhibiting activity, and the various systems that can be activated to induce tissue breakdown.

5.1. Therapeutic Targets: Bacteria

In normal infectious diseases the therapeutic strategy is obvious – use an antibiotic. While antibiotics are used in periodontal therapy the enormous prevalence of the periodontal diseases and the growing fears of antibiotic resistance precludes their universal use. A safer target would be the key bacterial virulence factors that drive the periodontal diseases. Unfortunately, it is at this point that we run into problems. A number of bacterial virulence factors have been identified in the periodontal diseases. The best known is LPS (18). Enteric LPSs are potent inflammatory mediators that can give rise to the lethal condition known as septic shock. It is less clear how biologically active oral LPSs are and how much they contribute to periodontal inflammation. We have compared the LPS, LPS-associated outer membrane proteins (LAPs) and the secreted proteins from *Actinobacillus actinomycetemcomitans* for their ability to stimulate human peripheral blood mononuclear cells to secrete pro-inflammatory cytokines and found that the LPS was a comparatively weak agonist for inducing cytokine synthesis compared to the other two bacterial fractions (19). However, if LPS is a therapeutic target then there are a number of ways in which activity could, in principle be blocked (Table 3). The methods that have or are being developed to

448

Table 3 Methods of inhibiting LPS bioactivity.

Neutralising anti-LPS monoclonal antibodies

Antibodies able to neutralise cytokines induced by LPS

Soluble cytokine receptors able to neutralise cytokines induced by LPS

IL-10

Intracellular signalling inhibitors which block LPS-induced cell signalling

LPS-binding antibiotics sich as polymyxin B

LPS-binding antibacterial peptides

LPS-binding proteins such as secretory leukocyte protease inhibitor (SLPI)

Endotoxin-neutralising protein from the horseshoe crab

Antibodies to CD14

CD14 itself

Bacterial permeability-inducing protein (BPI)

Antagonists of lipid A

Triacylglycerol-rich lipoproteins

Inhibitors of lipid A synthesis

block the biological activity of LPS include: neutralising antibodies, natural LPS-inhibiting proteins (e.g. bactericidal/permeability-inducing protein [BPI]), CD14, lipid A antagonists. Some of these therapeutic modalities have failed in the treatment of septic shock but may have more success if given locally to patients with periodontal disease.

Unfortunately, LPS is not the only oral bacterial component that has been demonstrated to induce cytokine synthesis or promote bone resorption. Many other molecules from bacteria have the ability to stimulate one or both of these activites (20,21). One of the most interesting bacterial virulence factors is the heat shock protein (molecular chaperone), chaperonin 60. Molecular chaperones are proteins which facilitate the folding and refolding of other proteins and are the gene products induced in the heat shock or cell stress response. During investigations of the potent bone resorbing activity secreted by cultured *A. actinomycetemcomitans* we discovered that the active protein was the molecular chaperone, chaperonin 60 (22). We also showed that the chaperonin 60 of *E. coli* (known as groEL) was a protein with potent bone resorbing actions (22). We have gone on to demonstrate that groEL is a powerful inducing factor for osteoclast development from bone marrow precursor cells (23) and that it is also a potent inducer of pro-inflammatory cytokine synthesis (24). Thus this protein may be a therapeutic target in, at least, localized juvenile periodontitis.

Other pro-inflammatory and/or osteolytic bacterial gene products have been recognised as being produced by periodontopathogenic bacteria. These may also be of therapeutic importance and it may be possible to develop methods of inactivating the major virulence factors of the key periodontopathogens. However, as many different virulence factors may be responsible for disease it may ultimately be impossible to develop specific therapy to inactivate bacterial virulence moieties.

5.1.1. Bacterial quorum sensing as a therapeutic target

One of the most exciting discoveries in modern bacteriology is the finding that bacteria indulge in intercellular signalling. One form of such signalling is the density-dependent gene activation process that goes under the name of quorum sensing. In this process bacteria produce and respond to a soluble product called an autoinducer. The autoinducer is generally a small molecule such as acyl homoserine lactones (AHLs) and peptides (reviewed in 1). Binding of the autoinducer to the bacterium switches on specific genes – in pathogenic bacteria these would be virulence genes. However, the amount of autoinducer required to stimulate these genes is high and thus gene activation only occurs when the cell density is high. It is possible that in the biofilms found in the oral cavities of patients with periodontal diseases the high cell density reached is controlled by some form of quorum sensing mechanism. It is now accepted that the quorum sensing mechanism is a therapeutic target for bacterial infections (25) and it may therefore be possible that inhibition of quorum signalling could have value in treating the periodontal diseases.

5.1.2. Human antibiotics as novel therapeutics

The role for antibiotics in the treatment of the periodontal diseases has been raised and it is generally accepted that conventional antibiotics are not suitable in the therapy of these conditions. However, over the past decade it has become clear that every living organism produces some form of peptide antibacterial agent. Many antibacterial peptides are now recognised and the oral cavity contains a number of such molecules (26). It is assumed that oral antibacterial peptides are involved in controlling the numbers of the oral microflora. The normal production of antibacterial peptides may be swamped by the vastly increased numbers of bacteria found in oral biofilms in the periodontal diseases. Thus it may be possible to supplement the oral antibacterial peptides by providing an exogenous source of artificial peptides. However, there could be problems with access of these peptides to the periodontal pocket. Moreover, as peptides, these molecules are susceptible to proteolytic breakdown. Another tactic would be to attempt to increase the normal rate of synthesis of antibiotic peptides by cells of the oral cavity. It is known that certain of these antibacterial peptides are able to be upregulated by bacterial signals such as LPS (27). If a method could be developed for upregulating antibiotic peptide synthesis without being, in itself, pro-inflammatory, then this could be an additional means of killing bacteria.

5.2. Therapeutic Targets: The Host

Targeting bacteria and their virulence factors is an attractive proposition for treating the periodontal diseases as such therapy will have selectivity. However, as discussed it is likely to be difficult to do. This leaves the therapeutic potential of targeting host-specific pathological mechanisms that are being driven by the signals emanating from the bacterial biofilm. This brings us into the purview of the prototypic human inflammatory diseases – rheumatoid arthritis and septic shock – which can be used to provide pointers for how one treats inflammatory diseases of either idiopathic or infectious causation. Indeed, in many ways the periodontal diseases resemble rheumatoid arthritis. In the latter, chronic inflammation of the synovial lining of the diarthrodial joint is associated with destruction of the adjacent articular cartilage and subchondral bone (28). This closely mimics the chronic inflammation of the gingiva and the destruction of the periodontal ligament and alveolar bone – the hallmarks of the periodontal diseases.

Studies of the pathomechanisms of inflammatory diseases such as rheumatoid arthritis over the past two decades have established a pecking order in terms of mediators and mechanisms and have focused on certain targets for therapy. Some of these may be relevant to the periodontal diseases.

5.2.1. Eicosanoid-generating systems

One of the major classes of drugs used for the treatment of rheumatoid arthritis are the compounds known as the non-steroidal anti-inflammatory drugs (NSAIDs). These work by inhibiting the activity of cyclooxygenases – enzymes that produce prostaglandins from arachidonic or eicosatetraenoic acid. The lipid products produced from eicosatetraenoic acid are called eicosanoids. Unfortunately, one of the cyclooxygenases (COXs) is utilised in the stomach as a cytoprotective mechanism and its inhibition accounts for the gastritis and gastric ulceration that often accompanies the ingestion of NSAIDs. These serious side-effects limit patient compliance, even in severe and painful diseases such as rheumatoid and osteoarthritis. Patient compliance in diseases that caused little discomfort, such as is the case with the periodontal diseases, would be minimal. However, during the past decade it has become established that the COX involved in inflammatory disease is a separate, and inducible, gene (COX-II). Drug companies have developed selective COX-II inhibitors and they are proving to be as effective as conventional NSAIDs but, as expected, lack the severe gastric problems (29). There is evidence that bone loss in the periodontal diseases can be inhibited by NSAIDs (30). If this claim is supported then it may be possible to use COX-II inhibitors to inhibit alveolar bone loss the periodontal diseases.

There are a number of cellular systems for metabolising eicosatetraenoic acid to produce a range of lipid mediators (31). The enzyme 5-lipoxygenase (5-

LO) metabolises eicosatetraenoic acid to produce the leukotrienes. It is now established that the leukotrienes are potent inducers of bone resorption with the ability to upregulate the recruitment of osteoclasts from precursor cells (32-34). It has been established that the major eicosanoids generated from inflamed gingival tissues are products of lipoxygenase action (35). Putting these two pieces of information together suggests that inhibition of lipoxygenase action may have therapeutic benefit for patients with periodontal disease. During the past few years a number of potent and selective inhibitors of 5-LO have been developed for the treatment of allergy and asthma (36). It would be sensible to determine if these compounds have any therapeutic potential in treating the periodontal diseases.

5.2.2. Pro-inflammatory cytokines as therapeutic targets
The paradigm has developed during the last decade or so that chronic inflammatory destructive diseases are controlled by a cascade of cytokines with the potent pro-inflammatory molecules, IL-1 and TNFα being at the top of the cascade (4,28). The production of IL-1 or TNF can lead to the synthesis of a range of other cytokines including the chemokines, IL-6, interferons and colony-stimulating factors. Counterregulatory cytokines, such as IL-1ra, IL-10 and TGFβ would normally regulate the production and actions of these pro-inflammatory proteins. However, it appears that in the chronic inflammatory diseases this normal regulatory pattern, or network, is not produced or does not function. Thus, at least in theory, it should be possible to inhibit chronic inflammatory diseases by removal of one or other of these key pro-inflammatory cytokines. In many experimental animal models of human inflammatory disesaes it has been established that neutralisation of IL-1 or TNF can block the induction or perpetuation of the disease (37).

There is now good evidence that neutralisation of the pro-inflammatory cytokine, TNFα, in patients with rheumatoid arthritis (38-40) or inflammatory bowel disease (41) can alleviate the major symptoms of these diseases. Use has also been made of a fusion protein composed of a soluble 75 kDa TNFα receptor complexed to a human Fc region for the treatment of rheumatoid arthritis (42). Thus even with a so-called autoimmune disease, in which the T lymphocyte is believed to be the major coordinator of disease, removal of one cytokine from the system seems able to negate most of the local and systemic pathology. It is not yet established if blockade of TNFα prevents the destruction of articular cartilage and bone.

Blockade of the activity of IL-1 by use of the natural antagonist, IL-1 receptor antagonist (IL-1ra) has shown mixed results in patients with sepsis. In patients with rheumatoid arthritis it is clear that the IL-1:IL-1ra balance is skewed in favour of the pro-inflammatory IL-1 (43). A number of clinical trials of IL-1ra in rheumatoid arthritis have now been conducted. In spite of the very short half-life of IL-1ra in the human circulation a number of these clinical trials have reported beneficial results (44).

Could anti-TNF reagents and/or IL-1ra be used for the treatment of the periodontal diseases. The answer is probably yes. One serious problem with such therapy in rheumatoid arthritis is the limited half-life of these protein reagents in the circulation. This could be overcome in the periodontal diseases if these proteins were administered locally in some slow release formulation.

Other methods currently under investigation to block the activity of these key pro-inflammatory cytokines include the use of protease inhibitors and inhibitors of cytokine-mediated intracellular signalling.

5.2.3. Inhibition of Tissue Proteinases

The cytokine cascades driven by bacterial factors stimulate many functions of the connective tissue cells and leukocytes present in the inflamed gingiva. Among the most important cell activation processes are those which lead to the transcription of connective tissue-degrading proteases. These include the soluble proteinases which go by the name of metalloproteinases or matrixins and include the collagenases, stromelysins and gelatinases (45). Another related grouping of these enzymes which has been discovered in recent years are the ADAMS (**a d**isintegrin **a**nd **m**etalloproteinase) or reprolysins. These are zinc-dependent metalloproteinases which are found on the outer surface of cells that have important functions in controlling many aspects of cell and cell-matrix behaviour. One of the ADAMS (TNFα-converting enzyme - TACE) is a major target of the drug industry as it cleaves the inactive precursor form of TNFα into the active 17kDa molecule (46). Blockade of the activity of this protease could prevent the production of active TNFα and have the same action as the TNF-neutralising antibodies or soluble receptors described earlier. Another ADAMs member has recently been isolated and claimed to be the key enzyme (known as aggrecanase) involved in the destruction of the matrix of articular cartilage (47). Aggrecan is the major proteoglycan of articular cartilage whose protein core is cleaved by aggrecanase resulting in loss of the articular cartilage matrix.

The various forms of zinc-dependent metalloproteinases described above could be therapeutic targets in the periodontal diseases. A number of pharmaceutical companies have now produced a range of potent metalloproteinase inhibitors (48). These have not had great success when used in patients for various reasons. However, clinical trials of a putative metalloproteinase inhibitor, which is an analogue of the antibacterial compound, tetracycline have proved some benefit (49). A more recent trial has combined doxycycline with ibuprofen (50).

6. Conclusions

The periodontium represents a 'hole' in the mucosal defences of the body and is therefore a fascinating place to view the interplay between the host and its microbial partners and enemies. This interplay must be honed by evolutionary forces, as the development of the periodontal diseases, and loss of the dentition, is the death sentence for any animal and must therefore have evolutionary impact. The periodontal diseases may represent one of the most complex biological and medical problems. Their causation is due to as yet undefined host and bacterial genetic and environmental factors that interplay in a complex manner made more complex by the bacterial biofilms to which the host is responding. In addition to the need to understand the pathological mechanisms that underly the periodontal diseases in order to be able to treat them there is increasing evidence that the oral biofilms that induce and perpetuate the periodontal diseases may also have important roles to play in systemic diseases such as the cardiovascular diseases. It is likely that the more we understand about the nature of the bacteria-host interactions that drive the periodontal diseases the more we will understand about the underlying nature of bacteria-host communication. Such information will be essential if we are to solve the perennial problem of theinfectious diseases.

References

1. Henderson B, Wilson M, McNab R, Lax AJ. *Cellular Microbiology: Bacteria-Host Interactions in Health and Disease.* John Wiley & Sons: Chichester 1999.
2. Landi L, Amar S, Polins AS, Van Dyke TE (1997) Host mechanisms in the pathogenesis of periodontal disease. *Curr Opin Periodontol* **4**: 3-10.
3. Meyer DH, Fives-Taylor PM (1997) The role of *Actinobacillus actinomycetemcomitans* in the pathogenesis of periodontal disease. *Trends Microbiol* **5**: 224-228.
4. Henderson B, Poole S, Wilson M. *Bacteria-Cytokine Interactions in Health and Disease.* Portland Press: London 1998.
5. Meager T. *The Molecular Biology of Cytokines.* John Wiley & Sons: Chichester 1998.
6. Medzhitov R, Janeway CA (1997) Innate immunity: the virtues of a nonclonal system of recognition. *Cell* **91**: 295-298.
7. Lenschow DJ, Walunas TL, Bluestone JA (1996) CD28/B7 system of T cell costimulation. *Annu Rev Immunol* **14**: 233-258.
8. Wright SD (1999) Toll, a new piece in the puzzle of innate immunity. *J Exp Med* **189**: 605-609.
9. Shimazu R, Akashi S, Ogata H, Nagai Y, Fukufome K, Miyake K, Kimoto M (1999) MD-2, a molecule that confers lipopolysaccharide responsiveness on Toll-like receptor 4. *J Exp Med* **189**: 1777-1782.
10. Henderson B, Poole S, Wilson M (1996) Bacterial modulins: a novel class of virulence factors which cause host tissue pathology by inducing cytokine synthesis. *Microbiol Revs* **60**: 316-341.
11. Henderson B, Poole S, Wilson M (1996) Microbial/host interactions in health and disease: who controls the cytokine network. *Immunopharmacol* **35**: 1-21.
12. Wilson M, Seymour R, Henderson B (1998) Bacterial perturbation of cytokine networks. *Infect Immun* **66**: 2401-2409.
13. Henderson B, Wilson M (1998) Commensal communism and the oral cavity. *J Dent Res* **77**: 1674-1682.
14. Sadlack B, Merz H, Schorle H *et al.* (1993) Ulcerative colitis-like disease in mice with a disrupted interleukin-2 gene. *Cell* **75**: 253-261.
15. Kuhn R, Lohler J, Rennick D, Rajewsky K, Muller W (1993) Interleukin-10-deficient mice develop chronic enterocolitis. *Cell* **75**: 263-274.
16. Madsen KL, Doyle JS, Jewell LD, Tavernini MM, Fedorak RN (1999) Lactobacillus species prevents colitis in interleukin-10 gene-deficient mice. *Gastroenterol* **116**: 1107-1114.
17. Hooper LV *et al.* (1998) Host-microbial symbiosis in the mammalian intestine: exploring an internal ecosystem. *Bioessays* **20**: 336-
18. Page RC (1998) The pathobiology of periodontal diseases ,may affect systemic diseases: inversion of a paradigm. *Ann Periodontol* **3**: 108-120.
19. Reddi K, Wilson M, Poole S, Meghji S, Henderson B (1996) Relative cytokine-stimulating activities of surface components of the periodontopathogenic bacterium Actinobacillus actinomycetemcomitans. *Cytokine* **7**: 534-541.
20. Wilson M, Reddi K, Henderson B (1996) Cytokine-inducing components of periodontopathogenic bacteria. *J Periodont Res* **31**: 393-407.
21. Nair SP, Meghji S, Wilson M, Reddi K, White P, Henderson B (1996) Bacterially-induced bone

destruction: Mechanisms and misconceptions. *Infect Immun* **64**: 2371-2380.

22. Kirby AC, Meghji S, Nair SP, White PA, Reddi K, Nishihara T, Nakashima K, Willis AC, Sim R, Wilson M, Henderson B (1995) The potent bone resorbing mediator of *Actinobacillus actinomycetemcomitans* is homologous to the molecular chaperone, groEL. *J Clin Invest* **96**: 1185-1194.

23. Reddi K, Meghji S, Nair SP, Arnett TR, Miller AD, Preuss M, Wilson M, Henderson B, Hill P (1998) The *Escherichia coli* chaperonin 60 (groEL) is a potent stimulator of osteoclast formation. *J Bone Miner Res* **13**: 1260-1266.

24. Tabona P, Reddi K, Khan S, Nair SP, Crean SV, Meghji S, Wilson M, Preuss M, Miller AD, Poole S, Carne S, Henderson B (1998) Homogeneous *Escherichia coli* chaperonin 60 induces IL-1β and IL-6 gene expression in hman monocytes by a mechanism independent of protein conformation. *J Immunol* **161**: 1414-1421.

25. Hartman G, Wise R (1998) Quorum sensing: potential means of treating gram-negative infections? *Lancet* **351**: 848-849.

26. Nilsson MF, Sandstedt B, Sorensen O *et al.* (1999) The human cationic antimicrobial protein (hCAP18), a peptide antibiotic, is widely expressed in human squamous epithelia and colocalises with interleukin-6. *Infect Immun* **67**: 2561-2566.

27. Schonwetter BS, Stolzenberg ED, Zasloff MA (1995) Epithelial antibiotics induced at sites of inflammation. Science **267**: 1645-1648.

28. Henderson B, Edwards JCW, Pettipher ER. *Mechanisms and Models in Rheumatoid Arthritis.* Academic Press 1995.

29. Schuna AA (1998) Update on treatment of rheumatoid arthritis. J Am Pharm Assoc Wash **38**: 728-735.

30. Williams RC, Jeffcoat MK, Howell TH *et al.* (1989) Altering the progression of human alveolar bone loss with the non-steroidal anti-inflammatory drug flurbiprofen. *J Periodontol* **60**: 485-490.

31. Serhan CN, Ward PA. *Molecular and Cellular Basis of Inflammation.* Humana Press: New Jersey, 1999.

32. Meghji S, Sandy JR, Scutt AM, Harvey W, Harris M (1988) Stimulation of bone resorption by lipoxygenase metabloites of arachidonic acid. *Prostaglandins* **36**: 139-149.

33. Gallwitz WE, Mundy GR, Lee CH *et al.* (1993) Lipoxygenase metabloites of arachidonic acid stimulate isolated osteoclasts to resorb calcified matrices. *J Biol Chem* **368**: 10087-10094.

34. Garcia C, Qiao M, Chen D *et al.* (1996) effects of synthetic peptido-leukotrienes on bone resorption in vitro. *J Bone Miner Res* **11**: 521-529.

35. El Attar TMA, Lin HS (1983) Relative conversion of arachidonic acid through lipoxygenase and cyclooxygenase pathways by homogenates of disease periodontal tissues. *J Oral Pathol* **12**: 7-10.

36. McGill KA, Busse WW (1996) Zileuton. *Lancet* **348**: 519-524.

37. Henderson B, Poole S (1994) Modulation of cytokine function: Therapeutic applications. *Adv Pharmacol* **25**: 53-115.

38. Elliott MJ, Maini RN, Feldmann M *et al.* (1993) Treatment of rheumatoid arthritis with chimeric monoclonal antibodies to TNFα. *Arthritis Rheum* **36**: 1681-1690.

39. Elliott MJ, MainiRN, Feldmann M *et al.* (1994) Randomised double-blind comparison of chimeric monoclonal antibody to tumour necrosis factor α (cA2) versus placebo in rheumatoid arthritis. *Lancet* **344**: 1105-1110.

40. Maini RN, Breedveld FC, Kalden JR *et al.* (1998) Therapeutic efficacy of multiple intravenous infusions of anti-tumour necrosis factor α monoclonal antibody combined with low-dose weekly methotrexate in rheumatoid arthritis. *Arthritis Rheum* **41**: 1552-1563.

41. Derkx B, Taminiau J, Radema S *et al.* (1993) Tumour necrosis factor-alpha antibody treatment in Crohn's disease. *Lancet* **342**: 173-174.

42. Weinblatt ME, Kremer JM, Bankhurst AD, *et al.* (1999) A trial of etanercept, a recombinant tumor necrosis factor receptor:Fc fusion protein, in patients with rheumatoid arthritis receiving methotrexate. *N Eng J Med* **340**: 253-259.

43. Firestein GS, Boyle DL, Yu C *et al.* (1994) Synovial interleukin-1 receptor antagonist and interleukin-1 balance in rheumatoid arthritis. *Arthritis Rheum* **37**: 644-652.

44. Smith MF. Interleukin-1 receptor antagonist. In Novel Cytokine Inhibitors (eds GA Higgs, B

Henderson) Birkhauser Verlag (in press 2000).

45. Nagase H (1997) Activation mechanisms of matrix metalloproteinases. *Biol Chem* **378**: 151-160.

46. Black RA, Rauch CT, Kozlosky CJ *et al.* (1997) A metalloproteinase disintegrin that releases tumour necrosis factor alpha from cells. *Nature* **385**: 729-733.

47. Tortorella MD, Burn TC, Pratta MA *et al.* (1999) Purification and cloning of aggrecanase-1: a member of the ADAMTS family of proteins. *Science* **284**: 1664-1666.

48. Denis LJ, Verweij J (1997) Matrix metalloproteinase inhibitors: present achievements and future prospects. *Invest New Drugs* **15**: 175-185.

49. Crout RJ, Lee HM, Schroeder K *et al.* (1996) The "cyclic" regimen of low dose doxycycline for adult periodontitis: A preliminary study. *J Periodontol* **67**: 506-514.

50. Ng VW, Bissada NF (1998) Clinical evaluation of systemic doxycycline and ibuprofen administration as an adjunctive treatment for adult periodontitis. *J Periodontol* **69**: 772-776.

MODERN METHODS FOR THE MECHANICAL CONTROL OF SUBGINGIVAL PLAQUE

Charles M. Cobb

*A translation by Johannes Channing (**De Chirurgia**) of Abu I Qasim's 10th century work notes that early treatment of periodontal disease consisted of "professional" cleaning of the teeth, over several days, facilitated by a set of fourteen scalers. Obviously, then, the use of manual scaling instruments has been ongoing for at least a thousand years although Egyptian hieroglyphics and medical papyri indicate that similar modes of periodontal therapy may extend back another three to four thousand years. "Modern methods" for the mechanical control of subgingival plaque consist primarily of design modifications leading to enhancement of the traditional scaling instrument and include piezoelectric, sonic, and ultrasonic scalers. In addition, various designs of rotary instrumentation have been developed and studied. However, the definitive title of "modern method" might belong to the evolving science of laser/biologic tissue interactions and the application of such concepts to the subgingival environment. Lastly, the commercial marketing claims presented on behalf of sonic and ultrasonic toothbrushes, specifically regarding control of subgingival plaque, place these instruments in the category of "modern methods". In spite of the purported advances in the control of subgingival plaque, manual scaling instrumentation, due to consistency of clinical response, remains the "gold standard" to which the more recently developed "modern methods" must be compared. Thus, comparative evaluations must include such outcomes as reductions in subgingival bacterial populations, change in clinical parameters such as bleeding on probing and probing depth, and changes in physical structure and/or chemical alterations in root surface tissues, i.e., cementum and dentin.*

Introduction

Paleoanthropological material from the East and South African Australopithecus era (2 to 3 million years ago) indicates that generalized periodontal disease was unusual although localized and severe lesions were frequently noted (Ward *et al.*, 1982; Clarke *et al.*, 1986; Ripamonti, 1989; Clark, 1990). However, by the European Neanderthal era (25,000 to 40,000 years ago), there is evidence that although dentitions were exempt from dental caries, the manifestations of generalized periodontal disease were well established. Specific evidence of horizontal loss of alveolar bone has been noted in the Ehringsdorf (Virchow, 1920) and Chapelle-aux-Saints (Choquet, 1909) specimens. In addition, skulls from Neolithic settlements (5800 to 3000 BC), similar to modern specimens, have been reported to exhibit increasing amounts of alveolar bone loss with increasing age of the individual (Mitsis and Taramidis, 1995). Based on such anthropological evidence, a legitimate argument can be made that the loss of alveolar bone due to periodontal disease shows an increasing prevalence as our ancestorial linage has evolved towards "modern" man.

Abu I-Qasim (Abulcasim) practicing during the 10th century in Cordova, seems to have been the first to give serious thought to the role played by calculus, whose presence under the gum (colored yellow, greenish or black) led to its "corruption". In his treatise, Al-Tasrif (later translated into Latin by Johannes Channing and entitled *De Chirurgia*), Abu I- Qasim recommended a "professional" cleaning of the teeth, over several days, which was facilitated by a set of fourteen scalers (Weinberger, 1948; Held, 1989). Thus, one may safely assume that the use of manual scaling instruments has been ongoing for at least a thousand years although Egyptian hieroglyphics and medical papyri indicate periodontal therapy may extend back another three to four thousand years (Weinberger, 1948).

Our ancient predecessors were unaware of the existence of bacteria. Their primary focus during scaling of the teeth was undoubtedly the removal calculus and extrinsic tooth stain. However, there is little debate that bacterial biofilms (and the inherent host response) when allowed to accumulate on tooth and root surfaces become the predominant etiologic factors in inflammatory periodontal disease. Consequently, the removal of sub- and supragingival plaque and calculus is an important part of any systematic treatment of periodontal disease.

Given the ancient history of periodontal therapy, more specifically manual scaling of teeth, what then are the "Modern Methods for the Mechanical Control of Subgingival Plaque"? Manual scaling instruments have been in continuous use for over a thousand years and have become, due to consistency of clinical response (Cobb, 1996), the "gold standard" to which more recently developed instrumentation must be compared. Modern methods for the mechanical control of subgingival plaque certainly should include those design modifications that enhance the performance of the traditional scaling instrument such as piezoelectric, sonic, and ultrasonic scalers. In addition, over the last decade, various designs of rotary instrumentation have received increasingly more attention. However, to date, the definitive title of "modern method" might be the applied to the evolving science of laser/biologic tissue interactions and the application of such concepts to the subgingival environment. Lastly, one might include, for the purposes of a complete discussion, an evaluation of the commercial marketing claims on behalf of sonic and ultrasonic toothbrushes with respect to the control of subgingival plaque. Accordingly, the following chapter will present a review and discussion of the merits and problems associated with all the aforementioned "modern methods" for the control of subgingival plaque.

Sonic, Ultrasonic, and Piezoelectric Scalers: Basic Design Concepts

The basic mechanical design of most sonic dental scalers consists of a vibrating rod activated by compressed air that generates an oscillatory frequency of 2 to 6 kHz (Gellin *et al.*, 1986; Loos *et al.*, 1987; Johnson *et al.*, 1989; Walmsley,

1989). The working tip of the sonic scaler operates in an elliptical pattern, with maximum oscillation at an air pressure of 260 N/m^2 (where N = Newton, or 1 m/sec) and no oscillation below 155 N/m^2 (Walmsley *et al.*, 1986; Gankerseer and Walmsley, 1987). The radius of oscillation decreases with increasing loads, to a maximum of 80 grams, at which no tip movement is observable. This contrasts with the ultrasonic scaler, which has an electrical feedback circuit that adjusts the power input to compensate for the load applied (Gankerseer and Walmsley, 1987). Shah *et al.* (1994) have reported notable variations in displacement amplitude between various commercial sonic scalers, resulting in significant differences in oscillation which, in turn, may affect clinical results.

The concept of ultrasonic instrumentation is based on the conversion of electrical energy into mechanical energy that generates surface vibrations in excess of 20 kHz. The magnetostrictive instrument is the traditional ultrasonic unit whose functional design is based on a stack of ferromagnetic metal in a high-frequency magnetic field. The stack undergoes alternate expansion and contraction in response to a fluctuating magnetic field that, in turn, causes vibration of the scaling tip at a rate of 25 to 30 kHz. The amplitude of the vibratory movement is about 0.06 to 0.1 mm. Depending on the mechanical design of the device, the working tip describes a linear, rectilinear, or elliptical movement. A simultaneous water flow, directed at the target area, functions both as a lavage and to minimize the effects of heat; approximately 60% of the energy used to power the instrument being converted to heat (Gottehrer and Reynolds, 1997).

Piezoelectric units constitute a new generation of ultrasonic instrument design in which the ferromagnetic stack is replaced by a quartz or ceramic crystal mechanism. When an oscillating voltage is applied, the crystal distorts to either side of resting position, resulting in an efficient high frequency tip vibration. The scaling tip motion is back-and-forth, i.e., a horizontal movement, generally at a frequency in the range of 40 to 42 kHz. (Zitterbart, 1987). Significantly less heat is generated by the piezoelectric design, thus effectively reducing the requirement of water as a cooling agent.

Sonic and Ultrasonic Scaling Tips:
Design Modifications

In recent years the working tips (scaling tips) for manual scalers and both sonic and ultrasonic instruments have undergone design modifications that enhance their subgingival application (Figures 1, 2 & 3). This is particularly apparent when compared to the ultrasonic working tips introduced in the mid 1950s. Originally, ultrasonic working tips were designed for supragingival scaling with little or no consideration for subgingival debridement. As such, these tips featured relatively bulky dimensions, were generally smooth and round in shape, or possessed cutting edges to facilitate removal of supragingival calculus deposits. In spite of such shortcomings, several studies have noted that ultrasonic working tips, with design specifications similar to those of the original inserts, were equal to manual instrumentation (curettes and scalers) when used

Charles M. Cobb

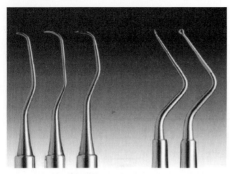

Figure 1 Design modifications in the Gracey curette. From left to right: 13 mm shank length with 3 mm "mini" blade (1/2 Gracey Mini Five*); 13 mm shank with 5 mm blade (1/2 Gracey After Five*); and the traditional 10 mm shank with 5 mm blade (1/2 Gracey*). At far right are new designs of furcation curettes (side view of the SOH 3/4 and frontal view of the SOH 1/2*). Original magnification of 2x.

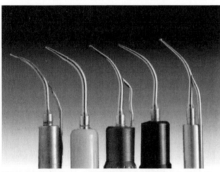

Figure 2 Design modifications in ultrasonic inserts. From left to right: 25 KHz P-10 insert[§], circa 1980; 25 KHz FSI-10 insert[§] with flow-thru design for water lavage; 25 KHz SF10S After Five™ insert*; FSI™ Slimline™ insert[§] with focused spray water delivery; and the 25KHz M6 ball furcation insert*. Original magnification of 3x.

---

* Hu-Friedy, Chicago, Illinois, 60618-5982, USA
§ Dentsply International, Inc., York, Pennsylvania, 17404, USA
‡ KaVo Dental GmbH, Biberach/Riss, Germany

to remove subgingival bacterial plaque and calculus deposits (Eschler and Rapley, 1991; Ritz *et al.*, 1991; Zappa *et al.*, 1991a; Jotikasthira *et al.*, 1992).

As can be seen in Figures 2 and 3, some of the more recent modifications in working tip design for sonic and ultrasonic instruments include fine-grit diamond-coated tips (Kocher and Plagmann, 1997; Yukna *et al.*, 1997), smooth ball tips designed for concavities and furcations, combinations of fine-grit diamond-coated and ellipsoid or ball shaped tips (Kocher *et al.*, 1998a, 1998b), file-shaped designs (Mengel *et al.*, 1994), elongated straight tips with diameters similar to that of a periodontal probe, sometimes referred to as "microultrasonic" tips (Kawanami *et al.*, 1988; Holbrook and Low, 1991; Clifford *et al.*, 1999), tips with a flow-through design for the concomitant delivery of a water lavage or liquid antimicrobials (Taggart *et al.*, 1990; Nosal *et al.*, 1991; Reynolds *et al.*, 1992), and rotary ultrasonic scaling tips that are essentially a modified dental bur (Radentz *et al.*, 1973).

Terminology:
Periodontal Debridement vs.
Scaling vs. Scaling and Root
Planing

Simply viewed, periodontal therapy consists of a variety of treatment techniques that are designed to achieve one or any combination of the following results: prevention of disease, arresting infection, restoration of lost dental tissues, and maintenance of a healthy and functional periodontium. In this regard, the mechanical removal of both supra- and subgingival bacterial plaque and calculus has proven an effective means of altering the progression and controlling the etiologic factors of inflammatory periodontal disease. The terms "mechanical control" or "mechanical therapy" refer to both supra- and subgingival scaling as well as root planing. In theory, these procedures are different but in the environment of a clinical practice they generally involve the same instruments and techniques and objectives of therapy. Scaling has been defined as the mechanical removal of plaque, calculus, and stains from the crown and root surfaces in which there is no deliberate attempt to remove tooth substance. Root planing, on the other hand, has been defined as the process by which residual calculus and portions of cementum are removed from the roots to yield a smooth, hard, and clean surface (Pattison and Pattison, 1996). From the clinician's point of view, the difference between scaling and scaling and root planing is simply a matter of degree.

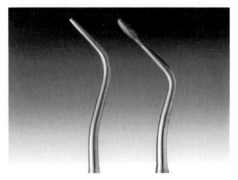

Figure 3 Sonic working tip designs. Left to right: a universal scaling tip[§] and a 15 μm grit diamond coated furcation tip[‡]. Original magnification of 3x.

* Hu-Friedy, Chicago, Illinois, 60618-5982, USA
§ Dentsply International, Inc., York, Pennsylvania, 17404, USA
‡ KaVo Dental GmbH, Biberach/Riss, Germany

The term "periodontal debridement" has recently been introduced to the dental literature. Smart *et al.* (1990) suggested the terminology to describe "a conservative instrumentation regime of overlapping strokes and light pressure utilized for only a limited time period". Such a definition would appear to apply only to sonic and ultrasonic instrumentation as scaling or scaling and root planing using manual instruments generally requires something greater than light pressures and is often described as arduous and time consuming (Drisko and Killoy, 1991; Drisko and Lewis, 1996).

Efficiency:
Manual vs. Sonic/Ultrasonic Instrumentation

Meticulous subgingival debridement and scaling and root planing by manual instrumentation is inherently a time consuming and difficult procedure requiring of the clinician considerable skill, perseverance, and stamina (Drisko and Killoy, 1991; Drisko and Lewis, 1996). The demanding nature of subgingival instrumentation using manual scalers and curettes and the recognition that the physical principles of ultrasonic wave generation could be applied to dentistry lead to the development of the first magnetostrictive ultrasonic scaler in the early 1950s. Since that time, numerous studies have reported on the comparative efficiency of sonic and/or ultrasonic vs. manual instrumentation. Collectively, these studies indicate that manual instrumentation generally takes longer to achieve the same clinical end-points than do sonic and/or ultrasonic scaling instruments (Badersten *et al.*, 1981, 1984a, 1985; Loos *et al.*, 1987 & 1989;

Kawanami *et al.*, 1988; Checchi and Pelliccioni, 1988; Laurell and Patterson, 1988; Laurell, 1990; Dragoo, 1992; Copulos *et al.*, 1993; Grant *et al.*, 1993; Boretti *et al.*, 1995; Drisko, 1995a; Kocher *et al.*, 1997; Yukna *et al.*, 1997). In fact, several studies have reported that use of sonic and/or ultrasonic instruments can result in a 20% to 50% savings in time compared to manual instrumentation when used for periodontal debridement procedures (Checchi and Pelliccioni, 1988; Dragoo, 1992; Copulos *et al.*, 1993; Drisko, 1995a).

The time required to achieve clinical endpoints is only one of several factors in the equation of instrument efficiency. For example, root anatomy, probing depth, tooth position within the dental arch, restricted access due mouth size, and variations in clinical expertise may impact on the effectiveness of scaling and root planing. Waerhaug (1975 & 1978) and later, Stambaugh *et al.* (1981) noted that the chances of removing all subgingival plaque from all tooth surfaces was fairly good if the probing depth was œ 3.0 mm. However, at probing depths of 3 to 5 mm, the chance of failure becomes greater than the chance of success. At probing depths ≥ 5.0 mm, the chance of failure becomes significantly dominate. In fact, Stambaugh *et al.* (1981) state that the removal of all subgingival plaque and calculus is unlikely to occur when the mean probing depth exceeds 3.73 mm.

Dragoo (1992) compared manual curettes, unmodified, and modified ultrasonic scaling tips for their ability to reach the most apical extension of pockets whose probing depths ranged from 5 to 8 mm. The modified ultrasonic tip featured a cross-sectional diameter similar to that of a periodontal probe (i.e., 0.5 mm), i.e., a so-called "microultrasonic" tip. Dragoo reported that only rarely did any of the instruments approach the most apical depth of the pocket. The mean distance from the instrument limit to the depth of the pocket was 1.25 mm for manual curettes, 1.13 for unmodified ultrasonic tips, and 0.78 mm for the modified ultrasonic tip. However, Clifford *et al.* (1999) have recently reported that a comparison of the standard ultrasonic and microultrasonic inserts, following in vivo use, showed that both types of working tips were able to reach and debride the apical plaque border in pockets in 4 to 6 mm and ≥ 7 mm pockets. Notwithstanding any apparent limitation in subgingival mechanical therapy, regardless of instrument type, the periodontal literature contains numerous reports supporting successful long-term maintenance following either surgical or non-surgical therapy (Hill *et al.*, 1981; Pihlstrom *et al.*, 1983; Lindhe and Nyman, 1984; Lindhe *et al.*, 1984; Kerry *et al.*, 1990; Kaldahl *et al.*, 1996a). This paradox can be explained, in part, by the concept of "critical mass" (WWP, 1989). As applied to non-surgical periodontal therapy, the concept of critical mass is best understood by assuming that a major goal of periodontal therapy is to reduce the quantity (mass) of bacterial plaque to a level (critical) that results in an equilibrium between the residual microbes and the host response, i.e., no clinical disease. Given the physical limitations, both anatomical and instrumentation, of subgingival scaling and/or root planing, it borders on mythical to assume that clinicians can remove all subgingival plaque and calculus. Indeed, it may be a myth to think that one must!

462

Control of Subgingival Bacterial Plaque:
Manual vs. Sonic/Ultrasonic Instrumentation

Treatment of a periodontal pocket using manual instrumentation for subgingival scaling generally results in a profound shift in the composition of the microbial flora (Listgarten *et al.*, 1978; Slots *et al.*, 1979; Mousques *et al.*, 1980; Singletary *et al.*, 1982; Greenwell and Bissada, 1984; Magnusson *et al.*, 1984; Hinrichs *et al.*, 1985; Lavanchy *et al.*, 1987; van Winkelhoff *et al.*, 1988; Southard *et al.*, 1989). Subgingival scaling effectively decreases the population of Gram-negative microbes while concomitantly allowing for an increase in the populations of Gram-positive rods and cocci. This shift towards a more dominate population of Gram-positive microbes is generally associated with gingival health (Listgarten *et al.*, 1978; Slots *et al.*, 1979; Mousques *et al.*, 1980; Singletary *et al.*, 1982; Greenwell and Bissada, 1984; Magnusson *et al.*, 1984; Hinrichs *et al.*, 1985; Harper *et al.*, 1987; Lavanchy *et al.*, 1987; van Winkelhoff *et al.*, 1988; Southard *et al.*, 1989; Sbordone *et al.*, 1990; Haffajee *et al.*, 1997). Although spirochetes, motile microbes, and *Bacteroides* species are routinely reduced in numbers after subginigival debridement, other species appear to be more resistant, such as *Actinobacillus actinomycetemcomitans* and *Porphyromonas gingivalis* (Slots and Rosling, 1983; Pihlstrom *et al.*, 1984; Christersson *et al.*, 1985; Harper *et al.*, 1987; van Winkelhoff *et al.*, 1988; Southard *et al.*, 1989; Renvert *et al.*, 1990; Sbordone *et al.*, 1990; Shiloah and Patters, 1994; von Troil-Lindén *et al.*, 1996; Haffajee *et al.*, 1997). The inability of subgingival instrumentation to eradicate *Actinobacillus actinomycetemcomitans* and *Porphyromonas gingivalis* has been attributed to their ability to invade the subjacent periodontal tissues (Slots *et al.*, 1983; Christersson *et al.*, 1985; Shiloah and Patters, 1994), existing high pretreatment levels, and deep initial probing depths (Mombelli *et al.*, 1994a, 1994b). In addition, several studies have demonstrated the presence of bacteria in root cementum and radicular dentin of periodontally diseased teeth. Such bacterial invasion of root structure may represent a reservoir of periodontopathic bacteria for recolonization and reinfection (Daly *et al.*, 1982; Adriaens *et al.*, 1988; Giuliana *et al.*, 1997). Lastly, subgingival therapy does little to address other oral sites that may act as a source for re-emerging periodontal pathogens, i.e., posterior tongue and peritonsillar areas (von Troil-Lindén *et al.*, 1996). It is recognized that shifts to a subgingival microbial flora representative of health appear to be transient. Thus, to sustain the positive effects of periodontal treatment, scaling and root planing must be performed periodically during the maintenance phase of therapy (Westfelt *et al.*, 1983; Lindhe and Nyman, 1984; Harper and Robinson, 1987; van Winkelhoff *et al.*, 1988; Renvert *et al.*, 1992; Shiloah and Patters, 1996).

Studies regarding the effect of ultrasonic instrumentation on the subgingival microbial flora and microbial toxins are relatively few but consistent in their findings. When this small number of investigations is evaluated as a collected body of literature, one common agreement appears to exist, that is, neither manual, sonic, or ultrasonic scalers effect the complete removal of subgingival bacterial plaque and calculus (Lie and Meyer, 1977; Thornton and Garnick, 1982; Hunter *et al.*, 1984; Eaton *et al.*, 1985; Lie and Leknes, 1985; Gellin *et al.*, 1986; Breininger *et al.*, 1987; Kawanami *et al.*, 1988; Coldiron *et al.*, 1990; Baehni *et al.*, 1992; Dragoo, 1992; Jotikasthira *et al.*, 1992; Bollen and Quirynen, 1996; Checchi *et al.*, 1997). Given the finality of this statement, one must also note that a comparative assessment of these studies is difficult due to the variety of instrumentation, study designs, and methods of quantitation. Yet, in spite of these limitations, several clinically relevant generalizations can be culled from the collected studies:

1. Regardless of instrument choice, interproximal areas, furcas, the cemento-enamel junction, and multirooted teeth are most likely to exhibit residual plaque and calculus following treatment (Hunter *et al.*, 1984; Gellin *et al.*, 1986; Breininger *et al.*, 1987; Fleischer *et al.*, 1989; Patterson *et al.*, 1989; Takacs *et al.*, 1993; Kocher *et al.*, 1998a, 1998b).
2. As probing depth increases, scaling and root planing becomes less effective at removing bacterial plaque and calculus (Waerhaug, 1978; Rabbani *et al.*, 1981; Stambaugh *et al.*, 1981; Caffesse *et al.*, 1986; Fleischer *et al.*, 1989). This statement, when applied to sonic and ultrasonic instrumentation, has been attributed to design limitations (Gellin *et al.*, 1986; Dragoo, 1992). However, some of the newly designed working tips (inserts) allow greater access to the traditional anatomic problem areas, e.g., the base of deeper pockets and furcations. (Dragoo, 1992; Kawanami *et al.*, 1988; Oda and Ishikawa, 1989; Takacs *et al.*, 1993; Kocher *et al.*, 1998a, 1998b; Clifford *et al.*, 1999).
3. When comparing manual and sonic/ultrasonic instrumentation, the manual instruments appear slightly more effective but require more effort, time, and expertise (Lie and Meyer, 1977; Hunter *et al.*, 1984), althoughnewly de-signed sonic/ultrasonic inserts appear to overcome this discrepancy (Dragoo, 1992; Takacs *et al.*, 1993; Kocher *et al.*, 1998a, 1998b).
4. Although there are few studies comparing sonic and ultrasonic instruments, there appears to be no appreciable difference in efficacy or clinical result (Lie and Leknes, 1985; Loos *et al.*, 1987; Baehni *et al.*, 1992).
5. The best clinical results are probably obtained by combining sonic and/or ultrasonic instrumentation with manual scaling (Fleischer *et al.*, 1989; Gellin *et al.*, 1986; Dragoo, 1992).

Copulos *et al.* (1993) compared manual scaling to a modified ultrasonic insert, designed to provide access to difficult root surface areas, and reported equal reductions in microbial populations up to 180 days post-treatment. The authors noted, however, that the equality of effect was achieved with a significant difference in time required for completion of instrumentation of treated sites; i.e., 3.9 minutes for ultrasonics versus 5.9 minutes for the manual instrument. Likewise, Oosterwal *et al.* (1987) comparing manual and ultrasonic instrumentation of deep pockets (6 to 9 mm), found the two methods to have an equal effect on reducing total microbial counts and colony-forming units. Interestingly, Ososterwal *et al.* (1987) noted that manual scaling resulted in a greater percentage of pockets reduced to 4 mm or less (54% versus 43%) and reduction in bleeding scores (29% versus 22%). Indirect evidence supporting the effectiveness of ultrasonic instrumentation in reducing subgingival microbial concentrations is offered by Badersten *et al.* (1981, 1984a) who reported equivalent clinical responses after treatment of moderate and severely advanced adult periodontitis with manual or ultrasonic instrumentation. In contrast to these studies, Leon and Vogel (1987) found ultrasonic instrumentation more effective than manual instruments at reducing spirochetes and motile rods when used to treat advanced furcation lesions.

Baehni *et al.* (1992) in an in vivo comparison of sonic and ultrasonic instrumentation, reported equally effective results with respect to reduction in microbial counts, particularly for spirochetes and motile rods. The impact of such instrumentation on spirochetes and motile rods was predictable given that Thilo and Baehni (1987) demonstrated, in vitro, that plaque samples exposed to 10 seconds of ultrasonication exhibited a sharp reduction in numbers of spirochetes and motile rods and viable microbes were no longer detectable after a 60-second exposure. Other studies have demonstrated that spirochetes, in particular, and Gram-negative microbes, in general, are destroyed at ultrasonic frequencies (Loesche and Laughon, 1982). In addition, Walmsley *et al.* (1988, 1990) support these observations by noting that the cavitational activity and acoustic mainstreaming generated by ultrasound in the presence of a fluid environment are effective mechanisms for removing microbial plaque.

Given the potential effect of acoustic and cavitational phenomena on microflora, it is interesting to note that Chapple *et al.* (1995) have reported that the healing response in cases of mild to moderate adult periodontitis is essentially the same whether the ultrasonic scaler is operated at half or full power. At both 1 and 6 months post-treatment, the authors reported a statistically significant increase in mean attachment gain for both half and full power settings above baseline but no difference between the two treatment groups.

In apparent contrast, O'Leary *et al.* (1997) using an in vitro acoustically-simulated pocket model, evaluated the possible bactericidal acoustic effect generated by an ultrasonic scaler. After treatment times of 2.5 and 5 minutes with controlled pocket temperatures ranging from 47°C to 53°C, aliquots of the treated specimens were incubated and the number of viable colonies of *Actinobacillus actinomycetemcomitans* and *Porphyromonas gingivalis* organisms was determined and found to be significantly reduced when compared to a non-activated control, regardless of time of exposure or temperature. The extent of any cavitation effect occurring with the pocket model to which the bactericidal activity could be attributed was determined by sonoluminescence and photomultiplication techniques. However, this method of evaluation failed to detect any significant sonoluminescence. Thus, the authors suggest that decreases in bacterial populations during ultrasonic instrumentation may, in fact, result from incidental increases in intrapocket temperatures.

Lastly, an in vivo comparison of manual instrumentation and the more aggressive rotary diamond burs, following surgical exposure of the root surfaces, for the removal of subgingival microbial plaque and calculus deposits has been reported by Schwarz *et al.* (1989). Evaluation of the treated sites by scanning electron microscopy, following extraction and staining, revealed no difference in the percentage of stained sites exhibiting residual microbial plaque; i.e., 6.9% for manual curettes versus 5.5% for teeth treated with the diamond burs.

Removal of Subgingival Calculus:
Manual vs. Sonic/Ultrasonic Scalers

Calculus contributes to the inflammatory periodontal disease process due to its inherent plaque retentive nature. Attempts to completely debride the root surface of calculus generally requires extensive instrumentation and often results in significant loss of cementum and/or dentin (Coldiron *et al.*, 1990; Kepic *et al.*, 1990; Smart *et al.*, 1990). In addition, the concept of removing all subgingival calculus and contaminated cementum has been shown to be unrealistic and quite likely unnecessary (Borghetti *et al.*, 1987; Breininger and O'Leary, 1987; Kepic *et al.*, 1990; Robertson, 1990; Sherman *et al.*, 1990a & 1990b; Eschler and Rapley, 1991; Fukazawa and Nishimura, 1994). Further, it appears that gingival wound healing will occur despite the presence of microscopic aggregates of residual root calculus (Nyman *et al.*, 1986; Blomlöf *et al.*, 1987; Buchanan and Robertson, 1987).

Even if complete removal of subgingival calculus is not likely to occur and removal of cementum is unnecessary, it appears that a considerable degree of root detoxification and gingival healing still occurs using multiple light strokes with a sonic or ultrasonic scaler (Badersten *et al.*, 1981, 1984a, 1984b; Nyman *et al.*, 1986; Checchi and Pelliccioni, 1988; Cheetham *et al.*, 1988; Chiew *et al.*, 1991; Smart *et al.*, 1990). Numerous studies have demonstrated that sonic or ultrasonic when compared to manual instrumentation achieves equal or superior treatment outcomes (Lie and Meyer, 1977; Torfason *et al.*, 1979; Thornton and Garnick, 1982; Badersten, 1984a & 1984b; Lie and Leknes, 1985; Loos *et al.*, 1987; Laurell, L. and Pattersson, 1988; Laurell, 1990; Copulos *et al.*, 1993).

Removal of Root Bound Endotoxin:
Manual and Sonic/Ultrasonic Scalers

In 1979, Nishimine and O'Leary reported on the relative effectiveness, in vivo, of manual and ultrasonic scalers in removing endotoxin from contaminated root surfaces. Although both types of instrumentation were effective when compared to untreated controls, the ultrasonic was considerably less effective than manual scaling. In contrast, several in vitro studies have shown that ultrasonic instrumentation is quite effective at removing adsorbed endotoxins (Cogen *et al.*, 1983, 1984; Checchi and Pelliccioni, 1988; Chiew *et al.*, 1991). The results of the in vitro studies would appear consistent with the demonstration that endotoxin is a surface phenomenon, i.e., lightly bound to but not penetrating cementum, and therefore easily removed (Nakib *et al.*, 1982; Hughes and Smales, 1986; Moore *et al.*, 1986; Chiew *et al.*, 1991) and that cavitational and acoustic mainstreaming phenomena associated with ultrasonics are particularly effective (Wilson *et al.*, 1986; Moore *et al.*, 1986; Walmsley *et al.*, 1988, 1990). Collectively, these findings suggest that clinicians may be over-instrumentating root surfaces under the guise of root surface detoxification (Adelson *et al.*, 1980; Loepez *et al.*, 1980; Cogen *et al.*, 1983; Checchi and Pelliccioni, 1988; Cheetham *et al.*, 1988; Smart *et al.*, 1990).

Root Surface Smoothness:
Manual vs. Sonic/Ultrasonic Instrumentation

It has long been assumed by clinicians that a smooth root surface is also a clean surface. Yet it remains to be determined that a smooth root surface is a desirable end-point of non-surgical periodontal therapy. There are relatively few reports dealing with the impact of root surface roughness on wound healing or in the reverse, the biocompatibility of a smooth root surface (Rosenberg and Ash, 1974; Khatiblou and Ghodssi, 1983; Lindhe *et al.*, 1984; Leknes *et al.*, 1996; Oberholzer and Rateitschak, 1996) Rosenberg and Ash (1974) were among the first to evaluate the influence of root surface roughness on bacterial plaque accumulation and presence of inflammation. They concluded that the differing degrees of roughness created by manual curettes and ultrasonic instruments had no significant effect on either parameter. These observations were later supported by Khatiblou and Ghodssi (1983) and Oberholzer and Rateitschak (1996) who reported that periodontal healing, reductions in probing depth, and attachment gains, were independent of root surface texture. However, such observations are in contrast to those of Waerhaug (1956) who noted that intentional roughening of subgingival enamel in dogs resulted in an increased deposition of bacterial plaque and calculus. Several other studies have noted the direct relationship between surface roughness and the rate of supragingival bacterial colonization (Turskey *et al.*, 1961; Keenan *et al.*, 1980; Budtz-Jorgensen and Kaaber, 1986; Quirynen and Listgarten, 1990; Leknes *et al.*, 1996). Further, both Quirynen and Bollen (1995) and Leknes *et al.* (1996) have noted that rough supragingival surfaces accumulate and retain more bacterial plaque. In addition, Quirynen and Bollen (1995) report that gingivitis and periodontitis is more frequently associated with teeth exhibiting a rough surface. Not so surprising, then, are the observations by Lindhe *et al.* (1984) who collectively have noted that smooth root surfaces were compatible with normal healing of the dento-gingival complex. Given that the more recent investigations seem to support the desirability of achieving a smooth root surface, it then follows that studies comparing manual scalers/curettes to sonic/ultrasonic instrumentation in this regard would be useful in determining the instrument of choice for the clinician.

The results of comparative studies concerning the effects of manual and power-driven instrumentation on root surfaces can only be described as inconsistent and discordant. For example, comparative studies have reported that manual curettes produce either a smoother root surface (Allen and Rhoads,

Figure 4 Low angle SEM view of an untreated periodontally diseased root surface. Bar = 0.1 mm at an original magnification of 326x.

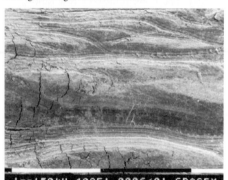

Figure 5 SEM view of diseased root surface following scaling with a Gracey curette. Bar = 1 mm at an original magnification of 40.8x.

Figure 6 SEM/ view of diseased root surface following scaling with a furcation curette (SOH 1/ 2*). Bar = 50 μm at an original magnification of 186x (left) and 558x (right).

* Hu-Friedy, Chicago, Illinois, 60618-5982, USA
‡ KaVo Dental GmbH, Biberach/Riss, Germany

1963; Rosenberg and Ash, 1974; Van Volkinburg *et al.* 1976; Benfenati *et al.*, 1987; Kerry, 1967; Jones *et al.*, 1972; Wilkinson and Maybury, 1973; Meyer and Lie, 1977; Nishimine and O'Leary, 1979; Hunter *et al.*, 1984; Cross-Poline *et al.*, 1995; Schlageter *et al.*, 1996) or a rougher surface than ultrasonic instrumentation (Moskow and Bressman, 1964; Pameijer *et al.*, 1972; Ewen *et al.*, 1976; Jacobson *et al.*, 1994) or the degree of roughness is essentially equal regardless instrument choice (Lie and Meyer, 1977). In addition, comparisons of sonic and ultra-sonic instrumentation report equivalence (Lie and Leknes, 1985; Schlageter *et al.*, 1996) or that the ultrasonic scaler was superior (Van Volkinburg *et al.*, 1976; Jotikasthira *et al.*, 1992) at producing smooth root surfaces. Figures 4 through 11 offer a visual comparison of root surface topography following in vivo treatment with various instrumentation.

Gantes *et al.* (1992), using scanning electron microscopy, reported that sonic scalers fitted with plastic working tips removed less root structure and produced a smoother surface than either manual curettes, a rubber cup with polishing paste, or the sonic scaler fitted with a metal tip. Lastly, Schlageter *et al.* (1996), using an in vitro study design, report an instrument hierarchy of smooth to rough root surfaces using an average roughness value (Ra) to be 15 μm rotating diamond (1.64

± 0.81), Gracey curette (1.90 ± 0.84), Perioplaner curette (2.10 ± 1.03), piezo electric scaler (2.48 ± 0.90), 75 μm rotating diamond (2.60 ± 1.06), and the sonic scaler (2.71 ± 1.12).

The significance of the study by Schlageter *et al.* (1996) lies in the Ra values, none of which achieve appear to achieve a surface smoothness threshold of Ra = 0.2 μm below which no impact on bacterial adhesion and/or colonization should be expected. However, surfaces with a roughness exceeding the 0.2 μm threshold should be expected to facilitate greater amounts of bacterial plaque accumulation (Quirynen *et al.*, 1993; Bollen *et al.*, 1996). In fact, a study using titanium implant abutments indicated that an Ra value of ≥ 0.8 μm resulted in a dramatic increase in subgingival plaque (25x) when compared to surfaces with an Ra value of 0.2 μm (Quirynen *et al.*, 1996). Thus, a comparison of the Ra values reported by Schlageter *et al.* (1996) with the threshold value of 0.2 μm would lead one to assume that achieving root surface smoothness with the instrumentation available at present is simply not possible. Given that the smoothest root surface in the study by Schlageter *et al.* (1996) had an Ra value roughly 8x greater than the threshold value of 0.2 μm, it would appear that for the foreseeable future subgingival microbes will continue to have a friendly surface for colonization.

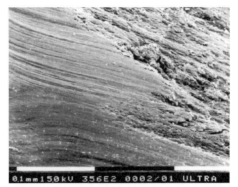

Figure 7 Areas of treated (left) and untreated (right) root surface. Treatment consisted of scaling with an ultrasonic (25 KHz) universal insert. Bar = 0.1 mm at an original magnification of 356x.

Figure 8 Area of diseased root surface treated with the ball furcation insert*. Note effect on crown margin (far right). Bar = 1 mm at an original magnification of 48.6x.

Figure 9 Area of diseased root surface treated with the 15 μm grit diamond coated sonic furcation insert‡. Bar = 0.1 mm at an original magnification of 203x.

* Hu-Friedy, Chicago, Illinois, 60618-5982, USA
‡ KaVo Dental GmbH, Biberach/Riss, Germany

Figure 10 Diseased root surface following treatment with a 12 fluted rotary bur. Bar = 1.0 mm at an original magnification of 53x.

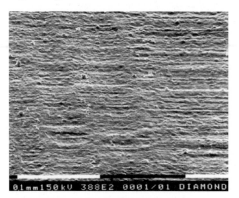

Figure 11 Diseased root surface following treatment with a 15 μm grit diamond coated rotary bur. Bar = 0.1 mm at an original magnification of 388x.

Obviously, more extensive in vivo studies evaluating the relationship of subgingival root surface roughness to bacterial plaque accumulation and to type of instrumentation would be helpful in establishing a clinically relevant treatment goal. Presently, it would appear that the best clinical results are likely to be obtained using a combination of sonic/ultrasonic instruments followed by manual scalers and curettes (Gellin *et al.*, 1986; Fleischer *et al.*, 1989; Dragoo, 1992).

An interesting dichotomy has been cited by Flemmig *et al.* (1998a) in suggesting that different instrument efficacies may be required for subgingival debridement in initial therapy and supportive periodontal therapy (SPT). Initial therapy, for instance, may require an instrument with high efficacy to remove moderate to heavy deposits of subgingival calculus whereas in SPT the instrument efficacy should be sufficient to achieve desired goals but low enough to avoid root damage. In the case of SPT, avoiding root damage is particularly critical as instrumentation will be performed repeatedly over multiple sequential SPT visits. Thus, the effects of changing the working parameters of power driven instrumentation on root surfaces assumes considerable importance. A clinical study by Chapple *et al.* (1995), designed to test the effects of ultrasonic scaling instrument power settings of one-half vs. full on clinical parameters, reported both settings to be equally effective at achieving reductions in bleeding on probing and increases in attachment levels. Flemmig *et al.* (1998a, 1998b) have reported that to prevent severe root damage while using an ultrasonic scaling instruments (25,000 and 42,000 Hz), it is necessary to use the scaler at a tip angulation approaching 0° with a 0.5 N to 1.0 N lateral force and low to medium power settings. Further, it was noted that significant root damage occurred as combinations of tip angle, lateral pressures, and power settings increased. In light of these results, it is interesting to note that Zappa *et al.* (1991b) have reported that the mean lateral force applied by clinical dentists during scaling and root planing (as separate modalities) were 5.7 N with a range of 1.01 to 10.35 N and 4.62 N and a range of 0.86 to 8.88 N, respectively. The corresponding values for dental hygienists were 5.38 N with a range of 1.52 to 15.73 N (scaling) and 4.58 N with a range of 1.56 to 10.59 N (root planing).

Changes in Clinical Parameters:
Manual vs. Sonic/Ultrasonic Instrumentation

Reduction in probing depth following mechanical instrumentation results from a combination of gain in clinical attachment and gingival recession (Hughes and Caffesse, 1978; Proye *et al.*, 1982). The magnitude of probing depth reduction and gains in attachment levels are related to the initial measurement, a phenomena supported by the collective data reported in various clinical studies over several decades (Cobb, 1996). For example, the mean reduction in probing depths with an initial depth of 1 to 3 mm has been calculated to be 0.03 mm with a mean net loss in attachment level of - 0.34 mm. For those pockets initially measuring 4 to 6 mm, the mean reduction in probing depth is approximately 1.29 mm with a net gain in clinical attachment levels of 0.55 mm. Periodontal pockets of ≥ 7.0 mm show a mean reduction in probing depth of 2.16 mm and a gain in attachment level of 1.19 mm (Cobb, 1996). The greatest change in probing depth reduction and gain in clinical attachment occurs within four weeks post-instrumentation, although gradual repair and maturation of the healing periodontium may occur over the following nine to twelve months (Morrison *et al.*, 1980; Badersten *et al.*, 1981; Proye *et al.*, 1982; Cercek *et al.*, 1983; Badersten *et al.*, 1984a; Kaldahl *et al.*, 1988). Thus, evaluation of the response of the periodontium to mechanical nonsurgical therapy should be performed no earlier than four weeks following treatment (Caton *et al.*, 1982; Kaldahl *et al.*, 1988; Dahlén *et al.*, 1992). Measurements taken prematurely will not be representative of completed healing and could, therefore, be misinterpreted as a poor clinical response.

Tables 1 through 4 present a summary of selected studies that have reported changes in various clinical parameters following treatment of moderate to severe periodontitis with either manual or sonic/ultrasonic instrumentation. A comparison of the mean decrease in probing depth and increases in attachment levels resulting from subgingival scaling with manual instruments (Table 1) to that obtained following use of sonic/ultrasonic instruments (Table 2) indicates little difference between to the two types of instrumentation. For example, six months post-treatment data for pockets with an initial probing depth of 4-6.0 mm shows a reduction in probing depths following manual scaling ranging from 0.75 to 1.25 mm vs. a range of 1.12 to 1.3 following sonic/ultrasonic instrumentation. Comparisons of attachment level increases for the same initial probing depth following manual scaling shows a range of 0.1 to 0.56 mm vs. 0.0 to 0.2 mm following sonic/ultrasonic instrumentation. Similar comparisons can be made between Tables 3 and 4 which provide data concerning reductions in the percentage of sites bleeding upon probing following treatment with manual scalers/curettes (Table 3) and sonic/ultrasonic instruments (Table 4).

Table 1 Summary from selected studies reporting the mean decrease in probing depth and changes in clinical attachment levels following non-surgical treatment of moderate to severe periodontitis using manual scalers/curettes.

Reference	IPD (mm)	Mean Decrease in Probing Depth (mm)					Change in Attachment Level (mm)				
		month: 1	3	6	9	12	month: 1	3	6	9	12
Torfason et al., 1979	5.00*	1.10§									
Badersten et al., 1981	4.30*	0.0‡		1.25		1.10	-0.1‡		0.25		0.1
Pihlstrom et al., 1981	4-6.0			0.94					0.56		
	≥6.0			1.66					1.40		
Caton et al., 1982	4-7.0		1.39					0.7			
Cercek et al., 1983	3.5-5		1.00					0.1			
Badersten et al., 1984a	5.70*		0.0‡	1.20	1.40	1.60	-0.1‡	0.10	0.2	0.2	
Becker et al., 1988	4-6.0					0.86					0.49
	≥7.0					1.54					1.54
Claffey et al., 1988	4-6.5					1.30					0.4
Laurell & Pattersson, 1988	≥4.0	26%#	66%#								
Kaldahl et al., 1988	5-6.0		1.23					0.96			
	≥7.0		2.18					1.66			
Copulos et al., 1993	5.07*		0.70	0.75							
Drisko et al., 1995	≥7.0					2.01					1.20
Haffajee et al., 1997	4-6.0		0.4‡	0.45	0.5			0.2‡	0.25	0.25	
	>6.0		1.0‡	1.2	1.7			0.5‡	0.50	0.45	

IPD Initial Probing Depth (* indicates mean IPD)
§ Mean for all pockets regardless of location.
‡ Calculated from data tables in paper and/or does not include decreases in probing depth or increases in attachment level due to oral hygiene.
# Percent reduction in the mean number of pockets of ≥ 4.0 at 1 and 4 months post-treatment.

Table 2 Summary from selected studies reporting the mean decrease in probing depth and changes in clinical attachment levels following non-surgical treatment of moderate to severe periodontitis using sonic or ultrasonic scaling instruments.

Reference	IPD (mm)	Mean Decrease in Probing Depth (mm)					Change in Attachment Level (mm)				
		month: 1	3	6	9	12	month: 1	3	6	9	12
Torfason et al., 1979	5.00*	1.00§									
Badersten et al., 1981	4.20*	0.60‡		1.12	1.40	1.20	-0.1‡		0.1		0.1
Badersten et al., 1984a	5.70*		0.1‡	1.20	1.30	1.60		-0.1‡	0.2	0.3	0.2
Loos et al., 1987	4 - 6.5		1.30	1.30	2.70			0.1	0.0	0.1	
	≥ 7.0		2.80	2.70				0.8	1.0	0.9	
Kawanami et al., 1988	5.50*	2.10									
Laurell & Pattersson, 1988	≥ 4.0	24%#	72%				1.1				
Laurell, 1990	≥ 4.0	28%##	78%		80%						
Reynolds et al., 1992	4 - 6.0	0.80									
	≥ 7.0	1.50									
Copulos et al., 1993	4.51*		0.62		0.72						
Forabosco et al., 1996	4 - 6.0					2.2					0.2‡‡
	≥ 7.0					2.5‡					0.4‡

IPD   Initial Probing Depth (* indicates mean IPD).

§   Mean percentages for all pockets regardless of location.

‡   Calculated from tables presented in paper and/or does not include decreases in probing depth or increases in attachment level due to oral hygiene.

Percent reduction in the mean number of pockets of ≥ 4.0 mm at 1 and 4 months post-treatment.

Percent reduction in the mean number of pockets of ≥ 4.0 mm at 1, 4, and 8 months post-treatment.

Table 3 Summary from selected studies reporting the percent decrease in bleeding on probing following non-surgical treatment of moderate to severe periodontitis using manual scalers/curettes.

Reference	IPD (mm)	% Decrease in Bleeding on Probing				
		month: 1	3	6	9	12
Torfason *et al.*, 1979	5.00*	42§				
Badersten *et al.*, 1981	4.30*	6‡		87		87
Caton *et al.*, 1982	4-7.0		48			
Proye *et al.*, 1982	3-7.0	38				
Badersten *et al.*, 1984a	5.70*		12‡	63	67	81
Laurell & Pattersson, 1988	≥ 4.0	34	80			
Al-Joburi *et al.*, 1989	≥ 4.0			55		
Kalkwarf *et al.*, 1989	5-6.0		42			
	≥ 7.0		30			
Hämmerle *et al.*, 1991	≥ 4.0		74			
Copulos *et al.*, 1993	4.50*		20			
Boretti *et al.*, 1995	5.60*	53				
Haffajee *et al.*, 1997	>4.0		10‡	12	21	

IPD   Initial Probing Depth (* indicates mean IPD)
GI   Gingival Index
§   Mean percentages for all pockets regardless of location.
‡   Calculated from data tables presented in paper and/or does not include decreases in probing depth or increases in attachment level due to oral hygiene.

Table 4 Summary from selected studies reporting the percent decrease in bleeding on probing following non-surgical treatment of moderate to severe periodontitis using sonic or ultrasonic scaling instruments.

Reference	IPD (mm)	% Decrease in Bleeding on Probing				
		month: 1	3	6	9	12
Torfason *et al.*, 1979	5.00*	43§				
Badersten *et al.*, 1981	4.20*	8‡		87		85
Badersten *et al.*, 1984a	5.70*		8‡	61	65	75
Loos *et al.*, 1987	4 - 6.5		17‡	35	39	37
	≥ 7.0					
Kawanami *et al.*, 1988	5.50*	75				
Laurell & Pattersson, 1988	≥ 4.0	34#	84			
Laurell, 1990	≥ 4.0	22##	93		96	
Forabosco *et al.*, 1996	4 - 6.0					76™
	≥ 7.0					76™

IPD   Initial Probing Depth (* indicates mean IPD)
GI   Gingival Index
§   Mean percentages for all pockets regardless of location.
‡   Calculated from data tables presented in paper and/or does not include decreases in probing depth or increases in attachment level due to oral hygiene.
#   1 and 4 months post-treatment.
1, 4, and 8 months post-treatment.
™   Percentage decrease in bleeding sites for all pocket depths.

Variations on a Theme:
Manual Scaling and Root Planing

Recently, Anderson *et al.* (1996) evaluated the effectiveness of calculus removal of a single episode of subgingival scaling and root planing versus that removed by three episodes of instrumentation. The single instrumentation was accomplished within 10 minutes per tooth and those teeth subjected to three sessions of root planing, each separated by at least a 24 hour interval, were limited to not more than 20 minutes total instrumentation time. Following their respective treatments, the teeth were extracted and by using stereomicroscopy with the grid method for assessment, the percent of residual calculus was determined. In the final analysis, the authors concluded that there was no significant difference in the effectiveness of calculus removal between single and multiple episodes of scaling and root planing. This confirms the earlier Badersten *et al.* (1984b) study which used changes in clinical parameters as the assessment end-point and also showed no difference between single and multiple episodes of instrumentation.

Recent studies comparing traditional consecutive sessions of quadrant scaling and root planing over time to a one-stage full-mouth "disinfection" report that significant clinical and microbiological improvements are associated with the latter approach (Quirynen *et al.*, 1995; Vandekerchhove *et al.*, 1996; Bollen *et al.*, 1996; Bollen *et al.*, 1998). In this series of studies, a full-mouth disinfection consisted of a definitive scaling and root planing in less than 24 hours, pocket irrigation with a 1% chlorhexidine gel (3 times in 10 minutes), oral rinsing with 0.2% chlorhexidine twice a day for 1 minute for 14 days, and daily tongue brushing. At two months post-treatment, the full-mouth disinfection treatment group exhibited a significant additional reduction in probing depth of 1.4 mm for multirooted teeth and 2.3 mm for single rooted teeth in pockets initially ≥ 7 mm. Differential phase contrast microscopy revealed significantly lower proportions of spirochetes and motile rods in the test group at one month post-treatment. Evaluation at eight months post-therapy confirmed the two month findings, i.e., reductions in probing depth and proportions of spirochetes and motile rods, although statistical significance of the differences between test and control groups disappeared after two months. Thus, based on this limited series of studies, one might conclude that, indeed, full-mouth "disinfection" suppresses the possibility of cross contamination between treated and untreated sites that may occur during the more traditional treatment protocol.

Treatment of Furcations:
Manual vs. Sonic/Ultrasonic Instrumentation

The vast majority of the investigations concerning the effectiveness of sonic and/or ultrasonic scaling instruments in the treatment of furcations have been in vitro studies and thus are difficult to extrapolate to the clinical situation. For example, Patterson *et al.* (1989) compared the effectiveness of two sonic and two ultrasonic scaler tips on artificial calculus removal from the furcations of mandibular molars. Individual specimens were evaluated by stereophotogrammetry and the results showed no significant difference between any of the tips with respect to residual calculus.

Takacs *et al.* (1993) reported on the efficacy of several sonic and ultrasonic working tip designs and a reciprocating handpiece insert in the removal of artificial calculus from the furcation areas of maxillary and mandibular molars. They noted that the sonic scaler with a universal insert and the ultrasonic with ball point inserts were significantly more effective than the reciprocating handpiece.

Otero-Cagide and Long (1997a & 1997b) compared small-blade manual curettes and ultrasonic inserts at removing paint from root trunks, furcation entrances, and the furcation area. In all three anatomical areas the curette proved significantly more effective than the ultrasonic instrument.

Recent studies by Kocher *et al.* (1998a, 1998b) report on the comparative abilities of manual curettes and 15 µm grit diamond-coated sonic scaler tips to effectively debride furcations of maxillary and mandibular molars. Due to furcation anatomy, i.e., width of entrance and presence of concavities and ridges in the interradicular root surface and furcal roof areas, the authors concluded that effective debridement was only possible through odontoplasty. To this end, the diamond-coated tips were significantly more effective than manual curettes at removing tooth structure and covering more surface area of root.

One of the very few in vivo studies comparing manual and ultrasonic instrumentation in the treatment of furcations was performed by Matia *et al.* (1986). They evaluated the proficiency of calculus removal from the furcation area of mandibular molars with and without surgical access utilizing manual or ultrasonic instrumentation. Their results showed significantly less residual calculus, regardless of instrument choice, when the furcas were surgical exposed (open approach). In the absence of surgery (closed approach), there was no significant difference in the mean percent of residual calculus for the manual curette versus the ultrasonic instrument. However, when teeth were divided and evaluated according to narrow and wide furcation entrance, the ultrasonic instrument was more significantly effective when used under the conditions of a closed approach.

Summary:
Manual vs. Sonic/Ultrasonic Instrumentation

Clinically, the mechanical control of subgingival microflora is accomplished primarily by periodontal debridement using sonic or ultrasonic instruments or by scaling and root planing using manual instrumentation. The objectives of the former treatment modality is to remove not only adherent and unattached bacterial plaque but, to a lesser extent, deposits of calculus. The primary objective of scaling and root planing is the removal of both calculus and contaminated cementum. The effectiveness of either procedure decreases with increasing probing depth, especially when probing depth exceeds 5 mm (Cobb, 1996). Clinically, there appears to be no specific or significant difference (except for the time required to achieve clinical end-points) between manual and sonic/ultrasonic instrumentation. Each method of instrumentation appears to yield the same degree of subgingival calculus removal and control of subgingival plaque, and both provoke a similar healing response (Walsh and Waite, 1978; Torfason *et al.*, 1979; Badersten *et al.*, 1984a & 1984b; Leon and Vogel, 1987; Oosterwaal *et al.*, 1987; Eschler and Rapley, 1991; Cobb, 1996). Equivalent results when evaluating manual and sonic/ultrasonic instrumentation appears to be generalizable, even when comparing closed (no surgery) to open (surgical exposure of the root surface) approaches. Thus, in consideration of the demands of clinical skill, time, and stamina, the of instrument of choice for universal application would appear to be either a sonic or ultrasonic scaler.

A single session of subgingival root planing can yield a significant reduction in the bacterial population, even without effective removal of all subgingival calculus (Breininger *et al.*, 1987). In fact, there appears to be no additional benefit from a single vs. multiple episodes of subgingival scaling and root planing (Badersten *et al.*, 1984b; Anderson *et al.*, 1996). However, recent studies indicate that the traditional quadrant by quadrant treatment separated by extended periods of time is less effective at controlling selected subgingival bacteria and yielding reductions in clinical parameters than a complete mouth treatment performed in one or two sessions separated by a few hours (Quirynen *et al.*, 1995; Vandekerchhove *et al.*, 1996; Bollen *et al.*, 1996; Bollen *et al.*, 1998).

Finally, one must not forget supragingival contributions to the subgingival bacterial population. It appears that the subgingival microbial flora has supragingival origins (Waerhaug, 1978; Mousques *et al.*, 1980; Magnusson *et al.*, 1984; Braatz *et al.*, 1985; McAlpine *et al.*, 1985; Sbordone *et al.*, 1990; Pedrazzoli *et al.*, 1991). However, Westfelt *et al.* (1998) have reported that in patients with advanced periodontal disease, control of supragingival plaque in the absence of subgingival therapy, fails to prevent further destruction of the periodontal tissues. This observation concurs with that of Kaldahl *et al.* (1996b) who noted continued attachment loss in patients with adult periodontitis that received only supragingival therapy. The results of these two studies would appear to be at odds with numerous previous studies. For example, it has been shown that meticulous supragingival plaque control may interfere with both the quantity and quality of the subgingival microbiota and the clinical symptoms associated with adult periodontitis. As the quantity, composition, and rate of subgingival plaque recolonization is, to some degree, dependent upon supragingival plaque accumulation (Dahlén *et al.*, 1992; Katsanoulas *et al.*, 1992; McNabb *et al.*, 1992; Hellström *et al.*, 1996) it would seem that effective supragingival control of microbial plaque would be absolutely critical if the clinician hopes to achieve long-term control of inflammatory periodontal disease (Lindhe and Nyman, 1975, 1984; Knowles *et al.*, 1979; Nyman and Lindhe, 1979; Axelsson and Lindhe, 1981a, 1981b; Westfelt *et al.*, 1983). The apparent conflict between the Westfelt *et al.*, (1998) and Kaldahl *et al.*, (1996b) studies and the other investigations noted above may simply be that supragingival plaque control is effective in early and moderate disease but not advanced periodontal disease. This would seem to make sense given the dramatic changes in microbial ecology that occurs as probing depths deepen.

Charles M. Cobb

Lasers and non-surgical periodontal therapy

Subgingival Instrumentation With The Dental Laser:
Concepts and Conflicts

The present use of lasers as a "non-surgical periodontal treatment" modality is based on the perceived benefits resulting from subgingival curettage and the associated disruption of bacterial plaque (Institute for Laser Dentistry, 1990; Tseng and Liew, 1990; Gold, 1991; Midda and Renton-Harper, 1991; Danesh-Meyer, 1992; Midda, 1992; Pick, 1993; Barr *et al.*, 1998; Pinero, 1998). The concept of a laser subgingival curettage raises two very fundamental questions that demand answers. First, does laser gingival curettage, when performed as a definitive therapy, offer any therapeutic benefit not inherent to traditional scaling and root planing? And second, can one reasonably expect to irradiate the soft tissue wall of a periodontal pocket, that is perform a laser curettage, without inflicting damage to the adjacent root surface? If the answer to either or both questions is no, then one must question if there are sufficient benefits to the patient to justify laser subgingival curettage.

The answer to the first question is rather direct and unequivocal. Over thirty years ago, gingival curettage was by no means universally accepted as a definitive treatment modality for achieving reduction in pocket depth or increases in attachment levels (WWP, 1966). A review of the chapters and discussions concerning non-surgical periodontal treatment from the three "World Workshops in Clinical Periodontics" glaringly indicate, by acts of omission, that gingival curettage is no longer a standard therapy (WWP, 1966; WWP, 1989; Cobb, 1996). Gingival curettage and debridement of the soft tissue wall of the pocket, as an adjunct to scaling and root planing, offers no advantage over scaling and root planing alone in the treatment of relatively shallow suprabony pockets (Echeverria and Caffesse, 1983; Lindhe and Nyman, 1985). Longer term treatment results (5 yrs) have confirmed this observation (Ramfjord *et al.*, 1987). Both the 1989 World Workshop in Clinical Periodontics and the 1993 Proceedings of the 1st European Workshop on Periodontology include rather definitive statements concerning gingival curettage, e.g., "The technique would not seem to be warranted in view of comparable clinical results achieved with root surface instrumentation alone ...."(Keiser, 1993) and "gingival curettage has no application in the treatment of adult periodontitis" (WWP, 1989).

An answer to the second question (i.e., Does subgingival curettage by laser result in damage to the adjacent root surface?) requires an understanding of the basic operating parameters of lasers and how changing various parameters effects the interaction of laser energy with biologic tissues.

Laser Parameters and Their Applications

The variable parameters of a laser over which the clinician has control, include wavelength, waveform (continuous or pulsed energy), power selection (Watts), diameter of the delivery tip, and duration and rate of tissue exposure, i.e., continuous energy or number and length of pulses per second (Dederich, 1991). Through manipulation of the various parameters, the clinician can effectively

478

control the power density (W/cm^2) and energy density (J/cm^2) delivered to the target tissue surface. The major variables of biologic tissue that influence laser-tissue interactions, over which the clinician has no control, include tissue composition, degree of pigmentation, and physical structure (Dederich, 1991; Ostertag *et al.*, 1997). Collectively, these tissue variables determine the optical absorption spectrum, that is, how much laser energy will be absorbed. The amount of energy absorption and distribution within the target tissue, in turn, determines tissue response and clinical outcome (Ostertag *et al.*, 1997).

The lasers most common to clinical periodontics have distinctly different wavelengths and, therefore, distinctly different characteristics, e.g., the CO$_2$ laser at 10.6 μm and the Nd:YAG laser at 1.06 μm. A comparison of these wavelengths offers a particularly relevant example of tissue-laser interaction and how each interacts with the hydroxyapatite mineral component of cementum and dentin. For example, the optical absorption spectrum for hydroxyapatite falls between 9.0 μm and 11.0 μm, which coincides with the CO$_2$ laser wavelength of 10.6 μm (Nelson *et al.*, 1986). Consequently, hydroxyapatite exhibits maximal absorption of CO$_2$ laser energy, whereas the Nd:YAG wavelength is such that more than 40% of the energy is reflected by the mineral component (Bohem *et al.*, 1977). Thus, to achieve comparable results using the two wavelengths on a root surface, the Nd:YAG would generally require either a higher power density (or higher energy density) and/or longer exposure times. On the other hand, the Nd:YAG laser wavelength is well suited for maximum absorption by pigmented tissues. Thus, the Nd:YAG laser can expedite hemostasis and vaporize pigmented bacteria and calculus deposits. Unlike the CO$_2$ laser, the Nd:YAG utilizes a fiber optic delivery system that can range in diameter from 0.4 mm to 1 mm. Obviously, the small diameter fiber optic delivery system of the Nd:YAG facilitates subgingival instrumentation.

Effects of Laser Irradiation on the Tooth Root

In 1992, a series of related studies were published that evaluated the in vitro effects of Nd:YAG irradiation on tooth root specimens. Collectively, these papers showed that use of parameters suggested by the manufacturer for root planing (energy densities ≈ 80 mJ/cm^2) resulted in changes in surface topography that included carbonization, fiber tracking, ablation crater formation, melting and resolidification of the mineral phase, porosity, and peeling of cementum that resulted in exposure of the underlying dentin (Trylovich, *et al*, 1992; Spencer *et al.*, 1992; Morlock *et al.*, 1992). In addition, laser treated surfaces were shown to be incompatible to in vitro attachment of gingival fibroblasts (Trylovich *et al.*, 1992). Fourier transform infrared photoacoustic spectroscopic (FTIR) analysis of laser treated surfaces revealed a peak at the 2015 cm^{-1} band which was initially attributed to ammonium derived from heat denaturization of the organic matrix components (Spencer *et al.*, 1992). In the latter study, the authors hypothesized that ammonium residues on the root surface were responsible for inhibition of the *in vitro* fibroblast attachment.

A subsequent study by Spencer *et al.* (1996) evaluated the effects on root surfaces following irradiation with the CO_2 and the Nd:YAG lasers, both with and without a surface cooling spray of air/water. The 2015 cm^{-1} band was again noted but reassigned to cyanamide and cyanate, both of which are cytotoxic ions. Reassignment of the 2015 cm^{-1} band was based on the earlier works of Dowker and Elloitt (1979 & 1983) who proposed that heating of hydroxyapatite in the presence of an NH_4^+ containing organic matrix, such as collagen, was responsible for the generation of the toxic by-products.

Thomas *et al.* (1994) demonstrated that the in vitro fibroblast attachment problem associated with lased root surfaces was reversible in specimens that were subsequently treated by root planing or an air-powder abrasive slurry. The authors also noted that fibroblasts refused to attach to areas of root surface that exhibited a residual carbonized (charred) layer. Based on the results of this series of in vitro studies (Trylovich *et al.*, 1992; Spencer *et al.*, 1992; Morlock *et al.*, 1992; Thomas *et al.*, 1994), one might conclude that to render a laser treated root surface biocompatible, the irradiated surface must be subjected to definitive root planing or some form of abrasive root conditioning.

In 1996, Maillet *et al.*, published the results of an in vivo study in which the apical 2 mm of the root of extracted teeth were subjected to irradiation with an Nd:YAG laser and portions of the remaining root surface, acting as the control, were subject to a dental bur. The root specimens were then implanted subcutaneously in rats and allowed to heal for time periods that varied from 3 to 90 days. There results showed a significant delay in tissue repair about the root surfaces of laser treated root surface areas when compared to those areas treated by dental bur.

The results of the Maillet *et al.* (1996) study were supported in a recently published study, using a canine experimental model, designed to evaluate the ability of surgical flaps to reattach to CO_2 laser-treated roots. This latter investigation by Gopin *et al.* (1997), confirmed the cell attachment problems noted in the earlier in vitro and in vivo studies. Following histologic examination of specimens at 28 day post-treatment, Gopin *et al.* (1997) noted that residual char layers left on the root surface consistently prevented flap connective tissue and/ or epithelial reattachment. This was not the case when lased roots were subsequently root planed. Additionally, although root planing was intentionally minimized with respect to the amount of manual pressure and the number of instrument strokes, an excessive amount of root surface was removed, indicating possible alterations in subsurface cementum and dentin as a result of laser irradiation. This latter observation is in keeping with the waveguide effect hypothesized by Altschuler and Grisimov (1990) which proposes the separation of dissimilar tissues due to the penetration, dissemination, and absorption of laser energy along the tissue interface.

The combined results of the in vivo and in vitro studies suggests an inherent danger of using a laser subgingivally where the clinician cannot visualize the root and, therefore, cannot determine the presence of a residual char layer (Figures 12, 13, 14, 15, 16 & 17). Furthermore, one must also question the advantages, if any, of using lasers as a primary or adjunctive instrument if the irradiated root surface must subsequently be root planed to achieve complete detoxification of the surface. As regards potential biological toxicity, it is interesting to note that other investigators have observed delayed healing of bone that exhibits a residual char layer following irradiation by Nd:YAG, Er:YAG, and CO_2 lasers (Williams *et al.*, 1995; El Montaser *et al.*, 1997; Friesen *et al.*, 1999).

With espect to the reported adverse effects of Er:YAG and Nd:YAG laser irradiation of root surfaces, it is interesting to note that orientation of the optical fiber to the target surface (perpendicular or parallel) apparently has minimal effect on the outcome, even when using relatively low power and energy densities. For example, two very recent studies using the Nd:YAG laser to debride root canals, where the fiber orientation can only be parallel to the surrounding walls of the canal, showed various degrees of melting and resolidification of the mineral phase (Takeda *et al.*, 1998a; Zhang *et al.*, 1998). Likewise, the argon laser when used to debride root canals, induced melting and resolidification similar to that seen when using the Nd:YAG (Takeda *et al.*, 1998a). In apparent contrast, the Er:YAG laser when used under similar conditions proved capable of removing the smear layer without inflicting heat-related damage (Takeda *et al.*, 1998a & 1998b).

Figure 12 Area of root surface following one pass with an Nd:YAG laser using a power density of 100 mJ/pulse. Bar = 1 mm at an original magnification of 75x.

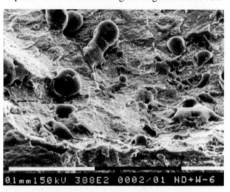

Figure 13 Melted and resolidified globules of root mineral within the ablation defect of a root surface irradiated by Nd:YAG laser using a power density of 100 mJ/pulse combined with a surface cooling spray of air/water. Bar = 0.1 mm at an original magnification of 388x.

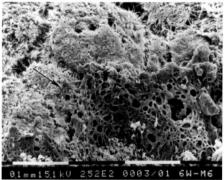

Figure 14 Area of calculus and surface bacterial plaque treated by CO_2 laser (lower right) using an energy density of 240 J/cm^2. Note the abrupt interface between the irradiated area and untreated plaque mass (arrow). Bar = 0.1 mm at an original magnification of 252x.

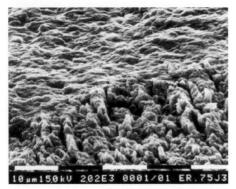

Figure 15 Interface between untreated root surface (top) and surface irradiated with an Er:YAG laser using an energy density of 0.75 J/cm² (bottom). Bar = 10 μm at an original magnification of 2,020x.

Figure 16 Periodontally diseased root surface irradiated with a CO_2 laser using an energy density of 138 J/cm² combined with a cooling surface spray of air/water. Bar = 1 mm at an original magnification of 89x.

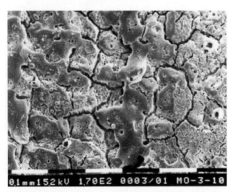

Figure 17 Root surface irradiated by CO_2 laser using an energy density of 206 J/cm². Surface texture is characterized by discontinuous sheet of melted and resolidified root mineral. Bar = 0.1 mm at an original magnification of 170x.

Numerous studies have noted heat induced surface cracking of root structure following irradiation by CO_2, Nd:YAG, and Er:YAG lasers, even at relatively moderate energy densities (Morlock *et al.*, 1992; Aoki *et al.*, 1994; Wilder-Smith *et al.*, 1995; Cobb *et al.*, 1995; Radvar *et al.*, 1995; Arakawa *et al.*, 1996; Fujii *et al.*, 1998). In an attempt to limit the amount of heat induced surface damage, the Nd:YAG laser has been combined with the simultaneous delivery of a surface cooling spray of air/water. The process of surface cooling is a direct result of the extensive thermal capacity of water and a process of thermal diffusion. In addition, due to the continual renewal of the air/water spray, simultaneous cooling of the tissue surface occurs by convection. However, the concept of combining a surface cooling spray of air/water with an Nd:YAG laser appears to be severely flawed. It should be remembered that the spatial extent and degree of tissue damage primarily depends on magnitude of power setting, exposure time, and absorption and distribution of heat within the target tissue. The deposition of laser energy, however, is not only a function of the various laser parameters, but also depends on tissue optical properties like absorption and scattering coefficients (Niemz, 1996). In biological tissue, absorption of laser energy is mainly due to the presence of free water molecules, proteins, pigments, and other

BioLine © 1999

macromolecules. The absorption coefficient is dependent on the wavelength of the incident laser radiation. The 1.06 μm wavelength of the Nd:YAG is not effectively absorbed in water, the absorption coefficient being 0.61 (α [cm^{-1}]) compared to 860 for the CO_2 wavelength of 10.6 μm (Niemz, 1996). Consequently, most of the beam energy from the Nd:YAG laser will simply pass through the surface cooling layer of water and penetrate the underlying target tissue.

Effects of Laser Irradiation on Subgingival Bacteria and Calculus
To date, there are only four peer-reviewed published studies (Cobb *et al.*, 1992; Hatit *et al.,* 1996; Neill and Mellonig, 1997; Moritz *et al.,* 1998) and two abstracts that report the results of treating human periodontal disease by the conservative application of laser irradiation. Three of these studies employed the Nd:YAG laser and one a diode laser, in clinical settings, and all reported reductions in pathogenic bacteria. More specifically, subgingival application of the dental laser is reported to be equal to scaling and root planing as regards reduction in probing depth, improvements in attachment levels or reductions in bleeding on probing (Neill and Mellonig, 1997; Moritz *et al.*, 1998); and superior in reducing numbers of Actinobacillus actinomycetemcomitans and Porphyromonas gingivalis and to a lesser extent Prevotella intermedia (Cobb *et al.*, 1992; Hatit *et al.,* 1996; Neill and Mellonig, 1997; Moritz *et al.*, 1998). Two of the studies noted evidence of irreparable root surface damage subsequent to subgingival laser treatment using parameters suggested by the manufacturer (Cobb *et al.*, 1992; Hatit *et al.*, 1996) whereas the remaining two studies (Neill and Mellonig, 1997; Moritz *et al.,* 1998) did not examine treated root surfaces for structural damage. Collectively, the four investigations involved a total of 57 laser treated patients and, therefore, represent insufficient data upon which to base treatment of the general public.

There are, however, numerous studies demonstrating the bactericidal effects of laser irradiation. Depending upon the choice of available parameters, lasers have the ability to either stimulate or inhibit the growth of bacteria, decrease bacterial populations, or to be bacteriocidal (Mullarky *et al.*, 1985; Schultz and Harvey, 1986; Dederich *et al.*, 1990; Tiphlova and Karu, 1991; Hatit *et al.*, 1996; Coffelt *et al.*, 1997; Klinke *et al.*, 1997; Moritz *et al.*, 1997). The CO_2, Nd:YAG and argon lasers have all been reported to be capable of destroying bacteria on instruments, culture media, glass slides, and in root canals (Mullarky *et al.*, 1985; Dederich *et al.*, 1990; Powell and Whisenant, 1991). Because of the bacteriocidal potential, manufacturers and researchers have suggested that lasers may be used in an adjunctive capacity to effectively reduce the microbial population of periodontal pockets (Tseng and Liew, 1990; Cobb *et al.*, 1992; Talebzadeh *et al.*, 1994; Hatit *et al.*, 1996; Coffelt *et al.*, 1997; Neill and Mellonig, 1997; Moritz *et al.*, 1998).

The ArF excimer, Er:YAG, Nd:YAG, CO_2 lasers have been used in various in vitro studies to remove plaque, calculus, and cementum without inducing significant changes in adjacent tissue layers. (Aoki *et al.*, 1994; Radvar *et al.*,

1995; Tucker *et al.*, 1996; Coffelt *et al.*, 1997). However, Radvar *et al.* (1995) offered some interesting observations concerning differences in susceptibility of calculus, dentin, and cementum to Nd:YAG laser irradiation. The authors used two different pulsed energy beams, each at two different power settings. The resulting four combinations were used for both 1 second and 5 second exposure durations. A clinically relevant observation was the consistent finding that specimens with complete evaporation of calculus always exhibited some degree of damage to the underlying cementum. None of the combination of parameters used in the study could differentiate between calculus and the underlying dental tissues, i.e., all were affected to some degree. Further, considerable variability was noted between specimens and within the same specimen regarding suscepti-bility of cementum and dentin to thermal damage when using a given combina-tion of parameters. Thus, given the variation in thickness of subgingival calculus and/or microbial plaque within the same periodontal pocket, one must question the in vivo use of an Nd:YAG laser on simple risk-to-benefit basis.

A study by Tucker *et al.* (1996) reported additional observations that have potential clinical significance. For example, the authors noted that laser (CO_2) vaporization of dental plaque was effective only within the beam path. Microbes lying peripheral to the beam path exhibited little or no morphologic evidence of thermal damage. Thus, complete eradication of microbial plaque deposits would require multiple overlapping passes of the energy beam - a feat rather difficult to accomplish with a manual curette or a laser unless surgical access is employed. The depth of laser energy penetration also varied between 125 mm to 250 mm. At first glance, this may appear sufficient to destroy a microbial mass, however, the mean generation time for bacterial plaque has been estimated at 3 to 4 hours (Socransky *et al.*, 1977). Thus, 3 to 5 day growth of an undisturbed mass of bacterial plaque may reach a thickness in excess of 0. 4 mm (Listgarten *et al.*, 1975). Tucker *et al.* (1996) also noted that dental calculus exposed to the laser energy underwent a phase transformation, i.e, meltdown followed by a resolidification during cooling. The results of this phase transformation included a porous surface texture and a rough, irregular surface topography. An in vivo root surface of similar texture and contour would require root planing by manual instrumentation in order to achieve long-term maintenance goals.

Lasers and Subgingival Periodontal Therapy: Summary

To date, there are no published, peer-reviewed, randomized controlled trials or longitudinal studies comparing lasers to traditional instrumentation for treatment of the subgingival environment, e.g., scaling and root planing vs. laser curettage. Given the lack of data, there remains only anecdotal evidence in support of using dental lasers as a treatment modality in non-surgical periodontal therapy. If gingival curettage has no inherent advantage over traditional scaling and root planing and if root planing is required to correct irregular laser-induced surface topography and cytotoxic residues, i.e., cyanamides and cyanates, then what is the advantage of the laser for non-surgical periodontal therapy? There are, however, numerous peer-reviewed articles from both in vivo and in vitro studies

484

that offer evidence of irreparable physical damage to root surfaces irradiated by Er:YAG, Nd:YAG or CO_2 lasers. Further, there is evidence that using lasers to remove subgingival calculus is likely no more efficient or predictable than traditional instrumentation and may, in fact, require root planing subsequent to laser therapy to achieve desired clinical goals. Lastly, a review of the 1966, 1989, and 1996 "World Workshops in Clinical Periodontics" and the last two "Proceedings of the European Workshop on Periodontology" clearly indicate that subgingival gingival curettage is unwarranted, particularly in light of the clinical results achieved with root planing alone. Indeed, the clinician must carefully weigh the patient's risk-to-benefit ratio and the ethical and legal ramifications before selecting the laser as the instrument of choice for non-surgical periodontal therapy.

The sonic and ultrasonic toothbrush
Concept
Plaque removal by manual tooth brushing remains the most common method of oral hygiene and has been shown to be quite effective when performed correctly, consistently, and for an appropriate duration (Axelsson *et al.*, 1991). However, given human susceptibility to lack of compliance, inattention to detail, and lack of manual dexterity, among other clinically relevant frailties, electro-mechanical toothbrushes were developed to compensate for poor brushing technique and the relative inefficiency of manual brushing when applied with less than optimal expertise.

As commercial technology has evolved, the electro-mechanical version of the traditional manual brush, featuring a back-and-forth movement, may be considered to constitute the first generation of mechanical brush designs. The second generation of mechanical brush design is characterized by rotary, counter-rotary, oscillating/rotating, etc. bristle motions and an increase in the number of brushing cycles per minute. Both manual and electro-mechanical toothbrushes create their desired clinical effect by a simple scrubbing action of the bristle tips when in contact with the tooth surface. The electro-mechanical toothbrush may generate, depending on design, two to seven thousand such bristle actions per minute. Obviously, the dramatic increase in bristle action when compared to that of a manual brush makes the electro-mechanical brush significantly more efficient at removing tooth-related bacterial plaque.

Sonic and ultrasonic toothbrushes constitute the third generation of electro-mechanical designs. The basic concept of sonic/ultrasonic toothbrushes involves an understanding of fluid dynamics. Simply put, the operational effect of a sonic or ultrasonic toothbrush is derived from using a combination of selected bristle frequencies and amplitude ranges, which in turn, translate into instantaneous velocity at the bristle tip. A typical sonic toothbrush (e.g., SenSonic' or Sonicare') generates 500 brush strokes per second (30,000/min) compared to 2,800 to 4,200 for popular electro-mechanical brushes (Braun Oral-B Plaque Remover' and Interplak', respectively). The ultrasonic toothbrush (e.g., UltraSonex') contains an emitter (transducer) embedded in the brush head that operates at 1.6 MHZ, creating a high-frequency, low-intensity sine-wave ultrasonic emission. The transducer contracts and expands volumetrically in tune with the impulses provided by the power supply (located in the brush handle), converting electric energy into ultrasonic waves. The ultrasonic waves, in turn, are transmitted from the transducer to the brush head and the bristles.

The bristle tip velocities created by sonic and ultrasonic brushes generate alternating pressure fields and create shear forces in the fluids surrounding the teeth (McInnes *et al.*, 1992, 1993, 1994). In theory, these alternating pressure fields produce a fluid flow velocity which is near that of the bristle tips, thereby causing a cleansing action beyond the actual reach of the bristles, e.g., disruption of biofilms in the interproximal and subgingival areas where the bristles cannot reach (Giuliani and Martin, 1992; Wu-Yuan *et al.*, 1994; Emling and Yankell, 1997). The action of the sonic or ultrasonic brush bristles results in a number of acoustical effects beyond the bristle tips that have disruptive potential in regards to bacterial plaque, such as: fluid-coupling, shear stress, abrasive erosion, and supersaturation with air.

The fluid-coupling effect refers to acoustical pressure, i.e., the alternating pressure field in the fluid medium produced by bristle movements. The tooth associated biofilm mass is believed to absorb the vibrational energy which results in disruption. If this process is conducted in the presence of a dentifrice or liquid antimicrobial, the vibrational stresses created in the biofilm may allow entry of chemically active agents. Shear stress, created by fluid velocity and frequency of bristle oscillation, when exceeding a critical value, may inhibit microbial adhesion through fatigue fracturing of pili or fimbriae. The abrasive erosion effect is created by movement of bristles in a fluid medium that also contains abrasive particles (e.g., toothpaste). The damage to a tooth associated biofilm increases with the bristle tip velocity, since the rate of impact as well as the momentum of the particles in the saliva also increases with velocity. Lastly, the supersaturation effect results from quantities of air being pulled into the saliva as a result of bristle velocity. Theoretically, the supersaturated saliva (or gingival crevicular fluid) is forced into subgingival regions, thereby exposing anaerobic bacteria to an increased oxygen tension.

Sonic/Ultrasonic Toothbrushes: Clinical Studies

Obviously, if all of the aforementioned phenomena were effective in the human mouth, then one might expect meaningful differences in clinical parameters in studies comparing sonic and ultrasonic brushes to manual or oscillating/rotating electric brushes. Indeed, several studies have shown the sonic (Johnson and McInnes, 1994; O'Beirne *et al.*, 1996; Tritten and Armitage, 1996; Ho and Niederman, 1997; Yankell *et al.*, 1997; Wolff *et al.*, 1998) and ultrasonic toothbrushes (Terezhalmy *et al.*, 1994; Terezhalmy *et al.*, 1995) to be more effective at removal of dental plaque and reducing gingival and bleeding index scores when compared to manual brushing, but less so when compared to oscillating/rotating electric (Grossman *et al.*, 1995; Van der Weijden *et al.*, 1996; Robinson *et al.*, 1997). However, several clinical studies and at least one in vitro

486

study have emphasized that the sonic brush is superior to either the manual or oscillating/rotating brushes at removing interproximal plaque (Johnson and McInnes, 1994; Tritten and Armitage, 1996; Robinson *et al.*, 1997; Yankell *et al.* 1997). Yet, in dramatic contrast, one recent study comparing an ultrasonic to manual toothbrushing for reductions in plaque, bleeding, and gingival indices and reported no differences over the 30-day experimental period (Forgas-Brockmann *et al.*, 1998).

If one considers the collective body of clinical studies comparing sonic or ultrasonic toothbrushes to either manual or oscillating/rotary brushes, as presented in Table 5, the problem of statistical vs. clinical significance becomes apparent. As an example, the Robinson *et al.* (1997) at the 180 day evaluation interval, reports a difference in plaque index of 0.28 (oscillating/rotary brush) vs. 0.36 (sonic brush) which in both instances equates to a 38% decrease in plaque score. In addition, the reported difference in probing depth between the oscillating/rotating brush vs. the sonic, was calculated to be 9% (in favor of the sonic brush) or a difference of 0.45 mm. Such differences in other clinical studies are likewise minimal, even if statistically significant. If changes in the various clinical parameters are converted to a common denominator, such as percentage in reduction, as done in Table 5, the minimal differences in clinical parameters, when comparing sonic and/or ultrasonic brushes to manual and/or oscillating/rotating brushes, become readily apparent.

Problems Associated with Applying the Physics of Fluid Dynamics to the Oral Cavity

Considering the almost 10-fold increase in brush stroke cycles of the sonic (or greater in the case of ultrasonics) compared to manual and/or oscillating/rotating brushes and the claims of effect due to fluid transmission of acoustic phenomena and shear stresses, etc., one might expect overwhelming changes in measurable clinical parameters. The lack of such dramatic evidence may have several levels of explanation. Changes in clinical parameters in head-to-head comparisons of manual and oscillating/rotating electric brushes with sonic or ultrasonic brushes may reflect nothing more than a difference in scrubbing efficiency based on the dramatic differences in stroke cycles. Optimal generation of alternating pressure fields and shear stresses in saliva and gingival crevicular fluids assumes that the brush bristles are not making contact with the teeth or gingivae and are immersed in a volume of liquid medium sufficient to transmit the amplitude and wave length of acoustic energy. Bristle-tooth surface or bristle-gingival contact disrupts bristle action and is likely to have a dampening effect. Furthermore, one could argue that in the case of the gingiva, the transmission of sonic or ultrasonic acoustic phenomena are further dampened by the fibrous and non-collagenous matrix components of the tissue. In addition, with respect to subgingival regions, the levels of gingival crevicular fluid (GCF) are insufficient to transmit acoustic phenomena. Although GCF is known to replenish its volume every 90 seconds, the average volume for a 5 mm pocket is only 0.5 µl (Binder *et al.* 1987; Goodson, 1989), which is insufficient for transmission of the amplitude

Charles M. Cobb

Table 5 Summary of clinical index scores, converted to percentage of reduction, from studies comparing sonic and ultrasonic vs. manual and oscillating/rotating toothbrushes.

Reference	Length of Study (days)	Plaque Index	Gingival Index	Bleeding Index	Reduction in Probing Depth
Terezhalmy *et al.*, 1994	30				
Manual		**	0	+12	
Ultrasonic			28	60	
Terezhalmy *et al.*, 1995	180				
Manual		**	63	0	
Ultrasonic			66	11	
Forgas Brockman *et al.*, 1998	30				
Manual		45	9	24	
Ultrasonic		50	12	24	
Johnson and McInnes, 1994	28				
Manual		9	19	36	
Sonic		26	14	29	
O'Beirne *et al.*, 1996	56				
Manual			70	72	19
Sonic			76	77	23
Tritten and Armitage, 1996	84				
Manual		12	16	24	
Sonic		17	20	27	
Ho and Niederman, 1997 (ortho pts.)	28				
Manual		10	3	9	6
Sonic		57	29	66	28
Wolf *et al.*, 1998 (implant pts.)	168				
Manual		53	61	54	12
Sonic		65	40	55	14
Grossman *et al.*, 1995	56				
Oscillating/Rotating		56	9		
Sonic		30	8		
Van der Weijden *et al.*, 1996	2 min				
Oscillating/Rotating	brushing	45			
Sonic	by pt.	40			
Robinson *et al.*, 1997	180				
Oscillating/Rotating		38		18	7
Sonic		18		32	16

** Method of scoring plaque reduction did not allow for comparisons between baseline and interval scores.

488

BioLine © 1999

and wave length of acoustic energy being generated by the sonic or ultrasonic brush.

Lastly, the viscosity of oral fluids, increased by toothpaste and dislodged plaque microbes, may dampen transmission of the acoustic effect. Normal human saliva is reported to contain 10^8 bacteria/ml (Marsh and Martin, 1992). Research studying the effects of acoustic energy on bacteria in fluid media has established that biological effects are reduced or inhibited at concentrations above 10^8 bacteria/ml (Hesselberg, 1952; Dakubu, 1976; McInnes *et al.*, 1992), suggesting that any shearing forces are likely to be attenuated.

Potential Effects of the Sonic Toothbrush on Oral Bacteria:
In Vitro Studies

The concept of using acoustic phenomena generated by sonic or ultrasonic toothbrush bristles to remove and disperse dental plaque by disrupting cell-to-cell and cell-to-substrate adhesion is, to date, based entirely on in vitro studies (McInnes *et al.*, 1992, 1993, 1994; Wu-Yuan *et al.*, 1994; Blanco *et al.*, 1997; MacNeill *et al.*, 1998). Several in vitro studies have demonstrated that the dynamic fluid activity produced by sonic toothbrushes is capable of: removing bacteria adhering to saliva-coated hydroxyapatite (McInnes *et al.*, 1992), inducing a dispersion of aggregated *Actinomyces viscosus* suspended in a fluid medium (Wu-Yuan *et al.*, 1994; MacNeill *et al.*, 1998), and removal or fragmenting of fimbriae from the cell wall of *Actinomyces viscosus* (McInnes *et al.*, 1993; MacNeill *et al.*, 1998). In addition, acoustic energy produced by a sonic toothbrush has also been shown to inflict irreparable damage, in vitro, on the cell walls of *Treponema denticola* (Blanco *et al.*, 1997). This latter observation should not be unexpected as Robrish *et al.* (1976) reported a hierarchy of microbial sensitivity to sonic energy with *Streptococcus mutans* being 600x more resistant than *Fusobacterium nucleatum*, 76x more resistant than *Bacteroides fragilis*, and 3x more resistant than *Actinomyces viscosus*. A similar study by Olsen and Socransky (1981) reported Gram-positive organisms to be more resistant to sonication than Gram-negative. Their hierarchy, in part, of most to least resistant Gram-negative anaerobes was: *Eikenella corrodens, Fusobacterium nucleatum, Actinobacillus actinomycetemcomitans,* and *Bacteroides melaninogenicus ss. intermedius (Prevotella intermedia). Treponema denticola, Selenomonas sputigena,* and *Wolinella (Campylobacter)* were the most susceptible to sonication.

A peculiar requirement of the sonic toothbrush in vitro studies is that brush bristles must be placed 2 mm into the fluid medium to achieve optimal transmission of the acoustic phenomena generated by the specific bristle frequency and amplitude that is inherent to the design specifications of the sonic toothbrush (Wu-Yuan *et al.*, 1994). If this minimal fluid depth is, indeed, an absolute requirement for optimal effect, then one may suggest that an attenuation of the acoustic phenomena occurs in the human oral cavity as such a fluid depth is seldom, if ever, in contact with the teeth. Ultimately, because of the dissimilarities between oral and in vitro conditions, the relevancy of the collective in vitro studies can only be established by appropriate clinical investigations. In vitro studies simply indicate potential mechanisms of action. To date, there have been no clinical studies demonstrating a subgingival effect that is directly related to the transmission of acoustic phenomena generated by and resulting from the use of a sonic or ultrasonic toothbrush.

References

Sonic/Ultrasonic Instrumentation

Adelson, L. J., Hanks, C. T., Ramfjord, S. J. and Caffesse, R. G. 1980. Cytotoxicity of periodontally diseased root surfaces. *J. Periodontol.*, **51**, 700-704.

Adriaens, P. A., De Boever, J. A. and Loesche, W. J. 1988. Bacterial invasion in root cementum and radicular dentin of periodontally diseased teeth in humans. *J. Periodontol.*, **59**, 222-230.

Al-Jabouri, W., Quee, T. C., Lautar, C., Iugovaz, I., Bourgouin, J., Delorme, F. and Chan, E. C. S. 1989. Effects of adjunctive treatment of periodontitis with tetracycline and spiramycin. *J. Periodontol.*, **60**, 533-539.

Allen, E. and Rhoades, R. 1963. Effects of high speed periodontal instruments on tooth surfaces. *J. Periodontol.*, **34**, 352-356.

Anderson, G. B., Palmer, J. A., Bye, f. L., Smith, B. A. and Caffesse, R. G. 1996. Effectiveness of subgingival scaling and root planing: Single versus multiple episodes of instrumentation. *J. Periodontol.*, **67**, 367-373.

Axelsson, P. and Lindhe, J. 1981a. Effect of controlled oral hygiene procedures on caries and periodontal disease in adults. Results after six years. *J. Clin. Periodontol.*, **8**, 239-248.

Axelsson, P. and Lindhe, J. 1981b. The significance of maintenance care in the treatment of periodontal disease. *J. Clin. Periodontol.*, **8**, 281-294.

Badersten, A., Nilvéus, R. and Egelberg, J. 1981. Effect of nonsurgical periodontal therapy. I. Moderately advanced periodontitis. *J. Clin. Periodontol.*, **8**, 57-72.

Badersten, A., Nilvéus, R. and Egelberg, J. 1984a. Effect of nonsurgical periodontal therapy. II. Severely advanced periodontitis. *J. Clin. Periodontol.*, **11**, 63-76.

Badersten, A., Nilvéus, R. and Egelberg, J. 1984b. Effect of nonsurgical periodontal therapy. III. Single versus repeated instrumentation. *J. Clin. Periodontol.*, **11**, 114-124.

Badersten, A., Nilvéus, R. and Egelberg, J. 1985. Effect of nonsurgical periodontal therapy. IV. Operator variability. *J. Clin. Periodontol.*, 1985, **12**, 190-200.

Baehni, P., Thilo, B., Chapuis, B. and Pernet, D. 1992. Effects of ultrasonic and sonic scalers on dental plaque microflora in vitro and in vivo. *J. Clin. Periodontol.*, **19**, 455-459.

Becker, W., Becker, B. E., Ochsenbein, C., Kerry, G., Caffesse, R., Morrison, E. C. and Prichard, J. 1988. A longitudinal study comparing scaling, osseous surgery and modified Widman procedures. Results after one year. *J. Periodontol.*, **59**, 351-365.

Benfenati, M. P., Montesani, M. T., Benfenati, S. P. and Nathanson, D. 1987. An SEM study of periodontal instrumented root surfaces, comparing sharp, dull, and damaged curettes and ultrasonic instruments. *Int. J. Periodontics Restorative Dent.*, **7**, 50-67.

Blomlöf, L., Lindskog, S., Appelgren, R., Jonsson, B., Weintraub, A. and Hammarström, L. 1987. New attachment in monkeys with experimental periodontitis with and without removal of the cementum. *J. Clin. Periodontol.*, **14**, 136-143.

Bollen, C. M. L., Papaioannou, W., Van Eldere, J., Schepers, E., Quirynen, M. and Van Steenberghe, D. 1996. The influence of abutment surface roughness on plaque accumulation and peri-implant mucositis. *Clin. Oral. Impl. Res.*, **7**, 201-211.

Bollen, C. M. L. and Quirynen, M. 1996. Microbiological response to mechanical treatment in combination with adjunctive therapy. A review of the literature. *J. Periodontol.*, **67**, 1143-1158.

Bollen, C. M. L., Vandekerckhove, B. N. A., Papaioannou W., Van Eldere, J. and Quirynen, M. 1996. Full- versus partial-mouth disinfection in the treatment of periodontal infections. A pilot study: Long-term microbiological observations. *J. Clin. Periodontol.*, **23**, 960-970.

Bollen, C. M. L., Mongardini, C., Papaioannou, W., van Steenberghe, D. and Quirynen, M. 1998. The effect of a one-stage full-mouth disinfection on different intra-oral niches. Clinical and microbiological observations. *J. Clin. Periodontol.*, **25**, 56-66.

Boretti, G., Zappa, U., Graf, H. and Case, D. 1995. Short-term effects of phase 1 therapy on crevicular cell populations. *J. Periodontol.*, **66**, 235-240.

Borghetti, A., Mattout, P. and Mattout, C. 1987. How much root planing is necessary to remove the cementum from the root surface? *Int. J. Periodontics Restorative Dent.*, **4**, 22-29.

Braatz, L, Garrett, S., Claffey, N. and Egelberg, J. 1985. Antimicrobial irrigation of deep pockets to supplement non-surgical periodontal therapy. II. Daily irrigation. *J. Clin. Periodontol.*, **12**, 630-638.

Breininger, D. R., O'Leary, T. J. and Blumenshine, R. V. H. 1987. Comparative effectiveness of ultrasonic and hand scaling for the removal of subgingival plaque and calculus. *J. Periodontol.*, **58**, 9-18.

Buchanan, S. A. and Robertson, P. B. 1987. Calculus removal by scaling and root planing with and without surgical access. *J. Periodontol.*, **58**, 159-163.

Budtz-Jorgensen, E. and Kaaber, S. 1986. Clinical effect of glazing denture acrylic resin bases using an ultraviolet curing method. *Scand. J. Dent. Res.*, **94**, 569-574.

Caffesse, R. G., Sweeney, P. L. and Smith, B. A. 1986. Scaling and root planing with and without periodontal flap surgery. *J. Clin. Periodontol.*, **13**, 205-210.

Caton, J. G., Proye, M. and Polson, A. 1982. Maintenance of healed periodontal pockets after a single episode of root planing. *J. Periodontol.*, **53**, 420-424.

Cercek, J. F., Kiger, R. D., Garrett, S. and Egelberg, J. 1983. Relative effects of plaque control and instrumentation on the clinical parameters of human periodontal disease. *J. Clin. Periodontol.*, **10**, 46-56.

Chapple, I. L. C., Walmsley, A. D., Saxby, M. S. and Moscrop, H. 1995. Effect of instrument power setting during ultrasonic scaling upon treatment outcome. *J. Periodontol.*, **66**, 756-760.

Checchi, L. and Pelliccioni, G. A. 1988. Hand versus ultrasonic instrumentation in the removal of endotoxins from root surfaces in vitro. *J. Periodontol.*, **59**, 398-402.

Checchi, L., Forteleoni, G., Pelliccioni, G. A. and Loriga, G. 1997. Plaque removal with variable instrumentation. *J. Clin. Periodontol.*, **24**, 715-717.

Cheetham, W. A., Wilson, M. and Kieser, J. B. 1988. Root surface debridement - an *in vitro* assessment. *J. Clin. Periodontol.*, **15**, 288-292.

Chiew, S. Y., Wilson, M., Davies, E. H. and Kieser, J. B. 1991. Assessment of ultrasonic debridement of calculus-associated periodontally-involved root surfaces by the limulus amoebocyte lysate assay. An in vitro study. *J. Clin. Periodontol.*, **18**, 240-244.

Choquet, J. 1909. Examen de l' appareil dentaire ducrâne de l'homme préhistorique de la Chapelle-aux-Saints. In: *Verhandlungen des 5. Internationalen Zahnärztlichen Kongresses*, vol. 1, p. 138., Berlin.

Christersson, L. A., Slots, J., Rosling, B. and Genco, R. 1985. Microbiological and clinical effects of surgical treatment of localized juvenile periodontitis. *J. Clin. Periodontol.*, **12**, 465-476.

Claffey, N., Loos, B., Gantes, B., Martin, M., Heins, P. and Egelberg, J. The relative effects of therapy and periodontal disease on loss of probing attachment after root debridement. *J. Clin. Periodontol.*, **15**, 163-169.

Clarke, N. G, Carey, S. E., Srikandi, W., Hirsch, R. S. and Leppard, P. I. 1986. Periodontal disease in ancient populations. *Am. J. Phys. Anthrop.*, **71**, 173-183.

Clarke, N. G. 1990. Periodontal defects of pulpal origin: Evidence in early man. *Am. J. Phys. Anthropol.*, **82**, 371-376.

Clifford, L. R., Needleman, I. G. and Chan, Y. K. 1999. Comparison of periodontal pocket penetration by conventional and microultrasonic inserts. *J. Clin. Periodontol.*, **26**, 124-130.

Cobb, C. M. 1996. Non-surgical pocket therapy: Mechanical. *Ann. Periodontol.*, **1**, 443-490.

Cogen, R. B., Garrison, D. C. and Weatherford, T. W. 1983. Effect of various surface treatments on the viability and attachment of human gingival fibroblasts. *J. Periodontol.*, **54**, 277-282.

Cogen, R. B., Al-Joburi, W., Gantt, D. G. and Denys, F. R. 1984. Effect of various root surface treatments on the attachment and growth of human gingival fibroblasts: Histologic and scanning electron microscopic evaluation. *J. Clin. Periodontol.*, **11**, 531-539.

Coldiron, N. B., Yukna, R. A., Weir, J. and Caudill, R. F. 1990. A quantitative study of cementum removal with hand curettes. *J. Periodontol.*, **61**, 293-299.

Copulos, T. A., Low, S. B., Walker, C. B., Trebilcock, Y. Y. and Hefti, A. F. 1993. Comparative analysis between a modified ultrasonic tip and hand instruments on clinical parameters of periodontal disease. *J. Periodontol.*, **64**, 694-700.

Cross-Poline, G. N., Stach, D. J. and Newman, S. M. 1995. Effects of curet and ultrasonics on root surfaces. *Am. J. Dent.*, **8**, 131-133.

Dahlén, G., Lindhe, J., Sato, K., Hanamura, H. and Okamoto, H. 1992. The effect of supragingival plaque control on the composition of the subgingival flora in periodontal pockets. *J. Clin. Periodontol.*, **19**, 802-809.

Daly, C., Seymour, G. Kieser, J. and Corbet, E. 1982. Histological assessment of periodontally involved cementum. *J. Clin. Periodontol.*, **9**, 266-274.

Dragoo, M. R. 1992. A clinical evaluation of hand and ultrasonic instruments on subgingival debridement. 1. With unmodified and modified ultrasonic inserts. *Int. J. Periodontics Restorative Dent.*, **12**, 310-323.

Drisko, C. L. and Killoy, W. J. 1991. Scaling and root planing: removal of calculus and subgingival organisms. *Curr. Opin. Dent.*, **1**, 74-80.

Drisko, C. L. 1995a. Periodontal debridement: Hand versus power-driven scalers. *Dent. Hyg. News*, Special Issue - Spring, 18-23.

Drisko, C. L., Cobb, C. M., Killoy, W. J., Michalowicz, B. S., Pihlstrom, B. L., Lowenguth, R. A., Caton, J. G., Encarnacion, M., Knowles, M. and Goodson, J. M. 1995b. Evaluation of periodontal treatments using controlled-release tetracycline fibers: Clinical response. *J. Periodontol.*, **19**, 692-699.

Drisko, C. L. and Lewis, L. H. 1996. Ultrasonic instruments and antimicrobial agents in supportive periodontal treatment and retreatment of recurrent or refractory periodontitis. *Periodontology 2000*, **12**, 90-115.

Eaton, K. A., Kieser, J. B. and Davies, R. M. 1985. The removal of root surface deposits. *J. Clin. Periodontol.*, **12**, 141-152.

Eschler, B. and Rapley, J. W. 1991. Mechanical and chemical root preparation in vitro: Efficiency of plaque and calculus removal. *J. Periodontol.*, **62**, 755-760.

Ewen, S. J., Scopp, I. W., Witkin, R. T. and Ortiz-Junceda, M. 1976. A comparative study of ultrasonic generators and hand instruments. *J. Periodontol.*, **47**, 82-86.

Fleischer, H. C., Mellonig, J. T., Brayer, W. K., Gray, J. L. and Barnett, J. D. 1989. Scaling and root planing efficacy in multirooted teeth. *J. Periodontol.*, **60**, 402-409.

Flemmig, T. F., Petersilka, G. J., Mehl, A., Hickel, R. and Klaiber, B. 1998a. Working parameters of a magnetostrictive ultrasonic scaler influencing root substance removal in vitro. *J. Periodontol.*, **69**, 547-553.

Flemmig, T. F., Petersilka, G. J., Mehl, A., Hickel, R. and Klaiber, B. 1998b. The effect of working parameters on root substance removal using a piezoelectric ultrasonic scaler in vitro. *J. Clin. Periodontol.*, **25**, 158-163.

Forabosco, A., Galetti, R., Spinato, S., Colao, P. and Casolari, C. 1996. A comparative study of a surgical method and scaling and root planing using the Odontoson ®. *J. Clin. Periodontol.*, **23**, 611-614.

Fujikawa, K., O'Leary, T. J. and Kafrawy, A. H. 1988. The effect of retained subgingival calculus on healing after flap surgery. *J. Periodontol.*, **59**, 170-175.

Fukazawa, E. and Nishimura, K. 1994. Superficial cemental curettage: its efficacy in promoting improved cellular attachment on human root surfaces previously damaged by periodontitis. *J. Periodontol.*, **65**, 168-176.

Gankerseer, E. J. and Walmsley, A. D. 1987. Preliminary investigation into the performance of a sonic scaler. *J. Periodontol.*, **58**, 780-784.

Gantes, B. G., Nilveus, R., Lie, T. and Leknes, K. N. 1992. The effect of hygiene instruments on dentin surfaces: Scanning electron microscopic observations. *J. Periodontol.*, **63**, 151-157.

Gellin, R. G., Miller, M. C., Javed, T., Engler, W. O. and Mishkin, D. J. 1986. The effectiveness of the Titan-S sonic scaler versus curettes in the removal of subgingival calculus. *J. Periodontol.*, **57**, 672-680.

Giuliana, G., Ammatuna, P., Pizzo, G., Capone, F. and D'Angelo, M. 1997. Occurrence of invading bacteria in radicular dentin of periodontally diseased teeth: Microbiological findings. *J. Clin. Periodontol.*, **24**, 478-485.

Gottehrer, N. and Reynolds, B. 1997. Power scalers: the new boom in contemporary periodontics. *Dent. Today*, **16**, 98-105.

Grant, D. A., Lie, T., Clark, S. M. and Adams, D. F. 1993. Pain and discomfort levels in patients during root surface debridement with sonic metal or plastic inserts. *J. Periodontol.*, **64**, 645-650.

Greenwell, H. and Bissada, N. F. 1984. Variations in subgingival microflora from healthy and intervention sites using probing depth and bacteriologic identification criteria. *J. Periodontol.*, **55**, 391-397.

Haffajee, A. D., Cugini, M. A., Dibart, S., Smith, C., Kent, R. L., Jr. and Socransky, S. S. 1997. The effect of SRP on the clinical and microbiological parameters of periodontal diseases. *J. Clin. Periodontol.*, **24**, 324-334.

Hämmerle, C. H. F., Joss, A. and Lang, N. P. 1991. Short term effects of initial periodontal therapy (hygienic phase). *J. Clin. Periodontol.*, **18**, 233-239.

Harper, S. and Robinson, P. 1987. Correlation of histometric, microbial, and clinical indicators of periodontal disease status before and after root planing. *J. Clin. Periodontol.*, **14**, 190-196.

Held, A.-J. 1989. *Periodontology: From its Origins up to 1980*, pp. 8-9, Birkhäuser, Berlin.

Hellström, M.-K., Ramberg, P., Krok, L. and Linhdhe, J. 1996. The effect of supragingival plaque control on the subgingival microflora in human periodontitis. *J. Clin. Periodontol.*, **23**, 934-940.

Hill, R. W., Ramfjord, S. P., Morrison, E. C., Appleberry, E. A., Caffesse, R. G., Kerry, G. J. and Nissle, R. R. 1981. Four types of periodontal treatment compared over 2 years. *J. Periodontol.*, **52**, 655-662.

Hinrichs, J., Wolff, L., Pihlstrom, B., Schaffer, E. M., Siljemark, W. F. and Brand, T. C. L. 1985. Effects of scaling and root planing on subgingival microbial proportions standardized in terms of their naturally occurring distribution. *J. Periodontol.*, **56**, 187-194.

Holbrook, T. and Low, S. 1991. Power-driven scaling and polishing instruments. In: Hardin, J., (ed.), *Clark's Clinical Dentistry*, pp. 1-24, J. B. Lippincott, Philadelphia.

Hughes, F. J. and Smales, F. C. 1986. Immunohistochemical investigation of the presence and distribution of cementum-associated lipopolysaccharides in periodontal disease. *J. Periodont. Res.*, **21**, 660-667.

Hughes, T. P. and Caffesse, R. G. 1978. Gingival changes following scaling and root planing and oral hygiene. A biometric evaluation. *J. Periodontol.*, **49**, 245-252.

Hunter, R. D., O'Leary, T. J. and Kafrawy, A. T. 1984. The effectiveness of hand versus ultrasonic instrumentation in open flap root planing. *J. Periodontol.*, **55**, 697-703.

Jacobson, L., Blomlöf, J. and Lindskog, S. 1994. Root surface texture after different scaling modalities. *Scand. J. Dent. Res.*, **102**, 1560-160.

Jones, S. J., Lozdan, J. and Boyde, A. 1972. Tooth surfaces treated in situ with periodontal instruments. *Br. Dent. J.*, **132**, 57-64.

Jotikasthira, N., Lie, T. and Leknes, K. 1992. Comparative in vitro studies of sonic, ultrasonic and reciprocating scaling instruments. *J. Clin. Periodontol.*, **19**, 560-569.

Kaldahl, W. B., Kalkwarf, K. L., Patil, K. D., Dyer, J. K. and Bates, R. E., Jr. 1988. Evaluation of four modalities of periodontal therapy. Mean proving depth, probing attachment level and recession changes. *J. Periodontol.*, **59**, 783-793.

Kaldahl, W. B., Kalkwarf, K. L., Patil, K. D., Molvar, M. P. and Dyer, J. K. 1996a. Long-term evaluation of periodontal therapy: I. Response to 4 therapeutic modalities. *J. Periodontol.*, **67**, 93-102.

Kaldahl, W. B., Kalkwarf, K. L., Patil, K. D., Molvar, M. P. and Dyer, J. K. 1996b. Long-term evaluation of periodontal therapy. II. Incidence of sites breaking down. *J. Periodontol.*, **67**, 103-108.

Kalkwarf, K. L., Kaldahl, W. B. and Patil, K. D. 1988. Evaluation of furcation region response to periodontal therapy. *J. Periodontol.*, **59**, 794-804.

Katsanoulas, T., Renee, I. and Attstrom, R. 1992. The effect of supragingival plaque control on the composition of the subgingival flora in periodontal pockets. *J. Clin. Periodontol.*, **19**, 760-765.

Kawanami, M., Sugaya, T., Kato, S., Iinuma, K., Tate, T., Hannan, M. A. and Kato, H. 1988. Efficacy of an ultrasonic scaler with a periodontal probe-type tip in deep periodontal pockets. *Adv. Dent. Res.*, **2**, 405-410.

Keenan, M. P., Schillingburg, H. T., Duncanson, M. G. and Wade, C. K. 1980. Effects of cast gold surface finishing on plaque retention. *J. Prosthet. Dent.*, **43**, 168-173.

Kepic, T. J., O'Leary, T. J. and Kafrawy, A. H. 1990. Total calculus removal: an attainable objective? *J. Periodontol.*, **61**, 16-20.

Kerry, G. J. 1967. Roughness of root surfaces after use of ultrasonic instruments and hand curettes. *J. Periodontol.*, **38**, 340-346.

Khatiblou, F. A. and Ghodssi, A. 1983. Root surface smoothness or roughness in periodontal treatment. A clinical study. *J. Periodontol.*, **54**, 365-367.

Knowles, J. W., Burgett, f. G., Nissle, R. R., Shick, R. A., Morrison, E. C. and Ramfjord, S. P. 1979. Results of periodontal treatment related to pocket depth and attachment level. Eight years. *J. Periodontol.*, **50**, 225-233.

Kocher, T. and Plagmann, H-C. 1997. The diamond-coated sonic scaler tip. Part I. Oscillation pattern of different sonic scaler inserts. *Int. J. Periodontics Restorative Dent.*, **17**:392-399.

Kocher, T., Rühling, a., Momsen, H. and Plagmann, H.-C. 1997. Effectiveness of subgingival instrumentation with power-driven instruments in the hands of experienced and inexperienced operators. A study on manikins. *J. Clin. Periodontol.*, **24**, 498-504.

Kocher, T., Gutsche, C. and Plagmann, H.-C. 1998a. Instrumentation of furcation with modified sonic scaler inserts: Study on manikins, Part I. *J. Clin. Periodontol.*, **25**, 388-393.

Kocher, T., Tersic-Orth, B. and Plagmann, H-C. 1998b. Instrumentation of furcation with modified sonic scaler inserts. A study on manikins (II). *J. Clin. Periodontol.*, **25**, 451-456.

Laurell, L. and Pettersson, B. 1988. Periodontal healing after treatment with either the Titan-S sonic scaler or hand instruments. *Swed. Dent. J.*, **12**, 187-192.

Laurell, L. 1990. Periodontal healing after scaling and root planing with the Kavo Sonicflex and Titan-S sonic scalers. *Swed. Dent. J.*, **14**, 171-177.

Lavanchy, D., Bickel., M. and Bachni, P. 1987. The effect of plaque control after scaling and root planing on the subgingival microflora in human periodontitis. *J. Clin. Periodontol.*, **14**, 295-299.

Leknes, K. N., Lie, T., Wikesjö, U. M. E., Böe, O. E. and Selvig, K. A. 1996. Influence of tooth instrumentation roughness on gingival tissue reactions. *J. Periodontol.*, **67**, 197-204.

Leon, L. E. and Vogel, R. I. 1987. A comparison of the effectiveness of hand scaling and ultrasonic debridement in furcations as evaluated by differential dark-field microscopy. *J. Periodontol.*, **58**, 86-94.

Lie, T. and Meyer, K. 1977. Calculus removal and loss of tooth substance in response to different periodontal instruments: A scanning electron microscope study. *J. Clin. Periodontol.*, **4**, 250-262.

Lie, T. and Leknes, K. N. 1985. Evaluation of the effect on root surfaces of air turbine scalers and ultrasonic instrumentation. *J. Periodontol.*, **56**, 522-531.

Lindhe, J. and Nyman, S. 1975. The effect of plaque control and surgical pocket elimination of the establishment and maintenance of periodontal health. A longitudinal study of periodontal therapy in cases of advanced disease. *J. Clin. Periodontol.*, **2**, 67-79.

Lindhe, J. and Nyman, S. 1984. Long-term maintenance of patients treated for advanced periodontal disease. *J. Clin. Periodontol.*, **11**, 504-514.

Lindhe, J., Westfelt, E., Nyman, S., Socransky, S. S. and Haffajee, A. D. 1984. Long-term effect of surgical/nonsurgical treatment of periodontal disease. *J. Clin. Periodontol.*, **11**, 448-458.

Listgarten, M. A., Lindhe, J. and Helldén, L. B. 1978. Effect of tetracycline and/or scaling on human periodontal disease. *J. Clin. Periodontol.*, **5**, 246-271.

Loesche, W. J. and Laughon, B. E. 1982. Role of spirochetes in periodontal disease. In:

Genco, R. J., Mergenhagen, S. E. (eds.), *Host-Parasite Interactions in Periodontal Disease,* pp. 62-75, American Society for Microbiology, Washington, D. C.

Loos, B., Kiger, R. and Engelberg, J. 1987. An evaluation of basic periodontal therapy using sonic and ultrasonic scalers. *J. Clin. Periodontol.*, **14**, 29-33.

Loos, B., Nylund, K., Claffey, N. and Egelberg, J. 1989. Clinical effects of root debridement in molar and non-molar teeth. *J. Clin. Periodontol.*, **16**, 498-504.

Lopez, N. J., Belvederessi, M. and De La Sotta, R. 1980. Inflammatory effects of periodontally diseased cementum studied by autogenous dental root implants in humans. *J. Periodontol.*, **51**, 583-593.

Magnusson, I., Lindhe, J., Yoneyama, T. and Liljenberg, B. 1984. Recolonization of a subgingival microbiota following scaling in deep pockets. *J. Clin. Periodontol.*, **11**, 193-207.

Matia, J. I., Bissada, N. F., Maybury, J. E. and Ricchetti, P. 1986. Efficiency of scaling of the molar furcation area with and without surgical access. *Inter. J. Periodontics Restorative Dent.*, **6**, 24-35.

McAlpine, R., Magnusson, I., Kiger, R, Crigger, M., Garrett, S. and Egelberg, J. 1985. Antimicrobial irrigation of deep pockets to supplement oral hygiene instruction and root debridement. I. Biweekly irrigation. *J. Clin. Periodontol.*, **12**, 568-577.

McNabb, H., Mombelli, A. and Lang, N. P. 1992. Supragingival cleaning 3 times a week. *J. Clin Periodontol.*, **19**, 348-356.

Mengel, R., Buns, C., Stelzel, M. and Flores-de-Jacoby, L. 1994. An in vitro study of oscillating instruments for root planing. *J. Clin. Periodontol.*, **21**, 513-518.

Meyer, K. and Lie, T. 1977. Root surface roughness in response to periodontal instrumentation studied by combined use of microroughness measurements and scanning electron microscopy. *J. Clin. Periodontol.*, **4**, 77-91.

Mitsis, F. J. and Taramidis, G. 1995. Alveolar bone loss on neolithic man: Remains on 38 skulls of Khirokitia's (Cyprus) inhabitants. *J. Clin. Periodontol.*, **22**, 788-793.

Mombelli, A., Gmür, R., Gobbi, C. and Lang, N. P. 1994a. *Actinobacillus actinomycetemcomitans* in adult periodontitis. I. Topographic distribution before and after treatment. *J. Periodontol.*, **65**, 820-826.

Mombelli, A., Gmür, R., Gobbi, C. and Lang, N. P. 1994a. *Actinobacillus actinomycetemcomitans* in adult periodontitis. II. Characterization of isolated strains and effect of mechanical periodontal treatment. *J. Periodontol.*, **65**, 827-834.

Moore, J., Wilson, M. and Kieser, J. B. 1986. The distribution of bacterial lipopolysaccharide (endotoxin) in relation to periodontally involved root surfaces. *J. Clin. Periodontol.*, **13**, 748-751.

Morrison, E. C., Ramfjord, S. P. and Hill, R. W. 1980. Short term effects of initial nonsurgical periodontal treatment (hygiene phase). *J. Clin. Periodontol.*, **7**, 199-211.

Moskow, B. S. and Bressman, E. 1964. Cemental response to ultrasonic and hand instrumentation. *J. Am. Dent. Assoc.*, **68**, 698-703.

Mousques, T., Listgarten, M. A. and Phillips, R. W. 1980. Effect of scaling and root planing on the composition of the human subgingival microbial flora. *J. Periodont. Res.*, **15**, 144-151.

Nakib, N. M., Bissada, N. F., Simmelink, J. W. and Goldstine, S. N. 1982. Endotoxin penetration into root cementum of periodontally healthy and diseased human teeth. *J. Periodontol.*, **53**, 368-378.

Nishimine, D. and O'Leary, T. J. 1979. Hand instrumentation versus ultrasonics in the removal of endotoxins from root surfaces. *J. Periodontol.*, **50**, 345-349.

Nosal, G., Scheidt, M., O'Neal, R. and Van Dyke, T. 1991. The penetration of lavage solution into the periodontal pocket during ultrasonic instrumentation. *J. Periodontol.*, **62**, 554-557.

Nyman, S. and Lindhe, J. 1979. A longitudinal study of combined periodontal and prosthetic treatment of patients with advanced periodontal disease. *J. Periodontol.*, **50**, 163-169.

Nyman, S., Sarhed, G., Ericsson, I., Gottlow, J. and Karring, T. Role of "diseased" root cementum in healing following treatment of periodontal disease. *J. Clin. Periodontol.*, **21**, 496-503.

Oberholzer, R. and Rateitschak, K. H. 1996. Root cleaning or root smoothing. An in vivo study. *J. Clin. Periodontol.*, **23**, 326-330.

Oda, S. and Ishikawa, I. 1989. In vitro effectiveness of a newly-designed ultrasonic scaler tip for furcation areas. *J. Periodontol.*, **60**, 634-639.

O'Leary, R., Sved, A. M., Davies, E. H., Leighton, T. G., Wilson, M. and Kieser, J. B. 1997. The bactericidal effects of dental ultrasound on *Actinobacillus actinomycetemcomitans* and *Porphyromonas gingivalis*. An in vitro investigation. *J. Clin. Periodontol.*, **24**, 432-439.

Oosterwaal, P. J. M., Matee, M. I., Mikx, F. H. M., van 't Hof, M. A. and Renggli, H. H. 1987. The effect of subgingival debridement with hand and ultrasonic instruments on the subgingival microflora. *J. Clin. Periodontol.*, **14**, 528-533.

Ortero-Cagide, F. J. and Long, B. A. 1997. Comparative in vitro effectiveness of closed root debridement with fine instruments on specific areas of mandibular first molar furcations. I. Root trunk and furcation entrance. *J. Periodontol.*, **68**, 1093-1097.

Ortero-Cagide, F. J. and Long, B. A. 1997. Comparative in vitro effectiveness of closed root debridement with fine instruments on specific areas of mandibular first molar furcations. II. Furcation area. *J. Periodontol.*, **68**, 1098-1101.

Pameijer, C. H., Stallard, R. E. and Hiep, N. 1972. Surface characteristics of teeth following periodontal instrumentation: A scanning electron microscope study. *J. Periodontol.*, **43**, 628-633.

Patterson, M., Eick, J. D., Eberhart, A. B., Gross, K. and Killoy, W. J. 1989. The effectiveness of two sonic and two ultrasonic scaler tips in furcations. *J Periodontol.*, **60**, 325-329.

Pattison, G. L. and Pattison, A. M. 1996. Principles of periodontal instrumentation. In: Carranza, F. A., Jr., *Clinical Periodontology*, 8th ed., p. 458, W. B. Saunders Company, Philadelphia.

Pedrazzoli, V., Kilian, M., Karring, T. and Kirkegaard, E. 1991. Effect of surgical and non-surgical periodontal treatment on periodontal status and subgingival microbiota. *J. Clin. Periodontol.*, **18**, 598-604.

Pihlstrom, B. L., Ortiz-Campos, C. and McHugh, R. B. 1981. A randomized four-year study of periodontal therapy. *J. Periodontol.*, **52**, 227-242.

Pihlstrom, B. L., McHugh, R. B. and Oliphant, T. H. 1984. Molar and nonmolar teeth compared over 6.5 years following two methods of periodontal therapy. *J. Periodontol.*, **55**, 499-504.

Proye, M., Caton, J. and Polson, A. 1982. Initial healing of periodontal pockets after a single episode of root planing monitored by controlled probing forces. *J. Periodontol.*, **53**, 296-301.

Quirynen, M. and Listgarten, M. 1990. The distribution of bacterial morphotypes around natural teeth and titanium implants ad modum Brånemark. *Clin Oral Implants Res.*, **1**, 8-12.

Quirynen, M., Van der Mei, H. C., Bollen, C. M. L., Schotte, A., Marechal, M., Doornbusch, G. I., Naret, I., Busscher, H. J. and Van Steenberghe, D. 1993. An in vivo study of the influence of surface roughness of implants on the microbiology of supra- and subgingival plaque. *J. Dent Res.*, **72**:1304-1309.

Quirynen, M., Bollen, C. M. L., Vandekerchhove, B. N. A., Dekeyser, C., Papaioannou, W. and Eyssen, H. 1995. Full- *vs.* partial-mouth disinfection in the treatment of periodontal infections: Short-term clinical and microbiological observations. *J. Dent. Res.*, **74**, 1459 1467.

Quirynen, M. and Bollen, C. M. L. 1995. The influence of surface roughness and surface-free energy on supra- and subgingival plaque formation in man. A review of the literature. *J. Clin. Periodntol.*, **22**, 1-14.

Quirynen, M., Bollen, C. M. L., Papaioannou, W., Van Eldere, J. and van Steenberghe, D. 1996. The influence of titanium abutment surface roughness on plaque accumulation and gingivitis: Short-term observations. *Int. J. Oral Maxillofac. Implants*, **11**, 169-178.

Rabbani, G. M., Ash, M. M. and Caffesse, R. G. 1981. The effectiveness of subgingival scaling and root planing in calculus removal. *J. Periodontol.*, **52**, 119-123.

Renvert, s., Wikström, M., Dahlén, G., Slots, J. and Egelberg, J. 1990. Effect of root debridement on the elimination of *Actinobacillus actinomycetemcomitans* and *Bacteroides gingivalis* from periodontal pockets. *J. Clin. Periodontol.*, **17**, 345-350.

Reynolds, M., Lavigne, D., Minah, G. and Suzuki, J. 1992. Clinical effects of simultaneous ultrasonic scaling and subgingival irrigation with chlorhexidine: Mediating influence of periodontal probing depth. *J. Clin. Periodontol.*, **19**, 595-600.

Ripamonti, U. 1989. The hard evidence of alveolar bone loss in early hominids of southern Africa. *J. Periodontol.*, **60**, 118-120.

Ritz, L., Hefti, A. and Rateitschak, K. 1991. An in vitro investigation on the loss of root substance in scaling with various instruments. *J. Clin. Periodontol.*, **18**, 643-647.

Robertson, P. B. 1990. Guest editorial: the residual calculus paradox. *J. Periodontol.*, **61**, 65.

Rosenberg, R. M. and Ash, M. M., Jr. 1974. The effect of root roughness on plaque accumulation and gingival inflammation. *J. Periodontol.*, **45**, 146-150.

Sbordone, L., Ramaglia, L., Gulletta, E. and Iacono, V. 1990. Recolonization of the subgingival microflora after scaling and root planing in human periodontitis. *J. Periodontol.*, **61**, 579-584.

Schlageter, L., Rateitschak-Plüss, E. M. and Schwarz, J-P. 1996. Root surface smoothness or roughness following open debridement. An in vivo study. *J. Clin. Periodontol.*, **23**, 460-464.

Schwarz, J. P., Guggenheim, R., Duggelin, M., Hefti, A. F., Rateitschak-Pluss, E. M. and Rateitschak, K. H. 1989. The effectiveness of root debridement in open flap procedures by means of a comparison between hand instruments and diamond burs: A SEM study. *J. Clin Periodontol.*, **16**, 510-518.

Shaw, S., Walmsley, A. D., Chapple, I. L. C. and Lumley, P. J. 1994. Variability of sonic scaling tip movement. *J. Clin. Periodontol.*, **21**, 705-709.

Sherman, P. R., Hutchens, L. H., Jr., Jewson, L. G., Moriarty, J. M., Greco, G. W. and McFall, W. T. 1990. The effectiveness of subgingival scaling and root planing. I. Clinical detection of residual calculus. *J. Periodontol.*, **61**, 3-8.

Sherman, P. R., Hutchens, L. H., Jr. and Jewson, L. G. 1990. The effectiveness of subgingival scaling and root planing. II. Clinical responses related to residual calculus. *J. Periodontol.*, **61**, 9-15.

Shiloah, J. and Patters, M. R. 1994. DNA probe analysis of the survival of selected periodontal pathogens following scaling, root planing, and intra-pocket irrigation. *J. Periodontol.*, **65**, 568-575.

Shiloah, J. and Patters, M. R. 1996. Repopulation of periodontal pockets by microbial pathogens in the absence of supportive therapy. *J. Periodontol.*, **67**, 130-139.

Singletary, M. M., Crawford, J. J. and Simpson, D. M. 1982. Dark-field microscopic monitoring of subgingival bacteria during periodontal therapy. *J. Periodontol.*, **53**, 671-681.

Slots, J., Mashimo, P. C., Levine, M. J. and Genco, R. J. 1979. Periodontal therapy in humans. Microbiological and clinical effects of a single course of periodontal scaling and root planing and of adjunctive tetracycline therapy. *J. Periodontol.*, **50**, 495-509.

Slots, J. and Rosling, B. 1983. Suppressing of the periodontopathic microflora in localized juvenile periodontitis by systemic tetracycline. *J. Clin. Periodontol.*, **10**, 465-486.

Smart, G. J., Wilson, M., Davies, E. H. and Kieser, J. B. 1990. The assessment of ultrasonic root surface debridement by determination of residual endotoxin levels. *J. Clin. Periodontol.*, **17**, 174-178.

Southard, S. S., Drisko, C., Killoy, W., Cobb, C. M. and Tira, D. E. 1989. The effect of 2% chlorhexidine digluconate irrigation on clinical parameters and the level of *Bacteroides gingivalis* in periodontal pockets. *J. Periodontol.*, **60**, 302-309.

Stambaugh, R. V., Dragoo, M., Smith, D. M. and Carasali, L. 1981. The limits of subgingival scaling. *Int. J. Periodontics Restorative Dent.*, **1**, 30-41.

Taggart, J. A., Palmer, R. M. and Wilson, R. F. 1990. A clinical and microbiological comparison of the effects of water and 0.02% chlorhexidine as coolants during ultrasonic scaling and root planing. *J. Clin. Periodontol.*, **17**, 32-37.

Takacs, V. J., Lie, T., Perala, D. G. and Adams, D. F. 1993. Efficacy of 5 machining instruments in scaling of molar furcations. *J. Periodontol.*, **64**, 228-236.

Thilo, B. E. and Baehni, P. C. 1987. Effect of ultrasonic instrumentation on dental plaque microflora in vitro. *J. Periodont. Res.*, **22**, 518-521.

Thornton, S. and Garnick, J. 1982. Comparison of ultrasonic to hand instruments in the removal of subgingival plaque. *J. Periodontol.*, **53**, 35-37.

Torfason, T., Kiger, R., Selvig, K. A. and Egelberg, J. 1979. Clinical improvement of gingival conditions following ultrasonic versus hand instrumentation of periodontal pockets. *J. Clin. Periodontol.*, **6**, 165-176.

Turesky, S., Renstrup, G. and Glickman, I. 1961. Histologic and histochemical observations regarding early calculus formation in children and adults. *J. Periodontol.*, **32**, 7-14.

Vandekerckhove, B. N. A., Bollen, C. M. L., Dekeyser, C., Darius, P. and Quirynen, M. 1996. Full-versus partial-mouth disinfection in the treatment of periodontal infections. Long-term clinical observations of a pilot study. *J. Periodontol.*, **67**, 1251-1259.

Van Volkinburg, J. W., Green, E. and Armitage, G. C. 1976. The nature of root surfaces after curette, cavitron and alpha-sonic instrumentation. *J. Periodont. Res.*, **11**, 374-381.

Van Winkelhoff, A. J., Van der Velden, U. and de Graff, J. 1988. Microbial succession in recolonizing deep periodontal pockets after a single course of supra- and subgingival debridement. *J. Clin. Periodontol.*, **15**, 116-122.

von Troil-Lindén, B., Saarela, M., Mättö, J., Alaluusua, S., Jousimies-Somer, H. and Asikainen, S. 1996. Source of suspected periodontal pathogens re-emerging after periodontal treatment. *J. Clin. Periodontol.*, **23**, 601-607.

Virchow, H. V. 1920. *Die menschlichen Skelettreste aus dem Kamf" schen Bruch in Travertin von Ehringsdorf bei Weimar,* p. 28-32, Fischer, Jena.

Waerhaug, J. 1956. Effect of rough surfaces upon gingival tissue. *J. Dent. Res.*, **35**, 323-325.

Waerhaug, J. 1978. Healing of the dentoepithelial junction following subgingival plaque control. II. As observed in human biopsy material. *J. Periodontol.*, **49**, 1-8.

Walmsley, A. D., Laird, W. R. E. and Williams, A. R. 1986. Inherent variability in the performance of the ultrasonic descaler. *J. Dent.*, **14**, 121-125.

Walmsley, A. D., Laird, W. R. E. and Williams, A. R. 1988. Dental plaque removal by cavitational activity during ultrasonic scaling. *J. Clin. Periodontol.*, **15**, 539-543.

Walmsley, A. D. 1989. Ultrasonic and sonic scalers. *Br. Dent. Surg. Asst.*, **48**, 26-29.

Walmsley, A. D., Walsh, T. F., Laird, W. R. and Williams, A. R. 1990. Effects of cavitational activity on the root surface of teeth during ultrasonic scaling. *J. Clin. Periodontol.*, **17**, 306-312.

Walsh, T. F. and Waite, I. M. 1978. A comparison of postsurgical healing following debridement by ultrasonic or hand instruments. *J. Periodontol.*, **49**, 201-205.

Ward, S. C., Johanson, D. C. and Coppens, Y. 1982. Subocclusal morphology and alveolar process relationships of hominid gnathic elements from the Hadar formation: 1974-1977 collections. *Am. J. Phys. Anthropol.,* **57**, 605-6630.

Weinberger, B. W. 1948. *An Introduction to the History of Dentistry*. Volume I. , pp. 49-87 and 205-207, C. V. Mosby Co., St. Louis.

Westfelt, E., Nyman, S., Socransky, S. and Lindhe, J. 1983. Significance of frequency of professional tooth cleaning for healing following periodontal surgery. *J. Clin. Periodontol.*, **10**, 148-156.

Westfelt, E., Rylander, H., Dahlén, G. and Lindhe, J. 1998. The effect of supragingival plaque control on the progression of advanced periodontal disease. *J. Clin. Periodontol.*, **25**, 536-541.

Wilkinson, R. F. and Maybury, J. E. 1973. Scanning electron microscopy of the root surface following instrumentation. *J. Periodontol.*, **44**, 559-563.

Wilson, M., Moore, J. E. and Kieser, J. B. 1986. Identity of limulus amoebocyte lysate-active root surface materials from periodontally involved teeth. *J. Clin. Periodontol.*, **13**, 743-747.

(WWP) *Proceedings of the World Workshop in Clinical Periodontics.* 1989. Nevins, M., Becker, W., Kornman, K. (eds.), pp. II-13, American Academy of Periodontology, Princeton, New Jersey..

Yukna, R. A., Scott, J. B., Aichelmann-Reidy, M. E., LeBlanc, D. M. and Mayer, E. T. 1997. Clinical evaluation of the speed and effectiveness of subgingival calculus removal on single-rooted teeth with diamond-coated ultrasonic tips. *J. Periodontol.*, **68**, 436-442.

Zappa, U., Smith, B., Simona, S., Graf, H., Case, D. and Kim, W. 1991a. Root substance removal by scaling and root planing. *J. Periodontol.*, **62**:750-754.

Zappa, U., Cadosch, J., Simona, C. Graf, H. and Case, D. 1991b. In vivo scaling and root planing forces. *J. Periodontol.*, **62**, 335-340.

Zitterbart, P.A. 1987. Effectiveness of ultrasonic scalers: A literature review. *Gen. Dent.*, **35**, 295-297.

The Laser and Non-Surgical Periodontal Therapy

Altschuler, G. B. and Grisimov, V. N. 1990. The effect of wave-guide light propagation in human tooth. *Dokl. Akad. Nauk. S. S. R.* (Russia), **310**, 1245-1248.

Aoki, A., Ando, Y., Watanabe, H. and Ishikawa, I. *1994.* In vitro studies on laser scaling of subgingival calculus with an erbium:YAG laser. *J. Periodontol.*, **65**, 1097-1106.

Arakawa, S., Cobb, C. M., Rapley, J. W., Killoy, W. J. and Spencer, P. 1996. Treatment of root fracture by CO_2 and Nd:YAG lasers: An *in vitro* study. *J. Endodont.*, **22**, 662-667.

Barr, R. E., Coluzzi, d. J., Monson, G. and Raffetto, N. 1998. Laser sulcular debridement: The newest weapon in fighting periodontitis. *Dent. Today*, **17** (September), 94-95 & 154-155.

Bohem, R., Baechler, T., Webster, J. and Jauke, S. 1977. Laser processes in preventive dentistry. *Optic. Eng.,* **16**, 493-496.

Cobb, C. M., McCawley, T. K. and Killoy, W. J. 1992. A preliminary study on the effects of the Nd:YAG laser on root surfaces and subgingival microflora *in vivo. J. Periodontol.*, **63**, 701-707.

Cobb, C. M., Spencer, P. and McCollum, M. H. 1995. Histologic comparison of the CO_2 and Nd:YAG with and without water/air surface cooling on tooth root structure. *SPIE (Soc. Photo-Optical Instrumentation Eng.)*, **2394**, 20-31.

Cobb, C. M. 1996. Non-surgical pocket therapy: Mechanical. *Ann. Periodontol.*, **1**, 443-490.

Coffelt, D. W., Cobb, C. M., MacNeill, S., Rapley, J. W. and Killoy, W. J. 1997. Determination of energy density threshold for laser ablation of bacteria: An *in vitro* study. *J. Clin. Periodontol.*, **24**, 1-7.

Danesh-Meyer, M. J. 1992. Current applications of lasers in periodontics. J. *New Zealand Soc. Periodontol.*, **74**, 17-21.

Dederich, D. N., Pickard, M. A., Vaughn, A. S., Tulip, J. and Zakariasen, K. L. 1990. Comparative bactericidal exposures for selected oral bacteria using carbon dioxide laser radiation. *Lasers Surg, Med.,* **10**, 591-594.

Dederich, D. N. 1991. Laser/tissue interaction. *Alpha Omegan,* **84**, 33-36.

Dowker, S. E. P. and Elliott, J. C. 1979. Infrared absorption bands from NCO⁻ and NCN²⁻ in heated carbonate-containing apatites prepared in the presence of NH₄⁺ ions. *Calcif. Tissue Int.,* **29**, 177-178.

Dowker, S. E. P. and Elliott, J. C. 1983. Infrared study of the formation, loss, and location of cyanate and cyanamide in thermally treated apatites. *J. Solid State Chem.,* **49**, 334-340.

Echeverria, J. J. and Caffesse, R. G. 1983. Effects of subgingival curettage when performed one mouth after root instrumentation. A biometric evaluation. *J. Clin. Periodontol.,* **10**, 277-285.

El Montaser, M. A., Devlin, H., Sloan, P. and Dickinson, M. R. 1997. Pattern of healing of calvarial bone in the rat following application of the Erbium-YAG laser. *Lasers Surg. Med.,* **21**, 255-261.

Friesen, L. R., Cobb, C. M., Rapley, J. W., Forgas-Brockman, L. and Spencer, P. 1999. Laser irradiation of bone: II. Healing response following treatment by CO_2 and Nd:YAG lasers. *J. Periodontol.,* **70**, ??-??.

Fujii, T., Baehni, P. C., Kawai, O., Kawakami, T., Matsuda K. and Kowashi, Y. 19998. Scanning electron microscopic study of the effects of Er:YAG laser on root cementum. *J. Periodontol.,* **69**, 1283-1290.

Gold, S. I. 1991. Application of the Nd:YAG laser in periodontics. *New York J. Dent,* **60**, 23-26.

Gopin, B. W., Cobb, C. M., Rapley, J. W. and Killoy, W. J. 1997. Histologic evaluation of soft tissue attachment to CO_2 laser treated root surfaces: An *in vivo* study. *Int. J. Periodontics Restorative Dent.,* **17**, 317-325.

Hatit, Y. B., Blum, R., Severin, C., Maquin, M. and Jabro, M. H. 1996. The effects of a pulsed Nd:YAG laser on subgingival bacterial flora and on cementum: An *in vivo* study. *J. Clin. Laser Med. Surg.,* **14**, 137-143.

Institute for Laser Dentistry. 1990. Curettage and assistance in scaling and root planing. Oct. 19, p. 6.

Kieser, J. B. 1993. Nonsurgical periodontal therapy. In: Lang, N. P., Karring, T. (eds.), *Proceedings of the 1ˢᵗ European Workshop on Periodontology*, p. 145, Quintessence Publishing Co., Ltd., London.

Klinke, T., Klimm, W. and Gutknecht, N. 1997. Antibacterial effects of Nd:YAG laser irradiation within root canal dentin. *J. Clin. Laser Med. Surg.,* **15**, 29-31.

Lindhe, J. and Nyman, S. 1985. Scaling and granulation tissue removal in periodontal therapy. *J. Clin. Periodontol.,* **12**, 374-388.

Listgarten, M. A., Mayo, H. E. and Tremblay, R. 1975. Development of dental plaque on epoxy resin crowns in man. *J. Periodontol.,* **46**, 10-26.

Maillet, W. A., Torneck, C. D. and Friedman, Sh. 1996. Connective tissue response to root surfaces resected with Nd:YAG laser or burs. *Oral Surg. Oral Med. Oral Pathol. Oral Radiol. Endod.,* **82**, 681-690.

Midda, M. and Renton-Harper, P. 1991. Lasers in dentistry. *Br. Dent. J.,* 170, 343-346.

Midda, M. 1992. The use of lasers in periodontology. *Curr. Opin. Dent.,* 2, 104-108.

Moritz, A., Doertbudak, O., Gutknecht, N., Goharkhay, K., Schoop, U. and Sperr, W. 1997. Nd:YAG laser irradiation of infected root canals in combination with microbiological examinations. *J. Am. Dent. Assoc.,* **128**, 1525-1530.

Moritz, A., Schoop, U., Goharkhay, K., Schauer, P., Doertbudak, O., Wernisch, J. and Sperr, W. 1998. Treatment of periodontal pockets with a diode laser. *Lasers Surg. Med.,* **22**, 302-311.

Morlock, B. J., Pippin, D. J., Cobb, C. M., Killoy, W. J. and Rapley, J. W. 1992. The effect of Nd:YAG laser exposure on root surfaces when used as an adjunct to root planing: An *in vitro* study. *J. Periodontol.,* **63**, 637-641.

Mullarky, M. B., Norris, C. W. and Goldberg, I. D. 1985. The efficacy of the CO_2 laser in the sterilization of skin seeded with bacteria: Survival at the skin surface and in the plume emissions. *Laryngoscope,* **95**, 186-187.

Neill, M. E. and Mellonig, J. T. 1997. Clinical efficacy of the Nd:YAG laser for combination periodontitis therapy. *Pract. Periodont. Aesthet. Dent.,* **9** (suppl 6), 1-5.

Nelson, D. G. A., Shariati, M., Glena, D., Shields, C. P. and Featherstone, J. D. B. 1986. Effect of pulsed low energy infrared laser irradiation on artificial caries-like lesion formation. *Caries Res.,* **20**, 289-299.

Niemz, M. H. 1996. *Laser-Tissue Interactions. Fundamentals and Applications*, pp. 64-65, Springer-

Verlag, Berlin.

Ostertag, M., McKinley, J. T., Reinsch, L., Harris, D. M. and Tolk, N. H. 1997. Laser ablation as a function of the primary absorber in dentin. *Lasers Surg. Med.,* **21**, 384-394.

Pick, R. M. 1993. Using lasers in clinical dental practice. *J. Am. Dent. Assoc.,* **124**, 37-47.

Pinero, J. 1998. Nd:YAG-assisted periodontal curettage to prevent bacteremia before cardiovascular surgery. *Dent. Today,* **17** (March), 84-87.

Powell, G. L. and Whisenant, B. K. 1991. Comparison of three lasers for dental instrument sterilization. *Lasers Surg. Med.,* **11**, 69-71.

Radvar, M., Creanor, S. L., Gilmour, W. H., Payne, A. P., McGadey, J., Foye, R. H., Whitters, C. J. and Kinane, D. F. 1995. An evaluation of the effects of an Nd:YAG laser on subgingival calculus, dentine and cementum. An *in vitro* study. *J. Clin. Periodontol.,* **22**, 71-77.

Ramfjord, S. P., Caffesse, R. G., Morrison, E. C. *et al.* 1987. 4 modalities of periodontal treatment compared over 5 years. *J. Clin. Periodontol.,* **14**, 445-452.

Schultz, R. J., Harvey, G. P., Fernandez-Beros, M. E., Krishnamurthy, S., Rodriguez ,J. E. and Cabello, F. 1986. Bactericidal effects of the neodymium:YAG laser: *In vitro* study. *Lasers Surg. Med.,* **6**, 445-448.

Socransky, S. S., Manganiello, A. D., Propas, D., Oram ,V. and van Houte, J. 1977. Bacteriological studies of developing supragingival plaque. *J. Periodont. Res.,* **12**, 90-106.

Spencer, P., Trylovich, D. J. and Cobb, C. M. 1992. Photoacoustic FTIR spectroscopy of lased cementum surfaces. *J. Periodontol.,* **63**, 633-636.

Spencer, P., Cobb, C. M., McCollum, M. H. and Wieliczka, D. M. 1996. The effects of CO_2 laser and Nd:YAG with and without water/air surface cooling on tooth root structure: Correlation between FTIR spectroscopy and histology. *J. Periodont. Res.,* **31**, 453-462.

Takeda, F. H., Harashima, T., Kimura, Y. and Matsumoto, K. 1998a. Efficacy of Er:YAG laser irradiation in removing debris and smear layer on root canal walls. *J. Endod.,* **24**, 548-551.

Takeda, F. H., Harashima, T., Kimura, Y. and Matsumoto, K. 1998b. Comparative study about the removal of smear layer by three types of laser devices. *J. Clin. Laser Med. Surg.,* **16**, 117-122.

Talebzadeh, N., Morrison, P. R. and Fried, M. P. 1994. Comparative cell targeting in vitro using the CO_2 laser. *Lasers Surg. Med.,* **14**, 164-167.

Thomas, D., Rapley, J. W., Cobb, C. M., Spencer, P. and Killoy, W. J. 1994. Effects of the Nd:YAG laser and combined treatments on *in vitro* fibroblast attachment to root surfaces. *J. Clin. Periodontol.,* **21**, 38-44.

Tiphlova, O. and Karu, T. 1991. Action of low-intensity laser radiation on *Escherichia coli. Crit. Rev. Biomed. Eng.,* **18**, 387-412.

Trylovich, D. J., Cobb, C. M., Pippin, D. J., Spencer, P. and Killoy, W. J. 1992. The effects of the Nd:YAG laser on *in vitro* fibroblast attachment to endotoxin-treated root surfaces. *J. Periodontol.,* **63**, 626-632.

Tseng, P. and Liew, V. 1990. The potential applications of a Nd:YAG dental laser in periodontal treatment. *Periodontology* (Australia), **11**, 20-22.

Tucker, D., Rapley, J. W., Cobb, C. M. and Killoy, W. J. 1996. Morphologic changes following *in vitro* CO_2 laser treatment of calculus-ladened root surfaces. *Lasers Surg. Med.,* **18**, 150-156.

Wilder-Smith, P., Arrastia, A. A., Schell, M. J., Liaw, L. H., Grill, G. and Berns, M. W. 1995. Effect of Nd:YAG laser irradiation and root planing on the root surface: Structural and thermal effects. *J. Periodontol.,* **66**, 1032-1039.

Williams, T. M., Cobb, C. M., Rapley, J. W. and Killoy, W. J. 1995. Histological evaluation of alveolar bone following CO_2 laser removal of connective tissue from periodontal defects. *Int. J. Periodontics Restorative Dent.,* **15**, 497-506.

(WWP) *World Work Shop in Periodontics. 1966.* Ramfjord, S. P., Kerr, D. A. and Ash, M. M. (eds.), p. 383, American Academy of Periodontology, Ann Arbor, Michigan.

(WWP) *Proceedings of the World Workshop in Clinical Periodontics.* 1989. Nevins, M., Becker, W., Kornman, K. (eds.), pp. V-1-23, American Academy of Periodontology, Princeton, New Jersey.

Sonic/Ultrasonic Toothbrush

Axelsson, P., Lindhe, J. and Nystrom, B. 1991. On the prevention of caries and periodontal disease. Results of a 15-year longitudinal study on adults. *J. Clin. Periodontol.,* **18**, 182-189.

Binder, T. A., Goodson, J. M. and Socransky, S. S. 1987. Gingival fluid levels of acid and alkaline phosphatase. *J. Periodont. Res.*, **22**, 14-19.

Blanco, V. L., Cobb, C. M., Williams, K. and Manch-Citron, J. N. 1997. In vitro effect of the SenSonic toothbrush on *Treponema denticola. J. Clin. Periodontol.*, **24**, 318-323.

Dakubu, S. 1976. Cell inactivation by ultrasound. *Biotech. Bioeng.*, **18**, 465-471.

Emling, R. C. and Yankell, S. L. 1997. The application of sonic technology to oral hygiene: The third generation of powered toothbrushes. *J. Clin. Dent.*, **8** (special issue), 1-3.

Forgus-Brockmann, L. B., Carter-Hanson, C. and Killoy, W. J. 1998. The effects of an ultrasonic toothbrush on plaque accumulation and gingival inflammation. *J. Clin. Periodontol.*, **25**, 375-379.

Giuliani, D. and Martin, R. W. 1992. United States Patent. GEMTech, Inc., Bellevue, Washington (Assignee), Application Number: 832,422, Filed: 7 February 1992.

Goodson, J. M. 1989. Pharmacokinetic principles controlling efficacy of oral therapy. *J. Dent. Res.*, **68** (special issue), 1625-1632.

Grossman, E., Dembling, W. and Proskin, H. M. 1995. A comparative clinical investigation of the safety and efficacy of an oscillating/rotating electric toothbrush and a sonic toothbrush. *J. Clin. Dent.*, **6**, 108-112.

Hesselberg, I. 1952. Investigations on the effect of ultrasonics on bacteria. *Acta Pathol. Microbiol. Scand.*, **93** (suppl.), 389-397.

Ho, H. P. and Niederman, R. 1997. Effectiveness of the Sonicare sonic toothbrush on reduction of plaque, gingivitis, probing pocket depth and subgingival bacteria in adolescent orthodontic patients. *J. Clin. Dent.*, **8**, 15-19.

Johnson, B. D. and McInnes, C. 1994. Clinical evaluation of the efficacy and safety of a new sonic toothbrush. *J. Periodontol.*, **65**, 692-697.

Marsh, P. D. and Martin, M. 1992. *Oral Microbiology*, pp. 56-97, Chapman & Hall, New York.

McInnes, C., Engel, d., Moncla, B. J. and Martin, R. W. 1992. Reduction in adherence of *Actinomyces viscosus* after exposure to low-frequency acoustic energy. *Oral Microbiol. Immunol.*, **7**, 171-176.

McInnes, C., Engel, D. and Martin, R. W. 1993. Fimbria damage and removal of adherent bacteria after exposure to acoustic energy. *Oral Microbiol. Immunol.*, **8**, 277-282.

McInnes, C., Johnson, B., Emling, R. C. and Yankell, S. L. 1994. Clinical and computer-assisted evaluations of the stain removal ability of the Sonicare' electronic toothbrush. *J. Clin. Dent.*, **5**, 13-18.

O'Beirne, G., Johnson, R. H., Persson, G. R. and Spektor, M. D. 1996. Efficacy of a sonic toothbrush on inflammation and probing depth in adult periodontitis. *J. Periodontol.*, **67**, 900-908.

Olsen, I. and Socransky, S. S. 1981. Ultrasonic dispersion of pure cultures of plaque bacteria and plaque. *Scan. J. Dent. Res.*, **89**, 307-312.

Robinson, P. J., Maddalozzo, D. and Breslin, S. 1997. A 6-month clinical comparison of the efficacy of the Sonicare and the Braun Oral-B electric toothbrushes on improving periodontal health in adult periodontitis patients. *J. Clin. Dent.*, **7** (special issue), 4-9.

Robrish, S. A., Grove, S. B., Bernstein, R. S., Marucha, P. T., Socransky, S. S. and Amdur, B. 1976. Effect of sonic treatment on pure cultures and aggregates of bacteria. *J. Clin. Microbiol.*, **3**, 474-479.

Terezhalmy, G. T., Gagliardi, V. B., Rybicki, L. A. and Kauffman, M. J. 1994. Clinical evaluation of the efficacy and safety of the UltraSonex® toothbrush: A 30-day study. *Compend. Contin. Educ. Dent.*, **7**, 866-874.

Terezhalmy, G. T., Iffland, H., Jelepis, C. and Waskowski, J. 1995. Clinical evaluation of the effect of an ultrasonic toothbrush on plaque, gingivitis, and gingival bleeding: A six-month study. *J. Prosthet. Dent.*, **73**, 97-103.

Tritten, C. B. and Armitage, G. C. 1996. Comparison of a sonic and a manual toothbrush for efficacy in supragingival plaque removal and reduction of gingivitis. *J. Clin. Periodontol.*, **23**, 641-648.

Van der Weijden, G. A., Timmerman, M. F., Reijerse, E., Snoek, C. M. and Van der Velden, U. 1996. Comparison of an oscillating/rotating electric toothbrush and a 'sonic' toothbrush in plaque-removing ability. A professional toothbrushing and supervised brushing study. *J. Clin. Periodontol.*, **23**, 407-411.

Wolff, L., Kim, A., Nunn, M., Bakdash, B. and Hinrichs, J. 1998. Effectiveness of a sonic toothbrush in maintenance of dental implants. A prospective study. *J. Clin. Periodontol.*, **25**, 821-828.

Wu-Yuan, C. D., Anderson, R. D. and McInnes, C. 1994. Ability of the Sonicare® electronic toothbrush to generate dynamic fluid activity that removes bacteria. *J. Clin. Dent.*, **5**, 89-93.

Yankell, S. L., Emling, R. C. and Shi, X. 1997. Interproximal access efficacy of Sonicare® plus and Braun Oral-B® Ultra compared to a manual toothbrush. *J. Clin. Dent.*, **8** (special issue), 26-29.

LABORATORY ASSESSMENT OF ANTIMICROBIALS FOR PLAQUE-RELATED DISEASES

Michael Wilson and Jonathan Pratten

There is great interest in the use of antimicrobial agents for the prevention and treatment of dental plaque-related diseases. In order to predict their likely effectiveness **in vivo**, *laboratory assessment of the antimicrobial susceptibility of the causative agents of these diseases requires that the organisms are tested when in the form of biofilms. However, surprisingly few studies of the suscepti- bility of oral biofilms to antimicrobial agents have appeared in the literature. There are, therefore, few data available regarding those characteristics of antimicrobials (e.g. their Biofilm Eliminating Concentrations) which could be used to judge their suitability for treating plaque-related diseases. Of those studies which have employed biofilms, a variety of systems have been used to generate oral bacterial biofilms for testing. These include: (a) growing the target bacteria on membrane filters (b) suspending hydroxyapatite discs in batch or continuous culture systems (c) the modified Robbins device and (d) the constant depth film fermentor. Using these devices, monospecies and multi- species biofilms, as well as microcosm dental plaques, have been grown and their susceptibility to antiseptics, antibiotics and new antimicrobial approaches has been determined. Oral microbiologists have also employed flow cell tech- nology to assess the ability of antimicrobials and anti-adhesives to prevent biofilm formation. Use of such biofilm-based laboratory models will aid the selection of agents suitable for further evaluation in clinical trials. The various laboratory devices which have been used to generate oral biofilms and assess their response to antimicrobials will be described and the results obtained with them will be reviewed.*

Introduction

The accumulation of bacterial biofilms on tooth surfaces results in two of the most prevalent infectious diseases of man - caries and periodontal diseases. Although prevention and control of these diseases may be achieved by daily mechanical removal of the biofilms, many individuals are either unable or unwilling to practice these procedures as regularly or as efficiently as is neces- sary. There is, therefore, great interest in the possibility of using chemicals to replace, or augment, mechanical preventive and therapeutic procedures (Marsh and Bradshaw, 1993; ten Cate and Marsh, 1994; Newman *et al.,* 1996). The attractions of such an approach are that both prevention and therapy would be easier for the patient and the dental practitioner. Unlike classical infectious diseases, in which chemical control invariably means the use of agents which kill (or inhibit the growth of) the target organism, diseases due to oral biofilms are amenable to control by chemical agents with properties other than bactericidal or bacteriostatic activities. The biofilmic nature of the causative organisms of these diseases, together with the topical location of these biofilms, enables the use of a variety of approaches to their control. Hence chemicals could be used to: (a) prevent the formation of biofilms, (b) disrupt existing biofilms, (c) prevent further growth of the biofilms, (d) kill particular organisms in the biofilm. While the latter two of these approaches could be achieved by chemicals with bactericidal or bacteriostatic activity, the first two do not necessitate the chemicals having any such properties. The laboratory evaluation of agents which might be useful for preventing biofilm formation or disrupting biofilms has involved the use of biofilm-based models such as steel wires immersed in a bacterial suspension (McCabe *et al.,* 1967) or more complex devices such as flow cells (Rundegren *et al.,* 1992; Herles *et al.,* 1994) or "artificial mouths" (Coulter and Russell, 1976). However, the evaluation of antimicrobial agents has usually utilised methodologies borrowed from diagnostic medical microbiology e.g. determination of the minimum inhibitory concentration - MIC - of the agent. However, the use of MIC determinations as a measure of the potential effectiveness of an antimicrobial for use against biofilm-related oral infections is inappropriate for a number of reasons (Wilson, 1993; Wilson, 1996). Firstly, there are now many studies which have demonstrated that the susceptibility of bacteria to antimicrobial agents is profoundly affected by the biofilm mode of growth (Nichols, 1989; Anwar *et al.,* 1990). Biofilms of a particular organism are considerably less susceptible to these agents than the planktonic form of the organism. Secondly, MIC determinations involve exposure of the target organism to a large excess of the antimicrobial agent for long periods of time - at least overnight in the case of most organisms but, for slow-growing oral species, this could be for several days. However, it is difficult to maintain high concentrations of an antimicrobial agent within the oral cavity for long periods of time - particularly in the case of supragingival regions. Thirdly, the MIC test involves the use of a static, closed system whereas oral biofilms *in vivo* constitute part of an open, dynamic system characterised by a continuous, but varying, flow of saliva which can remove the antimicrobial agent and deposit fresh organisms on the target biofilm. It is clear, therefore, that testing of the antimicrobial susceptibility of biofilms requires a methodology very different from that used in determining the MIC of planktonic bacteria. In recognition of the differences between the antimicrobial susceptibility of biofilms and planktonic cells, it has been suggested that the terms Biofilm Inhibitory Concentration (BIC) and Biofilm Killing (or Eliminating) Concentration (BKC or BEC), analogous to MIC and MBC should be used (Anwar and Costerton, 1990; Costerton et al., 1993; Nichols, 1994). Unfortunately, there are, as yet, no generally-agreed experimental protocols for determining these important characteristics of antimicrobial agents.

Despite the great interest in the use of antimicrobial agents for controlling oral biofilms there have been disappointingly few reported studies of the susceptibility of oral bacterial biofilms to antibiotics or antiseptics. The simplicity and rapidity of MIC determinations compared to the labour-intensive and time-consuming methods required to obtain values for the BIC, BKC or BEC of an agent have helped to maintain the pre-eminence of MICs as arbiters of the effectiveness of an antimicrobial agent for use against oral biofilms - despite their questionable relevance. During the last 10 years nearly 300 papers have been published on the antimicrobial susceptibility of bacteria in biofilms yet fewer than 5% of these have involved the use of oral bacteria. Furthermore, the studies which have been carried out have used very different laboratory models to evaluate biofilm susceptibility hence making it difficult to get a consensus view of the effectiveness of a particular agent. The ideal laboratory model should take account of the following important features of the oral environment which have a profound effect on the likely effectiveness of an antimicrobial agent *in vivo*:

1. the biofilms form on a solid substratum (enamel, cementum, restorative materials etc) and are in contact with a thin film of liquid (saliva or gingival crevicular fluid)
2. the fluid phase is continually being replaced
3. the bacteria are attached to the substratum via a conditioning film composed mainly of salivary glycoproteins or crevicular fluid proteins
4. the biofilms are subjected to mechanical and hydrodynamic shear forces
5. a wide variety of organisms are present in the biofilms
6. the system may be aerobic (supragingival) or anaerobic (subgingival)

This paper will summarise the data obtained from biofilm-based studies concerned with the antimicrobial susceptibility of oral bacteria, grouped according to the type of biofilm model used.

Closed culture biofilm models

These are systems in which there is no exchange of materials (particularly nutrients and waste products) with the external environment so that the system is constantly changing in terms of the concentration of these materials as well as physicochemical factors such as pH, redox potential etc. They are, therefore, fundamentally flawed as models of oral biofilms *in vivo* as one of the defining characteristics of the oral cavity is the continual flow-through of nutrients, organisms etc. However, their great attraction is that they are technically simple to perform and can be used in high-throughput primary screening of large numbers of compounds.

Growth on Agar Plates

If we define a biofilm as an assembly of bacteria embedded in a polymeric matrix then one of the simplest models of a biofilm is provided by a lawn of bacteria growing on an agar plate. This would constitute an example of a biofilm growing at a solid/air interface rather than one at a solid/liquid interface - the latter being more representative of pathological biofilms in man. There are a number of reports in which this simple model has been used to test the susceptibility of non-oral bacteria to antimicrobial agents (Kurian and Lorian, 1980; Al-Hiti and Gilbert, 1983). With regard to oral bacteria, the only reports of its use

505

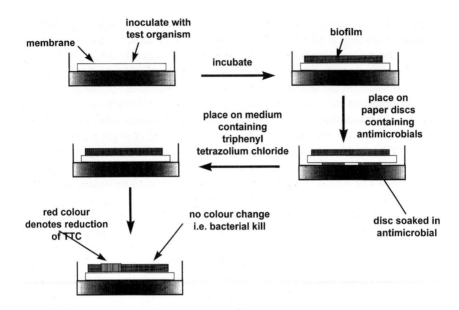

Figure 1 Membrane transfer method for determining susceptibility of oral biofilms to antimicrobial agents (Caufield *et al.*, 1987).

has been in the testing of their susceptibility to light-activated antimicrobial agents (Dobson and Wilson, 1992; Burns *et al.*, 1994). Dobson and Wilson (1992) grew biofilms of *Porphyromonas gingivalis, Fusobacterium nucleatum* and *Actinobacillus actinomycetemcomitans* on agar plates, added a solution of a photosensitising agent and then irradiated the biofilms with light from a low-power helium/neon laser for various periods of time. To determine whether a bactericidal effect had been achieved, sterile nitrocellulose membranes were placed over the irradiated portions of the biofilms and then removed, inverted, placed on the surfaces of fresh agar plates, incubated and examined for bacterial growth. A growth-free zone on the membrane indicated that at least some of the irradiated bacteria had been killed. Of a number of compounds tested, toluidine blue O was found to be an effective photosensitiser of all three organisms and kills were detectable using light energy doses of 73 mJ (energy density = 5.5 J/cm^2). The laser light had no detectable effect on the viability of any of the organisms in the absence of a photosensitiser. Light-activated drugs have also been shown to be effective against biofilms of cariogenic organisms (*Streptococcus mutans, Strep. sobrinus, Lactobacillus casei* and *Actinomyces viscosus*) using this model (Burns *et al.*, 1994).

Membrane Filter-based Model

Instead of growing the bacteria directly on the agar, a biofilm can be grown on a membrane filter placed on the agar surface. As this enables the membrane and associated biofilm to be removed it has certain technical advantages over the simpler model described above. The biofilms can be exposed to the test agent without the problems associated with antimicrobial-agar or antimicrobial-growth medium interactions and large numbers of biofilms may be grown on a single plate so aiding statistical analysis of results. The technique has been used for testing the antimicrobial susceptibility of oral bacteria (*Strep. sanguis* and a number of periodontopathogens) and *Pseudomonas aeruginosa* (Caufield *et al.*, 1987; Millward and Wilson, 1989; Nichols *et al.*, 1989). In the study of Caufield *et al* (1987), membranes with biofilms of periodontopathogenic species were transferred to another agar plate on the surface of which had been placed paper discs containing various concentrations of antimicrobial agents (Figure 1). After being left in contact with the discs for 5 mins, the membrane was transferred to another agar plate containing the redox indicator triphenyl tetrazolium chloride (TTC). As viable bacteria can reduce the TTC to a red product, a colourless zone on the membrane was indicative of a bactericidal effect hence the minimum concentration of the agents required to kill the organisms in the biofilms (i.e. the BKC) could be determined. Using this technique, the BKC of chlorhexidine, iodine, stannous fluoride and sodium fluoride for a number of oral bacteria were determined. The technique offers a simple means of determining the susceptibility of oral bacterial biofilms to antimicrobial agents. One potential problem associated with the use of redox dyes as indicators of cell "viability" is that non-viable bacteria may still be able to reduce the dye. When used in the manner described above, therefore, dye reduction may be apparent on plates containing antimicrobial concentrations greater than the BKC. This would lead to an erroneous value for the BKC and an underestimate of the effectiveness of the antibacterial agent (Stewart *et al.*,1994).

A membrane-based approach has also been used to determine the susceptibility of *Strep. sanguis* biofilms to chlorhexidine (Millward and Wilson, 1989). The organism was inoculated on to cellulose nitrate membrane filters placed on the surfaces of a blood-containing medium and incubated for various periods of time to provide biofilms of different age each containing approximately 10^7 cfu/cm^2 (Figure 2). The membrane-supported biofilms were then removed from the agar plates and exposed to chlorhexidine gluconate (CH) in experiments designed to study the effects of biofilm age, CH concentration, exposure time and the presence of blood on the kills attained. Older (72 h) biofilms were found to be less susceptible to CH than younger (24 h) ones, the BKC for a 4 h contact time being 200 µg/ml and 50 µg/ml respectively. The presence of blood was found to reduce the effectiveness of CH against the biofilms. The streptococci were also shown to be less susceptible to CH when in intact biofilms than when in disrupted biofilms, the BKC of CH being approximately twice its MBC for the disrupted biofilms.

The technique has also been used to study the relative effectiveness of CH and cetylpyridinium chloride (CPC), at concentrations recommended for clinical use, against biofilms of *Strep. mutans.* (Sutch *et al.,* 1995). There was no significant reduction in the viable count of 17 h biofilms (2.4 x 10^8 cfu/cm^2)

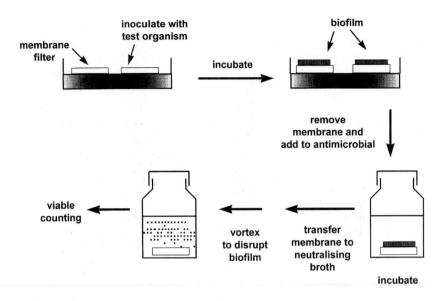

Figure 2 Determination of antimicrobial susceptibility of oral biofilms using the membrane filter method (Millward and Wilson, 1989).

after exposure to either 0.2 % (w/v) CH or 0.05 % (w/v) CPC for one minute. A five-minute exposure of the biofilms to CPC also had little effect on the viability of the streptococci in the biofilms whereas CH achieved a 2 $\log_{10}$ reduction in the viable count. Three day-old biofilms (2.2 x 10^8 cfu/cm²) proved to be less susceptible to both agents with no statistically significant decrease in the viability of the bacteria after a five-minute exposure to either antimicrobial. In contrast, exposure of planktonic cells of the organism (10^8 cfu/ml) to either agent resulted in 3 $\log_{10}$ and >4 $\log_{10}$ reductions in the viable count after only one and five minutes exposure respectively.

Biofilms of the periodontopathogenic organism, *Actinobacillus actinomycetemcomitans*, have been tested against three of the most commonly-used antimicrobial constituents of oral hygiene products - CH, CPC and triclosan (Thrower *et al.*, 1997). When used at concentrations found in commercial products, CH (0.2%) achieved the greatest bactericidal effect against 24 h and 72 h biofilms following exposure of the biofilms to the agents for 1,5 or 60 minutes (Figure 3). Triclosan (0.03%) proved to be the least effective of the agents tested.

Results obtained with closed culture biofilm models using a variety of oral bacteria and a range of agents enable three general conclusions to be drawn:
(a) biofilm-grown oral bacteria are less susceptible to antimicrobials than the corresponding planktonic cells,
(b) susceptibility decreases with biofilm age and
(c) susceptibility is decreased by the presence of blood.

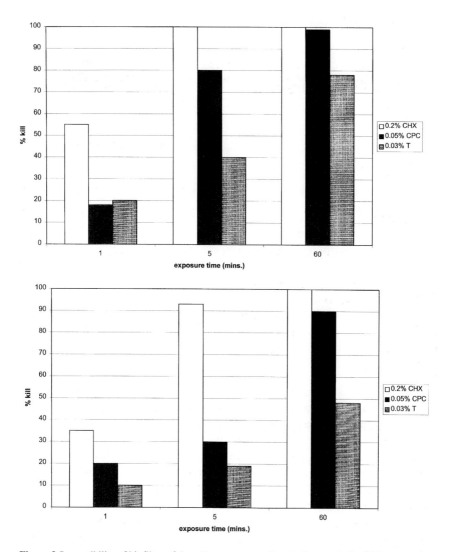

Figure 3 Susceptibility of biofilms of *A. actinomycetemcomitans* to three antimicrobial agents; a) one day old biofilms b) three day old biofilms. CHX = chlorhexidine, CPC = cetylpyridinium chloride, T = triclosan

Although the systems described above are technically simple and are likely to yield data more relevant to the *in vivo* situation than MIC values, they are poor models of dental plaques in their natural environment. The more noticeable defects of the models are:

1. the biofilms are produced at a solid/air interface rather than at a solid/liquid interface

2. the substratum (agar) is inappropriate

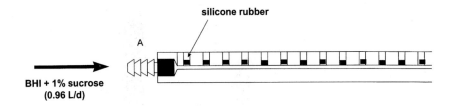

Figure 4 Modified Robbins device as used by Larsen and Fiehn (1996) to determine the susceptibility of *Strep. sanguis* to antimicrobial agents.

3. nutrients are supplied to the biofilm via the biofilm/substratum interface rather than from the biofilm/fluid interface
4. there is no simulation of salivary flow

Open continuous culture models

These models involve the exchange of materials and organisms with the external environment so that fresh nutrients may be continually added while waste products are removed. They may be sub-divided into two main types - those in which the biofilm reaches a steady state and those in which this does not occur.

Non-steady State Models

A variety of non-steady state continuous culture models have been used to study the antimicrobial susceptibility of oral biofilms and these will now be described.

Modified Robbins Device

One of the most commonly used devices used for evaluating the antimicrobial susceptibility of non-oral bacteria is the modified Robbins device (Lappin-Scott *et al.*, 1993). Surprisingly, however, it has been little-used in investigations involving oral bacterial biofilms. Larsen and Fiehn (1996) used the device to study the susceptibility of *Strep. sanguis* biofilms to chlorhexidine, amoxycillin and doxycycline. Following the establishment of the biofilms, the antimicrobial agents were pumped through the device continuously for 48 h (Figure 4). At concentrations 500 times their MIC for *S. sanguis*, the antibiotics were able to kill bacteria in the biofilms while chlorhexidine achieved this at a concentration 100 greater than its MIC for the organism. Although this device clearly has potential for evaluating antimicrobial agents, it is important that the system be adapted to mimic the environmental conditions existing in the oral cavity. The study described had several shortcomings; silicone rubber (rather than hydroxyapatite or enamel) was used as the substratum, brain heart infusion medium (instead of an artificial saliva or gingival crevicular fluid) was used as the fluid phase and the antimicrobial agents were maintained at very high concentrations for 48 h - this would be difficult to achieve *in vivo*.

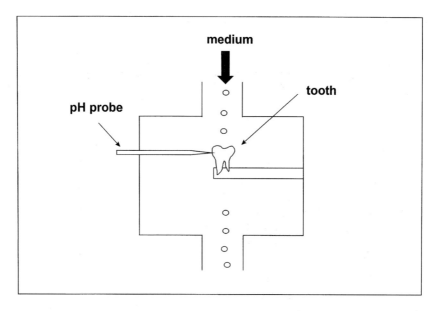

Figure 5 The artificial mouth as used by Coulter and Russell (1976) to determine the effect of chlorhexidine on microcosm dental plaques.

Artificial mouth models

A number of investigators have constructed devices which attempt to mimic the situation in the oral cavity - these have been termed artificial mouths. Coulter and Russell (1976) studied the effect of chlorhexidine on biofilm formation on the surface of a human tooth which was inoculated with human saliva and then supplied with a mucin-containing artificial saliva (Figure 5). They found that application to the tooth of a gel containing 0.5% chlorhexidine dramatically reduced plaque formation. Although the model used an appropriate substratum, fluid phase, atmospheric conditions and inoculum, its great disadvantage was that only a single biofilm was produced and the paper gave no indication of the reproducibility of the system. The number of biofilms was increased to four in the more-sophisticated device used by Zampatti *et al* (1994). In this system, as well as being supplied with an artificial saliva (although this did not contain glycoproteins - these are essential for the formation of an appropriate conditioning film), the biofilms were also periodically pulsed with both sucrose and other nutrients to simulate dietary intake (Figure 6). In order to study the effect of a chlorhexidine-containing toothpaste on the formation of biofilms of *Strep. mutans*, discs of the substratum (bovine enamel discs) were removed from the device every 8 h and treated with the toothpaste, a placebo or a control (water). Scanning electron microscopy of the enamel discs revealed that the toothpaste (containing 0.004% chlorhexidine) was able to inhibit (but not prevent) biofilm formation.

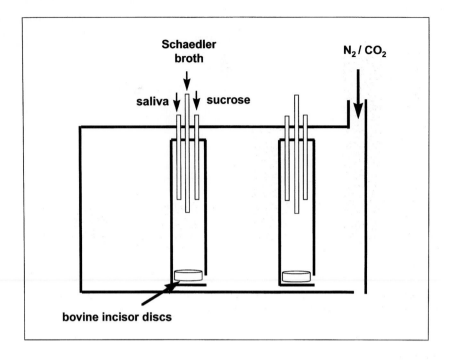

Figure 6 The artificial mouth used by Zampatti *et al.* (1994) to determine the effect of chlorhexidine on biofilm formation by *Strep.mutans*.

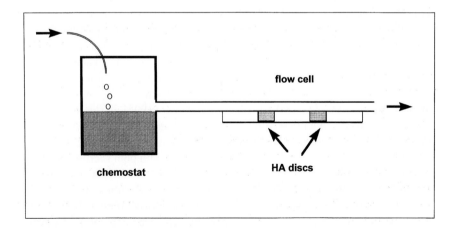

Figure 7 Use of a flow cell system to determine the susceptibility of a multi-species biofilm to triclosan (Herles *et al.*, 1994). HA = hydroxyapatite.

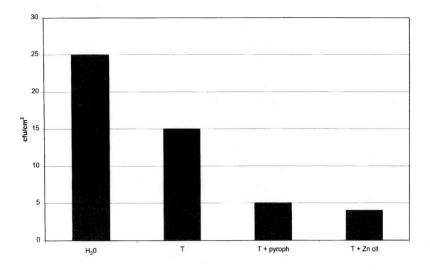

Figure 8 Results of a study of the effectiveness of triclosan on multi-species biofilms grown in a chemostat (Marsh and Bradshaw, 1993). T = triclosan, pyroph = pyrophosphate, Zn cit = zinc citrate.

Flow cells

Flow cells have been used extensively to study the adhesion of oral bacteria to surfaces (Bos *et al.*, 1999) but, surprisingly, there are few reports of their use in the assessment of antimicrobial agents. One such study (Herles *et al.,* 1994) used a chemostat to grow a five-membered community of oral bacteria and the effluent from this was passed through a flow cell containing hydroxyapatite discs which had been treated with human saliva to provide a conditioning film (Figure 7). The flow cells were then pulsed twice-daily with a mouthwash containing 0.03% triclosan. The antimicrobial-containing mouthwash caused a significant reduction in biofilm mass and in the viability of bacteria in the biofilm.

Chemostat models

Bradshaw *et al* (1990) have used the chemostat to grow stable communities of up to 10 species of oral bacteria in a mucin-containing medium and have included hydroxyapatite discs in the culture vessel to allow the formation of multi-species biofilms (Marsh and Bradshaw, 1994). The chemostat was then pulsed for one hour with triclosan (20 µg/ml), with or without zinc citrate or pyrophosphate, and the effects on the microbial composition of the biofilms determined (Figure 8). Triclosan reduced the viable count by approximately 40 % or less whereas it was reduced by 80 % when triclosan plus either zinc citrate or pyrophosphate was used. The reductions in viable counts achieved by the triclosan with either zinc citrate or pyrophosphate were due to an almost complete elimination of anaerobic Gram-negative bacteria resulting in biofilms dominated by Gram-positive facultatively anaerobic species.

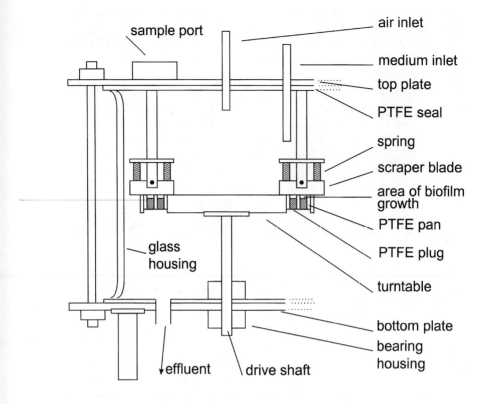

Figure 9 Diagram showing the main features of the constant depth film fermentor.

Steady State Models

Devices which enable the establishment of biofilms with a defined, reproducible composition include the perfused biofilm reactor and the constant depth film fermentor (CDFF). The former has been used to study the susceptibility of non-oral bacteria to antimicrobial agents (Gander and Gilbert, 1997) but has not, as yet, been used with oral bacteria. In contrast, there are now many reports of the use of the CDFF for investigating the susceptibility of a number of oral bacteria to a range of antimicrobial agents (Wilson, 1996; Wilson, 1999). This device enables the production of large numbers of identical biofilms under conditions which mimic those existing in the oral cavity. The CDFF consists of a glass vessel with stainless steel end-plates, the top one of which has ports for the entry of medium and gas and for sampling, while the bottom end-plate has a medium outlet (Figure 9). The vessel houses a stainless steel disc containing 15 polytetrafluoroethylene (PTFE) sampling pans and this rotates under a PTFE scraper bar which smears the incoming medium over the 15 pans and maintains the biofilms, once formed, at a constant pre-determined depth. Each sampling pan has up to 6 cylindrical holes containing PTFE plugs, on which the biofilms

514

form, with their upper surfaces recessed to a pre-determined depth below the surface of the steel disc. The PTFE plugs may also be used to support discs of hydroxyapatite, enamel, denture acrylic, restorative materials etc. enabling the formation of biofilms on a range of substrata. The sampling pans can be removed aseptically during the course of an experimental run and can then be exposed to antimicrobial agents. Alternatively, the agent can be delivered directly to the fermentor. It is particularly suitable for studies of biofilms of oral bacteria in that it can be set up to provide an environment similar to that found in the oral cavity i.e. a biofilm growing on a solid substratum with nutrients being provided in a thin film of liquid, continually replenished, trickling over the surface of the biofilm. Furthermore, the removal of the surfaces of the biofilms by the scraper blade simulates the continuous removal of the outermost layers of supragingival plaque due to mastication and tongue movements. The advantages of the system are:

1. it provides many replicates (up to 90) in a single run hence permitting good statistical analysis
2. it allows intermittent pulsing of antimicrobial agents and/or nutrients
3. it allows sampling of the biofilm (with large numbers of replicates) at various intervals during the course of a run
4. pure or mixed cultures of oral bacteria, saliva or homogenised plaque samples can be used as an inoculum. These can be added continuously or intermittently
5. it can be used to model supragingival or subgingival biofilms
6. the system is autoclavable and temperature-controlled
7. a number of substrata can be investigated e.g. hydroxyapatite, enamel, dental materials
8. the depth of the biofilms obtained can be varied
9. it can be used to study the effects of pre-treatment of substrata with antimicrobial agents on subsequent biofilm formation
10. the composition of the gaseous phase can be varied to create aerobic, anaerobic or intermediate conditions

The CDFF has been used to study the effects of antimicrobial agents on the formation of mono-species and multi-species biofilms of oral bacteria and on the survival of oral bacteria in biofilms. Furthermore, the effects of repeated pulsing of antimicrobial agents on biofilms has also been studied thus mimicking the way in which such agents are likely to be used by the public.

Effect of antimicrobial agents on biofilm formation
Pre-treatment of the substratum with certain antimicrobial-containing mouthwashes has been shown to have a dramatic effect on the formation of biofilms of *S. sanguis* (Pratten *et al.*, 1998a). When bovine enamel discs (coated with a conditioning film formed by immersion in a mucin-containing artificial saliva) were treated with mouthwashes containing 0.12% chlorhexidine, 0.03% triclosan or 0.05% CPC, the number of viable *S. sanguis* present on the discs after 4 h in the CDFF was reduced compared to a placebo and water control

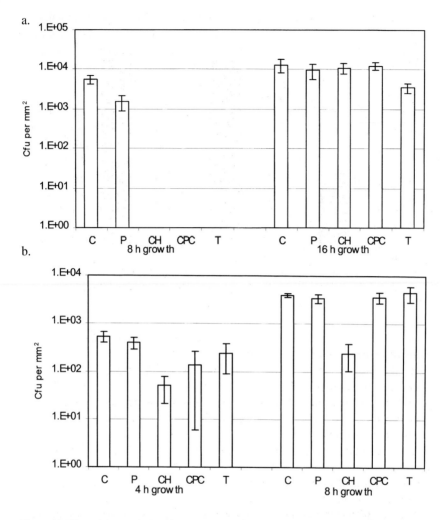

Figure 10 Effect of three antimicrobial agents on the formation of *Strep.sanguis* biofilms on (a) bovine enamel and (b) hydroxyapatite. C = control, P = placebo, CH = chlorhexidine, CPC = cetylpyridinium chloride, T = triclosan

(Figure 10). However, after 8 h, only discs which had been treated with chlorhexidine had reduced numbers of viable bacteria. The situation was very different when the substratum was hydroxyapatite. In this case, pre-treatment with a mouthwash containing any of the agents resulted in no detectable viable bacteria on the discs after 8 h. Even after 16 h in the CDFF, the number of viable bacteria on the discs treated with the triclosan-containing mouthwash was significantly lower than that on control discs. This study demonstrated for the first time that the nature of the substratum can influence the effectiveness of an antimicrobial agent against oral biofilms.

516

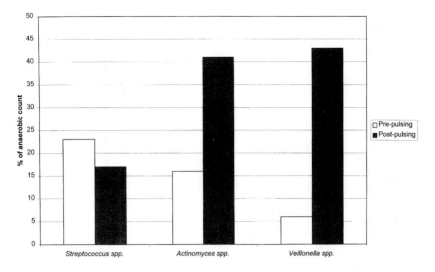

Figure 11 Effect of repeated pulsing with chlorhexidine on the bacterial composition of microcosm dental plaques.

Effect of antimicrobial agents on biofilm viability

The CDFF has been used in many studies of the susceptibility of biofilms (mono-species, multi-species and microcosm dental plaques) to antimicrobial agents (Table 1). A variety of agents have been employed including chlorhexidine, cetylpyridinium chloride, triclosan, amine fluorides and light-activated antimicrobial agents.

A number of general conclusions to be drawn from the results of these studies:

(a) monospecies, multispecies and microcosm biofilms are refractory to a variety of antimicrobial agents

(b) it is difficult to kill biofilms using short-term exposure to agents at clinically-acceptable concentrations

(c) antimicrobial agents can achieve shifts in the relative proportions of species in biofilms

(d) pre-treatment of the substratum with an antimicrobial agent followed by pulsing can reduce biofilm formation and growth

Studies of the effects of pulsing of the antimicrobial agent on multi-species biofilms are particularly interesting as they enable predictions of the likely effects on the oral microflora of long-term exposure to the agents. In one such study (Pratten *et al.,* 1998b) biofilms were grown on bovine enamel discs from a human saliva inoculum using a mucin-containing artificial saliva as the nutrient source. The composition of the microcosm dental plaques obtained were similar to that of approximal plaque in that they consisted of 25% streptococci, 19% *Actinomyces* spp. and 7% *Veillonella* spp. Corresponding figures for approximal

Table 1 Studies concerning the effect of antimicrobial agents on oral biofilms which have used the constant depth film fermentor.

Type of biofilm	Agents tested	Mode of application	Reference
S. sanguis	Light-activated antimicrobial agents (toluidine blue O and aluminium disulphonated phthalocyanine).	Single application	Wilson et al., 1996a
S. sanguis	Chlorhexidine gluconate and cetylpyridinium chloride	Single application	Wilson et al., 1996b.
Nine-membered community	Chlorhexidine	Twice-daily pulsing	Kinniment et al., 1996
Microcosm dental plaques	Chlorhexidine	Single application	Wilson et al., 1998
S. sanguis	Triclosan, cetylpyridinium chloride, chlorhexidine	Single application	Pratten et al.,1998a
S. sanguis	Chlorhexidine	Twice-daily pulsing	Pratten et al., 1998b
Microcosm dental plaques	Light-activated antimicrobial agent (toluidine blue)	Single application	Wilson, 1998
Three-membered community	Light-activated antimicrobial agent (toluidine blue)	Single application	Wilson, 1998
Six-membered community	Chlorhexidine	Single application	Pratten et al.,1998c
S. sanguis	Amine fluorides	Single application	Embleton et al., 1998
Microcosm dental plaques grown in sucrose	Chlorhexidine	Twice-daily pulsing	Pratten and Wilson, 1999
Microcosm dental plaques	Chlorhexidine	Twice-daily pulsing	Pratten et al., 1998b

plaque being 24%, 28% and 11% respectively. 10 ml of 0.2% chlorhexidine gluconate were pulsed into the CDFF twice daily and the initial pulse achieved a reduction in the viable count of approximately 90%. However, after 6 days of chlorhexidine pulsing, the viable count had returned to its pre-pulsing level although the bacterial composition of the biofilms had been substantially altered. The proportions of streptococci, *Actinomyces* spp. and *Veillonella* spp. after pulsing were 18%, 23% and 48% respectively which, when compared with the pre-pulsing composition (see above) represented a slight decrease in the proportion of streptococci but considerable increases in the proportions of *Actinomyces* spp. and *Veillonella* spp (Figure 11). Cryosectioning of the biofilms following exposure to an antimicrobial agent can also yield information concerning penetration of the agent. Hence, Figure 12 shows the results of viable counting of cryosectioning of microcosm dental plaques before and after exposure to 0.2% chlorhexidine gluconate for 60 s. Broadly speaking, approximately a one log reduction in the viable counts of most species occurred in most sections of the biofilm suggesting that the chlorhexidine had penetrated rapidly through the biofilm.

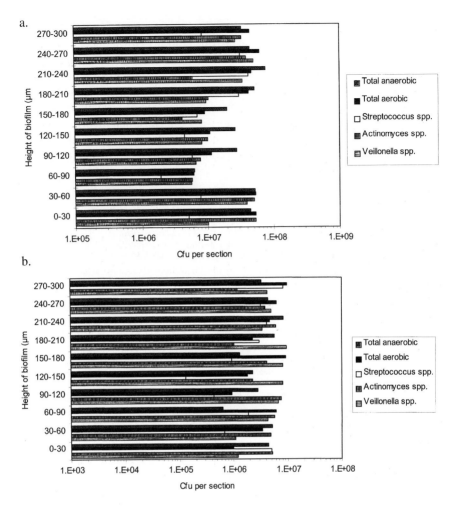

Figure 12 Distribution of viable bacteria at different levels within microcosm dental plaques before (a) and after (b) exposure to chlorhexidine for 60s.

Conclusions

From this comprehensive survey of the laboratory models which have been used for the evaluation of the susceptibility of oral biofilms to antimicrobial agents, it can be seen that, while the number of published studies has been very limited, the variety of models used has been wide. This illustrates two fundamental problems with current *in vitro* testing of antimicrobial agents for use in the treatment or prevention of plaque-related diseases. Firstly, not enough studies are employing biofilm-based models and secondly, there is no consensus emerging with regard to the type of model best suited to the task. In terms of the number of studies published using a particular model, the CDFF leads the field as at least ten such papers have been published using this model. This is undoubtedly a versatile model which is appropriate for testing the antimicrobial susceptibility of oral biofilms as it can provide biofilms grown under conditions similar to those which exist in the oral environment. The main advantages of the system have been referred to previously.

Clinical evaluation of antimicrobial agents for use in treating plaque-related diseases is expensive and, if the selection of the agents to be tested in this manner is based on inappropriate laboratory assessment, could involve a huge waste of resources. The use of biofilm-based models for such preliminary laboratory evaluation will enable the selection of agents that are more likely to be effective in clinical trials.

References

Al-Hiti, M..M.A. and Gilbert, P. 1983. A note on inoculum reproducibility: solid culture versus liquid culture. *J. Appl. Bacteriol.*, **55**, 173-176.

Anwar, H., Dasgupta, M.K. and Costerton J.W. 1990. Testing the susceptibility of bacteria in biofilms to antibacterial agents. *Antimicrob. Ag. Chemother.*, **34**, 2043-2046.

Anwar, H., Costerton, J.W. 1990. Enhanced activity of combinations of tobramycin and piperacillin for eradication of sessile biofilm cells of *Pseudomonas aeruginosa*. *Antimicrob. Ag. Chemother.*, **34**, 1666-1671.

Bradshaw, D.J., McKee, A.S., Marsh, P.D. 1990. Prevention of population shifts in oral microbial communities *in vitro* by low fluoride concentrations. *J. Dent. Res.*, **69**, 436-441.

Burns, T., Wilson, M. and Pearson, G. 1994. Sensitisation of cariogenic bacteria in biofilms to killing by low power laser light. *Proc. 4th Int. Con. Las. Dent.*, 66.

Caufield, P.W., Allen, D.N. and Childers, N.K. 1987. *In vitro* susceptibilities of suspected periodontopathogenic anaerobes as determined by membrane transfer assay. *Antimicrob. Ag. Chemother.*, **31**, 1989-93.

Costerton, J.W., Khoury, A.E., Ward, K.H. and Anwar, H. 1993. Practical measures to control device-related bacterial infections. *Int. J. Artif. Organs.*, **16**, 765-770.

Coulter, W.A. and Russell, C. 1976. Effect of chlorhexidine on plaque development in an artificial mouth. *Microbios.*, **16**, 21-28.

Dobson. J. and Wilson, M. 1992. Sensitisation of oral bacteria in biofilms to killing by light from a low-power laser. *Arch. Oral Biol.*, **37**, 883-887.

Embleton, J.V., Newman, H.N. and Wilson, M. 1998. Influence of growth mode and sucrose concentration on susceptibility of *Streptococcus sanguis* to amine fluoride and amine fluoride-inorganic fluoride combinations. *Appl. Environ. Microbiol.*, **64**, 3503-3506.

Gander, S. and Gilbert, P.J. 1997. The development of a small-scale biofilm model suitable for studying the effects of antibiotics on biofilms of gram-negative bacteria. *Antimicrob. Chemother.*, **40**, 329-34.

Herles. S., Olsen, S., Afflitto, J. and Gaffar, A. 1994. Chemostat flow cell system: an *in vitro* model for the evaluation of antiplaque agents. *J. Dent. Res.*, **73**, 1748-55.

Kinniment, S.L., Wimpenny, J.W., Adams, D. and Marsh, P.D. 1996. The effect of chlorhexidine on defined, mixed culture oral biofilms grown in a novel model system. *J. Appl. Bacteriol.*, **81**, 120-125.

Kurian, S. and Lorian, V. 1980. Discrepancies between results obtained by agar and broth techniques in testing of drug combinations. *J. Clin. Microbiol.*, **11**, 527-529.

Lappin-Scott, H.M., Jass, J. and Costerton, J.W. 1993. Microbial biofilm formation and characterization. In: Denyer SP, Gorman SP, Sussman M (eds.), *Microbial Biofilms: Formation and Control.* pp. 1-12, Blackwell Scientific Publications Ltd., Oxford.

Larsen, T. and Fiehn, N.E. 1996. Resistance of *Streptococcus sanguis* biofilms to antimicrobial agents. *A.P.M.I.S.*, **104**, 280-284.

Marsh, P.D. and Bradshaw, D.J. 1993. Microbiological effects of new agents in dentifrices for plaque control. *Int. Dent. J.*, **43**, 399-406.

McCabe, R.M., Keyes, P.H. and Howell, A. 1967. An *in vitro* method for assessing the plaque forming ability of oral bacteria. *Arch. Oral Biol.,* **12,** 1653-1656.

Millward, T.A. and Wilson, M. 1989. The effect of chlorhexidine on *Streptococcus sanguis* biofilms. *Microbios.,* **58,** 155-164.

Newman, H., Henderson, B. and Wilson, M. 1996. Chemical plaque control. In: Porter, S. and Scully, C. (eds.), *Innovations and developments in non-invasive oro-facial healthcare,* pp. 215-258. Science Reviews, Northwood.

Nichols, W.W. 1989. Susceptibility of biofilms to toxic compounds. In: Characklis, W.G and Wilderer, P.A. (eds.), *Structure and function of biofilms,* pp. 321-331. John Wiley, Chichester.

Nichols, W.M., Evans, M.J., Slack, M.P.E. and Walmsey, H.L. 1989. The penetration of antibiotics into aggregates of mucoid and non-mucoid *Pseudomonas aeruginosa. J. Gen. Microbiol.,* **135,** 1291-1303.

Pratten, J., Wills, K., Barnett, P. and Wilson, M. 1998a. *In vitro* studies of the effect of antiseptic-containing mouthwashes on the formation and viability of *Streptococcus sanguis* biofilms. *J. Appl. Microbiol.,* **84,** 1149-55.

Pratten, J., Smith, A.W. and Wilson, M. 1998b. Response of single species biofilms and microcosm dental plaques to pulsing with chlorhexidine. *J. Antimicrob. Chemother.,* **42,** 453-459.

Pratten, J., Barnett, P. and Wilson, M. 1998c. Composition and susceptibility to chlorhexidine of multi-species biofilms of oral bacteria. *Appl. Environ. Microbiol.,* **64,** 3515-3519.

Pratten, J. and Wilson, M. 1999. Antimicrobial susceptibility and composition of microcosm dental plaques supplemented with sucrose. *Antimicrob Ag Chemother* - in press

Stewart, P.S., Griebe, T., Srinivasan, R., Chen, C.I., Yu, F.P., deBeer, D. and McFeters, G.A. 1994. Comparison of respiratory activity and culturability during monochloramine disinfection of binary population biofilms. *Appl. Environ. Microbiol.,* **60,** 1690-1692.

Sutch, J.C.D., Pinney, R.J. and Wilson, M. 1995. Susceptibility of *Streptococcus mutans* biofilms to oral antiseptics. *Pharm. Sci.,* **1,** 395-398.

ten Cate, J.M. and Marsh, P.D. 1994. Procedures for establishing efficacy of antimicrobial agents for chemotherapeutic caries prevention. *J. Dent. Res.,* **73,** 695-703.

Thrower, Y., Pinney, R.J. and Wilson, M. 1997. Susceptibilities of *Actinobacillus actinomycetemcomitans* biofilms to oral antiseptics. *J. Med. Micro.,* **46,** 425-429.

Wilson, M. 1993. Laboratory assessment of antimicrobial agents for the treatment of chronic periodontitis. *Microb. Ecol. Health Dis.,* **6,** 143-145.

Wilson, M. 1996. Susceptibility of oral bacterial biofilms to antimicrobial agents. *J. Med. Microbiol.,* **44,** 79-87.

Wilson, M. 1998. Control of oral biofilms by light-activated antimicrobial agents. In: Busscher, H.J., Evans, L.V. (eds.), *Oral Biofilms and Plaque Control,* pp. 323-340, Harwood Academic Publishers, London.

Wilson, M. 1999. Use of the constant depth film fermentor in studies of biofilms of oral bacteria. In: Doyle, R. (Ed.), *Biofilms,* Academic Press - in press.

Wilson, M., Burns, T. and Pratten, J. 1996a. Killing of *Streptococcus sanguis* in biofilms using a light-activated antimicrobial agent. *J. Antimicrob. Chemother.,* **37,** 377-381.

Wilson, M., Patel, H. and Fletcher, J. 1996b. Susceptibility of biofilms of *Streptococcus sanguis* to chlorhexidine gluconate and cetylpyridinium chloride. *Oral Microbiol. Immunol.,* **11,** 188-192.

Wilson, M., Patel, H. and Noar, J.H. 1998. Effect of chlorhexidine on multi-species biofilms. *Current Microbiol.,* **36,** 13-18.

Zampatti, O., Roques, C. and Michel, G. 1994. An *in vitro* mouth model to test antiplaque agents: preliminary studies using a toothpaste containing chlorhexidine. *Caries Res.,* **28,** 35-42.

NON-ANTIBIOTIC PLAQUE CHEMOTHERAPY

Connie Hastings Drisko

Introduction

The primary prevention and control of periodontal disease is through the mechanical removal of bacterial plaque (biofilm). If however, mechanical plaque control is insufficient to prevent disease, then use of chemical antiplaque agents to supplement mechanical hygiene is warranted (Cummins, 1997). Likewise, if professional cleaning is unable to control the plaque using mechanical procedures including surgical and non-surgical periodontal debridement, use of adjunctive antimicrobial therapy could benefit the patient. To date, no one cleaning device, antimicrobial toothpaste, mouthrinse, or sustained delivery agent has been able to completely prevent or arrest the reaccumulation of supragingival and subgingival plaque. In addition, certain side effects such as tooth staining make the most efficacious products containing chlorhexidine less desirable and accepted by the public because of their detrimental cosmetic effects.

This review of selected non-antibiotic antiplaque and antigingivitis agents includes a brief historical overview of each product used for the treatment and prevention of plaque, gingivitis and periodontitis and the evidence related to toothpastes, mouthrinses, and sustained local delivery of chlorhexidine. The majority of the studies reviewed are based on plaque accumulation and experimental gingivitis models or intervention studies including subjects with existing plaque, gingivitis, or periodontitis. Due to space limitations, the very large body of current literature on antimicrobials, and the dynamic nature of the development of antimicrobial agents, all products and experimental formulations could not be included in the overview. Likewise, anticaries activity exists for many of the antiplaque and antigingivitis agents, however, caries is beyond the focus of this paper.

Drug-antimicrobial contact and clearance times

In order for an antimicrobial agent to exert its bacteriostatic or bactericidal effects, the targeted microorganisms must be exposed for an adequate amount of time with a drug of minimum inhibitory concentration (MIC) or minimum bactericidal concentration (MBC). If the desired affect is aimed at supragingival plaque, then the salivary turnover rate must be considered (Goodson, 1989). The efficacy of most oral antimicrobials is largely dependent on their ability to attach to the pellicle on tooth and soft tissue surfaces before being released over time into the saliva to kill or inhibit the salivary bacteria or the bacteria attached to epithelial cells (Cummins and Creeth, 1992). Prolonged drug activity is usually referred to as substantivity, with chlorhexidine being the most substantive agent " the gold standard", to which most agents are compared over time.

Within a moderate-sized periodontal pocket, about 0.5 µl volume of pocket fluid is turned over many times every hour (Goodson, 1989). This turnover rate has been shown to increase when gingival tissue inflammation is present (Cimasoni, 1982). Oosterwaal *et al.* (1990) reported a 2-log decrease in a sodium fluorescent dye within 5 minutes of subgingival placement. This rapid clearance of fluid from the pocket addresses the limitations that are encountered when most antimicrobial agents are used subgingivally. If the agent does not have the ability to bind to the tooth and oral tissues or is not incorporated into a sustained release delivery system, the drug is usually cleared quickly and bacteria soon repopulate the oral tissues and saliva.

Drug concentrations
Effective Drug Concentrations on Biofilms
Wilson (1996) points out many publications have reported the results of studies where minimum inhibitory concentrations (MIC) of agents for cariogenic and periodontopathogenic bacteria have been determined by testing organisms in aqueous suspensions. In the laboratory assessment of antimicrobial agents aimed at the treatment of plaque-related diseases, the target organisms should be in the form of biofilms (Wilson 1996). Laboratory evaluations of chemical agents for the prevention of plaque have generally employed biofilm-based models, while agents used in the treatment of gingivitis and periodontitis generally have not (Wilson, 1996). This lack of evidence may profoundly influence the clinical outcomes of therapy aimed at treating periodontal diseases, if the biofilm-eliminating concentrations or biofilm-killing concentrations differ significantly from concentrations derived from evidence based on bacteria in their planktonic form.

When the effects of three antimicrobial-containing mouthwashes were tested on biofilm formation and bacterial viability on hydroxyapatite and enamel, the abiltiy of antimicrobial agents to prevent the accumulation of viable bacteria was found to depend onthe nature of the substratum (Pratten *et al.*, 1998a). The authors suggest the biofilm-based model used in this study is useful for studies of biofilms of oral bacteria becuase it provides an environment that is very similar to the oral cavity ie., a solid substratum where nutrients are provided in a thin film of liquid and continually replenished. Specific bacterial species have been test using three-day biofilms versus planktonic suspensions to test concentrations of chlorhexidine digluconate, cetylpyridinium chloride or triclsosan used in commercial mouthwases (Thrower *et al.*, 1997). The results of this study showed that bacterial films are much more resistant to antimicrobial agents than planktonically grown cells. Chlorhexidine in this study was far superior to the other agents in inhibiting the growth of *A. actinomycetemcomitans*, followed by cetylpyridinium chloride then triclosan. Other evidence of the efficacy of CHX in biofilms was reported by Pratten *et al.* (1998b). Their results demonstrated that chlorhexidine kills biofilms in vitro after pulsing twice daily over a period of 4 days. They propose that using a microcosm of plaque mimics the in-vivo environment more closely than when single species are used, and that interactions between bacteria of the same and different species is important in the formation and maturation of dental plaque. By using microcosm plaques similar to supra-gingival plaque, they predict more reproducible testing of compounds in vitro for their antiplaque effectiveness (Pratten et al, 1998). However, using a constant-depth film fermentor and a six-membered biofilm community, Pratten *et al.*, 1998c) found that exposure to a 0.2% chlorhexidine rinse for up to 5 minutes had minimal effect on the biofilm. These results indicate the refractory reaction of biofilms to antimicrobial agents, where exposure to 0.2% chlorhexidine mouthrinse for 1 minute had no significant effect on bacterial viability. Substantial reductions in bacterial viability were seen after 60-minute exposure, illustrating the importance of substantivity for effectiveness in antimicrobial agents designed to work intra-orally. These findings were consistent with the results of an earlier study by Wilson *et al.* (1997).

A clinical study comparing plaque accumulation using an essential oil mouthrinse or an amine fluoride/stannous fluoride mouthrinse resulted in the essential oil mouthrinse being superior to the amine fluoride/stannous fluoride mouthrinse using a kill kinetics assay and a plaque biofilm kill assay.

When biofilms of *Streptococcus sanguis* and planktonic cells of the bacteria were exposed to chlorhexidine gluconate and cetylpyridinium chloride at concentrations normally used in the clinic, *S. sanguis* exhibited a lower susceptibility to both antiseptics when it was in a biofilm rather than in the planktonic form (Wilson *et al.*, 1996). No viable bacteria were seen after 5 minutes of exposure of planktonic cells to 0.2% (w/v) of CHX or 0.05% (w/v) of cetylpyridinium chloride, where viable bacteria survived in biofilms of *S. sanguis* even after exposure to the antiseptics for 4 hours. Minimum inhibitory concentration determinations showed that chlorhexidine gluconate is more effective against *S. sanguis* than cetylpyridinium chloride, however on a molar basis, cetylpyridinium chloride was the more effective of the two antiseptics. This study suggests that the minimum inhibitory concentration is not a reliable predictor of the relative effectiveness of antimicrobial agents against *S. sanguis* biofilms, and raises questions regarding previous work where antiseptics have generally been tested against planktonic cells rather than biofilms.

Effective Drug Concentrations on Plaque

There appears to be little if any difference in the activity of 0.12% and 0.2% formulations of CHX regarding relative substantivity or plaque inhibition (Addy et al 1991a). Studies have been conducted in the laboratory using a membrane transfer technique to determine the in vitro antimicrobial concentrations needed to kill *F. nucleatum, A. actinomycetemcomitans, P. gingivalis, and P. intermedia* within a 5-minute period (Caufield *et al.*, 1987). Iodine showed 5-minute bactericidal action against the test organisms at concentrations that would be clinically attainable in subgingival sites (0.25% to 0.5%) (Rams and Slots, 1996). When the water-soluble form of povidone iodine (iodine plus the hydrophilic polymer polyvinylpyrrolidone) was used, rapid bactericidal effects against the above organisms were observed in addition to Streptococcus intermedius and E. corrodens (Higashitsutsumi *et al.,* 1993, Maruniak *et al.*, 1992,

Müller *et al.*, 1989). Chlorhexidine by comparison, required concentrations of 0.5% to 2% to achieve the 5-minute bactericidal affect for test organisms.

Currently, of CHX products, only 1% CHX gel (available only outside the USA) and chlorhexidine chips are formulated for use in concentrations that would reach or exceed the 0.5% minimal CHX concentration needed for bactericidal activity against most pathogens (Caufield *et al.*, 1987). This may explain why subgingival applications of weaker solutions of CHX have generally have little or no effect on clinical and microbial parameters following single or multiple applications with irrigators or hand held syringes (Krust *et al.*, 1991, Bratz *et al.*, 1985, Soh *et al.*, 1982, Watts *et al.*, 1986)

Other environmental conditions that alter the in vivo concentrations of antimicrobial agents may exist. Chlorhexidine, for example, can be partially inactivated in periodontal pockets due to binding to the serum proteins (Wade and Addy, 1989) that are greatly elevated in the gingival crevicular fluid in inflamed tissues (Cimasoni, 1983).

Stannous fluoride also requires concentrations of 0.5% to 2.0% to show bactericidal activity, concentrations again that generally exceed that found in commercially available products (Caufield *et al.*, 1987, Oosterwaal *et al.*, 1990). A 1.64% stannous fluoride gel, applied professionally without the benefit of root debridement has been shown to reduce gingival inflammation and decrease proportions of subgingival motile organisms over 6 to 10 weeks in one study (Schmid *et al.*, 1985) however when used in conjunction with debridement, no additional benefits have been noted (Krust *et al.*, 1993, Oosterwaal *et al.*, 1991, Perry *et al.*, 1984).

Maruniak *et al.* (1992) and Mayasaki *et al.* (1986) report that the bactericidal effect of povidone-iodine (PVP-I) is potentiated in vitro when combined with hydrogen peroxide. These observations support the clinical and microbial improvements shown in clinical trials.

Chlorhexidine mouthrinse

One of the most widely used chemotherapeutic agents in periodontics is chlorhexidine gluconate (CHX) and is best known for its ability to inhibit plaque and gingivitis. Chlorhexidine is an antimicrobial agent that is a cationic bisbiguanide with a strong affinity for binding to skin and mucous membranes, with low mammalian toxicity and a broad antibacterial activity (Denton 1991). In 1970, Löe and Schiött employed an experimental gingivitis model to test the antiplaque properties of CHX. They reported that new plaque formation was totally inhibited and that gingivitis was prevented when a 0.2% chlorhexidine mouthrinse was applied twice daily over a 21-day period. Two other earlier long-term, well-controlled studies have shown that CHX can reduce plaque and gingivitis in test groups (Grossman *et al.*, 1986 Lang *et al.*, 1973). The substantivity of CHX is central to its superior performance as a plaque reduction agent by allowing a prolonged contact with the soft and hard tissues in the oral cavity (Bonesvoll, 1977, Rölla *et al.*, 1971). Four hours after a chlorhexidine rinse, the number of bacterial cells attached to epithelial cells is significantly

526

reduced (Vaahtoniemi *et al.,* 1994). At 12 hours post-rinse, salivary bacterial counts have been shown to be suppressed (Schiött, 1973). Toothbrushing with a conventional toothpaste further reduces the number of bacterial cells adhering to the gingival and mucosal epithelial cells. These findings confirm earlier studies that suggest the antibacterial effect of chlorhexidine is potentiated by its sustained binding to the oral mucosa (Bonesvoll *et al.,* 1974b and Gjermo *et al.* 1974).

Other evidence presented by Jenkins et al, 1988, has shown that bacterial attachment to enamel surfaces is not entirely inhibited, however bacterial growth is delayed by the bacteriostatic effects at the tooth surface. This implies that the chlorhexidine bound to the tooth surface may be of major importance in preventing plaque formation, and may work in concert with the antimicrobial effects that CHX has on salivary and epithelial-bound bacteria. Because of its superior antimicrobial activity, Kornman describes chlorhexidine as a second generation drug (Kornman, 1985) with the first generation antimicrobials being those that have limited therapeutic value because of their short period of bioactivity and substantivity.

The mechanisms of action of chlorhexidine are based on its behavior as a cationic molecule as it binds to anionic compounds in the tooth surfaces and oral mucosa. At the tooth surface, the resultant action is the reduction of the adsorption of the salivary proteins to form a pellicle. Chlorhexidine molecules bind to the tooth and other oral mucosal surfaces and are released over the next 8 to 12 hours in active form (Rölla and Melsen, 1975, Bonesvoll *et al.,* 1974). The prolonged bacteriostatic effect of chlorhexidine is an important complement to its high initial bactericidal activity. Chlorhexidine is active against Gram-positive and Gram-negative bacteria, yeasts, dermatophytes, and some lipophilic viruses (Denton, 1991). Chlorhexidine solutions are effective in killing or inhibiting supra-and subgingival plaque in vitro (Stanley *et al.,* 1989) and in vivo (Netuschil *et al.,* 1989). Chlorhexidine has been shown to inhibit a wide range of proteolytic and glycosidic enzymes produced by dental plaque bacteria. It has a bacteriostatic effect at low concentrations and a rapidly bactericidal activity at higer concentrations which vary between bacterial species (Beighton *et al.,* 1991, Denton, 1991).

There is some disagreement in the literature as to the degree of cytotoxicity exhibited by chlorhexidine on human tissue cells. Pucher and Daniel (1992) have used human cultured fibroblasts to demonstate various cell functions such as collagen gel contraction and protein synthesis and proliferation may be negatively affected by CHX. Protein synthesis and DNA synthesis are inhibited in vitro in fibroblasts and in epithelial cells (Goldschmidt *et al.,* 1977, Helgeland *et al.* 1971).

Early animal experiments provided evidence of the primary route of CHX excretion being the feces (Winrow, 1973). Long-term use studies show it is poorly absorbed and exhibits a very low toxicity and lack of teratogenicity (Winrow, 1973, Faulkes, 1973).

Clinical uses of chlorhexidine rinse

In addition to its antiplaque and antigingivitis activity, wound healing is enhanced by the topical application of CHX, evidenced by more favorable healing of oral lesions (Lindhe *et al.*, 1970, Hamp *et al.*, 1975). In a variety of immunocompromised hosts and ulcerative type oral lesions, CHX has shown earlier healing times and reduced symptoms (Beumer *et al.*, 1979, Carl, 1983, Overholser *et al.*, 1982). Nyman *et al.* (1977) demonstrated clearly that surgery performed in patients with insufficient plaque control, a "plaque infected dentition", leads to increased loss of clinical attachment. Westfelt *et al.*, (1983) found that use of a chlorhexidine rinse as a plaque control measure following surgical treatment enhanced clinical outcomes and gain of clinical attachment. Two-minute rinses applied twice daily can be used as an alternative to regular professional prophylaxis during the healing phase following periodontal surgery.

Use of chlorhexidine in dressings has been shown to be of benefit (Asboe-Jörgensen *et al.*, 1974). Lang *et al.*, 1994, Bragger *et al.*, 1994, and Hermesch *et al.*, 1998) have recommended the use of 0.12% CHX starting 2 days after tooth extraction for reduction in probing depth and gingival inflammation at sites adjacent to the extraction. Their studies reinforce the findings of Lagarth and Munster-Swendsen (1977) that rinsing with 0.2% CHX for the first week postoperatively significantly reduces the incidence of dry sockets following removal of third molars by 13.7% compared to 7.5% of controls.

Although chlorhexidine mouthrinse has many advantages over other antimicrobial rinses, it produces side effects not usually found to the same degree in other formulations including; tooth surface and tongue staining, altered taste sensation, increased calculus deposits, burning or dryness, and mucositis. Sensitivity to this agent is rare, but there are limited reports citing anaphylaxis or fixed drug reaction (Moghadam *et al.*, 1991.) following exposure to CHX.

Long-term clinical trials have not shown any serious local or systemic side effects after 2 years of continuous use (Schiott CR *et al.*, 1976). Chlorhexidine is an American Food and Drug Administration (FDA) Category B pregnancy drug, meaning it has been tested in animals and failed to demonstrate a risk to the fetus; no human studies are available.

The usual dose of 15 ml of chlorhexidine mouthrinse twice a day is sufficient to reduce most plaque and gingivitis by approximately 30-40% (Gjermo, 1989). However, according to Jones (1997), in order to maintain its anti-plaque and gingivitis properties, it should not be used immediately following toothpaste since the interaction with the anionic surfactants found in most toothpaste formulations could reduce the effect the delivery of chlorhexidine to the tooth surface in its active form. If toothpaste is used prior to using a chlorhexidine rinse, the excess toothpaste should be rinsed away with water prior to using the CHX mouthrinse. Staining following antimicrobial use has been investigated by Addy *et al.* (1991b, 1991c, 1977). They report that staining is most likely due to the local precipitation occurring between tooth-bound chlorhexidine and chromogens found in foodstuffs and beverages. They suggest that the effect may be minimized if these particular foods and beverages, such as beets, red wine,

528

and tea are avoided in the immediate period after rinsing.

Several studies show chlorhexidine chewing gum to be associated with the control of dental plaque formation including a double-blind crossover design by Tellefsen *et al.* (1996), showing CHX chewing gum to be more effective than xylitol and sorbitol containing products.

Essential oils

Phenolic agents have been used for over a century in compounds that are contained in commercially available mouthrinses for use as antiseptic and disinfectants. The essential phenolic oils found in these products are; thymol, eucalyptol, menthol and methy salicylate (Otomo-Corgel, J. 1992). Fornell *et al.* (1975) was one of the first to conduct a cross-over study on a small number of patients using a three times daily rinse protocol for controlling dental plaque and gingivitis. Fine *et al.* (1985) have studied harvested plaque and reported significant reductions after 9 months of twice-daily use along with toothbrusing.

Most other larger studies of longer duration have followed the ADA Council on Dental Therapeutics (1986) study design recommendations; the study population should be typical users of the product in a normal regimen and should be compared with a placebo control or active control, the study should be randomized, double-blind, and of at least 6-months in duration. Several studies using this general design have shown essential oil mouthrinses to be effective in reducing plaque formation and gingival inflammation (Lamster *et al.*, 1983, Gordon *et al.*, 1985, DePaola *et al.*, 1989, Overholser *et al.*, 1990).

Walker *et al.* (1989) have shown no emergence of opportunistic organism or pathogenic bacteria following after 6 months of essential oil mouthrinse use. When 124 healthy adults with pre-existing plaque and gingivitis were enrolled in a comparison study (76), chlorhexidine mouthrinse was significantly more effective at reducing plaque formation than the essential oil rinse. However, there were no significant differences between rinses in their effects on reducing gingival inflammation and gingival bleeding. Stain and calculus formation were significantly increased in the chlorhexidine mouthrinse group compared to the essential oils group. The essential oils rinse was the first to receive the Seal of Acceptance of the Council on Dental Therapeutics of the American Dental Association.

Recent data indicate that compared to an amine fluoride/stannous fluoride-containing mouthrinse and a positive chlorhexidine control, both the CHX and the essential oil-containing mouthrinses significantly reduce plaque and plaque accumulation compared to the fluoride containing mouthrinse. (Reip *et al.*, 1999).

Laspisa *et al.* (1994) have shown the essential oils mouthrinse is useful following periodontal surgery in reducing plaque accumulation, gingival inflammation, and initial wound healing compared to a control rinse.

Dental implants must be maintained as free of plaque and inflammation as natural teeth. Ciancio *et al.* (1994), have demonstrated twice-daily use of essential oil mouthrinse in a subgingival irrigation device significantly reduces gingival inflammation around dental implants compared to irrigation with a control agent.

Metal salts in dentifrices (fluoride, zinc ions, copper salts)

Evidence of the first successfully formulated fluoride containing dentifrice was reported by Muhler and Radike in 1957. Although the fluoride salt form is beneficial in the prevention of caries, it has not routinely exhibited antimicrobial properties for controlling gingival inflammation (Gjermo, 1989, Boyd, 1994, Tinanoff *et al.*, 1989). Early studies suffered from the problem of the difficulties related to the instability of the stannous fluoride.

Recent formulations have shown the positive effects of a stabilized stannous fluoride toothpaste on plaque and gingival inflammation (Beiswanger *et al.*, 1995, Perlich *et al.*, 1995). In both well controlled studies, gingival inflammation and gingival bleeding were reduced by approximately 20% and 30% respectively, without significant reductions in plaque scores. The increased pellicle protein layer may inhibit the ability to read the plaque score (Rykke, *et al.*, 1991, Tinnanoff and Weeks, 1979) or fluoride may improve gingival health by reducing the plaque virulence without reducing its mass (Hastreiter, 1989, Leverett *et al.*, 1984, Skjorland *et al.*, 1978). Staining was significantly more in stannous group than in the control. Comparing a mouthrinse to a stabilized stannous fluoride to another toothpaste or mouthrinse, demonstrated the highest antimicrobial effect for the stannous fluoride toothpaste followed by the essential oil rinse in gingivitis reduction (Beiswanger *et al.*, 1997).

Zinc salts have been shown to be effective in aqueous solutions as plaque inhibitors (Addy *et al.*, 1980, Harrap *et al.*, 1983), where stannous fluoride has not been used much for mouthwashes and gels most likely because of the difficulty in stabilizing the stannous.

One three-year study reported a 42% reduction in plaque accumulation between subjects using a zinc toothpaste versus control (Jones *et al.*, 1988). Reduction of the development of gingival inflammation was accomplished at the 25% level using a 21-day experimental gingivitis model (Saxton and Cummins, 1989). Sanz *et al.* (1994) compared a zinc and chlorhexidine dentifrice formulation chlorhexidine rinse and a placebo in a 6 month controlled trial. Results of this study showed significant improvement in both chlorhexidine groups over placebo for plaque, gingivitis, and bleeding sites. Increased calculus formation was only statistically significant for the CHX rinse, but the control rinse demonstrated significantly higher score for staining than the control or experimental dentifrice.

Copper salts have not been used in toothpaste or mouthrinse formulations because of their unpleasant taste, potential to cause stain, and potential toxicity (Jackson, 1997).

Phenols

Phenols have been used as antiseptic and disinfectants for years, however in the last ten years triclosan, which is a chlorinated phenol, has been incorporated into dentifrices to inhibit plaque and gingivitis. After experimenting with various formulations, it was discovered that the addition of Gantrez, a copolymer of methoxyethylene and maleic acid enhanced the adsorption of triclosan to tooth enamel which eventually led to a successful formulation that inhibited plaque formation (Jackson and McDonald, 1994). Saxton et al, (1988) also demonstrated that zinc would enhance the activity of triclosan, in particular, by reducing the rate of bacterial proliferation in existing plaque.

Five large clinical trials using dentifrice containing triclosan and zinc citrate that satisfy the ADA guidelines for agents to reduce plaque and gingivitis have been conducted by Svatun *et al.* (1987, 1989a, 1989b, 1993), and Stephen *et al.* (1990). Plaque Index scores were significantly reduced by 25%-55% in the groups of subjects using the triclosan-zinc citrate dentifrice versus controls. Gingival inflammation was reduced overall by an average of 33% to 69% in these five studies. Stephen *et al.* (1990) also evaluated the microbial shifts in the oral flora, and found no detrimental effects following use of the triclosan-zinc mouthrinse for 6 months.

Results of earlier controlled clinical trials using triclosan-zinc combinaions in mouthrinses have not confirmed the usefulness of these mouthrinse formulations in reducing gingivitis (van der Hoeven *et al.*, 1993). However, combining triclosan and the co-polymer Gantrez has been studied and shown to reduce Gingival Index scores by approximately 20%-30%, and to reduce Plaque Index scores by 12-60%. Again, no reported shifts in the microflora have been reported following extended use of triclosan-Gantrez (Bonta *et al.*, 1992, Walker *et al.*, 1994).

Two studies have described the effect of twice-daily brushing with a dentifrice containing the triclosan-copolymer compared to a control. (Lindhe *et al.*, 1993, and Triratana *et al.*,1993). Both studies showed the mean Gingival Index score of patients using the triclosan-Gantrez formulation was reduced by approximately 20-30% compared to controls. Numerous other dentifrice studies using the same formulations and ADA guidelines have confirmed these findings.

Furuichi *et al.* (1999) have recently studied the effect of a triclosan/copolymer dentifrice to enhance healing following non-surgical periodontal therapy at sites with progressive attachment loss in periodontitis-susceptible subjects. Results of this study show modest improvement in the control groups, with more marked improvement (27.5%) in the test group. Probing depths were reduced in both groups, but were significantly greater in the test group (1.7mm versus 0.6mm for control). At the 3 year follow up, attachment levels had improved in both groups, however they were significantly higher in the test than control (1.8mm versus 0.7mm). It would appear from this study that the use of triclosan co-polymer toothpaste is clinically relevant to the treatment and follow-up care of periodontitis subjects with a past history of difficult-to-treat disease. Others have confirmed that the subgingival microbiota is significantly reduced both quantitatively and qualitatively in adult periodontitis subjects using triclosan/copolymer containing dentifrice, which may account for the clinical improvements seen in other clinical trials and the prevention of the recurrence of periodontal pockets (Rosling *et al.*, 1997a, Rosling *et al.*, 1997b).

As a mouthrinse, triclosan has shown reduction of Plaque Index by 24% to 36% and modest reductions in Gingival Index of 19% to 23% (Worthington *et al.*, 1993, Ayad *et al.*, 1995, Triratana *et al.*, 1995).

Topical use of povidone iodine (PVP-I)

Povidone iodine is one of the best all-around antiseptics. It is active against bacteria, fungi, spores, yeasts, protozoa and viruses. Most bacteria are killed within 10 seconds by a 1% solution, within 1 minute by a 0.05% solutions, and within 10 minutes by a 0.0002% solution. A 0.15% solution may kill wet bacterial spores, amebic cysts, and enteric viruses in about 16 minutes, but dry spores may require hours, even with 1:30000 concentration. On the skin, a 1% tincture will kill 90% of the bacteria in 90 seconds. The standard undiluted 10% aqueous polyvinyl pyrrolidine with iodine (PVP-I) solutions are formulated to contain 1% available iodine. PVP-I is a common iodophor that has many benefits over non-iodophor iodines. PVP-I produces less staining, is water soluble, and much less volatile, thereby producing less odor, and is far less irritating than non-iodophor iodines.

Povidone iodine is an Federal Food and Drug Administration category D pregnancy drug, indicating that there is evidence of definite human fetal risks. The drug may be given in spite of risks if needed in life-threatening conditions. In other words, intraoral use of povidone iodine should be approached cautiously in women of child bearing age. It is definitely contraindicated during pregnancy and lactation, and in people with sensitivity to shell fish or other known allergies to iodine.

In a well-controlled clinical trial, Rosling *et al.* (1986), and Christersson *et al.* (1987) studied the clinical and microbiological value of povidone-iodine irrigation in periodontitis subjects as an adjunct to subgingival debridement (currettage) or modified flap surgery. At 12-months post-treatment, 2 mm or more in probing attachment gain was observed in the ultrasonic/povidone-iodine solution group compared to the ultrasonic/saline group (Rosling *et al.*, 1986). Healing appeared to be related to the superior suppression subgingival periodontopathic organisms using the PVP-I as the ultrasonic lavage (Christersson *et al.*, 1987). The adjunctive benefit of PVP-I was in the non-surgical currettage groups but not the surgical groups. Povidone-iodine lavage along with ultrasonic curretage to bone resulted in significantly more gain of attachment than the water lavage group, and significantly better attachment gain than either surgical group using water or PVP-I as the ultrasonic lavage. Forabosco *et al.* (1996) have reported similar results when PVP-I lavage was compared to water during ultrasonic debridement (no intentional soft tissue currettage). In maintenance patients with recurrent pockets of _ 5mm that bled upon probing, ultrasonic debridement with water significantly reduced clinical and microbial parameters. Campbell (1999) reported that when 0.05% PVP-I was added to the ultrasonic lavage along with a full mouth decontamination protocol consisting of a pre-procedural tongue brush and gargle with 10% PVP-

532

I, further reductions in probing depths and bleeding on probing were seen in addition to further gains in attachment

Other studies have shown positive clinical and microbiological outcomes when PVP-I irrigation was used along with the treatment of periodontitis of molars and furcation lesions (Rosling *et al.*, 1983, Hamada *et al.*, 1986). In the absence of any other treatment, PVP-I irrigation has been shown to significantly decrease gingival inflammation, reduce the number of plasma cells, and the density of infiltrated gingival connective tissue in advanced periodontitis sites (24). Pocket irrigation with a diluted povidone-iodine solution of 0.2% has been shown to produce a > 2 log decrease in black-pigmented, Gram-negative anaerobic rods (Nakagawa *et al.*, 1990).

Topical use of histatins and delmopinol hydrochloride mouthrinses

Human saliva contains histidine-rich proteins that have been shown to have antifungal activity in vitro. Candidacidal activity of histatin 3 has been shown to involve interaction with the cell, and is not limited exclusively to binding at the cell surface (Xu *et al.*, 1999). Histatin-derived basic antimicrobial peptides have been reported to have a significant effect on reducing viable counts of bacteria in a model for oral biofilm as well as in isolated oral biofilms in vitro (Helmerhorst et al, 1999). Animal studies have shown reduction of plaque and gingivitis with salivary histatins, P-113, and P-113D (Paquette *et al.*, 1997).

Delmopinol is a surface modifying agent that has shown moderate antiplaque and antigingivitis efficacy in both short-term and long-term trials. (Freitas *et al.*, 1991, Lang *et al.*, 1998, Claydon *et al.*, 1996, Collaert et. Al., 1994). When compared to chlorhexidine, delmopinol had higher plaque and gingivitis scores than CHX, but lower stain and calculus (Lang *et al.*, 1998).

Treatment of malodor with chlorhexidine gels and rinses

Oral malodor affects a large portion of the population world wide, and is generally attributed to conditions within the oral cavity (Newman, M.G.,1996). Quirynen *et al.* (1998) have reported a 1-stage full-mouth disinfection in periodontitis patients (scaling and root planing of all pockets within 24 hours along with the topical application of chlorhexidine for 2 months) resulted in a significant improvement in malodor compared to a more traditional approach of quadrant scaling and root planing. The extensive use of chlorhexidine in this study included brushing the dorsum of the tongue for 60 seconds with a 1% chlorhexidine gel, rinsing twice with chlorhexidine 0.2% solution during 1 minute, two applications of a 0.2% spray to the tonsil area, and subgingival irrigation (3x repeated within 10 minutes) with chlorhexidine 1% gel of all pocket with a syringe and blunt needle. Patients were also asked to rinse twice daily with 0.2% CHX for 2 months following initial therapy. Most researchers agree that the increased microbial density on coated tongues is the main etiology for oral malodor, however the results of this study did not confirm a relationship between the presence of tongue coating and the organoleptic scores; pigmented bacteria were significantly reduced on the tongue, which may have partially accounted for the reduction in malodor.

The translocation of bacteria from one intraoral "niche" to another has been shown by Quirynen *et al.*, 1996, and Bollen *et al.*, 1998). Based on these observation, it is logical that breath malodor caused by oral bacteria will benefit more from a full-mouth disinfection than from a local periodontal debridement or from tongue cleaning alone. This group of researchers have shown previously that full-mouth disinfection results in a significant reduction in the number of pigmented bacteria sampled from the tongue (Bollen *et al.*, 1998, Quirynen *et al.*, 1995). More importantly, clinical outcomes were significantly improved indicated by significant improvements in microbial counts and attachment levels, with significantly less recession using the full mouth disinfection protocol versus traditional quadrant scaling and root planing.

Bosy *et al.* (1994) and De Boever *et al.* (1996) have used chlorhexidine rinses to treat oral malodor in periodontitis subjects and have reported improvements in malodor due to the reduction in total bacterial load in the oral cavity, particularly on the mucosal surface of the tongue. Vanderkerckhove *et al.* (1996) also reported additional pocket reduction using the chlorhexidine full mouth disinfection protocol compared to scaling and root planing alone.

Kolovsky *et al.* (1996) have tested a 2-phase oil:water mouthrinse for controlling oral malodor, gingivitis, and plaque. Results of their study showed significantly greater reduction of oral malodor in the test versus control groups. The control reduced plaque significantly compared to the test, and no difference were seen between microbial levels, bleeding index or gingival index between groups.

Antimicrobials as pre-procedural rinses

The possibility of cross-infection from microbes is great and remains a critical issue in dentistry today. Infection control and the use of barrier protection by the practitioner and staff is commonplace and serves an important role in containing noxious infectious agents. Several studies have shown that prior to dental procedures, a prerinse with either an essential oil antiseptic or chlorhexidine is very effective in reducing salivary and aerosolized bacteria (Balbuena *et al.*, 1998, Fine *et al.*, 1993, Veksler *et al.*, 1991, Buckner *et al.*, 1994). As a prerinse, one 30-patient study showed chlorhexidine or an essential oil antiseptic reduces bacterial colony count significantly at 1 hour compared to a saline solution in healthy human subjects. At four hours, 0.12% CHX reduced total bacterial colony counts by 85% where essential oils were no different than placebo (Balbuena *et al.*, 1998). Results of two double-blind controlled clinical studies of 18 patients each found pre-procedural rinsing with an essential oil mouthrinse during instrumentation with an ultrasonic scaler (Fine *et al.* 1993) significantly reduces aerosolized bacteria by 92.1% for 40 minutes in a simulated dental treatment period. Veksler *et al.*, 1991, used 40 subjects to find that pre-procedural rinsing (2 consecutive 30-second rinses) with 0.12% chlorhexidine gluconate immediately reduced aerobic salivary bacteria by 97% and that this reduction persisted for 60 minutes during scaling and root planing procedures.

Others have repeated a similar experiment and tested the effect of a single 30-second rinse of 0.12% CHX on salivary aerobes and anaerobes and found they were significantly reduced for over 5 hours following active therapy (Buckner *et al.*, 1994). The authors suggest that the adsorption and persistence of chlorhexidine in the oral cavity after a 30 second rinse could be considered a "chemical barrier" that it prevents the possible spread of contagion in the dental office.

Antimicrobials in special patient care

The application of antiseptics to the oral mucous membranes is indicated to prevent wound infections following surgical intervention in patients with leukemia, AIDS, immunosuppressant therapy and patients undergoing anti-neoplastic radiation or chemotherapy. Patients receiving cytotoxic antineoplastic therapy often require treatment for stomatitis. In patients with cancer undergoing intensive chemotherapy, prophylactic chlorhexidine rinses reduce oral mucositis and microbial burden (Ferretti *et al.* 1990). Chlorhexidine is effective against candida infections and is useful in combination with antifungal agents (Simonetti *et al.*, 1988). In the management of immunocompromized people, including those receiving chemotherapy or radiotherapy and bone marrow transplants, chlorhexidine enhances treatment if initiated as a preventive agent, prior to the appearance of oral or systemic complications (Ferretti et al, 1990, Toth *et al.*, 1990).

A variety of studies have been conducted using mouthrinse and spray for plaque control among physically and mentally challenged individuals, especially those who are institutionalized. Results of these studies generally show modest improvements in plaque and gingivitis scores following daily topical applications of chlorhexidine (Francis *et al.*, 1987, Storhaug, 1977, Kalaga, 1989a, 1989b).

Poorly controlled diabetics have been shown to benefit from ultrasonic debridement with 0.12% CHX or 0.05% povidone iodine lavage in addition to systemic antibiotic therapy compared to water and placebo controls (Grossi *et al.*, 1997).

Chlorhexidine irrigation supragingivally around the gingival margin has been shown to reduce the instance of bacteremia (MacFarlane *et al.*, 1984). Ciancio *et al.* (1994) have reported anaerobic and aerobic bacterial populations are greatly reduced when essential oils are delivered subgingivally prior to instrumentation. These antimicrobial effects following the use of chlorhexidine and Listerine irrigation may be useful in patients requiring antibiotic premedication to prevent bacterial endocarditis. However at this time, neither the American Heart Association nor the American Academy of Periodontology recommend subgingival antimicrobial irrigation as part of a routine prophylactic protocol.

Anti-inflammatory effects of mouthrinses and toothpastes

Antiseptics such as chlorhexidine, sanguinarine, cetylpyridinium chloride and listerine are commonly used as chemical plaque control agents. It is also been shown by Firatli *et al.* (1994) that in addition to their antiseptic or antimicrobial effects, these agents have an antioxidative activity against spontaneous oxidation possibly due to the inhibition of free oxygen radical activity (Table 1). The mechanism of inhibition of oxidation is unclear, but it appears that the drugs may interact with the biological membranes and probably with the oxidation process that occurs within the tissues during gingival inflammation.

Phenols have been shown to have a clinically significant effect on gingival inflammation, indicating an antiinflammatory component to the formula (Rosling *et al.*, 1997a, 1997b). See the section on phenols for details.

Antiinflammatory rinses containing ketoprofen have been shown to reduce bone loss and gingival crevicular fluid PGE2 levels compared to placebo and systemic flurbiprofen (Jeffcoat *et al.*, 1995). Other antiinflammatory agents, such as acetlsalicylic acid have been used in marginal irrigation for treating gingivitis and have shown no additional beyond that of water alone (Flemmig *et al.*, 1995).

Irrigation with antimicrobials

The efficacy of applied antimicrobials depends largely on their ability to be delivered to the site at adequate concentrations for sufficient time to kill or inhibit the growth of target organisms (Goodson, 1989). Since most topical antimicrobials have been designed as toothpastes and mouthrinses aimed at the reduction of supragingival plaque and gingivitis, it is not surprising that many have failed to fulfill all of the necessary efficacy criteria when applied subgingivally in aqueous formulations. Mouthrinses penetrate into the gingival areas only 0.2 mm (Perry *et al.*, 1984, Wolf *et al.* 1989) and toothbrushes penetrate the sulcus up to 0.9 mm on average (Waerhaug, 1981), thus the opportunity to deliver an antimicrobial agent via toothpaste or mouthrinse subgingivally is generally limited.

A conventional pulsed oral irrigator at moderate to high settings will deliver an aqueous solution to approximately 50% of the distance up to the most coronal connective tissue attachment (Eakle *et al.* 1986) whether the standard blunt jet tip is aimed at either a 45° or 90° angle. It has been observed that investigators in these studies and other similar studies may have underestimated the penetration of solutions, since most did not take into account the width of the epithelial attachment which is usually located 1 to 2 mm coronal to the gingival connective tissues in vivo.

Subgingival plaque has been shown to be disrupted up to 6 mm in clinical and microscopic studies without forcing bacteria into the soft tissue or causing any detectable injury to the pocket epithelium (Cobb *et al.* 1988, Drisko *et al.*, 1987). When a soft cone-shaped rubber tip device is used with an irrigator, penetration of an aqueous solution is possible up to 90% of the depth of ≤ 6 mm sites, and up to 64% of the depth of sites that are ≥ 7 mm (Braun *et al.*, 1992). Calculus deposits interfere with the flow of the agents into the periodontal pockets, making it more efficient to use irrigation after the pockets have been

536

thoroughly debrided of adherent deposits (Larner *et al.*, 1993). Irrigation of unscaled sites for 6 to 12 weeks with water or saline may reduce clinical and microbial parameters, but does not usually result in any gain in attachment (Boyd *et al.*, 1985, Flemmig *et al.*, 1995, Itic and Serfaty, 1992). Comparatively, when 0.02% stannous fluoride solution was used, periodontal attachment levels were improved in addition to clinically significant probing and bleeding reduction (Boyd *et al.*, 1985).

Using a hand-held syringe or oral irrigator, personally or professionally applied antimicrobials have been shown to reach the full depth of the pocket if the tip is advanced at least 3 mm subgingivally beyond the gingival margin (Hardy *et al.*, 1982, Perry *et al.*, 1984, Wunderlich *et al.*, 1984). Daily home placement of chlorhexidine (0.02% to 2%) with a manual syringe or blunt needle reduces gingival inflammation but not probing depths compared to a placebo or oral hygiene (Bratz *et al.*, 1985, Soh *et al.*, 1982, Watts *et al.*, 1986). When CHX (0.2%-0.4%) is delivered by an oral irrigator with either a standard jet tip or cone-shaped subgingival tip, clinical benefits include reductions in probing depths and gingival inflammation (Walsh *et al.*, 1992).

Limited data show reduction of bacteria and clinical improvements when 1% CHX gel is used in combination with a 0.2% CHX rinse as part of a full mouth disinfection protocol (Quirynen *et al.,* 1995, Bollen *et al.*, 1996, Vandekerckhove *et al.*, 1996, Bollen *et al.*, 1998). Others have shown that multiple irrigations with 2.0% CHX has short-term benefits in microbial reduction and improvements in attachment levels, probing depths and bleeding on probing (Southard *et al.* 1989, Bray *et al.*, 1993).

Most of the literature points to minimal or insignificant adjunctive clinical improvements following chlorhexidine irrigation or gel placement into periodontal pockets during mechanical root debridement. Studies representing this finding include MacAlpine *et al.*, 1985, Haskel *et al.*, 1986, Wennström *et al.*, 1987, Krust *et al.*, 1991). It appears that a single or multiple irrigation with chlorhexidine during scaling and root planing has no adjunctive effect unless multiple applications of at least a 2% gel or solution are applied subgingivally over a 3-4 week period (Bray *et al.*, 1993, Southard *et al.*, 1989). Essential oils mouthrinses used in oral irrigators have been shown to reduce bleeding on probing and gingival inflammation (Fine *et al.*, 1994). Diluted iodine solution (0.0004%) has not been shown to be particularly useful in home irrigation (Wolff *et al.*, 1989).

Novel treatment with povidone-iodine, sodium chloride, hydrogen peroxide and sodium bicarbonate

Highly successful outcomes have been reported earlier in treating periodontitis subjects with adjunctive local antimicrobial agents. Rosling *et al.*, (1983a) first documented the therapeutic value of a professionally applied subgingival paste of sodium bicarbonate, sodium chloride and hydrogen peroxide following by pocket irrigation of a povidone-iodine solution. Greater reduction in the subgingival microbiota and statistically significant gains in probing attachment and alveolar bone mass were seen in a 12-month post-treatment trial comparing the multi-agent approach to traditional scaling and root planing (SRP) alone. As with most treatment regimens, the deeper sites that were ≥ 7 mm benefited the most from the test antimicrobial treatment. Subtraction radiography revealed at six months, compared to baseline, 73% of sites receiving the adjunctive therapy increased in bone density compared to 28% of SRP sites. Since all ingredients have some antimicrobial activity, it is not known what effect each individual agent had on these rather remarkable outcomes.

Antimicrobial ultrasonic lavage

Ultrasonic devices have been used to deliver antimicrobial agents into periodontal pockets with varying success (Reynolds *et al.* 1992, Rosling et al, 1986). Three studies (Reynolds *et al.*, 1992 and Chapple *et al.* 1992, Taggart *et al.* 1990) have shown there is little or no benefit in using 0.02%,0.06% or 0.2% chlorhexidine as the lavage during ultrasonic scaling compared to water when using standard sized tips. When thinner tips have been tested that more nearly resemble the size of a periodontal probe, the base of deep periodontal pocket bases can be reached with the instrument or the irrigating solution (Dragoo, 1992, Clark, 1990). Complete penetration in 96% of sites ranging from 3 mm to 9 mm has been successfully demonstrated using an erythrocin dye, however the dispersion from the ultrasonic tip was shown to have very little lateral dispersion, necessitating multiple overlapping strokes to evenly distribute the solution (Nosal *et al.*, 1991).

Sustained local drug delivery of chlorhexidine

The rationale for using local sustained antimicrobials to augment mechanical therapy was brought to the profession by Goodson *et al.* (1979) over two decades ago. The first local drug delivery system period for the treatment of periodontitis was a non-resorbable polyvinyl ether fiber that released the antibiotic tetracycline into the periodontal pocket over a 10 day period of time. Since then, a second generation non-antibiotic formulation of the antiseptic chlorhexidine (2.5 mg of chlorhexidine gluconate) in a resorbable hydrolyzed gelatin matrix (chip) has been developed for the adjunctive treatment of adult periodontitis. Chlorhexidine concentrates in the gingival crevicular at levels of 1,444 µg/ml during the first 4 hours and drops to about 125 µg/ml by 7 days which is still an effective concentration to kill most suspected pathogens associated with periodontal disease (Soskolne *et al.*, 1998, Stanley *et al.*, 1989). Multicenter studies (Soskolne *et al.*, 1997, Jeffcoat *et al.*, 1998) have tested the CHX chip as an adjunct to scaling and root planing compared to scaling alone and scaling plus placebo.

Results of two large trials for a total of 447 subjects, confirm that by 9 months, probing depths were significantly reduced in the chlorhexidine group compared to controls (Jeffcoat *et al.*, 1997, Jeffcoat *et al.*, 1998). The proportion of sites that had 2 mm or more of probing depth reduction was 30% compared to 16% in controls. Modest attachment gains in the treatment groups were

538

maintained throughout the study and bleeding was also significantly improved in the chlorhexidine group compared to those receiving scaling and root planing alone. Local drug delivery agents have expanded the use of highly concentrated drugs to sucessfully treat recurrent adult periodontitis, and are effective adjuncts to scaling and root planing.

Discussion

Most adjunctive antimicrobials to date have been shown to provide modest benefits when used to enhance the effects of oral hygiene or periodontal debridement. Collins and Creeth, (1992) have designated the following as key properties for topical antiplaque agents for supragingival plaque control: 1) high inherent biological activity pertinent to the specific mode of action, 2) high oral substantivity at the sites of biological action, 3) low acute and chronic toxicity, 4) and low permeability. Since antimicrobials may react quite differently within in vivo biofilms versus a planktonic layer of cells in vitro, antimicrobial efficacy must still be tested in well designed randomized controlled clinical trials. Most of the agents available today have not been studied on biofilms to any large degree, therefore further reliability data is needed to support long-term effects.

Since the oral mucosa constitutes the largest area of retention for clinically proven antiplaque agents, it is reasonable to assume agents that reduce the bacterial load at mucosal sites, will in turn affect the bacterial load in the saliva and possibly the tooth and root surfaces, pellicle and plaque. Cummins and Creeth (1992) propose that the clinically proven antiplaque agents act "multifunctionally" and at multiple sites, by reducing the metabolism of the plaque bacteria in both the saliva and on the tooth surface, in addition to reducing the potential recolonization of adherent plaques.

In the future, as with caries research, it may be more cost effective and efficient to study the antimicrobials used to treat periodontal diseases in the laboratory in artificial, highly controlled environments that will allow for more in-depth study of the mechanisms of action and bioavailability of these agents. Slavkin, (1997) states that "opportunities exist for researchers to revisit previously held assumptions and investigate the complexities of biofilms and to guide the development of "smart therapies" and approaches to inhibit or eliminate microbes under various environmental conditions". The host immune response to pathogenic organisms is frequently not able to control or remove the biofilm, which confirms the need to develop other chemotherapeutic agents or other biologic approaches that will help the patient maintain a healthy equilibrium between pathogenic and non-pathogenic organisms in the oral environment.

References

Addy, M., Prayitno, S., Taylor, L., Cadogan, L. 1979. An in vitro study of the role of dietary factors in the etiology of tooth staining associated with the use of chlorhexidine. *J. Periodontal. Res.*, **14**,403-410.

Addy, M., Richards, J., Williams, G. 1980. Effect of a zinc citrate mouthwash on dental plaque and salivary bacteria. *J. Clin. Periodontol.*, **7**, 309-315.

Addy, M, Jenkins, S., Newcombe, R. 1991a. The effect of some chlorhexidine-containing mouthrinses on salivary bacterial counts. *J. Clin. Periodontol.,* **18**,90-93.

Addy, M., Al-Arrayed, F., Moran, J. 1991b. The use of an oxidising mouthwash to reduce staining associated with chlorhexidine. Studies in vitro and in vivo. *J. Clin. Periodontol.,* **18**, 267-271.

Addy, M., Wade, W., Goodfield, S. 1991c. Staining and antimicrobial properties in vitro of some chlorhexidine formulations. *Clin. Prev. Dent.,* **6**, 13-17.

Allen, D.R., Davies, R., Bradshaw, B., Ellwood, R., Simone, A.J., Robinson, R., Mukerjee, C., Petrone, M.E., Chaknis, P., Volpe, A.R., Proskin, H.M. 1998. Efficacy of a mouthrinse containing 0.05% cetylpyridinium chloride for the control of plaque and gingivitis: a 6-month clinical study in adults. *Compend. of Cont. Educ. in Dent.,* **19**(2)Suppl),20-26.

Anonymous. Council on Dental Therapeutics. Guidelines for acceptance of chemotherapeutic products for the control of supragingival plaque and gingivitis. *J. Am. Dent. Assoc.* **112**, 529-532.

Asboe-Jörgensen, V., Attström, R., Lang, N.P., Löe, H. 1974. Effect of chlorhexidine dressing on healing after periodontal surgery. *J. Periodontol,.* **45**,13-17.

Ayad, F., Berta, R., Petrone, M., DeVizio W., Volpe. 1995. Effect on plaque removal and gingivitis of a triclosan-co-polymer pre-brush rinse: a six-month study in Canada. *J. Can. Dent. Assoc.,* **61**, 53-56, 59-61.

Balbuena, L., Stambaugh, K.I., Ramirez, S.G., Yeager, C. 1998. Effects of topical oral antiseptic rinses on bacterial counts of saliva in healthy human subjects. *Otolaryngology-Head & Neck Surgery,* **118**(5),625-629.

Beighton, D., Decker, J., Homer, K.A. 1991. Effects of chlorhexidine on proteolytic and glycosidic enzyme activities of dental plaque. *J. Clin. Periodontol.,* **18**,85-89.

Beumer, J., Curtis, T., Harrison, R.E. 1979. Radiation therapy of the oral cavity: sequelae and management. *Head Neck Surg.,* 1:301-312.

Beiswanger, B.B., McClanahan, S.F., Bartizek, M.S. *et al.* 1997. The comparative efficacy of stabilized stannous fluoride dentifrice, peroxide/baking soda dentifrice, and essential oil mouthrinse for the prevention of gingivitis. *J. Clin. Dent.* (**Special issue**) 46-53.

Beiswanger, B.B., Doyle, P.M., Jackson, R.D., Mallett, M.E., Mau, M.S., Bollmer, B.W., Crisanti, M.M., Guay, C.B., Lanzlaco, A.C., Lukacovic, M.F., Majeti, S., McClanahen, S.F. 1995. The clinical effect of dentifrices containing stabilized stannous fluoride on plaque formation and gingivitis-a six-month study with ad libitum brushing. *J. Clin. Dent.* **6**(spec issue), 46-53.

Bollen, C.M.L., Moangardini, C., Papaioannou, W., Van Steenberghe, D., Quirynen, M. 1998. The effect of a one-stage full-mouth disinfection on different intra-oral niches. Clinical and microbiological observations. *J. Clin. Periodontol.,* **25**,56-66.

Bollen, C.M.L., Vandekerckhove B.N.A., Papaioannou, W., Van Eldere, J., Quirynen, M. 1996. Full-versus partial-mouth disinfection in the treatment of periodontal infections. A pilot study: long-term microbiological observations. *J. Clin. Periodontol.,* **23**, 960-970.

Bonesvoll, P. 1977. Oral pharmacology of chlorhexidine. *J. Clin. Periodontol.,* **4**,49-65.

Bonesvoll, P., Lokken, P., Rölla, G., Paus, P.N. 1974. Retention of chlorhexidine in the human oral cavity after mouthrinses. *Arch. Oral Biol.,* 19, l209-1212.

Bonesvoll, P., Olsen, I. 1974b. Influence of teeth, plaque and denture on the retention of chlorhexidine in the human oral cavity. *J. Clin. Periodontol.,* **1**,214-221.

Bonta, C.Y., Reynolds, H.S., Dunford, R.G., Zambon, J.J. 1992. Effect of a triclosan/co-polymer dentifrice on oral microflora. *J. Dent. Res.* **71**. 557 (abstr).

Bosy, A., Kulkarni, G.V., Rosenberg, M., McCulloch, C.A.G. 1994. Relationship of oral malodor to periodontitis: evidence of independence in discrete subpopulations. *J Periodontol.* **65**, 37-46.

Boyd, R.L., Leggott, P., Quinn, R., Buchanan S., Eakle, W., Chambers, D. 1985. Effect of self-administered daily irrigation with 0.02% SnF2 on periodontal disease activity. *J. Clin. Periodontol.,* **12**, 420-431.

Boyd, R.L., Chun Y.S. 1994. Eighteen months evaluation of the effects of a 0.4% stannous fluoride gel on gingivitis in orthodontic patients. *Am. J. Orthod. Dentofac. Orthop.,* **105**, 35-41.

Bragger, U., Schild, U., Lang, H.P. 1994. Effect of chlorhexidine rinses on periodontal tissue healing after tooth extraction (II). Radiographic parameters. *J. Clin. Periodontol.,***21**.(6), 422, 430.

Braatz, L. Garrett, S, Claffey, N., Egelberg, J. 1985. Antimicrobial irrigation of deep pockets to supplement non-surgical periodontal therapy. II. Daily irrigation. *J. Clin. Periodontol.* 12, 630-638.

Braun, R.E., Ciancio S.G. 1992. Subgingival delivery by an oral irrigation device. *J.Periodontol.,*

540

63,469-472.

Bray, K.S., Drisko, C.L., Cobb C.M. 1993. Adjunctive effects of irrigation with 0.5% and 2.0% chlorhexidine gel. *J. Dent. Res.*, **72,** 2956, (abstr).

Brex, M.C. and Theilade, J. 1984. Effect of chlorhexidine rinses on the morphology of early dental plaque formed on plastic films. *J. Clin. Periodontol.,* **11,**553-564.

Buckner, R.Y., Kayrouz, G.A., Briner, W. 1994. Reduction of oral microbes by a single chlorhexidine rinse. *Compend. Contin. Educ. Dent.* **4,**512-516.

Burchard, W.B., Cobb, C., M., Drisko, C.L., Killoy, W.J. 1991. Effects of chlorhexidine and stannous fluoride on fibroblast attachment to different implant surfaces. *Int. J. oral Maxillofac. Implants*, **6**. 418-426.

Campbell, D.A. 1999. Enhanced maintenance using povidone iodine (PVP-I) full mouth decontamination (PVP-I-FMD) and ultrasonic debridement in patients with recurrent periodontitis: Clinical and microbial results. M.S. thesis, University of Louisville, Louisville, Kentucky.

Carl, W. **1983.** Oral complications in cancer patients. *Am. Fam. Physician.*, **27,**161-170.

Caufield, P.W., Allen, D.N., Childers, N.K. 1987. In vitro susceptibilities of suspected periodontopathic anaerobes as determined by membrane transfer assay. *Antimicrob. Agents Chemother.*, **31**, 1989-1993.

Chapple, I.C., Walmsley, A.D., Saxby, M.S., Moscrop, H. 1992. Effect of subgingival irrigation with chlorhexidine during ultrasonic scaling. *J. Periodontol.*, **63**,812-816.

Christersson, L.A., Rosling, B.G., Dunford R.G., Wikesjö U.M.E., Zambon, J.J., Genco, R.J. 1987. Monitoring of subgingival Bacteroides gingivalis and Actinobacillus actinomycetemcomitans in the management of advanced periodontitis. *Adv. Dent. Res.*, **2**, 382-388.

Ciancio, S.G., Laucillo, F., Shilby, O., Vitello, M. Mather, M. 1995. The effect of an antiseptic mouthrinse on implant maintenance: plaque and per-implant gingival tissues. *J. Periodontol.* **66**, 962-965.

Ciancio, S.G. 1994. Expanded and future use of mouthrinses. *J. Am. Dent. Assoc.* **125**(suppl 2), 29S-32S.

Cimasoni, F. 1983. Crevicular fluid updated. *Monographs in Oral Science* **12**, III-VII.

Clark, S.M. 1990. The influence of two ultrasonic tips on root surfaces- in vivo. Gen. Dent.,**38,**125-128.

Claydon, N., Hunter, L., Moran, J., Wade, W., Kelly, E., Movert, R., Addy, M. 1996. A 6 month home usage trial of 0.1% and 0.2% delmopinol mouthwashes (1) effects on plaque, gingivitis, supragingival calculus and tooth staining. *J. Clin. Periodontol.*, **23**, 220-228.

Cobb, C.M., Rodgers, R.L., Killoy, W.J. 1988. Ultrastructural examination of human periodontal pockets following the use of an oral irrigation device in vivo. *J. Periodontol.*, **59**, 155-163.

Collaert, B., Attstrom, R., Edwardsson, S., Hase, J.C., Astrom, M., Movert, R. 1994. Short term effects of topical application of delmopinol on salivary microbiology plaque and gingivitis. *Scand. J. Dent. Res.*, **102**, 17-23.

Corbet, E.F., Tam, J.O., Zee, K.Y., Wong, M.C., Lo, E.C., Mombelli, A.W., Lang, N.P. 1997. Therapeutic effects of supervised chlorhexidine mouthrinses on untreated gingivitis. *Oral Diseases,*,**3**(1):9-18.

Cummins, D. Vehicles: how to deliver the goods. *Periodontology 2000*, **15**, 84-99.

Davies, A. 1973. The mode of action of chlorhexidine. *J. Periodontal Res.*, **12**(suppl 8),68-75.

De Boever, E.H., Loesche, W.H. 1996. The tongue microbiota and tongue surface characteristics contribute to oral malodor. In: van Steenberghe D., Rosengerg M. eds. *Bad breath. A multidisciplinary Approach*. Leuven Univeristy Press. 111-121.

DePaola, L.G., Overholser, C.D., Meiller, T.F., Minah, G.E., Niehaus, C. 1989. Chemotherapeutic inhibition of supragingival plaque and gingivitis development. *J. Clin. Periodontol.* **6**, 311-315.

Denton, G.W. 1991. In: Block S.S., ed. *Disinfection, sterilization and preservation*. 4th edn. Lea and Febiger, Philadelphia.

Dragoo, M.A. 1992. A clinical evaluation of hand and ultrasonic instruments on subgingival debridement. I. With unmodified and modified ultrasonic inserts. *Int. J. Periodontics & Restorative Dent.*, **12,**310-323.

Drisko, C.L., White, C.L., Killoy W.J., Mayberry W.E. 1987. Comparison of dark-filed microscopy and a flagella stain for monitoring the effect of a Water Pik on bacterial motility. *J. Periodontol.*

58, 381-386.

Eakle, W.S., Ford, C.L., Boyd, R.L. 1986. Depth of penetration in periodontal pockets with oral irrigation. *J. Clin. Periodontol.*, **13**,39-44.

Eldridge, K.R., Finnie, S.F., Steephens, J.A., Mauad, A.M., Munoz, C.A., Kettering, J.D. 1998. Efficacy of an alcohol-free chlorhexidine mouthrinse as an antimicrobial agent. *J. Pros. Dent.*, **80**(6),685-690.

Ernst, C.P., Prockl, K. Willershausen, B. 1998. The effectiveness and side effects of 0.1% and 0.2% chlorhexidine mouthrinses: a clinical study. *Quintessence International*, **29**(7),443-448.

Felo, A., Shibly, O., Ciancio, S.G., Lauciello, F.R., Ho, A. 1997. Effects of subgingival chlorhexidine irrigation on peri-implant maintenance. *American Journal of Dentistry*, **10**(2),107-110.

Ferretti, G., Hansen D.M.D., Whittenburg, K., Brown, A.T., Lillich T.T., Ash, R.C. 1987. Therapeutic use of chlorhexidine in bone marrow transplant patients: case studies. *Oral Surg. Oral Med. Oral Pathol. Oral Radiol. Endod.*, **63**,683-687.

Ferretti, G.A., Raybould, T.P., Brown, A.T., Jacdonal, J.S. Greenwood, M., Maruyama Y., Geil, J., Lillich, T.T., Ash, R.C. 1990. Chlorhexidine prophylaxis for chemotherapy- and radiotherapy-induced stomatitis: a randomized double-blind trial. *Oral Surg. Oral. Med. Oral Pathol.*, **69**(3),331-338.

Fine, D.H., Letizia, J., Mandel, I.D. 1985. The effect of rinsing with Listerine antiseptic on the properties of developing dental plaque. *J. Clin. Periodontol.*, **12**, 660-666.

Fine, D.H., Harper, D.S., Gordon, J.M., Hovliaras, C.A., Charles, C.H. 1994. Short-term microbiological and clinical effects of subgingival irrigation with an antimicrobial mouthrinse. *J. Periodontol.*, **65**, 30-36.

Firatli, E., Unal. T., Onan, U., Sandalli, P. 1994. Antioxidative activities of some chemotherapeutics. A possible mechanism in reducing gingival inflammation. *J. Clin. Periodontol.*, **21**, 680-683.

Flemmig, T.F., Epp, B., Funkenhauser, Z., Newwman, M.G., Kornman, K.S., Haubitz, I., Klaiber., B. 1995. Adjunctive supragingival irrigation with acetylsalicylic acid in periodontal supportive therapy. *J. Clin. Periodontol.*, **22**, 427-433.

Forabasco, A., Galetti, R., Spinato, S., Colao, C., Casolari, C. 1996. A comparative study of a surgical method and scaling and root planing using the Odontoson. *J. Clin. Periodontol.* **23**, 611-614.

Fornell, J., Sundin, Y., Lindhe, J. 1975. Effect of Listerine on dental plaque and gingivitis. *Scand. J. Dent. Res.* **83**, 18-25.

Foulkes, D.M. 1973. Some toxicological observations on chlorhexidine. *J. Periodontal Res.*, **12**,56-60.

Francis, J.R., Humter, B., Addy, M. 1987. A comparison of three delivery methods of chlorhexidine in handicapped children. 1. Effects on plaque, gingivitis and toothstaining. *J. Periodontol.* **58**, 451-455.

Furuichi, Y., Rosling, B., Volpe, A.R., Lindhe, J. 1999. The effect of a triclosan/copolymer dentifrice on healing after non-surgical treatment of recurrent periodontitis. *J. Clin. Perdontol.,* **26**, 63-66.

Gjermo, P., Bonesvoll, P., Rölla, G. 1974. Relationship between plaque-inhibiting effect and retention of chlorhexidine in the human oral cavity. *Arch. Oral. Biol.*, **19**,1031-1034.

Gjermo, P. 1989. Chlorhexidine and related compounds. *J. Dent. Res.*, **68**(spec issue), 1602-1608.

Goldschmidt, P., Cogen, R., Taubman, S. 1977. Cytopathologic effects of chlorhexidine on human cells. J. Periodontol., **48**,212-215.

Goodson, J.M. , Haffajee, A., Socransky, S.S. 1979. Periodontal therapy by local delivery of tetracycline. *J. Clin. Periodontol.*, **6**, 83-92.

Goodson, J.M. 1989. Pharmacokinetic principles controlling efficacy of oral therapy. J. Dent. Res., **68**,1625-1632.

Gordon, J. M., Lamster, I.B., Seiger, M.C. 1985. Efficacy of Listerine antiseptic in inhibiting the development of plaque and gingivitis. *J. Clin. Periodontol.*, **12**, 697-704.

Grossi, S.G., Skrepcinski, F.B., DeCaro, T., Robertson, D.C., Ho, A.W., Dunford, R.G., Genco R.J. 1997. Treatment of periodontal disease in diabetics reduces glycated hemoglobin. *J Periodontol.*, **68**, 713-719.

Grossman, E., Reiter, G., Sturzenberg, M., De la Rosa, M., Dickinson, T.D., Ferretti, G.A., Ludlam, G.E., Meckel, A.H. 1986. Six months study of the effects of a chlorhexidine mouthrinse on gingivitis in adults. *J. Periodontal. Res.*, **21** (suppl 16), 33-43.

Hamada, N., Arai, S., Kobayashi, H., Saito, K., Kamoi, K. 1986. Clinical evaluation of Odontoson

4N special. *J. Jpn. Assoc. Periodontol.*, **28**, 1180-1187.

Hamp, S.E., Rosling, B., Lindhe, J. 1975. Effect of chlorhexidine on the gingival wound healing in the dog. A Histometric study. *J. Clin. Periodontol.*, **2**,143-152.

Hardy, J.H., Newman, H.N., Strahan, J.D. 1982. Direct irrigation and subgingival plaque. *J.Clin. Periodontol.*, **9,** 57-65.

Harrap, G.J., Best, J.S., Saxton, C.A. 1983. Inhibition of plaque by zinc salts. *J. Periodont. Res.*, **18**, 634-642.

Hase, J.C., Edwardsson, S., Rundegren, J., Attstrom, R., Kelty, E. 1998. 6-month use of 0.2% delmopinol hydrochloride in comparison with 0.2% chlorhexidine digluconate and placebo (II). Effect on plaque and salivary microflora. *J. Clin. Periodontol.*, **25**(11 Pt 1),841-849.

Haskel, E., Esquenasi, J., Yussim, L. 1986. Effects of subgingival chlorhexidine irrigation in chronic moderate periodontitis. *J. Periodontol.*, **57**, 305-310.

Hastreiter, R.J. 1989. Is 0.4% stannous fluoride gel an effective agent for the prevention of oral diseases? *J. Am. Dent. Assoc.*, **118**, 634-642.

Helgeland, K., Heyden, G., Rölla, G. 1971. Effect of chlorhexidine on animal cells in vitro. *Scand. J. Dent. Res.*,**79**, 209-215.

Helmerhorst, E.J., Hodgson, R., van 'tHof, W., Veerman, E.C.I., Allison, C., Nieiw. A.v. 1999. The effects of histatin-derived basic antimicrobial peptides on oral biofilm. *J. Dent. Res.* **78**, 1245-1250.

Hermesch, C.B., Hilton, T.J., Biesbrock, A.R., Baker, R.A., Cain-Hamlin J., McClanahan, S.F., Gerlach, R.W. 1998. Perioperative use of 0.12% chlorhexidine gluconate for the prevention of alveolar osteitis: efficacy and risk factor analysis. Oral. Surg., *Oral Medicine, oral Pathology, Oral Radiology, & Endodontics*, **85**,(4),381-387.

Higashitsutsumi, M., Kamoi, K., Miyata, H., Nishizawa, S., Sakamoto, M., Tuchiya, T., Hatae, S. 1993. Bactericidal effects of povidone-iodine solution to oral pathogenic bacteria in vitro. *Postgrad. Med. J.*, **69**, (suppl 3),S10-S14.

Jackson, R.J., and McDonald, F.E. 1994. The effect of pyrophosphate on triclosan activity. *J. Dent. Res.* **73**(abstract), 848.

Jackson, R.J. 1997. Metal salts, essential oils and phenols- old or new? *Periodontology 2000*, **15**, 63-73.

Jeffcoat, M., Palcanis, K., Offenbacher, S. *et al.* 1997. Multicenter evaluation of a biodegradable chlorhexidine/gelatin chip for the treatment of adult periodontitis. J. Dent., Res., 76, 153 (abstract).

Jeffcoat, M.K., Bray, K.S., Ciancio S.G., Dentino, A.R., Fine, D.H., Gordon, J.M., Gunsolley, J.C., Killoy, W.J., Lowenguth, R.A., Magnusson, N.I., Offenbacher, S., Palcanis, K.G., Proskin, H.M., Finkelman, R.D., Flashner, M. 1998. Adjunctive use of a subgingival controlled release chlorhexidine chip (PerioChip) reduces probing pocket depth and improves attachment level compared with scaling and root planing alone. *J. Periodontol.*, **69**, 989-997.

Jeffcoat, M.K., Reddy, M.D., Haigh, S., Buchanan, W., Doyle, M.J., Meredith, M.P., Nelson, S.L., Goodale, M.B., Wehmeyer, K.R. 1995. A comparison of topical ketorolac, systemic flurbiprofen, and placebo for the inhibition of bone loss in adult periodontitis. *J. Periodontol.*, **66**, 329-338.

Jones, C.L., Stephen, K.W., Richie, J.A., Huntington, E., Saxton C.A., van der Ouderaa, F. 1988. Long term exposure of plaque to zinc citrate. Caries Res., **22**, 84-90.

Jones, C.G. 1997. Chlorhexidine: is it still the gold standard? *Periodontology 2000*, **15**, 55-62.

Kalaga, A., Addy M, Hunter, B. 1989a. Comparison of chlorhexidine delivery by mouthwash and spray on plaque accumulation. *J. Periodontol.* **60**, 127-130.

Kalaga, A., Addy M, Hunter, B. 1989b. The use of a 0.2% chlorhexidine spray as an adjunct to oral hygiene and gingival health in physically and mentally handicapped adults. *J. Periodontol.* **60**, 381-385.

Kozlovsky, A., Goldberg, S., Natour, I., Rogatky-Gat, A., Gelernter, I., Rosenberg, M. 1996. Efficacy of a 2-phase oil:water mouthrinse in controlling oral malodor, gingivitis, and plaque. *J. Periodontol.*, **67**, 577-582.

Kornman, K.S. 1986. The role of supragingival plaque in the prevention and treatment of periodontal diseases. A review of current concepts. *J. Periodont. Res.*, **21**(suppl), 5-22.

Krust, K.S., Drisko, C.L., Gross, K., Overman, P., Tira, D.D. 1991. The effects of subgingival irrigation with chlorhexidine and stannous fluoride. A preliminary investigation. *J. Dent. Hyg.* **65**, 289-295.

Lamster, I.B., Alfano, M.C., Seiger, M.C., Gordon, J.M. 1983. The effect of Listerine antiseptic on reduction of existing plaque and gingivitis. *Clin. Prev. Dent.*, **5**, 12-16.

Lang N.P., Hotz P., Graf H.,. Greing, A.H., Saxen, U.P, Sturzenberger, O.P., Meckel, A.H. Effects of supervised chlorhexidine mouthrinses in children. A longitudinal clinical trial. *J. Periodontol.Res.*, **17**,101-111.

Lang, N.P., Hase, J.C., Grassi, M., Hammerle, C.H., Weigel, C., Kelty, E., Frutig, F. 1998. Plaque formation and gingivitis after supervised mouthrinsing with 0.2% delmopinol hydrochloride, 0.2% chlorhexidine digluconate and placebo for 6 months. *Oral Diseases*, **4**(2),105-113.

Lang, N.P., Schild, U., Brägger, U. 1994. Effect of chlorhexidine (0.12%) rinses on periodontal tissue healing after tooth extraction (I) Clinical parameters. *J. Clin. Periodontol.*, **21**,425-421.

Lang, N.P., Hase, J.C., Grassi, M., Hamerle, C.H., Weigel, C., Kelty, E., Frutig, F. 1998. Plaque formation and gingivitis after supervised mouthrinsing with 0.2% delmopinol chdrochloride, 0.2% chlorhexidine digluconate and placebo for 6 months. *Oral Dis.*, **4**, 105-113.

Larner, J.R., Greenstein, G. 1993. Effect of calculus and irrigator tip design on depth of subgingival irrigation. *Int. J. Periodontics Restorative Dent.*, **13**, 288-297.

Laspisa, S., Singh, S., Deasy, M. 1994. Efficacy of Listerine as a post-surgical antimicrobial rinse. *Am. J. Dent.,* **7**, 5-8.

Leverett, D.H., McHugh, W.D., Jenson, Q.E. 1984. Effect of daily rinsing with stannous fluoride on plaque and gingivitis. Final report. *J. Dent. Res.*, **63**, 1083-1086.

Lindhe, J., Heyden, G., Svanberg, G., Löe, H., Schiött, C.R. 1970, Effect of local applications of chlorhexidine on the oral mucosa of the hamster. *J. Periodontal. Res.*, **5**,177-182.

Lindhe, J., Rosling, B., Socransky, S.S., Volpe, A.R. 1993. The effect of a triclosan containing dentifrice on established plaque and gingivitis. *J. Clin. Periodontol.* **20**, 227-334.

Löe H., and Schiött, C.R. 1970. The effect of suppression of the oral microflora upon the development of dental plaque and gingivitis. McHugh W.E., ed. *Dental plaque*. Edinburgh, Churchill Livingston.

Löe, H. and Schiött, C.R., 1970. The effect of mouthrinses and topical application of chlorhexidine on the development of dental plaque and gingivitis in man. *J. Periodontal Res.*, **5**,79-83.

MacAlpine, R., Magnusson, I., Kiger, R., Crigger, M., Garrett, S., Egelberg, J. 1985. Antimicrobial irrigation of deep pockets to supplement oral hygiene instruction and root debridement. I. Biweekly irrigation. *J. Clin. Periodontol.*, **12**, 568-577.

MacFarlane, T.W., Ferguson, M.M., Mulgrew, D.J. 1984. Post-extraction bacteraemia: role of antiseptics and antibiotics. *Br. Dent. J.*, **156**, 179-181.

Machuca, G., Valencia, S., Lacalle, J.R., Machuca, C., Bullon, P. 1997. A clinical assessment of the effectiveness of a mouthwash based on triclosan and on Aea mays L used as supplements to brushing. *Quintessence International*, **28**(5),329-335.

Maruniak, J., Clark, W.B., Walder, C.B., Magnusson, I., Marks, R.G., Taylor, M., Clouser, B. 1992. The effect of 3 mouthrinses on plaque and gingivitis development. *J. Clin. Periodontol.*, **19**,19-23.

Moghadam, B.K., Drisko, C.L., Gier, R.E. 1991. Chlorhexidine mouthwash-induced fixed drug eruption. Case report and review of the literature. *Oral Surg. Oral Med. Oral Pathol.* **71**, 431-434.

Muhler, J., Radike, A.W. 1957. Effect of a dentifrice containing stannous fluoride on dental caries in adults II. Results at the end of two years of unsupervised use. *J. Am. Dent. Assoc.*, **58**, 196-198.

Müller, R.F., Höpfner, C., Lange,D.E. Wirksamkeit eines PVP-Jod-Präparates in vitro auf ausgewählte mundhöhlenkeime. *Dtsch. Zahnärztl.* **44**,366-369.

Nakagawa, T., Saito, A., Hosaka, Y., Yamada, S., Tsunoda, M., Sato, T., Ishikawa T. 1990. Bactericidal effects on subgingival bacteria of irrigation with a povidone-iodine solution. *Bull Tokyo Dent. Coll.*, **31**,199-203.

Netuschi,l L., Reich, E., Brecx, M. 1989. Direct measurement of the bactericidal effect of chlorhexidine on human dental plaque. *J. Clin. Periodontol.*, **16**,240-249.

Newman, M.G. 1996. The role of periodontitis in oral malodor: Clinical perspectives. In: van Steenberghe D., eds. *Bad Breath: A multidisiplinary Approach.* Leuven University Press., 3-14.

Nosal, K.G., Scheidt, M.J., O'Neal, R., Van Dyke, T.E. 1991. The penetration of lavage solution into the periodontal pocket during ultrasonic instrumentation. *J. Periodontol.*, **62**,554-557.

Nyman, S., Lindhe, J., Rosling, B. 1977. Periodontal surgery in plaque infected dentitions. *J. Clin.*

Periodontol., **3**,240-249.

Olmez, A., Can, H., Ayhan, H., Okur, H. 1998. Effect of an alum-containing mouthrinse in children for plaque and salivary levels of selected oral microflora. *J. Clin. Pediatric Dent.*, VOLUME 335-340.

Oosterwaal, P.J.M., Mikx, F.H.M., Renggli, H.H. 1990. Clearance of a topically applied fluorescein dye from periodontal pockets. *J. Clin. Periodontol.*, **17**,613-615.

Otomo-Corgel, J. 1992. Over-the-counter and prescription mouthwashes-an update for the 1990s. *Compendium Dent. Educ. Dent.*, **13**, 1086-1090.

Olverholser, C.D., Meiller, T.F., DePaola, L.G., Minah, G.E., Niehaus, C. 1990. Comparative effects of 2 chemotherapeutic mouthrinses on the development of supragingival dental plaque and gingivitis. *J. Clin. Periodontol.*, **17**, 575-579.

Overholser, C.D., Peterson, D.E., William, L.T., *et al.* 1982. Periodontal infection in patients with acute nonlymphocytic leukemia: prevalence of acute exacerbations. *Ach. Intern. Med.*, **142**,551.

Pan, P.H., Finnegan, M.B., Sturdivant, L., Barnett, M.L. 1999. Comparative anatimicrobial activityof an essential oil and an amine fluoride/stannous fluoride mouthrinse in vitro. *J. Clin. Periodontol.*, **26**, 474-476.

Paquette, D. W., Waters, G.S., Stefanidou, V.L., Lawrence, H.P., Friden, P.M., O'Connor, S.M., Sperati, J.D., Oppenheim, F.G., Hutchens, L.H., Williams, R.C. 1997. Inhibition of experimental gingivitis in beagle dogs with topical salivary histatins. J Clin Periodontol., 24, 216-222.

Perry, D.A., Newman, M.G., Carranza, F.A., Mazza, J., Hamamoto, D., Yale, C. 1984. Stannous fluoride adjunct to root planing: clinical and microbiological effects. *J. Dent. Res.*, **63**(abstr 702),249.

Perlich, M.A., Bacca, L.A., Bollmer, B.W., Lanzalaco, A.C., McClanahan, S.F., Sewal,L.K., Beiswanger. B.B., Eichold, W.A., Hull, J.R., Jackson, R.D., Mau, M.S. 1995. The clinical effect of a stabilized dentifrice on plaque formation, gingivitis, and gingival bleeding: a six-month study. *J. Clin. Dent.*, **6**(spec issue), 54-58.

Pratten, J., Wills, K., Barnett, P., Wilson, M. 1998a. In vitro studies of the effect of antiseptic-containing mouthwashes on the formation and viability of Streptococcus sanguis biofilms. *J. Appl. Microbiol.*, **84**, 1149-1155.

Pratten J., Smith, A.W., Wilson, M. 1998b. Response of single species biofilms and microcosm dental plaques to pulsing with chlorhexidine. *J. Antimicrobial Chemotherapy.* **42**, 453-459.

Pratten, J., Barnett, P., Wilson, M. 1998c. Composition and susceptibility to chlorhexidine of multispecies biofilms of oral bacteria. *Applied and Environmental Microbiology.* **64**, 3515-3519.

Preshaw, P.M., Lauffart, B., Brown, P., Zak E., Heasman, P.A. 1998. Effects of ketorolac tromethamine mouthrinse (0.1%) on crevicular fluid prostaglandin E2 concentrations in untreated chronic periodontitis. *J. Periodontol.*, **69**(7),777-783.

Pucher,J.J., Daniel, J.C., 1992. The effects of chlorhexidine digluconate on human fibroblasts in vitro. *J. Periodontol.* **63**, 526-532.

Quirynen, M., Mongardini, C., van Steenberghe, D. 1998. The effect of a 1-stage full-mouth disinfection on oral malodor and microbial colonization of the tongue in periodontitis patients. A pilot study. *J. Periodontol.*, **69**, 374-382.

Quirynen, M., Bollen, C.M.L., Vandekerckhove, B.N.A., Dekeyser, C., Papaioannou, W., Eyssen, H. 1995. Full- vs. Partial-mouth disinfection in the treatment of periodontal infections: short-term clinical and microbiological observations. *J Dent. Res.* **74**. 1456-1467.

Quirynen, M., Papaioannou, W., van Steenberghe, D. 1996. Intra-oral transmission and the colonization or oral hard surfaces. *J. Periodontol.*, **67**, 986-993.

Reip, B.G., Bernimoulin, J.P., Barnett, M.L. 1999. Comparative antiplaque effectiveness of an essential oil and amine fluoride/stannous fluoride mouthrinse. *J. Clin. Periodontol.*, **26**,164-168.

Reynolds, M.A., Lavigne, C.K., Minah, G.E., Suzuki, J.B. 1992. Clinical effects of simultaneous ultrasonic scaling and subgingival irrigation with chlorhexidine. *J. Clin. Periodontol.*, **19**,595-600.

Roberts, W.R., Addy, M. 1981. Comparison of the in vivo and in vitro antibacterial properties of antiseptic mouthrinses containing chlorhexidine, alexidine, cetylpyridinium chloride and hexetidine. Relevance to mode of action. bisbiguanide antiseptics alexidine and chlorhexidine. I Effect on plaque accumulation and salivary bacteria. *J. Clin. Periodontol.*, **8**, 295-310.

Rölla, G., Löe, H., Schiöt, C.R. 1971. Retention of chlorhexidine in the human oral cavity. *Arch. Oral. Biol.*, **16**, 1109-1116.

Rölla, G., Melson, B. 1975. On the mechanisms of the plaque inhibition by chlorhexidine. *J. Dent. Res.*(special issue B) **54**, 57-62.

Rosling, B.G., Slots, J., Webber, R.L., Christersson, L.A., Genco R.J. 1983. Microbiological and clinical effects of topical subgingival antimicrobial treatment on human periodontal disease. *J. Clin. Periodontol.*, **10**, 487-514.

Rosling, B. G., Slots, J., Christersson, L.A., Genco, R.J. 1984. Clinical and microbiological effects of surgical and non-surgical treatment of multi-rooted teeth in adult periodontitis. *J. Dent. Res.,* **63**, 205-abstr 311.

Rosling, B.G., Slots, J., Christersson, L.A., Gröndahl, H.G., Genco, R.J. 1986. Topical antimicrobial therapy and diagnosis of subgingival bacteria in the management of inflammatory periodontal disease. *J. Clin. Periodontol.*, **13**, 975-981.

Rosling, B., Dahlen, G., Volpe, A., Furuichi, Y, Ramberg, P., Lindhe, J. 1997a. Effect of triclosan on the subgingival microbiota of periodontitis-susceptible subjects. *J. Clin. Periodontol.,* **24**, 881-887.

Rosling, B., Wannfors, B., Volpe, A., Furuichi, Y, Ramberg, P., Lindhe, J. 1997b. The use of a triclosan/copolymer dentifrice may retard the progression of periodontitis. *J. Clin. Periodontol.*, **24**, 873-880.

Rykke. M., Ellingsen, J.E., Sönju, T. 1991, Chemical analysis and scanning-electron microscopy of acquired pellicle formed in vivo on stannous fluoride treated enamel. *Scand. J. Dent. Res.*, **99**, 205-211.

Sanz, M., Vallcorba, N., Fabregues, S., *et al.* 1994. The effect of a dentifrice containing chlorhexidine and zinc on plaque, gingivitis, calculus, and tooth staining. *J. Clin. Periodontol.,* **21**, 431-437.

Saxton, C.A., Svatun, B., Lloyd, A.M. 1988. Antiplaque effects and mode of action of a combination of zinc citrate and a nonionic antimicrobial agent. *Scand. J. Dent. Res.* **96**, 212-217.

Saxton, C.A., Cummins, D. 1989. The effect of zinc citrate dentifrices on the development of gingivitis. *J. Dent. Res.* **68**(abstract),971.

Schiött, C.R. 1973. Effect of chlorhexidine on the microflora of the oral cavity. *J. Periodontal. Res.***8**(suppl), 7-10.

Schmid, E., Kornman, K., Tinanoff, N. 1985. Changes of subgingival total colony forming units and black pigmented Bacteroides after a single irrigation of periodontal pockets with 1.64% SnF2. *J. Periodontol.*, **56**, 330-333.

Scully, C., El-Kabi,R M., Greenman, J., Porter, S.R., Mutlu, S., Barton, I., Adair, R. 1999. The effects of mouthrinses and dentifrice-containing magnesium monoperoxyphthalate (mmpp) on oral microflora, plaque reduction, and mucosa. *J. Clin. Periodontol.*, **26**(4),234-238.

Shibly, O., Ciancio, S.G., Kazmierczak, M., Cohen, R.E., Mather, M.L., Ho, A., Bessinge,R. M. 1997. Clinical evaluation of the effect of a hydrogen peroxide mouthrinse, sodium bicarbonate dentifrice, and mouth moisturizer on oral health. *J. Clin. Dent.*, **8**(5),145-149.

Simonetti N., D'Aurin, F.D., Strippoli, V., Lucchetti, G. 1988 Itraconazole: increased activity of chlorhexidine. *Drugs Exp. Clin. Res.*, **14**, 19-23.

Skjorland, K., Gjermo, P, Rölla, G. 1978. Effect of some polyvalent cations on plaque formation in vivo. *Scand. J. Dent. Res.*, **86**, 103-107.

Slavkin, H.C. 1997. biofilms, microbial ecology and Antoni Van Leeuwenhoek. *JADA*, **128**, 492-495.

Soh, L.L, Newman, H.N., Strahan, J.D. 1982. Effects of subgingival chlorhexidine irrigation on periodontal inflammation. *J. Clin. Periodontol.* 9, 66-74.

Soskolne, W.A. 1998. An in vivo study of the CHX release profile of the PerioChip in the gingival crevicular fluid, plasma and urine. *J. Clin. Periodontol.*, **25**, 1017-1021.

Soskolne W., Heasman, P., Stabholz, A. *et al.* 1997. Sustained local delivery of chlorhexidine in the treatment of periodontitis: a multi-center study. *J. Periodontol.*, **68**, 32-38.

Spetz-Happonen, S., Seppa, L., Korheonen, A., Alakuijala, P. 1998. Accumulation of strontium and fluoride in approximal dental plaque and changes in plaque microflora after rinsing with chlorhexidine-fluoride-strontium solution. *Oral Diseases*, 4(2),114-119.

Stanley, A., Wilson, M., Newman, H.N. 1989. The in vitro effects of chlorhexidine on subgingival plaque bacteria. *J. Clin. Periodontol.*, **16**,259-264.

Stephen, K.W., Saxton, C.A., Jones, C.L., Ritchie, J.A., Morrison, T. 1990. Control of gingivitis and calculus by a dentifrice containing a zinc salt and triclosan. J. Periodontol. **61**, 674-679.

Storhaug, K. 1977. Hibitane in oral disease in handicapped patients. *J. Clin. Periodontol.*, **4**, 102-107.

Taggart, J.A., Palmer, R.M., Wilson, R.F. 1990. A clinical and microbiological comparison of the effects of water and 0.02% chlorhexidine as coolants during ultrasonic scaling and root planing. *J. Clin. Periodontol.*, **17**,32-37.

Tellefsen, G., Larsen, G., Kalihithi, R., Zimmerman, G.J., Wikesjö. 1996. Use of chlorhexidine chewing gum significantly reduces dental plaque formation compared to use of similar xylitol and sorbitol products. *J. Periodontol.*, **67**, 181-183.

Thrower, Y., Pinney, R.J., Wilson, M. 1997. Susceptibilities of Actinobacillus actinomycetemcomitans biofilms to oral antiseptics. *J. Med. Microbiol.* **46**, 425-429.

Tinnanoff, N. , Manwell., M.A., Zameck, R.L., Grasso, J.E. 1989. Clinical and microbiological effects of daily brushing with either NaF or Snf2 gels in subjects with fixed or removable dental prostheses. *J. Clin. Periodontol.*, **16**, 284-290.

Tinnanoff, N., Weeks, D.B. 1979. Current status of Snf2 as an antiplaque agent. *Pediatr. Dent.* **1**, 199-204.

Triratana, T., Tuongratanaphan, S., Rustogi, K.N., Petrone, M., Volpe, A.R., Petrone, D. 1993. Plaque/gingivitis effect of a triclosan/copolymer dentifrice. *J. Dent. Res.* **72**, 334 (abstr).

Triratana, T., Kraivaphan, P., Amornchat, C., Rustogi, K., Petrone, M.P., Volpe, A.R. 1995. Effect of a triclosan/copolymer prebrush mouthrinse on established plaque formation and gingivitis: a six-month study in Thailand. *J. Clin. Dent.* **6**, 142-147.

Turesky S, Warner V, Lin Sun P, et al 1977. Prolongation of antibacterial activity of chlorhexidine absorbed to teeth: Effect of sulfates. *J. Periodontol.*, **48**.646-649.

Vaahtoniemi, L.H., Räiänen, S., Stenfors, L.E. 1994. Effect of chlorhexidine and toothbrushing on the presence of bacteria on gingival and buccal epithelial cells. *Oral Microbiol. Immuno.,* **9**,315-317.

van der Hoeven, J.S., Cummins, D., Schaeken, M.J., van der Ouderaa, F.J. 1993. The effect of chlorhexidine and zinc/triclosan mouthrinses on the production of acids in dental plaque. *Caries Res.*, **27**, 298-302.

Vandekerckhove, B. N. A., Bollen, C.M.L., Dekeyser, C., Darius, P., Quirynen. M. 1996. Full-versus partial-mouth disinfection in the treatment of periodontal infections. Long-term clinical observations of a pilot study. *J. Periodontol.*, **67**, 1251-1259.

Van der Weijden, G.A., Timmer, C.J., Timmerman, M.F., Reijerse, E., Mantel, M.S., van der Velden, U. 1998. The effect of herbal extracts in an experimental mouthrinse on established plaque and gingivitis. *J. Clin. Periodontol.*, **25**(5),399-403.

Veksler, A., Ghassan, A., Kayrouz, Newman, M. Reduction of salivary bacteria by pre-procedural rinses with chlorhexidine 0.12%. *J Periodontol*, **62**, 649-651.

Wade, W.G., Addy, M. 1989. In vitro activity of a chlorhexidine-containing mouthwash against subgingival bacteria. *J. Periodontol.*, **60**, 521-525.

Waerhaug, J. 1981. Effect of toothbrushing on subgingival plaque formation. *J. Periodontol.*, **52**,30-34.

Walker, C., Clark, W., Tyler, K. 1989. Evaluation of microbial shifts following long-term antiseptic use. *J. Dent. Res.* **21**(abstr), 60.

Walker, C., Borden, L.C., Zambon, J.J., Bonta, C.Y., DeVizio, W., Volpe, A.R. 1994. The effects of a 0.3% triclosan-containing dentifrice on the microbial composition of supragingival plaque. *J. Clin. Periodontol.*, **21**, 334-341.

Walsh, T.F., Glenwirght, H.D., Hull, P.S. 1992. Clinical effects of pulsed oral irrigation with 0.2% chlorhexidine digluconate in patients with adult periodontitis. *J. Clin. Periodontol.*, **19**.245-248.

Watts. E.A., Newman, H.N. 1986. Clinical effects on chronic periodontitis of a simplified system of oral hygiene including subgingival pulsated jet irrigation with chlorhexidine. *J. Clin. Periodontol.*, **13**, 666-670.

Wennström, J.L., Heijl, L., Dahlön, G., Gröndahl, K. 1987. Periodic subgingival antimicrobial irrigation of periodontal pockets. I. Clinical observations. *J. Clin. Periodontol.*, **14**, 541-550.

Westfelt, E., Nyman, S., Lindhe, J., and Socransky, S.S. 1983. Use of chlorhexidine as a plaque control measure following surgical treatment of periodontal disease. *J. Clin. Periodontol.*, **10**,22-36.

Wilson, M. 1996. Susceptibility of oral bacterial biofilms to antimicrobial agents. *J. Med. Microbiol.* **44**, 79-87.

Wilson, M., Patel, H., Fletcher, J.,. 1996. Susceptibility of biofilms of *Streptococcus sanguis* to chlorhexidine gluconate and cetylpyridinium chloride. *Oral. Microbiol. Immunol.*, **11**, 188-192.

Wilson M, Patel, H., Noar, J.H. 1998. Effect of chlorhexidine on multi-species biofilms. *Current Microbiology*, **36**, 13-18.

Winrow, M.J. 1973. Metabolic studies with radiolabeled chlorhexidine in animals and man. *J. Periodontal. Res.*, **8**,45-48.

Wolff, L.F., Pihlstrom B.L., Bandt, C.L. 1989. The effect of professional and home subgingival irrigation with antimicrobial agents on gingivitis and early periodontitis. *J. Dent. Hyg.*, **63**,222-241.

Worthington, H.V., Davies, R.M., Blinkhorn, A.S., Mankodi, S., Petrone, M., DeVizio, W., Volpe. A.R. 1993. A six-month clinical study of the effect of a pre-brush rinse on plaque removal and gingivitis. *Br. Dent. J.*, **175**, 322-326.

Xu, Y., Ambudkar, I., Yamagishi, H., Swaim W., Walsh, T.J., O'Connol, B.C. 1999. Histatin 3-Mediated killing of candida albicans: effect of extracellular salt concentration on binding and internalization. *Antimicrob. Agents Chemother.*, **43**, 2256-2262.

ANTIBIOTICS AND CONTROL OF PLAQUE-RELATED DISEASES

J.M. Goodson, M. Feres, S. Som and S.S. Socransky

Eight subjects with periodontal disease were treated by scaling and root planing followed by systemically administered doxycycline (immediate adminis- tration of 200 mg and 100 mg/day for 14 days). This treatment created doxycy- cline concentrations of 0.1 to 4 µg/ml in gingival crevice fluid (GCF). These treatments did not substantially alter gross plaque composition. In addition, organisms still susceptible to concentrations occurring in GCF were isolated after two weeks of systemic antibiotic administration. These observations suggest that systemically administered doxycycline may not be reaching all environments that harbor susceptible organisms. Oral biofilm characteristics which effectively exclude antibiotics offer a possible explanation for this observation.

*Evaluation of the proportions of 40 periodontal bacteria by DNA:DNA hybridization revealed that only **T. denticola** was significantly reduced by the administration of doxycycline using the defined protocol. Regression analysis at all time points studied indicated that the percentage of **T. denticola** was reduced in proportion to the concentration of GCF doxycycline, even one year after its administration. Data also suggested that the reduction in **T. denticola** propor- tions may have occurred early in therapy (after only three days of administra- tion) and may require substantial GCF concentrations before any persistent affect can occur. Taken together, these data suggest that a shorter duration with higher dosage of doxycycline could be a more effective therapeutic strategy for periodontal treatment than that used in this study. Future investigations that test groups of subjects under various dosage and time intervals using antibacterial outcome variables offer a means to optimize systemic antibiotic therapy for periodontal treatments.*

Introduction

Systemically administered antibiotics have long been considered reasonable adjunctive treatments to be included with other forms of periodontal therapy. Their clinical effectiveness, however, has not been convincingly demonstrated. For example, systemically administered doxycycline has been reported to have positive clinical effects in two studies (Crout *et al.,* 1996; Schroeder *et al.,* 1992), but little or no effects in two other studies (Chaves E *et al.,* 1995; Ng & Bissada, 1998). Few investigations have been undertaken to study the microbio- logical consequences of this type of periodontal therapy.

More recently, the biology of biofilms has suggested a possible reason for the difficulty in obtaining meaningful clinical results when systemic antibiotics are used as adjuncts in periodontal therapy. Oral bacteria removed from the mouth and placed on antibiotic-containing agar plates, or in antibiotic-contain- ing media can be killed by extremely low concentrations of the agents. Oral

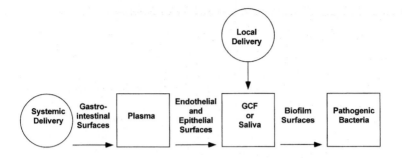

Figure 1 Surface penetration of systemic and local antibiotic delivery systems to reach bacteria within the plaque biofilm.

bacteria protected within a complex biofilm on a tooth surface pose an entirely different problem. Some of the complexities of bringing the antibiotic to the pathogenic oral bacterium are illustrated in Figure 1.

Systemically administered antibiotics first must traverse multiple membrane surfaces within the body to reach the GCF or saliva while locally delivered antibiotics may be placed directly into the GCF or saliva. However, this is not the end of the road for either mode of delivery. The antibiotic must penetrate the plaque biofilm in order to reach the pathogenic bacterial target. To fail at this step is to fail in therapy.

It is now clear that dental plaque is a complex biofilm that dramatically reduces effectiveness of many antibiotics. It seems likely that the use of antibiotics in the treatment of oral diseases depends largely on their ability to permeate the dental biofilm. This conclusion is based on a series of observations that will be described in this manuscript in which the concentration of doxycycline in GCF, as well as the corresponding effects on bacteria of the periodontal pocket are measured.

One way to demonstrate the clinical significance of the plaque biofilm effect, is to establish and maintain a GCF concentration for a defined time period and measure the susceptibility of bacterial isolates to that antibiotic at that concentration. If a large fraction of the plaque bacteria remain susceptible at the measured GCF concentration, one must conclude that susceptible species evaded elimination by what would be a toxic antibiotic concentration in an in vitro situation. To make this experiment more clinically meaningful the plaque mass can be disrupted by performing full-mouth scaling and root planing.

Materials and methods

The experiment illustrated in Figure 2 was designed to test the antibacterial effects of oral administration of doxycycline in conjunction with scaling and root planing. By this protocol, three groups of parameters were measured on 6 selected test teeth in each of 8 subjects. The measured parameters were GCF concentration of doxycycline, plaque susceptibility at the end of antibiotic

550

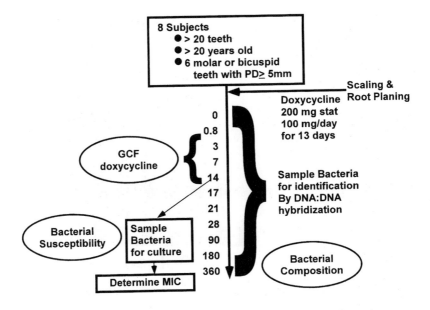

Figure 2 Experimental protocol to investigate short-term and long-term microbiologic effects of antibiotics on periodontal plaque biofilms. GCF samples for measurement of doxycycline were taken at 0.8, 3, 7 and 14 days. Samples for culture were taken at 14 days for measurement of antibiotic susceptibility. Samples for DNA:DNA hybridization assay were taken at 0, 3, 7, 14, 17, 21, 28, 90, 180 and 360 days.

therapy (14 days) and changes in bacterial composition. Associations between drug concentration and bacterial composition were evaluated by comparing doxycycline concentration and bacterial changes at the same sites.

Subject Population

Eight test subjects were selected with periodontal disease as evidenced by having 6 molar or bicuspid teeth with a pocket depth of greater than or equal to 5 mm. All subjects were greater than 20 years of age and had at least 20 teeth. None of the subjects were pregnant, lactating or had any known allergy to tetracycline or to local anesthetics. All subjects requiring antibiotic coverage for routine periodontal procedures or with known systemic disease that could affect periodontitis (such as diabetes or AIDS) or having had periodontal or antibiotic therapy in the previous 6 months were excluded.

Therapy

All subjects were treated by full-mouth scaling and root planing (SRP) under local anesthesia. The test group was administered 200 mg doxycycline immediately following completion of scaling. They were also given thirteen 100 mg capsules of doxycycline to be taken once daily for the following 13 days.

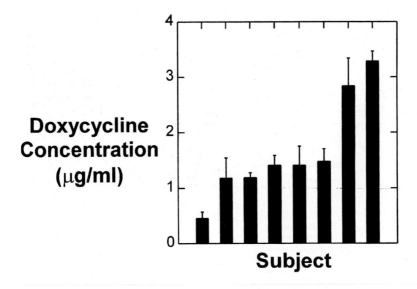

Figure 3 Mean GCF doxycycline concentration in 8 subjects (averaged over 2 hour, 3 day, 7 day and 14 day samples of six sites/subject).

Antibiotic Concentration

Filter paper samples of gingival crevice fluid (GCF) were taken from the mesiobuccal surface of six pre-selected teeth. GCF samples were taken at 2 hours and at 3,7 and 14 days following the initiation of systemic doxycycline administration. The fluid volume of each sample was measured (Periotron). These samples were analyzed by bioassay for doxycycline concentration as previously described (Gordon *et al.*, 1980).

Microbiological Sampling

Subgingival plaque samples were taken from the mesial aspect of all teeth in the mouth using a sterile periodontal scaler at 0, 90, 180 and 360 days for identification of 40 bacterial species by DNA:DNA hybridization (Socransky S.S. *et al.*, 1994). In addition, samples were taken at 3, 7 and 14 days from two of six randomly paired posterior teeth during doxycycline administration and again on days 17 ,21 and 28. Samples were taken at the same time points from the control group treated by SRP alone.

Aliquots of plaque samples taken on day 14 were grown on non-selective blood agar plates and 50 randomly selected colonies from each plate were transferred into a 96 well microtiter plate containing 2% Mycoplasma broth (BBL). Enriched Mycoplasma agar plates containing serial dilutions of doxycycline (0.5, 1, 2, 4 and 8 µg/ml) were prepared in disposable polystyrene MIC 2000 inoculum trays (Dynatech Laboratories, Chantilly VA) as well as the same medium without doxycycline. The suspensions from the 96 well plates were then stamped on the 5 test media and on the control agar plate using an MIC-

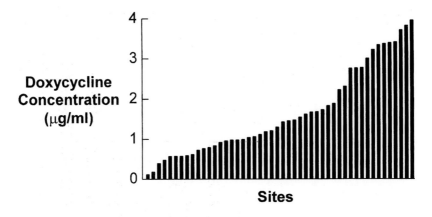

Figure 4 Mean and standard error of GCF doxycycline concentration in 48 sites (averaged over 2 hour, 3 day, 7 day and 14 day samples).

2000 Automatic Inoculator (Dynatech Laboratories) and then incubated for 7 days at 35° C in 80%N_2, 10% CO_2 and 10% H_2. After the incubation period, the minimum inhibitory concentration (MIC), defined as the lowest concentration allowing no detectable growth, was determined on 378 isolates.

Data Analysis

Mean percentage composition of bacterial complexes were computed using published definitions (Socransky *et al.,* 1998). Percent of sites colonized (prevalence) of bacteria was computed as the percent of sites within the detection limit of the DNA:DNA hybridization assay (10^4 bacteria) divided by the number of sites sampled (48 at baseline 90, 180 and 360 days).

Target species that may have been affected by systemic doxycycline administration were identified by considering the association between microbial presence and doxycycline concentration. This was facilitated by computing Pearson correlation coefficients between average doxycycline concentration at a site (average of 2 hour, 3, 7, and 14 day samples) and average percentage of the organism in the sample of that site (average of 3, 7, 14, 17, 21, 28, 90, 180 and 365 day samples). In this procedure, a positive correlation between doxycycline concentration and reduction in percentage of the organism was sought to identify target species. Upon identification of these species, functional relationships were investigated by linear regression at each microbial sampling time.

Results

Doxycycline Concentration

Average GCF concentration of doxycycline (Figure 3) varied greatly between subjects (average concentrations varied from 0.5 to 3.2 µg/ml). An even larger variation in GCF doxycycline concentration between sites (Figure 4) was observed (average concentrations varied from 0.1 to 4 µg/ml).

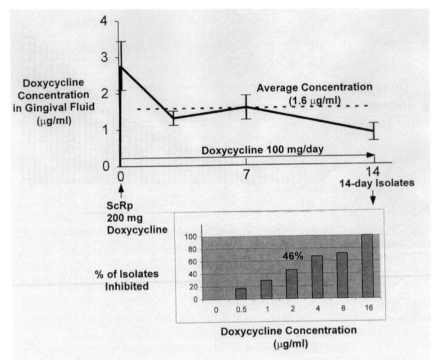

Figure 5 GCF doxycycline concentration and antibiotic susceptibility of periodontal plaque samples isolated after 14 days of drug administration. Susceptibility testing indicated that 46% of 378 isolates tested were sensitive to 2% doxycycline, the approximate concentration measured in GCF.

Bacterial Sensitivity

The average GCF doxycycline concentration and sensitivity of bacteria isolated from the periodontal pocket are illustrated in Figure 5. The upper panel indicates that the highest doxycycline concentration occurred 2 hours following administration of the loading dose of 200 mg. The concentration then dropped to a plateau level. No signs of a cumulative increase were noted. The average GCF concentration of doxycycline over the 14-day treatment period was 1.6 µg/ml. Sensitivity testing of isolates from periodontal pockets indicated that the growth of 46% of the isolates was inhibited by 2 µg/ml. doxycycline (Figure 5 lower panel).

Taken together, these data indicate that approximately half the bacteria in samples of dental plaque from teeth that were meticulously scaled and exposed to an average GCF concentration of 1.6 mg/ml for two weeks somehow were unaffected by the systemically administered doxycycline.

Characterization of Antimicrobial Effects of Doxycycline.

Figure 6 illustrates the total bacterial counts over 28 days. None of the changes in total counts represent a significant change. Similarly, the changes in the proportions of different complexes following doxycycline administration

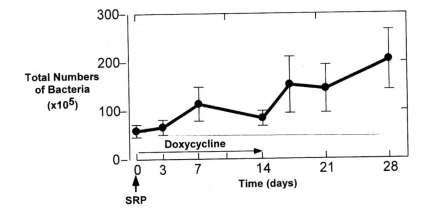

Figure 6 The total numbers of bacteria from sites treated by scaling and root planing followed by adjunctive systemic administration of doxycycline. Observed changes were small and statistically insignificant.

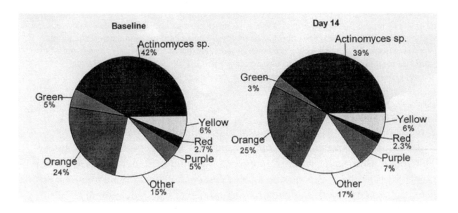

Figure 7 Distribution of bacterial complexes at baseline and after 14 days of doxycycline administration after full mouth scaling and root planing. All differences were 3% or less.

(Figure 7) were minimal. Changes in bacterial complexes (as defined by Socransky *et al.*, 1998) from baseline to the completion time of antibiotic administration (14 days) were 3% or less.

   Identification of Bacterial Changes Related to Systemic Antibiotic Therapy. To identify bacterial species that might have changed as a result of the systemic antibiotic therapy, the correlation between average GCF doxycycline and percentage reduction (DNA%) for each species was computed. A plot of these values is illustrated in Figure 8. From this presentation, it is clear that

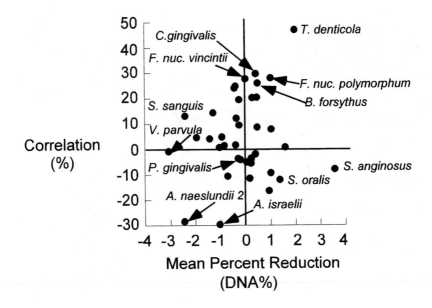

Figure 8 Correlation between average GCF doxycycline concentration and mean reduction in bacterial percentage from baseline. The analysis indicates that of the 40 species tested, only *T. denticola* reduction had a high positive correlation with GCF doxycycline concentration.

T. denticola had the greatest reduction in percentage composition associated with the highest correlation with the average GCF concentration in the pocket. This relationship suggest that *T. denticola* was unique in that, under the conditions of this study, it was the only species associated with both a high correlation between site doxycycline concentration and percentage reduction in bacteria.

The percent of sites colonized (prevalence) at baseline by *T. denticola, B. forsythus* and *P. gingivalis* at baseline was 85.1%, 35.4% and 34% respectively. The prevalence of *T. denticola* decreased by approximately 30% following therapy and remained lower relative to baseline values up to one year (Figure 9). The percent of sites colonized by *B. forsythus* was also reduced, but to a smaller degree (12.4%), and tended to increase by the end of a year. The percentage of sites colonized by *P. gingivalis* did not show any reduction, continually increasing over the monitored period.

The effect of systemic doxycycline administration on percentage of *T. denticola* was examined by regression analysis of site concentration with percentage reduction at each time point. The values obtained are recorded in Table 1.

These data indicate that, in general, there was a positive association at each time point between the average site concentration of doxycycline during the therapeutic period and the percentage of *T. denticola*. This association appeared

556

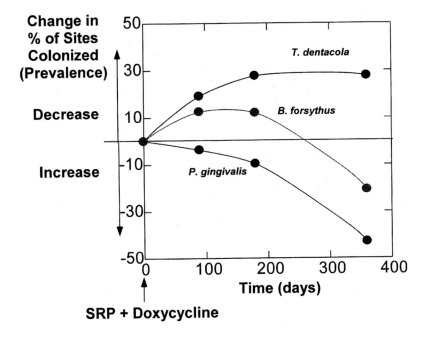

Figure 9 Change in percent of sites colonized by "red complex" periodontal pathogens (prevalence). The baseline prevalence of *T. denticola, B. forsythus* and *P. gingivalis* was 85.1%, 35.4% and 34.0% respectively. Although a small transient decrease in the proportions of *B. forsythus* occurred following therapy, the only persistant reduction in proportions maintained over time was that of *T. denticola*. The prevalence of *P. gingivalis* infected sites continued to increase over the period studied.

as early as 3 days with borderline significance (p=0.1) and was highly significant at 90, 180 and 365 days after the study was initiated. These data indicate that on average, the percentage of *T. denticola* was reduced by 3.6% per μg/ml doxycycline in GCF, an effect that persisted for one year following therapy. None of the proportions of other "red complex" members (*P. gingivalis* and *B. forsythus*) were significantly related to GCF doxycycline concentration.

Figure 10 illustrates a regression analysis of Table 1 at 365 days following the 14-day period of antibiotic administration. No trend in bacterial composition occurred until the doxycycline concentration was approximately 1 μg/ml. Thereafter, the percentage reduction was 2.47 %/mg/ml doxycycline. These data suggest that the microbiological effect obtained in therapy can be long lasting and depends on the antibiotic concentration achieved in GCF.

Discussion
These observations indicate that systemically administered antibiotics have less effect on plaque bacteria than that observed in the laboratory on agar plates. This implies there may be considerable clinical significance to the effect of

Table 1 Analysis of relationship between mean change in percentage of *T. denticola* at each site and average site doxycycline concentration over the 14-day therapeutic period by regression analysis. The parameters of slope, intercept, p and correlation coefficient were computed for each time point following therapy by scaling and root planing with adjunctive systemic doxycycline administration.

Time (days)	p	Correlation coefficient	Number of sites	Slope ($\%/\mu g/ml$)	Intercept (%)
3	0.1	0.46	13	2.90	-2.68
7	0.07	0.50	14	1.62	-0.78
14	0.1	0.44	14	8.99	8.99
17	0.1	0.39	15	1.99	-0.91
21	0.01	0.60	16	1.72	-0.81
28	0.2	0.32	16	7.85	7.85
90	0.007	0.39	46	1.34	-0.07
180	0.0000	0.59	46	3.09	-3.84
365	0.0002	0.52	46	2.47	-2.69
Average				3.6	0.6

biofilm formation in dental plaque. The findings in this study may be summarized as follows:

1. The effects of systemically administered doxycycline with scaling and root planing on total bacterial counts and composition were modest.
2. The GCF doxycycline concentration varied greatly between subjects and sites.
3. The growth of approximately 50% of bacteria exposed to what would be considered sensitive in vitro antibacterial levels of doxycycline were not inhibited in vivo.
4. Of 40 bacterial taxa tested, only the presence of *T. denticola* was significantly affected by systemic administration of doxycycline at usual doses.
5. The magnitude of effect of doxycycline on *T. denticola* was proportional to the GCF concentration.

The modest effects of doxycycline therapy were in sharp contrast to the widely held view of its effectiveness on the periodontal microbiota: that antibiotic administration is the equivalent of launching a nuclear war on the periodontal flora. Far from this viewpoint, in this study only subtle changes occurred and the great mass of bacteria remained intact.

Variability in site and subject concentrations of tetracyclines in GCF samples has been reported. In a recent study (Sakellari *et al.*, 2000), 20 subjects were administered 100 mg doxycycline and the concentration of doxycycline in GCF was measured two hours following administration of the antibiotic. The GCF concentration at sites within subjects varied greatly. Some sites had concentrations below detection limits of the assay (0.03 $\mu g/ml$) and some had concentrations as high as 8 $\mu g/ml$. Approximately 50% of the subjects tested had GCF

558

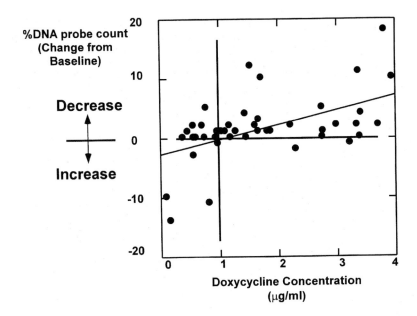

Figure 10 Relationship of mean change in percentage of *T. denticola* to mean site doxycycline concentration 365 days after a 14-day therapeutic period. The plot suggests that a long-term change in proportions occurred. It appears that no effect occurred at GCF concentrations less than 1 µg/ml but that a positive association between GCF concentration and decreased bacterial proportions occurred at higher GCF levels.

concentrations less than 1 µg/ml. The principle component related to GCF concentration was plasma concentration, indicating that absorption may have been one limiting factor. This variability, seen also in the current study, could provide the basis for much of the controversy concerning claims of adjunctive efficacy using systemic antibiotics.

The observation that almost 50% of bacteria isolated from a periodontal site are susceptible to inhibition in vitro by doxycycline at approximately the same concentration measured in GCF suggest that they are somehow protected in the periodontal environment. Several mechanisms have been proposed whereby this might occur (Gilbert *et al.,* 1997). These include direct interaction between the exopolymer matrices affecting drug diffusion, modified environment and suppression of growth rate within the biofilm, and development of biofilm/ attachment-specific phenotypes. Whatever the mechanism, clearly antibiotic-susceptible species survive despite combined mechanical disruption by scaling and root planing and systemically administered doxycycline.

In laboratory culture, all members of the "red complex" were susceptible to tetracyclines at concentrations of 1 µg/ml (Goodson 1994). Although initially surprising, the effect of doxycycline on *T. denticola* might be explained by its motility. Unlike *B. forsythus* and *P. gingivalis, T. denticola* can move in and out of a plaque biofilm. Although little is known of doxycycline susceptibility of this species, based on experience with other tetracyclines it can be expected to be doxycycline sensitive. The difference in in vitro efficacy is potential for exposure. After two weeks of systemic doxycycline therapy, virtually all motile species would likely encounter effective concentrations of the antibiotic. *B. forsythus* and *P. gingivalis*, on the other hand, could easily be protected by the biofilm.

Considering the greater than 10-fold variation in GCF doxycycline concentration, a comparable variability in microbiological responses to systemic antibiotic administration would seem likely. For example the microbiological effect on *T. denticola*, the single species that appeared to respond to doxycycline therapy in this study, was directly proportional to the antibiotic concentration. Such findings could explain the variability in clinical responses reported with adjunctive systemic antibiotic administration.

The observation that the effect of systemically administered doxycycline on *T. denticola* depends on GCF concentration also suggests a strategy by which antibiotic therapy may be optimized for the treatment of periodontal diseases. Clearly, higher site concentrations produce better results. Results from locally delivered tetracycline where concentrations were approximately 1,500 mg/ml have a powerful effect on elimination of *P. gingivalis* (Mombelli *et al.*, 1996), a species not affected by the systemic regime used in this study. In a recent report of different doses of doxycycline (Sakellari *et al.*, 2000) a single 400 mg dose produced peak GCF concentrations up to 15 µg/ml, almost 10 times the average concentration observed in this study. Considering also that the effects on *T. denticola* seemed to occur within three days of the initiation of antibiotic therapy, we came to an important conclusion. It seems possible that optimal dosage for systemic antibiotics used in periodontal therapy should be higher than generally recommended and that the required duration may be shorter.

References

Chaves E, Ryerson C., Snyder B. & Jeffcoat M. 1995. Effect of systemic tetracycline therapy on specific bacterial antigens and bone height. *J Dent Res*, **26**, 114(Abstract).

Crout, R.J., Lee, H.M., Schroeder, K., Crout, H., Ramamurthy, N.S., Wiener, M. & Golub, L.M. 1996. The "cyclic" regimen of low-dose doxycycline for adult periodontitis: a preliminary study. *Journal of Periodontology*, **67**, 506-514.

Gilbert, P., Das, J. & Foley, I. 1997. Biofilm susceptibility to antimicrobials. [Review] [77 refs]. *Advances in Dental Research*, **11**, 160-167.

Goodson, J.M. 1994. Antimicrobial strategies for treatment of periodontal diseases. [Review] [171 refs]. *Periodontology 2000*, **5**, 142-168.

Gordon, J.M., Walker, C.B., Goodson, J.M. & Socransky, S.S. 1980. Sensitive assay for measuring tetracycline levels in gingival crevice fluid. *Antimicrobial Agents and Chemotherapy* **17**, 193-198.

Mombelli, A., Tonetti, M., Lehmann, B. & Lang, N.P. 1996. Topographic distribution of black-pigmenting anaerobes before and after periodontal treatment by local delivery of tetracycline. *Journal of Clinical Periodontology*, **23**, 906-913.

Ng, V.W. & Bissada, N.F. 1998. Clinical evaluation of systemic doxycycline and ibuprofen administration as an adjunctive treatment for adult periodontitis. *Journal of Periodontology*, **69**, 772-776.

Sakellari, D., Goodson, J.M., Socransky S.S., Kolokotronis, A. & Konstantinidis, A. 2000. Concentration of 3 tetracyclines in plasma, gingival crevice fluid and saliva. *J Clin Periotontol,*

Schroeder, K., Ramamurthy, N.S. & Sczepanek KA 1992. Low-dose doxycycline prevents attachment loss in adult periodontitis. *J Dent Res,* **71**, 758(Abstract).

Socransky S.S., Smith, C., Martin, L., Paster, B.J., Dewhirst, F.E. & Levin, A.E. 1994. "Checkerboard" DNA-DNA Hybridization. *Biotechniques,* **17**, 788-792.

Socransky, S.S., Haffajee, A.D., Cugini, M.A., Smith, C. & Kent, R.L., Jr. 1998. Microbial complexes in subgingival plaque. *Journal of Clinical Periodontology,* **25**, 134-144.

PROSPECTS FOR VACCINATION AGAINST PLAQUE-RELATED ORAL DISEASES

Roy C. Page and Laura S. Houston

*There is a need for new approaches to prevention of the onset and progression of periodontitis in individuals and large populations. There is evidence that development of a periodontitis vaccine is possible and could be used for this purpose. In most industrialized countries approximately 15% of the population has enhanced risk for moderate to severe periodontitis. The disease is caused by infection by gram-negative, anaerobic bacteria including **Porphyromonas gingivalis** and **Bacteroides forsythus**. There is evidence that **P. gingivalis** is a key pathogen. Using ligature-induced periodontitis in the nonhuman primate **Macaca fascicularis** as a model, we immunized 10 animals using intact killed **P. gingivalis** and SAF-M adjuvant and 10 controls using adjuvant only. The vaccine, containing 250 µg protein/ml, was injected subcutaneously in the neck and into the deltoid muscle (0.5ml each site) at baseline and weeks 3, 6, and 12 weeks, and the mandibular posterior teeth ligated at week 16. At weeks 30 and 36 changes in alveolar bone, measured using digital subtraction radiography, was used as the outcome measure. Even though periodontitis in humans and in this animal model is a polymicrobial disease, immunization with a vaccine containing a single bacterial species, **P. gingivalis**, induced protection. Of all the **P. gingivalis** components that have been studied, the cysteine proteases have the greatest potential as vaccine antigens. In a pilot study using the same protocol, we have shown that porphypain-2 purified from **P. gingivalis** is effective in inducing protection. Although opsonization and bacterial cell killing may be involved in protection, other mechanisms such as antibody mediated reduction of levels of inflammatory mediators such as PGE_2 and neutralization of virulence factors may be important. In neither the whole cell vaccine nor the purified cysteine protease vaccine studies were signs of toxicity observed.*

Introduction

Microbial plaque forms on the surfaces of the teeth and becomes organized into structures known as biofilms. These structures consist of large numbers of bacterial species organized into communities and embedded in matrix material which they produce (Costerton *et al.*, 1994). Biofilms have the capacity to cause any of several diseases including dental caries and inflammatory diseases of the periodontal tissues. Among the latter are gingivitis including acute necrotizing ulcerative gingivitis and several kinds of periodontitis including adult periodontitis and various early onset forms. There is great diversity among these diseases in their natural history, etiology and pathogenesis, and in the composition of their associated microbial biofilms. Considerable effort has been expended on development of vaccines for caries and periodontitis (Page and Genco, 1996;

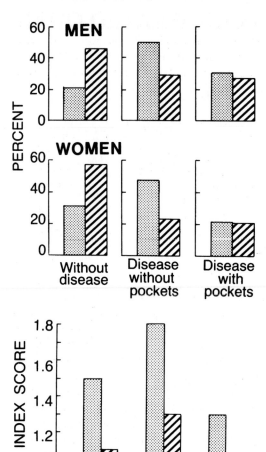

Figure 1A Proportion of adults aged 18 to 79 years by periodontal disease status listed by sex and year of survey. Differences in proportion of persons within each disease category between surveys are significant at P < 0.001 for men and women without disease and with disease without pockets, and at P < 0.01 for men with disease with pockets. Data from 1960-1962 indicated by the stippled bars, and that for 1971-1974 by bars with hash marks. From Douglass, *et al.,* 1983 (with permission).

Figure 1B Average simplified oral hygiene scores for adults by sex and year of survey, mean index scores between surveys are statistically significant at P < 0.001. Data from 1960-1962 indicated by the stippled bars , and that from 1971-1974 by bars with hash marks. From Douglass *et al.,* 1983 (with permission).

Taubman *et al.,* 1998), but virtually nothing is known about the potential for vaccines for the other plaque-associated diseases. The opportunities available and the problems encountered in development of vaccines differ greatly for caries and periodontal disease. This paper is limited, therefore, to prospects for development of a vaccine for periodontitis.

The discovery roughly fifty-five years ago of the effectiveness of fluoride in reducing susceptibility and preventing dental caries (see Carlos, 1988) resulted in an enormous reduction in disease prevalence and severity especially in children, and to revolutionary changes in methods of caries management and prevention. Following the discoveries of the direct association between bacteria in microbial plaque and gingivitis and periodontitis (Keyes and Jordan, 1964; Loe *et al.,* 1965; Lindhe *et al.,* 1975), intensive efforts were made in many countries to effectively control microbial plaque accumulation through daily oral hygiene and periodic profession tooth cleaning. These efforts combined with improved oral hygiene devices and products had a positive effect as manifested by a reduction in plaque scores and in the prevalence of gingivitis, but not periodontitis (Figure 1) (Douglass *et al.,* 1983). However no break-through comparable to the use of fluoride for the prevention of caries has occurred for periodontal diseases. Today, essentially all of our efforts at prevent-ing periodontitis continue to focus exclusively on control of microbial plaque. Clearly, there are boundaries beyond which most individuals cannot go in achieving daily plaque removal. New approaches for prevention of periodontal diseases in individuals and in large populations are badly needed and vaccines may provide a solution.

A great deal of progress has been made in the last decade in improving vaccines for use in prevention of infections as well as many other diseases such as some cancers. Much improved adjuvants designed specifically for use in humans are now becoming available (Allison and Byars, 1986; 1991; Byars and Allison, 1987). Production of vaccines using highly purified and well character-ized antigens synthesized using recombinant DNA techniques has greatly reduced potential toxic side effects and increased safety. Relatively inexpensive, safe vaccines that can be administered to large populations even in countries and locations that have little or no biomedical infrastructure can now be developed. The purpose of this paper is to summarize progress made on development of a vaccine for use in prevention of periodontitis in human populations. A success-ful vaccine appears to offer the best opportunity for prevention of periodontitis not only in industrialized countries but also in emerging countries where professional periodontal services and adequate oral hygiene measures are unlikely to become available in the foreseeable future. There is rapidly increas-ing evidence that periodontitis significantly enhances risk for many systemic diseases that are potentially causes of death including atherosclerosis, coronary heart disease, stroke and complications of diabetes mellitus (Beck *et al.,* 1996; Taylor *et al.,* 1996). A successful periodontal vaccine could have health benefits extending far beyond periodontal disease prevention.

Rationale for a periodontal vaccine
Prevalence of Periodontitis
Periodontitis is a chronic destructive inflammatory disease of the connective tissues and bone housing the teeth. The disease has an infectious etiology and it is a major cause of tooth loss in adults. The prevalence of periodontal diseases in most human populations is relatively high. Mild to moderate periodontitis affects about one-half of working American adults between ages 18 and 65 years (Brown *et al.,* 1990; Brown and Loe, 1993; Albander *et al.,* 1999). In contrast, progressive periodontal destruction of a magnitude sufficient to endanger the survival of the dentition occurs in approximately 13% - 15% of the population (Brown *et al.,* 1990; Brown and Loe 1993; Albander *et al.,* 1999). This is true not only in industrialized countries but also for populations in other countries where

the availability of dental care has been limited or unavailable (Loe *et al.*, 1986; Pilot *et al.*, 1986), for populations of treated patients maintained on recall where deterioration continues in 5 to 15% (Hirshfeld and Wasserman, 1978), and for untreated patients where in most cases, although not all, deterioration is infrequent and episodic (Lindhe *et al.*, 1983). Thus a discrete but significant proportion of the general population, as well as patients receiving adequate periodontal therapy, is considered to be at risk for progressive periodontal deterioration. The use of a vaccine for these groups would likely be more practical, cost-effective, and workable than currently used methods of prevention aimed exclusively at improved oral hygiene.

Periodontitis Is An Infectious Disease

The modern era of periodontal microbiology began with the work of Socransky, Macdonald and Gibbons and their colleagues at the Forsyth Dental Center in Boston in the early 1960s (Socransky *et al.*, 1963). By 1970 sufficient evidence existed to support a consensus among periodontal investigators that human periodontitis is an infectious disease caused by bacteria in microbial plaque (Genco *et al.*, 1969; Keyes, 1970; Socransky, 1970; Ellison *et al.*, 1970). Subsequently investigators determined that specific species of predominantly gram-negative, anaerobic, black-pigmenting bacteria were associated with these diseases and were likely to be involved in the etiology (Newman *et al.*, 1976; Slots, 1976; Tanner *et al.*, 1979). The subgingival flora associated with periodontitis is complex. It may contain more than a hundred different microbial species that incorporate themselves into highly structured biofilms (Tanner *et al.*, 1979; Slots, 1986; Loesche, 1976; 1984; Zambon, 1988; Costerton *et al.*, 1994; Darveau *et al.*, 1997). During the decade of the 1980s, up to 20 to 25 different species were shown to be associated with human periodontitis. The idea that multiple species of bacteria were involved hampered research on the role of the immune response in patients with periodontitis and led many investigators to conclude that development of a vaccine for the disease would not be possible. However, there is now considerable evidence to the contrary.

Periodontitis is caused by a group of predominantly anaerobic, gram-negative bacteria present in subgingival biofilms that form on the crowns and root surfaces of the teeth (Tanner *et al.*, 1979; Costerton *et al.*, 1994; Darveau *et al.*, 1997). Although a very large number of different bacterial species can be found in the biofilms, there is evidence that *Porphyromonas gingivalis*, *Bacteriodes forsythus* and Spirochete sp. are the most strongly linked to the etiology of periodontitis in adults (Grossi *et al.*, 1994; Haffajee and Socransky, 1994; Consensus Report 1996). *P. gingivalis* appears be a key microorganism that plays a special role (Darveau *et al.*, 1995)

Humoral Immune Response to Periodontal Bacterial Antigens

It is enigmatic that while most bacterial infections induce an immune response which plays a significant role in recovery, and conveys protection against subsequent infections by the same or closely related microorganisms, this seems

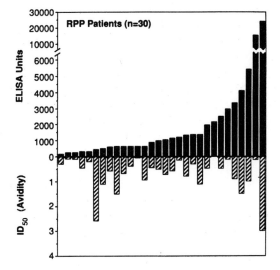

Figure 2A IgG antibody titers in ELISA Units (black bars) and avidity reported as ID-50 (cross-hashed bars) of whole IgG reactive with sonicate antigens of *P. gingivalis* for 30 untreated patients with rapidly progressive periodontitis (RPP). From Whitney *et al.,* 1992 (with permission).

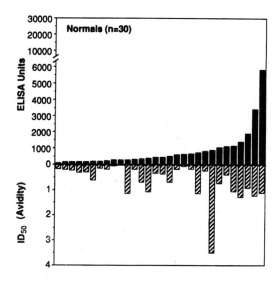

Figure 2B IgG antibody titers in ELISA Units (black bars) and avidity reported as ID-50 (cross-hatched bars) for 30 age, gender and race related periodontally normal control individuals. From Whitney *et al.,* 1992 (with permission).

not to be the case in periodontitis. In this family of diseases, infections frequently recur following successful treatment or continue unabated in spite of treatment, necessitating continuing treatment or maintenance every three or four months. Numerous studies have demonstrated that many, although not all, patients with periodontitis mount a humoral immune response during the course of their spontaneously occurring periodontal infections (Mouton *et al.,* 1981; Tew *et al.,* 1985; Vincent *et al.,* 1985; Ebersole *et al.,* 1986; Ishikawa *et al.,* 1988; Murayama *et al.,* 1988; Ogawa *et al.,* 1990). In our studies, only about

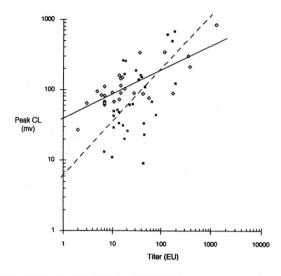

Figure 3 Regression analysis of relationship between peak chemiluminescence (CL) values (broken line) , a surrogate measure for bacterial cell killing by PMN, and IgG titer (solid line) for RPP patients and normal serum groups. Solid squares are for patient sera and open diamonds are for control sera. The slopes of the two lines are significantly different with P = 0.04. From Sjöström et al., 1992 (with permission).

one-half of untreated patients with rapidly progressive periodontitis were seropositive (Figure 2) (Chen et al., 1991; Whitney et al., 1992; Sjöström et al., 1994). Why some patients respond by producing serum antibodies reactive with antigens of their infecting bacteria while others do not remains unknown.

Not only does a large proportion of the periodontitis patients remain seronegative but the antibodies produced during the course of periodontal infection by seropositive patients may be relatively ineffective in providing protection. For example, antibodies specific for antigens of infecting periodontal bacteria of the IgG2 subclass, followed by IgG3, IgG1 and IgG4 predominate in the sera of patients with early onset periodontitis (Whitney et al., 1992; Ling et al., 1993). IgG2 antibodies do not fix complement nor enhance opsonization and phagocytosis and killing by neutrophils as effectively as IgG1 (Roitt et al., 1989). Although serum antibody titers may be rather high in some patients, measures of antibody function such as avidity and enhancement of killing may be significantly lower in patient than in normal control sera (Chen et al., 1991; Sjöström et al., 1992; 1994). In Figure 2, mean avidity value for normal control sera is significantly higher than for patients. Indeed, low-titer sera from periodontally normal individuals were more effective at enhancing phagocytosis and killing than low-titer sera from patients (Figure 3) (Sjöström et al., 1992), suggesting that immediately following infection, individuals who are resistant to development of periodontitis may produce antibodies that are effective in cleaning the organisms prior to the onset of clinical signs of disease, while susceptible individuals may be unable to do so, and clinical disease develops.

Although there is some evidence to the contrary (see above; Ebersole et al., 1991), the bulk of the published data indicate that serum antibodies are protective. Ranney et al. (1982) observed fewer affected teeth and less severe disease

568

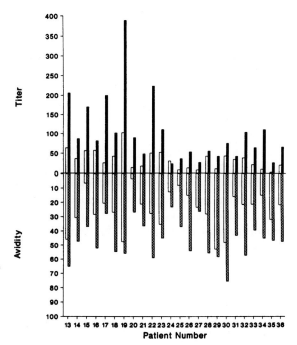

Figure 4 Pre- and Post-treatment titers (open bars and closed bars respectively, upper part of the figure), and pre- and post-treatment avidities (open bars and closed bars respectively, lower part of the figure) for 24 seronegative patients. Samples were defined as seronegative if the titers were lower than two standard deviations of the median titer for normal control sera. From Chen *et al.,* 1991, with permission.

in young adults having high levels of precipitating serum antibodies to antigens of periodontopathic bacteria than in those with lower titers. Similarly, Gunsolley *et al.,* (1987) found an inverse relationship between levels of serum antibodies reactive with antigens of *A. actinomycetemcomitans* and *P. gingivalis* and the number of teeth having attachment loss. In addition, a negative correlation has been reported between specific serum IgG antibody and the number of pockets deeper than 4 mm (Schenck *et al.,* 1987).

Immunologic Effects of Periodontal Therapy

Periodontal therapy has a marked effect on the humoral immune response to antigens of periodontopathic bacteria (Ebersole *et al.,* 1985; Vincent *et al.,* 1987; Murayama *et al.,* 1988). Treatment by scaling and root planing or by surgery significantly enhances serum antibody titers and avidities to antigens of *P. gingivalis* and induces seronegative patients to seroconvert (Figure 4) (Ebersole *et al.,* 1985; Chen *et al.,* 1991; Sjöström *et al.,* 1994). Following treatment, Chen *et al.,* (1991) observed a significant negative correlation between antibody avidity to *P. gingivalis* antigens and both mean pocket depth and mean bone loss. In another study, sera harvested 6 and 12 months following scaling and root planing significantly enhanced neutrophil chemiluminescence, phagocytosis and killing of *P. gingivalis* relative to pretreatment sera (Sjöström *et al.,* 1994). A portion of the clinical improvement observed following treatment appears to result from immune activation (Pawlowski *et al.,* 1998).

Animal Studies

Animal experiments also support the idea that protective humoral immunity may be induced. Immunization with a vaccine containing killed *P. gingivalis* provides protection in the *P. gingivalis*-induced skin-abscess model in rodents (Chen *et al.*, 1990). Immunization of mice with *P. gingivalis* by gastric lavage protects against alveolar bone loss (Baker *et al.*, 1994). Likewise, immunization with *P. gingivalis* and with the purified *P. gingivalis* antigen fimbrillin, suppresses alveolar bone loss in the monoinfected rat model (Evans *et al.*, 1992). Genco *et al.* (1998) using the mouse chamber model recently showed that immunization with a peptide from the catalytic domain of gingipain provided protection against *P. gingivalis* infection, although peptides from the hemagglutinin or adhesion domains failed to protect. Moritz *et al.*, (1998) immunized *M. fascicularis* with a vaccine containing the purified *P. gingivalis* cysteine protease porphypain-2. They were able to achieve very high specific antibody titers and the extent of alveolar bone loss was reduced in the immunized relative to the control animals but the differences did not reach statistical significance.

Summary

In summary, there is a strong rationale for development of a vaccine for human periodontitis. Only a segment of most populations manifest an enhanced susceptibility for severe periodontitis. Methods to identify those at high risk are now becoming available (Page and Beck, 1997; Kornman *et al.*, 1997). Periodontitis is an infectious disease caused by a group of predominantly anaerobic gram-negative bacteria among which *P. gingivalis* is a key species. Roughly half of patients do not mount a humoral immune response during the course of their spontaneously occurring infection, and in those who do, functional characteristics of the antibodies produced are low. Periodontal therapies such as scaling and root planing result in bacteremia and cause seroconversion in most seronegative patients. The antibodies produced have enhanced functional properties. We suggest the probability is high that intentional immunization with an appropriate purified antigen in an appropriate adjuvant will provide protection against periodontal infection and tissue destruction. Experiments described below have been performed to test this hypothesis.

Strategy for vaccine development

Formulation of a plan for development of a periodontal vaccine requires answers to several key questions. More than a hundred species of microorganisms can be found in the human oral cavity. Human periodontitis has traditionally been considered to be a polymicrobial infection involving as many as 20 to 25 bacterial species (Haffajee and Socransky, 1994). Under these conditions, development of a successful vaccine would seem to be impossible. That, however, may not be the case. There is evidence that most of the species associated with periodontitis are likely to be bystanders or contributors to the biofilm structure, with only one or a few being key disease-causing participants.

570

In ranking bacteria species on the strength of their association with disease, Haffajee and Socransky (1994) gave *P. gingivalis* and *B. forsythus* their highest ranking. Experts have agreed that these two species are not only associated with but are etiologic agents for human periodontitis (World Workshop in Clinical Periodontics, 1996). In an epidemiological study, Grossi *et al.,* (1994) found that *P. gingivalis* and *B. forsythus* were the only microorganisms significantly associated with the presence of periodontitis in adults. At the World Workshop on Clinical Periodontics, recognized experts in the field agreed that *P. gingivalis* and *B. forsythus* were not only associated with but are etiologic agents for periodontitis (Consensus Report 1996). Notably, these two species are know to share cross-reactive antigenic epitopes (Vasel *et al.,* 1996). Furthermore, there is evidence that *P. gingivalis* may play a special and essential role. Darveau *et al.,* (1995) have shown that *P. gingivalis* does not activate vascular endothelial cells to express of E-selectin and it blocks expression induced by other gram-negative bacteria such as *Escheria coli*. Thus, *P. gingivalis* can block this initial step in the inflammatory response and host defense, and may, thereby, permit not only *P. gingivalis* but also other periodontal pathogens to colonize, infect and cause disease. For these reasons, we concluded that development of a vaccine for periodontitis has a high probability of success, and we selected *P. gingivalis* as the species upon which to focus for vaccine development.

A choice had to be made between use of an oral vaccine to induce an IgA response and mucosal immunity, or use subcutaneous or intramuscular injection to induce a systemic serum IgG response. While a strong case for mucosal immunity can be made (See Page and Genco, 1996), the latter was chosen for the following reasons. High titers of salivary IgA specific for antigens of periodontopathic bacteria can be induced, and such antibodies could affect adhesion and colonization of the oral cavity by these organisms. However, multiple mechanisms of bacterial adhesion are known to exist and this decreases the likelihood of successful antibody blocking of colonization. Of more impor- tance, salivary components do not have access to periodontal pockets, the location of the subgingival biofilms, that cause periodontitis. In contrast, serum IgG antibodies are transported into gingival sulci and periodontal pockets in the gingival crevicular fluid (GCF) and continuously bathe the subgingival biofilms. These antibodies can opsonize bacteria, activate the complement cascade and enhance bacterial phagocytosis and killing by PMNs.

We chose SAF-M as the adjuvant for the vaccine. This adjuvant was de- signed for human use and has been used in other human vaccines (Allison and Byars, 1986; 1991;Byars and Allison, 1987). It is chemically defined and contains threonyl-muramyl dipeptide, squalene, pluronic-L-121 and tween 80. SAF-M selectively elicits antibodies of protective isotypes and suppresses hypersensitiv- ity reactions. It also elicits cell-mediated as well as humoral immunity, and is relatively free of undesirable properties.

Vaccine development requires selection and use of an animal model. This presents special problems since no analogue of human periodontitis exists (Page and Schroeder, 1982). The only animal models in which immunization against

Design of Study

Figure 5 Design the *M. fascicularis* immunization study using the killed intact *P. gingivalis* vaccine. Injections were given at baseline and 3, 6, and 16 weeks and ligatures placed at 16 weeks. Blood and GCF samples were harvested and clinical data collected at each time point indicated on the horizontal axis, and radiographs were taken at baseline and 30 and 36 weeks.

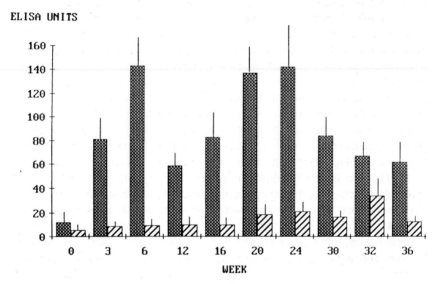

Figure 6 Mean serum antibody titers reported as ELISA units (EU) and standard error bars for control and immunized animals at baseline and for weeks 3 through 36 following vaccination. Stippled bars, immunized; cross-hatched bars, controls. From Persson *et al.,* 1994, with permission.

periodontal infections has been studied are rodents and nonhuman primates. Rodent models of periodontal disease include germ-free rats monoinfected with *P. gingivalis* (Klausen *et al.,* 1993; Evans *et al.,* 1992), mice infected with *P. gingivalis* by gastric lavage (Baker *et al.,* 1994), ligated hamster teeth (Okuda *et al.,* 1988), subcutaneous abscess in mice (van Steenbergen *et al.,* 1982) and subcutaneous chamber models in rabbits and mice (Dahlen and Slots, 1989; Genco *et al.,* 1991; 1998). The rodent studies have recently been reviewed (Page and Genco 1996). Immunization studies using the ligature-induced periodontitis model in nonhuman primates have also been conducted using squirrel monkeys (*Saimiri scuireus*) (McArthur *et al.,* 1989; Clark *et al.,* 1991) and in macaques

(*Macaca fascicularis* and *M. mulatta*) (Offenbacher *et al.*, 1987; 1989; Ebersole *et al.*, 1991; Moritz *et al.*, 1998).

We chose to use the ligature-induced model of periodontitis in *M. fascicularis*. This model of periodontitis is very similar to the clinical, microbiological, histologic and immunological features of disease seen in humans (Kornman *et al.*, 1981; Breckx *et al.*, 1985, 1986; Holt *et al.*, 1988; Ebersole *et al.*, 1987, 1991; Giardino *et al.*, 1996; Persson *et al.*, 1994; Ebersole and Kornman 1991; Moritz *et al.*, 1998). The subgingival flora of macaques contains most if not all of the major bacterial species considered to be pathogenic in humans including *P. gingivalis, B. forsythus, Actinobacillus actinomycetemcomitans, Camplobacter recta, Fusobacterium nucleatum,* and *Prevotella intermedia,* and the animals can mount a strong and enduring humoral immune response to the antigens of these bacteria (Persson *et al.*, 1993). Host defenses of nonhuman primates more nearly mimic those of humans than do other possible models such as rodents. Although not observed as frequently as in humans, nonhuman primates develop age-related periodontitis with attachment loss, pocket formation and loss of alveolar bone in their older years (Page *et al.*, 1975; Page and Schroeder 1982; Persson *et al.*, 1993). Although we measured gingival inflammation, pocket depth and attachment loss, we used changes in alveolar bone as assessed by digital subtraction radiography as the primary outcome measure. The presence of ligatures interferes with accuracy of pocket depth and attachment loss measures, while digital subtraction radiography has a very high level of sensitivity and specificity (Jeffcoat *et al.*, 1984).

We chose to use intact killed *P. gingivalis* as antigen rather than a *P. gingivalis* fraction, or a highly purified *P. gingivalis* protein or other component. We reasoned that use of an intact killed cell vaccine would be best for proof of principle. In addition, the availability of an animal model in which we achieved protection using the whole cell vaccine would permit us to evaluate various cell fractions and highly purified components to identify the most effective purified antigen.

Proof of principle

We screened and enrolled 10 young adult *M. fascicularis* animals in a control group and 10 in an experimental group. For enrollment, animals were required to have detectable mild to moderate gingival inflammation but no periodontal pockets, and *P. gingivalis* in the flora. Following the schedule illustrated in Figure 5, control animals received vaccine containing adjuvant but no antigen and experimental animals received complete vaccine (250 µg protein/ml, 0.5ml subcutaneously in the neck and 0.5ml into the deltoid muscle) (Persson *et al.*, 1994). As shown in Figure 6, mean serum IgG antibody titers peaked at about 6 weeks then began to decrease. Following an additional booster injection at 16 weeks, titers peaked again at 24 weeks, followed by a decrease to about one-half peak titer by week 36. Ligation and immunization had effects on the subgingival flora. *P. gingivalis* in the flora increased markedly in both control and immunized animals immediately following placement of the ligatures. By weeks 30

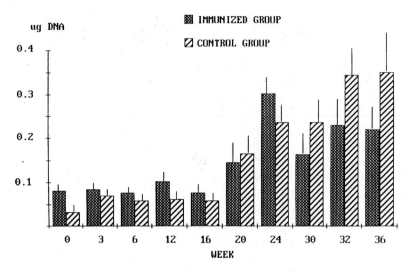

Figure 7 Mean amount of *P. gingivalis* present and standard error bars for the subgingival microflora of immunized and control animals from ligated sextants at baseline and at 3 through 36 weeks, reported as micrograms of *P. gingivalis*-specific DNA per sample, measured by slot blot with a *P. gingivalis*-specific DNA probe. From Persson *et al.,* 1994, with permission.

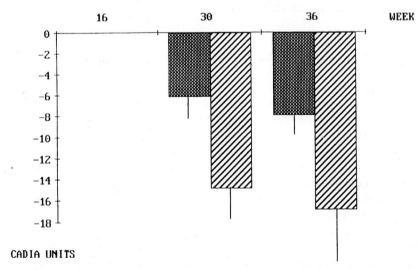

Figure 8 Mean change and standard error bars in alveolar bone housing mandibular test teeth, reported in terms of CADIA units from week 16 when the ligatures were placed to weeks 30 and 36 (values at week 16 were considered as zero). Stippled bars, immunized animals; cross-hatched bars, control animals. From Persson *et al.,* 1994, with permission.

and 36, levels of *P. gingivalis* in the subgingival flora from the control animals were significantly greater than in the immunized animals (Figure 7). As shown in Figure 8, alveolar bone loss at weeks 30 and 36 were significantly reduced in

574

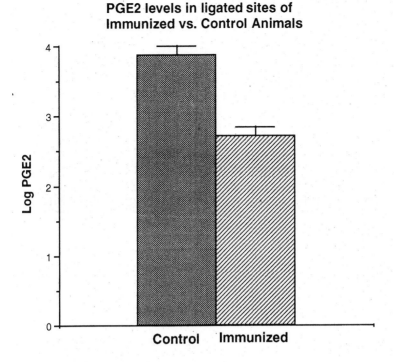

Figure 9 PGE2 levels in ligated sites in GCF samples from immunized (cross-hatched bar) and control (stippled bar) animals.

the immunized animals. We saw no signs of toxicity either at the injections sites or systemically.

Our studies show that even though periodontitis in humans and in this animal model is considered to be a polymicrobial disease, immunization using a single bacterial species, *P. gingivalis*, reduced levels of *P. gingivalis* in the subgingival flora and suppressed the progression of periodontitis as assessed by alveolar bone loss. Although immunization did suppress levels of *P. gingivalis*, very large numbers of these microorganisms were still present. We suspected that mechanisms other than or in addition to antibody enhancement of bacterial phagocytosis and killing by PMNs could be involved in immune suppression of alveolar bone loss. Subsequent studies on samples of GCF demonstrated significant reductions in levels of PGE2 in the immunized animals (Figure 9) and a significant correlation between elevated PGE2 levels in GCF and in-creased alveolar bone loss (Figure 10). In additional studies, we demonstrated that serum from the immunized but not the control animals had the capacity to inhibit production and secretion of PGE2 from blood monocytes maintained in culture and activated using lipopolysaccharide (Figure 11) (Bainbridge *et al.,* 1997). We suggest that this blocking activity may account in part for the ob-

PGE₂ Levels v. CADIA

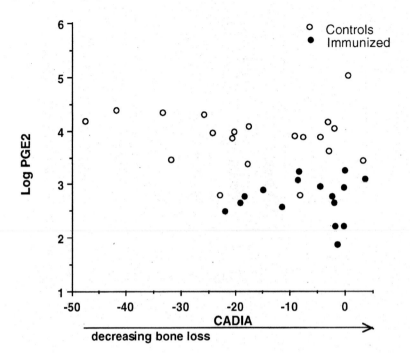

Figure 10 Relationship between GCF PGE2 levels and alveolar bone loss as measured by CADIA for immunized (closed circles) and control (open circles) animals.

served immune suppression of alveolar bone loss. We concluded that this study provided proof of the principle that immunization can affect the composition of the subgingival flora and inhibit the onset and progress of periodontitis in this animal model.

Search for a purified antigen

The next step in development of a periodontitis vaccine was to identify the *P. gingivalis* component(s) responsible for induction of immune protection. That has been a difficult task. *P. gingivalis* has a complex clonal structure (Loos *et al.,* 1993; Menard and Mouton 1995; Teanpaisan *et al.,* 1996). To date four specific serotypes (Ebersole *et al.,* 1995; Nagata *et al.,* 1991), five fimbrial types (Lee *et al.,* 1991) and more than 35 clonal types of *P. gingivalis* have been identified (Ali *et al.,* 1997). The causation of periodontitis in humans cannot be attributed to any single serotype or clonal type or even to a small group of clonal

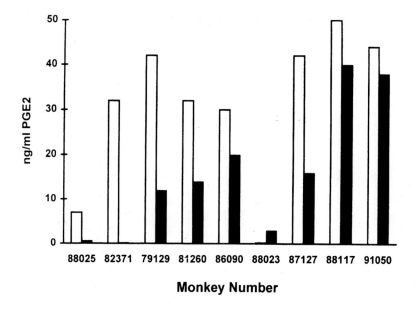

Figure 11 Inhibitors of *P. gingivalis* LPS-stimulated PGE2 production by individual preligation monkey sera. PBMCs were stimulated in the presence of 1% preimmune (open bars) or immune (solid bars) monkey serum. Each stimulation was performed at least three times. Percent inhibition did not vary between experiments by more than 28% for any given monkey. From Bainbridge *et al.,* 1997, with permission.

types. Thus the antigen in any broadly protective vaccine must have epitopes that are shared among serotypes and clonal types. In addition, the component(s) should be nontoxic, present in large amounts and accessible on the bacterial cell surface, available in highly purified, preferably recombinant form, and must elicit a T-cell dependent anamnestic immune response yielding enduring high titers of biologically effective serum antibodies.

In searching for an appropriate antigen, we and others have examined a group of cell surface carbohydrates designated as K-antigens (Schifferle *et al.,* 1989; Laine *et al.,* 1996, 1997; Choi *et al.,* 1998; Sims *et al.,* 1999), lipopolysaccharides (LPS) (Vasel *et al.,* 1996; Schenck *et al.,* 1987; Ou *et al.,* 1997; Gu *et al.,* 1997), and various proteins including fimbriae and fimbrillin and the Mr 53 k and Mr 67 k cell surface proteins (Kokeguchi *et al.,* 1990; Yoshimura *et al.,* 1989; Watanabe *et al.,* 1992; Fan *et al.,* 1999), hemagglutinin (McBride *et al.,* 1990) and cysteine proteases (Lantz *et al.,* 1993; Ciborowski *et al.,* 1994; Pike *et al.,* 1994; Pavloff *et al.,* 1997; Rangarajan *et al.,* 1997a, 1997b; Barkocy-Gallagher *et al.,* 1996).

We have focused on the proteins as potential vaccine candidates because carbohydrate and LPS antigens generally induce mostly IgM and IgG2 responses that are not anamnestic, and the K-antigens are not shared among clonal

Monkey IgG Response (n=5)

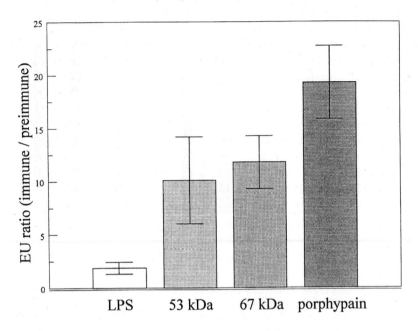

Figure 12 IgG antibody titers for purified *P. gingivalis* lipopolysaccharide, the 53 k and 67 k cell surface proteins, and cysteine protease (porphypain) in sera from five monkeys immunized using the killed intact cell *P. gingivalis* vaccine as described in Persson *et al.*, 1994.

types. In addition, use of LPS as a vaccine antigen poses special problems because of its toxicity. Fimbria and the monomer fimbrillin are present on most *P. gingivalis* strains, and they induce high titers of highly opsonic antibody (Lee *et al.*, 1991; Evans *et al.*, 1992l; Fan *et al.*, 1999), however anti-fimbria/fimbrillin antibodies are not cross reactive among serotypes and ribotypes (Lee *et al.*, 1991; Fan *et al.*, 1999). The Mr 53 k and Mr 67 k proteins induce opsonic antibodies in rabbits but titers are lower than those induced by fimbriae and cysteine protease, and neither protein is present in all serotypes and clonal types of *P. gingivalis* .

Of all of the *P. gingivalis* components studied to date, the cysteine proteases (porphypain, gingipains) show the most promise for use in a potentially successful vaccine. It is now clear that lysine-specific gingipain (KGP) and arginine-specific gingipain (RGP, HRGP, RGP-1) account for most of the trypsin-like activity of *P. gingivalis*. (Potempa *et al.*, 1995a, b) The cysteine proteases are present in large quantities on the cell surface of *P. gingivalis* (Lantz *et al.*, 1993), and they can account for much of the virulence including unusually potent proteolytic activity, and hemagglutination and adhesion activities (Potempa and

578

Travis, 1996; Potempa *et al.,* 1995b). They can inactivate host proteinase inhibitors, degrade IgA, IgG and IgM, degrade iron transporting and sequestering proteins, activate the coagulation, kinin and complement cascades, degrade components of the extracellular matrix and destroy bactericidal proteins and peptides (Potempa *et al.,* 1995a,b; Travis *et al.,* 1995, 1997; Potempa and Travis 1996; Lantz, 1997). Cysteine proteases were present in all of more than 100 isolates of *P. gingivalis* studied by Booth *et al.* (1996), as well as in the ribotypes and serotypes we have studied. No cysteine protease-negative clones have been reported except for created mutants.

There is strong evidence that cysteine proteases are excellent candidate antigens for a vaccine. In monkeys protected by immunization with the whole cell *P. gingivalis* vaccine (Persson *et al.,* 1994), serum antibody titers to cysteine protease were higher than for any other antigens tested except whole cell sonicate (Figure 12). Both KGP and RGP induce high enduring titers of highly opsonic specific antibody in rabbits, and these antibodies are cross reactive among serotypes and ribotypes (Nakawaga *et al.*, 1999). Local application of an anti-cysteine protease monoclonal antibody in periodontal pockets in humans prevented recolonization by *P. gingivalis* for up to nine months (Booth *et al.,* 1996).

Immunization with a cystein protease vaccine

In a pilot study, we immunized five *M. fascicularis* with a vaccine containing SAF-M adjuvant and porphypain-2 purified as described by Ciborowski *et al.,* (1994). Compared to controls, bone loss was reduced significantly in the immunized animals (P = 0.0079). The effect of immunization on the subgingival flora was relatively minor, as has been reported previously (Ebersole *et al.,* 1991; Persson *et al.,* 1994;Holt *et al.,* 1995), while levels of PGE_2 in GCF were significantly reduced at weeks 6, 16, and 20 (P < 0.032). There was an association between the PGE_2 level at any given site and the extent of bone loss at the same site (P< 0.001) (Page *et al.,* 1998; Houston *et al.,* 1998). No signs of toxicity were seen in any of the animals.

Summary

There is a need for new approaches to prevention of the onset and progression of periodontitis in individuals and large populations. There is evidence that development of a periodontitis vaccine is possible and could be used for this purpose. Even though periodontitis in humans and in this animal model is polymicrobial, immunization with a vaccine containing a single bacterial species, *P. gingivalis*, induces protection. Of all of the *P. gingivalis* components that have been studied, the cysteine proteases have the greatest potential as vaccine antigens. In a pilot study we have shown that porphypain-2 purified from *P. gingivalis* is more effective than whole cells in inducing protection. Although opsonization and bacterial cell killing may be involved in protection, other mechanisms such as antibody mediated reduction of levels of inflammatory mediators such as PGE_2 and neutralization of virulence factors may be important. In neither the whole cell vaccine nor the purified cysteine protease vaccine studies were signs of toxicity observed. There is rapidly increasing evidence that periodontitis significantly enhances risk for many potentially fatal systemic diseases including atherosclerosis, coronary heart disease and complications of diabetes mellitus (Beck *et al.*, 1996;Taylor *et al.*, 1996). A successful vaccine for periodontitis could have health benefits far exceeding the prevention of periodontitis.

References

Albander JM, Brunelle JA, Kingman A. Destructive periodontal disease in adults 30 years of age and older in the United States, 1988-1994. *J. Periodontol.* 70:13-29, 1999.

Ali RW, Martin L, Haffajee AD, Socransky SS. Detection of identical ribotypes of *Porphyromonas gingivalis* in patients residing in USA, Sudan, Romania and Norway. *Oral Microbiol. Immunol.* 12:106-111, 1997.

Allison AC, Byars NE. An adjuvant formulation that selectively elicits the formation of antibodies of protective isotypes and of cell-mediated immunity. *J. Immunol. Methods* 95:157-168, 1986.

Allison AC, Byars NE. Immunological adjuvants: desirable properties and side-effects. *Mol. Immunol.* 28:279-284, 1991.

Bainbridge BW, Page RC, Darveau RP. Serum antibodies to *Porphyromonas gingivalis* block the prostaglandin E$_2$ response to lipopolysaccharide by mononuclear cells. *Infect. Immun.* 65:4801-4805, 1997.

Baker PJ, Evans T, Roopenian DC. Oral infection with *Porphyromonas gingivalis* and induced alveolar bone loss in immunocompetent and severe combined immunodeficient mice. *Arch. Oral Biol.* 39:1035-1040, 1994.

Barkocy-Gallagher GA, Hian M, Patti JM, Whitlock J, Progulske-Fox A, Lantz MS. Analysis of the prtP gene encoding porphypain, a cysteine proteinase of *Porphyromonas gingivalis*. *J. Bacteriol.* 178:2734-2741, 1996.

Beck JD, Garcia R, Heiss G, Vokonas PS, Offenbacher S. Periodontal disease and cardiovascular disease. *J. Periodontol.* 67:1123-1137, 1996.

Bhogal PS, Slakeski N, Reynolds EC. A cell-associated protein complex of *Porphyromonas gingivalis* W50 composed of Arg- and Lys-specific cysteine proteinases and adhesions. *Microbiology* 143:2485-2495, 1997.

Booth V, Ashley FP, Lehner T. Passive immunization with monoclonal antibodies against *Porphyromonas gingivalis* in patients with periodontitis. *Infect. Immun.* 64:422-427, 1996.

Breckx MC, Nalbandian J, Kornman KS, Robertson PB. Morphological studies on periodontal disease in the cynomolgus monkey II. Light microscopic observations on ligature-induced periodontitis. *J. Periodont. Res.* 20:165-175, 1985.

Brown JL, Loe H. Prevalence, extent, severity and progression of periodontal disease. *Periodontology 2000* 2:57-71, 1993.

Brown JL, Oliver RC, Loe H. Evaluating periodontal status of U.S. employed adults. J Am Dent Assoc 121:226-232, 1990.

Byars NE, Allison AC. Adjuvant formulation for use in vaccines to elicit both cell-mediated and humoral immunity. *Vaccine* 5:223-228, 1987.

Calkins CC, Platt K, Potempa J, Travis J. Inactivation of tumor necrosis factor-alpha by proteinases (Gingipains) from the periodontal pathogen *Porphyromonas gingivalis*. *J. Biol. Chem.* 273:6611-6614, 1998.

Carlos JP, Wolfe MD. Historic and current perspectives. Compendium Contin. Dent. Edu. Suppl. No. 11., S354-366, 1988.

Chen HA, Johnson BD, Sims TJ, Darveau RP, Moncla BJ, Whitney CW, Engel D, Page RC. Humoral immune response to *Porphyromonas gingivalis* before and following therapy in rapidly progressive periodontitis patients. *J. Periodontol.* 62:781-791, 1991.

Chen PB, Davern LB, Schifferle R, Zambon JJ. Protective immunization against experimental *Bacteroides (Porphyromonas) gingivalis* infection. *Infect. Immun.* 58:3394-3400, 1990.

Choi JI, Schifferle RE, Yoshimura F, Kim BW. Capsular polysaccharide-fimbrial protein conjugate vaccine protects against *Porphyromonas gingivalis* infection in SCID mice reconstituted with human peripheral blood lymphocytes. *Infect. Immun.* 66:391-393, 1998.

Ciborowski P, Nishikata MM, Allen RD, Lantz MS. Purification and characterization of two forms of a high-molecular weight cysteine proteinase (porphypain) from *Porphyromonas gingivalis. J. Bacteriol.* 176:4549-4557, 1994.

Clark WB, Magnusson I, Beem JE, Jung JM, Marks RG, McArthur WP. Immune modulation of *Prevotella intermedia* colonization in squirrel monkeys. *Infect Immun.* 59:1927-1931, 1991.

Consensus report on periodontal diseases: pathogenesis and microbial factors. *Ann Peridontol* 1:926-932, 1996.

Costerton JW, Lewandowski Z, DeBeer D, *et al.,* Biofilms, the customized microniche. *J Bacteriol* 176:2137-2142, 1994.

Dahlen G, Slots J. Experimental infection by *Bacteroides gingivalis* in nonimmunized and immunized rabbits. *Oral Microbiol. Immunol..* 4:6-11, 1989.

Darveau RP, Cunningham MD, Bailey T, Seachord C, Ratcliffe K, Bainbridge B, Dietsch M, Page RC, Aruffo A. Ability of bacteria associated with chronic inflammatory disease to stimulate E-selectin expression and promote neutrophil adhesion. *Infect. Immun.* 63:1311-1317, 1995.

Darveau RP, Tanner A, Page RC. The microbial challenge in periodontitis. *Periodontol. 2000* 14:12-32, 1997.

Douglass CW, Gillings D, Sollecito W, Gammon M; National trends in the prevalence and severity of periodontal diseases. *J. Am . Dent. Assoc.* 107:403-412, 1983.

Ebersole JL, Kornman KS. Systemic antibody responses to oral microorganisms in the cynomolgous monkey: Development of methodology and longitudinal responses during ligature-induced disease. *Res. Immunol.* 142:829-839, 1991.

Ebersole JL, Steffen MJ. Human antibody responses to outer envelope antigens of *Porphyromonas gingivalis* serotypes. *J. Periodont. Res.* 30:1-14, 1995.

Ebersole JL, Steffen MJ, Holt SC, Kornman KS. Effect of immunization with *Porphyromonas gingivalis* and *Prevotella intermedia* on disease progression in ligature induced periodontitis in the nonhuman primate, *Macaca fascicularis. Infect. Immun.* 59:3351-3359, 1991.

Ebersole JL, Steffen MJ, Holt SC, Kornman KS. Antibody in the cynomolgus monkey to periodontal bacteria. *J. Dent. Res.* 66:121-125, 1987.

Ebersole JL, Taubman MA, Smith DJ, Frey DE. Human immune responses to oral microorganisms: Patterns of systemic antibody levels to *Bacteroides* species. *Infect. Immun.* 51:507-513, 1986.

Ebersole JL, Taubman MA, Smith DJ, Haffajee AD. Effect of subgingival scaling on systemic antibody responses to oral microorganisms. *Infect. Immun.* 48:534-539, 1985.

Ellison SA. Oral bacteria and periodontal disease. *J Dent Res* 49:198-202, 1970.

Evans RT, Klausen B, Sojar HT, Bedi GS, Sfintescu C, Ramamurthy NS, Golub LM, Genco RJ. Immunization with *Porphyromonas (Bacteroides) gingivalis* fimbriae protects against periodontal destruction. *Infect. Immun.* 60:2926-2935, 1992.

Fan Q, Sims T, Sojar H, Genco R, Page RC. Opsonic antiserum against the fimbriae of *Porphyromonas gingivalis* significantly enhances phagocytosis and killing by human polymorphonuclear leukocytes. *Oral Microbiol Immunol,* Submitted 1999.

Genco CA, Cutler CW, Kapczynski DR, Maloney K, Arnold RR. A novel mouse model to study virulence of and host response to *Porphyromonas (Bacteroides) gingivalis. Infect. Immun.* 59:1255-1263, 1991.

Genco CA, Odusanya BM, Potempa J, Mikolajczyk-Pawlinska J, Travis J. A peptide domain on gingipain R which confers immunity against *Porphyromonas gingivalis* infection in mice. *Infect. Immun.* 66:4108-4114, 1998.

Genco RJ, Evans RT, Ellison SA. Dental research in microbiology with emphasis on periodontal disease. *J Am Dent Assoc* 78:1016-1036, 1969.

Giardino AG, Ebersole JL, Holt SC. Characteristics of systemic antibody responses of nonhuman primates following active immunization with *Porphyromonas gingivalis, Prevotella intermedia* and *Bacteroides fragilis. Oral Microbiol. Immunol.* 11:79-87, 1996.

Grossi SG, Zambon JJ, Ho AW, Kock G, Dunford RG, Machtei EE, Norderyd OM, Genco RJ. Assessment of risk for periodontal disease. I. Risk indicators for attachment loss. *J. Periodontol* 65:260-267, 1994.

Gu K, Bainbridge B, Darveau RP, Page RC. Antigenic components of *Actinobacillus actinomycetemcomitans* lipopolysaccharide recognized by sera from patients with localized juvenile periodontitis. *Oral Microbiol. Immunol.* 12:11-19, 1997.

Gunsolley JC, Burmeister JA, Tew JG, Best AM, Ranney RR. Relationship of serum antibody to attachment level patterns in young adults with juvenile periodontitis or generalized severe periodontitis. *J. Periodontol.* 58:314-320, 1987.

Haffajee AD, Socransky SS. Microbial etiologic agents of destructive periodontal diseases. *Peridontology 2000* 5:78-lll, 1994.

Hirshfeld L, Wasserman B. A long-term survey of tooth loss in 600 treated periodontal patients. *J. Periodontol.* 49:225-237, 1987.

Holt SC, Brunsvold M, Jones A, Wood R, Ebersole JL. The effect of immunization with isolated cell envelope antigens from *Porphyromonas gingivalis* and *Prevotella intermedia* on the progression of ligature-induced periodontitis in the primate *Macaca fascicularis*. *Oral Microbiol. Immuol.* 10:321-343, 1995.

Holt SC, Ebersole JL, Felton J, Brunsvold M, Kornman KS. Implantation of *Bacteroides gingivalis* in nonhuman primates initiates progression of periodontitis. *Science* 239:55-57, 1988.

Houston LS, Persson GR, Lantz MS, Jeffcoat MK, Mancl LC, Lukehart SA, Page RC. Immunization with *Porphyromonas gingivalis* cysteine protease decreases local prostaglandin E2 in experimental periodontitis. Program and Abstracts, Annual Meeting IADR, Vancouver BC Abst. #1512, 1999.

Ishikawa I, Watanabe H, Horibe M, Izumi Y. Diversity of IgG antibody responses in patients with various types of periodontitis. *Adv. Dent. Res.* 2:334-338, 1988.

Jeffcoat MK, Williams R, Ruttiman R. Relationship between linear and area measurements of radiographic bone levels utilizing simple computerized techniques. *J. Periodontol. Res.* 19:191-198, 1984.

Keyes PH, Jordan HN Periodontal lesions in the Syrian hamster. III. Findings related to an infectious and transmissible component. *Arch Oral Biol* 9:377-400, 1964.

Keyes PH. Are periodontal pathoses caused by bacterial infections on cervicoradicular surfaces of teeth? *J Dent Res* 49:223-228, 1970.

Klausen B, Evans RT, Genco RJ. Vaccination against *Porphyromonas gingivalis* in experimental animals. In: Biology of the Species *Porphyromonas gingivalis*. HN Shah, D Mayrand and RJ Genco (eds.) CRC Press, Boca Raton, FL.

Kokeguchi S, Kato K, Kurihara H, Nishimura F, Murayama Y. Purification and characterization of two major outer membrane proteins from *Porphyromonas gingivalis*. *Dentistry in Japan* 27:29-34, 1990.

Kornman KS, Crane A, Wang HY *et al.,* The interleukin-l genotype as a severity factor in adult periodontal disease. *J Clin Peridontol* 24:72-77, 1997.

Kornman KS, Holt SC, Robertson PB. The microbiology of ligature-induced periodontitis in the cynomolgus monkey. *J. Periodont. Res.* 15:363-371, 1981.

Laine ML, Appelmelk BJ, van Winkelhoff AJ. Novel polysaccharide capsular serotypes in *Porphyromonas gingivalis*. *J. Periodont. Res.* 31:278-284, 1996.

Laine ML, Appelmelk BJ, van Winkelhoff AJ. Prevalence and distribution of six capsular serotypes of *Porphyromonas gingivalis* in periodontitis patients. *J. Dent. Res.* 76:1840-1844, 1997.

Lantz MS. Are bacterial proteases important virulence factors? *J. Periodont. Res.* 32:126-132, 1997.

Lantz MS, Allen RD, Ciborowski P, Holt SC. Purification and immunolocalization of a cysteine protease from *Porphyromonas gingivalis*. *J. Periodont. Res.* 28:467-469, 1993.

Lee JY, Sojar HT, Bedi GS, Genco RJ. *Porphyromonas (Bacteroides) gingivalis* fimbrillin: size, amino terminal sequence and antigenic heterogeneity. *Infect. Immun.* 59:383-389, 1991.

Lindhe J, Haffajee AD, Socransky SS. Progression of periodontal disease in adult subjects in the absence of periodontal therapy. *J Clin Perio*dontol 10:433-442, 1983.

Lindhe J, Hamp S-E, Loe H. Plaque induced periodontal disease in beagle dogs. 4-year clinical, roentgenographical and histometrical study. *J Periodont Res* 10:243-255, 1975.

Ling TY, Sims TJ, Chen HA, Whitney C, Moncla B, Engel LD, Page RC. Titer and subclass distribution of serum IgG antibody reactive with *Actinobacillus actinomycetemcomitans* in localized juvenile periodontitis. *J. Clin. Immunol.* 123:100-111, 1993.

Loe H, Anerud A, Boysen H, Morrison E. Natural history of periodontal disease in man. *J. Clin Periodontol* 13:431- check, 1986.

Loe H. Theilade E, Jensen SB. Experimental gingivitis in man. *J Periodontol* 36:177-187, 1965.

Loesche WJ. Chemotherapy of dental plaque infections. Oral Sci Rev 9:65-107, 1976.

Loesche WJ. Possibilities for treating periodontal disease as specific anaerobic infections. J Canadian Dent Assoc Symposium 25:467-472, 1984.

Loos BG, Dyer DS, Whittam TS, Selander RK. Genetic structure of populations of *Porphyromonas gingivalis* associated with periodontitis and other oral infections. *Infect. Immun.* 61:204-212, 1993.

McArthur WP, Magnusson I, Marks RG, Clark WB. Modification of colonization by black-pigmented *Bacteroides* species in squirrel monkeys by immunization with *Bacteroides gingivalis*. *Infect. Immun* 57:2313-2317, 1989.

McBride BC, Joe A, Singh U. Cloning of *Bacteroides gingivalis* surface antigens involved in adherence. *Archs. Oral Biol.* 35(Suppl):59S-68S, 1990.

Menard C, Mouton C. Clonal diversity of the taxon *Porphyromonas gingivalis* assessed by random amplified polymorphic DNA fingerprinting. *Infect. Immun.* 63:2522-2531, 1995.

Moritz AJ, Cappelli D, Lantz MS, Holt SC, Ebersole JL. Immunization with *Porphyromonas gingivalis* cysteine protease: Effects on experimental gingivitis and ligature-induced periodontitis in *Macaca fascicularis*. *J. Periodontol.* 69:686-697, 1998.

Mouton C, Hammond PG, Slots J, Genco RJ. Serum antibodies to oral Bacteroides asaccharolyticus (Bacteroides gingivalis): relationship to age and periodontal disease. *Infect Immun.* 31(1):182-92, 1981.

Murayama Y, Nagai A, Okamura K, Kurihara H, Nomura Y, Kokeguchi S, Kato K. Serum immunoglobulin G antibody to periodontal bacteria. *Adv. Dent. Res.* 2:339-345, 1988.

Nagata A, Man Y-T, Sato M, Nakamura R. Serological studies of *Porphyromonas (Bacteroides) gingivalis* and correlation with enzyme activity. *J. Periodont. Res.* 26:184-190, 1991.

Newman MG, Socransky SS, Savitt ED, Propas DA, Crawford A. Studies of the microbiology of periodontosis. *J. Periodontol.* 47:373-379, 1976.

Offenbacher S, Braswell LD, Loos AS, Johnson HG, Hall CM, McClure H, Orkin JL, Strobert EA, Green MD, Odle BM. Effects of fluorbiprofen on the progression of periodontitis in *Macaca mulatta*. *J. Periodont. Res.* 22:473-481, 1987.

Offenbacher S, Odle BM, Brawell LD, Johnson HG, Hall CM, McClure H, Orkin JL, Strobert EA, Green MD. Changes in cyclooxygenase metabolism in experimental periodontitis in *Macaca mulatta*. *J. Periodont. Res.* 24:63-74, 1989.

Ogawa T, Kusumoto Y, Hamada S, McGhee JR, Kiyono H. *Bacteroides gingivalis*-specific serum IgG and IgA subclass antibodies in periodontal diseases. *Clin. Exp. Immunol.* 82:318-325, 1990.

Okuda K, Kato T, Naito Y, Takazoe I, Kikuchi Y, Nakamura KT, Kiyoshige T, Sasaki S. Protective efficacy of active and passive immunization against experimental infections with *Bacteroides gingivalis* in ligated hamsters. *J Dent Res* 67:807-811, 1988.

Ou JG, Bainbridge BW, Sims TJ, Whitney CS, Darveau RP, Chen HA, Houston LS, Page RC. Recognition of antigenic epitopes in lipopolysaccharide and protein from *Actinobacillus actinomycetemcomitans* by serum antibodies in untreated rapidly progressive periodontitis patients. *Oral Microbiol. Immunol.* 12:11-19, 1997.

Page RC, Beck JD. Risk assessment for periodontal diseases. *Internatl Dent. J.* 47:61-87, 1997.

Page RC, Genco RJ. Mucosal immunity and periodontitis. In *Mucosal Vaccines*. Ed. Kiyono, Academic Prides, San Diego, pp. 437-449, 1996.

Page RC, Lantz M, Persson GR, Houston L, Lukehart S, Jeffcoat M, Mancl L, Weinberg A, Braham P, Darveau R. Immunization with *Porphyromonas gingivalis* cysteine protease attenuates alveolar bone loss. Program and Abstracts, Annual Meeting IADR, Vancouver BC, Abst. #1511, 1999.

Page RC, Schroeder HE. Periodontitis in Man and Other Animals. S. Karger, Basel, pp. 193-212, 1982.

Page RC, Simpson DM, Ammons WF. Host tissue response in chronic periodontal disease. IV. The periodontal and dental status of a group of aged great apes. *J. Periodontol.* 46:144-155, 1975.

Pavloff N, Pemberton PA, Potempa J, Chen WC, Pike RN, Prochazka V, Kiefer MC, Travis J, Barr PJ. Molecular cloning and characterization of *Porphyromonas gingivalis* lysine-specific gingipain. A new member of an emerging family of pathogenic bacterial cysteine proteinases. *J. Biol. Chem.* 272:1595-1600, 1997.

583

Pawlowski A, Chen A, Speakerman C, Page RC. Vaccine effects of scaling and root planing. Clinical, microbiological and radiographic outcomes. Program and Abstracts, Annual Meeting IADR, Nice, France, Abst. #1923, 1998.

Persson GR, Engel LD, Moncla BJ, Page RC. *Macaca nemestrina*: a nonhuman primate model for studies of periodontal disease. *J. Periodont. Res.* 28:294-300, 1993.

Persson GR, Engel D, Whitney C, Darveau R, Weinberg A, Brunsvold M, Page RC. Immunization against *Porphyromonas gingivalis* inhibits progression of periodontitis in nonhuman primates. *Infect. Immun.* 62:1026-1031, 1994.

Pike R, McGraw W, Potempa J, Travis J. Lysine- and arginine-specific proteinases from *Porphyromonas gingivalis*. Isolation, characterization and evidence for the existence of complexes with hemagglutinins. *J. Biol. Chem.* 269:406-411, 1994.

Pilot T, Barmes DE, Leclercqs MH, McCombie BJ, Infirri JS. Periodontal conditions in adults, 34-44 years of age: An overview of CPITN data in the WHO global oral data bank. *Commun.. Dent. Oral Epidemiol.* 14:310-312, 1986.

Potempa J, Pike R, Travis J. The multiple forms of trypsin-like activity present in various strains of *Porphyromonas gingivalis* are due to the presence of either Arg-gingipain or Lys-gingipain. *Infect . Immun.* 63:1176-1182, 1995a.

Potempa J, Pike R, Travis J. Host and *Porphyromonas gingivalis* proteinases in periodontitis: A biochemical model of infection and tissue destruction. *Perspectives in Drug Discovery and Design* 2:445-458, 1995b.

Potempa P, Travis J. *Porphyromonas gingivalis* proteinases in periodontitis, a review. *Acta Biochim. Polonica* 43:455-466, 1996.

Rangarajan M, Aduse-Opoku J, Slaney JM, Young KA, Curtis MA. The prpR1 and prpR2 arginine-specific protease genes of *Porphyromonas gingivalis* W50 produce five biochemically distinct enzymes. *Mol. Microbiol.* 23:599-565, 1997.

Rangarajan M, Smith SJ, Curtis MA. Biochemical characterization of the arginine-specific proteases of *Porphyromonas gingivalis* W50 suggests a common precursor. *Biochem. J.* 323:701-709, 1997.

Ranney RR, Yanni NR, Burmeister JA, Tew JG. Relationship between attachment loss and serum antibody to *Actinobacillus actinomycetemcomitans* in adolescents and young adults having severe periodontal destruction. *J. Periodontol.* 53:1-7, 1982.

Roitt I, Brostoff J, Male D. *Immunology* 2nd ed. p. 75, kCV Mosby Co, St. Louis, 1989,

Schenck K, Helgeland K, Tollefsen T. Antibodies against lipopolysaccharide from *Bacteroides gingivalis* before and after periodontal treatment. *Scand. J. Dent. Res.* 95:112-118, 1987.

Schifferle RE, Reddy MS, Zambon JJ, Genco RJ. Characterization of a polysaccharide antigen from *Bacteroides gingivalis*. *J. Immunol.* 143:3035-3042, 1989.

Sims T, Schifferle RE, Ali R, Skaug N, Page RC. Serum IgG reactivity of periodontitis patients to K antigens of *Porphyromonas gingivalis*. Program and Abstracts, Annual Meeting, IADR, Vancouver BC, 1999.

Sjöström K, Darveau R, Page RC, Whitney C, Engel D. Opsonic antibody activity against *Actinobacillus actinomycetemcomitans* in patients with rapidly progressive periodontitis. *Infect. Immun.* 60:4819-4825, 1992.

Sjöström K, Ou J, Whitney C, Johnson B, Darveau R, Engel D, Page RC. Effect of treatment on titer, function and antigen recognition of serum antibodies to *Actinobacillus actinomycetemcomitans* in patients with rapidly progressive periodontitis. *Infect. Immun.* 62:145-151, 1994.

Slots J. The predominant cultivable organisms in juvenile periodontitis. *Scand J Dent Res* 84:1-10, 1976.

Socransky SS. Relationship of bacteria to the etiology of periodontal disease. *J Dent Res* 49:203-222, 1970.

Socransky SS, Gibbons RJ, Dale AC, Bortnick L, Rosenthal E, Macdonald JB. The microbiota of the gingival crevice area of man I. Total microscopic and viable counts and counts of specific organisms. *Arch oral Biol* 8:275-280, 1963.

Tanner ARC, Haffer C, Bratthall GT, Visconti RA, Socransky SS. A study of the bacteria associated with advancing periodontitis in man. *J Clin Periodontol* 6:278-307, 1979.

Taubman MA, Page RC, Genco RJ. Mucosal vaccines for dental diseases. <u>Mucosal Immunology</u> 2nd

BioLine © 1999

ed., edited by Tearay, Ogra L., Academic Press, 1999.

Taylor GW, Burt BA, Becker MP, Genco RJ, Schlossman M, Knowles WC, Pettitt, DJ. Severe periodontitis and risk for poor glycemic control in patients with non-insulin-dependent diabetes mellitus. *J. Periodontol.* 67(suppl; 10): 1085-1093, 1996.

Teanpaisan R, Douglas CWI, Eley AR, Walsh TF. Clonality of *Porphyromonas gingivalis, Prevotella intermedia* and *Prevotella nigrescens* isolated from periodontally diseased and healthy sites. *J. Periodont. Res.* 31:423-432, 1996.

Tew JG, Marshall DR, Moore WEC, Best AM, Palcanis UG, Ranney RR. Serum antibody reactive with predominant organisms in the subgingival flora of young adults with generalized severe periodontitis. *Infect. Immun.* 48:303-311, 1985.

Travis J, Pike R, Imamura T, Potempa J. *Porphyromonas gingivalis* proteinases as virulence factors in the development of periodontitis. *J. Periodont. Res.* 32:120-125, 1997.

Travis J, Potempa J, Maeda H. Are bacterial proteinases pathogenic factors? *Trends in Microbiology* 3:405-407, 1995.

Van Steenbergen TJM, Kastelein P, Touw JJA, de Graaff J. Virulence of black-pigmented Bacteroides strains from periodontal pockets and other sites in experimentally induced skin lesions in mice. *J. Peridont. Res.* 17:41-49, 1982.

Vasel D, Sims T, Bainbridge B, Weinberg A, Houston L, Page RC. Shared antigens of *Porphyromonas gingivalis* and *Bacteroides forsythus. Oral Microbiol. Immunol.* 11:226-235, 1996.

Vasel D, Sims TJ, Bainbridge B, Weinberg A, Houston L, Page RC. Shared antigens of *Porphyromonas gingivalis* and *Bacteroides forsythus. Oral Microbiol. Immunol.* 11:226-235, 1996.

Vincent JW, Suzuki JB, Falker WA Jr, Cornett WC. Reaction of human sera from juvenile periodontitis, rapidly progressive periodontitis, and adult periodontitis patients with selected periodontopathogens. *J. Periodontol.* 56:464-469, 1985.

Watanabe K, Takasawa T, Yoshimura F, Ozeki M, Kawanami J, Kato H. Molecular cloning and expression of a major surface protein (the 75-kDa protein of *Porphyromonas (Bacteroides) gingivalis* in *Escherichia coli. FEMS Microbiol. Letters* 92:47-56, 1992.

Whitney C, Ant J, Moncla B, Johnson B, Page RC, Engel D. Serum immunoglobulin G antibody to *Porphyromonas gingivalis* in rapidly progressive periodontitis: Titer, avidity and subclass distribution. *Infect. Immun.* 60:2194-2200, 1992.

Yoshimura F, Watanabe K-I, Takasawa T, Kawanami M, Kato H. Purification and properties of a 75-kilodalton major protein, an immunodominant surface antigen, from the oral anaerobe *Bacteroides gingivalis. Infect. Immun.* 57:3646-3652, 1989.

Zambon JJ, Umemoto T, DeNardin E, Nakazawa F, Christersson LA, Genco RJ. *Actinobacillus actinomycetemcomitans* in the pathogenesis of human periodontal disease. *Adv. Dent. Res.* 2:269-274, 1988.

REPLACEMENT THERAPY OF DENTAL CARIES

Jeffrey D. Hillman

*There are many examples of positive and negative interactions between different species of bacteria inhabiting the same ecosystem. This observation provides the basis for a novel approach to preventing microbial diseases called replacement therapy. In this approach, a harmless effector strain is permanently implanted in the host's microflora. Once established, the presence of the effector strain prevents the colonization or outgrowth of a particular pathogen. In the case of dental caries, replacement therapy has involved construction of an effector strain called BCS3-L1, which was derived from a clinical **Streptococcus mutans** isolate. Recombinant DNA technology was used to delete the gene encoding lactate dehydrogenase in BCS3-L1 making it entirely deficient in lactic acid production. This effector strain was also designed to produce elevated amounts of a novel peptide antibiotic called mutacin 1140 which gives it a strong selective advantage over most other strains of **S. mutans.** In laboratory and rodent model studies, BCS3-L1 was found to be genetically stable and to produce no apparent deleterious side effects during prolonged colonization. BCS3-L1 was significantly less cariogenic than wild-type **S. mutans** in gnotobiotic rats, and it did not contribute at all to the cariogenic potential of the indigenous flora of conventional Sprague-Dawley rats. And, its strong colonization properties indicated that a single application of the BCS3-L1 effector strain to human subjects should result in its permanent implantation and displacement over time of indigenous, disease-causing **S. mutans** strains. Thus, BCS3-L1 replacement therapy for the prevention of dental caries is an example of biofilm engineering that offers the potential for a highly efficient, cost effective augmentation of conventional prevention strategies. It is hoped that the eventual success of replacement therapy for the prevention of dental caries will stimulate the use of this approach in the prevention of other bacterial diseases.*

The theory of replacement therapy

The normal human oral flora is composed of more than 300 species of bacteria that collectively number in the billions. It is remarkable that the challenge presented by this very large variety and number of microorganisms does not lead to frequent manifestations of oral disease, but, in fact, the predominant human condition is one of health. This observation accords with the Gene-for-Gene Hypothesis (Person, 1967) which states, in specific regard to indigenous microorganisms, that host-parasite interactions are inherently unstable. Over eons of time, natural selection will favor mutations in the parasite that reduce its virulence and mutations in the host that promote its resistance. Ultimately, a climax state is reached wherein the parasite becomes a stable and innocuous member of the host's indigenous flora.

Empirically, most members of human dental plaque are climax organisms.

However, there are certain species that have not completed this evolutionary process and retain some pathogenic potential. Also, in other instances, certain organisms may have been forced out of their climax state by the influences of civilization, as seen when modern sanitation methods resulted in polio epidemics or when increased reliance on dietary carbohydrates resulted in increased dental caries.

In the case of dental caries, we can confidently assume that evolution will continue to act on the principle etiologic agent, *Streptococcus mutans,* to bring it into a new climax state wherein it no longer expresses a pathogenic potential. However, for natural selection to act on spontaneous mutations to eliminate this organism's residual virulence may require many thousands of years to complete.

The intention of modern day replacement therapy, as it applies to diseases caused by indigenous microorganisms, is to greatly speed this natural evolutionary process. By careful study of the pathogen, it may be possible to identify and modify certain of its genes to create, in a relatively short span of time, an effector strain that presages the climax organism that evolution would eventually select. The effector strain is used to intentionally colonize the niche in susceptible host tissues that is normally colonized by the pathogen. By being better adapted, a properly constructed effector strain will prevent colonization of the pathogen by blocking attachment sites, competing for essential nutrients, or other mechanisms. In this fashion, the host is protected for as long as the effector strain persists as a member of the indigenous flora which, ideally, is for the lifetime of the host.

An historical summary
As reviewed by Florey (1946), the use of bacteria to fight bacteria began over a century ago when Cantani attempted to treat tuberculosis by insufflation of a presumed harmless organism referred to as "Bacto. Termo". Since then, there have been dozens of reports describing positive and negative bacterial interactions in which the presence of a particular indigenous microorganism promotes or deters the presence of a pathogen. For the most part, these interactions were detected during *in vitro* cultivation, and their occurrence *in vivo* was inferred from correlations provided by cultivation studies. For example, the predominant microorganism in the pharynx of healthy neonates is one or more species of alpha-hemolytic streptococci, and the absence of these species was shown to correlate with a significantly increased risk of infections including sepsis, meningitis, pneumonia, and cystitis (reviewed by Sprunt and Leidy, 1988). Strain 215 is a naturally occurring alpha-hemolytic streptococcus that was chosen to serve as an effector strain based largely on its ability to inhibit a variety of common pathogens that initially colonize the pharynx. A nasopharyngeal dose of 10^6 cells was given to a group of infants lacking an indigenous alpha-hemolytic streptococcus in their throat flora. In most instances, strain 215 rapidly became the predominant microorganism in pharyngeal cultures, the numbers of potential pathogens declined to low or undetectable levels, and the infants suffered a significantly lower incidence of infections than uninoculated

588

controls (Sprunt *et al.,* 1980). Also, in older individuals, natural or antibiotic-induced low levels of alpha-hemolytic streptococci in the pharynx has been shown to correlate with increased susceptibility to *S. pyogenes* infections (Crowe and Sanders, 1973; Fujimori *et al.,* 1997; Sanders, 1969; Sanders *et al.,* 1976). This suggests the potential for replacement therapy in the prevention of streptococcal pharyngitis in susceptible subjects.

Application of replacement therapy to diseases caused by *Staphylococcus aureus* has also been very instructive. In recent years, *S. aureus* is the most commonly isolated pathogen causing nosocomial infections. It is also the etiologic agent of chronic furunculosis. Considerable work has been done to prevent these infections (Shinefield *et al.,* 1971; Perl and Golub, 1998), including replacement therapy using strain 502A, a naturally occurring *S. aureus* strain of low virulence. Implantation of strain 502A on the nasal mucosa and umbilical stumps of newborn infants has been very successful in curtailing epidemics of staphylococcal disease in the nursery. Persistent nasal carriage of pathogenic staphylococci has also been interrupted in adults by implantation of strain 502A after antibiotic suppression of the indigenous strain. After gaining relatively widespread acceptance in the 1960's and '70's, 502A has been little used partly because of lack of need and partly because of infections that have been reported following its use (Drutz *et al.,* 1966; Blair and Tull, 1969; Houck *et al.,* 1972). Although the benefits of using strain 502A far outweigh the hazards (Light *et al.,* 1967; Houck *et al.,* 1972), this work emphasized the potential difficulty of using naturally occurring effector strains that may have residual pathogenic potential.

The molecular basis for bacterial interference has rarely been proven, even in the best studied models. Organisms that occupy the same or similar niche would be expected to compete for essential nutrients, which accounts, at least in part, for the ability of alpha-hemolytic streptococci to interfere with colonization by *S. pyogenes* (Sanders, 1969). The same or overlapping habitats would make competition for attachment sites a logical basis for interference. This is probably the basis for the ability of 502A to sterically interfere with the colonization of disease-causing *S. aureus* strains (Bibel *et al.,* 1983). Recently, it was postulated that cross-inhibition by autoinducing molecules could serve as a basis for bacterial interference in quorum sensing species such as *S. aureus* (Ji *et al.,* 1997). If shown to occur *in vivo,* this mechanism would be similar to other instances where the production of a metabolic end-product or antibiotic-like substance by one microorganism has been proven to prevent colonization by another sharing the same habitat. Mutant analysis was used to prove that hydrogen peroxide production by *S. oralis* (previously *S. sanguis* type II) inhibited the growth of *Actinobacillus actinomycetemcomitans in vitro* and in an animal model (Hillman and Shivers, 1988). However, inability to obtain persistent colonization by *S. oralis* has hindered its use as an effector strain in prevention or treatment of localized juvenile periodontitis (J.D. Hillman, unpublished result). As detailed below in the case of mutacin production by *S. mutans,* persistent colonization by an effector strain is usually an important feature of replacement therapy that is difficult to satisfy.

Application of replacement therapy to dental caries

An effector strain for replacement therapy of dental caries called BCS3-L1 has been constructed (Hillman *et al.,* submitted) that took into account the following logical prerequisites:

1. It must have a significantly reduced pathogenic potential;
2. It must persistently and preemptively colonize the *S. mutans* niche, thereby preventing colonization by wild-type strains whenever the host comes in contact with them;
3. Ideally, it should be able to aggressively displace indigenous strains of *S. mutans*, thereby allowing even previously infected subjects to be treated with replacement therapy;
4. It must be generally safe and not predispose the host to other disease conditions.

Pathogenicity

Several different approaches have been examined to satisfy the first of these prerequisites for effector strain construction. In accord with the acidogenic theory of dental caries, lactic acid production by *S. mutans* has long been considered to be the main pathogenic mechanism for production of caries lesions. Consequently, mutants of *S. mutans* with reduced acidogenicity were tested for their cariogenic potential. Lactate dehydrogenase (LDH; Johnson *et al.,* 1980; Fitzgerald *et al.,* 1989) and intracellular polysaccharide mutants (Tanzer and Freedman, 1978) proved to have significantly reduced cariogenicity both *in vitro* and in various animal models. Rather than directly reducing acid production by *S. mutans,* several groups have exploited another oral viridans streptococcus, *S. salivarius,* for its ability to serve as an effector strain. This organism is naturally less cariogenic than *S. mutans,* but normally occupies its own distinct niche. Tanzer *et al.* (1985) isolated a naturally occurring *S. salivarius* variant that competed effectively for the *S. mutans* niche. The basis for this strain's altered colonization properties was not determined. More recently, the urease gene has been cloned from *S. salivarius* with the idea of constructing a urease-producing effector strain (Chen *et al.,* 1996). It is imagined that such an effector strain could metabolize environmental or exogenously supplied urea to neutralize acids in plaque produced by *S. mutans* and other acidogenic bacteria. To test this hypothesis, an *S. gordonii* strain harboring a plasmid containing the cloned urease gene produced significantly less environmental acidification *in vitro* when as little as 2 mM urea was added to the cell suspension along with glucose. A ureolytic strain of *S. mutans* has been constructed and shown to have a significantly decreased cariogenic potential in a rat model (R. Burne, personal communication).

For construction of BCS3-L1, which is an *S. mutans* strain, LDH deficiency was chosen as the approach for reducing acidogenicity. Earlier work with a closely related *S. rattus* strain had provided convincing evidence for the effectiveness of this approach. LDH-deficient mutants were virtually non-cariogenic in gnotobiotic rats and did not contribute significantly to the cariogenic potential

590

of the indigenous flora in conventional pathogen-free rats (Johnson *et al.,* 1980). Although the mutants used in these studies were either induced by ethylmethane sulfonate treatment or spontaneous, reversion studies strongly suggested that cryptic mutations were not responsible for the observed decrease in pathogenicity. In fact, these data provided the most direct proof of the acidogenic theory of dental caries.

Attempts to transfer these findings directly to *S. mutans* proved to be difficult. LDH-deficient mutants of various strains of *S. mutans* were not found using the same screening methods used to isolate mutants of *S. rattus.* Abhyankar *et al.* (1985) identified two strains that were exceptions to this rule. Both strains appeared to possess one or more preexisting mutations that affected pyruvate metabolism as evidenced by their unusually high production of ethanol, acetate, and acetoin when grown in the presence of limiting glucose. These strains were mutable to LDH-deficiency using N-methyl-N'-nitro-N-nitrosoguanidine, although it was not demonstrated that they harbored single gene mutations. Cloning the structural gene encoding the *S. mutans* LDH (Hillman *et al.,* 1990) provided the basis for solving this puzzle. Standard insertional mutagenesis methods failed to yield LDH-deficient clones suggesting that LDH-deficiency was a lethal mutation in most *S. mutans* strains (Duncan and Hillman, 1991). This hypothesis was definitively proven by creation of a temperature sensitive LDH mutant (Chen *et al.,* 1994). This isolate grew well at 30°C but did not grow at 42°C under a variety of cultivation conditions. Chemostat studies indicated that some aspect of glucose metabolism was toxic during growth under the non-permissive condition (Hillman *et al.,* 1996). The toxic effect could be overcome by limiting the amount of environmental glucose. This and other data accorded with studies of *S. mutans* central intermediary metabolism indicating that this organism has enzymatic activities, including pyruvate formate-lyase (Abbe *et al.,* 1982; Takahashi *et al.,* 1982) and pyruvate dehydrogenase (Carlsson *et al.,* 1985; Hillman *et al.,* 1987a), for pyruvate dissimilation. However, at high sugar concentrations, the levels of activity of these enzymes are apparently insufficient to compensate for the absence of LDH. It was found (Hillman *et al.,* 1996) that a supplemental alcohol dehydrogenase (ADH) activity, when expressed in the temperature sensitive LDH mutant, could complement LDH deficiency.

With this background of information, BCS3-L1 construction started with the *ldh* gene cloned into an appropriate suicide vector for *S. mutans.* Essentially the entire gene except for transcription and translation signal sequences was deleted, and it was replaced with the *Zymomonas mobilis* open reading frame (ORF) for alcohol dehydrogenase (ADH) II. Transformation of the recombinant molecule into the *S. mutans* starting strain, JH1140, and allelic exchange resulted in the isogenic mutant, BCS3-L1. This effector strain has no measurable LDH activity and ca. 10-fold elevated levels of ADH activity relative to its parent. Fermentation end-product analysis showed that BCS3-L1 makes no detectable lactic acid. As predicted, much of the metabolized carbon is converted to the neutral end-products, ethanol and acetoin. Under various cultivation conditions, including growth on a variety of sugars and polyols, such as sucrose, fructose, lactose, mannitol, and sorbitol, BCS3-L1 yielded final pH values that were 0.4 to 1.2 pH units higher than those of JH1140.

The reduced acidogenic potential of BCS3-L1 was reflected in its decreased cariogenic potential. Gnotobiotic Fisher rats and conventional, pathogen-free Sprague Dawley rats infected with BCS3-L1 and fed a sucrose-containing diet had less than half the incidence and severity of caries lesions compared to animals infected with the parent strain, JH1140 (Hillman *et al.,* submitted). Caries scores of conventional animals infected with BCS3-L1 did not differ from the scores of control animals that remained *S. mutans*-free throughout the experiment, indicating that it did not contribute to the cariogenic potential of the indigenous flora. The results of these studies provide strong evidence that an LDH-deficient *S. mutans* strain has significantly reduced pathogenic potential, and thus satisfies the first prerequisite for use as an effector strain in replacement of dental caries.

Colonization

Transmission of mutans streptococci within the human population has been extensively studied. Most studies support the idea that this organism is usually transmitted from mother (primary caretaker) to child within a several year period following the onset of tooth eruption (Alaluusua, 1991; Berkowitz and Jones, 1985; Caufield and Walker, 1989; Davey and Rogers, 1984; Genco and Loos, 1991). However, there is some recent conflicting evidence that a significant proportion of children may acquire mutans streptococci from sources outside their immediate family (de Soet *et al.,* 1998; Emanuelsson *et al.,* 1998). These studies were fairly evenly divided on whether individual subjects harbored one or more than one strain of mutans streptococci. According to a recent report (Alaluusua *et al.,* 1996), the acquisition of multiple strains may depend on the frequency of sugar consumption. No longitudinal studies have been conducted to determine if two or more strains can persistently colonize a subject or if one strain eventually displaces the other(s). Numerous studies (Krasse *et al.,* 1967; Jordan *et al.,* 1972; Ruangsri and Orstavik, 1977; Svanberg and Krasse, 1981; Tanzer *et al.,* 1982) have documented the difficulty of persistently introducing laboratory strains of mutans streptococci into the mouths of humans, particularly if they already harbored an indigenous strain of this organism.

From the standpoint of replacement therapy of caries, these results suggest that implantation of an effector strain would best be accomplished in children immediately after the onset of tooth eruption and before their acquisition of a wild-type strain. In order to prevent supercolonization by wild-type strains when the host comes in contact with them, an effector strain should have some significant selective advantage to colonization. This would also enable subjects who have already been infected with wild-type *S. mutans* to be treated by replacement therapy. The ability of an effector strain to preemptively colonize the human oral cavity and aggressively displace indigenous wild-type strains

592

was initially thought to be a complex phenomenon dependent on a large number of phenotypic properties. However, it was discovered that a single phenotypic property could provide the necessary selective advantage. A naturally occurring strain (JH1000) of *S. mutans* was isolated that produces a bacteriocin called mutacin 1140 capable of killing virtually all other strains of mutans streptococci against which it was tested (Hillman *et al.*, 1984). Mutants were isolated that produced no detectable mutacin 1140 or that produced approximately three-fold elevated amounts. The mutants were used to correlate mutacin production to preemptive colonization and aggressive displacement in a rat model. Although a number of studies (for example, Huis in 't Veld *et al.*, 1982; Kestrup and Gibbons, 1969; Rogers *et al.*, 1978; Smith and Huggins, 1974; Takazoe *et al.*, 1984) performed over the years suggested a role for bacteriocins in the natural history of infection by various bacteria, this experiment provided the first strong evidence that at least certain ones are important in colonization.

A correlation was also made between mutacin 1140 production and the ability of *S. mutans* to persistently colonize the oral cavities of human subjects and aggressively displace indigenous mutans streptococci (Hillman *et al.*, 1985; Hillman *et al.*, 1987b). Three years following a single, 3 minute infection regimen involving brushing and flossing of a concentrated cell suspension onto and between the teeth, all of the subjects remained colonized by the mutacin up-producing mutant of JH1000 (Hillman *et al.*, 1989). No other strains of mutans streptococci were observed in saliva and plaque samples. The same results were found recently, 14 years after colonization, for at least two of three subjects who are still available for testing. These results indicate that this strain of *S. mutans* succeeded in satisfying the second and third prerequisites for use as an effector strain in replacement therapy: It persistently and preemptively colonized the *S. mutans* niche in the human oral cavity and it aggressively displaced indigenous strains of this organism. Consequently, strain JH1140, which has a spontaneous mutation resulting in ca. 3-fold elevated production of mutacin 1140, served as the starting strain for construction of BCS3-L1 described above.

The effect of LDH deficiency on colonization potential was tested in several ways (Hillman *et al.*, submitted). First, it was found that BCS3-L1 produced as much mutacin 1140 as did its parent, JH1140, indicating that LDH-deficiency did not affect this important phenotypic property. BCS3-L1 actually formed significantly more plaque than JH1140 when grown in the presence of sucrose. This phenomenon was previously reported for LDH-deficient mutants of *S. rattus* (Hillman, 1978), and is likely to be a reflection of pH dependence of glucosyl transferase activities. Using previously described methods (Hillman *et al.*, 1984), BCS3-L1 and JH1140 were shown to be nearly identical in their ability to preemptively colonize the teeth of conventional rats and aggressively displace an indigenous strain of *S. mutans*. These results lend strong support to the idea that BCS3-L1 retains its parent's selective advantage for colonization, and will serve as a useful effector strain in replacement therapy of dental caries.

Safety

To serve as an effector strain in replacement therapy of dental caries, BCS3-L1 must be safe in several important regards. First, it must be genetically stable. Reacquisition of an acidogenic phenotype by spontaneous reversion is extremely unlikely because construction of BCS3-L1 involved deletion of essentially all of the *ldh* ORF. No acidogenic revertants were observed among 10^5 independent colonies screened on glucose tetrazolium medium (Hillman *et al.*, submitted). Horizontal transmission of an *ldh* gene is possible. Repeated attempts have failed to demonstrate transduction of *S. mutans* by bacteriophage (A. Delisle, personal communication). Transformability is known to be very strain dependent (Perry and Kuramitsu, 1981; Westergran and Emilson, 1983) and BCS3-L1, like its parent, is very poorly transformable (Chen *et al.*, 1994; Hillman *et al.*, submitted). This feature made BCS3-L1 construction difficult but helps to assure its long-term stability. Certain *S. mutans* strains have been shown to serve as recipients for conjugation by *S. faecalis* and possibly other species (LeBlanc *et al.*, 1978). BCS3-L1 has not been studied in this regard, but acidogenic mutants of BCS3-L1 were not recovered from conventional Sprague-Dawley rats harboring a complex indigenous flora after 6 months of colonization. Plaque from subjects infected for 14 years with the mutacin up-producing strain will serve as a good source of material to further study the occurrence and potential problems posed by horizontal transmission of DNA.

Mutacin 1140 has been shown (Hillman *et al.*, 1998) to be a member of a small class of antibiotics called lantibiotics. It is a small (2,263 Da), very stable peptide containing modified amino acids, lanthionine, methyllanthione, didehydroalanine and didehydrobutyrine, characteristic of lantibiotics. Sufficient mutacin 1140 has not been purified to directly test its toxicity. However, the prototype lantibiotic, nisin, is known to have extremely low toxicity (Hurst, 1981), and has been developed as a food preservative that is "generally recognized as safe" by the FDA. Mutacin 1140 is very poorly immunogenic in rabbits (J.D. Hillman, unpublished result). A long-term toxicity study found that after colonization for 6 months, the mean weights of conventional Sprague-Dawley rats colonized with BCS3-L1 did not differ significantly from animals colonized with JH1140 or *S. mutans*-free control animals. Histopathological examination revealed no treatment-related lesions in any of the major organs examined, including liver, spleen kidney, bladder, adrenal gland, pituitary, salivary glands, mandibular and mesenteric lymph nodes, thyroid, parathyroid, trachea, esophagus, heart, thymus, lungs, stomach, pancreas, intestines, testes, prostate, skin, mammary gland, tongue, palate, brain, bone and eyes.

Mutacin production by BCS3-L1 and the change in fermentation products resulting from LDH deficiency could conceivably upset plaque ecology and lead to the bloom of another microorganism with pathogenic potential. Recent studies (reviewed by Costerton, 1995) have provided an appreciation for the complicated structural architecture of biofilms, presumably including dental plaque. Following specific initial attachment to a surface, the growth of cells leads to the formation of a thick layer of differentiated mushroom- and pillar-like structures consisting of cells embedded in their extracellular polysaccharide matrix. Between these cellular structures are water-filled spaces that serve as channels for the introduction of nutrients and the elimination of waste products. In biofilms consisting of two or more species of bacteria, each cellular structure may be pure or mixtures of cells depending on the pressures imposed by positive and negative bacterial interactions. These interactions may also extend over a finite area to affect the general composition of plaque in a particular habitat. Clearly, however, there is a physical limit to this sphere of influence. The mutacin 1140 up-producing strain of *S. mutans* eliminated mutacin-sensitive indigenous strains of this species but had no effect on indigenous *S. oralis* strains which were equally sensitive to mutacin killing *in vitro* (Hillman *et al.*, 1987b). These results indicate that *S. mutans* has a physically distinct habitat that is separated from the *S. oralis* habitat by a distance sufficient for dilution to reduce the concentration of mutacin below its minimal inhibitory concentration. A similar explanation could account for the failure to observe a change in plaque composition associated with the change in fermentation end-products following colonization of conventional rats by an LDH-deficient mutant (Stashenko and Hillman, 1989).

A final aspect of replacement therapy safety is the requirement for controlled spread of the effector strain within the population. Mutacin 1140 up-production clearly provides a selective advantage to BCS3-L1 colonization, but the minimal infectious dose has not been determined for this strain or any *S. mutans* strain in humans. As described above, horizontal transmission of natural strains appears to be a rare event, but mutacin up-production may promote its occurrence. It has been reported that mutacin production appears to promote mother to child transmission (Gronroos *et al.*, 1998). Wives and children of the two subjects colonized with the mutacin up-producing *S. mutans* strain were not colonized when tested 14 years after the initial infection regimen (J.D. Hillman, unpublished result). Clearly, additional studies with larger populations will have to be performed to properly measure the potential for horizontal transmission. It is expected that, like wild-type strains of *S. mutans*, vertical transmission of BCS3-L1 from mother to child will occur at a high frequency. Control of this phenomenon, and unregulated transmission in general, could be achieved by introducing a mutation into BCS3-L1 that would make it dependent on a nutritional supplement not normally part of the human host diet. As an example, persistent survival of a strain harboring a mutation in the gene encoding alanine racemase would probably require daily D-alanine supplements, perhaps in the form of a mouthwash or chewing gum.

Conclusions

In general, replacement therapy using a properly constructed effector strain provides a number of advantages over conventional prevention strategies. In the case of dental caries, a single colonization regimen that leads to persistent colonization by the effector strain should provide lifelong protection. In the event that the effector strain does not persist in some subjects indefinitely, reapplication could be performed as the need arises without added concern for safety or effectiveness.

One of the greatest advantages of replacement therapy is that there is no need for patient compliance. Conscientious use of conventional prevention methods, (brushing, flossing, topical fluoride, controlled sugar consumption, etc.) is sufficient in most cases to maintain the *S. mutans* level below its minimal pathogenic dose. The fact that dental caries remains as one of the most common infectious diseases afflicting humans is a clear indication that the effectiveness of a prevention strategy is inversely related to its need for patient compliance.

In previous studies, subjects have received a pumice and rubber cup prophylaxis prior to implantation to reduce the number of indigenous *S. mutans* on teeth. The need for this step has not been experimentally determined, and may possibly be eliminated in the future. Research-based application of BCS3-L1 has used the cells from 100 ml cultures concentrated 20-fold in fresh medium. Ultimately, the cells could be provided to the practitioner frozen in glycerol or lyophilized and reconstituted chairside by the addition of water. In either case, a blunt, curved tip syringe would be used to deliver the cell suspension onto and between the subject's teeth. After 5 minutes, unattached cells would be removed by several rinses with water. The price of both labor and materials to accomplish this process is expected to make replacement therapy quite cost effective compared to other prevention strategies, and it is particularly suitable for use in developing countries.

Most of the pertinent safety issues with regard to BCS3-L1 stability and mutacin 1140 toxicity have already been addressed. Two others can be briefly mentioned. First, it should be noted that spontaneous resistance to mutacin 1140 does not readily occur in sensitive species. In one experiment, plating of over 10^{12} cells of several different streptococcal species on medium containing mutacin 1140 failed to give rise to a single, genetically stable resistant clone (J.D. Hillman, unpublished result). Thus, outgrowth of resistant variants does not seem to be a likely problem. And second, although dental treatments in general do not seem to be a risk factor for infective endocarditis (Strom *et al.*, 1998), the possibility of bacteremia during implantation will be minimized by directing the stream of cells away from the gingival sulcus and any observable mucosal lesions. Antibiotic prophylaxis will be performed in subjects with conditions deemed to be high or medium risk as defined by the American Heart Association (Dajani *et al.*, 1997).

Finally, although experimental data obtained to date indicates that horizontal transmission of BCS3-L1 is not likely to occur, vertical transmission from mother to child is expected. Thus, treatment of one generation would lead to protection of future generations. In this regard, replacement therapy with BCS3-L1 will mimic the climax organism that evolution would eventually select.

It is clear from the current resurgence of various infectious diseases that traditional and antibiotic-based therapies alone will not suffice. The continued study of bacterial interactions as they occur *in vivo* will inevitably lead us to more naturally occurring effector strains for the replacement therapy of various infections. Hopefully, the success of using genetic engineering to tailor an effector strain for replacement therapy of dental caries will encourage similar efforts to prevent other infectious diseases.

References

Abbe, K., Takahashi, S. and Yamada, T. 1982. Involvement of oxygen-sensitive pyruvate formate-lyase in mixed-acid fermentation by *Streptococcus mutans* under strictly anaerobic conditions. *J. Bacteriol.* **152,** 175-182.

Abhyankar, S., Sandham, H.J. and Chan, K.H. 1985. Serotype c *Streptococcus mutans* mutable to lactate dehydrogenase deficiency. *J. Dent. Res.* **64,** 1267-1271.

Alaluusua, S. 1991. Transmission of mutans streptococci. *Proc. Finn. Dent. Soc.* **87,** 443-447.

Alaluusua, S., Matto, J., Gronroos, L., Innila, S., Torkko, H., Asikainen, S., Jousimeis-Somer, H. and Saarela, M. 1996. Oral colonization by more than one clonal type of mutans streptococcus in children with nursing-bottle dental caries. *Arch. Oral Biol.* **41,** 167-173.

Berkowitz, R.J. and Jones, P. 1985. Mouth-to-mouth transmission of the bacterium *Streptococcus mutans* between mother and child. *Arch. Oral Biol.* **30,** 377-379.

Bibel, D.J., Aly, R., Bayles, C., Strauss, W.G., Shinefield, H.R. and Maibach, H.I. 1983. Competitive adherence as a mechanism of bacterial interference. *Can. J. Microbiol.* **29,** 700-703.

Blair, E.B. and Tull, A.H. 1969. Multiple infections among newborns resulting from colonization with *Staphylococcus aureus* 502A. *Am. J. Clin. Pathol.* **52,** 42-49.

Carlsson, J., Kujala, U. and Edlund, M.-B.K. 1985. Pyruvate dehydrogenase activity in *Streptococcus mutans. Infect. Immun.* **49,** 674-678.

Caufield, P.W. and Walker, T.M. 1989. Genetic diversity within *Streptococcus mutans* evident from chromosomal DNA restriction fragment polymorphisms. *J. Clin. Microbiol.* **27,** 274-278.

Chen, A., Hillman, J.D. and Duncan, M. 1994. L(+)-lactate dehydrogenase deficiency is lethal in *Streptococcus mutans. J. Bacteriol.* **176,** 1542-1545.

Chen, Y.-Y.M., Clancy, K.A. and Burne, R.A. 1996. *Streptococcus salivarius* urease: genetic and biochemical characterization and expression in a dental plaque streptococcus. *Infect. Immun.* **64,** 585-592.

Costerton, J.W. 1995. Overview of microbial biofilms. *J. Indust. Microbiol.* **15,** 137-140.

Crowe, C.C. and Sanders, Jr., E.S. 1973. Bacterial interference. II. Role of the normal throat flora in prevention of colonization by group A *streptococcus. J. Infect. Dis.* **128,** 527-532.

Dajani, A.S., Taubert, K.A., Wilson, W., Bolger, A.F., Bayer, A., Ferrieri, P., Gewitz, M.H., Shulman, S.T., Nouri, S., Newburger, J.W., Hutto, C., Pallasch, T.J., Gage, T.W., Levison, M.E., Peter, G. and Zuccaro, G. 1997. Prevention of bacterial endocarditis. Recommendations by the American Heart Association. *J. Amer. Med. Assoc.* **277,** 1794-1801.

Davey, A.L. and Rogers, A.H. 1984. Multiple types of the bacterium *Streptococcus mutans* in the human mouth and their intra-family transmission. *Arch. Oral Biol.* **29,** 453-460.

De Soet, J.J., Bokhout, B., Buijs, J.F., van Loveren, C., de Graaff, J. and Prahl-Andersen, B. 1998. Transmission of mutans streptococci between mothers and children with cleft lip and/or palate. *Cleft Palate Craniofac. J.* **35,** 460-464.

Drutz, D.J., van Way, M.H., Schaffner, W. and Koenig, M.G. 1966. Bacterial interference in the therapy of recurrent staphylococcal infections: multiple abscesses due to implantation of the 502A strain of staphylococcus. *N. Engl. J. Med.* **275,** 1161-1165.

Duncan, M.J. and Hillman, J.D. 1991. DNA sequence and *in vitro* mutagenesis of the gene encoding the fructose-1,6-diphosphate-dependent L-(+)-lactate dehydrogenase of *Streptococcus mutans. Infect. Immun.* **59,** 3930-3934.

Emanuelsson, I.R., Li, Y. and Bratthall, D. 1998. Genotyping shows different strains of mutans streptococci between father and child and within parental pairs in Swedish families. *Oral Microbiol. Immunol.* **13,** 271-277.

Fitzgerald, R.J., Adams, B.O., Sandham, H.J. and Abhyankar, S. 1989. Cariogenicity of a lactate dehydrogenase-deficient mutant of *Streptococcus mutans* serotype c in gnotobiotic rats. *Infect. Immun.* **57,** 823-826.

Florey, H.W. 1946. The use of micro-organisms for therapeutic purposes. *Yale J. Biol. Med.* **19,** 101-117.

Fujimori, I., Kikushima, K., Hisamatsu, K., Nozawa, I., Goto, R. and Murakami, Y. 1997. Interaction between oral alpha-streptococci and group A streptococci in patients with tonsilitis. *Ann. Otol. Rhinol. Laryngol.* **106,** 571-574.

Genco, R.J. and Loos, B.G. 1991. The use of genomic DNA fingerprinting in studies of the epidemiology of bacteria in periodontitis. *J.Clin. Periodontol.* **18,** 396-405.

Gronroos, L., Saarela, M., Matto, J., Tanner-Salo, U., Vuorela, A. and Alaluusua, S. 1998. Mutacin production by *Streptococcus mutans* may promote transmission of bacteria from mother to child. *Infect. Immun.* **66,** 2595-6000.

Hillman, J.D. 1978. Lactate dehydrogenase mutans of *Streptococcus mutans*: isolation and preliminary characterization. *Infect. Immun.* **21,** 206-212.

Hillman, J.D., Johnson, K.P. and Yaphe, B.I. 1984. Isolation of a *Streptococcus mutans* strain producing a novel bacteriocin. *Infect. Immun.* **44,** 141-144.

Hillman, J.D., Yaphe, B.I. and Johnson, K.P. 1985. Colonization of the human oral cavity by a strain of *Streptococcus mutans. J. Dent. Res.* **64,** 1272-1274.

Hillman, J.D. andrews, S.W. and Dzuback, A.L. 1987a. Acetoin production by wild-type strains and a lactate dehydrogenase-deficient mutant of *Streptococcus mutans. Infect. Immun.* **55,** 1399-1402.

Hillman, J.D., Dzuback, A.L. and Andrews, S.W. 1987b. Colonization of the human oral cavity by a *Streptococcus mutans* mutant producing increased bacteriocin. *J. Dent. Res.* **66,** 1092-1094.

Hillman, J.D. and Shivers, M. 1988. Interaction between wild-type, mutant and revertant forms of the bacterium *Streptococcus sanguis* and the bacterium *Actinobacillus actinomycetemcomitans in vitro* and in the gnotobiotic rat. *Arch. Oral Biol.* **33,** 395-401.

Hillman, J.D. andrews, S.W., Painter, S. and Stashenko, P. 1989. Adaptive changes in a strain of *Streptococcus mutans* during colonization of the human oral cavity. *Microbial Ecol. Health Dis.* **2,** 231-239.

Hillman, J.D., Duncan, M.J. and Stashenko, K.P. 1990. Cloning and expression of the gene encoding the fructose-1,6-diphosphate-dependent L-(+)-lactate dehydrogenase of *Streptococcus mutans. Infect. Immun.* **58,** 1290-1295.

Hillman, J.D., Chen, A., Duncan, M. and Lee, S.-W. 1994. Evidence that L(+)-lactate dehydrogenase deficiency is lethal in *Streptococcus mutans. Infect. Immun.* **62,** 60-64.

Hillman, J.D., Chen, A. and Snoep, J.L. 1996. Genetic and physiological analysis of the lethal effect of L-(+)-lactate dehydrogenase deficiency in *Streptococcus mutans*: complementation by alcohol dehydrogenase from *Zymomonas mobilis. Infect. Immun.* **64,** 4319-4323.

Hillman, J.D., Novak, J., Sagura, E., Gutierrez, J.A., Brooks, T.A., Crowley, P.J., Azziz, A., Leung, K.-P., Cvitkovitch, D., Bleiweis, A.S. 1998. Genetic and biochemical analysis of mutacin 1140, a lantibiotic from *Streptococcus mutans. Infect. Immun.* **66,** 2743-2749.

Hillman, J.D., Brooks, T., Michalek, S.M., Harmon, C.C. and Snoep, J.L. Construction and characterization of an effector strain of *Streptococcus mutans* for replacement therapy of dental caries. *J. Dent. Res.* Submitted.

Houck, P.W., Nelson, J.D. and Kay, J.L. 1972. Fatal septicemia due to *Staphylococcus aureus* 502A. *Amer. J. Dis. Child.* **123,** 45-48.

Huis in 't Veld, J.H., Drost, J.S. and Havenaar, R. 1982. Establishment and localization of mixtures of *Streptococcus mutans* serotypes in the oral cavity of the rat. *J. Dent. Res.* **61,** 1199-1205.

Hurst, A. 1981. Nisin. In: Perlman and Laskin (eds.), *Advances in Applied Microbiology*, vol. 27, pp. 85-123. Academic Press, London.

Ji, G., Beavis, R. and Novick, R.P.1997. Bacterial interference caused by autoinducing peptide variants. *Science* **276,** 2027-2030.

Johnson, C.P., Gross, S.M., Hillman, J.D. 1980. Cariogenic potential *in vitro* in man and *in vivo* in the rat of lactate dehydrogenase mutants of *Streptococcus mutans. Arch Oral Biol* **25,** 707-713.

Jordan, H.V., Englander, H.R., Engler, W.O. and Kulczyk, S. 1972. Observations on the implantation and transmission of *Streptococcus mutans* in humans. *J. Dent. Res.* **51,** 515-518.

Kelstrup, J. and Gibbons, R.J. 1969. Inactivation of bacteriocins in the intestinal canal and oral cavity. *J. Bacteriol.* **99,** 888-890.

Krasse, B., Edwardsson, S., Svensson, I. and Trell, L. 1967. Implantation of caries-inducing streptococci in the human oral cavity. *Arch. Oral Biol.* **12,** 231-236.

LeBlanc, D., Hawley, R.J., Lee, L.N. and St. Martin, E.J. 1978. Conjugal transfer of plasmid DNA

598

among oral streptococci. *Proc. Natl. Acad. Sci. U.S.A.* **75,** 3484-3487.

Light, I.J., Walton, L., Sutherland, J.M., Shinefield, H.R. and Brackvogel, V. 1967, Use of bacterial interference to control a staphylococcal nursery outbreak: deliberate colonization of all infants with the 502A strain of *Staphylococcus aureus. Amer. J. Dis. Child.* **113,** 291-300.

Perl, T.M. and Golub, J.E. 1998. New approaches to reduce *Staphylococcus aureus* nosocomial infection rates: Treating *S. aureus* nasal carriage. *Ann. Pharmacother.* **32,** S7-16.

Perry, D. and Kuramitsu, H.K. 1981. Genetic transformation of *Streptococcus mutans. Infect. Immun.* **32,** 1295-1297.

Person, C. 1967. Genetical adjustment of fungi to their environment. In: Ainsworth, G.C. and Sussman, A.S. (eds.), *The Fungi,* vol. 3, pp. 395-415, Academic Press, New York.

Rogers, A.H., van der Hoeven, J.S. and Mikx, F.H. 1978. Inhibition of *Actinomyces viscosus* by bacteriocin-producing strains of *Streptococcus mutans* in the dental plaque of gnotobiotic rats. *Arch. Oral Biol.* **23,** 477-483.

Ruangsri, P. and Orstavik, D. 1977. Effect of the acquired pellicle and of dental plaque on the implantation of *Streptococcus mutans* on tooth surfaces in man. *Caries Res.* **11,** 204-210.

Sanders, E. 1969. Bacterial interference. I. Its occurrence among the respiratory tract flora and characterization of inhibition of group A streptococci by viridans streptococci. *J. Infect. Dis.* **120,** 698-707.

Sanders, C.C., Sanders, W.E. and Harrowe, D.J. 1976. Bacterial interference: effects of oral antibiotics on the normal throat flora and its ability to interfere with group A streptococci. *Infect. Immun.* **13,** 808-812.

Shinefield, H.R., Ribble, J.C. and Boris, M. 1971. Bacterial interference between strains of *Staphylococcus aureus,* 1960 to 1970. *Amer. J. Dis. Child.* **121,** 148-152.

Smith, N.W. and Huggins, M.B. 1974. Further observation on the association of the colicin V plasmid of *Escherichia coli* with pathogenicity and survival in the alimentary tract. *J. Gen. Microbiol.* **92,** 335-350.

Sprunt, K., Leidy, G. and Redman, W. 1980. Abnormal colonization of neonates in an ICU: conversion to normal colonization by pharyngeal implantation of alpha hemolytic streptococcus strain 215. *Pediatr. Res.* **14,** 308-313.

Sprunt, K. and Leidy, G. 1988. The use of bacterial interference to prevent infection. *Can. J. Microbiol.* **34,** 332-338.

Stashenko, K.P. and Hillman, J.D. 1989. Microflora of plaque in rats following infection with an LDH-deficient mutant of *Streptococcus mutans. Caries Res.* **23,** 375-377.

Strom, B.L., Abrutyn, E., Berlin, J.A., Kinman, J.L., Feldman, R.S., Stolley, P.D., Levison, M.E., Korzeniowski, O.M. and Kaye, D. 1998. Dental and cardiac risk factors for infective endocarditis. A population-based, case-control study. *Ann. Intern. Med.* **129,**761-769.

Svanberg, M. and Krasse, B. 1981. Oral implantation of saliva-treated *Streptococcus mutans* in man. *Arch. Oral Biol.* **26,** 197-201.

Takahashi, S., Abbe, K. and Yamada, T. 1982. Purification of pyruvate formate-lyase from *Streptococcus mutans* and its regulatory properties. *J. Bacteriol.* **149,** 1034-1040.

Takazoe, I., Nakamura, T. and Okuda, K. 1984. Colonization of the subgingival area by *Bacteroides gingivalis. J. Dent. Res.* **63,** 422-426.

Tanzer, J.M. and Freedman, M.L. 1978. Genetic alterations of *Streptococcus mutans* virulence. *Adv. Exp. Med. Biol.* **107,** 661-672.

Tanzer, J.M., Krasse, B., Svanberg, M. 1982. Conditions for implantation of *Streptococcus mutans* mutant 805 in adult human mouths (abstract). *J. Dent. Res.* 61 (Spec. Iss.):334.

Tanzer, J.M., Kurasz, A.B. and Clive, J. 1985. Competitive displacement of mutans streptococci and inhibition of tooth decay by *Streptococcus salivarius* TOVE-R. *Infect. Immun.* **48,** 44-50.

Westergren, G. and Emilson, C.G. 1983. Prevalence of transformable *Streptococcus mutans* in human dental plaque. *Infect. Immun.* **41,**1386-1388.